STIMULUS SAMPLING THEORY

HOLDEN-DAY SERIES IN PSYCHOLOGY

ROBERT R. BUSH, *Editor*

STIMULUS
SAMPLING
THEORY

E. D. Neimark

Rutgers, the State University

W. K. Estes

Stanford University

HOLDEN-DAY

San Francisco, Cambridge, London, Amsterdam

PREFACE

As is more or less customary in enterprises of this character, we begin with an apology and an explanation. First, we wish to apologize to the authors of many important articles, in or bordering on the area of stimulus sampling theory, whose contributions we could not include. The fact that we had difficult problems of selection will surprise no one, for a volume of this sort would not be needed had not the relevant literature grown to such proportions that the interested but uninitiated investigator or student can scarcely come to grips with it unaided. We have tried to assemble a collection of articles in which the principal ideas and methods of stimulus sampling theory, as we see them, are represented, while keeping to dimensions dictated by considerations of cost, portability, and usefulness. Our problems of organization have been simplified somewhat by the ready availability of excellent presentations of the mathematical methods involved in stimulus sampling theories. For an introduction to these, the reader is referred to Atkinson, Bower, and Crothers (1965), and for a more intensive follow-up, to Luce, Bush, and Galanter (1963). Thus we have been in a position to organize the present volume in terms of concepts, rather than methods, with special attention to the close interplay between theory and experiment which has characterized the development of this branch of learning theory.

The explanation we propose to offer is simply our answer to the question, "What is stimulus sampling theory?" The answer cannot be had simply by reference to some appropriate one of the remaining articles in the volume, for in each is represented only some particular model, usually with some specific empirical interpretation. The property of being a theory belongs, if anywhere, to the whole collection rather than to any one element. Following customary usage in psychology (which differs somewhat from that of such logicians as Tarski, 1941), we mean by *model* a set of assumptions together with implications deduced from them by mathematical reasoning. Usually in a scientific context we find that the terms of the model are interpreted via correspondences with operations or events in an experimental situation, and then we speak of a model for the particular type of experiment. Over the last fifteen years, a very large number of stimulus sampling models have been formulated and applied to experimental phenomena. In a few instances, particular models have worked out very well for particular situations and have continued to be used virtually unchanged. More often models have been found to be faulty in some degree and consequently have been rejected outright, combined with other models, or modified in other ways. The term *stimulus sampling theory* refers, in a sense, to the whole collection of models and applications, but more importantly to certain communalities of conception, method, and outlook. As in the case of a rapidly growing child, these communalities may not be easy to discern in a rapidly evolving discipline unless one attends, somewhat, to its course of development over a period of time. We shall not attempt to express these communalities in capsule form, but we have attempted to organize the volume in such a way that the reader will have a reasonable opportunity of arriving at them for himself by induction.

The project of preparing this volume grew out of a suggestion from Robert R. Bush, who patiently awaited its completion and offered helpful comments on the final draft. The final plan of organization and the selection of materials are the joint responsibility of the two editors; whereas chapter introductions and reviews of related literature are primarily the work of one of us (E. D. N.), whose efforts were partially supported under grant No. MH 11026 from U.S. Public Health Service. The patience of Frederick H. Murphy, of Holden-Day, Inc., throughout a long sequence of missed deadlines has been appreciated and will be, we hope, ultimately rewarded.

We wish, also, to thank the many individual authors who generously granted permission to reprint their papers. We regret that, due to practical considerations, some of them have been deprived of the satisfaction of seeing their work reprinted. A number of publishers have also granted permission for reprinting, and their permission is gratefully acknowledged. Finally, we wish to express our appreciation to Mary Tanner and Chris Holder who, in the course of typing almost endless revisions, have become expert at deciphering dreadful handwriting.

E. D. N.
New Brunswick, N.J.

W. K. E.
Stanford, California

INTRODUCTION

All learning theories are concerned both with developing rules or principles which aid in predicting learning phenomena and with building up some kind of picture of the events and processes that go on in the organism during learning. But emphases differ greatly. At one extreme, the physiologically-oriented theory of D. O. Hebb develops rather elaborate hypotheses concerning the particular kinds of neural events involved in learning but exhibits little concern for actual prediction of experimental phenomena. At the other, the stochastic learning models associated with, for example, the work of R. R. Bush and F. Mosteller are almost exclusively concerned with developing simple and manageable schemes for the description and prediction of quantitative experimental data. The position characteristic of stimulus sampling theory is intermediate, though rather closer to the latter extreme than to the former.

To elucidate by means of an analogy, suppose that one's task were to describe, not a learning organism, but a new computing machine. One might begin by describing the principal component parts and the ways in which they interact with each other as the machine operates; or, at the other extreme, one might simply present a set of rules telling how the output of the machine is affected if one operates this knob or that knob on the console. A third starting point, the intermediate position, would be to begin by characterizing the machine in general terms—for example, whether it is basically digital or analog, its capacity for receiving, storing, and retrieving information. Then the rules for operating the console would be presented, not simply in terms of the effects on output, but in terms of the kinds of processes going on in the machine—entering items in memory storage, moving them from one address to another, transferring items from core memory to buffer storage, and the like.

A common thread running through the many particular formulations and reformulations of stimulus sampling theory during the past fifteen years is provided by some rather general concepts and orienting assumptions which appeared in the earliest papers. In all variants of stimulus sampling theory the learning organism is conceived to operate in important respects like a digital machine, or switching network. The effect of a learning experience is conceived to be the production of discrete, all-or-none changes of state in certain behavioral elements, which may be termed memory traces or stimulus response connections; the name is immaterial, all that matters being the properties assigned these elements. The most ubiquitous property characterizing the learning mechanism is multiplicity. Whatever the physical entities underlying elementary associations may be, many lines of evidence indicate that there must be a vast degree of duplication in the changes induced by a learning experience; for learned associations are found to survive not only radical changes in the organism's external situation, and changes in the organism itself owing to normal physiological processes such as growth, sleep, and aging, but even radical alterations of the nervous system by drugs or surgery. The multiplicity of associations between components or aspects of a stimulus situation and the organism's responses assumed in the theory not only makes for robustness of learned habits in the face of various kinds of disturbances, but also provides a natural basis for transfer of learning from one situation to another. Common elements in any two stimulus situations are assumed to activate common associative elements, and thus to produce transfer of learning roughly in proportion to the degree of communality between the situations. The basic multiplicity of the associative process, together with an assumption of constant random variation over time in the state of activity or inactivity of each associative element, makes the learning mechanism, as conceived in stimulus sampling theory, one which not only is prepared to deal with an ever-changing environment, but one which indeed thrives on variability.

The first chapter of this volume will, thus, bring together a number of papers in which are developed these general ideas of multiple, elementary stimulus response processes, learning via all-or-none changes of state, transfer by means of common elements, and random variation in elementary processes over time. An important characteristic of this series of papers, which may puzzle the student at first, is that the same fundamental ideas keep reappearing in superficially rather different mathematical clothing. In the final paper of this first chapter, it will become clear, at least to the reader reasonably well-versed in probability theory, that most of the formal differences among specific stimulus sampling models arise from variations in particular assumptions about the sampling mechanisms. In many cases, the choice among particular alternative sampling assumptions (for example, between sampling with and without replacement) has little empirical import, but it does have important consequences regarding mathematical tractability and convenience when one is working with the theory in a particular context. A particularly happy discovery in this regard was finding that, with suitable simplifying assumptions, the entire mathematical machinery of Markov chains can be brought to bear for purposes of deriving testable implications of the theory for many kinds of experimental situations.

Beyond the elucidation of a few basic ideas and general mathematical methods for working with them, we feel that stimulus sampling theory can best be understood by concentrating on what it does rather than what it is. As with any scientific theory, whatever significance stimulus sampling theory may prove to have for psychology lies in the kinds of experiments it leads to, the ways in which investigators working within the theoretical framework are led to analyze and interpret their data.

Following out this motif, we intersperse the basic theoretical papers of Chapter I with experimental articles. More importantly, in the succeeding three chapters we bring together three major series of theoretical and experimental articles in which the basic conceptual machinery of Chapter I is worked out and elaborated in specific research areas. In each instance, it will be seen that the results are: first, the development of specific mathematical models ("miniature theories") for particular types of experiments; second, the generation of new empirical phenomena, for example, the existence of discrete performance levels in a variety of learning situations, various types of probability matching, functions of nonreinforced trials in multiple choice learning. These chapters have been arranged more in order of simplicity than chronology, and roughly parallel the order of introduction of mathematical topics in Atkinson, Bower, and Crothers, *Introduction to Mathematical Learning Theory* (1965).

The last two chapters of the volume include contributions representative of several main lines of current theoretical modification and innovation. The first of these foci of current research interest has to do with the matter of stimulus units and the problem of patterning. In the earlier work on stimulus sampling theory, investigators were concerned, not so much with the question of what a stimulus element might be, but with the prior questions: whether the concept were a useful one at all, and if so, what general properties should be assumed to characterize these entities. Only when a reasonable body of logical and mathematical machinery for developing testable implications of hypotheses about elements had become available was it feasible to begin looking more directly at the empirical correspondents of the elements of the theory. Initial steps in this direction have been to seek to determine for a number of situations just what aspects of a stimulus situation enter into unitary relationships with responses as a result of a single learning experience. A major question as to whether "higher-order" elements develop as a result of a process of patterning has just begun to receive attention; it seems likely to be an important focus of research in the near future.

The importance of selective sampling of stimuli, which is treated in quite different ways in the several principal lines of research represented in Chapter V, is so widely appreciated by investigators of learning that one may well wonder why this concept did not appear in the earliest formulations of stimulus sampling theory. The answer seems to be twofold: first, in classical theories of learning, the potential importance of random sampling processes had been largely overlooked; second, although the situation could not readily have been foreseen, it has turned out in fact that mathematical techniques for dealing with random sampling of stimuli are far simpler and more tractable than those needed to deal with selective sampling processes. Thus, major efforts have been required to develop each of the approaches to selective sampling represented—namely, those based on adaptation of cues and observing responses. In neither case have the mathematical problems yet been solved fully enough to permit adequate differential testing of the empirical implications of these two conceptions. The third principal approach to selective sampling is associated with models for "vicarious trial and error" behavior at a choice point. Though originally developed in connection with interpretations of discrimination learning, models of this class appear to be of greater potential importance in other contexts, and in particular for providing linkages between stimulus sampling theory and other bodies of psychological theory. This function is exemplified by several papers concerned with treatments of psychophysical judgments and choice behavior. Also, it should be noted that the concept of scanning of choice point cues is extended to the scanning of implicit response sequences in the papers of Chapter III which deal with multiple-choice learning in relation to reward values and probabilities. Although no new basic concepts are involved, the elementary processes assumed in earlier formulations of stimulus sampling theory are concatenated or pyramided to form a rather complex theoretical structure.

The picture of the learning organism which emerges from the most recent developments of stimulus sampling theory in relation to reward learning and choice behavior is a far cry from the bundle of simple stimulus response connections envisaged in the earliest treatments of conditioning—and still identified with stimulus sampling theory in the minds of virtually all psychologists except those few working actively with the theory. The conceptual organism now assumed exhibits behavior of quite different orders of complexity in different situations. In the simple conditioning experiment, its responses are evoked by the cues it samples without any complex intervening processes, and its state of learning is described by the state of a single set of associative elements. In discriminative situations, the organism's responses are not directly evoked by random samples of impinging stimuli. Rather, the behavior of responding discriminatively breaks down into two principal phases—the scanning of cues and the determination of the final overt response, not by the whole stimulus complex presented, but only by those cues or aspects selected by the scanning process. In choice situations involving rewards and punishments, still a third phase appears. The organism scans the cues presented at the beginning of an experimental trial; as each cue is sampled it generates a covert, or implicit, representation of the response with which it is associated; the implicit response leads in turn to recall of the rewarding or punishing outcome which followed previous overt occurrences of that response; and the final overt choice response is the result of selection from these covert responses and their anticipated outcomes.

To some it will doubtless seem a great waste of time to have gone through 15 years of research in order to arrive at a realization that choice behavior is as complex as every layman knows it to be. But it is one thing to appreciate that behavior is complex and quite another to discern simple properties and simple constituent processes which may enable one to predict or control complex phenomena in new situations. There are easy and difficult routes to any conclusion, the latter often repaying the extra effort by deepened understanding. We have tried to arrange this volume to make the long route available to readers who have not had the sometimes rewarding, more often frustrating, but in any event interesting experience of participating in these developments.

CONTENTS

CHAPTER IV.   SINGLE PROCESS MODELS FOR
           GENERALIZATION AND DISCRIMINATION

CHAPTER V.   MULTIPROCESS MODELS FOR DISCRIMINATION AND CHOICE

STIMULUS SAMPLING THEORY

CHAPTER I

Development and General Theory
of Stimulus Sampling

The term "stimulus sampling theory" refers to a number of theories differing with respect to special assumptions and their mathematical expression, yet sharing a common approach to conceptual representation of the stimulus situation and the formation of associative connections, rather than to a single coherent set of assumptions formulated to apply to all the experimental procedures employed in the study of learning. The present chapter begins with a brief sketch of the historical development of stimulus sampling theory. The central concepts of stimulus elements, sampling of elements, and connection of elements to responses are then introduced and the consequences of three alternative mathematical formulations of the nature of the sampling process are explored. The remainder of this volume is concerned with models derived from focusing upon a special assumption or from lifting some of the restrictions of the initial theory. The final section of the present chapter deals with one example of the effect of removing restrictions: namely, the consequences of assuming that the stimulus situation does not remain constant, but rather that the availability of individual elements changes as a result of the passage of time or the manipulation of experimental variables.

Background.   The intellectual climate of psychology in the 1940's was marked by a number of trends which influenced the nature and early development of statistical learning theory: (a) intense interest in the principles of theory construction; (b) the decline of monolithic systems accompanied by the accumulation of a mass of orderly data obtained in relatively comparable experimental situations; and (c) a continuing interest in quantitative formulation of psychological theory. The first trend was reflected in the preoccupation of experimental psychologists with logical positivism. Although the revolutionary interactions of the philosophy of science and physical theory occurred in the 1920's and 1930's, self-conscious examination of the process of theory construction

1

really infected psychologists—and most especially learning theorists—in the late 1930's and early 1940's (Boring et al., 1945). During this time, psychologists in major graduate departments were busily catechizing their students in the mysteries of hypothetical constructs, intervening variables (MacCorquodale and Meehl, 1948), and empirical testability. Eventually some of this evangelical zeal was channeled into the constructive task of translating belief into practice. A notable application of principles to practice was the appearance of *Modern Learning Theory* (Estes et al., 1954), the product of a conference held at Dartmouth in the summer of 1950 for the purpose of examining existing learning theories from the standpoint of adequacy of construction. The appearance of that book may be taken to mark the culmination of the second trend: the decline of monolithic systems.

The period of the 1930's saw the accumulation of a body of data obtained in similar experimental situations and the development of a number of learning theories (Guthrie, 1935; Hull, 1943; Skinner, 1938; Tolman, 1932). These theories were developed with meticulous attention to principles of general methodology and, with their announced intent of accounting for all learning phenomena in terms of a limited set of concepts and principles, were well calculated to capture enthusiastic adherents. The principal weakness of most of these theories, which ultimately led to disillusionment and set the stage for new approaches in the 1950's, was that the elaboration of constructs and postulates was not accompanied by commensurate development of logical and mathematical methods for bringing the theories into closer alignment with experimental data. It became increasingly evident that the theories influential in the 1940's were but a sample of a very large number of possible theories which could be constructed to account for the general aspects of learning phenomena and for the gross qualitative and semi-quantitative results of standard experiments. Future selection among the various approaches would certainly depend upon the development of theoretical machinery permitting more detailed predictions of experimental phenomena and a resulting sharper testing of theoretical assumptions. On the other hand, all the data collected in T-mazes, runways, and Skinner boxes remained as evidence of functional relationships which constituted both a starting point and a preliminary test of more quantitative formulations.

The third historical trend, interest in quantitative theory, had characterized experimental psychology from its inception: Fechner's attempt at rational derivation of the relation between physical and psychological events. Fechner's derivational technique was to establish a differential equation which could then be integrated to yield an expression for changes in response as a function of the independent variables (stimulus intensity in the case of psychophysics; trials in the case of learning). Rational learning curves were derived in this fashion by a number of investigators (Graham and Gagne, 1940; Gulliksen and Wolfle, 1938; Thurstone, 1930).However, it was in the later versions of Hull's theory (1943, 1951) that efforts toward rational quantitative formulation were first associated with a major continuing program of research on learning. To a considerable extent Hull's program established the goals for the kind of mathematical learning theory represented in this volume and in other contemporary approaches (Vol. II of Luce, Bush, and Galanter, 1963).

With the increasing emphasis upon statistical analysis of data, psychologists became familiar with probability theory and the techniques of mathematical statistics. It was almost inevitable that someone should eventually apply these tools not simply to analysis of the wealth of orderly data available, but also to a description of the underlying processes which generate the data. A number of such probabilistic theories appeared in the early 1950's: Bush and Mosteller (1951), Estes (1950), Miller and McGill (1952). All three departed from the Hullian approach in the mathematical techniques employed, in their adoption of more limited objectives, and in their increased attention to the development of logical and mathematical tools for exploring evolving theories. Furthermore, they worked as closely as possible at the level of observable events instead of constructing elaborate superstructures of hypothetical constructs.

As psychologists became more familiar with recent developments in probability theory, models describing a variety of behaviors, in increasing detail, appeared at a positively accelerated rate. At the same time, new experimental procedures were developed expressly to test the models, and new statistical techniques were developed for assessing the adequacy of theoretical description. In retrospect, it is now obvious that experimental procedures involving rats in Skinner boxes and runways, which had once seemed, on intuitive grounds, to provide the ultimate in simplicity, were quite complex from the standpoint of mathematical description. On the other hand, human learning of, for example, paired-associates and concept identification, has turned out to be simpler in some respects.

The fundamental concepts of stimulus sampling. In 1950 Estes first formulated the fundamental assumptions of stimulus sampling theory and applied them to a very simple conditioning situation. All stimulating conditions which can arise during the course of the experiment are viewed as comprising a population of stimulus elements from which a sample is drawn on each experimental trial. The responses which the subject can emit in this situation are classified as members of one of two mutually exclusive and exhaustive categories: the experimental response, class A, and all other responses, class $\bar{A}$. At all times, each element is connected to one response class or the other, but its conditioning status may change as a result of experimental events on a trial on which it is sampled. A change in conditioning status of an element occurs on an all-or-none basis; in other words, the elements are, in effect, digital. For example, in a simple conditioning experiment, the presentation of a conditional stimulus (CS) is treated as presentation of a sample of elements. The probability that a response of class A will be evoked by the CS is determined by the proportion of elements in the sample which are already connected to A (which, because of the assumption of random sampling from a large population, presumably is close to the population proportion). By virtue of the fact that an unconditional stimulus (US) is consistently paired with CS, the experimental procedure ensures that, regardless of the response evoked at onset of the CS, a member of class A will occur at the termination of the trial. Thus, all elements associated with the CS which have been sampled should be connected to class A when they are returned to the population at the end of the trial. The newly connected elements, along with those previously conditioned, whose status is unchanged, are returned to the population with the result that the total number of conditioned elements in the population—hence, theoretical response probability which is based upon the ratio of conditioned elements to total elements—increases.

It will be noted that the concept of the stimulus element is not defined in terms of observable events; it has the status of a primitive term within the theory. Although there have been some attempts at relating experimental manipulations to a stimulus sampling parameter (Burke, Estes, and Hellyer, 1954; Schoeffler, 1954; Anderson, 1965), success in this endeavor is by no means a necessary requirement for the derivation of testable predictions. To the extent that directly testable implications of the theory are supported by evidence, the concepts of stimulus sampling remain tenable.

In return for some deliberate oversimplification of both stimulus and response concepts, this simple formulation offers both power and parsimony. For example, variability becomes a natural property of the stimulus situation and need not be tacked on as an additional explanatory principle. Similarly, conditions within the organism, for example, motivation (Estes, 1958, 1961), can be described in terms of subsets of elements of varying weight in the population. Additional detail on applications of the original form of statistical learning theory to data is available in Estes (1959a).

Alternative descriptions of stimulus sampling. The process of sampling from a population of stimulus elements on successive experimental trials may be described quantitatively in a variety of ways (Estes, 1959b; Atkinson and Estes, 1964). In his 1950 paper Estes assumed that there is a large population of elements, N in number, from which a sample of fixed size s is drawn with replacement on each experimenal trial; all elements are assumed to have the same probability of sampling, that is, s/N. In a later paper, Estes and Burke (1953) removed the restrictions of fixed sample size and equal sampling probability by allowing each element to have its own sampling probability (θ_i for the ith element) which was assumed constant throughout the course of the experiment. With this formulation of sampling, sample size can vary from one trial to another, and, depending upon the number of elements in the population, there may be trials on which no elements are sampled.

A comparison of learning curves for the case in which θ may vary with comparable curves for the case in which all elements have the same sampling probability $\bar{\theta}$, shows that initially curves for the equal θ case rise more slowly than for the unequal case, but that the two curves cross only once and the equal θ curve becomes asymptotic more quickly. Certainly this consequence is in accord with intuition. In general, predictions for the two cases are very similar and approach the same limiting values as the number of elements in the population becomes large. There is one property of equal θ models which is not generally characteristic of models in which sampling probability may vary: change in response probability from trial n to trial $n + 1$ is a function only of the experimental outcome on trial $n,$ and is independent of the prior sequence of reinforced and nonreinforced trials. This "independence of path" property has been the subject of some discussion and investigation (see Chapter III). Since the equal θ case leads to greater mathematical tractability, it has been employed in most of the extensions covered in Chapters III and IV.

Both sampling assumptions reviewed above are alike in assuming a very large (but usually finite) population of elements from which a finite (and, again, usually large) sample is drawn on each trial. Models incorporating these assumptions are usually described as *component* models to distinguish them from *pattern* models based upon a third sampling assumption to which we now turn. In this instance, the sample of stimulus elements is viewed as a coherent entity, or pattern, rather than in terms of the individual elements which comprise it.

It is a convenient abstraction to assume that, under some circumstances, exactly one element is sampled from the population on each trial, that is, $s = 1$. If there are only two possible conditioning states, namely, connection to response class A or to $\bar{A}$, then all possible changes in conditioning state from the outset to the termination of an experimental trial may be described for that element in terms of a 2×2 matrix of transition probabilities (and, of course, the same reasoning would apply for any finite number of conditioning states greater than two). In these instances, it is easy to apply the simple and elegant mathematics of Markov processes to derive predictions for a great many properties of experimental data. The Markov property, itself, is independent of the value of s. The very special case of a one-element model, however, dramatizes the assumption of all-or-none connection and, in addition, makes it possible to obtain rather sharp tests of the assumption under suitably simplified conditions. Chapter II is devoted to a fuller examination of the application of such models to the data of, for example, paired-associate learning. For a more detailed explanation of sampling assumptions and a comparison of their consequences, see Estes (1959b) in this chapter.

Models providing for systematic change in the composition of stimulus samples.   The applicability of the early conditioning models, (Estes, 1950, 1953) to experimental data is severely restricted by the requirements that (a) the experimental situation is assumed constant throughout the course of the experiment, and (b) the response in question is consistently reinforced (acquisition) or consistently nonreinforced (extinction). Models developed for experimental tasks in which the second restriction is removed deal with reinforcement variables and are considered in greater detail in Chapter III. Derivation of models for experimental situations in which the first restriction is removed depends upon the class of experimental procedures under consideration. For example, when training is spread over a number of experimental sessions on subsequent days, it is unreasonable to assume that the experimental environment remains constant. In such instances, it is natural to assume a process of stimulus drift over time, in which some previously available elements become unavailable, whereas other elements, previously unavailable, enter the population available for sampling. This assumption may be expressed by partitioning the population into subsets, S and S', of available and unavailable elements and by introducing two new terms, j and j', to describe the probability of drift from S to S' or from S' to S in a given unit of time. The resulting model (Estes, 1955a) has been applied with some success to the description of spontaneous recovery (Homme, 1956; McConnell, 1959; Witte, 1959; Cole and Abraham,

1962) and retroactive interference (Frankmann, 1957). Furthermore, this type of formulation provides a basis for describing the effects of changes in motivational conditions (Estes, 1958, 1961).

An assumption of systematic change in stimulus conditions within an experimental session (Estes, 1955b) provides a basis for analyzing the effect of distribution and spacing of trials. A slightly different set of assumptions has been proposed by Prokasy (1961), who assumes an interchange of elements between the effective sample and the population, rather than a change in the subset of available elements. An assumption of this sort would seem to be especially applicable, for example, to massed trials where one might expect the stimulus situation on trial $n + 1$ to be composed, at least in part, of elements arising from the aftereffects of trial n. Models incorporating this property have been developed by Burke and Estes (1957, see Chapter IV), and tested by Straughan (1956).

Still another source of systematic change in stimulus conditions within an experimental session is provided by assuming that individual elements may change in status or relative importance during the course of training. Some assumption of this sort is required for the description of many discrimination experiments; the example included in this chapter (La-Berge, 1959), however, is applicable to simpler learning situations. LaBerge provides one mechanism for differential weighting by assuming that, at the outset of training, some elements are "neutral," that is, not connected to any recorded response class. With the introduction of neutral elements, it is possible to provide a basis for describing data on such phenomena as changes in latency and differential transfer effects.

In learning situations involving discrimination and stimulus generalization, many experimental tasks may quite naturally be conceptualized in terms of a population of elements, unique (but in general not disjoint) subsets of which are associated with each of the discriminative stimuli. Models employing this natural extension of the treatment of simple learning and conditioning are reviewed in Chapter IV. To the extent that there is overlap among the stimulus subsets, generalization is readily predicted, but perfect discrimination is not. On the other hand, by assuming nonoverlapping subsets, or patterns, one can readily predict perfect discrimination. Representative models based upon pattern assumptions are treated in Chapters II and IV. Chapter V deals with models for discrimination and choice, which require that special assumptions be added to the sampling models reviewed in this chapter in order to describe perfect discrimination.

Development of mathematical techniques. In discussing theoretical assumptions, we have referred to a number of mathematical techniques employed in deriving testable implications of the assumptions. In this section the techniques are described and a number of useful references are cited. No attempt is made to introduce the reader to the mechanics of each technique; rather, our emphasis is upon the psychological assumptions underlying a number of applications of stimulus sampling theory. For an explanation of the mathematical techniques employed in exploring these assumptions, see Atkinson, Bower, and Crothers (1965).

In building something new, one usually begins with available tools and materials. For learning theorists, the materials were data on the simple learning of rats in runways, mazes, and Skinner boxes; the tools were techniques of differential and integral calculus which have been successfully employed in the physical sciences since the time of Newton and Leibniz. The calculus is most appropriately applied in analyzing a continuous process into a large number of infinitesimally small changes which may be expressed in a differential equation. Most learning tasks, however, proceed in a number of discrete steps—trials. On structural grounds, therefore, one would expect a calculus of finite differences to provide a more appropriate mathematical tool. With a calculus of finite differences, one proceeds similarly by solving a basic difference equation (Jordan, 1950; Goldberg, 1961) This procedure was first applied to learning data by Bush and Mosteller (1951). Since the techniques and theorems of finite differences are quite similar to those of differential calculus, it is not surprising that the result of expressing statistical learning theory assumptions in finite difference form (Estes and Burke, 1953) was quite similar to the earlier (Estes, 1950) differential equation results. Although the general approach of solving a basic difference equation has been widely used (especially in dealing with the problems of Chapter III), it has severe limitations; once one gets outside the class of linear difference equations of the first order, there are many difference equations which, in practice, cannot be solved (some of these are encountered in the contingent case of Chapter III). Although numerical solutions for specific application may be obtained through the use of Monte Carlo methods (see, e.g., Bush and Mosteller, 1955), particular solutions are never as satisfying as exact general solutions.

A branch of probability theory is concerned with *stochastic processes*—random or probabilistic processes which change through time. As psychologists became familiar with the mathematical treatment of stochastic processes, it was apparent that many learning phenomena could naturally be interpreted in terms of this class of models. A major consequence of this approach, first systematically exploited by Bush and Mosteller (1955), is that it leads to detailed predictions for a variety of sequential properties of learning data—formerly a relatively neglected class of dependent variables. For a general discussion of stochastic processes, the interested reader should consult Feller (1957) or Parzen (1962); for applications of stochastic models in learning theory, see Kemeny, Snell, and Thompson (1957), Bush and Estes (1959), or Luce, Bush, and Galanter (1963).

A subclass of stochastic processes, characterized by the property that the state probabilities on trial $n + 1$ are exclusively determined by the state on trial n, is known as *Markov chains*. The simplest possible example of a Markov chain in learning would involve a single stimulus element which can either be conditioned to the response in question, or not; the probability that it will be conditioned on a given trial is a constant c; once it is conditioned it remains so. These assumptions describe a 2×2 matrix of transition probabilities which, when applied to initial response probabilities, can provide a complete description of the course of learning in this simple situation. For such instances, the description of learning is extensive and simple. Lest the reader assume that such Markov models have only a vacuous mathematical simplicity, it should be noted that they have profound psychological implications. They provide a basis for analyzing behavior into simpler, discrete units; since psychology has never been blessed with an abundance of natural units of analysis, this is no mean accomplishment. Examples of this type of analysis are covered in Chapters II and V. In some instances (for example, in the experimental situation of Chapter III), it is possible to examine the same task from the standpoint of a number of different stimulus sampling assumptions and to explore the consequences with a variety of mathematical tools; some of these comparisons are given in Estes (1959b). In general, many gross predictions of, for example, mean learning curves, are relatively unchanged by the nature of the sampling assumption or its mathematical formulation. On the other hand, other descriptive statistics, such as the variance of the distribution of response probabilities, do differ. For fuller discussion of the application of Markov processes to psychological data, see Suppes and Atkinson (1960), Miller (1952), and Atkinson, Bower, and Crothers (1965).

REFERENCES

Anderson, N. H. Test of a prediction of stimulus sampling theory in probability learning. *J. exp. Psychol.*, 1966, **71,** 499–510.

Atkinson, R. C., Bower, G. H., and Crothers, C. J. *Introduction to mathematical learning theory*. New York: Wiley, 1965.

Boring, E. G., Langfeld, H. S., Bridgman, P. W., Feigl, H., Israel, H. E., Pratt, C. C., and Skinner, B. F. Symposium on operationism. *Psychol. Rev.*, 1945, **52,** 241–294.

Burke, C. J. and Estes, W. K. A component model for stimulus variables in discrimination learning. *Psychometrika*, 1957, **22,** 133–145.

Burke, C. J., Estes, W. K., and Hellyer, S. Rate of verbal conditioning in relation to stimulus variability. *J. exp. Psychol.*, 1954, **48,** 153–161.

Bush, R. R. and Estes, W. K. (Eds.) *Studies in mathematical learning theory*. Stanford, Calif.: Stanford Univ. Press, 1959.

Bush, R. R. and Mosteller, F. A mathematical model for simple learning. *Psychol. Rev.*, 1951, **58,** 313–323.

Bush, R. R. and Mosteller, F. *Stochastic models for learning*. New York: Wiley, 1955.

Cole, M. and Abraham, F. Extinction and spontaneous recovery as a function of amount of training and extinction intertrial interval. *J. comp. physiol. Psychol.*, 1962, **55,** 978–982.

Estes, W. K. Toward a statistical theory of learning. *Psychol. Rev.*, 1950, **57,** 94–107.

Estes, W. K. Statistical theory of spontaneous recovery and regression. *Psychol. Rev.*, 1955(a), **62,** 145–154.

Estes, W. K. Statistical theory of distributional phenomena in learning. *Psychol. Rev.*, 1955(b), **62,** 369–377.

Estes, W. K. Stimulus response theory of drive. In M. R. Jones (Ed.), *Nebraska symposium on motivation*. Vol. 6, Lincoln, Nebraska: Univ. of Nebraska Press, 1958, 35–69.

Estes, W. K. The statistical approach to learning theory. In S. Koch (Ed.), *Psychology, a study of a science*, Vol. 2. New York: McGraw-Hill, 1959(a).

Estes, W. K. Component and pattern models with Markovian interpretations. In R. R. Bush and W. K. Estes (Eds.), *Studies in mathematical learning theory*. Stanford, Calif.: Stanford Univ. Press, 1959(b), 9–53.

Estes, W. K. and Burke, C. J. A theory of stimulus variability in learning. *Psychol. Rev.*, 1953, **60,** 276–286.

Estes, W. K., Koch, S., MacCorquodale, D., Meehl, P. E., Mueller, C. G., Jr., Schoenfeld, W. N., and Verplanck, W. S. *Modern learning theory*. New York: Appleton-Century-Crofts, 1954.

Feller, W. *An introduction to probability theory and its applications*, Vol. 1 (2nd ed.), New York: Wiley, 1957.

Frankmann, J. P. Effect of amount of interpolated learning and time interval before test on retention in rats. *J. exp. Psychol.*, 1957, **54,** 462–466.

Goldberg, S. *Introduction to difference equations*. New York: Wiley, 1961.

Graham, C. H. and Gagne, R. M. The acquisition, extinction, and spontaneous recovery of a conditioned operant response. *J. exp. Psychol.*, 1940, **26,** 251–281.

Gulliksen, H. and Wolfle, D. L. A theory of learning and transfer. *Psychometrika*, 1938, **3,** 127–149, 225–261.

Guthrie, E. R. *The psychology of learning*. New York: Harper, 1935.

Hilgard, E. R. *Theories of learning*. (2nd ed.) New York: Appleton-Century-Crofts, 1956.

Homme, L. E. Spontaneous recovery and statistical learning theory. *J. exp. Psychol.*, 1956, **51,** 205–212.

Hull, C. L. *Principles of behavior*. New York: Appleton-Century-Crofts, 1943.

Hull, C. L. *A behavior system*. New Haven: Yale Univ. Press, 1951.

Jordan, C. *Calculus of finite differences*. New York: Chelsea, 1950.

Kemeny, J. G., Snell, J. L., and Thompson, G. L. *Introduction to finite mathematics*. Englewood Cliffs, N.J.: Prentice-Hall, 1957.

LaBerge, D. A model with neutral elements. In R. R. Bush and W. K. Estes (Eds.), *Studies in mathematical learning theory*. Stanford, Calif.: Stanford Univ. Press, 1959, 53–64.

Luce, R. D., Bush, R. R., and Galanter, E. (Eds.) *Handbook of mathematical psychology*. Vol. I, Vol. II. New York: Wiley, 1963. Vol. III, 1965.

MacCorquodale, K. and Meehl, P. E. On a distinction between hypothetical constructs and intervening variables. *Psychol. Rev.*, 1948, **55**, 95–107.

McConnell, D. Spontaneous regression and recovery in a sequence of discrimination periods. *J. exp. Psychol.*, 1959, **57**, 121–129.

McConnell, D. An augmented model for spontaneous regression and recovery. *Psychometrika*, 1959, **24**, 145–155.

Miller, G. A. Finite Markov processes in psychology. *Psychometrika*, 1952, **17**, 149–167.

Miller, G. A. and McGill, W. J. A statistical description of verbal learning. *Psychometrika*, 1952, **17**, 369–396.

Parzen, E. *Stochastic processes*. San Francisco: Holden-Day, 1962.

Prokasy, W. Nonrandom stimulus sampling in statistical learning theory. *Psychol. Rev.*, 1961, **68**, 219–224.

Schoeffler, M. S. Probability of response to compounds of discriminated stimuli. *J. exp. Psychol.*, 1954, **48**, 323–329.

Skinner, B. F. *The behavior of organisms: An experimental analysis*. New York: Appleton-Century-Crofts, 1938.

Suppes, P. and Atkinson, R. C. *Markov learning models for multi–person interactions*. Stanford, Calif.: Stanford Univ. Press, 1960.

Straughan, J. H. Human escape learning in relation to reinforcement variables and intertrial conditions. *J. exp. Psychol.*, 1956, **52**, 1–8.

Thurstone, L. L. The learning function. *J. gen. Psychol.*, 1930, **3**, 469–493.

Tolman, E. C. *Purposive behavior in animals and men*. New York: D. Appleton-Century, 1932. (Reprinted, Univ. of Calif. Press, 1949.)

Witte, R. A stimulus-trace hypothesis for statistical learning theory. *J. exp. Psychol.*, 1959, **57**, 273–283.

Toward a Statistical Theory of Learning[*]

WILLIAM K. ESTES, *Indiana University*

Improved experimental techniques for the study of conditioning and simple discrimination learning enable the present day investigator to obtain data which are sufficiently orderly and reproducible to support exact quantitative predictions of behavior. Analogy with other sciences suggests that full utilization of these techniques in the analysis of learning processes will depend to some extent upon a comparable refinement of theoretical concepts and methods. The necessary interplay between theory and experiment has been hindered, however, by the fact that none of the many current theories of learning commands general agreement among researchers. It seems likely that progress toward a common frame of reference will be slow so long as most theories are built around verbally defined hypothetical constructs which are not susceptible to unequivocal verification. While awaiting resolution of the many apparent disparities among competing theories, it may be advantageous to systematize well established empirical relationships at a peripheral, statistical level of analysis. The possibility of agreement on a theoretical framework, at least in certain intensively studied areas, may be maximized by defining concepts in terms of experimentally manipulable variables, and developing the consequences of assumptions by strict mathematical reasoning. This essay will introduce a series of studies developing a statistical theory of elementary learning processes. From the definitions and assumptions which appear necessary for this kind of formulation, we shall attempt to derive relations among commonly used measures of behavior and quantitative expressions describing various simple learning phenomena.

PRELIMINARY CONSIDERATIONS

Since propositions concerning psychological events are verifiable only to the extent that they are reducible to predictions of behavior under specified environmental conditions, it appears likely that greatest economy and consistency in theoretical structure will result from the statement of all fundamental laws in the form

$$R = f(S),$$

where R and S represent behavioral and environmental variables respectively. Response-inferred laws, as for example those of differential psychology, should be derivable from relationships of this form. The reasoning underlying this position has been developed in a recent paper by Spence (8). Although developed within this general framework, the present formulation departs to some extent from traditional definitions of S and R variables.

Many apparent differences among contemporary learning theories seem to be due in part to an oversimplified definition of stimulus and response. The view of stimulus and response as elementary, reproducible units has always had considerable appeal because of its simplicity. This simplicity is deceptive, however, since it entails the postulation of various hypothetical processes to ac-

[*] For continual reinforcement of his efforts at theory construction, as well as for many specific criticisms and suggestions, the writer is indebted to his colleagues at Indiana University, especially Cletus J. Burke, Douglas G. Ellson, Norman Guttman, and William S. Verplanck.

This article appeared in *Psychol. Rev.*, 1950, **57**, 94–104, 106–107 (abridged).

count for observed variability in behavior. In the present formulation, we shall follow the alternative approach of including the notion of variability in the definitions of stimulus and response, and investigating the theoretical consequences of these definitions.

It will also be necessary to modify the traditional practice of stating laws of learning in terms of relations between isolated stimuli and responses. Attempts at a quantitative description of learning and extinction of operant behavior have led the writer to believe that a self-consistent theory based upon the classical *S-R* model may be difficult, if not impossible, to extend over any very wide range of learning phenomena without the continual addition of *ad hoc* hypotheses to handle every new situation. A recurrent difficulty might be described as follows. In most formulations of simple learning, the organism is said originally to "do nothing" in the presence of some stimulus; during learning, the organism comes to make some predesignated response in the presence of the stimulus; then during extinction, the response gradually gives way to a state of "not responding" again. But this type of formulation does not define a closed or conservative system in any sense. In order to derive properties of conditioning and extinction from the same set of general laws, it is necessary to assign specific properties to the state of not responding which is the alternative to occurrence of the designated response. One solution is to assign properties as needed by special hypotheses, as has been done, for example, in the Pavlovian conception of inhibition. In the interest of simplicity of theoretical structure, we shall avoid this procedure so far as possible.

The role of competing reactions has been emphasized by some writers, but usually neglected in formal theorizing.

The point of view to be developed here will adopt as a standard conceptual model a closed system of behavioral and environmental variables. In any specific behavior-system, the environmental component may include either the entire population of stimuli available in the situation or some specified portion of that population. The behavioral component will consist in mutually exclusive classes of responses, defined in terms of objective criteria; these classes will be exhaustive in the sense that they will include all behaviors which may be evoked by that stimulus situation. Given the initial probabilities of the various responses available to an organism in a given situation, we shall expect the laws of the theory to enable predictions of changes in those probabilities as a function of changes in values of independent variables.

DEFINITIONS AND ASSUMPTIONS

1. *R-variables.* It will be assumed that any movement or sequence of movements may be analyzed out of an organism's repertory of behavior and treated as a "response," various properties of which can be treated as dependent variables subject to all the laws of the theory. (Hereafter we shall abbreviate the word response as *R,* with appropriate subscripts where necessary.) In order to avoid a common source of confusion, it will be necessary to make a clear distinction between the terms *R*-class and *R*-occurrence.

The term *R*-class will always refer to a class of behaviors which produce environmental effects within a specified range of values. This definition is not without objection (*cf.* 4) but has the advantage of following the actual practice of most experimenters. It may be possible eventually to coordinate *R*-classes defined in terms of environmental effects with *R*-classes defined in terms of effector activities.

By R-occurrence we shall mean a particular, unrepeatable behavioral event. All occurrences which meet the defining criteria of an R-class are counted as instances of that class, and as such are experimentally interchangeable. In fact, various instances of an R-class are ordinarily indistinguishable in the record of an experiment even though they may actually vary with respect to properties which are not picked up by the recording mechanism.

Indices of tendency to respond, *e.g.*, probability as defined below, always refer to R-classes.

These distinctions may be clarified by an illustration. In the Skinner-type conditioning apparatus, bar-pressing is usually treated as an R-class. Any movement of the organism which results in sufficient depression of the bar to actuate the recording mechanism is counted as an instance of the class. The R-class may be subdivided into finer classes by the same kind of criteria. We could, if desired, treat depression of a bar by the rat's right forepaw and depression of the bar by the left forepaw as instances of two different classes provided that we have a recording mechanism which will be affected differently by the two kinds of movements and mediate different relations to stimulus input (as for example the presentation of discriminative stimuli or reinforcing stimuli). If probability is increased by reinforcement, then reinforcement of a right-forepaw-bar-depression will increase the probability that instances of that subclass will occur, and will also increase the probability that instances of the broader class, bar-pressing, will occur.

2. S-variables. For analytic purposes it is assumed that all behavior is conditional upon appropriate stimulation. It is not implied, however, that responses can be predicted only when eliciting stimuli can be identified. Ac-cording to the present point of view, laws of learning enable predictions of changes in probability of response as a function of time under given environmental conditions.

A stimulus, or stimulating situation, will be regarded as a finite population of relatively small, independent, environmental events, of which only a sample is effective at any given time. In the following sections we shall designate the total number of elements associated with a given source of stimulation as S (with appropriate subscripts where more than one source of stimulation must be considered in an experiment), and the number of elements effective at any given time as s. It is assumed that when experimental conditions involve the repeated stimulation of an organism by the "same stimulus," that is by successive samples of elements from an S-population, each sample may be treated as an independent random sample from S. It is to be expected that sample size will fluctuate somewhat from one moment to the next, in which case s will be treated as the average number of elements per sample over a given period.

In applying the theory, any portion of the environment to which the organism is exposed under uniform conditions may be considered an S-population. The number of different S's said to be present in a situation will depend upon the number of independent experimental operations, and the degree of specificity with which predictions of behavior are to be made. If the experimenter attempts to hold the stimulating situation constant during the course of an experiment, then the entire situation will be treated as a single S. If in a conditioning experiment, a light and shock are to be independently manipulated as the CS and US, then each of these sources of stimulation will be treated as a separate S-population, and so on.

It should be emphasized that the division of environment and behavior into elements. is merely an analytic device adopted to enable the application of the finite-frequency theory of probability to behavioral phenomena. In applying the theory to learning experiments we shall expect to evaluate the ratio s/S for any specific situation from experimental evidence, but for the present at least no operational meaning can be given to a numerical value for either S or s taken separately.

3. *Probability of response.* Probability will be operationally defined as the average frequency of occurrence of instances of an R-class relative to the maximum possible frequency, under a specified set of experimental conditions, over a period of time during which the conditions remain constant. In accordance with customary usage the term probability, although defined as a relative frequency, will also be used to express the likelihood that a response will occur at a given time.

4. *Conditional relation.* This relation may obtain between an R-class and any number of the elements in an S-population, and has the following implications.

(a) If a set of x elements from an S are conditioned to (*i.e.*, have the conditional relation to) some R-class, R_1, at a given time, the probability that the next response to occur will be an instance of R_1 is x/S.

(b) If at a given time in an S-population, x_1 elements are conditioned to some R-class, R_1, and x_2 elements are conditioned to another class, R_2, then x_1 and x_2 have no common elements.

(c) If all behaviors which may be evoked from an organism in a given situation have been categorized into mutually exclusive classes, then the probabilities attaching to the various classes must sum to unity at all times.

We consider the organism to be always "doing something." If any arbitrarily defined class of activities may be selected as the dependent variable of a given experiment, it follows that the activity of the organism at any time must be considered as subject to the same laws as the class under consideration. Any increase in probability of one R-class during learning will, then, necessarily involve the reduction in probability of other classes; similarly, while the probability of one R decreases during extinction, the probabilities of others must increase. In other words, learning and unlearning will be considered as transfers of probability relations between R-classes.

5. *Conditioning.* It is assumed that on each occurrence of a response, R_1, all new elements (*i.e.*, elements not already conditioned to R_1) in the momentarily effective sample of stimulus elements, s, become conditioned to R_1.

An important implication of these definitions is that the conditioning of a stimulus element to one R automatically involves the breaking of any pre-existing conditional relations with other R's.

6. *Motivation.* Experimental operations which in the usual terminology are said to produce motives (*e.g.*, food-deprivation) may affect either the composition of an S or the magnitude of the s/S ratio. Detailed discussion of these relations is beyond the scope of the present paper. In all derivations presented here we shall assume motivating conditions constant throughout an experiment.

7. *Reinforcement.* This term will be applied to any experimental condition which ensures that successive occurrences of a given R will each be contiguous with a new random sample of elements from some specified S-population. Various ways of realizing this definition experimentally will be discussed in the following sections.

SIMPLE CONDITIONING: REINFORCEMENT BY CONTROLLED ELICITATION

Let us consider first the simplest type of conditioning experiment. The system to be described consists of a subpopulation of stimulus elements, S_c, which may be manipulated independently of the remainder of the situation, S, and a class, R, of behaviors defined by certain measurable properties. By means of a controlled original stimulus, that is, one which has initially a high probability of evoking R, it is ensured that an instance of R will occur on every trial contiguously with the sample of stimulus elements which is present. In the familiar buzz-shock conditioning experiment, for example, S_c would represent the population of stimulus elements emanating from the sound source and R would include all movements of a limb meeting certain specifications of direction and amplitude; typically, the R to be conditioned is a flexion response which may be evoked on each training trial by administration of an electric shock.

Designating the mean number of elements from S_c effective on any one trial as s_c, and the number of elements from S_c which are conditioned to R at any time as x, the expected number of new elements conditioned on any trial will be

$$\Delta x = s_c \frac{(S_c - x)}{S_c}. \qquad (1)$$

If the change in x per trial is relatively small, and the process is assumed continuous, the right hand portion of (1) may be taken as the average rate of change of x with respect to number of trials, T, at any moment, giving

$$\frac{dx}{dT} = s_c \frac{(S_c - x)}{S_c}. \qquad (2)$$

This differential equation may be integrated to yield

$$x = S_c - (S_c - x_0)e^{-qT}, \qquad (3)$$

where x_0 is the initial value of x, and q represents the ratio s_c/S_c. Thus x will increase from its initial value to approach the limiting value, S_c, in a negatively accelerated curve. A method of evaluating x in these equations from empirical measures of response latency, or reaction time, will be developed in a later section.

If the remainder of the situation has been experimentally neutralized, the probability of R in the presence of a sample from S_c will be given by the ratio x/S_c. Representing this ratio by the single letter p, and making appropriate substitutions in (3), we have the following expression for probability of R as a function of the number of reinforced trials.

$$p = 1 - (1 - p_0)e^{-qT}. \qquad (3')$$

Since we have not assumed any special properties for the original (or unconditioned) stimulus other than that of regularly evoking the response to be conditioned, it is to be expected that the equations developed in this section will describe the accumulation of conditional relations in other situations than classical conditioning, provided that other experimental operations function to ensure that the response to be learned will occur in the presence of every sample drawn from the S-population.

OPERANT CONDITIONING: REINFORCEMENT BY CONTINGENT STIMULATION

In the more common type of experimental arrangement, various termed operant, instrumental, trial and error, etc. by different investigators, the response to be learned is not elicited by a controlled original stimulus, but has some initial strength in the experimental situation and occurs originally as part of so-called "random activity." Here the response cannot be evoked concurrently with the presentation of each new stimulus sample, but some of the same effects can be secured by making changes in the stimulating situation contingent upon occurrences of the response. Let us consider a situation of this sort, assuming that the activities of the organism have been catalogued and classified into two categories, all movement sequences characterized by a certain set of properties being assigned to class R and all others to the class R_e, and that members of class R are to be learned.

If changes in the stimulus sample are independent of the organism's behavior, we should expect instances of the two response classes to occur, on the average, at rates proportional to their initial probabilities. For if x elements from the S-population are originally conditioned to R, then the probability of R will be x/S; the number of new elements conditioned to R if an instance occurs will be $s[(S-x)/S]$, s again representing the number of stimulus elements in a sample; and the mathematically expected increase in x will be the product of these quantities, $sx[(S-x)/S^2]$. At the same time, the probability of R_e will be $(S-x)/S$, and the number of new elements conditioned to R_e if an instance occurs will be sx/S; multiplying these quantities, we have $sx[(S-x)/S^2]$ as the mathematically expected decrease in x. Thus we should predict no average change in x under these conditions.

In the acquisition phase of a learning experiment two important restrictions imposed by the experimenter tend to force a correlation between changes in the stimulus sample and occurrences of R. The organism is usually introduced into the experimental situation at the beginning of a trial, and the

trial lasts until the pre-designated response, R, occurs. For example, in a common discrimination apparatus the animal is placed on a jumping stand at the beginning of each trial and the trial continues until the animal leaves the stand; a trial in a runway experiment lasts until the animal reaches the end box, and so on. Typically the stimulating situation present at the beginning of a trial is radically changed, if not completely terminated, by the occurrence of the response in question; and a new trial begins under the same conditions, except for sampling variations, after some pre-designated interval. The pattern of movement-produced stimuli present during a trial may be changed after occurrences of R by the evocation of some uniform bit of behavior such as eating or drinking; in some cases the behavior utilized for this purpose must be established by special training prior to a learning experiment. In the Skinner box, for example, the animal is trained to respond to the sound of the magazine by approaching it and eating or drinking. Then when operation of the magazine follows the occurrence of a bar-pressing response during conditioning of the latter, the animal's response to the magazine will remove it from the stimuli in the vicinity of the bar and ensure that for an interval of time thereafter the animal will not be exposed to most of the S-population; therefore the sample of elements to which the animal will next respond may be considered very nearly a new random sample from S.

In the simplest operant conditioning experiments it may be possible to change almost the entire stimulus sample after each occurrence of R (complete reinforcement), while in other cases the sampling of only some restricted portion of the S-population is correlated with R (partial reinforcement). We shall consider the former case in some detail in the remainder of this section.

By our definition of the conditional relation, we shall expect all R-classes from which instances actually occur on any trial to be conditioned to stimulus elements present on that trial. The first movement to occur will be conditioned to the environmental cues present at the beginning of the trial; the next movement will be conditioned to some external cues, if the situation is not completely constant during a trial, and to proprioceptive cues from the first movement, and so on, until the predesignated response, R, occurs and terminates the trial. If complete constancy of the stimulating situation could be maintained, the most probable course of events on the next trial would be the recurrence of the same sequence of movements. In practice, however, the sample of effective stimulus elements will change somewhat in composition, and some responses which occur on one trial may fail to occur on the next. The only response which may never be omitted is R, since the trial continues until R occurs. This argument has been developed in greater detail by Guthrie (4). In order to verify the line of reasoning involved, we need now to set these ideas down in mathematical form and investigate the possibility of deriving functions which will describe empirical curves of learning.

Since each trial lasts until R occurs, we need an expression for the probable duration of a trial in terms of the strength of R. Suppose that we have categorized all movement sequences which are to be counted as "responses" in a given situation, and that the minimum time needed for completion of a response-occurrence is, on the average, h. For convenience in the following development, we shall assume that the mean duration of instances of class R is approximately equal to that of class R_e. Let the total number of stimulus elements available in the experimental situation be represented by S, the sample effective on any one trial by s, and the ratio s/S by q. The probability, p, of class R at the beginning of any trial will have the value x/S; if this value varies little within a trial, we can readily compute the probable number of responses (of all classes) that will occur before the trial is terminated. The probability that an instance of R will be the first response to occur on the trial in question is p; the probability that it will be the second is $p(1-p)$; the probability that it will be the third is $p(1-p)^2$; etc. If we imagine an indefinitely large number of trials run under identical conditions, and represent the number of response occurrences on any trial by n, we may weight each possible value of n by its probability (i.e., expected relative frequency) and obtain a mean expected value of n. In symbolic notation we have

$$\bar{n} = \Sigma n p (1 - p)^{n-1} = p \Sigma n (1 - p)^{n-1}.$$

The expression inside the summation sign will be recognized as the general term of a well-known infinite series with the sum $1/(1 - (1 - p))^2$. Then we have, by substitution,

$$\bar{n} = p/(1 - (1 - p))^2 = 1/p.$$

Then $\bar{L}$, the average time per trial, will be the product of the expected number of responses and the mean time per response.

$$\bar{L} = \bar{n}h = h/p = Sh/x.$$

Since R will be conditioned to all new stimulus elements present on each trial, we may substitute for x its equivalent from equation (3), dropping the subscripts from S_c and s_c, and obtaining

$$\bar{L} = \frac{Sh}{S - (S - x_0)e^{-qT}}$$

$$= \frac{h}{1 - \frac{(\bar{L}_0 - h)e^{-qT}}{\bar{L}_0}}. \quad (4)$$

Thus, $\bar{L}$ will decline from an initial value of $\bar{L}_0$ (equal to Sh/x_0) and approach the asymptotic minimum value h over a series of trials.

A preliminary test of the validity of this development may be obtained by applying equation (4) to learning data from a runway experiment in which the conditions assumed in the derivation are realized to a fair degree of approximation. In Fig. 1 we have plotted acquisition data reported by Graham and Gagné (3). Each empirical point represents the geometric mean latency for a group of 21 rats which were reinforced with food for traversing a simple elevated runway. The theoretical curve

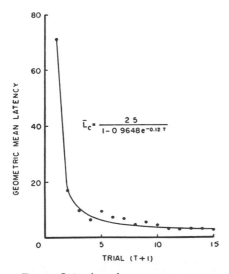

FIG. 1. Latencies of a runway response during conditioning, obtained from published data of Graham and Gagné (3), are fitted by a theoretical curve derived in the text.

in the figure represents the equation

$$\bar{L} = \frac{2.5}{1 - .9648e^{-.12T}},$$

where values of $\bar{L}_0$, h, and q have been estimated from the data. This curve appears to give a satisfactory graduation of the obtained points and, it might be noted, is very similar in form to the theoretical acquisition curve developed by Graham and Gagné. The present formulation differs from theirs chiefly in including the time of the first response as an integral part of the learning process. The quantitative description of extinction in this situation will be presented in a forthcoming paper.

In order to apply the present theory to experimental situations such as the Skinner box, in which the learning period is not divided into discrete trials, we shall have to assume that the intervals between reinforcements in those situations may be treated as "trials" for analytical purposes. Making this assumption, we may derive an expression for rate of change of conditioned response strength as a function of time in the experimental situation, during a period in which all responses of class R are reinforced.

$\bar{L}$, as defined above, will represent the time between any two occurrences of R. Then if we let t represent time elapsed from the beginning of the learning period to a given occurrence of R, and T the number of occurrences (and therefore reinforcements) of R, we have from the preceding development

$$\bar{L} = Sh/x.$$

Since $\bar{L}$ may be considered as the increment in time during a trial, we can write the identity

$$\frac{\Delta x}{\Delta t} = \frac{\Delta x}{\Delta T} \cdot \frac{\Delta T}{\Delta t}.$$

Substituting for $\Delta x/\Delta T$ its equivalent from (1), without subscripts, and for

$\Delta T/\Delta t$ its equivalent from the preceding equation, we have

$$\frac{\Delta x}{\Delta t} = \frac{s(S - x)}{S} \cdot \frac{x}{hS} = \frac{s(S - x)x}{hS^2}. \quad (5)$$

If the change in x per reinforcement is small and the process is assumed continuous, the right hand portion of equation (5) may be taken as the value of the derivative dx/dt and integrated with respect to time—

$$x = \frac{S}{1 + \dfrac{(S - x_0)}{x_0}e^{-Bt}}, \quad (6)$$

where $B = s/Sh$. In general, this equation defines a logistic curve with the amount of initial acceleration depending upon the value of x_0. Curves of probability (x/S) vs. time for $S = 100$, $B = 0.25$, and several different values of x_0 are illustrated in Fig. 2.

Since we are considering a situation in which a reinforcement is administered (or a new "trial" is begun) after each occurrence of R, we are now in a position to express the expected rate of occurrence of R as a function of time. Representing rate of occurrence of R by $r = dR/dt$, and the ratio $1/h$ by w, we have

$$r = \frac{dR}{dt} = \frac{dT}{dt} = \frac{wx}{S} = \frac{w}{1 + \dfrac{(S - x_0)}{x_0}e^{-Bt}}$$

and if we take the rate of R at the beginning of the experimental period as $r_0 = wx_0/S$ this relation becomes

$$r = \frac{w}{1 + \dfrac{(w - r_0)}{r_0}e^{-Bt}}. \quad (7)$$

To illustrate this function, we have plotted in Fig. 3 measures of rate of

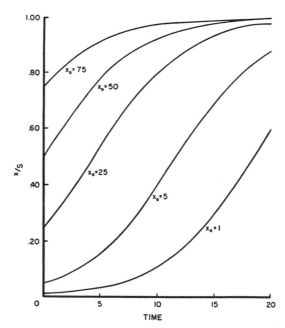

FIG. 2. Illustrative curves of probability vs. time during conditioning; parameters of the curves are the same except for the initial x-values.

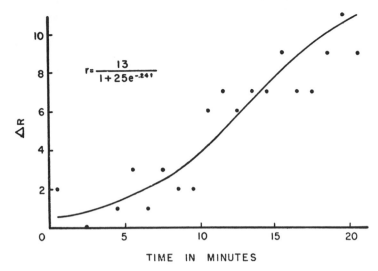

FIG. 3. Number of responses per minute during conditioning of a bar-pressing habit in a single rat; the theoretical curve is derived in the text.

responding during conditioning of a bar-pressing response by a single rat. The apparatus was a Skinner box; motivation was 24 hours thirst; the animal had previously been trained to drink out of the magazine, and during the period illustrated was reinforced with water for all bar-pressing responses. Measures of rate at various times were obtained by counting the number of responses made during the half-minute before and the half-minute after the point being considered, and taking that value as an estimate of the rate in terms of responses per minute at the midpoint. The theoretical curve in the figure represents the equation

$$r = \frac{13}{1 + 25e^{-.24t}}.$$

A considerable part of the variability of the empirical points in the figure is due to the inaccuracy of the method of estimating rates. In order to avoid this loss of precision, the writer has adopted the practice of using cumulative curves of responses vs. time for most purposes, and fitting the cumulative records with the integral of equation(7):

$$R = wt + \frac{w}{B} \log \left(\frac{r_0}{w} + \frac{(w - r_0)}{w} e^{-Bt} \right), \quad (8)$$

where R represents the number of responses made after any interval of time, t, from the beginning of the learning period. The original record of responses vs. time, from which the data of Fig. 3 were obtained, is reproduced in Fig. 4. Integration of the rate equation for this animal yields

$$R = 13t + 125 \log_{10} (.038 + .962e^{-.24t}).$$

Magnitudes of R computed from this equation for several values of t have been plotted in Fig. 4 to indicate the goodness of fit; the theoretical curve has not been drawn in the figure since it would completely obscure most of the empirical record. In an experimental report now in press (2), equation (8) is fitted to several mean conditioning curves for groups of four rats; in all cases, the theoretical curve accounts for

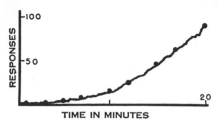

Fig. 4. Reproduction of the original cumulative record from which the points of Fig. 3 were obtained. Solid circles are computed from an equation given in the text.

more than 99 per cent of the variance of the observed R values. Further verification of the present formulation has been derived from that study by comparing the acquisition curves of successively learned bar-pressing habits, obtained in a Skinner-type conditioning apparatus which included two bars differing only in position. It has been found that the parameters w and s/S can be evaluated from the conditioning curve of one bar response, and then used to predict the detailed course of conditioning of a second learned response.

The overall accuracy of these equations in describing the rate of conditioning of bar-pressing and runway responses should not be allowed to obscure the fact that a small but systematic error is present in the initial portion of most of the curves. It is believed that these disparities are due to the fact that experimental conditions do not usually fully realize the assumption that only one R-class receives any reinforcement during the learning period.

DISCUSSION

The foregoing sections will suffice to illustrate the manner in which problems of learning may be handled within the framework of a statistical theory. The extent to which the formal system developed here may be fruitfully applied to interpret experimental phenomena can only be answered by a considerable program of research. A study of concurrent conditioning and extinction of simple skeletal responses which realizes quite closely the simplified conditions assumed in the derivations of the present paper has been completed, and a report is now in press. Other papers in preparation will apply this formulation to extinction, spontaneous recovery, discrimination, and related phenomena.

The relation of this program to contemporary theories of learning requires little comment. No attempt has been made to present a "new" theory. It is the purpose of our investigation to clarify some of the conceptions of learning and discrimination by stating important concepts in quantitative form and investigating their interrelationships by mathematical analysis. Many similarities will be noted between functions developed here and "homologous" expressions in the quantitative formulations of Graham and Gagné (3) and of Hull (6). A thorough study of those theories has influenced the writer's thinking in many respects. Rather than build directly on either of those formulations, I have felt it desirable to explore an alternative point of view based on a statistical definition of environment and behavior and doing greater justice to the theoretical views of Skinner and Guthrie. A statistical theory seems to be an inevitable development at the present stage of the science of behavior; agreement on this point may be found among writers of otherwise widely diverse viewpoints, *e.g.*, Brunswik (1), Hoagland (5), Skinner (7), and Wiener (9). It is to be expected that with increasing rigor of definition and continued interplay between theory and experiment, the various formulations of learning will tend to converge upon a common set of concepts.

It may be helpful to outline briefly the point of view on certain controversial issues implied by the present analysis.

Stimulus-response terminology. An attempt has been made to overcome some of the rigidity and oversimplification of traditional stimulus-response theory without abandoning its principal advantages. We have adopted a definition of stimulus and response similar to Skinner's (7) concept of generic classes, and have given it a statistical interpretation. Laws of learning developed within this framework refer to behavior systems (as defined in the introductory section of this paper) rather than to relations between isolated stimulus-response correlations.

The learning curve. This investigation is not intended to be another search for "the learning function." The writer does not believe that any simple function will be found to account for learning independently of particular experimental conditions. On the other hand, it does seem quite possible that from a relatively small set of definitions and assumptions we may be able to derive expressions describing learning under various specific experimental arrangements.

Measures of behavior. Likelihood of responding has been taken as the primary dependent variable. Analyses presented above indicate that simple relations can be derived between probability and such common experimentally obtained measures as rate of responding and latency.

Laws of contiguity and effect. Available experimental evidence on simple learning has seemed to the writer to require the assumption that temporal contiguity of stimuli and behavior is a necessary condition for the formation of conditional relations. At the level of differential analysis, that is of laws relating momentary changes in behavior to changes in independent variables, no other assumption has proved necessary at the present stage of the investi-

gation. In order to account for the accumulation of conditional relations in favor of one R-class at the expense of others in any situation, we have appealed to a group of experimental operations which are usually subsumed under the term "reinforcement" in current experimental literature. Both Guthrie's (4) verbal analyses and the writer's mathematical investigations indicate that an essential property of reinforcement is that it ensures that successive occurrences of a given R will be contiguous with different samples from the available population of stimuli. We have made no assumptions concerning the role of special properties of certain after-effects of responses, such as drive-reduction, changes in affective tone, etc. Thus the quantitative relations developed here may prove useful to investigators of learning phenomena regardless of the investigators' beliefs as to the nature of underlying processes.

SUMMARY

An attempt has been made to clarify some issues in current learning theory by giving a statistical interpretation to the concepts of stimulus and response and by deriving quantitative laws that govern simple behavior systems. Dependent variables, in this formulation, are classes of behavior samples with common quantitative properties; independent variables are statistical distributions of environmental events. Laws of the theory state probability relations between momentary changes in behavioral and environmental variables.

From this point of view it has been possible to derive simple relations between probability of response and several commonly used measures of learning, and to develop mathematical expressions describing learning in both classical conditioning and instrumental learning situations under simplified conditions.

No effort has been made to defend

the assumptions underlying this formulation by verbal analyses of what "really" happens inside the organism or similar arguments. It is proposed that the theory be evaluated solely by its fruitfulness in generating quantitative functions relating various phenomena of learning and discrimination.

REFERENCES

1. BRUNSWIK, E. Probability as a determiner of rat behavior. *J. exp. Psychol.*, 1939, 25, 175–197.
2. ESTES, W. K. Effects of competing reactions on the conditioning curve for bar-pressing. *J. exp. Psychol.* (in press).
3. GRAHAM, C. H., & GAGNÉ, R. The acquisition, extinction, and spontaneous recovery of a conditioned operant response. *J. exp. Psychol.,* 1940, 26, 251–280.
4. GUTHRIE, E. R. Psychological facts and psychological theory. *Psychol Bull.,* 1946, 43, 1–20.
5. HOAGLAND, H. The Weber-Fechner law and the all-or-none theory. *J. gen. Psychol.,* 1930, 3, 351–373.
6. HULL, C. L. *Principles of behavior.* New York: Appleton-Century, 1943.
7. SKINNER, B. F. *The behavior of organisms.* New York: Appleton-Century, 1938.
8. SPENCE, K. W. The nature of theory construction in contemporary psychology. PSYCHOL. REV., 1944, 51, 47–68.
9. WIENER, N. *Cybernetics.* New York: Wiley, 1948.

[MS. received July 15, 1949]

A Theory of Stimulus Variability in Learning[1]

W. K. ESTES and C. J. BURKE, *Indiana University*

There are a number of aspects of the stimulating situation in learning experiments that are recognized as important by theorists of otherwise diverse viewpoints but which require explicit representation in a formal model for effective utilization. One may find, for example, in the writings of Skinner, Hull, and Guthrie clear recognition of the statistical character of the stimulus concept. All conceive a stimulating situation as made up of many components which vary more or less independently. From this locus of agreement, strategies diverge. Skinner (17) incorporates the notion of variability into his stimulus-class concept, but makes little use of it in treating data. Hull states the concept of multiple components explicitly (13) but proceeds to write postulates concerning the conditions of learning in terms of single components, leaving a gap between the formal theory and experimentally defined variables. Guthrie (11) gives verbal interpretations of various phenomena, e.g., effects of repetition, in terms of stimulus variability; these interpretations generally appear plausible but they have not gained wide acceptance among investigators of learning, possibly because Guthrie's assumptions have not been formalized in a way that would make them easily used by others. Statistical theories of learning differ from Hull in making stimulus variability a central concept to be used for explanatory purposes rather than treating it as a source of error, and they go beyond Skinner and Guthrie in attempting to construct a formalism that will permit unambiguous statements of assumptions about stimulus variables and rigorous derivation of the consequences of these assumptions.

It has been shown in a previous paper (7) that several quantitative aspects of learning, for example the exponential curve of habit growth regularly obtained in certain conditioning experiments, follow as consequences of statistical assumptions and need not be accounted for by independent postulates. All of the derivations were carried out, however, under the simplifying assumption that all components of a stimulating situation are equally likely to occur on any trial. By removing that restriction, we are now in a position to generalize and extend the theory in several respects. It will be possible to show that regardless of whether assumptions as to the necessary conditions for learning are drawn from contiguity theories or from reinforcement theories, certain characteristics of the learning process are invariant with respect to stimulus properties while other characteristics depend in specific ways upon the nature of the stimulating situation.

THE GENERALIZED SET MODEL: ASSUMPTIONS AND NOTATION

The exposure of an organism to a stimulating situation determines a set

[1] This paper is based upon a paper reported by the writers at the Boston meetings of the Institute of Mathematical Statistics in December 1951. The writers' thinking along these and related lines has been stimulated and their research has been facilitated by participation in an interuniversity seminar in mathematical models for behavior theory which met at Tufts College during the summer of 1951 and was sponsored by SSRC.

This article appeared in *Psychol. Rev.*, 1953, **60**, 276–286.

of events referred to collectively as stimulation. These events constitute the data of the various special disciplines concerned with vision, audition, etc. We wish to formulate our model of the stimulus situation so that information from these special disciplines can be fed into the theory, although utilization of that information will depend upon the demands of learning experiments.

For the present we shall make only the following very general assumptions about the stimulating situation: (*a*) The effect of a stimulus situation upon an organism may be regarded as made up of many component events. (*b*) When a situation is repeated on a series of trials, any one of these component stimulus events may occur on some trials and fail to occur on others; as a first approximation, at least, the relative frequencies of the various stimulus events when the same situation (as defined experimentally) occurs on a series of trials, may be represented by independent probabilities. We formulate these assumptions conceptually as follows:

(*a*) With any given organism we associate a set S^* of N^* elements.[2] The N^* elements of S^* are to represent all of the stimulus events that can occur in that organism in any situation whatever with each of these possible events corresponding to an element of the set. (*b*) For any reproducible stimulating situation we assume a distribution of values of the parameter θ; we represent by θ_i the probability that the stimulus event corresponding to the ith element of S^* occurs on any given trial.

[2] In the sequel, various sets will be designated by the letter S, accompanied by appropriate subscripts and superscripts. The letter N, with the same arrangement of subscripts and superscripts, always denotes the size of the set.

It is assumed that any change in the situation (and we shall attempt to deal only with controlled changes corresponding to manipulations of experimental variables) determines a new distribution of values of the θ_i. By repeating the "same" situation, we mean the same as described in physical terms, and we recognize that, strictly speaking, repetition of the same situation refers to an idealized state of affairs which can be approached by increasing experimental control but possibly never completely realized.

It is recognized that some sources of stimulation are internal to the organism. This means that in order to have a reproducible situation in a learning experiment it is necessary to control the maintenance schedule of the organism and also activities immediately preceding the trial. In the present paper we shall not use the term "trial" in a sufficiently extended sense to necessitate including in the θ distribution movement-produced-stimulation arising from the responses occurring on the trial.

We have noted that the behavior on a given trial is assumed to be a function of the stimulus elements which are sampled on that trial. If in a given situation certain elements of S^* have a probability $\theta = 0$ of being sampled, those elements have a negligible effect upon the behavior in that situation. For this reason we often represent a specific situation by means of a reduced set S. An element of S^* is in S if and only if it has a non-zero value of θ in the given situation. These sets are represented in Fig. 1. In this connection, we must note that a probability of zero for a given event does not mean that the event can never occur "accidentally"; this probability has the weaker meaning that the relative frequency of occurrence of the event is zero in the long run. For a

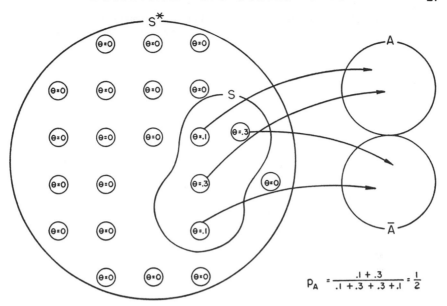

F$_{IG}$. 1. A schematic representation of stimulus elements, the stimulus space S^*, the reduced set S containing elements with non-zero θ values for a given stimulating situation, and the response classes A and $\bar{A}$. The arrows joining elements of S to the response classes represent the partition of S into S_A and $S_{\bar{A}}$

more detailed explication of this point the reader is referred to Cramér (5).

It should be clearly understood that the probability, θ, that a given stimulus event occurs on a trial may depend upon many different environmental events. For example, a stimulus event associated with visual stimulation may depend for its probability upon several different light sources in the environment. Suppose that for a given stimulus element, the associated probability θ in a given situation depends only upon two separately manipulable components of the environment, a and b, and that the probabilities of the element's being drawn if only a or b alone were present are θ_a and θ_b, respectively. Then the probability attached to this element in the situation with both components present will be

$$\theta = \theta_a + \theta_b - \theta_a\theta_b.$$

THE RESPONSE MODEL

The response model formulated in a previous paper (7) will be used here without any important modification. We shall deal only with the simple case of two mutually exclusive and exhaustive response classes. The response class being recorded in a given situation will be designated A and the complementary class, $\bar{A}$. The dependent variable of the theory is the probability that the response occurring on a given trial is a member of class A. It is recognized that in a learning experiment the behaviors available to the organism may be classified in many different ways, depending upon the interests of the experimenter. The response class selected for investigation may be anything from the simplest reflex to a complex chain of behaviors involving many different groups of effectors. Adequate treatment of all levels of response specification would require the formulation of a model for the response space and will not be attempted in the present paper. Preliminary investigation of this problem leads us to believe that when a response model is elaborated, the theory developed in this paper will be found to hold rigorously for the most elementary response components and to a first approximation for simple response classes that do not involve chaining. For experimental verification of the present theory we shall look to experiments involving response classes no more complex than flexing a limb, depressing a bar, or moving a key.

Conditional Relations and Response Probability

We assume that the behavior of an organism on any trial is a function, not of the entire population of possible stimulus events, but only of those stimulus events which occur on that trial; further, when learning takes place, it involves a change in the dependency of the response upon the stimulus events which have occurred on the given trial.

Conditional relations, or for brevity, connections, between response classes and stimulus elements are defined as in other papers on statistical learning theory (3, 7). The response classes A and $\bar{A}$ define a partition of S^* into two subsets S_A^* and $S_{\bar{A}}^*$. Elements in S_A^* are said to be "connected to" or "conditioned to" response A; those in $S_{\bar{A}}^*$ to response $\bar{A}$. The concept of a partition implies specifically that every element of S^* must be connected either to A or to $\bar{A}$ but that no element may be connected to both simultaneously.[3] Various features of the model are illustrated in Fig. 1.

[3] The argument of this section could as well be given in terms of the set S as of S^*, defin-

For each element in S^* we define a quantity $F_i(n)$ representing the probability that the element in question is connected to response A, i.e., is in the subset S_A^*, at the end of trial n. The mean value of $F_i(n)$ over S^* is, then, simply the expected proportion of elements connected to A, and if all of the θ_i were equal, it would be natural to define this proportion as the probability, $p(n)$, that response A occurs on trial $n + 1$. In the general case, however, not all of the θ_i are equal and the contribution of each element should be weighted by its probability of occurrence, giving

$$(1) \quad p(n) = \frac{\sum_i \theta_i F_i(n)}{\sum_i \theta_i} = \frac{1}{N^* \bar{\theta}} \sum_i \theta_i F_i(n).$$

It will be seen that in the equal θ case, expression (1) reduces to

$$(2) \quad p(n) = \frac{\theta}{N^* \theta} \sum_i F_i(n) = E(F_i(n))$$

which, except for changes in notation, is the definition used in previous papers (6, 7).

The quantity p is, then, another of the principal constructs of the theory. It is referred to as a probability, firstly because we assume explicitly that quantities p are to be manipulated mathematically in accordance with the axioms of probability theory, and secondly because in some situations p can be given a frequency interpretation. In any situation where a sequence of responses can be obtained under conditions of negligible learning and independent trials (as at the asymptote of a simple learning experiment carried out with discrete, well-spaced trials) the numerical value of p is taken as the average relative frequency of response A. For all situations the construct p is assumed to

ing S_A and $S_{\bar{A}}$ as the partition of S imposed by the response classes A and $\bar{A}$.

correspond to a parameter of the behavior system, and we do not cease to speak of this as a probability in the case of a situation where it cannot be evaluated as a relative frequency. It has been shown in a previous paper (7) that p can be related in a simple manner to rate or latency of responding in many situations; thus in all applications of the theory, p is evaluated in accordance with the rules prescribed by the theory, either from frequency data or from other appropriate data, and once evaluated is treated for all mathematical purposes as a probability.

REPRESENTATION OF LEARNING PROCESSES

In order to account for the gradual course of learning in most situations, a number of the earlier quantitative theories, e.g., those of Hull (13), Gulliksen and Wolfle (10), Thurstone (18) have assumed that individual connections are formed gradually over a series of learning trials. Once we adopt a statistical view of the stimulating situation, however, it can be shown rigorously that not only the gradual course of learning but the form of the typical learning curve can be accounted for in terms of probability considerations even if we assume that connections are formed on an all-or-none basis. This being the case, there seems to be no evidence whatsoever that would require a postulate of gradual formation of individual connections. Psychologically an all-or-none assumption has the advantage of enabling us to account readily for the fact that learning is sudden in some situations and gradual in others; mathematically, it has the advantage of great simplicity. For these reasons, recent statistical theories of learning have adopted some form of the all-or-none assumption (3, 7, 15).

Under an all-or-none theory, we must specify the probabilities that any stimulus element that is sampled on a given trial will become connected to A or to $\bar{A}$. For convenience in exposition, we shall limit ourselves in this paper to the simplest special case, i.e., a homogeneous series of discrete trials with probability equal to one that all elements occurring on a trial become connected to response A.

We begin by asking what can be said about the course of learning during a sequence of trials regardless of the distribution of stimulus events. It will be shown that our general assumptions define a family of mathematical operators describing learning during any prescribed sequence of trials, the member of the family applicable in a given situation depending upon the θ distribution. We shall first inquire into the characteristics common to all members of a family, and then into the conditions under which the operators can be approximated adequately by the relatively simple functions that have been found convenient for representing learning data in previous work.

Let us consider the course of learning during a sequence of trials in the simplified situation. Each trial in the series is to begin with the presentation of a certain stimulus complex. This situation defines a distribution of θ over S^* so that each element in S^* has some probability, θ_i, of occurring on any trial, and we represent by S the subset of elements with non-zero θ values; any element that occurs on a trial becomes connected to A (or remains connected to A if it has been drawn on a previous trial). For concreteness the reader might think of a simple conditioning experiment with the CS preceding the US by an optimal interval, and with conditions arranged so that the UR is evoked on each trial and decremental factors are negligible; the situation represented by S is that obtaining from the onset of the CS to the onset of the US, and the response probability p will refer to the probability of A in this situation. The number of elements in S will be designated by N. For simplicity we shall suppose in the following derivations that none of the elements in S are connected to A at the beginning of the experiment. This means that the learning curves obtained all begin with N_A and p equal to zero. No loss of generality is involved in this simplification; our results may easily be extended to the case of any arbitrary initial condition.

The ith element in S will still remain in $S_{\bar{A}}$ after the nth trial if and only if it is not sampled on any of the first n trials; the likelihood that this occurs is $(1 - \theta_i)^n$. Hence, if $F_i(n)$ represents the expected probability that this element is connected to A after the nth trial, we obtain:

$$(3) \qquad F_i(n) = 1 - (1 - \theta_i)^n.$$

The expected number of elements in S connected to A after the nth trial, $E[N_A(n)]$, will be the sum of these expected contributions from individual elements:

$$
\begin{aligned}
(4) \quad E[N_A(n)] &= \sum_i F_i(n) \\
&= \sum_i \left[1 - (1 - \theta_i)^n \right] \\
&= N - \sum_i (1 - \theta_i)^n.
\end{aligned}
$$

We are now in a position to express p, the probability of response A, as a function of the number of trials in this situation. By substituting for the term $F_i(n)$ of equation (1) its equivalent from equation (3), we obtain the relation

$$
\begin{aligned}
(5) \quad p(n) &= \frac{1}{N\bar{\theta}} \sum_i \theta_i \left[1 - (1 - \theta_i)^n \right] \\
&= 1 - \frac{1}{N\bar{\theta}} \sum_i \theta_i (1 - \theta_i)^n.
\end{aligned}
$$

Equation (5) defines a family of learning curves, one for each possible θ distribution, and it has a number of simple properties that are independent of the distribution of the θ_i. It can easily be verified by substitution that there is a fixed point at $p = 1$, and this will be the asymptote approached by the curve of $p(n)$ vs. n as n increases over all bounds. Members of the family will be monotonically increasing, negatively accelerated curves, approaching a simple negative growth function as the θ_i tend toward equality. If all of the θ_i are equal to $\bar{\theta}$, equation (5) reduces to

$$(6) \qquad p(n) = 1 - (1 - \bar{\theta})^n$$

which, except for a change in notation, is the same function derived previously (7) for the equal θ case [4] and corresponds to the linear operator used by Bush and Mosteller (2) for situations where no decremental factor is involved. In mathematical form, equation (6) is the same as Hull's well-known expression for growth of habit strength, but the function does not have the same relation to observed probability of responding in Hull's theory as in the present formulation.

Except where the distribution function of the θ_i either is known, or can be assumed on theoretical grounds to be approximated by some simple expression, equation (5) will not be convenient to work with. In practice we are apt to assume equal θ_i and utilize equation (6) to describe experimental data. The nature of the error of approximation involved in doing this can be stated generally. Immediately after the first trial, the curve for the general case must lie above the curve for the

[4] This is essentially the same function developed for the equal θ case in a previous paper (7); the terms $\bar{\theta}$ and n of equation (6) correspond to the terms $q = s/S$, and T of that paper.

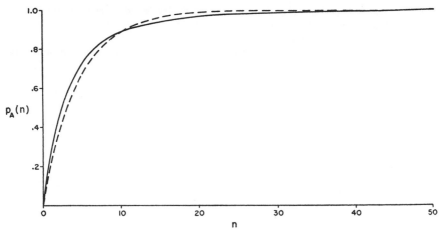

FIG. 2. Response probability, in S, as a function of number of trials for the numerical examples presented in the text. The solid curve is the exact solution for a population of elements, half of which have $\theta = 0.1$ and half $\theta = 0.3$. The dashed curve describes the equal θ approximation with $\bar{\theta} = 0.2$. Initially no elements of S are conditioned to A.

equal θ case; the difference between the two curves increases for a few trials, then decreases until they cross (in constructing hypothetical θ distributions of diverse forms we have usually found this crossing in the neighborhood of the fourth to eighth trial); after crossing, the curves diverge to a smaller extent than before, then come together as both go to the same asymptote at $p = 1$. It can be proved that the curves for the general and special case cross exactly once as n goes from one to infinity. We cannot make any general statement about the maximum error involved in approximating expression (5) with expression (6), but after studying a number of special cases, we are inclined to believe that the error introduced by the approximation will be too small to be readily detectable experimentally for most simple learning situations that do not involve compounding of stimuli.

The development of equations (5) and (6) has necessarily been given in rather general terms, and it may be helpful to illustrate some of the considerations involved by means of a simple numerical example. Imagine that we are dealing with some particular conditioning experiment in which the CS can be represented by a set S, composed of two subsets of stimulus elements, S_1 and S_2, of the sizes $N_1 = N_2 = N/2$, where N is the number of elements in S. Assume that for all elements in S_1 the probability of being drawn on any trial is $\theta_1 = 0.3$ and for those in S_2, $\theta_2 = 0.1$. Now we wish to compute the predicted learning curve during a series of trials on which A responses are reinforced, assuming that we begin with all elements connected to $\bar{A}$. Equation (5) becomes

$$p(n) = 1 - \frac{1}{0.2N}[N_1(0.3)$$
$$\times (1-0.3)^n + N_2(0.1)(1-0.1)^n]$$
$$= 1 - \frac{1}{0.4}[0.3(0.7)^n + 0.1(0.9)^n].$$

Plotting numerical values computed from this equation, we obtain the solid curve given in Fig. 2.

Now let us approach the same problem, but supposing this time that we know nothing about the different θ values in the subsets S_1 and S_2 and are given only that $\bar{\theta} = 0.2$. We now obtain predicted learning curves under the equal θ approximation. Equation (6) becomes:

$$p(n) = 1 - (1 - 0.2)^n$$

and numerical values computed from this yield the dashed curve of Fig. 2.

Inspection of Fig. 2 shows that the exact treatment leads to higher values of $p(n)$ on the early trials but to lower values on the later trials, the difference becoming negligible for large n. The reason, in brief, for the steeper curvature of the exact curve is that elements with high θ values are likely to be drawn, and therefore conditioned to A, earlier in the learning process than elements with low θ values, and then because they will tend to recur frequently in successive samples, to lead to relatively high values of p. During the late stages of learning, elements with low θ values that have not been drawn on the early trials will contribute more unconnected elements per trial than would be appearing at the same stage with an equal θ distribution and will depress the value of p below the curve for the equal θ approximation.

It should be emphasized that the generality of the present approach to learning theory lies in the concepts introduced and the methods developed for operating with them, not in the particular equations derived. Equation (5), for example, can be expected to apply only to an extremely narrow class of learning experiments. On the other hand, the methods utilized in deriving equation (5) are applicable to a wide variety of situations. For the interest of the experimentally oriented reader, we will indicate briefly a few of the most obvious extensions of the

theory developed above, limiting ourselves to the equal θ case.

As written, equation (6) represents the predicted course of conditioning for a single organism with an initial response probability of zero. We can allow for the possibility that an experiment may begin at some value of $p(0)$ other than zero by rewriting (6) in the more general form

$$(7) \qquad p(n) = 1 - [1 - p(0)](1 - \bar{\theta})^n$$

which has the same form as (6) except for the initial value.

If we wish to consider the mean course of conditioning in a group of m organisms with like values of $\bar{\theta}$ but varying initial response probabilities, we need simply sum equation (7) over the group and divide by m, obtaining

$$(8) \qquad \bar{p}(n) = \frac{1}{m} \sum p(n)$$
$$= 1 - [1 - \bar{p}(0)](1 - \bar{\theta})^n.$$

The standard deviation of $p(n)$ under these circumstances is simply

$$(9) \qquad \sigma_p(n) = \sqrt{\frac{1}{m} \sum p^2(n) - \bar{p}^2(n)}$$
$$= (1 - \bar{\theta})^n \sigma_p(0)$$

where $\sigma_p(0)$ is the dispersion of the initial p values for the group. Variability around the mean learning curve decreases to zero in a simple manner as learning progresses.

The treatment of counter-conditioning, i.e., extinguishing one response by giving uniform reinforcement to a competing response, follows automatically from our account of the acquisition process. Returning to equation (6) and recalling that the probabilities of A and $\bar{A}$ must always sum to unity, we note that while response A undergoes conditioning in accordance with (6), response $\bar{A}$ must undergo extinction in accordance with the function

$$p_{\bar{A}}(n) = 1 - p_A(n) = (1 - \bar{\theta})^n.$$

If, then, we begin with any arbitrary $p(0)$ and arrange conditions so that $\bar{A}$ is evoked and conditioned to all elements drawn on each trial, the extinction of response A will be given by the simple decay function

$$(10) \qquad p(n) = p(0)(1 - \bar{\theta})^n.$$

Again the mean and standard deviation of $p(n)$ can easily be computed for a group of organisms with like values of $\bar{\theta}$ but varying values of $p(0)$:

$$(11) \qquad \bar{p}(n) = \bar{p}(0)(1 - \bar{\theta})^n$$

$$(12) \qquad \sigma_p(n) = (1 - \bar{\theta})^n \sigma_p(0).$$

As in the case of acquisition, variability around the mean curve decreases to zero in a simple manner over a series of trials.

Since variability due to variation in $p(0)$ is reduced during both conditioning and counter-conditioning, it will be seen that in general we should expect less variability around a curve of relearning than around a curve of original learning for a given group of subjects.

APPLICATION OF THE STATISTICAL MODEL TO LEARNING EXPERIMENTS

Since our concern in this paper has been with the development of a stimulus model of considerable generality, it has been necessary in the interests of clear exposition to omit reference to most of the empirical material upon which our theoretical assumptions are based. The evaluation of the model must rest upon detailed interpretation of specific experimental situations. It is clear, however, that the statistical model developed here cannot be tested in isolation; only when it is taken together with assumptions as to how learning occurs and with rules of correspondence between terms of the theory and experimental variables, will experimental evaluation be possible. Limitations of space preclude a detailed theoretical analysis of individual learning situations in this paper. In order to indicate how the model will be utilized and to suggest some of its explanatory potentialities we shall conclude with a few general remarks concerning the interpretation of learning phenomena within the theoretical framework we have developed.

Application of the model to any one isolated experiment will always involve an element of circularity, for information about a given θ distribution must be obtained from behavioral data. This circularity disappears as soon as data are available from a number of related experiments. The utility of the concept is expected to lie in the possibility of predicting a variety of facts once the parameters of the θ distribution have been evaluated for a situation. The methodology involved has been illustrated on a small scale by an experiment (6) in which the mean θ value for an operant conditioning situation was estimated from the acquisition curve of a bar-pressing habit and then utilized in predicting the course of acquisition of a second bar-pressing habit by the same animals under slightly modified conditions.

When the statistical model is taken together with an assumption of association by contiguity, we have the essentials of a theory of simple learning. The learning functions (5), (6), and (10) derived above should be expected to provide a description of the course of learning in certain elementary experiments in the areas of conditioning and verbal association. It must be emphasized, however, that these functions alone will not constitute an adequate theory of conditioning, for a number of relevant variables, especially those controlling response decrement, have not been taken into account in our derivations. In conditioning experiments where decremental factors are minimized, there is considerable evidence (1, 4, 9, 14, 16) that the curve of conditioning has the principal properties of our equation (5) and can be well approximated by the equal θ case (7). The fact that functions derived from the model can be fitted to certain empirical curves is a desirable outcome, of course, but cannot be regarded as providing a very exacting test of the theory; probably any contemporary quantitative theory will manage to accomplish this much. On the other hand, the fact that the properties of our learning functions follow from the statistical nature of the stimulating situation is of some interest; in this respect the structure of the present theory is simpler than certain others, e.g., that of Hull (13), which require an independent postulate to account for the form of the conditioning curve.

It should also be noted that deviations from the exponential curve form may be as significant as instances of good fit. From the present model we must predict a specific kind of deviation when the stimulating situation contains elements of widely varying θ values. If, for example, curves of conditioning to two stimuli taken separately yield significantly different values of $\bar{\theta}$, then the curve of conditioning to a compound of the two stimuli should be expected to deviate further than either of the separate curves from a simple growth function. The only relevant experiment we have discovered in the literature is one reported by Miller (16); Miller's results appear to be in line with this analysis, but we would hesitate to regard this aspect of the theory as substantiated until additional relevant data become available.

Although we shall not develop the argument in mathematical detail in the present paper, it may be noted that the statistical association theory yields certain specific predictions concerning the effects of past learning upon the course of learning in a new situation. In general, the increment or decrement in p during any trial depends to a certain extent upon the immediately preceding sequence of trials. Suppose that we have two identical animals each of which has $p(n)$ equal, say, to 0.5 at the end of trial n of an experiment, and suppose that for each animal response A is reinforced on trial $n + 1$. The histories of the two animals are presumed to differ in that the first animal has arrived at $p(n) = 0.5$ via a sequence of reinforced trials while the second animal has arrived at this value via a sequence of unreinforced trials. On trial $n + 1$, the second animal will receive the greater increment to p (except in the equal θ case); the reason is, in brief, that for both animals the stimulus elements most likely to occur on trial $n + 1$ are those with high θ values; for the first animal these elements will have occurred frequently during the immediately preceding sequence of trials and thus will tend to be preponderantly connected to A prior to trial $n + 1$; in the case of the second animal, the high θ elements will have been connected to $\bar{A}$ during the immediately preceding sequence and thus when A is reinforced on trial $n + 1$, the second animal will receive the greater increment in weight of connected elements. From this analysis it follows that, other things equal, a curve of reconditioning will approach its asymptote more rapidly than the curve of original conditioning unless extinction has actually been carried to zero. How important the role of the unequal θ distribution will prove to be in accounting for empirical phenomena of relearning cannot be adequately judged until further research has provided means for estimating the orders of magnitude of the effects we have mentioned here.

SUMMARY

Earlier statistical treatments of simple associative learning have been refined and generalized by analyzing the stimulus concept in greater detail than heretofore and by taking account of the fact that different components of a stimulating situation may have different probabilities of affecting behavior.

The population of stimulus events corresponding to an independent experimental variable is represented in the statistical model by a mathematical set. The relative frequencies with which various aspects of the stimulus variable affect behavior in a given experiment are represented by set operations and functions.

The statistical model, taken together with an assumption of association by contiguity, provides a limited theory of certain conditioning phenomena. Within this theory it has been possible to distinguish aspects of the learning process that depend upon properties of the stimulating situation from those that do not. Certain general predictions from the theory concerning acquisition, extinction, and relearning, are compared with experimental findings.

Salient characteristics of the model elaborated here are compared with other quantitative formulations of learning.

REFERENCES

1. BROGDEN, W. J. Animal studies of learning. In S. S. Stevens (Ed.), *Handbook of experimental psychology*. New York: Wiley, 1951.
2. BUSH, R. R., & MOSTELLER, F. A mathematical model for simple learning. *Psychol. Rev.*, 1951, 58, 313–323.
3. BUSH, R. R., & MOSTELLER, F. A model for stimulus generalization and discrimination. *Psychol. Rev.*, 1951, 58, 413–423.
4. CALVIN, J. S. Decremental factors in conditioned-response learning. Unpublished Ph.D. thesis, Yale Univer., 1939.
5. CRAMÉR, H. *Mathematical methods of statistics.* Princeton: Princeton Univer. Press, 1946.
6. ESTES, W. K. Effects of competing reactions on the conditioning curve for bar pressing. *J. exp. Psychol.*, 1950, 40, 200–205.
7. ESTES, W. K. Toward a statistical theory of learning. *Psychol. Rev.*, 1950, 57, 94–107.
8. FELLER, W. *An introduction to probability theory and its applications.* New York: Wiley, 1950.
9. GRANT, D. A., & HAKE, H. W. Dark adaption and the Humphreys random reinforcement phenomenon in human eyelid conditioning. *J. exp. Psychol.*, 1951, 42, 417–423.
10. GULLIKSEN, H., & WOLFLE, D. L. A theory of learning and transfer. *Psychometrika*, 1938, 3, 127–149.
11. GUTHRIE, E. R. Psychological facts and psychological theory. *Psychol. Bull.*, 1946, 43, 1–20.
12. HILGARD, E. R., & MARQUIS, D. G. *Conditioning and learning.* New York: Appleton-Century, 1940.
13. HULL, C. L. *Principles of behavior.* New York: D. Appleton-Century, 1943.
14. HUMPHREYS, L. G. Acquisition and extinction of verbal expectations in a situation analogous to conditioning. *J. exp. Psychol.*, 1939, 25, 294–301.
15. MILLER, G. A., & McGILL, W. J. A statistical description of verbal learning. *Psychometrika*, in press.
16. MILLER, J. The rate of conditioning of human subjects to single and multiple conditioned stimuli. *J. gen. Psychol.*, 1939, 20, 399–408.
17. SKINNER, B. F. *The behavior of organisms.* New York: Appleton-Century-Crofts, 1938.
18. THURSTONE, L. L. The learning function. *J. gen. Psychol.*, 1930, 3, 469–493.

[MS. received November 12, 1952]

Probability of Response to Compounds of Discriminated Stimuli[1]

MAX S. SCHOEFFLER, *Indiana University*

This study is designed to determine the probability of a response when the stimulating situation that is presented is composed in part of a stimulus to which that response has been conditioned, and in part of a stimulus to which a competing response has been conditioned. The experiment goes beyond a related study by Gulliksen (2) in that it utilizes training and test conditions which can be readily related to a theory which provides quantitative predictions regarding response probability in such a compounded stimulus situation.

In the present study, a group of 24 lights was randomly divided for each O into three distinct groups of eight lights each (S_I, S_{II}, S_{III}). A group of Os was conditioned to respond by moving a lever in one direction when S_I was presented, and by moving it in the other direction when S_{II} was presented. When Os had learned to make the correct responses with a high probability of success, a trial was presented on which predetermined proportions of lights from S_I, S_{II}, and S_{III} were presented simultaneously. The proportion of Os responding to the side that had been associated with S_I during the discrimination training was taken as a measure of the probability of a response in the S_I direction under this compound stimulation.

[1] This study was taken from a dissertation submitted to the Department of Psychology of Indiana University in partial fulfillment of the requirements for the Ph.D. degree in psychology. The writer is greatly indebted to Professor W. K. Estes under whose direction this investigation was conducted.

The set theoretical model of learning developed by Estes and Burke (1) provides quantitative predictions regarding the probability of a response in the S_I direction. In this theory, the sets of lights, S_I, S_{II}, and S_{III}, are conceived of as nonoverlapping stimulus situations, each of which consists of a large number of stimulus elements. If, for example, the lights comprising set S_I are lighted on a given trial, it is assumed that a random sample of the elements associated with these lights is presented to O. Each light is assumed to have the same number of elements associated with it, and to each element there is associated a probability that it will be sampled when its light is presented. For purposes of simplification, it can be assumed that all elements have the same probability (θ) of being sampled when their corresponding lights are presented. The parameter θ, then, also represents the proportion of elements in a set that are sampled when the set is presented. These elements can become conditioned to a response, and under the conditions assumed in the present study, the probability of a response is equal to the proportion of elements in a set which are conditioned to that response. The Os learn the discrimination until they reach a high probability of success. If it is assumed that the discrimination is perfect, all the elements in S_I are considered to be conditioned to a given movement of the lever, and all the elements in S_{II} to the opposing response.

Prediction as to the probability of a

This article appeared in *J. exp. Psychol.*, 1954, **48**, 323–329.

movement in the direction associated with S_I, when lights from S_I, S_{II}, and S_{III} appear simultaneously, follows directly. If, for example, all the lights from S_I appear together with half of the lights from S_{II} on a test trial, it is possible to make the following analysis. Since all the elements associated with the S_I lights are conditioned to a certain response, the quantity $N\theta$, of conditioned elements is present, N being the total number of elements in any one of the sets. But at the same time half of the elements from S_{II} appear and none of these elements are conditioned to this response since they all have been conditioned to the opposing response. The proportion of the elements appearing that are conditioned to the response in the S_I direction is then $\dfrac{N\theta}{N\theta + \dfrac{N\theta}{2}}$, and the probability of this response is $\frac{2}{3}$.

This theoretically derived probability can be quantitatively compared with the observed proportion of Os responding to the side conditioned to S_I.

In a similar way, exact predictions can be made for other proportions of lights from S_I, S_{II}, and S_{III} presented simultaneously. If the lights from S_{III} are presented on a trial, it is assumed that since these lights have never appeared previously, half the elements corresponding to these lights are connected to a left movement and the other half to a right movement—the only responses available to the O.

METHOD

Subjects.—The Os for this experiment were 234 men and women undergraduates at Indiana University. The majority of Os were obtained from introductory psychology classes on a promise of extra points in their course work. The remainder were recruited singly without the offer of a reward.

Apparatus.—Facing O, there was a panel of $\frac{1}{2}$-in. plywood, 24 in. wide and 23 in. high. It was painted black and contained four rows and six columns of holes behind each of which was mounted a 6-w. light bulb. The distance between centers of adjacent holes was 4 in., in both the horizontal and vertical directions. In order to prevent the light from shining through an adjacent hole, a 1-in. piece of aluminum tubing was inserted into each hole reducing the inside diameter of the hole to $\frac{3}{8}$ in. The tubing was flush with the panel on the side toward O, and a rubber washer with an inside diameter of $\frac{3}{16}$ in. was placed between the tube and the bulb on the other side. The rest of the bulb was then painted black so that light from the bulb could pass only through the hole in front of it. Centered directly above the panel were two additional lights, one marked R and one marked L.

In front of the panel toward O, there was a black wooden box. A $\frac{1}{4}$-in. brass rod projected from this box toward O. This lever could be moved either to the right or to the left until it actuated a microswitch. The lever was spring loaded by means of rubber bands so as to be self-centering, and it projected 12 in. from the panel. The lever was $4\frac{3}{4}$ in. above the table, and O was seated so as to be in a comfortable position to move the lever. There was a distance of approximately 3 ft. between the front of the panel and the eyes of O. The E sat on the opposite side of the panel from O, and a 30-w. fluorescent bulb was placed behind E to permit recording. The whole apparatus was mounted on a table in a sound- and lightproof room.

The lights on top of the panel facing O were arranged so that when O moved the lever on a training trial, one of the lights (either R or L) would go on, depending on which pattern of panel lights was presented. This light then remained on as long as O kept the lever to the side or until the timing device terminated the trial. On the test trials, neither the R nor the L light came on. Each trial was automatically timed to last for a period of 2 sec. after which the apparatus was inoperative for 4 sec., the time of a complete cycle being 6 sec.

Procedure.—At the beginning of a session, O was read the following set of instructions:

"The purpose of the experiment is to find out how people learn to react correctly to different sets of stimuli. In front of you there is a panel of lights. When the experiment starts, some of those lights will go on for a period of 2 sec. As soon as the lights go on you are to move that lever in front of you either to the right or to the left. As soon as you have moved it, one of the lights on top—the ones marked R and L—one of those two lights will go on, indicating which way you should have moved the lever. If you make a mistake, do not attempt to correct it, but try to respond correctly on the next trial. You are to try to move the lever to the correct side on as many trials as possible—that is, to make as few errors as possible.

"On some trials neither light will go on so that in this case you will not know whether you have responded properly or not.

"Sometimes you may have difficulty trying to decide to which side to move the lever. If this happens make sure that you nevertheless move it during the 2 sec. in which the lights are on. If you have not moved before the lights go out again, it will count as an error, so even if you cannot make up your mind, move the lever immediately anyway, because you may have it correct.

"Are there any questions? Well, practice moving that lever a few times so that you get the feel of it. Well, we're ready to start now. Remember that you move the lever while the lights are on. Ready?"

If O had any questions, the appropriate parts of the instructions were reread until he stated that he had no further questions.

After these instructions had been read to O, S_I and S_{II} were presented in a random sequence (constructed separately for each O) with the restriction that within each block of ten trials there must be five S_I trials and five S_{II} trials. For half the Os, every time S_I was presented, the light marked L flashed when O responded and every time S_{II} was presented, the light marked R operated. For the other half of the Os, these conditions were reversed.

Thirty of these training trials were given to each O. If O made more than one error during the last ten trials he was dismissed. The Os who made either one or no errors during the last ten trials were continued in the experiment, and will hereafter be called "used" Os. On Trial 31, all these used Os were given the first of ten test trials. Between any two of these test trials some more training trials were given. The number of these varied randomly from three to five, with the restriction that for each O, three pairs of test trials were to be separated by three training trials, three pairs by four training trials, and three pairs by five training trials. In this way, all Os received the same total number of training trials (66 trials). There were nine different kinds of test patterns and each O received all of these. On the tenth test trial a given O again received the same condition he had had as his first test trial. This was done in order to permit analysis to determine the effect of additional training encountered when a test trial came late in the series. The nature of the test trials is described below.

The nine different kinds of test patterns corresponded to the varying proportions of

TABLE 1

THE PROPORTIONS OF LIGHTS FROM S_I, S_{II}, AND S_{III} PRESENTED ON A GIVEN KIND OF TEST TRIAL

Kind of Trial	Proportion			Total Number of Lights
	S_I	S_{II}	S_{III}	
1	1	1		16
2	1	$\frac{1}{2}$		12
3	1	$\frac{1}{4}$		10
4	$\frac{1}{2}$	$\frac{1}{4}$		6
5	1	$\frac{1}{2}$	1	20
6	1	$\frac{1}{4}$	1	18
7	$\frac{1}{2}$	$\frac{1}{4}$	1	14
8	1		1	16
9	1	1	1	24

lights from S_I, S_{II}, and S_{III} that were presented. A description of these trials is given in Table 1.

As mentioned previously, the 24 lights were divided randomly for each O into three groups of eight lights each. In order to determine which lights would be included in a given test pattern, the necessary number of lights was chosen randomly from each of the previously determined sets of eight, separately for each O and each test condition.

In order to balance for practice effect resulting from the fact that each O received all test patterns, the used Os were divided into nine groups of 20 Os each, and the test patterns were presented in the same order for all Os within each group. Each group received the test patterns in the order prescribed by the randomly chosen latin square in Table 2. The rows represent the different groups of 20 Os; the columns represent the ordinal positions of the test trials; and the entries in the cells represent the types of test trials.

Each of the groups of 20 Os arrived at in this way was further subdivided into two groups of ten each, half of the Os being trained to move right for S_I and the other half being trained to move left for S_I. The Os were assigned to groups haphazardly as they appeared for their appointments, but no group was permitted at any time to have more than two used Os in excess of any other group. In this way Os were added to each group until all groups had their quotas of 20 used Os. Altogether, 234 Os took part in the experiment, including 54 who were discarded for not fulfilling the criterion of no more than one incorrect response in the last 10 of the first 30 trials.

RESULTS

Figure 1 shows the curve describing the learning of the discrimination

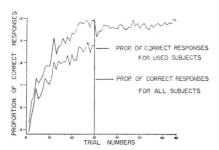

FIG. 1. Discrimination learning curves for all *O*s and for "used" *O*s. Test trials appearing after 30th training trial in curve for "used" *O*s are not shown.

based upon the two nonoverlapping sets of lights. The proportion of correct responses on each of the 30 training trials is plotted for all *O*s who served in the experiment, including the *O*s who did not fulfill the criterion of at least nine out of the last ten responses being correct, and who were

thereafter discarded from the rest of the experiment. Also shown is a curve constructed for only *O*s fulfilling the learning criterion; and this curve is extended for the complete set of 66 trials that these *O*s received. It must be noted here that the test trials which were given to the used *O*s after Trial 30 and at three to five trial intervals thereafter are not shown on this curve.

The number of *O*s responding to the S_I side on the test trials is given in Table 2. The test pattern associated with each cell is indicated by a roman numeral. The total possible entry in each cell is 20.

An analysis of this latin square indicates that there are significant differences among conditions but no significant differences with respect to groups or positions of test trials. The

TABLE 2

Latin-Square Arrangement Showing Number of Responses to S_I
Made by Each Group of *O*s to Each Test Pattern

Groups of *O*s N = 20	Ordinal Position of Test Pattern								
	1	2	3	4	5	6	7	8	9
1	I 14	VIII 16	VI 11	V 15	IV 9	II 18	III 18	IX 8	VII 12
2	V 11	VI 11	III 18	I 9	VIII 11	IX 8	II 16	VII 11	IV 10
3	IX 11	I 9	II 15	IV 12	VII 13	III 17	VIII 13	VI 15	V 12
4	VIII 14	IV 12	VII 10	II 16	III 15	VI 14	I 9	V 13	IX 13
5	III 15	II 17	IX 16	VIII 14	VI 12	VII 12	V 13	IV 13	I 10
6	VI 14	V 15	IV 14	IX 9	I 9	VIII 16	VII 9	III 16	II 14
7	IV 14	III 16	VIII 17	VII 10	V 13	I 12	IX 10	II 14	VI 16
8	II 16	VII 10	V 9	III 16	IX 11	IV 11	VI 14	I 13	VIII 15
9	VII 11	IX 12	I 12	VI 14	II 16	V 11	IV 18	VIII 15	III 15

<table>
<tr><td colspan="4" align="center">TABLE 3</td></tr>
</table>

TABLE 3

LATIN-SQUARE ANALYSIS OF THE RESULTS
GIVEN IN TABLE 2

Source	df	Sum of Squares	F
Groups	8	29	0.931
Positions	8	12	0.385
Conditions	8	316	10.146*
Residual (error)	56	218	

* $p < .01$.

results of the analysis are given in Table 3.

As an additional test to determine whether it is important at which point in the experiment a particular test pattern is given, each O was presented on the last trial of the experiment (the tenth test trial) with the same test pattern as had been presented to him on his first test trial. Thus the 20 Os in Group 1 were given Test Pattern 1 on their first test trial and again on their last test trial. Similarly, Group 2 Os were given Test Pattern 5 on their first and last test trials, and so on. The numbers of responses each group made to the S_I side when the repeated test pattern appeared in the first and in the last positions were then compared. These values, together with the result of a t test for paired measures, are given in Table 4. The value of $t(1.34)$ indicates that the position of the test trial in relation to the other test trials is not an important variable, a result which is in accord with the nonsignificant F for

TABLE 4

NUMBER OF RESPONSES TO THE S_I SIDE
FOR THE REPEATED TEST PATTERN

Position	Test Pattern								
	1	2	3	4	5	6	7	8	9
First	14	16	15	14	11	14	11	14	11
Last	12	13	17	14	10	15	9	15	6

$t = 1.34$; $df = 8$

TABLE 5

COMPARISONS OF EXPECTED AND OBTAINED
PROPORTIONS OF S_I RESPONSES
TO THE TEST PATTERNS

Test Pattern	Expected Proportion to S_I Side	Obtained Proportion to S_I Side	t	p
1	.500	.539	1.05	.294
2	.667	.789	3.49	.0004
3	.800	.811	.37	.712
4	.667	.628	1.11	.266
5	.600	.622	.61	.542
6	.667	.672	.14	.888
7	.571	.544	.70	.484
8	.750	.728	.69	.490
9	.500	.544	1.19	.234

ordinal position obtained in the latin-square analysis.

In order to test the theoretical predictions concerning compounding, a computation was made of the total proportion of Os who responded to the S_I side in the presence of each of the different test patterns. For this purpose the responses were combined for the various groups in the latin square. The proportions for the various test patterns were then compared with the proportions expected on theoretical grounds. The comparisons are given in Table 5.

These comparisons show that none of the differences between obtained and predicted values even approach significance except for the one for Test Pattern 2. Another test of

TABLE 6

COMPARISON OF EXPECTED ORDER OF GROUPS
ACCORDING TO MAGNITUDE
WITH OBTAINED ORDER

Test Pattern	Expected Proportion to S_I Side	Observed Proportion to S_I Side
3	.80	.811
8	.75	.728
6,4,2	.667	.696
5	.60	.622
7	.571	.544
9,1	.50	.542

agreement between theory and data was obtained by ordering the expected proportions with respect to size. This ordering was then compared with the ordering of the obtained proportions. For this purpose, the test conditions for which the same proportions were expected were averaged. An identical ordering of the two sets of numbers resulted, as may be seen in Table 6. The probability of this identity in order occurring on the basis of chance is one in 720.

DISCUSSION

The experiment was in effect done in two stages. In the first stage, Os learned to respond differentially to two stimulus situations. After they had mastered this discrimination with a high probability of success, they were presented with different situations in which the stimulation was compounded of various proportions of the stimuli to which different responses had previously been conditioned. Thus, in one stage of the experiment, responses were measured in relation to isolated segments of a field of stimulation, and in the second stage, the segments of the field were combined in various ways to provide data concerning the effect of such combinations on the behavior of O, and to test in a quantitative manner some predictions which were derived from the set theoretical model of learning developed by Estes and Burke.

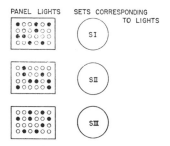

Fig. 2. Schematic diagram of disjoint sets of panel lights corresponding to the three stimulus sets S_I, S_{II}, and S_{III}

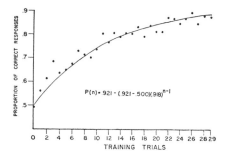

$$P(n) = .921 - (.921 - .500)(.918)^{n-1}$$

Fig. 3. Discrimination learning curve for all Os together with a theoretical curve obtained by minimizing the squared deviations

The two stages of the experiment and the results obtained in them will be discussed separately below.

Discrimination learning.—In the present experiment, the probability of occurrence of a response in the presence of a given stimulus, is related to the proportion of elements in the corresponding stimulus set that are connected to that response. There are only two responses available to O, and he is trained to make one of these consistently to a given stimulus set, and the other response to the other stimulus set. When this is achieved, all the elements in one stimulus set are considered to be conditioned to one response, and all the elements in the other stimulus set, to the other response. The schema diagrammed in Fig. 2 may clarify the conceptual interpretation of the experiment. The probability of a correct response on the nth trial $[p(n)]$ can be now described by an equation of the form: $p(n) = A - [A - p(1)]B^{n-1}$. The derivation of this equation is described elsewhere (3).

The trial-by-trial learning curve for all Os, shown in Fig. 1, is presented again in Fig. 3 together with a least-squares fit of the theoretical curve based on the above equation.

Compounding of stimuli.—In order to derive predictions from the Estes-Burke theory described earlier concerning the probability of response in the presence of compounded stimulation, certain assumptions are made, and the extent to which they are met must be considered.

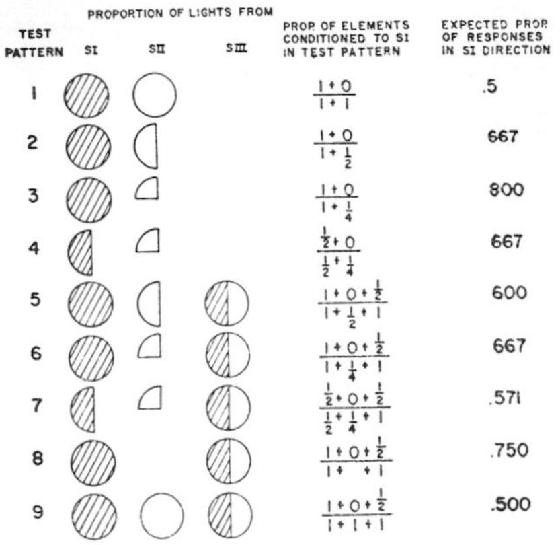

TEST PATTERN	PROPORTION OF LIGHTS FROM			PROP OF ELEMENTS CONDITIONED TO SI IN TEST PATTERN	EXPECTED PROP OF RESPONSES IN SI DIRECTION
	SI	SII	SIII		
1				$\frac{1+0}{1+1}$	.5
2				$\frac{1+0}{1+\frac{1}{2}}$	667
3				$\frac{1+0}{1+\frac{1}{4}}$	800
4				$\frac{\frac{1}{2}+0}{\frac{1}{2}+\frac{1}{4}}$	667
5				$\frac{1+0+\frac{1}{2}}{1+\frac{1}{2}+1}$	600
6				$\frac{1+0+\frac{1}{2}}{1+\frac{1}{2}+\frac{1}{4}}$	667
7				$\frac{\frac{1}{2}+0+\frac{1}{2}}{\frac{1}{2}+\frac{1}{2}+1}$	.571
8				$\frac{1+0+\frac{1}{2}}{1+\ +1}$	.750
9				$\frac{1+0+\frac{1}{2}}{1+1+1}$	.500

FIG. 4. Proportions of lights from each of the stimulus sets comprising the test patterns, together with probability of a response in the direction associated with S_I. Shaded areas represent elements in the set conditioned to a response in the S_I direction.

The assumption that the proportion of lights presented corresponds to the proportion of elements from the theoretical stimulus set seems reasonable, since the lights are separately manipulable, randomly drawn, and of equal wattage rating. Further, since only those Os which showed a well-learned discrimination were used in this part of the experiment, it can be reasonably assumed that all of the elements in S_I are conditioned to one response and all of the elements in S_{II} are conditioned to the other.

With the relation between the theory and the experiment thus clarified, and with other variables such as side preference and interactions among test conditions under experimental control, it is possible to derive predictions of response probability in the combined stimulation of S_I, S_{II}, and S_{III}. The way in which these predictions are made has been discussed in the introduction. Figure 4 shows these probabilities for each of the test patterns.

The close agreement between the expected and the observed results indicated in Tables 5 and 6 lends considerable support to the Estes-Burke set theoretical model of learning. It also indicates that the theory is fruitful for the enterprise of gaining information as to how to apply the results of the innumerable experiments which have been done in the artificially stable field where only one segment is allowed to vary, to situations which are more complex, i.e., where this stability does not obtain.

SUMMARY

The experiment was performed to determine the probability of a response in stimulus situations composed in part of stimuli to which this response had been conditioned, in part of stimuli to which an opposing response had been conditioned, and in part of stimuli to which neither response had been conditioned. The experiment also permitted a comparison between the obtained response probabilities and exact quantitative predictions of these probabilities derived from the set theoretical model of learning developed by Estes and Burke.

The subjects ($N = 234$) were trained to discriminate between two disjoint sets of lights, and were then given a series of test trials on which lights from the two discriminated sets, and lights that had not been presented previously, appeared simultaneously in varying proportions. The results indicated that: (a) the discrimination curve is a negatively accelerated, increasing function as predicted by theory; and (b) the probability of a response in the presence of a given test pattern is equal to the proportion of component stimuli that are conditioned to that response. Observed response proportions on test trials were in close agreement with the predictions derived from the set theoretical model.

REFERENCES

1. ESTES, W. K., & BURKE, C. J. A theory of stimulus variability in learning. *Psychol. Rev.*, 1953, **60**, 276–286.
2. GULLIKSEN, H. Transfer of response in human subjects. *J. exp. Psychol.*, 1932, **15**, 496–516.
3. SCHOEFFLER, M. S. Probability of response to compounds of discriminated stimuli. Unpublished doctor's dissertation, Indiana Univ., 1953.

(Received February 15, 1954)

Component and Pattern Models with Markovian Interpretations[1]

WILLIAM K. ESTES, *Indiana University*

All of the stimulus-sampling models appearing in the contemporary literature (e.g., [5], [7], [24], [25]) have been developed primarily for purposes of representing situations in which the learner is conceived to be sampling a population of components or aspects (elements) of a stimulating situation from trial to trial. In these models it is assumed that the conditioning of individual elements to responses occurs independently as the elements are sampled in conjunction with reinforcing events, and that response probability in the presence of a sample containing a number of elements is determined by an averaging rule. The main consideration has been to account for variability of response to an apparently constant stimulus situation by assuming random fluctuation from trial to trial in the particular sample of stimuli affecting the learner. Also, stimulus sampling models have provided a mechanism for effecting a reconciliation between the picture of gradual change usually exhibited by the learning curve and the all-or-none law of association along the lines proposed earlier by Guthrie [17]. With one exception ([7], chap. 2), sampling models have assumed that the sample of stimuli effective on any trial becomes conditioned to the reinforced response on an all-or-none basis; but probability of response, depending on the proportion of stimuli in the population conditioned to the response, may nevertheless change gradually.

In most empirical applications of stimulus sampling models to date, it has seemed natural, or at least has proved advantageous for mathematical reasons, to assume that N, the number of elements in the stimulus population, is large. Then, if sampling probabilities of individual elements are constant, the law of large numbers ensures that the proportion of elements in any trial sample connected to a given response differs negligibly from the corresponding proportion in the population. A number of sampling models presented elsewhere* depend on the large N assumption to make derivations and computations manageable. With the additional assumption

---

[1] The mathematical researches reported in this chapter were largely completed during the academic year 1955-56 while the writer was a fellow at the Center for Advanced Study in the Behavioral Sciences, Stanford, California.

Reprinted from *Studies in mathematical learning theory* (pp. 9–53), Robert R. Bush and William K. Estes, editors, with the permission of the publishers, Stanford University Press. © Copyright 1959 by the Board of Trustees of Leland Stanford Junior University.

that all elements in a given population have equal sampling probabilities, laws of learning derived from large N sampling models take the form of linear transformations on the response probabilities. A large literature has already grown up around these "linear models" ([1], [2], [7], [9], [11], [23]).

Recent developments in both experiment and theory indicate the desirability of deriving a comparable body of mathematical methods for handling situations in which sampling is assumed, either for psychological or for mathematical reasons, to occur from populations that are too small for the law of large numbers to effect any simplifications. In such cases, trial-to-trial variation in sample proportions, even at the asymptote of learning, cannot be considered negligible, and reinforcing events change the response probabilities of individual learners by step-functions rather than by linear transformations. Interest in methods for dealing with small N sampling models arises in part from experiments in which sampling probabilities of different components of a stimulus situation are manipulated by the experimenter ([6], [10], [13], [14], [25]). Interest arises also from the circumstance that in some simple learning situations, e.g., those involving incomplete knowledge of results and those involving two-person interactions, recursive expressions for means and other moments of the individual response probabilities cannot be solved even at asymptote. In these cases, one may be led to consider small N sampling models simply because they yield definite, detailed predictions where large N, or linear, models do not.

It has been noted by several writers on learning theory ([3], [7], [11], [19]) that mathematical models which treat response probabilities as dependent variables can be interpreted as Markov processes.[2] Whether there is any profit in such an interpretation depends on particular circumstances. If the Markov process associated with a particular theory is a finite chain, then a large body of theorems and computational methods is available for immediate application; this proves to be the case for the statistical learning theories developed by Estes [8] and Estes and Burke [12], and a main concern of this paper will be the interpretation of these theories as Markov processes. If the Markov process associated with a theory is not finite, as proves to be the case for Bush and Mosteller's stochastic model [7], then the Markovian interpretation offers few immediate dividends. It will, however, be instructive to compare the finite and infinite models within the common mathematical framework provided by the Markovian interpretations.

The learning theories to be discussed are concerned with three kinds of events: responses, stimuli, and reinforcing events. The behaviors available to the subject (by " subject " we refer to the organism whose learning is under consideration) in a given experimental situation are categorized into mutually exclusive and exhaustive response classes (A_1, A_2, $\cdots$, A_r). The

---

[2] In this paper we assume that the reader is familiar with the elements of Markov theory at the level of the presentations by Kemeny, Snell, and Thompson [21] or Miller [22]. To work with the stimulus-sampling models in theoretical research, one would require also a mastery of the basic derivational and calculational methods as given, e.g., by Feller [16], Bartlett [4], or Kemeny and Snell [20].

stimulating situation is represented by a set S of N "stimulus elements" which is sampled by the subject at the beginning of each trial. The possible outcomes of a trial (e.g., giving or withholding of rewards, unconditioned stimuli, knowledge of results) are classified according to their effects on response probabilities and are represented by a mutually exclusive and exhaustive set of "reinforcing events" $(E_0, E_1, \cdots, E_r)$, where E_i, for $i \neq 0$, represents the event "response A_i is reinforced," and E_0 represents any trial outcome whose effect is "neutral" (i.e., reinforces none of the A_i). Learning is defined in terms of trial-to-trial changes in the conditional probabilities of responses to stimuli, and laws of learning take the form of rules specifying the probabilities of these changes under various experimental conditions.

For our purposes it is useful to distinguish three types of stochastic models: (a) finite models with unrestricted transitions, (b) finite models with restricted transitions, and (c) infinite models. Type (a) is exemplified by the set-theoretical model of Estes and Burke [12]. In this model it is assumed that each stimulus element in the set S has a fixed probability θ of being sampled on any learning trial; thus the number of elements sampled per trial is a random variable. At any time, each element is "connected" to exactly one of the responses $(A_1, A_2, \cdots, A_r)$, and the probability of a given response is a function of the subset of elements connected to it. It is assumed that all elements sampled on a trial become connected to the response that is reinforced. Since the set S is assumed to be finite, there is a finite set of possible values for the probability of any given response, and in general it is possible to shift from any one of these values to any other on a single trial. The probabilities of the various possible transitions depend on the θ values and on the probabilities of the various reinforcing events.

Set models of type (b)—see e.g., [8]—differ from those just described only in that the sample size, rather than the sampling probabilities of the elements, is fixed; it is assumed that from the set of N elements exactly s are sampled on each trial, s being a constant for a given experimental situation. Therefore the possible shifts in response probability on a single trial are restricted as compared to those permitted in an otherwise identical model of type (a). If, for example, s were equal to 1 and probability of a given response were equal to p on a given trial, the possible values for probability of that response on the next trial would be $p - (1/N)$, p, and $p + (1/N)$.

Given an instance of either type of finite model, we can define a corresponding infinite model. The infinite model will have the same sets of responses, reinforcing events, and reinforcement probabilities, and a single free parameter θ' which has the same value as θ in the corresponding finite model of type (a) or s/N in the corresponding finite model of type (b). In the infinite model, the probability of a given response can shift from its current value, p, to one of the new values $[(1 - \theta')p + \theta']$, $(1 - \theta')p$, or p, depending on whether the given response, an alternative response, or neither is reinforced. The infinite model can be regarded either as a special case of the finite model, obtained by letting N become infinite while θ or s/N remains fixed, or as a special case of Bush and Mosteller's model, obtained by imposing special restrictions on the parameters. In the following sections we shall develop the mathematical theory of the finite models in some detail and compare important theorems and computational formulas with those derived elsewhere for corresponding infinite models. Although many of the theorems of the infinite models have been derived independently by several different investigators, it will be convenient for the present exposition to use as a basis of comparison the theorems given in Chapter 8 of *Studies in mathematical learning theory.*[†]

It will be convenient to begin by considering models with restricted transitions, since their mathematical properties are in some respects the simplest. When this type of model was introduced in an earlier paper by the writer [8], the only case considered was that in which both population size and sample size are large. In this presentation we shall go to the opposite extreme and give most attention to the case in which, although N is unrestricted, exactly one element is sampled per trial $(s = 1)$. From a mathematical viewpoint this is merely the simplest type of finite sampling model. From a psychological viewpoint, however, the interpretation is quite different from that of the other sampling models to be considered. Consequently the $s = 1$ case will be presented as a separate model, to be designated the *pattern model*. Both the psychologically interesting features of the pattern model and the advantages of introducing Markovian interpretations and techniques in the simplest possible context make this model a good point of departure.

The Pattern Model

Assumptions. Under many circumstances, quantitative properties of learning can be accounted for in considerable detail by models that assume discrete and independent associations ("connections") between responses and the various independently variable components of a stimulating situation. (For a full discussion of this point, see [11].) But in some cases predictions from component models fail and it appears that a simple account of the course of learning requires the assumption that responses become associated, not with separate components or aspects, but with total patterns of stimulation considered as units [10]. The model presented in this section is intended to represent such cases. In it we assume that an experimentally defined stimulating situation can be conceived as an assemblage of mutually exclusive patterns of stimulation, each of which becomes connected to responses on an all-or-none basis according to laws strictly analogous to those assumed in previous formulations of statistical learning theory (e.g., [8], [11], [12]). By "mutually exclusive," it is implied, *not* that different patterns must have no observable stimuii or stimulus properties in common, but simply that exactly one of the patterns occurs (is sampled by the subject) on each trial. At any time, each pattern is connected to exactly one of the alternative responses A_i; thus, given the pattern sampled on a trial, the response connected to it must occur. For simplicity in this presentation, we shall limit consideration to cases in which patterns are sampled randomly with

---

*See, for example, *Studies in mathematical learning theory.* Stanford: 1959. Chaps. 2, 4, 5.
[†]Frequent references to this chapter appear throughout the rest of this article.

equal probabilities so that, if there are N patterns, each has probability $1/N$ of being sampled on any trial. Also, if m of the N patterns are connected to a particular response A_i, then the probability of A_i is equal to m/N.

It would be unnecessarily restrictive to require of the model a priori that the stimulus pattern occurring on a trial should invariably become connected to the reinforced response. Even if we should wish to make the assumption of invariable conditioning for some situations, we would wish also to be in a position to test it. Consequently, we shall define at the outset a "conditioning parameter" c. The value of c is presumed to be fixed for any one experiment (i.e., for any given subject and set of experimental conditions). We may formally interpret c as the probability that the pattern occurring on a trial, if not at the time connected to A_i, becomes connected to A_i if the corresponding reinforcing event E_i occurs. Now, within the theory, testing the assumption of invariable conditioning amounts to testing the hypothesis $c = 1$. One might generalize the present model by defining different parameters c_i, one corresponding to each possible reinforcing event E_i, but we shall not discuss such possibilities in this paper.

Before we can begin to apply the methods of Markov theory, we must define the notion of a *state*. Although it is not an essential restriction, we shall limit consideration to cases in which there is a one-to-one correspondence between states and response probabilities. Thus, in the pattern model for two-choice situations, we shall say that the subject is in state m when exactly m of the N patterns are connected to response A_1. We have a Markov process (see [16] for a more elaborate definition) if the probability of a transition from any state to any other depends at most on the state existing on the trial preceding the transition. In the pattern model, the subject can go from state m only to one of the three states $m - 1$, m, or $m + 1$ on any one trial. The probabilities of these transitions depend on the value of c, the probabilities of reinforcement, and the value of m. Thus we can satisfy the Markov condition by limiting ourselves to reinforcement schedules in which the probability of a reinforcing event E_k depends at most on the response of the given trial, i.e., in conventional terminology, to simple noncontingent and simple contingent reinforcement. This restriction will be assumed throughout the present exposition except for a few sections in which we explicitly consider various lines of generalization.

The Special Case of $N = 1$. Although the theory to be developed is relatively elementary from a mathematical standpoint, a rather formidable notational apparatus will be required. Consequently, it may help if we introduce the basic ideas in terms of a simplified example before proceeding with a systematic presentation of the general model. For concreteness let us imagine that we are studying an experiment in which the subject's task is to guess whether red or black will come up in a series of spins of a roulette wheel. We shall assume that the ready signal given by the experimenter, together with associated background cues, constitutes a single pattern of stimulation which recurs at the beginning of each trial. Following the signal, the subject makes a response A_1 or A_2, corresponding to a guess of red or black, respectively.

Finally, the wheel spins and the reinforcing event E_1 (stop on red) or E_2 (stop on black) occurs.

In our Markovian representation of this situation, we recognize two possible states of the system. We say that the subject is in state 1 if the single stimulus pattern is connected to response A_1, and in state 0 if it is not connected to A_1 (therefore is connected to A_2). The probability of A_1 will be 1 or 0 on any trial according as the subject is in state 1 or 0, respectively, at the beginning of the trial. Assuming that the experimenter-determined probabilities of the reinforcing events E_1 and E_2 are π and $1 - \pi$, respectively, we can now write down the matrix of transition probabilities

$$Q = \begin{pmatrix} 1 - c + c\pi & c(1 - \pi) \\ c\pi & 1 - c\pi \end{pmatrix}.$$

The element in the ith row and jth column of this matrix represents the probability q_{ij} of a transition from state i to state j in a single trial; as written, the first row and first column refer to state 1, the second row and second column to state 0. To obtain the entry q_{11} in the upper left, we note that a transition from state 1 to state 0 can occur only on an E_2 trial, and then only with probability c; thus the probability of the transition is $c(1 - \pi)$, and the probability that the transition does not occur is $1 - c(1 - \pi)$, which is the entry for q_{11}. The entry q_{01} in the lower left follows immediately from the fact that a transition to state 1 from state 0 can occur only on an E_1 trial, and then only with probability c. The other two entries can be obtained by subtraction, since each row of Q must sum to unity.

Numerous predictions about the course of learning in this example are ascertainable by study of the matrix Q and its powers Q^n. It will readily be apparent that if the elements of Q give the probabilities of one-step transitions between states, the elements of Q^n must give the probabilities of n-step transitions. In our example, a transition from state i to state j in two steps can occur if the system remains in state i for one trial and passes to state j on the next, or if it passes from i to j on the first trial and remains there on the next; adding the probabilities of these two alternatives, we obtain

$$q_{ij}^{(2)} = q_{ii}q_{ij} + q_{ij}q_{jj},$$

which is simply the element in the ith row and jth column of the matrix Q^2. Similarly, the probability that the system will be found in state j on trial n, given that it began in state i on trial 1, is $q_{ij}^{(n)}$, the element in the ith row and jth column of the matrix Q^n. We can easily compute the powers of Q. By direct multiplication, we obtain for Q^2

$$Q^2 = \begin{pmatrix} \pi + (1 - \pi)(1 - c)^2 & (1 - \pi)[1 - (1 - c)^2] \\ \pi[1 - (1 - c)^2] & 1 - \pi[1 - (1 - c)^2] \end{pmatrix},$$

and we can prove by induction that in general,

$$Q^n = \begin{pmatrix} \pi + (1 - \pi)(1 - c)^n & (1 - \pi)[1 - (1 - c)^n] \\ \pi[1 - (1 - c)^n] & 1 - \pi[1 - (1 - c)^n] \end{pmatrix}.$$

We see from inspection of Q^n that, regardless of which state the subject has started in, after a large number of trials the probability of being in state 1 tends to the limiting value $q_1 = \pi$, and the probability of being in state 0 tends to the limiting value $q_0 = 1 - \pi$.

In experimental applications of the model we will not usually know the initial states. Consequently, we may be less concerned with the probability of a transition from i to j in n trials than with the probability of being in j after n trials, given a distribution of initial probabilities. We shall define $q_1^{(n)}$ and $q_0^{(n)}$ to be the probabilities of states 1 and 0, respectively, after n trials and $\mathbf{q}^{(n)}$ to be the row vector

$$\mathbf{q}^{(n)} = (q_1^{(n)}, \; q_0^{(n)}) .$$

Then we can verify by direct multiplication that

$$\mathbf{q}^{(1)} = \mathbf{q}^{(0)} Q$$

and by induction that

$$\mathbf{q}^{(n)} = \mathbf{q}^{(0)} Q^n$$
$$= (\pi - [\pi - q_1^{(0)}](1 - c)^n, \; 1 - \pi - [1 - \pi - q_0^{(0)}](1 - c)^n) .$$

According to the assumptions of the model, $p_{1,n}$, the probability of an A_1 response on trial n, is equal to the probability that the single stimulus pattern is connected to A_1 at the end of trial $n - 1$; therefore,

$$p_{1,n} = 1 \cdot q_1^{(n-1)} + 0 \cdot q_0^{(n-1)}$$
$$= \pi - [\pi - p_{1,1}](1 - c)^{n-1} .$$

It will be noted that this expression for $p_{1,n}$ is identical with the one previously derived ([9], [23]) by difference equation methods for the type of experiment involved in this illustration. One must not, however, leap to the conclusion that response probability will always be independent of N, either in the pattern model or in component models; we shall see in later sections that independence of N holds for some, but not all, special cases of each type of sampling model.

The illustrative example will have served its purpose if it has given the reader some intuitive familiarity with the relationships between states, state probabilities, transition probabilities, and response probabilities which are fundamental to the model. Now we shall introduce formulas for the elements of the transition matrix in the general case of the pattern model with N unrestricted, and then derive various expressions of experimental interest and, where appropriate, compare them with corresponding expressions obtainable from the linear model. It is recommended that the general reader proceed directly to the section on discrimination learning (p. 33) and defer for later study the intervening sections concerned with detailed derivations for various cases of simple learning.

Transition Probabilities. In general, for two response alternatives,[3] we shall recognize $N + 1$ states, one corresponding to each possible number of stimulus

[3] For simplicity, we shall limit consideration to the case of two alternatives throughout this chapter, except for a few sections in which extensions to $r > 2$ are explicitly mentioned. For a systematic treatment of the general case of r alternatives, see [15].

patterns $(0, 1, \cdots, N)$ which may be connected to the A_1 response. Then our assumptions yield the following rules for transitions from one state to another:

If the system is in state m and an E_1 occurs,

$$(1) \qquad q'_{mm} = 1 - c + c\frac{m}{N}, \qquad q'_{m(m+1)} = c\frac{(N-m)}{N};$$

if the system is in state m and an E_2 occurs,

$$(2) \qquad q'_{mm} = 1 - c + c\frac{(N-m)}{N} = 1 - c\frac{m}{N}, \qquad q'_{m(m-1)} = c\frac{m}{N};$$

if the system is in state m and an E_0 occurs,

$$(3) \qquad q'_{mm} = 1,$$

where the q'_{ij} are the one-step transition probabilities, conditional upon the indicated reinforcing events, and E_1, E_2, and E_0 are interpreted (cf. Chapter 8) as reinforcement of A_1, reinforcement of A_2, and nonreinforcement, respectively.

From these rules we can obtain immediately the elements of the transition matrix for the Markov process. A transition upward can occur only when a pattern unconnected to A_1 is sampled on an E_1 trial, and a transition downward only when a pattern connected to A_1 is sampled on an E_2 trial; thus we have

$$(4) \qquad q_{m(m+1)} = c\frac{(N-m)}{N}P(E_1 \mid s^0 m),$$

$$(5) \qquad q_{m(m-1)} = c\frac{m}{N}P(E_2 \mid s^1 m),$$

and

$$(6) \qquad q_{mm} = 1 - c + c\left[\frac{m}{N}P(E_1 \mid s^1 m) + \frac{(N-m)}{N}P(E_2 \mid s^0 m) + P(E_0 \mid m)\right],$$

where $q_{m(m+1)}$ is the unconditional probability of a transition from m to $m+1$ on any trial; $P(E_1 \mid s^1 m)$ is the probability of an E_1, given that the system is in state m and a pattern connected to A_1 is sampled; and so on. Here and in subsequent derivations, we let s^1 indicate occurrence of a stimulus pattern connected to A_1 and s^0 occurrence of one not connected to A_1.

In the noncontingent case, $P(E_j \mid m)$ and $P(E_j \mid s^i m)$ are both simply equal to a constant π_j. In the contingent case, $P(E_j \mid m)$ and $P(E_j \mid s^i m)$ can be expressed in terms of response probabilities and constant conditional probabilities π_{ij}:

$$P(E_1 \mid m) = \pi_{11}P(A_1 \mid m) + \pi_{21}P(A_2 \mid m)$$
$$= \pi_{11}\frac{m}{N} + \pi_{21}\frac{(N-m)}{N},$$
$$P(E_1 \mid s^1 m) = P(E_1 \mid A_1) = \pi_{11},$$
$$P(E_1 \mid s^0 m) = P(E_1 \mid A_2) = \pi_{21}.$$

As we have seen in the case of the illustrative example, the probabilities $q_m^{(n)}$ that the system is in state m after n trials, starting from any specified initial distribution, can be defined recursively in terms of the transition probabilities; thus in general

$$(7) \qquad q_m^{(n)} = q_0^{(n-1)} q_{0m} + q_1^{(n-1)} q_{1m} + \cdots + q_N^{(n-1)} q_{Nm} .$$

Response Probabilities and Moments. Designating by p_{mn} the probability of the A_1 response on trial n given that the subject is in state m, and by p_n the probability of A_1 over the whole sample space, we note that as a consequence of our assumptions

$$(8) \qquad p_{mn} = \frac{m}{N}$$

and

$$(9) \qquad p_n = \sum_{m=0}^{N} \frac{m}{N} q_m^{(n-1)} .$$

The latter expression, together with Equation 7, serves as the basis for a general recursion in the response probability p_n,

$$p_n = \sum_{m=0}^{N} \frac{m}{N} \sum_{j=0}^{N} q_j^{(n-2)} q_{jm} ;$$

now, substituting for q_{jm} in terms of Equations 4, 5, and 6 and simplifying, we find

$$(10) \qquad p_n = \left[1 - \frac{c}{N} + \frac{c}{N} P(E_{0,n-1} \mid A_{1,n-1}) \right] p_{n-1} + \frac{c}{N} P(E_{1,n-1}) ,$$

where $A_{i,n-1}$ and $E_{j,n-1}$ denote the events " A_i occurred on trial $n-1$ " and " E_j occurred on trial $n-1$," respectively. In the determinate case (i.e., the E_0 event has zero probability for all n), this last result reduces to

$$(11) \qquad p_n = \left(1 - \frac{c}{N} \right) p_{n-1} + \frac{c}{N} P(E_{1,n-1}) ,$$

which, with c/N taking the same role as θ, is identical with the recursion for response probability in the corresponding case of the linear model (see Chapter 8, Sec. 5). In the simple noncontingent case, for example, the recursion becomes simply

$$(12) \qquad p_n = \left(1 - \frac{c}{N} \right) p_{n-1} + \frac{c}{N} \pi ,$$

with the solution

$$(13) \qquad p_n = \pi - (\pi - p_1) \left(1 - \frac{c}{N} \right)^{n-1} ,$$

where π denotes probability of the E_1 event. Clearly, in the determinate case at least, predictions concerning forms and asymptotes of learning curves are exactly the same for the pattern model as for the appropriate special case of Bush and Mosteller's stochastic model ([7], p. 109) or for stimulus component models under the assumption of large N ([5], [15]). This is not to say, however, that even in the determinate case *all* predictions derivable from the pattern model are identical with those derivable from the others.

Although p_n, which may be regarded as the mean of the response probabilities p_{mn} associated with individual states, is the same for the various models, higher moments of the p_{mn} differ. It will be convenient to illustrate this point by calculating the variance of p_{mn} for the determinate case of the pattern model. The second raw moment, $V_{2,n}$ in the notation used elsewhere in this book, is of course given by

$$V_{2,n} = \sum_{m=0}^{N} \frac{m^2}{N^2} q_m^{(n-1)} = \sum_{m=0}^{N} \frac{m^2}{N^2} \sum_{j=0}^{N} q_j^{(n-2)} q_{jm} \ .$$

Substituting for the transition probabilities q_{jm} in terms of Equations 4, 5, and 6, we obtain after some algebraic rearrangement

(14) $\qquad V_{2,n} = (1 - c)V_{2,n-1} + c\left[\left(1 - \frac{2}{N}\right)V_{2,n-1}\right.$

$$\left. + \frac{1}{N}\left\{\frac{1}{N} + 2P(E_{1,n-1}) - \frac{2}{N}P(E_{1,n-1})\right\} p_{n-1} + \frac{1}{N^2}P(E_{1,n-1})\right].$$

Now, letting $P(E_{1,n-1}) = \pi$ and subtracting the square of p_n, as given by Equation 12, from $V_{2,n}$, we obtain for the variance in the simple, noncontingent case:

(15) $\qquad \sigma_n^2 = \left(1 - \frac{2c}{N}\right)\sigma_{n-1}^2 + \frac{c\pi}{N^2} - \frac{c^2\pi^2}{N^2} + \frac{c}{N^2}(1 - 2\pi + 2c\pi) + \frac{c}{N^2}p_{n-1} - \frac{c^2}{N^2}p_{n-1}^2.$

At asymptote we can set $\sigma_n^2 = \sigma_{n-1}^2 = \sigma_\infty^2$, and $p_{n-1} = \pi$; then Equation 15 reduces to

(16) $\qquad\qquad\qquad\qquad \sigma_\infty^2 = \frac{\pi(1 - \pi)}{N} \ ,$

which, interestingly enough, proves to be independent of the conditioning parameter c. This result may be compared with the asymptotic variance,

$$\sigma_\infty^2 = \frac{\theta}{2 - \theta}\pi(1 - \pi) \ ,$$

of the large N component model or the linear model (cf. Chapter 8, Sec. 8). The second and higher moments of the response probabilities are of experimental interest primarily because they enter into expressions for various sequential statistics of the data. We shall see in a later section that for the determinate case, at least, it is by no means easy to derive readily testable predictions differentiating the pattern model from the linear model.

On the other hand, comparing our recursion for response probability in the nondeterminate case $[P(E_0) > 0]$ with the corresponding expression for the linear model (cf. Chapter 8, Sec. 5), we see that the pattern model and the linear model have somewhat different properties. If, for example, both models are applied to Atkinson's study [2], in which noninformative trial outcomes served as E_0 events, different predictions are generated for the asymptotic response probabilities. The source of the difference is that in the pattern model an E_0 event on an A_1 trial has the same effect as an E_1, and an E_0 event on an A_2 trial has the same effect as an E_2; while in the linear model the effect of an E_0 is always quite distinct from that of any other reinforcing event. Since in Atkinson's study the linear model gave a good account of the data, it may be desirable to reinterpret the effect of an E_0 event in the pattern model. If we assume that when the subject is in state m, an E_0 event serves to reinforce the A_1 response with probability m/N and to reinforce other responses with probability $(N - m)/N$, then the recursion for p_n can be shown to be[4]

$$(17) \qquad p_{n+1} = \left(1 - \frac{c}{N}\right)p_n + \frac{c}{N}P(E_{1,n}) + \frac{c}{N} \sum_m \frac{m}{N}P(E_{0,n} \mid m)q_m^{(n-1)} ,$$

which is identical in form to the corresponding expression in the linear model and which yields the same predictions concerning bounds on asymptotic response probabilities for Atkinson's study as does the linear model. Technically, more precise predictions can be derived from the pattern model than from the linear model for experiments involving the kind of reinforcement contingency employed in Atkinson's study, but further analysis of this special case is beyond the scope of the present paper.

Asymptotic Distribution of Response Probabilities. For all cases to which it is applicable, the pattern model has one particularly advantageous feature as compared with the linear model or with any of the component models that have appeared in the literature. This unique feature is a simple calculational procedure for generating the complete distribution of asymptotic state probabilities, and therefore of asymptotic response probabilities. The only restriction we require is that the elements q_{jk} of the matrix of transition probabilities should all be constant (i.e., independent of n). The derivation to be given will assume also that the q_{jk} are all nonzero; the same technique can be applied if there are zero entries, except, of course, that in forming ratios of transition probabilities one must keep the zeros out of the denominators.

The gist of the theorem to be proved is that all of the asymptotic state probabilities q_m can be expressed recursively in terms of q_0; since the q_m must sum to unity, this recursion suffices to determine the entire distribution. We begin by noting that since by Equation 7

$$q_0 = q_0q_{00} + q_1q_{10} ,$$

it follows obviously that

$$(18) \qquad \frac{q_0}{q_1} = \frac{q_{10}}{1 - q_{00}} = \frac{q_{10}}{q_{01}} .$$

---

[4] For a full derivation of this theorem, and of others given in this chapter without proof, see [15].

Now we shall prove by induction that a similar relation holds for any adjacent pair of states, i.e., that if $j = i + 1$, then

(19)
$$\frac{q_i}{q_j} = \frac{q_{ji}}{q_{ij}} .$$

For any state j, we have by Equation 7

$$q_j = q_i q_{ij} + q_j q_{jj} + q_k q_{kj} ,$$

where $j = i + 1$ and $k = j + 1$. Rearranging, we have

$$q_j(1 - q_{jj}) = q_i q_{ij} + q_k q_{kj} ,$$

and replacing q_i by its equivalent $q_j q_{ji}/q_{ij}$ under the inductive hypothesis,

$$q_j(1 - q_{jj}) = q_j \frac{q_{ji}}{q_{ij}} q_{ij} + q_k q_{kj}$$

$$= q_j q_{ji} + q_k q_{kj} ,$$

or

$$q_j(1 - q_{jj} - q_{ji}) = q_k q_{kj} .$$

However, $1 - q_{jj} - q_{ji} = q_{jk}$ since by definition $q_{ji} + q_{jj} + q_{jk} = 1$, and therefore

$$\frac{q_j}{q_k} = \frac{q_{kj}}{q_{jk}} . \qquad \text{Q.E.D.}$$

Thus we can write

$$q_1 = \frac{q_{01}}{q_{10}} q_0 , \qquad q_2 = \frac{q_{12}}{q_{21}} \frac{q_{01}}{q_{10}} q_0 ,$$

etc., and, since the q_m must sum to unity, q_0 is determined also.

It may be instructive to illustrate the application of our technique for generating asymptotic probabilities in terms of some of the familiar special cases. In the simple noncontingent case, for example, the probabilities of upward and downward transitions between neighboring states are, by Equations 4 and 5,

$$q_{k(k+1)} = c \frac{(N - k)}{N} \pi \qquad \text{and} \qquad q_{k(k-1)} = c \frac{k}{N} (1 - \pi) ,$$

respectively. Applying the technique of the preceding paragraph, we have immediately

$$\frac{q_1}{q_0} = \pi c \left/ \frac{(1 - \pi)c}{N} \right. = \frac{N\pi}{1 - \pi} , \qquad \frac{q_2}{q_1} = \pi c \frac{(N - 1)}{N} \left/ (1 - \pi)c \frac{2}{N} \right. = \frac{\pi(N - 1)}{(1 - \pi)2} ,$$

and in general,

(20)
$$\frac{q_k}{q_{k-1}} = \pi c \frac{(N - k + 1)}{N} \left/ (1 - \pi)c \frac{k}{N} \right. = \frac{\pi(N - k + 1)}{(1 - \pi)k} .$$

This last result has two interesting aspects. First, it is clear that the asymptotic probabilities are independent of the conditioning parameter c. Second, the ratio of q_k to q_{k-1} is the same as that of neighboring terms

$$\binom{N}{k}\pi^k(1-\pi)^{N-k} \quad \text{and} \quad \binom{N}{k-1}\pi^{k-1}(1-\pi)^{N-k+1}$$

in the expansion of $[\pi + (1 - \pi)]^N$. Therefore the asymptotic probabilities in this case are binomially distributed; in a population of subjects whose learning is described by the model, the limiting proportion of subjects having all N stimulus patterns connected to the A_1 response is π^N, the proportion having all but one of the N patterns connected to A_1 is $N\pi^{N-1}(1 - \pi)$, and so on.

In the simple contingent case, the transition probabilities required are

$$q_{k(k+1)} = \frac{(N-k)}{N}\pi_{21}c \quad \text{and} \quad q_{k(k-1)} = \frac{k}{N}\pi_{12}c \,,$$

and the ratio of adjacent state probabilities is

(21)
$$\frac{q_k}{q_{k-1}} = \frac{(N-k+1)\pi_{21}c}{N} \bigg/ \frac{k\pi_{12}c}{N}$$
$$= \frac{(N-k+1)\pi_{21}}{k\pi_{12}} \,.$$

Again the asymptotic probabilities prove to be independent of c. This time we note that the ratio of q_k to q_{k-1} is the same as that of

$$\binom{N}{k}\pi_{21}^k\pi_{12}^{N-k} \quad \text{to} \quad \binom{N}{k-1}\pi_{21}^{k-1}\pi_{12}^{N-k+1} \,;$$

therefore the asymptotic state probabilities are simply the terms in the expansion of

$$\left(\frac{\pi_{21}}{\pi_{21}+\pi_{12}} + \frac{\pi_{12}}{\pi_{21}+\pi_{12}}\right)^N .$$

Thus the limiting probability that all N stimulus patterns are connected to A_1 is

$$\left(\frac{\pi_{21}}{\pi_{21}+\pi_{12}}\right)^N ;$$

the probability that all but one are connected to A_1 is

$$N\left(\frac{\pi_{21}}{\pi_{21}+\pi_{12}}\right)^{N-1}\left(\frac{\pi_{12}}{\pi_{21}+\pi_{12}}\right) ;$$

and so on.

It will not always be the case that the asymptotic probabilities conform to some familiar distribution such as the binomial. Even when they do not, however, the probabilities can be calculated by means of the ratio rule (Equation 19). Thus not only mean asymptotic probabilities, or response proportions, but also medians and any other desired statistical parameters of the asymptotic distribution can be calculated and compared with statistics of experimental data.

Calculation of State Probabilities. Given the transition matrix Q, we can in principle (subject to the restrictions on Q stated above) always compute the probabilities $q_{jk}^{(n)}$ that the subject is in state k, and therefore has response probability k/N, n trials after beginning in state j. Unless explicit formulas for the $q_{jk}^{(n)}$ are available, however, the computations require a priori decisions as to the values of c, q_j, and N. We shall limit consideration here to the simple noncontingent case (with E_0 events excluded), for which explicit formulas can be derived with relative ease.

Except for a few special cases in which formulas for Q^n can be established directly by induction, calculations of $q_{jk}^{(n)}$ depend on the fact that the transition matrix can be expressed as

$$(22) \qquad\qquad Q = Y \varLambda Y^{-1} ,$$

where Y is a square matrix with the same number of rows as Q and $\varLambda$ is the diagonal matrix whose nonzero elements are the latent roots (eigenvalues) of Q, i.e.,

$$\varLambda = \begin{pmatrix} \lambda_N & 0 & \cdots & 0 & 0 \\ 0 & \lambda_{N-1} & \cdots & 0 & 0 \\ \vdots & \vdots & & \vdots & \vdots \\ 0 & 0 & \cdots & \lambda_1 & 0 \\ 0 & 0 & \cdots & 0 & \lambda_0 \end{pmatrix} .$$

Then by simple matrix algebra,

$$(23) \qquad\qquad Q^n = Y \varLambda^n Y^{-1} ,$$

so that, once the λ_i and the elements of Y and its inverse have been determined, the computation of Q^n, and therefore of $q_{jk}^{(n)}$, reduces to the computation of λ_i^n for $i = N, N-1, \cdots, 0$.

Once the λ_i are known, determination of the elements of Y and Y^{-1} is simply a matter of solving systems of $N+1$ linear equations in $N+1$ unknowns (for full detail see [4], chap. 2, or [16], chap. 16), since it follows immediately from Equation 22 that

$$(24) \qquad\qquad Y^{-1}Q = \varLambda Y^{-1} \quad\text{and}\quad QY = Y\varLambda .$$

In view of the central role of $\varLambda$, it is fortunate that an explicit formula can be derived for λ_i in terms of the two parameters N and c of the pattern model. For reasons that will become apparent, it will be convenient first to obtain the latent roots for the special case of $c = 1$, and then to extend our results to the general case.

When $c = 1$, the elements of Q reduce to

$$q_{m(m+1)} = \pi\frac{(N-m)}{N} , \quad q_{m(m-1)} = (1-\pi)\frac{m}{N} , \quad q_{mm} = \pi\frac{m}{N} + (1-\pi)\frac{(N-m)}{N} ,$$

as may be seen by making the appropriate simplifications in Equations 4, 5, and 6. We shall demonstrate that in this case the latent roots of Q_1, the transition matrix, are simply

$$\lambda'_m = \frac{m}{N} \qquad (m = 0, 1, \cdots, N).$$

The proof will be accomplished by using a similarity transformation $AQ_1A^{-1} = Q'_1$ to reduce Q_1 to a triangular matrix having the same latent roots. First let us see how the transformation works in a simple special case. When $N = 2$, we have

$$Q_1 = \begin{pmatrix} \pi & 1-\pi & 0 \\ \dfrac{\pi}{2} & \dfrac{1}{2} & \dfrac{1-\pi}{2} \\ 0 & \pi & 1-\pi \end{pmatrix}.$$

A suitable matrix A proves to be

$$A = \begin{pmatrix} 1 & 0 & 0 \\ 1 & -1 & 0 \\ 1 & -2 & 1 \end{pmatrix},$$

which has the property $A^2 = I$, where

$$I = \begin{pmatrix} 1 & 0 & 0 \\ 0 & 1 & 0 \\ 0 & 0 & 1 \end{pmatrix}.$$

Then the desired transformation is simply $Q'_1 = AQ_1A$. By direct multiplication we find

$$AQ_1 = \begin{pmatrix} \pi & 1-\pi & 0 \\ \dfrac{\pi}{2} & \dfrac{1}{2}-\pi & -\dfrac{1-\pi}{2} \\ 0 & 0 & 0 \end{pmatrix},$$

and

$$Q'_1 = AQ_1A = \begin{pmatrix} 1 & -(1-\pi) & 0 \\ 0 & \dfrac{1}{2} & -\dfrac{1-\pi}{2} \\ 0 & 0 & 0 \end{pmatrix}.$$

The latent roots of a triangular matrix are simply the elements on the main diagonal, so we see immediately that for this example

$$\lambda'_2 = 1, \qquad \lambda'_1 = 1/2, \qquad \lambda'_0 = 0,$$

as anticipated.

The only difficult step in carrying out a similar proof for arbitrary N is that of locating a suitable "transforming matrix" A. The solution in this instance (suggested by Dr. Herman Chernoff) is a matrix with the elements

$$a_{ij} = (-1)^{j+1}\binom{i-1}{j-1} \quad \text{when } j \le i,$$

and

$$a_{ij} = 0 \quad \text{when } j > i.$$

As in the $N = 2$ case, $A^2 = I$, so the required transformation is again simply

$Q'_1 = AQ_1A$. For the remainder of this one proof, in order to simplify the subscript notation, the rows of Q_1, and correspondingly those of A, are considered to be numbered $1, 2, \cdots, N+1$ from top to bottom. With this numbering system, the elements of Q_1 are

$$q_{k(k+1)} = (1 - \pi)\frac{(N - k + 1)}{N}, \qquad q_{k(k-1)} = \pi\frac{(k - 1)}{N},$$

$$q_{kk} = \pi\frac{(N - k + 1)}{N} + (1 - \pi)\frac{(k - 1)}{N},$$

as will be clear from the correspondence

State (No. cond. el.) N $N-1$ $\cdots$ $N-k+1$ $\cdots$ 0
Row of Q_1 $\cdots\cdots$ 1 2 $\cdots$ k $\cdots$ $N+1$.

Now for any diagonal element b_{ii} of Q'_1, we find by direct multiplication

$$b_{ii} = \sum_{j=1}^{N+1} \sum_{k=1}^{N+1} a_{ij}q_{jk}a_{ki}.$$

Then, making the appropriate substitutions,

$$(25) \quad b_{ii} = \sum_{j=1}^{i} \sum_{k=1}^{N+1} (-1)^{j+1}\binom{i-1}{j-1}(-1)^{i+1}\binom{k-1}{i-1}q_{jk}$$

$$= \sum_{j=1}^{i} (-1)^{j+i+2}\binom{i-1}{j-1}\binom{j-1}{i-1}q_{jj} + \sum_{j=1}^{i} (-1)^{j+i+2}\binom{i-1}{j-1}\binom{j}{i-1}q_{j(j+1)}$$

$$= (-1)^{2(i+1)}q_{ii} + (-1)^{2i+1}\binom{i-1}{i-2}q_{(i-1)i} + (-1)^{2(i+1)}\binom{i}{i-1}q_{i(i+1)}$$

$$= \left[\pi\frac{(N - i + 1)}{N} + (1 - \pi)\frac{(i - 1)}{N}\right] - (i - 1)(1 - \pi)\frac{(N - i + 2)}{N}$$

$$+ i(1 - \pi)\frac{(N - i + 1)}{N}$$

$$= \frac{N - i + 1}{N}.$$

Next we must consider elements of Q'_1 falling below the main diagonal, i.e., b_{ij} with $i > j$. Proceeding as above, we can write

$$(26) \quad b_{ij} = \sum_{k=1}^{N+1} \sum_{m=1}^{N+1} a_{ik}q_{km}a_{mj}$$

$$= \sum_{k=1}^{i} \sum_{m=j}^{i} (-1)^{k+1}\binom{i-1}{k-1}(-1)^{j+1}\binom{m-1}{j-1}q_{km}$$

$$= \sum_{k=1}^{i} (-1)^{j+k+2}\binom{i-1}{k-1}\left[q_{k(k-1)}\binom{k-2}{j-1} + q_{kk}\binom{k-1}{j-1} + q_{k(k+1)}\binom{k}{j-1}\right]$$

$$= \frac{\pi}{N}\sum_{k=j+1}^{i} (-1)^{j+k}\binom{i-1}{k-1}\binom{k-2}{j-1}(k - 1)$$

$$+ \sum_{k=j}^{i} (-1)^{j+k}\binom{i-1}{k-1}\binom{k-1}{j-1}\left[\pi\frac{(N - k + 1)}{N} + (1 - \pi)\frac{(k - 1)}{N}\right]$$

$$+ \frac{(1 - \pi)}{N}\sum_{k=j-1}^{i} (-1)^{j+k}\binom{i-1}{k-1}\binom{k}{j-1}[N - (k - 1)].$$

Now a lengthy series of algebraic reductions establishes that for $i > j$, $b_{ij} = 0$. All the reductions are similar, so we shall take the first part of the last summation in Equation 26 as an example:

$$\frac{N}{N} \sum_{k=j-1}^{i} (-1)^{j+k} \binom{i-1}{k-1}\binom{k}{j-1} = \sum_{k=j-1}^{i} (-1)^{j+k} \frac{(i-1)!}{(k-1)!(i-k)!} \cdot \frac{k!}{(j-1)!(k-j)!}$$

$$= \frac{(i-1)!}{(j-1)!(i-j+1)!} \sum_{k=j-1}^{i} (-1)^{j+k} k \binom{i-j+1}{k-j+1}$$

$$= \frac{(i-1)!(-1)^{2j-1}}{(j-1)!(i-j+1)!} \sum_{r=0}^{i-j+1} (-1)^r \left\{ r\binom{i-j+1}{r} + (j-1)\binom{i-j+1}{r} \right\},$$

where $r = k + j - 1$. Thus we have come down to two sums of the form

$$\sum_{r=0}^{n} (-1)^r r\binom{n}{r} \quad \text{and} \quad \sum_{r=0}^{n} (-1)^r \binom{n}{r},$$

which are well known to equal zero ([16], p. 61).

Since the elements falling below the main diagonal of Q_1' are all equal to zero, the latent roots of Q_1', and therefore of Q_1, are

$$\lambda_i' = \frac{N-i+1}{N} \quad (i = 1, 2, \cdots, N+1),$$

or, if we index the λ's in terms of states,

$$\lambda_m' = \frac{m}{N} \quad (m = 0, 1, \cdots, N),$$

since obviously the two sets of values are identical.

Now with the roots of Q_1 in hand, we wish to determine those of Q, which has c as a parameter. As a preliminary step we note that the matrix Q can be written in the form

(27) $$Q = (1 - c)I + cQ_1.$$

The identity will be apparent if we consider the case of $N = 2$, for which Equations 4 to 6 prescribe

$$Q = \begin{pmatrix} 1 - c + c\pi & c(1 - \pi) & 0 \\ c\frac{\pi}{2} & 1 - \frac{c}{2} & c\frac{(1-\pi)}{2} \\ 0 & c\pi & 1 - c\pi \end{pmatrix}.$$

We can rewrite Q as a sum of two matrices

$$Q = \begin{pmatrix} 1-c & 0 & 0 \\ 0 & 1-c & 0 \\ 0 & 0 & 1-c \end{pmatrix} + \begin{pmatrix} c\pi & c(1-\pi) & 0 \\ c\frac{\pi}{2} & \frac{c}{2} & c\frac{(1-\pi)}{2} \\ 0 & c\pi & c(1-\pi) \end{pmatrix}.$$

Factoring $(1 - c)$ out of the first matrix on the right and c out of the second, we arrive at

$$Q = (1 - c)\begin{pmatrix} 1 & 0 & 0 \\ 0 & 1 & 0 \\ 0 & 0 & 1 \end{pmatrix} + c\begin{pmatrix} \pi & 1 - \pi & 0 \\ \dfrac{\pi}{2} & \dfrac{c}{2} & \dfrac{1 - \pi}{2} \\ 0 & \pi & 1 - \pi \end{pmatrix},$$

or

$$Q = (1 - c)I + cQ_1 .$$

Now it is easy to show that if λ' is a root of Q_1, then $1 - c + c\lambda'$ is a root of Q. Letting λ be a root of Q, and recalling that by definition of a latent root the determinant of $Q - \lambda I$ must vanish, we can write

$$\begin{aligned} |Q - \lambda I| &= |(1 - c)I + cQ_1 - \lambda I| \\ &= |cQ_1 - (c + \lambda - 1)I| \\ &= c^{N+1}\left|Q_1 - \frac{\lambda + c - 1}{c}I\right| \\ &= 0 . \end{aligned}$$

Therefore, provided $c > 0$,

$$\frac{\lambda + c - 1}{c} ,$$

which we may denote by λ', is the root of Q_1 corresponding to the root λ of Q. Solving the equation $(\lambda + c - 1)/c = \lambda'$, we obtain $\lambda = 1 - c + c\lambda'$. Since we previously demonstrated that the roots of Q_1 are $\lambda'_m = m/N$ for $m = 0, 1, \cdots, N$, we now have established that the roots of Q are

$$(28) \qquad \lambda_m = 1 - c + c\frac{m}{N} \qquad (m = 0, 1, \cdots, N) .$$

We can illustrate the function of the λ's in a relatively simple context and at the same time obtain some experimentally useful expressions by calculating $q_{jk}^{(n)}$ for the case of uniform reinforcement (i.e., the simple noncontingent case with $\pi = 1$).

Having the values of λ_m in hand, we know both Q and Λ in Equation 24, and it turns out that explicit solutions for Y and Y^{-1} are readily obtainable by standard methods. We find for elements of Y

$$y_{jm} = \frac{\dbinom{m}{j}}{\dbinom{N}{j}} ,$$

and for elements of Y^{-1}

$$y_{mj}^{-1} = \binom{N - m}{j - m}(-1)^{j-m} .$$

Since the systems of linear equations arising from Equation 24 are homogeneous, the solutions involve $N + 1$ arbitrary constants, k_m. But using the fact that $Y^{-1}Y = I$, we can express these constants in terms of the other parameters; by direct multiplication of the row and column of Y^{-1} and Y, respectively, associated with the root λ_m, and therefore the same constant k_m,

$$k_m \sum_{j=0}^{N} y_{jm} y_{mj}^{-1} = 1 ,$$

and when appropriate expressions for y_{jm} and y_{mj}^{-1} have been substituted and the summation has been carried out, we find

$$k_m = \frac{1}{\binom{N}{m}} .$$

Finally, multiplying out the right-hand side of Equation 23, after all the necessary substitutions have been made in terms of the quantities just computed, we find that the element in the jth row and kth column of Q^n is

(29)
$$q_{jk}^{(n)} = \sum_{m=j}^{k} \left(1 - c + c\frac{m}{N}\right)^n \frac{\binom{m}{j}}{\binom{N}{j}} \binom{N-m}{k-m}(-1)^{k-m}\binom{N}{m} ,$$

which can also be written

$$q_{jk}^{(n)} = \binom{N-j}{N-k} \sum_{m=j}^{k} \left(1 - c + c\frac{m}{N}\right)^n (-1)^{k-m}\binom{k-j}{m-j} .$$

As a check on our somewhat lengthy computations, we might evaluate Equation 29 for a transition that we already know, viz.,

$$q_{j(j+1)}^{(1)} = \left(1 - c + c\frac{j}{N}\right) \cdot \frac{1}{\binom{N}{j}}(N-j)(-1)\binom{N}{j}$$

$$+ \left[1 - c + c\frac{(j-1)}{N}\right] \frac{(j+1)}{\binom{N}{j}}\binom{N-j+1}{0}\binom{N}{j+1}$$

$$= -(N-j)\left(1 - c + c\frac{j}{N}\right) + (N-j)\left[1 - c + c\frac{(j+1)}{N}\right]$$

$$= c\frac{(N-j)}{N} ,$$

in agreement with Equation 4. In its general form, Equation 29 is a bit cumbersome for practical purposes, but in many particular cases it simplifies greatly. For example, the probability of remaining in state 0 for n trials turns out to be simply $q_{00}^{(n)} = (1 - c)^n$; the probability of terminating in state N (i.e., having all N patterns conditioned to A_1) regardless of the initial state is

$$q_{jN}^{(\infty)} = \frac{\binom{N}{j}}{\binom{N}{j}}\binom{N-N}{N-N}(-1)^{N-N}\binom{N}{N} = 1;$$

and the probability that, for a subject beginning in state 0, all N patterns will be conditioned to A_1 at the end of the first N trials is

$$q_{0N}^{(N)} = \sum_{m=0}^{N}\left(1 - c + c\frac{m}{N}\right)^{N}(-1)^{N-m}\binom{N}{m}.$$

For $N = 1$, this last expression reduces to

$$q_{01}^{(1)} = (1 - c)(-1) + 1 = c;$$

for $N = 2$,

$$q_{02}^{(2)} = (1 - c)^2 + \binom{2}{1}(-1)\left(1 - c + \frac{c}{2}\right)^2 + 1 = \frac{c^2}{2};$$

for $N = 3$,

$$q_{03}^{(3)} = (-1)^3(1 - c)^3 + c\left(1 - c + \frac{c}{3}\right)^3 + 3(-1)\left(1 - c + \frac{2c}{3}\right)^3 + 1 = \frac{2}{9}c^3;$$

and so on.

Absorption Probabilities. By an "absorbing state," in the terminology of Markov chains, one means a state from which escape is impossible. If state j is absorbing, then obviously we must have $q_{jj} = 1$. In the case of uniform reinforcement ($\pi = 1$) considered in the preceding section, state N has $q_{NN} = 1$, and when we calculated $q_{jN}^{(n)}$, we found that all of these transition probabilities tend to 1 as a limit when n becomes large. It is quite possible to have more than one absorbing state; an example would be the case of simple, contingent reinforcement with $\pi_{11} = \pi_{22} = 1$, where states N and 0 are both absorbing. In such a case, we know from the general theory of finite Markov chains [16] only that the subject must end up in one or another of the absorbing states. For the present model, probabilities of absorption in any particular absorbing state are obtainable by the technique given in the section above on asymptotic probabilities.

New questions of experimental interest that arise for cases involving absorbing states concern the number of trials which a subject may be expected to spend in any given nonabsorbing state. All such questions can be dealt with once we have calculated for each pair of nonabsorbing states the statistic t_{ij}, which represents the expected number of trials the subject will spend in state j, given that he started in state i. A simple method for calculating the t_{ij} is presented in [21]. Here we shall illustrate the method and obtain some useful results by treating the case of uniform reinforcement.

To carry out the desired calculations, we require a matrix Q_{-a} formed by deleting the row and column of the transition matrix Q corresponding to state N. (For cases involving more than one absorbing state, the procedure is the same, except that the reduced matrix Q_{-a} is formed by deleting the rows and columns corresponding to all of the absorbing states.) From Equations 4 to 6, the matrix Q_{-a} takes the form

$$Q_{-a} = \begin{pmatrix} 1 - c/N & 0 & 0 & \cdots & 0 \\ 2c/N & 1 - 2c/N & 0 & \cdots & 0 \\ 0 & 3c/N & 1 - 3c/N & \cdots & 0 \\ \vdots & \vdots & \vdots & & \vdots \\ 0 & 0 & \cdots & Nc/N & 1 - Nc/N \end{pmatrix},$$

where all entries except those on the main diagonal and the one below it are zeros. Now the quantities t_{ij} are the elements of the matrix $T = (I - Q_{-a})^{-1}$. Subtracting Q_{-a} from the identity matrix I, we have

$$I - Q_{-a} = \begin{pmatrix} c/N & 0 & 0 & \cdots & 0 \\ -2c/N & 2c/N & 0 & \cdots & 0 \\ 0 & -3c/N & 3c/N & \cdots & 0 \\ \vdots & \vdots & \vdots & & \vdots \\ 0 & 0 & \cdots & -Nc/N & Nc/N \end{pmatrix},$$

where, again, all entries off the main diagonal and the one below it are zeros. The inverse of $I - Q_{-a}$ is readily found to be

$$T = (I - Q_{-a})^{-1} = \begin{pmatrix} N/c & 0 & 0 & \cdots & 0 \\ N/c & N/2c & 0 & \cdots & 0 \\ N/c & N/2c & N/3c & \cdots & 0 \\ \vdots & \vdots & \vdots & & \vdots \\ N/c & N/2c & N/3c & \cdots & N/Nc \end{pmatrix},$$

where the rows, from bottom to top, correspond to states $0, 1, \cdots, N - 1$. That is,

$$(30) \qquad t_{ij} = \begin{cases} \dfrac{N}{c(N - j)} & \text{if } i \leq j \\ 0 & \text{if } i > j, \end{cases}$$

where $i, j = 0, 1, \cdots, N - 1$. Since all the nonzero entries in each column of T are identical, it is apparent that the expected number of trials a subject will spend in any attainable nonabsorbing state is independent of his initial state.

The expected total number of trials to absorption (i.e., to the completion of learning) for any subject is simply the sum of the entries in the row of T corresponding to his initial state, thus

$$(31) \qquad \sum_{j=i}^{N-1} t_{ij} = \frac{N}{c} \sum_{j=i}^{N-1} \frac{1}{N - j}.$$

If we regard an A_1 as a correct response and an A_2 as an error in a given learning situation, then when the subject is in state j, the probability of an error is $(N-j)/N$. Hence, the expected total number of errors during learning is given by

$$(32) \qquad e_i = \sum_{j=i}^{N-1} t_{ij} \frac{N-j}{N} = \frac{N}{c} \sum_{j=i}^{N-1} \frac{1}{N-j} \cdot \frac{N-j}{N} = \frac{N-i}{c} .$$

This expression can be put in a form more convenient for some purposes if we divide numerator and denominator by N, obtaining

$$e_i = \frac{1 - \dfrac{i}{N}}{\dfrac{c}{N}} = (1 - p_i) \frac{N}{c} .$$

We have encountered the term c/N before, in the role of slope parameter of the mean learning curve (Equation 13), and we will see later that it appears also in expressions for various sequential statistics. Of course, p_i here is the initial probability of a correct response for a subject starting in state i.

Sequential Statistics. We can further our understanding of the model and at the same time augment our stock of methods for estimating the parameters by deriving expressions for probability of the A_1 response contingent on all possible combinations of responses and reinforcing events on the preceding trial. As in the treatment of state probabilities, we limit ourselves to the simple, noncontingent case. We shall write in terms of two alternatives, A_1 and A_2, but all of the results hold for any number of alternatives. If there are r alternatives in a given experimental application, any one response can be denoted A_1 and the rest regarded as members of a single class A_2.

1. Probability of A_1 given that it occurred and was reinforced on the preceding trial: It is convenient to deal first with the joint probability $P(A_{1,n+1}E_{1,n}A_{1,n})$ and then conditionalize at the final step. We begin by introducing the identity

$$P(A_{1,n+1}E_{1,n}A_{1,n}) = \sum_m \sum_i P(A_{1,n+1}E_{1,n}A_{1,n}s^i m) ,$$

where the summation is over the two types of stimulus patterns (s^1 conditioned to A_1 and s^0 not conditioned to A_1) and all possible states on trial n. The right-hand side of the identity can be expanded into the form

$$\sum_m q_m^{(n-1)}[P(A_{1,n+1} \mid E_{1\,n}A_{1,n}s^0 m)\pi P(A_{1,n} \mid s^0 m)P(s^0 \mid m)$$
$$+ P(A_{1\,n+1} \mid E_{1,n}A_{1,n}s^1 m)\pi P(A_{1,n} \mid s^1 m)P(s^1 \mid m)] .$$

The first term inside the brackets equals zero, since an A_1 cannot occur in the presence of s^0. The factor in the second term involving $A_{1,n}$ is equal to unity since A_1 must occur in the presence of s^1; the factor involving $A_{1,n+1}$ is equal to m/N, since the stimulus pattern present together with the E_1 event on trial n was already conditioned to A_1; and the probability of s^1 given state m is m/N; thus the summation reduces to

$$\pi \sum_m q_m^{(n-1)} \frac{m^2}{N^2} = \pi V_{2,n} \, ,$$

where $V_{2,n}$ denotes the second raw moment of the response probabilities on trial n. To conditionalize, we need only divide this result by πp_n, the probability of the joint event $E_1 A_1$ on trial n, obtaining

$$(33) \qquad P(A_{1,n+1} | E_{1,n} A_{1,n}) = V_{2,n}/p_n \, .$$

Derivations of the other three conditional probabilities are similar and will be given more briefly.

2. Probability of A_1 given that it was reinforced although A_2 occurred on the preceding trial:

$$\sum_m \sum_i P(A_{1,n+1} E_{1,n} A_{2,n} s^i m)$$

$$= \sum_m q_m^{(n-1)} P(A_{1,n+1} | E_{1,n} A_{2,n} s^0 m) \pi P(A_{2,n} | s^0 m) P(s^0 | m)$$

$$= \sum_m q_m^{(n-1)} \pi \left[(1 - c) \frac{m}{N} + c \frac{(m+1)}{N} \right] \frac{(N - m)}{N}$$

$$= \pi \left(p_n + \frac{c}{N} - V_{2,n} - \frac{c}{N} p_n \right) ,$$

and therefore

$$(34) \qquad P(A_{1,n+1} | E_{1,n} A_{2,n}) = \frac{\left[\left(1 - \frac{c}{N} \right) p_n + \frac{c}{N} - V_{2,n} \right]}{1 - p_n} .$$

3. Probability of A_1 given that it occurred but that A_2 was reinforced on the preceding trial:

$$\sum_m \sum_i P(A_{1,n+1} E_{2,n} A_{1,n} s^i m)$$

$$= \sum_m q_m^{(n-1)} P(A_{1,n+1} | E_{2,n} A_{1,n} s^1 m)(1 - \pi) P(A_1 | s^1 m) P(s^1 | m)$$

$$= \sum_m q_m^{(n-1)} (1 - \pi) \left[(1 - c) \frac{m}{N} + c \frac{(m-1)}{N} \right] \frac{m}{N}$$

$$= (1 - \pi) \left(V_{2,n} - \frac{c}{N} p_n \right) ,$$

and therefore

$$(35) \qquad P(A_{1,n+1} | E_{2,n} A_{1,n}) = \frac{V_{2,n} - \frac{c}{N} p_n}{p_n} .$$

4. Probability of A_1 given that A_2 occurred and was reinforced on the preceding trial:

$$\sum_m \sum_s P(A_{1,n+1} E_{2,n} A_{2,n} s^i m)$$

$$= \sum_m q_m^{(n-1)} P(A_{1,n+1} | E_{2,n} A_{2,n} s^0 m)(1 - \pi) P(A_2 | s^0 m) P(s^0 | m)$$

$$= \sum_m q_m^{(n-1)} \frac{m}{N} \frac{(N - m)}{N} (1 - \pi)$$

$$= (1 - \pi)(p_n - V_{2,n}) ,$$

and therefore

$$(36) \qquad P(A_{1,n+1}|E_{2,n}A_{2,n}) = \frac{p_n - V_{2,n}}{1 - p_n} \; .$$

With the basic equations 33 to 36 in hand, we need only elementary probability theory to obtain expressions for dependencies of responses on responses or responses on events, viz.,

$$(37) \qquad P(A_{1,n+1}|A_{1,n}) = \frac{V_{2,n}}{p_n} - \frac{c}{N}(1 - \pi) \; ,$$

$$(38) \qquad P(A_{1,n+1}|A_{2,n}) = \frac{p_n - V_{2\,n}}{1 - p_n} + \frac{c}{N}\pi \; ,$$

$$(39) \qquad P(A_{1,n+1}|E_{1,n}) = \left(1 - \frac{c}{N}\right)p_n + \frac{c}{N} \; ,$$

$$(40) \qquad P(A_{1,n+1}|E_{2,n}) = \left(1 - \frac{c}{N}\right)p_n \; .$$

In some respects these results deviate from what one might have intuitively expected. Since an E_1 event can have no effect when a pattern already conditioned to A_1 is sampled, and since an A_1 can occur only when such a pattern is sampled, one might suppose that the conditional probability $P(A_{1,n+1}|A_{1,n})$ would be unaffected by the additional information that an E_1 occurred on trial n. But, comparing Equations 33 and 37, we see that, except for the special case when $\pi = 1$, $P(A_{1,n+1}|E_{1,n}A_{1,n})$ is always greater than $P(A_{1,n+1}|A_{1,n})$. Similarly, except in the special case when $\pi = 0$, $P(A_{1,n+1}|E_{2,n}A_{1,n})$ is always smaller than $P(A_{1,n+1}|A_{1,n})$. Comparing Equations 33 to 40 with corresponding expressions for the linear model (Chapter 8, Sec. 8), we see that the two models differ somewhat with respect to the formulas for all but the last two conditional probabilities. For example, in the case of A_1 probability following the joint occurrence of E_1A_1, the result given by the pattern model in Equation 33,

$$P(A_{1,n+1}|E_{1,n}A_{1,n}) = \frac{V_{2,n}}{p_n} \; ,$$

may be compared with that generated by the linear model of Chapter 8,

$$P(A_{1,n+1}|E_{1,n}A_{1,n}) = (1 - \theta)\frac{V_{2,n}}{p_n} + \theta \; .$$

It is interesting to note that, although many of the expressions for sequential statistics differ between the two models, estimation procedures may fail to reveal these differences in empirical applications. In order to get rid of the term $V_{2,n}$, which appears in Equations 33 to 38 but which has no direct empirical interpretation, one frequently forms differences such as

$$P(A_{1,n+1}|E_{1,n}A_{1,n}) - P(A_{1,n+1}|A_{1,n}) = (1 - \pi)\frac{c}{N} \; ,$$

$$P(A_{1,n+1}|A_{2,n}) - P(A_{1,n+1}|E_{2,n}A_{2,n}) = \pi\frac{c}{N},$$

$$P(A_{1,n+1}|E_{1,n}) - P(A_{1,n+1}|E_{2,n}) = \frac{c}{N}.$$

These difference expressions are formally identical to those derivable from the linear model, with c/N in the pattern model having the same role as θ in the linear model.

Since we have previously derived formulas for P_n and $V_{2,n}$ in the pattern model (Equations 13 and 14), we can substitute the asymptotic forms of these expressions into Equations 33 to 38 to obtain asymptotic formulas for the conditional probabilities, which we indicate by dropping the n subscripts:

$$P(A_1|E_1A_1) = \pi + \frac{1-\pi}{N}, \qquad P(A_1|E_2A_2) = \pi - \frac{\pi}{N},$$

$$P(A_1|E_1A_2) = \pi\left(1 - \frac{1}{N}\right) + \frac{c}{N}, \qquad P(A_1|A_1) = \pi + \frac{(1-\pi)(1-c)}{N},$$

$$P(A_1|E_2A_1) = \pi\left(1 - \frac{1}{N}\right) + \frac{1-c}{N}, \qquad P(A_1|A_2) = \pi - \frac{\pi(1-c)}{N}.$$

It will be noted that these expressions provide a convenient means for estimating the parameters c and N separately for experiments in which N is an unknown parameter.

Finally, we state without proof the one remaining formula that is needed as a basis for computing serial correlation coefficients and variances of sums of response frequencies over trials:

$$(41) \qquad P(A_{1,n+k}A_{1,n}) = \pi p_n - \left[\pi p_n - P(A_{1,n+1}A_{1,n})\right]\left(1 - \frac{c}{N}\right)^{k-1}.$$

This equation is an identity for $k = 1$, and is readily established by induction to hold for all integral $k \geq 1$.

Discrimination Learning. Although the simple mathematical properties of the pattern model make it a serious competitor to other extant models in the analysis of simple learning, it was originally conceived as a possible solution to the problem of overlap in discrimination learning. As Restle brings out in Chapter 20, one of the principal focal points of recent research in discrimination theory has been the problem of accounting for the fact that, under many circumstances, organisms can learn to discriminate with 100 per cent accuracy between stimulus situations which have so many components or aspects (cues) in common that initially there is substantial generalization between them. Without elaborating calculational machinery in full detail, we shall now consider briefly how the model developed in the preceding sections can be applied to standard discrimination learning experiments.

1. Discrimination between situations having no common stimulus patterns: This case is mathematically the simplest, requiring only the direct application of techniques derived in connection with simple learning. Typically, a discrimination of this type requires the subject to learn differential responses to two sets

of stimulus patterns, which we may denote S_1 and S_2, containing N_1 and N_2 patterns, respectively. In the usual procedure ([5], [18], [24]), patterns of S_1 occur on a proportion β (usually one-half) of trials and are followed by reinforcement of A_1 with probability 1; patterns of S_2 occur on a proportion $1 - \beta$ of trials and are followed by reinforcement of A_2 with probability 1, the order of S_1 and S_2 trials being randomized.

In order to make completely clear the important distinction between *common cues* and *common patterns*, let us consider a hypothetical experiment in which the subject is to learn a discrimination between two sets of printed symbols. We shall denote the symbols (cues) by A, B, C, D, and E, and suppose they occur in the following combinations (patterns). On a proportion $\beta = 1/2$ of trials, the experimenter exhibits either ABC or ABD and reinforces response A_1 (thus ABC and ABD comprise S_1); on the remaining trials, he presents either BCD or BDE and reinforces response A_2 (i.e., BCD and BDE comprise S_2). Now it is clear that S_1 and S_2 have common *cues*, but they have no common *patterns* (assuming experimental conditions are such that the subject sees all three of the symbols that are presented on each trial). In Restle's terminology (Chapter 20, [24]), B and C are *irrelevant cues* (since they are randomly associated with the reinforcing events); A and E are *relevant cues*; and D, since its correlation with the reinforcing events is intermediate between zero and unity, is a *partially relevant* cue.

Now if we assume that, within each of the sets S_1 and S_2, all the patterns are equally likely to occur when the set is available for sampling, then the entire theory developed previously for the case of simple learning with uniform reinforcement can be applied to learning relative to each of the two sets separately. Thus the probability of correct response to set S_i is given by Equation 12 or 13, with $\pi = 1$ and with n replaced by n_i, the number of trials on which set S_i has been available for sampling. Similarly, state probabilities in set S_i are given by Equation 29, expected trials in a nonabsorbing state by Equation 30, and expected total errors to patterns of set S_i by Equation 32, in each case with n replaced by n_i. The equations for response probability and state probability can easily be adjusted to express the dependent variables as functions of total trials, n, rather than n_i. For example, Equation 12 becomes

$$(42) \quad p_n = \beta\left[\left(1 - \frac{c}{N_1}\right)p_{n-1} + \frac{c}{N_1}\right] + (1 - \beta)\left[\left(1 - \frac{c}{N_2}\right)p_{n-1} + \frac{c}{N_2}\right]$$

$$= \left[1 - \frac{\beta c}{N_1} - \frac{(1 - \beta)c}{N_2}\right]p_{n-1} + \frac{\beta c}{N_1} + \frac{(1 - \beta)c}{N_2} ,$$

where p_n now represents probability of correct responding.

Regardless of the values of N_1, N_2, and β, the probability of correct responding goes asymptotically to unity in this case. The rate of discrimination learning depends on the values of N_i. Adding either relevant or irrelevant cues will retard discrimination learning if and only if it leads to increases in the number of patterns N_i.

2. Discriminations between situations having common stimulus patterns:

To illustrate this case, let us consider a hypothetical experiment in which the experimenter presents the symbol pair AB on a proportion β of trials, always accompanied by reinforcement of response A_1, and the symbol pair BC on the remaining trials, accompanied by reinforcement of A_2. But in this instance, let us assume experimental conditions such that the subject is able to see only one of the symbols exhibited on each trial. If the subject is equally likely to see either of the symbols belonging to the pair shown on a trial, then we have the following contingencies of reinforcement upon effective stimulus patterns (recall that a pattern constitutes all of the stimulation actually affecting the subject on a given trial):

Pattern	$P(E_1\|\text{pattern})$
A	1
B	β
C	0

Now states can be defined and a transition matrix set up analogously to the case of simple learning. One might, for example, define states as follows:

State	Patterns conditioned to A_1
1	A, B, C
2	A, B
3	A, C
4	B, C
5	A
6	B
7	C
8	none

This, of course, is not the only possibility. For purposes of calculating expressions for probability of correct responding, it is convenient to bypass the transition matrix and follow the procedure used by Burke and Estes ([5], [12]) with component models, designating by $F_{i1,n}$ the probability that pattern i is conditioned to response A_1 on trial n. For the present example, recursions for these probabilities take the form

$$F_{A1,n} = \left(1 - \frac{\beta}{2}\right)F_{A1,n} + \frac{\beta}{2}[(1-c)F_{A1,n} + c] = \left(1 - \frac{\beta c}{2}\right)F_{A1,n} + \frac{\beta c}{2},$$

$$F_{B1,n} = \frac{1}{2}F_{B1,n} + \frac{1}{2}[(1-c)F_{B1,n} + \beta c] = \left(1 - \frac{c}{2}\right)F_{B1,n} + \frac{\beta c}{2},$$

and

$$F_{C1,n} = \left[1 - \frac{(1-\beta)}{2}\right]F_{C1,n} + \frac{(1-\beta)}{2}(1-c)F_{C1,n} = \left[1 - c\frac{(1-\beta)}{2}\right]F_{C1,n}.$$

To obtain, for example, $F_{A1,n}$, we observe that this probability can change only on a trial when the experimenter exhibits combination AB and the subject sees symbol A, the probability of this joint event being $\beta \cdot 1/2$; then $F_{A1,n}$ goes to unity with probability c (the probability that the stimulus pattern, if not already conditioned to A_1, becomes so conditioned when response A_1 is reinforced).

Probability of correct responding is now a weighted combination of the $F_{i1,n}$, viz.,

$$p_n = \beta\left(\frac{F_{A1,n}}{2} + \frac{F_{B1,n}}{2}\right) + (1 - \beta)\left[\frac{1 - F_{B1,n}}{2} + \frac{1 - F_{C1,n}}{2}\right]$$

$$= \frac{1}{2}[\beta F_{A1,n} + (2\beta - 1)F_{B1,n} + (1 - \beta)(2 - F_{C1,n})],$$

which goes asymptotically to $p_\infty = 1 - \beta + \beta^2$. If, for example, the experimenter presents AB and BC equally often, so that $\beta = 1/2$, then $p_\infty = 3/4$, as one would have anticipated without formal analysis since obviously patterns A and C would eventually become conditioned to the correct responses, A_1 and A_2, respectively, while pattern B would be equally likely to be conditioned to either response on any trial. In general, it is clear that in this case asymptotic probability of correct responding is inversely related to the number of patterns the two situations undergoing discrimination, S_1 and S_2, have in common.

3. Paired-associate learning: A paired-associate problem typically involves K different stimulus patterns and K responses, one response being designated "correct" for each stimulus (i.e., being reinforced whenever that stimulus is presented). One can view a simple paired-associate experiment as K different learning processes, all going on concurrently and independently. Then the simplest case of the pattern model ($N = 1$ and $\pi = 1$) can be applied to each of the separate processes.

For most purposes, however, it is more convenient to reinterpret the situation as one in which there are only two classes of responses, "correct" and "incorrect," the former being reinforced in the presence of each of the K stimuli. With this interpretation, p_n is the mean probability of a correct response (expected proportion of correct responses) at the beginning of the nth showing of the list, it being assumed that the order of stimuli in the list is randomized before each successive presention; and the subject is said to be in state k when exactly k of the K stimuli are conditioned to correct responses. The elements of the transition matrix take the form

$$(43) \qquad q_{k(k+v)} = \binom{K - k}{v}c^v(1 - c)^{K-k-v},$$

since, when k stimuli are already conditioned to correct responses, there are $\binom{K-k}{v}$ ways of selecting v unconditioned ones and there is probability $c^v(1 - c)^{K-k-v}$ that exactly these v stimuli become conditioned on the given trial. By writing out the matrix for a particular example, say $K = 3$,

$$Q = \begin{pmatrix} 1 & 0 & 0 & 0 \\ c & 1 - c & 0 & 0 \\ c^2 & \binom{2}{1}c(1 - c) & (1 - c)^2 & 0 \\ c^3 & \binom{3}{2}c^2(1 - c) & \binom{3}{1}c(1 - c)^2 & (1 - c)^3 \end{pmatrix},$$

we see immediately that the latent roots are, in general,

(44) $\lambda_K = 1, \quad \lambda_{K-1} = 1 - c, \quad \cdots, \quad \lambda_0 = (1 - c)^K.$

Given the λ's, and the benefit of the large number of zeros in the transition matrix, it is easy to solve Equations 24 for any given K and to express Q^n in the form of Equation 23, $Q^n = YA^nY^{-1}$. For $K = 3$, we find

$$Y = \begin{pmatrix} 1 & 0 & 0 & 0 \\ 1 & 1 & 0 & 0 \\ 1 & 2 & 1 & 0 \\ 1 & 3 & 3 & 1 \end{pmatrix},$$

$$A = \begin{pmatrix} 1 & 0 & 0 & 0 \\ 0 & 1-c & 0 & 0 \\ 0 & 0 & (1-c)^2 & 0 \\ 0 & 0 & 0 & (1-c)^3 \end{pmatrix},$$

and

$$Y^{-1} = \begin{pmatrix} 1 & 0 & 0 & 0 \\ -1 & 1 & 0 & 0 \\ 1 & -2 & 1 & 0 \\ -1 & 3 & -3 & 1 \end{pmatrix}.$$

Multiplying out these three matrices yields for Q^n the matrix

$$\begin{pmatrix} 1 & 0 & 0 & 0 \\ 1-(1-c)^n & (1-c)^n & 0 & 0 \\ [1-(1-c)^n]^2 & 2(1-c)^n[1-(1-c)^n] & (1-c)^{2n} & 0 \\ [1-(1-c)^n]^3 & 3(1-c)^n[1-(1-c)^n]^2 & 3(1-c)^{2n}[1-(1-c)^n]^2 & (1-c)^{3n} \end{pmatrix}$$

It will be apparent that, starting from state k, the probability of having all K stimuli conditioned to correct responses after n trials is $[1 - (1 - c)^n]^{K-k}$; the probability that no conditioning occurs in n trials is $(1 - c)^{(K-k)n}$; and in general the probability of going from state k to state $k + v$ in n trials is

(45) $q_{k(k+v)}^{(n)} = \binom{K-k}{v}(1 - c)^{(K-k-v)n}[1 - (1 - c)^n]^v .$

Since there is only one absorbing state, $k = K$, eventually all stimuli must become conditioned to correct responses. To calculate the expected number of trials, t_{ij}, that a subject will spend in a nonabsorbing state j, given that he started in state i, we proceed as in the derivation of Equation 30. Continuing to illustrate the technique for the case of $K = 3$, we have for the reduced matrix Q_{-a},

$$Q_{-a} = \begin{pmatrix} 1-c & 0 & 0 \\ \binom{2}{1}c(1-c) & (1-c)^2 & 0 \\ \binom{3}{2}c^2(1-c) & \binom{3}{1}c(1-c)^2 & (1-c)^3 \end{pmatrix}.$$

Subtracting Q_{-a} from the identity matrix yields

$$I - Q_{-a} = \begin{pmatrix} c & 0 & 0 \\ -2c(1-c) & 1-(1-c)^2 & 0 \\ -3c^2(1-c) & -3c(1-c)^2 & 1-(1-c)^3 \end{pmatrix},$$

whose inverse is

$$(I-Q_{-a})^{-1} = \begin{pmatrix} \dfrac{1}{c} & 0 & 0 \\ \dfrac{2(1-c)}{1-(1-c)^2} & \dfrac{1}{1-(1-c)^2} & 0 \\ \dfrac{3c(1-c)[1+(1-c)^2]}{[1-(1-c)^2][1-(1-c)^3]} & \dfrac{3c(1-c)^2}{[1-(1-c)^2][1-(1-c)^3]} & \dfrac{1}{1-(1-c)^3} \end{pmatrix}.$$

The expected total number of errors during learning, e_i, for a subject beginning in state i is obtainable as in the case of Equation 32, and, although the t_{ij} are different in the present instance, e_i proves to be the same:

$$e_1 = \frac{1}{c}, \qquad e_2 = \frac{2(1-c)}{1-(1-c)^2} + \frac{2}{1-(1-c)^2} = \frac{2}{c},$$

and in general

(46) $$e_i = \frac{K-i}{c} = \frac{K}{c}(1-p_i),$$

where p_i is probability of a correct response for a subject in state i.

Component Models with Fixed Sample Size

Assumptions. Representation of a simple learning experiment in terms of this type of model is based on the assumption of a population S consisting of N stimulus elements. On every trial the subject draws a sample of s elements from S; the value of s is constant throughout any given experiment, and all possible samples of size s are equally likely to occur. At any time, each element of S is connected to exactly one of the response alternatives, A_1, A_2, $\cdots$, A_r, and each possible distribution of m_1 elements to A_1, m_2 to A_2, $\cdots$, m_r to A_r defines a state in the Markovian interpretation. In general there are $\binom{N+1}{r-1}$ different states, but in this paper we shall limit consideration to cases involving $r = 2$ and, therefore, $N + 1$ states. In the learning theory associated with component models (see, e.g., [8], [11], [12]), it is assumed that probability of a response is equal to the proportion of elements connected to that response in the trial sample. With the assumption of equal sampling probabilities, however, the expected proportion of elements connected to a given response A_i in the sample is equal to the proportion in the population. Therefore in this paper we shall identify the probability, p, of an A_1 response in a two-alternative situation with m/N, where m is the number of elements in S connected to A_1.

Conditioning assumptions are similar to those of the pattern model, given above, and the linear model (Chapter 8). At the termination of a trial when reinforcing event E_1 or E_2 occurs, all elements in the trial sample are connected to A_1 or A_2, respectively. When the "neutral" event E_0 occurs, the conditioned status of elements in the sample does not change. As in the pattern model, the transition probabilities q_{ij} are functions of the probabilities of reinforcing events and of the set-theoretical parameters, here s and N. Again, we shall limit consideration to cases in which probabilities of reinforcement depend at most upon the response of the given trial, a restriction which guarantees that all elements of the transition matrix Q will be constant over trials. One might expect that the component model would include a "conditioning parameter" defined analogously to the parameter c of the pattern model; in this case c would be the probability that the elements of a trial sample previously unconditioned to response A_i become so conditioned if the sample occurs in conjunction with reinforcing event E_i. In the literature of statistical learning theory, however, this parameter has been assumed equal to unity, and the assumption will be maintained in this paper except where otherwise specified. At a few points, we shall note the respects in which relaxation of the restriction $c = 1$ would change the formulation.

Transition Probabilities and Classification of States. The transition probabilities take the form

$$(47) \qquad q_{m(m+v)} = \frac{\binom{N-m}{v}\binom{m}{s-v}}{\binom{N}{s}} P(E_1 | s' m) ,$$

where v is an integer and s' is a sample of size s including exactly $s - v$ elements connected to A_1;

$$(48) \qquad q_{m(m-v)} = \frac{\binom{N-m}{s-v}\binom{m}{v}}{\binom{N}{s}} P(E_2 | s'' m) ,$$

where s'' is a sample of size s including exactly v elements connected to A_1; and

$$(49) \qquad q_{mm} = \frac{\binom{m}{s}}{\binom{N}{s}} P(E_1 | s''' m) + \frac{\binom{N-m}{s}}{\binom{N}{s}} P(E_2 | s'''' m) + P(E_0 | m) ,$$

where s''' and s'''' are samples of size s having all and none of their elements, respectively, connected to A_1. To obtain Equation 47, for example, we note that to go from state m to state $m + v$, the subject must draw exactly v elements from the $N - m$ not already connected to A_1, and that the probability of doing this is the number of ways of drawing samples with this property over the total number of ways of drawing samples of size s; once an appropriate sample is drawn, it must be accompanied by an E_1 event, and $P(E_1|s'm)$ is our notation for the probability of an E_1 given the state m and the prescribed type of sample.

One of the advantages of interpreting the model as a Markov process is that even in cases where recursive expressions for response probability defy solution and computation of the higher-order transition probabilities is impractical, general theorems drawn from the theory of Markov chains may provide considerable information about the behavior of the system.

Whenever general formulas are available for the transition probabilities, inspection of these formulas permits classification of the states into one or more of the following types: absorbing, transient, periodic, or ergodic. (For detailed discussion of the classification and for derivation of probabilistic theorems cited here without proof, the reader is referred to Feller [16], chaps. 15, 16.)

a. A state is said to be absorbing if transition from it to any other state is impossible, i.e., if $q_{mm} = 1$. Absorbing states arise in the present model only when some of the reinforcement probabilities π_{ij} are equal to zero or unity.

b. A state is said to be transient if the probability of its recurrence (in an infinite sequence of trials) is less than unity. When any case of this model includes absorbing states, the remaining states are all transient.

c. A state is said to be periodic with period k (k being an integer) if its recurrence is impossible except in k, $2k$, $3k$, $\cdots$ steps. Periodic states do not occur in any of the cases discussed in this paper.

d. States of a finite chain which are neither absorbing, transient, nor periodic are said to be ergodic. Ergodic states are certain to recur infinitely often in an infinite sequence of trials. In all cases of the present model that we will consider, all states are necessarily ergodic if none of the π_{ij} are equal to zero or unity.

Once the states are classified for any case of the model, general theorems are adducible to predict the asymptotic behavior of the system. For example:

a. If all states are ergodic, the state probabilities, and therefore the response probabilities, converge to unique asymptotic values that are independent of the initial state or initial distribution of states. Further, the expected asymptotic response probability, p_∞, must have a value intermediate between zero and unity.

b. If there is a single absorbing state, the asymptotic probability of this state is unity and those of all other states are zero.

c. If there are two or more absorbing states, the asymptotic probabilities of these states sum to unity. The distribution of asymptotic probabilities over the set of absorbing states (and therefore the distribution of asymptotic response probabilities) depends on the initial state or initial distribution of states.

To exhibit some of the more detailed properties of the model and to illustrate the derivation of experimentally testable results, we now turn to the special cases that arise when specific assumptions are made concerning the parameters.

Simple Noncontingent Reinforcement. When the reinforcement schedule prescribes that only the two events E_1 and E_2 occur, and these with fixed probabilities π and $1-\pi$, respectively, Equations 47 to 49 for the transition probabilities reduce to

$$q_{m(m+v)} = \pi\frac{\binom{N-m}{v}\binom{m}{s-v}}{\binom{N}{s}}, \quad q_{m(m-v)} = (1-\pi)\frac{\binom{N-m}{s-v}\binom{m}{v}}{\binom{N}{s}},$$

$$q_{mm} = \pi\frac{\binom{m}{s}}{\binom{N}{s}} + (1-\pi)\frac{\binom{N-m}{s}}{\binom{N}{s}}.$$

It is apparent at once that the only possible absorbing states are state N, when $\pi=1$, and state 0, when $\pi=0$. Otherwise all states are ergodic.

A recursion for p_n, the probability of A_1 over the sample space of all possible event sequences, is obtainable by the same technique used in the case of Equation 10, and proves to be

$$(50) \qquad p_n = \left(1 - \frac{s}{N}\right)p_{n-1} + \frac{s}{N}\pi,$$

with the solution

$$(51) \qquad p_n = \pi - (\pi - p_1)\left(1 - \frac{s}{N}\right)^{n-1}.$$

Equations 50 and 51 are identical in form to those derived for the same case of the linear model (Chapter 8, Sec. 8), with the sampling ratio s/N taking on the role of the rate parameter θ in the linear model. However, the variances of the response probabilities differ. The asymptotic variance for the model with fixed sample size is

$$(52) \qquad \sigma^2 = \pi(1-\pi)\frac{[N+(N-2)s]}{N(2N-s-1)}.$$

When we let $s/N = \theta$ and rewrite this result in the form

$$\sigma^2 = \pi(1-\pi)\frac{[1+(N-2)\theta]}{N(2-\theta)-1},$$

we see that it is greater than the variance

$$\sigma^2 = \pi(1-\pi)\frac{\theta}{2-\theta}$$

for the same case of the linear model when N is finite, but converges to the latter expression as $N \to \infty$.

By the same technique used with the noncontingent case of the pattern model, it is possible to show that the latent roots of the transition matrix for this case of the fixed-sample-size model are

$$\text{(53)} \qquad \lambda_N = 1, \ \lambda_{N-1} = \frac{\binom{N-1}{s}}{\binom{N}{s}}, \ \lambda_{N-2} = \frac{\binom{N-2}{s}}{\binom{N}{s}}, \ \cdots, \ \lambda_s = \frac{1}{\binom{N}{s}},$$

and $\lambda_m = 0$ for $m < s$.

To illustrate the use of the λ's in calculating state probabilities, let us consider the case of $N = 3$ and $s = 2$; for this case the transition matrix is

$$Q = \begin{pmatrix} \pi & 0 & 1-\pi & 0 \\ \dfrac{2}{3}\pi & \dfrac{\pi}{3} & \dfrac{2(1-\pi)}{3} & \dfrac{1-\pi}{3} \\ \dfrac{\pi}{3} & \dfrac{2\pi}{3} & \dfrac{1-\pi}{3} & \dfrac{2(1-\pi)}{3} \\ 0 & \pi & 0 & 1-\pi \end{pmatrix}$$

and the roots are $\lambda_3 = 1$, $\lambda_2 = 1/3$, $\lambda_1 = \lambda_0 = 0$. Solving Equations 24 for the first two columns of Y and the first two rows of Y^{-1}, we find for the column and row associated with λ_3

$$\begin{pmatrix} 1 \\ 1 \\ 1 \\ 1 \end{pmatrix} \ (\pi^2, \ \pi(1-\pi), \ \pi(1-\pi), \ (1-\pi)^2) \, ,$$

and for the column and row associated with λ_2

$$\begin{pmatrix} 3\pi - 3 \\ 3\pi - 2 \\ 3\pi - 1 \\ 3\pi \end{pmatrix} \ (-\pi, \ \pi, \ -(1-\pi), \ (1-\pi)) \, .$$

Now to obtain the coefficient of λ_m^n in the expression for $q_{ij}^{(n)}$, we need only multiply the ith row of the associated column by the jth column of the associated row. Thus we find

$$q_{33}^{(n)} = \pi^2 + \pi(1-\pi)\left(\frac{1}{3}\right)^{n-1}, \qquad q_{23}^{(n)} = \pi^2 + \pi\left(\frac{2}{3}-\pi\right)\left(\frac{1}{3}\right)^{n-1},$$

$$q_{32}^{(n)} = \pi(1-\pi)\left[1 - \left(\frac{1}{3}\right)^{n-1}\right], \quad \text{etc.}$$

Having the elements of Q^n, we can premultiply this matrix by the row vector of initial state probabilities to obtain formulas for state probabilities n trials after starting from an arbitrary initial distribution:

$$q^{(n)} = q^{(0)}Q^n$$
$$= (\pi^2, \ \pi(1-\pi), \ \pi(1-\pi), \ (1-\pi)^2)$$
$$- \left(\frac{1}{3}\right)^{n-1}\left[q_3^{(0)}(1-\pi) + q_2^{(0)}\left(\frac{2}{3}-\pi\right) + q_1^{(0)}\left(\frac{1}{3}-\pi\right) - q_0^{(0)}\pi\right]$$
$$\cdot (-\pi, \ \pi, \ -(1-\pi), \ 1-\pi)$$

$$= (\pi^2, \ \pi(1-\pi), \ \pi(1-\pi), \ (1-\pi)^2)$$
$$-\left(\frac{1}{3}\right)^{n-1}(p_1 - \pi)(-\pi, \ \pi, \ -(1-\pi), \ (1-\pi)) \ ,$$

since

$$\sum_m q_m^{(0)} = 1 \qquad \text{and} \qquad \sum_m q_m^{(0)}\frac{1}{m} = p_1 \ .$$

From these results and the obvious substitutions, we obtain

$$p_n = \sum_{m=0}^{3} q_m^{n-1}\frac{1}{m} = \pi - (\pi - p_1)\left(\frac{1}{3}\right)^{n-1} \ ,$$

in agreement with the result obtainable by specialization of Equation 51.

Introduction of the conditioning parameter, c, in the noncontingent case, has little effect on quantitative properties of the model. The elements $q_{m(m+v)}$ and $q_{m(m-v)}$ of the transition matrix are simply multiplied by c, and the diagonal elements q_{mm} become

$$1 - c + c\left[\pi\frac{\binom{m}{s}}{\binom{N}{s}} + (1-\pi)\frac{\binom{N-m}{s}}{\binom{N}{s}}\right].$$

Therefore the new transition matrix, Q_c, can be written

$$(54) \qquad Q_c = (1-c)I + cQ \ ,$$

where I is the identity matrix with $N+1$ rows and columns. It is easy to see that the elements of Q_c^n must approach the same asymptotes as the elements of Q^n when n becomes large. The limit of Q^n as $n \to \infty$ is a matrix Q^∞ whose elements, the asymptotic state probabilities, may be obtained by solving the equations

$$(55) \qquad Q^\infty Q = Q Q^\infty = Q^\infty \ .$$

But in view of the relation 54, it must follow that $Q^\infty Q_c = Q_c Q^\infty = Q^\infty$, and therefore Q^∞ must be the limit matrix of Q_c as well as of Q. By the same technique used in the derivation of Equation 28, one can show further that the latent roots of Q_c are given by

$$\lambda_m = 1 - c + c\frac{\binom{m}{s}}{\binom{N}{s}} \qquad (m = s, \ s+1, \ \cdots, \ N) \ ,$$

the factor

$$\frac{\binom{m}{s}}{\binom{N}{s}}$$

being the corresponding root of Q. Finally, we note that the recursion for response probability, derived in the usual way, takes the form

$$p_{n+1} = \left(1 - \frac{cs}{N}\right)p_n + \frac{cs}{N}\pi \ .$$

In concluding this section, we might point out that although we have written our results specifically for the special case of two response alternatives, they all hold for the general case of r alternatives. To apply the various formulas to experimental situations with $r > 2$, one need only designate any desired response as A_1 and class the remainder together as A_2. The same will not be true, however, for the contingent case, to which we now turn.

Simple Contingent Case. When the probability of E_0 events is zero but the probabilities of E_1 and E_2 depend on whether the subject has made an A_1 or an A_2 response on the given trial, the transition equations 47, 48, and 49 specialize to

$$q_{m(m+v)} = \left[\frac{(s-v)}{s}\pi_{11} + \frac{v}{s}\pi_{21}\right]\frac{\binom{m}{s-v}\binom{N-m}{v}}{\binom{N}{s}} \ ,$$

$$q_{m(m-v)} = \left[\left(\frac{v}{s}\right)\pi_{12} + \left(\frac{s-v}{s}\right)\pi_{22}\right]\binom{m}{v}\binom{N-m}{s-v} \ ,$$

$$q_{mm} = \frac{\binom{m}{s}}{\binom{N}{s}}\pi_{11} + \frac{\binom{N-m}{s}}{\binom{N}{s}}\pi_{22} \ ,$$

where again π_{jk} represents the probability of E_k given A_j.

Using these expressions for the transition probabilities, we find the recursion for response probability to be

$$p_n = \left[1 - \frac{s}{N}(1 - \pi_{11} + \pi_{21})\right]p_{n-1} + \frac{s}{N}\pi_{21} \ ,$$

which, with s/N taking the role of θ, is the same as the corresponding relation in the linear model (Chapter 8, Sec. 5).

When both π_{11} and π_{22} have values intermediate between zero and unity, the same must be true of q_{mm} for all m, and therefore all states are ergodic. State probabilities can be calculated by the techniques demonstrated previously, but the expressions are not generally very simple in form. When either π_{11} or π_{22} equals unity, the corresponding state, $m = N$ or $m = 0$, respectively, is absorbing.

In the case of two absorbing states, a problem arises that we have not encountered previously. We know from the general theory that all subjects will end up in one or the other of the absorbing states. But we would like to go further and specify the probability that a subject starting from state j will be absorbed at state N with an asymptotic A_1 probability of unity, rather than at state 0 with an asymptotic A_1 probability of zero.

Methods of handling this problem can conveniently be illustrated in terms of the special case used before, i.e., $N = 3$ and $s = 2$, but this time with $\pi_{11} = \pi_{22} = 1$. The transition matrix for this case is

$$Q = \begin{pmatrix} 1 & 0 & 0 & 0 \\ \tfrac{1}{3} & \tfrac{1}{3} & \tfrac{1}{3} & 0 \\ 0 & \tfrac{1}{3} & \tfrac{1}{3} & \tfrac{1}{3} \\ 0 & 0 & 0 & 1 \end{pmatrix},$$

and the usual techniques for calculating the higher-order transition probabilities yield

$$Q^n = \begin{pmatrix} 1 & 0 & 0 & 0 \\ \tfrac{2}{3} & 0 & 0 & \tfrac{1}{3} \\ \tfrac{1}{3} & 0 & 0 & \tfrac{2}{3} \\ 0 & 0 & 0 & 1 \end{pmatrix} + \left(\tfrac{2}{3}\right)^n \begin{pmatrix} 0 & 0 & 0 & 0 \\ -\tfrac{1}{2} & \tfrac{1}{2} & \tfrac{1}{2} & -\tfrac{1}{2} \\ -\tfrac{1}{2} & \tfrac{1}{2} & \tfrac{1}{2} & -\tfrac{1}{2} \\ 0 & 0 & 0 & 0 \end{pmatrix}$$

$$= A + \left(\tfrac{2}{3}\right)^n B .$$

Clearly the elements of the first and last columns of the first matrix on the right, A, are the limiting probabilities of absorption at N or 0, respectively, starting from any given state. If we preferred, we could obtain the elements of A, without computing Q^n, simply by solving the linear equations

(56) $\qquad a_{ij} = \sum_{v=0}^{N} q_{iv} a_{vj} \quad$ and $\quad \sum_{j} a_{ij} = 1 \qquad (i, j = 0, 1, \cdots, N) ,$

with N in this instance equal to 3.

Inspecting the limit matrix A, above, we are led to surmise that for the general case with N and s unrestricted, the probability a_{iN} that a subject starting from i will be absorbed at N is always equal to i/N. An attempt to demonstrate this relation by solving Equations 56 for the general case runs into some unwieldy algebra. However, we can satisfy ourselves that the relation holds by utilizing the following dodge. We note first that substituting into the left-hand equation in terms of our hypothesis yields, for any initial state i, the following equation, which must be satisfied if the hypothesis is true:

(57) $\qquad q_{iN}\dfrac{N}{N} + q_i(N-1)\dfrac{N-1}{N} + \cdots + q_{i1}\dfrac{1}{N} = \dfrac{i}{N} .$

But the expression on the left represents also the expected probability of the A_1' response on a given trial for all subjects who were in state i on the preceding trial; and this conditional probability can be derived independently: Letting s^v represent a sample on trial n containing v elements connected to A_1, and i the state on trial n, we can write

$$P(A_{1,n+1}|i) = \sum_{k}\sum_{j}\sum_{v} P(A_{1,n+1}E_{k,n}A_{j,n}s^v|i)$$

$$= \sum_{v=0}^{s} \frac{\binom{i}{v}\binom{N-i}{s-v}}{\binom{N}{s}} \left[\frac{v}{s}\,\frac{(i+s-v)}{N} + \frac{(s-v)}{s}\,\frac{(i-v)}{N} \right]$$

$$= \sum_{v=0}^{s} \frac{\binom{i}{v}\binom{N-i}{s-v}}{\binom{N}{s}} \left[\frac{i}{N}\right]$$

$$= \frac{i}{N} ,$$

and therefore Equation 57 is satisfied.

The probability of absorption in state j after starting from an arbitrary distribution of initial state probabilities is given by

(58) $$a_j = \sum_i q_i^{(0)} a_{ij} .$$

Using the expression just established for a_{ij} in conjunction with Equation 58, we find for the unconditional probability of absorption at state N,

$$a_N = q_N^{(0)} + q_{N-1}^{(0)} \frac{N-1}{N} + q_{N-2}^{(0)} \frac{N-2}{N} + \cdots + q_1^{(0)} \frac{1}{N} .$$

However, the right side of this last equation is also an expression for the expected proportion of elements connected to A_1 after zero trials, i.e., on trial 1, so we conclude that $a_N = p_1$, and, similarly, $a_0 = 1 - p_1$.

The Role of Neutral Events. In the noncontingent case, the changes in properties of the model that ensue when neutral (E_0) events are permitted can be very simply described. The transition probabilities become

$$q_{m(m+v)} = \pi_1 \frac{\binom{N-m}{v}\binom{m}{s-v}}{\binom{N}{s}} \qquad q_{m(m-v)} = \pi_2 \frac{\binom{m}{v}\binom{N-m}{s-v}}{\binom{N}{s}} ,$$

$$q_{mm} = \pi_0 + \pi_1 \frac{\binom{m}{s}}{\binom{N}{s}} + \pi_2 \frac{\binom{N-m}{s}}{\binom{N}{s}} ,$$

where π_1, π_2, and π_0 are constants representing the probabilities of E_1, E_2, and E_0, respectively. These transition equations give rise to a recursion for response probability,

(59) $$p_n = \left(1 - \frac{s}{N} + \frac{s}{N}\pi_0\right)p_{n-1} + \frac{s}{N}\pi_1 ,$$

which, with s/N replacing θ, is the same as the one derived from the linear model and tested experimentally by Neimark [23] and Anderson and Grant [1].

Comparing the modified q_{ij} formulas with those given above for the simple noncontingent case, we note that the transition matrix, Q_0, of the present case may be expressed in the form

$$Q_0 = \pi_0 I + (1 - \pi_0)Q' ,$$

where I is the identity matrix with $N+1$ rows, and Q' is identical with the matrix Q of the simple (non-E_0) case except that the reinforcement parameters

π and $1 - \pi$ of the latter are replaced by

$$\pi' = \frac{\pi_1}{1 - \pi_0} \qquad \text{and} \qquad 1 - \pi' = \frac{\pi_2}{1 - \pi_0} ,$$

respectively. The limit matrix of Q_0^n is the same as that of Q^n since if $Q'^\infty Q' = Q'^\infty$, then

$$Q'^\infty Q_0 = \pi_0 Q'^\infty + (1 - \pi_0)Q'^\infty = Q'^\infty .$$

Therefore the asymptotic state probabilities of the case with E_0 events are the same as those of the simpler case, except for the substitution of π' for π.

The latent roots of Q_0 are easily shown to be $\lambda_m^{(0)} = \pi_0 + (1 - \pi_0)\lambda_m$, where λ_m, the corresponding root of Q', is (by Equation 53) equal to

$$\binom{m}{s} \bigg/ \binom{N}{s} .$$

The proof of this relation is analogous to that of Equation 28.

From these results it is apparent that if the value of π_0 is increased while the ratio of π_1 to π_2 remains constant, the rate of learning is reduced, but asymptotic properties of the model having to do with the relative frequencies of A_1 and A_2 are unchanged.

Properties of the model in the contingent case with E_0's cannot be characterized in comparable detail. The expressions for upward and downward transition probabilities are unaltered in form, but the diagonal element of the transition matrix becomes

$$q_{mm} = \frac{\binom{m}{s}}{\binom{N}{s}} \pi_{11} + \frac{\binom{N-m}{s}}{\binom{N}{s}} \pi_{22} + \frac{m}{N} \pi_{10} + \left(1 - \frac{m}{N}\right)\pi_{20} .$$

Inspection of this equation reveals that states other than N and 0 can be absorbing only in the degenerate case when neither response is ever reinforced, i.e., when $\pi_{10} = \pi_{20} = 1$. States N and 0 are absorbing when $\pi_{11} + \pi_{10} = 1$ and when $\pi_{22} + \pi_{20} = 1$, respectively. In all other cases, all states are ergodic and the state probabilities tend to a stationary asymptotic distribution independent of the initial conditions. The recursion for response probability is

$$(60) \qquad p_n = \left[1 - \frac{s}{N}(1 - \pi_{11} + \pi_{21} - \pi_{20})\right]p_{n-1} + \frac{s}{N}\pi_{21} + \frac{s}{N}(\pi_{10} - \pi_{20})V_{2,n-1} ,$$

where

$$V_{2,n-1} = \sum_m \left(\frac{m}{N}\right)^2 q_m^{(n-2)} .$$

It is apparent that Equation 60, like the analogous expression in the linear model (Chapter 8, Sec. 5), cannot be solved, even for the asymptotic mean, except in the special case when $\pi_{10} = \pi_{20}$. In all cases, however, provided only that N is not so large as to overtax one's resources for solving systems of $N + 1$ linear equations, the complete asymptotic distribution can be obtained by solution of $Q^\infty Q = Q^\infty$, where, as usual, Q represents the transition matrix and Q^∞ the limit matrix of Q^n.

Component Models with Fixed Sampling Probabilities

All the assumptions of the preceding section hold for this one except for those having to do with the sampling process. In the present instance, we assume that the elements of the stimulus set, S, are sampled independently on each trial, each element having some fixed probability of being drawn. In the general model ([5], [12]), the sampling probabilities may vary from element to element, but we shall limit consideration here to the special case in which all elements have the same sampling probability, θ. A new problem that arises with the fixed-θ model concerns the possibility of trials on which no elements are sampled. The assumptions we have stated previously must be supplemented by some convention prescribing response probability in the presence of an empty sample. Probably in most situations one would be willing to assume this probability equal to $1/r$ (e.g., $1/2$ in the case of two response alternatives), but experimental or theoretical considerations might dictate a different assumption in some instances. As a result of the null-sample problem, recursions for response probability in the fixed-θ model are not generally the same as those in the fixed-sample-size model. However, although the derivation is somewhat complex (see [15]), it can be shown that recursions for the expected proportion of elements conditioned to a given response are identical for the two models under all conditions of reinforcement. The second and higher moments of the conditioned proportions are not generally the same for the two models, but, as one might intuitively expect, expressions for these moments, and in fact for all statistics of the fixed-θ model, converge to those of the fixed-sample-size model as N becomes large [15].

Simple Noncontingent Case. The transition equations differ from the corresponding set for the fixed-sample-size model only in that the factors representing sample probabilities are terms of the binomial rather than of the hypergeometric distribution; for $v > 0$,

$$q_{m(m+v)} = \binom{N-m}{v}\theta^v(1-\theta)^{N-m-v}\pi\,, \qquad q_{m(m-v)} = \binom{m}{v}\theta^v(1-\theta)^{m-v}(1-\pi)\,,$$

$$q_{mn} = (1-\theta)^{N-m}\pi + (1-\theta)^m(1-\pi)\,.$$

These transition probabilities lead to the recursive expression

$$(61) \qquad p_n = (1-\theta)p_{n-1} + \theta\pi$$

for the expected proportion of elements conditioned to A_1, and to

$$(62) \qquad \sigma^2 = \frac{\pi(1-\pi)}{2-\theta}\left[\theta + \frac{2(1-\theta)}{N}\right]$$

for the asymptotic variance of the conditioned proportions. The former is, of course, identical in form with that of the fixed-sample-size model (Equation 50), but the latter is not. Subtracting the right side of Equation 52 from the right side of Equation 62, we find that if $N = 1$, the two variances are equal; that if $N > 1$, the variance for the fixed-θ model is always the larger; and that as $N \to \infty$, the two variances converge to a common limit, which is the same as the variance,

$$\sigma^2 = \frac{\pi(1 - \pi)\theta}{2 - \theta} \ ,$$

of the linear model (Chapter 8, Sec. 8).

Calculation of state probabilities is again facilitated by the availability of a simple formula for the latent roots of the transition matrix. In the case of uniform reinforcement ($\pi = 1$), the entire matrix takes on a very simple form:

$$Q = \begin{pmatrix} 1 & 0 & 0 & 0 & 0 & \cdots & 0 \\ \theta & (1 - \theta) & 0 & 0 & 0 & \cdots & 0 \\ \theta^2 & 2\theta(1 - \theta) & (1 - \theta)^2 & 0 & 0 & \cdots & 0 \\ \theta^3 & 3\theta^2(1 - \theta) & 3\theta(1 - \theta)^2 & (1 - \theta)^3 & 0 & \cdots & 0 \\ \vdots & \vdots & \vdots & \vdots & \vdots & \ddots & \vdots \\ \theta^N & N\theta^{N-1}(1 - \theta) & \binom{N}{2}\theta^{N-2}(1 - \theta)^2 & & & \cdots & (1 - \theta)^N \end{pmatrix},$$

and we can see immediately that the latent roots are

$$\lambda_N = 1, \quad \lambda_{N-1} = (1 - \theta), \quad \cdots, \quad \lambda_0 = (1 - \theta)^N \ .$$

Further, we can establish by induction that for $\pi = 1$,

(63) $$q_{ik}^{(n)} = \binom{N - i}{k - i}[1 - (1 - \theta)^n]^{k-i}(1 - \theta)^{n(N-k)} \ .$$

First, we note that for $n = 1$, Equation 63 reduces to the transition equation given previously for $q_{m(m+v)}$ with $m = i$ and $v = k - i$. Next, we introduce the inductive hypothesis into the general recursion for $q_{ik}^{(n)}$:

$$q_{ik}^{(n)} = \sum_{j=0}^{N} q_{ij}q_{jk}^{(n-1)}$$

$$= \sum_{u=0}^{k-i} \binom{N - i}{u}\theta^u(1 - \theta)^{N-i-u}[1 - (1 - \theta)^{n-1}]^{k-i-u}(1 - \theta)^{(n-1)(N-k)}\binom{N - i - u}{k - i - u}$$

$$= (1 - \theta)^{n(N-k)}\binom{N - i}{N - k}\sum_{u=0}^{k-i}\theta^u(1 - \theta)[1 - (1 - \theta)^{n-1}]^{k-i-u}\binom{k - i}{u}$$

$$= (1 - \theta)^{n(N-k)}\binom{N - i}{N - k}[1 - (1 - \theta)^n]^{k-i} \ ,$$

since the summation in the preceding line is simply the binomial expansion of

$$\{\theta + (1 - \theta)[1 - (1 - \theta)^{n-1}]\}^{k-i} = [1 - (1 - \theta)^n]^{k-i} \ .$$

With θ replacing c, the transition matrix of the present case is identical with that of the pattern model for paired associate learning, considered previously. Consequently, the results obtained above for the expected number of trials a subject will spend in any given nonabsorbing state apply here also. In the present case, however, the expected number of errors (A_2 responses) per trial spent in state m is given by

$$\frac{(N-m)}{N}[1-(1-\theta)^N]+(1-\rho)(1-\theta)^N ,$$

where ρ is the probability of an A_1 response in the presence of an empty sample.

In the ergodic case, when $0 < \pi < 1$, the higher-order state transitions can be calculated by the same methods as before, although the expressions quickly become cumbersome as N increases. When $N = 2$, for example, solution of $Q^\infty Q = Q^\infty$ yields for the asymptotic state probabilities,

$$q_2^{(\infty)} = \pi^2 + \frac{\pi(1-\pi)\theta}{2-\theta} , \qquad q_1^{(\infty)} = 2\pi(1-\pi)\left(1 - \frac{\theta}{2-\theta}\right) ,$$

$$q_0^{(\infty)} = (1-\pi)^2 + \frac{\pi(1-\pi)\theta}{2-\theta} .$$

The latent roots of the transition matrix Q prove to be $\lambda_2 = 1$, $\lambda_1 = 1 - \theta$, and $\lambda_0 = (1-\theta)^2$, suggesting that as in the case of $\pi = 1$, the roots are in general

$$\lambda_m = (1-\theta)^{N-m} \qquad (m = N, N-1, \cdots, 0) .$$

The full expression for Q^n in this $N = 2$ case can be written

$$Q^n = Q^\infty + (1-\theta)^n Q_1 + (1-\theta)^{2n} Q_0 ,$$

where the limit matrix Q^∞ has all entries of the first, second, and third columns, respectively, equal to $q_2^{(\infty)}$, $q_1^{(\infty)}$, and $q_0^{(\infty)}$; Q_1 is the matrix

$$\begin{pmatrix} 2(1-\pi) \\ (1-2\pi) \\ -2\pi \end{pmatrix} (\pi, \ 1-2\pi, \ -(1-\pi)) ,$$

and Q_0 is the matrix

$$-\frac{1}{2-\theta}\begin{pmatrix} (1-\pi)(2\pi+\theta-2) \\ 2\pi(1-\pi) \\ \pi(\theta-2\pi) \end{pmatrix} (1, \ -2, \ 1) .$$

For larger values of N, there does not seem to be any simple, closed formula for the asymptotic state probabilities, but Kemeny and Snell [19] have derived a useful recursive expression for these quantities.

Other Cases. In the contingent case, the transition equations are considerably more complex than those of the fixed-sample-size model:

$$q_{m(m+v)} = \binom{N-m}{v}\theta^v(1-\theta)^{N-m-v}\sum_{u=0}^{m}\left(\frac{u}{u+v}\pi_{11} + \frac{v}{u+v}\pi_{21}\right)\binom{m}{u}\theta^u(1-\theta)^{m-u} ,$$

$$q_{m(m-v)} = \binom{m}{v}\theta^v(1-\theta)^{m-v}\sum_{u=0}^{N-m}\left(\frac{v}{u+v}\pi_{12} + \frac{u}{u+v}\pi_{22}\right)\binom{N-m}{u}\theta^u(1-\theta)^{N-m-u} ,$$

$$q_{mm} = (1-\theta)^N + (1-\theta)^{N-m}\pi_{11}[1-(1-\theta)^m] + (1-\theta)^m\pi_{22}[1-(1-\theta)^{N-m}] ,$$

so that for N greater than 2 or 3 the transition matrix becomes most unwieldy. Simple asymptotic results can, however, be established for absorbing cases. Consider, for example, that of $\pi_{11} = \pi_{22} = 1$, with states N and 0 both absorbing. For $N = 2$, the transition matrix is

$$
Q = \begin{pmatrix} 1 & 0 & 0 \\ \dfrac{\theta^2}{2} & 1 - \theta^2 & \dfrac{\theta^2}{2} \\ 0 & 0 & 1 \end{pmatrix},
$$

and we find readily by the usual technique that

$$
Q^n = \begin{pmatrix} 1 & 0 & 0 \\ 1/2 & 0 & 1/2 \\ 0 & 0 & 1 \end{pmatrix} - (1 - \theta)^{2n} \begin{pmatrix} 0 & 0 & 0 \\ 1/2 & -1 & 1/2 \\ 0 & 0 & 0 \end{pmatrix}.
$$

This result suggests that perhaps in general the probability, a_{mN}, that a subject beginning in state m will be absorbed at N is equal to m/N. We know that the absorption probabilities must satisfy the relation

$$
a_{mN} = \sum_{i=1}^{N} q_{mi} a_{iN} .
$$

Replacing the factors a_{iN} at the right in terms of our hypothesis and breaking up the summation preparatory to substituting from the transition equations yields

$$
a_{mN} = \sum_{v=1}^{N-m} q_{m(m+v)} \frac{m+v}{N} + q_{mm} \frac{m}{N} + \sum_{v=1}^{m} q_{m(m-v)} \frac{m-v}{N} .
$$

Noting that the coefficients of m/N sum to unity and substituting for $q_{m(m+v)}$ and $q_{m(m-v)}$ the expressions given above, we have

$$
a_{mN} = \frac{m}{N} + \sum_{v=1}^{N-m} \frac{v}{N} \binom{N-m}{v} \theta^v (1 - \theta)^{N-m-v} \sum_{u=0}^{m} \frac{u}{u+v} \binom{m}{u} \theta^u (1 - \theta)^{m-u}
$$
$$
- \sum_{v=1}^{m} \frac{v}{N} \binom{m}{v} \theta^v (1 - \theta)^{m-v} \sum_{u=0}^{N-m} \frac{u}{u+v} \binom{N-m}{u} \theta^u (1 - \theta)^{N-m-u} .
$$

But for each positive term in the first double summation, there is an identical term with negative sign in the second double summation; therefore, under our hypothesis the equation is an identity with $a_{mN} = m/N$.

The roles of E_0 events and of the conditioning parameter, c, in this model are essentially the same as in the model with fixed sample size, so we need not give them detailed consideration here. Methods and results relative to the application of component models to various cases of discrimination learning have been presented elsewhere [5].

REFERENCES

1. Anderson, N. H., and Grant, D. A. A test of a statistical learning theory model for two-choice behavior with double stimulus events. *J. exp. Psychol.*, 1957, **54**, 305–17.
2. Atkinson, R. C. An analysis of the effect of nonreinforced trials in terms of statistical learning theory. *J. exp. Psychol.*, 1956, **52**, 28–32.

3. Atkinson, R. C., and Suppes, P. An analysis of two-person game situations in terms of statistical learning theory. *J. exp. Psychol.*, 1958, **55**, 369–78.

4. Bartlett, M. S. *Stochastic processes*. Cambridge: Cambridge University Press, 1955.

5. Burke, C. J., and Estes, W. K. A component model for stimulus variables in discrimination learning. *Psychometrika*, 1957, **22**, 133–45.

6. Burke, C. J., Estes, W. K., and Hellyer, S. Rate of verbal conditioning in relation to stimulus variability. *J. exp. Psychol.*, 1954, **48**, 153–61.

7. Bush, R. R., and Mosteller, F. *Stochastic models for learning*. New York: Wiley, 1955.

8. Estes, W. K. Toward a statistical theory of learning. *Psychol. Rev.*, 1950, **57**, 94–107.

9. Estes, W. K. Theory of learning with constant, variable, or contingent probabilities of reinforcement. *Psychometrika*, 1957, **22**, 113–32.

10. Estes, W. K. Of models and men. *Amer. Psychologist*, 1957, **12**, 609–17.

11. Estes, W. K. The statistical approach to learning theory. In S. Koch (ed.), *Psychology: A Study of a Science* (New York: McGraw-Hill, 1959), II, 383–491.

12. Estes, W. K., and Burke, C. J. A theory of stimulus variability in learning. *Psychol. Rev.*, 1953, **60**, 276–86.

13. Estes, W. K., and Burke, C. J. Application of a statistical model to simple discrimination learning in human subjects. *J. exp. Psychol.*, 1955, **50**, 81–88.

14. Estes, W. K., Burke, C. J., Atkinson, R. C., and Frankmann, Judith P. Probabilistic discrimination learning. *J. exp. Psychol.*, 1957, **54**, 233–39.

15. Estes, W. K., and Suppes, P. Foundations of statistical learning theory, II. Stimulus sampling models for simple learning. Technical Report No. 4, Contract Nonr 225 (17), Applied Mathematics and Statistics Laboratory, Stanford University, Stanford, Calif., 1959.

16. Feller, W. *Probability theory and its applications*. New York: Wiley, 1950.

17. Guthrie, E. L. *The psychology of learning*, 2d ed. New York: Harper, 1952.

18. Hilgard, E. R., and Marquis, D. G. *Conditioning and learning*. New York: Appleton-Century-Crofts, 1940.

19. Kemeny, J. G., and Snell, J. L. Markov processes in learning theory. *Psychometrika*, 1957, **22**, 221–30.

20. Kemeny, J. G., and Snell, J. L. *Finite Markov chains*. Princeton, N. J: Van Nostrand, in press.

21. Kemeny, J. G., Snell, J. L., and Thompson, G. L. *Introduction to finite mathematics*, Englewood Cliffs, N. J: Prentice-Hall, 1957.

22. Miller, G. A. Finite Markov processes in psychology. *Psychometrika*, 1952, **17**, 149–68.

23. Neimark, Edith D. Effects of type of non-reinforcement and number of alternative responses in two verbal conditioning situations. *J. exp. Psychol.*, 1956, **52**, 209–20.

24. Restle, F. A theory of discrimination learning. *Psychol. Rev.*, 1955, **62**, 11–19.

25. Schoeffler, M. S. Probability of response to compounds of discriminated stimuli. *J. exp. Psychol.*, 1954, **48**, 323–29.

Statistical Theory of Spontaneous Recovery and Regression[1]

WILLIAM K. ESTES, *Indiana University*

From the viewpoint of one interested in constructing a learning theory, it would be convenient if an organism's habits of responding with respect to any given situation were modifiable only during periods of exposure to the situation. In that case, it would not be unreasonable, prima facie, to hope that all of the empirical laws of learning could be stated in terms of relations between behavioral and environmental variables. Nothing in psychology is much more certain, however, than that orderly changes in response tendencies—e.g., spontaneous recovery, forgetting—do occur during intervals when the organism and the situation are well separated.

How are these "spontaneous" changes to be accounted for? It is easy enough to construct a law expressing some behavioral measure as a function of time, but an unfilled temporal interval never remains permanently satisfying as an explanatory variable. The temporal gap has to be filled with events of some sort, observed or inferred, in the environment or in the organism. The favorite candidate for the intervening position has usually been a postulated state or process, either neural or purely hypothetical, which varies spontane-

ously during rest intervals in whatever manner is required to account for the behavioral changes. The difficulty with this type of construct is that it is always much easier to postulate than to unpostulate. Few hypothetical entities are so ill-favored that once having secured a foothold they cannot face out each new turn of empirical events with the aid of a few *ad hoc* assumptions.

The approach to time-dependent learning phenomena which will be illustrated in this paper attempts to shift the burden of explanation from hypothesized processes in the organism to statistical properties of environmental events. The very extensiveness of the array of hypothetical constructs—e.g., set, reactive inhibition, memory trace—which now compete for attention in this area suggests that postulates of this type have entered the scene prematurely. Until more parsimonious explanatory variables have been fully explored, it will scarcely be possible either to define clearly the class of problems which require explanation or to evaluate the various special hypotheses that have been proposed.

By "more parsimonious" sources of explanation, I refer to the variables, ordinarily stimulus variables, which are intrinsic to a given type of behavioral situation and thus must be expected to play a role in any interpretive schema.

[1] This paper was prepared during the author's tenure as a faculty research fellow of the Social Science Research Council.

This article appeared in *Psychol. Rev.*, 1955, **62**, 145–154.

In the present instance we are interested specifically in the way learned response tendencies change during rest intervals following experimental periods. And we note that there are two principal ways in which stimulus variables could lead to modification in response tendencies during rest intervals. The first is the direct effect that changes in the stimulus characteristics of experimental situations from trial to trial or period to period may have upon response probability. The second is the learning that may occur between periods if the stimulating situations obtaining within and between periods have elements in common. The former category can again be subdivided according as the environmental variation is systematic or random.

The random component has been selected as our first subject of investigation for several reasons. One is that it has received little attention heretofore in learning theory. Another is that in other sciences apparently spontaneous changes in observables have frequently turned out to be attributable to random processes at a more molecular level. Perhaps not surprisingly, considerable analysis has been needed in order to ascertain how random environmental fluctuations during intervals of rest following learning periods would be expected to influence response probabilities. It will require the remainder of this paper to summarize the methods and results of this one phase of the over-all investigation.

GENERAL THEORY OF STIMULUS FLUCTUATION

Even prior to a detailed analysis, we can anticipate that whenever environmental fluctuation occurs, the probability of a response at the end of one experimental period will not be the same as the probability at the beginning of the next. If conditioning is carried out during a given period, some of the newly conditioned stimulus elements [2] will be replaced before the next period by elements which have not previously been available for conditioning. Similarly, during the interval following an extinction period, random fluctuation will lead to the replacement of some of the just extinguished stimulus elements by others which were sampled during conditioning but have not been available during extinction. In either case, the result will be a progressive change in response probability as a function of duration of the rest interval.

In order to make these ideas testable, we must state more formally and explicitly the concepts and assumptions involved. Once this is done, we will have in effect a fragmentary theory, or model, which may account for certain apparently spontaneous changes in response tendencies. At a minimum, this formal model will enable us to derive the logical consequences of the concept of random environmental fluctuation so that they may be tested against experimental data. If the correspondence turns out to be good, we may wish to incorporate this model into the conceptual structure of S-R learning theory, viewing it as a limited theory which accounts for a specific class of time-dependent phenomena.

Most of the assumptions we shall require have been discussed elsewhere (8) and need only be restated briefly for our present purposes.

a. Any environmental situation, as constituted at a given time, determines for a given organism a population of

[2] For reasons of mathematical simplicity and convenience I shall develop these ideas in terms of the concepts of statistical learning theory. It will be apparent, however, that within the Hullian system a similar argument could be worked out in terms of the fluctuation of stimuli along generalization continua.

stimulus events from which a sample affects the organism's behavior at any instant; in statistical learning theories the population is conceptualized as a set of stimulus elements from which a random sample is drawn on each trial.

b. Conditioning and extinction occur only with respect to the elements sampled on a trial.

c. The behaviors available to an organism in a given situation may be categorized into mutually exclusive and exhaustive response classes.

d. At any time, each stimulus element in the population is conditioned to exactly one of these response classes.

On the basis of these assumptions, functions have been derived by various investigators (2, 5, 8, 16, 21) to describe the course of learning predicted for an idealized situation in which the physical environment is perfectly constant and the organism samples the stimulus population on each trial. No idealized situations are available for testing purposes, but the theory seems to give good approximations to empirical learning functions obtained in short experimental periods under well-controlled conditions.

In the present paper we turn our attention from behavioral changes that occur within experimental periods to the changes that occur as a function of the intervals between periods. Correspondingly, we replace the simplifying assumption of a perfectly constant situation with the assumption of a randomly fluctuating situation.[3] Specifically, it will be assumed that the availability of stimulus elements during a given learning period depends upon a large number of independently variable components or aspects of the environ-

mental situation, all of which undergo constant random fluctuation.

Now let us consider the type of experiment in which an organism is run for more than one period in the same apparatus. In dealing with the behavior that occurs during any given experimental period, the total population S_* of stimulus elements available in the situation at any time during the experiment can be partitioned into two portions: the subset S of elements which are available during that period and the subset S' of elements which are not. Under the conditions considered in this paper, the probability of a response at any given time during the period is equal to the proportion of elements in the available set S that are conditioned to that response. Owing to environmental fluctuation, there is some probability j that an element in the available set S will become unavailable, i.e., go into S', during any given interval Δt, and a probability j' that an element in S' will enter S. These ideas are illustrated in Fig. 1 for a hypothetical situation.

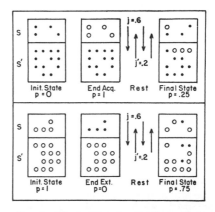

Fig. 1. Fluctuations in stimulus sets during spontaneous regression (upper panel) and spontaneous recovery from extinction (lower panel). Circles represent elements connected to response *A*. Values of *p* represent probabilities of response *A* in the available set *S*.

---

[3] It is possible now to go back and "correct" the functions derived earlier to allow for this random variation, but we will not be able to go into this point in the present paper.

The relevance of the scheme for learning phenomena arises from the fact that both conditioned and unconditioned elements will constantly be fluctuating in and out of the available set S. During an experimental period in which conditioning or extinction occurs, the proportion of conditioned elements in S will increase or decrease relative to the proportion in S'. But during a subsequent rest interval, these proportions will tend toward equality as a result of the fluctuation process.

INTERPRETATION OF SPONTANEOUS RECOVERY AND REGRESSION [4]

The essentials of our treatment of spontaneous recovery and regression will be clear from an inspection of Fig. 1. The upper panel illustrates a case in which, starting from a zero level, conditioning of a given response A is carried out during one period until the probability of A in the available situation represented by the set S is unity. At the end of the conditioning period we will have, neglecting any fluctuation that may have occurred during the period, all of the elements in S conditioned to A and all of the temporarily unavailable elements in S' unconditioned. During the first interval Δt of the ensuing rest interval, the proportion $j = .6$ of the conditioned elements will escape from S, being replaced by the proportion $j' = .2$ of the unconditioned elements from S'. During further intervals the interchange will continue, at a progressively decreasing rate, until the system arrives at the final state of statistical equilib-

rium in which the densities of conditioned elements in S and S' are equal. The predicted course of spontaneous regression in terms of the proportion of conditioned elements that will be in S at any time following the conditioning period is given by the topmost curve in the upper panel of Fig. 2. The equation of the curve will be derived in a later section.

In an analogous fashion the essentials of the spontaneous recovery process are schematized in the lower panel of Fig. 1. We begin at the left with a situation following maximal conditioning so that all elements are conditioned to response A. During a single period of extinction, all elements in the available set S are conditioned to the class of competing responses $\bar{A}$ and the probability of A goes temporarily to zero. Then during a recovery interval, the random interchange of conditioned and unconditioned elements between S and S' results in a gradual increase in the proportion of conditioned elements in S until the final equilibrium state is reached. The predicted course of spontaneous recovery as a function of time is given by the topmost curve in the lower panel of Fig. 3.

According to this analysis, spontaneous regression and recovery are to be regarded as two aspects of the same process. In each case the form of the process is given by a negatively accelerated curve with the relative rate of change depending solely upon the characteristics of the physical situation embodied in the parameters j and j'. Rates of regression and recovery should, then, vary together whenever the variability of the stimulating situation is modified.

It cannot be assumed, however, that amounts of regression and recovery should be equal and opposite in all experiments. The illustrative example of Fig. 1 meets two special conditions that do not always hold: (*a*) the condition-

[4] The term *spontaneous regression* will be used here to refer to any decrease in response probability which is attributable solely to stimulus fluctuation. It is assumed that over short time intervals the empirical phenomenon of forgetting may be virtually identified with regression, but that over longer intervals forgetting is influenced to an increasing extent by effects of interpolated learning.

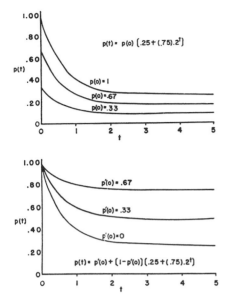

FIG. 2. Families of spontaneous regression curves. In the upper panel the proportion of conditioned elements in S' at the end of conditioning is zero and the proportion in S is the parameter. In the lower panel the proportion of conditioned elements in S at the end of conditioning is unity and the proportion in S' is the parameter.

ing and extinction series start from initial response probabilities of zero and unity, respectively; and (b) conditioning and extinction are carried to comparable criteria within the experimental period preceding the rest interval.

PREDICTIONS CONCERNING EFFECTS OF EXPERIMENTAL VARIABLES

Terminal level of conditioning or extinction. If other conditions remain fixed, the level of response probability attained at the end of a single learning period will determine both the initial value and the asymptote of the curve of regression or recovery. For the situation represented by the upper panel of Fig. 1, the curve of conditioning goes to unity, and the predicted course of spontaneous regression is

given by the top curve in the upper panel of Fig. 2. If in the same situation, conditioning has been carried only to a probability level of, say, .67, then the total number of conditioned elements will be smaller and the curve of regression will not only start at a lower value, but will run to a lower asymptote, and so on. Similarly, if in the situation represented by the lower panel of Fig. 1, response probability goes to zero during the extinction period, the predicted course of spontaneous recovery is given by the lowest curve in the upper panel of Fig. 3; if extinction terminates at higher probability levels, we obtain the successively higher recovery curves shown in the figure.

Number of preceding learning periods. Increasing the number of preceding acquisition periods would tend to increase the total number of condi-

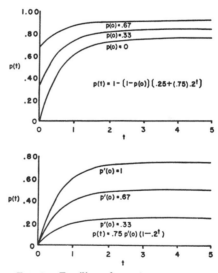

FIG. 3. Families of spontaneous recovery curves. In the upper panel the proportion of conditioned elements in S' at the end of extinction is unity and the proportion of conditioned elements in S at the end of extinction is the parameter. In the lower panel, the proportion of conditioned elements in S' at the end of extinction is the parameter and the proportion in S is zero.

tioned elements in S_* and therefore the asymptote of the curve of regression. If level of response probability at the end of the last acquisition period is fixed at some one value, say unity, then variation in the proportion of conditioned elements in S' yields the family of regression curves illustrated in the lower panel of Fig. 2, all curves starting at the same point but diverging to different asymptotes. This curve family will be recognized as corresponding to the well-known relationship between retention and amount of overlearning, where overlearning is defined in terms of additional training beyond the point at which response probability in the temporarily available situation reaches unity.

Analogous considerations apply in the case of spontaneous recovery. Increasing the number of preceding extinction periods would tend to decrease the proportion of conditioned elements remaining in S' at the end of extinction and thus the asymptote of the curve of spontaneous recovery, as illustrated in the lower panel of Fig. 3. On the other hand, increasing the number of conditioning periods prior to extinction would tend to increase the density of conditioned elements in S' and thus the asymptote of the curve of recovery following a period of extinction.

The experimental phenomenon of "extinction below zero" corresponds to a case in which additional extinction trials are given beyond the point at which temporary response probability first reaches zero. The results of this procedure will clearly depend upon the conditioning history. Consider, for example, the situation illustrated in the top row of Fig. 1. If extinction were begun immediately following the conditioning period, then we would expect extinction below zero to have little effect, for at the end of the first extinction period the set S would be ex-

hausted of conditioned elements and there would be few or none in S' to fluctuate back into S during further periods of extinction. If, however, extinction began long enough after the end of the acquisition period so that an appreciable number of conditioned elements were in S' during the first extinction period, the additional extinction would further reduce the total number of conditioned elements and thus increase the amount of training that would be required for reconditioning. If conditioning extended over more than one period, then there would be conditioned elements in S' at the end of conditioning, and similar effects of extinction below zero would be expected even if extinction began immediately after the last conditioning period.

Distribution of practice. In general, amount of spontaneous regression should vary inversely with duration of the intertrial interval during conditioning, and spontaneous recovery should vary inversely with duration of the intertrial interval during extinction. In each case, the length of the intertrial interval will determine the extent to which the stimulating situation can change between trials, and thus the proportion of the elements in the stimulus population S_* which will be sampled during a given number of trials. These relationships will be treated in more detail in a forthcoming paper (7).

MATHEMATICAL DEVELOPMENT OF FLUCTUATION THEORY

Stimulus fluctuation model. Let the probability that any given element of a total set S_* is in the available set S at time t be represented by $f(t)$, the probability that an element in S escapes into the unavailable set S' during a time interval Δt by j, and the probability that an element in S' enters S during an interval Δt by j'. Then by elementary probability theory we have for the probability that an element is in S at the end of the $(t + 1)$st interval Δt following an experimental period:

$$f(t + 1) = [1 - f(t)]j' + f(t)(1 - j).$$

This difference equation can be solved by standard methods (2, 12) to yield a formula for $f(t)$ in terms of t and the parameters:

$$f(t) = \frac{j'}{j+j'}$$
$$- \left[\frac{j'}{j+j'} - f(0) \right] (1 - j - j')^t$$
$$= J - [J - f(0)]a^t \qquad [1]$$

where $f(0)$ is the initial value of $f(t)$; J represents the fraction $j'/j + j'$; and a represents the quantity $(1 - j - j')$. Since a is bounded between -1 and $+1$ by the definition of j and j', the probability that any element [5] is in S will settle down to the constant value J after a sufficiently long interval of time, and the total numbers of elements in S and S' will stabilize at mean values N and N', respectively, which satisfy the relation.

$$N = J(N + N'). \qquad [2]$$

Spontaneous recovery and regression. Curves of spontaneous recovery and regression can now be obtained by appropriate application of Equation 1.

[5] For simplicity, it has been assumed in this paper that all of the elements in S_* have the same values of j and j'. In dealing with some situations it might be more reasonable to assume that different parameter values are associated with different elements. For example, data obtained by Homme (11) suggest that in the Skinner box a portion of the elements should be regarded as fixed and always available while the remainder fluctuate. Application of an analytic method described elsewhere (8) shows that conclusions in the general case will differ only quantitatively from those given in this paper.

Let us designate by $p(t)$ and $p'(t)$ the proportions of conditioned elements, and therefore the response probabilities, in S and S' respectively at time t following an experimental period. The set of conditioned elements in S at time t will come in part from the conditioned elements, $p(0)N$ in number, that were in S at the end of the experimental period, and in part from the conditioned elements, $p'(0)N'$ in number, that were in S'. The probabilities of finding elements from these two sources in S at time t are obtained from Equation 1 by setting $f(0)$ equal to 1 and 0 respectively. With these relations at hand we are ready to write the general expression for spontaneous recovery and regression:

$$p(t) = \frac{1}{N} [p(0)\{J - (J - 1)a^t\}N + p'(0)J(1 - a^t)N']$$
$$= p(0)[J - (J - 1)a^t] + p'(0)(1 - a^t)(1 - J), \qquad [3]$$

the parameters N and N' having been eliminated by means of Equation 2.

The functions illustrated by the curve families of Fig. 2 and 3 are all special cases of Equation 3. In the upper panel of Fig. 2, $p'(0)$ has been set equal to 0; in the lower panel, $p(0)$ has been set equal to 1. In the upper panel of Fig. 3, $p'(0)$ has been set equal to 1; in the lower panel, $p(0)$ has been set equal to 0.

EMPIRICAL RELEVANCE AND ADEQUACY

General considerations. The theoretical developments of the preceding sections present two aspects, one general and one specific, which are by no means on the same footing with regard to testability. It will be necessary to discuss separately the general concept of stimulus fluctuation and the specific mathematical model utilized for pur-

poses of deriving its testable consequences.

The reason why the fluctuation concept had to be incorporated into a formal theory in order to be tested was,
of course, the difficulty of direct ob-
servational check. Thus for the present this concept must be treated with
the same reserve and even suspicion
as any interpretation which appeals to
unobservable events. This remoteness
from direct observation may, however,
represent only a transitory stage in the
development of the theory. Relatively
direct attacks upon certain aspects of
the stimulus element concept are provided by recent experiments (1, 21) in
which the sampling of stimulus populations has been modified experimentally
and the outcome compared with theoretical expectation. Further, it should
be noted that the idea of stimulus
fluctuation is well grounded in physical considerations. Surely no one would
deny that stimulus fluctuation must occur continuously; the only question is
whether fluctuations are large enough
under ordinary experimental conditions
to yield detectable effects upon behavior. The surmise that they are is not
a new one; the idea of fluctuating environmental components has been used
in an explanatory sense by a number
of investigators in connection with particular problems: e.g., by Pavlov (19)
and Skinner (22) in accounting for
perturbations in curves of conditioning
or extinction, by Guthrie (10) in accounting for the effects of repetition,
and recently by Saltz (20) in accounting for disinhibition and reminiscence.

Considered in isolation, the concept
of stimulus fluctuation is not even indirectly testable; it must be incorporated into some broader body of theory
before empirical consequences can be
derived. In the present paper we have
found that when this concept is taken
in conjunction with other concepts and

assumptions common to contemporary
statistical learning theories (2, 5, 8,
16), the result of the union is a mathematical model which yields a large number of predictions concerning changes
in response probability during rest intervals. Once formulated, this model
is readily subject to experimental test.
Its adequacy as a descriptive theory of
spontaneous recovery and regression can
be evaluated quite independently of the
merits of the underlying idea of stimulus fluctuation.

Spontaneous recovery. Space does
not permit the detailed discussion of
experimental studies, and we shall have
to limit ourselves to a brief summary of
empirical relationships derivable from
the theory, together with appropriate
references to the experimental literature. To the best of my knowledge,
the references cited include all studies
which provide quantitative data suitable for comparison with predicted
functions.

a. The curve of recovery is exponential in
form (3, 9, 17) with the slope independent
of the initial value (3).

b. The asymptote of recovery is inversely
related to the degree of extinction (3, 11).

c. The asymptote of recovery is directly
related to the number of conditioning periods given prior to extinction (11).

d. The asymptote of recovery is directly
related to the spacing of preceding conditioning periods (11).

e. Amount of recovery progressively decreases during a series of successive extinction periods (4; 13; 19, p. 61).

It may be noted that items c and d
represent empirical findings growing out
of a study conducted expressly to test
certain aspects of the theory. Many
additional predictions derivable from
the theory must remain unevaluated
until appropriate experimental evidence
becomes available, e.g., the inverse relation between asymptote of recovery
and spacing of extinction trials or periods, and the predictions concerning "ex-

tinction below zero" mentioned in a previous section.

Spontaneous regression. Predictions concerning functional relationships between spontaneous regression and such experimental variables as trial spacing or degree of learning parallel those given above for spontaneous recovery, but in the case of regression there are fewer data available for purposes of verification. The predicted exponential decrease in amount of regression as a function of number of preceding learning periods has been observed in several studies (6, 11, 13, 14). Predictions concerning regression in relation to spacing of learning periods have not been tested in conditioning situations, but they seem to be in agreement with rather widely established empirical relationships between spacing and retention in human learning (15, pp. 156–158; 18, p. 508).

Finally, the question may be raised whether there are no experimental facts that would embarrass the present theory. If a claim of comprehensiveness had been made for the theory, then negative instances would be abundantly available. Under some conditions, for example, recovery or regression fails to appear at all following extinction or conditioning, respectively. Since, however, we are dealing with a theory that is limited to effects of a single independent variable, stimulus fluctuation, instances of that sort are of no special significance. Like any limited theory, this one can be tested only in situations where suitable measures are taken and where the effects of variables not represented in the model are either negligible or else quantitatively predictable. And subject to these qualifications, available evidence seems to be uniformly confirmatory. The danger of continually evading negative evidence by *ad hoc* appeals to other variables cannot be entirely obviated, but

it may be progressively reduced if we are successful in bringing other relevant independent variables into the theoretical fold by further applications of the analytical method illustrated here.

SUMMARY

In this paper we have investigated the possibility that certain apparently spontaneous behavioral changes, e.g., recovery from extinction, may be accounted for in terms of random fluctuation in stimulus conditions. Taken in isolation, the concept of random stimulus fluctuation has proved untestable, but when incorporated into a model it has led to quantitative descriptions of a variety of already established empirical relationships concerning spontaneous recovery and regression and to the determination of some new ones. A forthcoming paper in which the same model is applied to the problem of distribution of practice will provide further evaluation of its scope and usefulness in the interpretation of learning phenomena.

REFERENCES

1. BURKE, C. J., ESTES, W. K., & HELLYER, S. Rate of verbal conditioning in relation to stimulus variability. *J. exp. Psychol.,* 1954, **48**, 153–161.
2. BUSH, R. R., & MOSTELLER, F. *Stochastic models for learning.* New York: Wiley, in press.
3. ELLSON, D. G. Quantitative studies of the interaction of simple habits: I. Recovery from specific and generalized effects of extinction. *J. exp. Psychol.,* 1938, **23**, 339–358.
4. ELLSON, D. G. Successive extinctions of a bar-pressing response in rats. *J. gen. Psychol.,* 1940, **23**, 283–288.
5. ESTES, W. K. Toward a statistical theory of learning. *Psychol. Rev.,* 1950, **57**, 94–107.
6. ESTES, W. K. Effects of competing reactions on the conditioning curve for bar pressing. *J. exp. Psychol.,* 1950, **40**, 200–205.
7. ESTES, W. K. Statistical theory of distributional phenomena in learning. *Psychol. Rev.,* in press.

8. ESTES, W. K., & BURKE, C. J. A theory of stimulus variability in learning. *Psychol. Rev.*, 1953, **60**, 276–286.

9. GRAHAM, C. H., & GAGNÉ, R. M. The acquisition, extinction, and spontaneous recovery of a conditioned operant response. *J. exp. Psychol.*, 1940, **26**, 251–280.

10. GUTHRIE, E. R. *The psychology of learning.* New York: Harper, 1952.

11. HOMME, L. E. Spontaneous recovery from extinction in relation to number of reinforcements, spacing of acquisition, and duration of initial extinction period. Unpublished Ph.D. thesis, Indiana Univer., 1953.

12. JORDAN, C. *Calculus of finite differences.* New York: Chelsea, 1950.

13. LAUER, D. W., & ESTES, W. K. Successive acquisitions and extinctions of a jumping habit in relation to schedule of reinforcements. *J. comp. physiol. Psychol.*, 1955, **48**, 8–13.

14. LAUER, D. W., & ESTES, W. K. Rate of learning successive discrimination reversals in relation to trial spacing. *Amer. Psychologist*, 1953, **8**, 384. (Abstract)

15. MCGEOCH, J. A., & IRION, A. L. *The psychology of human learning.* New York: Longmans, Green, 1952.

16. MILLER, G. A., & McGILL, W. J. A statistical description of verbal learning. *Psychometrika*, 1952, **17**, 369–396.

17. MILLER, N. E., & STEVENSON, S. S. Agitated behavior of rats during experimental extinction and a curve of spontaneous recovery. *J. comp. Psychol.*, 1936, **21**, 205–231.

18. OSGOOD, C. E. *Method and theory in experimental psychology.* New York: Oxford Univer. Press, 1953.

19. PAVLOV, I. P. *Conditioned reflexes.* (Trans. by G. V. Anrep.) London: Oxford Univer. Press, 1927.

20. SALTZ, E. A single theory for reminiscence, act regression, and other phenomena. *Psychol. Rev.*, 1953, **60**, 159–171.

21. SCHOEFFLER, M. S. Probability of response to compounds of discriminated stimuli. *J. exp. Psychol.*, 1954, **48**, 323–329.

22. SKINNER, B. F. *The behavior of organisms.* New York: Appleton-Century-Crofts, 1938.

(Received April 18, 1954)

Spontaneous Recovery and Statistical Learning Theory[1]

Lloyd E. Homme,[2] *Indiana University*

To be reported here are two experiments designed to uncover relationships between spontaneous recovery and (*a*) number of reinforcements, and (*b*) spacing of reinforcements. Further, the experiments are designed so that the results may be compared with predictions from statistical learning theory (1, 2).

In Estes' original model (1) a stimulating situation is represented as a single set of elements which remains fixed during the experimental period. While this single-set notion seems adequate for dealing with many events taking place in one session, it has been found necessary, when the problems of spontaneous recovery and related phenoma (2) are considered, to postulate that the set of elements available during any one experimental period is a random sample from a larger total set of elements available to the organism, and further, that the elements in the experimental set are replaced, over any period of time, by random sampling from the larger set. The assumption is made throughout that the probability of occurrence of a response, *R*, is equal to the proportion of elements conditioned to *R* in the experimental subset.

To show how the model may be related to experimental events, we shall consider an initial Skinner-box learning session for a naive animal. At the beginning of the

session there are, let us assume, no elements conditioned to bar-pressing. This is illustrated in Fig. 1A, by letting the larger circle, S^*, represent the total available elements, and S the portion of the total set available on any experimental period. At the end of the conditioning period all of the elements, let us say, in the experimental subset are conditioned, but, neglecting interchanges during the experimental period, none of the elements outside this subset are conditioned ones. This state of affairs is represented in Fig. 1B.

Now, if we allow 24 hr. to elapse before replacing S in the apparatus for extinction, it is apparent that the sample of stimulus elements present during the extinction period will not include all the elements that were conditioned the previous day; some conditioned elements may be thought of as having "drifted out" of the sample, while some unconditioned elements have "drifted in," as in Fig. 1C.

Now if we carry out extinction until all the elements in S are extinguished

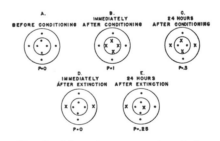

Fig. 1. Schematic representation of stimulus element situation in relation to some experimental operations. *X*'s represent elements conditioned to *R*; dots represent elements not conditioned to *R* (conditioned to $\bar{R}$). The larger circle represents the total available population of elements; the smaller circle represents the portion of elements available on a single experimental session.

[1] This report is a revised portion of a dissertation submitted to Indiana University in partial fulfillment of the requirements for the degree of Doctor of Philosophy. The writer is deeply indebted to Professor W. K. Estes for his generous advice and assistance.

[2] Now at the University of Pittsburgh.

This article appeared in *J. exp. Psychol.*, 1956, **51**, 205–212.

(Fig. 1D) and then allow 24 hr. to elapse before replacing S in the apparatus, some of the extinguished elements will have drifted out to be replaced by conditioned ones (Fig. 1E). The probability of response now will be greater than at the end of the previous extinction period; spontaneous recovery will have occurred.

From the foregoing considerations it may be seen that several predictions can be made concerning the effect of *number of reinforcements and spacing of reinforcements* on spontaneous recovery from extinction. Below are statements of the pertinent predictions regarding these variables deducible from Fig. 1 on a verbal basis. Mathematical expression of these predictions will be given in a later section.

In statistical learning theory it is specified that the number of elements conditioned in a single experimental period is an increasing exponential function of the number of reinforcements, so that, in terms of Fig. 1, as the number of reinforcements is increased there would result a greater number of conditioned elements in S. Now, with the simplifying assumption that all elements have an equal and independent probability of being drawn on any one experimental period, it is clear that the number of conditioned elements present at the beginning of a first extinction period will depend on the number originally conditioned. It also follows that after the first extinction period, in which all the conditioned elements in S become unconditioned, the number of conditioned elements remaining outside S will also depend on the degree of original conditioning. If this is true, the likelihood that conditioned elements will drift back into S before the test for spontaneous recovery will also depend on the number of reinforcements during conditioning. From these considerations, then, the

following predictions emerge: (*a*) initial probability in extinction should be an increasing (exponential) function of the number of reinforcements, (*b*) the level of recovery 24 hr. after a first extinction period should be an increasing function of the number of reinforcements, and (*c*) the total number of responses over the extinction series should be an increasing function of the number of reinforcements.

By the relationships of the model presented above, a given number of reinforcements spaced over several periods should result in more responses during extinction than the same number of reinforcements in one period. This prediction is a consequence of stimulus fluctuation between acquisition periods. With massed acquisition only S elements are available for conditioning; with spaced acquisition more of S^* is available since several samples of size S are drawn. Therefore, with spaced acquisition more *different* elements will be present at some time during the course of the reinforced trials and on statistical grounds we should expect more elements to become conditioned than in the case of masses acquisition. The predictions are, then, that (*a*) initial probability in extinction should be greater for the spaced groups, (*b*) there should be a higher level of recovery 24 hr. after extinction for the spaced groups, (*c*) the total number of responses over the extinction series should ·be greater for the spaced groups, and (*d*) there should be a greater difference between a group with five spaced acquisition periods and its massed acquisition control than between a group with two spaced acquisition periods and its control group.

These predictions are tested in the conditions of the investigations that are to be described and reported here.

Predictions from other theories of recovery.—Although these experiments were specifically designed to test a set of predictions from a statistical theory of learning, it is likely that other theories of extinction and recovery could mediate many of the same predictions. An extended review of extinction "theories" may be found in Razran (9) and will not be attempted here. Estes' theory of extinction, from which we will derive quantitative expressions for treatment of the present data in a later section, might be thought of as a more formal and testable statement of notions characteristic of Guthrie (4) and Wendt (11), in that the animal is considered to be learning a competing response in the presence of a situation which previously set the occasion for a conditioned response. Hull's theory, on the other hand, might be thought of as combining certain features of Pavlovian inhibition theory and Guthrian competing response theory (cf. Spence [10]). Because of the relatively incomplete specification of the sI_R construct, the design of the experiments and treatment of the data reported here have been organized in terms of the more quantitative relationships derivable from the statistical theory.

METHOD

Design.—Six groups of Ss were used. Groups 1–4 received 15, 50, 100, or 250 reinforcements, respectively, during a single experimental period. These groups will be compared to evaluate the effects of number of reinforcements on extinction and spontaneous recovery. Group 5 received 100 reinforcements spaced 50 per day for two days; Group 6 received 250 reinforcements spaced 50 per day for five days. Groups 5 and 6 will be compared in conjunction with Groups 3 and 4 as in a factorial design in order to evaluate the effects of spacing, number of reinforcements, and the interaction between these two variables on extinction and spontaneous recovery.

Subjects.—The Ss were 144 albino rats 70 to 90 days old obtained in six shipments of 24 each from the Windsor Biology Gardens, Bloomington, Indiana. One shipment consisted of males, the other five of females. The Ss in each shipment were randomly assigned to the six experimental groups with the restriction that four go into each group. Each experimental group, then, contained a total of 4 males and 20 females.

Apparatus.—The apparatus consisted of eight identically constructed Skinner-type boxes. The rat was contained in a chamber $10\frac{1}{2} \times 12 \times 10$ in. having a floor of hardware cloth, side and rear panels of fiberboard covered with wire-mesh screen, and a front panel of aluminum. From the left side of the front panel a 2-in. wide bar (with the leading edge rounded to reduce the frequency of bar-biting) protruded $\frac{5}{8}$ in. For this experiment the bar and rotary microswitch were adjusted so that a 4-gm. weight on the leading edge would close a circuit activating the water-dipper mechanism when the bar was depressed $\frac{3}{8}$ in. from its original position $3\frac{1}{4}$ in. from the floor. During extinction the dipper mechanism was shunted out so that only the recorder was in the circuit. Each of the experimental chambers was enclosed in a $28\frac{1}{2} \times 13\frac{3}{4} \times 14\frac{1}{2}$ in. partially soundproofed box. A 10-w. bulb mounted between the rear wall of the experimental chamber and the outer box furnished sufficient illumination so that S could be observed through a Plexiglas aperture cut in the top of the soundproofed outer box. Responses were recorded in an adjoining room by means of an Esterline-Angus Operations Recorder.

Procedure.—The Ss in each shipment were assigned to four squads, each containing one member of each experimental group. All Ss in a squad were run simultaneously in six of the eight Skinner boxes. (The other two boxes were used for a related experiment.) Counterbalancing was employed to control for box differences, three Ss in each group being assigned to each of the eight Skinner boxes.

All Ss were tamed by handling for at least three days prior to the experiment and were placed on a 22-hr. water-deprivation schedule for at least six days prior to experimentation. Food was available in the home cages at all times.

After taming and watering-schedule training, Ss were conditioned to run to the dipper and drink at the sound of the "dipper click," a characteristic sound produced when the dipper solenoid retracted the dipper into the water reservoir and released it. This dipper training, carried on for 1 hr. per day for three days, was accomplished by placing Ss in Skinner boxes in which the bars had been covered with a metal shield. The boxes were equipped with a timer which operated the dippers and a counter every 5 min. In each day's 1-hr. session, then, the dipper click followed by water presentation occurred 12 times.

Intermittent observations by E through the top of the box showed that all Ss learned to approach and drink from the magazine at the sound of the click.

Conditioning.—After Ss had received three days' dipper training, the metal shields were removed from the bars and the bar circuit was switched in so that whenever bars were depressed, the dippers and counters would operate. When the predetermined number of bar presses had been made, Ss were removed from the apparatus and watered for 1 hr.

Extinction.—On the day following the final acquisition period, the dipper mechanism was shunted out of the circuit so that only the recorder was activated when bar-pressing occurred. After the apparatus was tested and the dippers were dried, Ss were placed in the boxes and left there for 1 hr. At the end of this time Ss were watered for 1 hr. after being returned to their home cages. This procedure was repeated daily for five extinction periods.

RESULTS

The mean total extinction responses during successive 60-min. periods for Groups 1–4, where number of reinforcements during a single session was varied, are shown in Table 1. It was predicted that initial probability would differ among groups receiving differing numbers of reinforcements. Since it is specified in statistical learning theory that rate of responding is directly related to probability, the cumulated totals for the first 3 min. (by the third minute the totals have lined up in the order which is maintained over all totals) have been compared. The means (14.62, 22.67, 23.71, and 24.96 for Groups 1–4, respectively) were found by analysis of variance to differ significantly ($F = 6.43$, df 3 and 80, $P < .01$).[3] The prediction with respect to initial probability will be discussed further in connection with the p_0 parameter in the theoretical equations.

Mean response totals for the first day of extinction are in agreement with other studies of the number-of-

[3] In this instance and those to follow, wherever a significant P is reported, Bartlett's test for homogeneity of variance has yielded a nonsignificant value.

TABLE 1

OBTAINED AND PREDICTED MEAN TOTAL RESPONSES DURING 60–MIN.
EXTINCTION SESSIONS ON SUCCESSIVE DAYS

Group	Reinforcements	Measure	Extinction Day									
			1		2		3		4		5	
			Mean	SD	Mean	SD	Mean	SD	Mean	SD	Mean	SD
1	15	Obtained	88.5	35.1	28.9	19.9	21.3	12.6	16.9	11.7	14.0	9.8
		Predicted	88.3		34.5		23.0		17.9		15.3	
2	50	Obtained	94.7	49.6	20.1	14.8	23.9	17.0	17.9	15.3	15.1	12.8
		Predicted	94.7		35.0		23.2		17.9		15.4	
3	100	Obtained	110.8	56.8	37.5	23.0	22.0	8.9	19.1	14.6	19.4	15.1
		Predicted	110.5		35.9		23.5		18.2		15.4	
4	250	Obtained	119.1	39.7	42.1	20.1	24.6	12.3	25.3	24.7	18.1	14.4
		Predicted	119.1		36.3		23.6		18.2		15.5	
5	50 × 2	Obtained	102.2	36.9	40.9	23.9	21.0	8.4	20.0	11.9	13.8	9.4
		Predicted	102.4		35.6		23.4		18.1		15.4	
6	50 × 5	Obtained	149.9	55.5	57.1	23.8	35.5	21.8	26.2	16.4	19.3	13.9
		Predicted	150.5		36.9		23.9		18.3		15.5	

reinforcements variable (8, 12, 13, 14), although the F obtained in analysis of variance is not significant ($F = 2.26$; F required at .05 level is 2.72 for 3 and 80 df). Mean totals for the five extinction sessions (169.6, 181.7, 208.8, and 229.7 for Groups 1-4, respectively) fall in the predicted order. Analysis of variance yields an F value of 2.36; 2.72 is required at the .05 level with df 3 and 80.

The mean daily extinction totals for Groups 3-6, where number and spacing of reinforcements was varied, are also shown in Table 1.

Initial probabilities in terms of rate of responding were evaluated as in a factorial experiment with two variables, number of reinforcements and spacing. Neither variable yielded a significant F but the interaction term was significant at well beyond the .05 level ($F = 6.28$, 1 and 80 df).

It will be noted in Table 1 that, for the extended spacing group (50 × 5 reinforcements), there are, as predicted, more responses than for its control (250 massed reinforcements). In the case of spacing over two periods (50 × 2) versus one (100 reinforcements), this difference is not observed. Similar relationships are to be seen throughout the five extinction sessions. The totals over all periods are 208.8 and 197.9 for the 100 vs. 50 × 2 reinforcement groups and 229.7 and 288.0 for the 250 vs. 50 × 5 reinforcement groups. Evaluating the differences between these as in a factorial experiment, analysis of variance yields a significant F for the reinforcement variable ($F = 10.03$; $P < .01$, 1 and 80 df). Neither the F for spacing nor the F for interaction attains significance at the .05 level.

When the mean totals for Day 1 are analyzed in the same way, the number of reinforcements variable is significant at the .01 level ($F = 8.15$, 1 and 80 df), and the interaction term is significant at the .05 level ($F = 4.01$), but the spacing variable is not significant ($F = 1.29$). The significant interaction term is of particular interest because it supports the prediction of a greater difference between the five-period spacing group and its control than between the two-period spacing group and its control group. The t statistics computed between the mean total on Day 1 for Group 6 and its control, Group 4, is significant at the .05 level ($t = 2.21$, 46 df). The difference between Groups 3 and 5 is not significant.

RELATIONSHIPS BETWEEN DATA AND THEORY

In the introductory verbal statement of the model an important simplifying assumption was made that all elements have an equal and independent probability of being drawn on each session. Quantitative predictions utilizing this assumption will be presented and compared with the data.

Let us suppose there are, altogether, C_o elements conditioned in S_* (cf. Fig. 1) at the end of conditioning. Now, on the assumption that all elements fluctuate and have equal probabilities of being drawn, there will be available, at the beginning of the first extinction period, only the fraction $\frac{S}{S_*}$ of those originally conditioned. Letting $N_{e,1}$ be the number of conditioned elements available at the beginning of the first extinction period, then

$$N_{e,1} = \frac{S}{S_*} \cdot C_o \qquad (1)$$

Now, if extinction has been carried out until probability of responding approaches zero in this session, C_o will have been reduced by this amount, $\frac{S}{S_*} C_o$, so that with a sufficient recovery period the number of elements available at the beginning of the second extinction period,

$N_{e,2}$, is

$$N_{e,2} = \frac{S}{S_*}\left(C_o - \frac{S}{S_*}C_o\right)$$

$$= \frac{S}{S_*}C_o\left(\frac{S^* - S}{S_*}\right). \quad (2)$$

Letting $(1 - j) = \dfrac{S_* - S}{S_*}$, we may generalize Equation 2. The number of conditioned elements available at the beginning of the mth session is given by

$$N_{e,m} = \frac{S}{S_*}C_o(1 - j)^{m-1}, \quad (3)$$

where m is the ordinal number of the extinction session.

Relating number of elements, $N_{e,m}$ to probability we have, letting p_{om} be probability at the beginning of the mth session,

$$p_{o,m} = \frac{N_{e,m}}{S} = \frac{C_o}{S_*}(1 - j)^{m-1}. \quad (4)$$

Now in statistical learning theory (1) an equation for the cumulated number of bar-pressing responses is given. On the assumption that extinction is the learning of competing behaviors, Equation 5 follows directly (See [5] for a fuller derivation).

$$R = \frac{1}{\theta}ln(1 - p_o) \quad (5)$$

where θ equals the proportion of elements effective at a given moment, p_o is the initial probability in extinction, and R is total number of responses during a period. Now, by substituting Equation 4 into Equation 5, we may write for the number of responses on the mth day, R_m, the following:

$$R_m = \frac{1}{\theta}ln[1 - (p_o)(1 - j)^{m-1}]. \quad (6)$$

The values obtained with Equation 6 are shown in Table 1 opposite the designation, *predicted*. The numerical form of Equation 6 from which these values were obtained is

$$R_m - 12 = 28.7\,ln[1 - (p_o)\,.585^{m-1}].$$

The p_o values used were .930, .944, .968, and .976, for the 15, 50, 100, and 250 reinforcement groups, respectively; for the 50 × 2 and 50 × 5 groups the p_o values used were .957 and .991. The $\dfrac{1}{\theta}$ used here is the value found in fitting acquisition data from comparable animals in a different experiment using the same apparatus (4). The $(l - j)$ is from curve fitting by approximation, the p_o values are adjusted so that the predicted and obtained first day's totals coincide, and an operant rate of 12 responses per hour has been subtracted each day to approximate the theoretical requirement that rate of responding go to zero each session. (Homme found in an independent experiment [4] with comparable animals in the same apparatus, that, for 12 days' extinction the mean operant rate was 11.67 responses per hour for the last three days.) It should be emphasized that j and θ are constant for all predictions; only p_o is permitted to vary.

It seems that the discrepancies between data and predicted curves are not of a nature to require rejection of the hypothesis that the predicted curves are of the required form and that the obtained curves have the same slope. It will not be overlooked, however, that there are systematic discrepancies between these curves and the data. For the low reinforcement groups too many responses are predicted, and for the high reinforcement groups, too few. Secondly, to ensure that the first theoretical and obtained points coincide, p_o values required are higher than the unmodified assumption of random fluctuation of stimulus elements permits; even if all of the elements in an experimental sample (S of Fig. 1) were conditioned during massed acquisiton, p_o at the beginning of extinction 24 hr. later could not exceed j, which in this case is .415.

It is worth noting that the deviations mentioned above are strikingly similar to the sort to be expected if there were a "common core" of stimulus elements having a very high probability of being drawn, which are present on *all* experimental sessions. It seems reasonable to suppose that there are certain components of the stimulating situation which *are* almost inevitably present on every trial, e.g., some of the proprioceptive cues attendant on bar-pressing, and some which are not, e.g., the visual stimulation attendant on bar-pressing. (Although the bar must go down in a particular way on each response, this is not primarily contingent on the rat's visual orientation.) The assumption that the probability of being drawn on a given trial varies among stimulus elements has already been given explicit theoretical treatment in Estes' and Burke's discussion of the "θ distribution" (3). The common-core notion may be viewed as an instance or special case of the θ distribution hypothesis, making the simplifying assumption that the distribution is made up of two components, the very high probability elements constituting the common core, and the fluctuating elements whose probabilities are within a range such that serious error is not introduced by dealing with their mean. The consequences of the common-core assumption are that initial probability as well as total responses on the first extinction period ought to be greater than can be accounted for by the unmodified random fluctuation rule. By the same reasoning, fewer responses on succeeding sessions are to be expected to the extent that already extinguished elements of the common core continue to occupy the sample space but do not, of course, contribute to response strength.

It can be shown quantitatively that the common-core assumption will increase the correspondence between obtained and predicted total daily extinction responses and that this effect is particularly noticeable on the Day 2 values. Also the required initial probabilities will assume more theoretically reasonable values. In view of the variability exhibited in the obtained data, however, it is not clearly certain that this theoretical modification is required at the present time.

SUMMARY

Investigations are reported of the theoretical and empirical relationships between spontaneous recovery from extinction and (*a*) number of reinforcements and (*b*) spacing of acquisition. The experiments utilized albino rats in a Skinner-type conditioning situation.

To study the effect of number of reinforcements, four groups received 15, 50, 100, or 250 reinforcements on the same day, followed by five daily 60-min. extinction sessions. It was concluded that the data offer considerable support for predictions from Estes' statistical theory of learning concerning: (*a*) initial probability of responding during extinction, (*b*) ordering of day-to-day curves of total responses in extinction, and (*c*) the convergence and slope of the curves.

To study the effect of massed versus spaced acquisition, two massed acquisition groups received 100 or 250 reinforcements on the same day and two spaced groups received 50 reinforcements on each of the two days, or 50 reinforcements on each of five days. All groups received five daily 60-min. extinction sessions. Theoretical predictions concerning higher initial probabilities and higher totals of responding during extinction following spaced acquisition were supported only by the differences between the five-day spaced acquisition group and its control. Predictions concerning the differential effect of five-day versus two-day spacing and the form and shape of the day-to-day curves of total responses in extinction are supported.

The statistical learning theory which the investigations were designed to test assumes that all elements in the stimulus population fluctuate randomly in and out of the effective stimulating situation. It was mentioned that a better quantitative account of the data could be obtained if this assumption were modified to allow for a common core of stimulus elements which remain fixed while the remainder of the population is subject to random fluctuations.

REFERENCES

1. ESTES, W. K. Toward a statistical theory of learning. *Psychol. Rev.*, 1950, **57**, 94–107.
2. ESTES, W. K. Statistical theory of spontaneous recovery and regression. *Psychol. Rev.*, 1955, **62**, 145–154.
3. ESTES, W. K., & BURKE, C. J. A theory of stimulus variability in learning. *Psychol. Rev.*, 1953, **60**, 276–286.
4. GUTHRIE, E. R. *The psychology of learning.* New York: Harper, 1935.
5. HOMME, A. S. Rate of reconditioning as a function of amount of extinction. Unpublished doctor's dissertation, Indiana Univ., 1953.
6. HOMME, L. E. Spontaneous recovery from extinction in relation to number of rein-

forcements, spacing of reinforcements, and duration of initial extinction period. Unpublished doctor's dissertation, Indiana Univ., 1953.

7. HULL, C. L. *Principles of behavior.* New York: Appleton-Century, 1943.

8. PERIN, C. T. Behavior potentiality as a joint function of the amount of training and the degree of hunger at the time of extinction. *J. exp. Psychol.,* 1942, **30**, 93–113.

9. RAZRAN, G. H. S. The nature of the extinctive process. *Psychol. Rev.,* 1939, **46**, 264–297.

10. SPENCE, K. W. Theoretical interpretations of learning. In S. S. Stevens (Ed.), *Handbook of experimental psychology.* New York: Wiley, 1951. Pp. 690–730.

11. WENDT, G. R. An interpretation of inhibition of conditioned reflexes as competition between reaction systems. *Psychol. Rev.,* 1936, **43**, 258–281.

12. WILLIAMS, S. B. Resistance to extinction as a function of the number of reinforcements. *J. exp. Psychol.,* 1938, **23**, 506–521.

13. WYCKOFF, L. B. Resistance to extinction of the lever-pressing response in the white rat as a function of number of reinforcements. Unpublished master's thesis, Indiana Univ., 1950.

14. YAMAGUCHI, H. G. Superthreshold reaction potential (sE_R) as a function of experimental extinction (n). *J. exp. Psychol.,* 1951, **41**, 391–400.

(Received March 31, 1955)

Growth and Function of Mathematical Models for Learning

WILLIAM K. ESTES, *Stanford University*

Attempts to formulate mathematical descriptions of learning and forgetting are as old as experimental psychology. But for a half-century dating, say, from the work of Ebbinghaus, little issued from these efforts that could be expected to excite wide interest or enthusiasm among students of learning. The status of this line of research at the time when I was a graduate student is epitomized by its treatment in McGeoch's *Psychology of Human Learning*.[18] For my generation of students, as for many to follow, this erudite text was the last word on the subject, without whose support no Ph.D. candidate would dare face preliminary examinations. One could not help noting, even upon the most casual inspection, that all of the material on learning curves and equations was carefully segregated in a special chapter—one which had nothing whatever to do with the rest of the book and was customarily assigned only because it provided such a gold mine of multiple choice questions. (I blush to admit that my own first undergraduate classes were required to master the esoteric terminology of positive and negatively accelerated curves, plateaus, and physiological limits—about as sterile an exercise as could well be devised.) The status of quantitative formulations of learning at that time was succinctly summarized by McGeoch in a footnote:[18,p.65] ". . . equational statements of learning are of secondary importance to the subject at the present time, although it may confidently be expected that they will become more and more important as the quantification of our knowledge of learning increases."

It will be noted that McGeoch identifies mathematical formulations with equations for learning curves, reflecting accurately the prevailing viewpoint among psychologists in the early 1940's. In order to illustrate for you the progress that has occurred over a fifty-year period in formulating equations for learning curves, I have assembled a longitudinal sample in Figure 1. The data points represent cumulative errors per trial in a standard paired-associates learning experiment run by B. L. Hopkins and myself (unpublished). The three empirical curves represent the same data and have simply been displaced up the ordinate to eliminate overlapping of the theoretical curves. The uppermost of the fitted curves has been computed from the "autocatalytic function" proposed by the chemist T. B. Robertson (1908);[21] the middle curve represents the model advanced by Thurstone in 1930;[23] and the lowermost curve is derived from contemporary statistical

This article appeared in *Current trends in psychological theory*, R. Glaser, editor. Pittsburgh, Pa.: Univ. of Pittsburgh Press, 1961, 144–151.

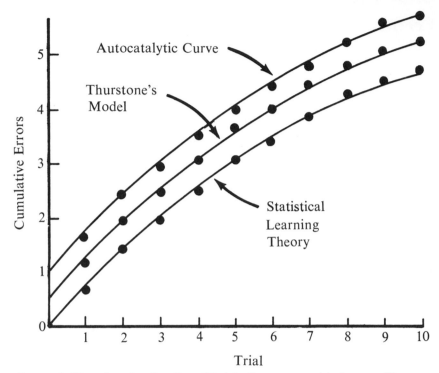

FIGURE 1. Three learning functions fitted to the same empirical curve. The upper curves are displaced up the ordinate.

learning theory by a line of reasoning that I shall explain a bit later. It is interesting to note that however we measure progress in this area, it is not simply by the accuracy with which theoretical curves fit the data; although differences in goodness of fit among the three plots are difficult to distinguish by eye, the fact is that Robertson's equation provides the best fit of the three by a least squares criterion.

Some differences among the theoretical functions that do not show up in a graphic presentation will become apparent if we inspect the equations of the curves:

$$\text{Robertson:} \quad \log \frac{x}{A - x} = at - b$$

$$\text{Thurstone:} \quad e_n = \frac{n}{a + bn}$$

$$\text{Statistical learning theory:} \quad q_n = \left(1 - \frac{1}{N}\right)(1 - c)^n$$

In the first of these, adapted from Chaisson (1930),[5] x is the response measure;* t is time, in this case the duration of a trial being the unit; and A, a, and b are constants. In the second equation, e_n represents cumulative errors through trial n, and a and b are constants. In the third q_n represents probability of an error on trial n, N is the number of items in the list, and c is a constant. Thus Robertson's equation has three free parameters to be evaluated from the data, Thurstone's two, and the function drawn from statistical learning theory only one. Although the adequacy of description differs little among models appearing over a fifty-year span, the output in terms of data fitted per free constant has improved considerably.

To bring out some still more important differences among the three approaches, let us consider a related experiment. The paired-associate data previously shown were obtained with a list of eight stimuli (consonant syllables) and eight different responses (numbers 1 through 8). Concurrently with that group of subjects, we ran another group under identical conditions except that there were only two responses (numbers 1 and 2) each paired with four of the stimuli. It seems reasonable to ask what the various models will permit us to predict about the results of the two-response group, given the data for the eight-response group. For the first model the answer is simple—nothing. Robertson's equation includes three constants that must be evaluated by curve-fitting methods for each set of data the equation is applied to; before it can be used to describe the two-response data, the values of the constants must be re-evaluated for those data; possibly some of them would turn out to have the same values, but there is no underlying rationale to specify which, if any, should carry over to the new condition and therefore no predictions can be made.

In Thurstone's model, an attempt has been made to provide the missing psychological rationale. Thurstone conceived learning to be a process of sampling from a population of acts, some correct and some incorrect for any given task, with the successful acts being retained and the unsuccessful ones having some fixed probability of elimination on each trial. In the equation shown, the parameter b is assumed to vary inversely with the total number of available acts, and therefore with difficulty of the task. Thus one might hope that by making some simple adjustment in the value of the b constant, while holding the other constant fixed, one could generate a prediction for the two-response condition. However, according to my calculations, no such procedure yields a satisfactory prediction in the present case.

In the case of the statistical model, there is even more underlying theory, and consequently fewer degrees of freedom in carrying over the equation

---

* To calculate the plotted curves, $(A - x)/A$ has been taken to represent probability of an incorrect response, and the function has been integrated over time with this quantity as the dependent variable.

to a new situation. The principal assumption is that each stimulus and its correct response become associated on an all-or-none basis. The parameter c represents the probability that any one stimulus will become associated with its correct response on any given trial (if learning has not previously occurred). Therefore, the term $(1 - c)^n$ in the equation is simply the probability that any given item is still unlearned after n training trials. When the correct response to a particular stimulus has not yet been learned, the subject may still get a correct response by guessing, and the probability of doing so is $1/N$ (on the simplest assumptions). Therefore, the probability

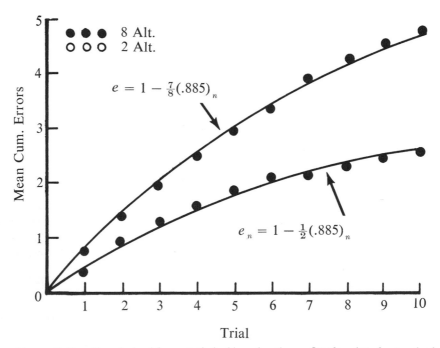

FIGURE 2. Equation derived from statistical learning theory fitted to data from paired-associate with eight stimuli and either eight responses (upper curve) or two responses (lower curve). The slope parameter was evaluated from the eight-response data only.

that a subject will fail to get any given item right on a test after n training trials is $(1 - 1/N)(1 - c)^n$, and by summing this expression over trials we obtain the desired curve for cumulative errors. There is only one free constant, c, and once it has been evaluated for this experimental situation and population of subjects from the eight-response curve, we should be able to predict the curve for the two-response group simply by replacing $\frac{1}{8}$ by $\frac{1}{2}$ in the factor $(1 - 1/N)$ representing the guessing allowance. The result of doing this is shown in Figure 2. The upper curve simply reproduces the one shown before for the eight-response condition. The lower curve shows how well we have been able to predict the results of the two response condition by means of an equation which uses *none* of the two-response data for curve-fitting.

There is still another difference among the three developmental stages in quantitative theorizing that is worth mention. It concerns not the models per se but the purposes they serve. In the earliest period, the question at issue was simply that of whether equations, *any* equations, could be found that would describe the course of learning in standard experimental situations. By 1930, not only had this question been answered, but in fact an inconveniently large number of equations had been proposed, all with much the same ability to fit "typical" learning curves. In order to obtain any differential evaluations among them it was necessary to go deeper than the surface of the graph paper. The first substantial move in this direction was taken by Thurstone, who set himself the task of finding plausible psychological assumptions from which one could deduce equations for learning curves. His apparently promising start did not come to immediate fruition, perhaps simply because Thurstone's theoretical work was not associated with an active experimental program; but progress during subsequent years has begun to show an encouraging tendency to follow the same autocatalytic function that the early quantifiers thought they saw mirrored in the performance of individual subjects. The "learning curve" for this line of endeavor shows no signs of approaching an asymptote, but it has reached a point at which we can afford to divide our attention between continuing efforts to improve our formulations and explorations of the utility that models already in hand may be prepared to offer in the service of other theoretical objectives.

One of the main functions of mathematical models, once they have attained some standing as descriptive devices, is to serve as tools to aid in testing substantive theories and hypotheses. The case of two-vs.-eight response alternatives in the paired-associate problem illustrates this point. The data shown in Figure 2 were not collected for purposes of testing the model. A number of previous studies had provided adequate evidence that the model yields a serviceable description of paired-associate learning under any one set of conditions. What we were concerned with was the role of number of alternatives as an independent variable. The few studies dealing with this variable had reported faster learning with fewer alternatives. However, we felt that none had fully controlled for the differential guessing allowances associated with differing numbers of responses and that consequently there had been no critical test of the hypothesis that learning is basically identical, and proceeds at the same rate, regardless of the number of alternatives. I do not mean to criticize the previous investigators; for the fact is that in the absence of a theory no suitable allowance for the guessing factor can be made. Guessing occurs only on unlearned items, and there is no way to tell by direct observation just how many items have been learned and how many have been guessed correctly on any given trial. With the aid of the model, we can make an exact estimate of the contribution of learning and guessing at every point of the performance curve, and thus evaluate the c parameter which represents rate of learning. Then if our assumptions are correct, the rate of learning will be the same when the number of alternatives is changed, and we can predict the result of this manipulation in advance by combining our estimate of learning rate with a new guessing allowance. As you have seen in the last figure, our data proved to support the hypothesis that rate of learning is independent of the number of alternatives. This is just one example of the type of case in which a model for learning serves the experimenter by helping him evaluate or partial out the effects of variables that cannot be separated by direct manipulation.

An important factor in making it possible for contemporary models to begin rendering these service functions is that, unlike earlier models which assumed a particular form for "the learning curve," the more recent ones typically express assumptions in the form of mathematical operators describing changes in response tendencies on single trials. Given the assumptions of a theory in the latter form, curves can be deduced for an infinite variety of experiments run with differing initial and boundary conditions. One main branch of research in mathematical learning theory (e.g., Bush and Mosteller;[4] Burke and Estes;[2] Bush and Estes Part II) is concerned with deriving a body of theorems and formulas that follow from the assumption that learning on any one trial is described by a simple linear transformation of the response probabilities. These "linear models" are primarily descriptive, but they may also serve explanatory functions. Not explanation, as psychologists most often think of it, in terms of hypothetical neural mechanisms, but explanation of a sort familiar in physical science which accounts for the course of a process over a period of time by showing it to be a result of simple effects of variables operating on single trials. A contemporary illustration in psychology is afforded by an episode that may appropriately be termed "the case of the irrational rats."

The facts of the case are in essence that rats offered repeated trials in a T-maze with, e.g., .75–.25 probabilities of reward on the two sides, show remarkable ingenuity in avoiding the optimal strategy of always choosing the more frequently rewarded side. With a procedure that permits the animal to correct errors, several investigators (Brunswik,[1] Estes and Lauer, cited in Estes,[9] Parducci and Polt,[19] Hickson,[12]) have found that probability of a given response tends to approach the probability of reward.

When animals are run under similar reward schedules except for a non-correction procedure, so that some trials go entirely unrewarded, the results are quite different. The majority of animals come to choose the more frequently rewarded side virtually 100 per cent of the time, while a few become equally fixated on the less favorable side. A typical result is that of Hickson and Carterette;[13] over the last sixteen daily trials of a fifty-six-day series run with a .75–.25 noncorrection schedule, they found that for a group of eleven rats, eight went sixteen times and one fifteen to the .75 side while the remaining two went fourteen and sixteen times to the .25 side. Clearly, what one would usually think of as a minor difference in procedure leads to a rather striking difference in results. And in neither the correction nor the noncorrection case does the outcome agree entirely with expectation based on traditional law of effect theory.

To analyze this two-choice situation in terms of the linear model, we consider the various types of trial outcomes that may arise; letting L and R designate responses and rewards on the left and right sides of the T-maze, p the probability of a left choice, and θ ($0 \leq \theta \leq 1$) the learning rate parameter, these can be summarized as follows for the experiment with correction procedure:

Choice	Reward	New Probability of L Choice
L	$\left.L\right\}$	
R	L	$p + \theta(1 - p)$
L	$\left.R\right\}$	
R	R	$p - \theta p$

The basis for the right-hand column is, of course, the usual assumption that reward on a given side increases the probability of that choice and decreases the probability of the other choice. The formulas given here for the new probabilities following rewards on either side are not the only ones that have been used in recent researches, but they are the simplest and will suffice for our purposes. Considering this schema, it is easy to see why, if the formulas are even approximately correct, the rats do not maximize their incomes by going always to the more frequently rewarded side when reward possibilities are intermediate between zero and unity. If, say, probabilities of reward on the left and right are .75–.25, the probability of a left choice will be more often moved toward unity than toward zero, and thus, if it starts near .50, will initially start to drift toward unity. But even if p is brought near unity by an unusually long sequence of rewards on the left, eventually rewards will occur on the right and p will be driven back toward zero. Since on the average increments occur three times as often as decrements under this schedule, it seems intuitively reasonable that after a sufficient number of trials p will be found fluctuating around a mean value of .75, and this is what the model predicts.

Under a noncorrection procedure, the effects of rewarded trials must be assumed to be the same as under the correction procedure, but we now have also nonrewarded trials to contend with. There is considerable evidence from studies of partial reinforcement in the runway and T-maze to indicate that after a reasonably long partial series, a nonrewarded trial has very little effect on response probability (see, e.g., Weinstock[24]). Thus we would expect that at least over the portion of an experiment for which asymptotic data are collected, the effects of reward and nonreward will be approximated by the following set of operators

Choice	Reward	New Probability of L Choice
L	L	$p + \theta (1 - p)$
L	None $\}$	p
R	None	
R	R	$p - \theta p$

The probability at the beginning of a trial, p, would be increased by a reward, decreased by reward on the opposite side, and left unchanged by nonreward. Now under a .75–.25 schedule, p will again tend on the average to drift toward unity; but here the similarity to the other case ends. If under this procedure p reaches unity,* no further rewards can occur on the right side to drive it away; similarly, if under a run of ill fortune (from the rat's point of view) p drops to zero, no further rewards on the left can occur and the animal will be expected to remain fixated on the right side even though this yields a much less than optimal return in terms of rewards per run. Predicting the exact proportion of animals that will be "absorbed" at unity rather than at zero, starting from any given initial probability, is a matter of considerable mathematical difficulty (see Bush and Estes,[3] Part II), but it is safe to say that under the conditions of initial probability and reward probability characterizing most studies that have been reported, a high percentage of animals should be predicted to end up choosing the more frequently rewarded side all of the time.

We recognize that the task of explanation is not complete for this class of experiments. We still would like to know, for example, precisely why the effect of nonreward changes during a partially reinforced series so that eventually nonreward is virtually neutral in its effects while at the same time the effect of reward remains essentially constant. But even while we

* Strictly speaking, a linear model (Bush and Estes,[3] Part II; Bush and Mosteller[4]), as distinguished from a stimulus sampling model (Burke and Estes,[2] Bush and Estes,[3] Part I), does not permit p actually to reach unity; however, p may come so close to unity that the probability of its ever again decreasing is negligible.

continue looking for answers to these deeper questions, we may feel that our mathematical models have shed considerable light on a puzzling set of experimental results concerning matching and maximizing under partial reinforcement schedules.

Although we have not explicitly mentioned it so far, a noteworthy characteristic distinguishing the contemporary mathematical models we have considered both from earlier ones and from such theories as those of Hull[16] and Hebb,[11] is the strategy of operating almost exclusively at the level of observable events. The probabilistic models for paired-associate learning and for maze learning have relied on careful analyses of observable stimulus and response variables in these situations and on assumptions formulated in terms of changes in probabilities of these variables as a function of reinforcing operations. It would be premature, however, to leap to the conclusion that the trend in the development of mathematical learning theory is toward complete elimination of any reference to un-observables, i.e., inferred or assumed events, or constructs. The fact seems to be that for any limited empirical area, taken by itself, hypothetical entities or mechanisms have trouble proving their worth and usually turn out to be clearly dispensable. Sometimes they play a useful role in suggest-ing the form of laws or models, but once the latter become operational, the hypothetical constructs can be discarded, much like the scaffolding after completion of a building. Only when we wish to bridge the gap be-tween superficially distinct problem areas and to integrate hitherto un-related findings do we find that interpretations in terms of hypothetical, "molecular" events turn out to be of critical importance. To illustrate this point, we turn to a final example of current mathematical theorizing, this time one beginning with the problem of retention and transfer but ending in an area customarily falling under quite a different chapter heading.

By reference to Figure 3 we can conveniently review the principal as-sumptions of a statistical model for stimulus fluctuation that have been applied to a number of studies of retention and transfer (e.g., Homme,[15] Frankmann,[10] McConnell[17]) since its original publication a few years ago (Estes[7]). The set-theoretical schema shown in this figure conceptualizes the idea that within any experimental situation there is constant, random fluc-tuation over any period of time in the particular stimulus components, or cues, that are available for sampling by the organism. If one of the rectangles shown in the figure is taken to represent the population of all stimuli, internal as well as external in origin, that may be available for sampling by the subject at any time during an experiment, then the portion, labeled S, above the horizontal dividing line corresponds to the cues that are available for sampling during a given short experimental period, and

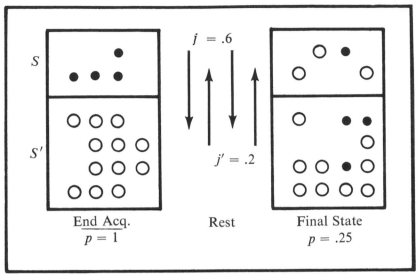

FIGURE 3. Theoretical schema from stimulus fluctuation model for retention loss following an acquisition period. Filled circles represent elements conditioned and open circles elements unconditioned to the reinforced response. Subsets S and S', respectively, represent elements that are or are not available for sampling during a given period.

the portion below corresponds to the part of the stimulus population that is temporarily unavailable. The left-hand rectangle illustrates the state of affairs at the end of an acquisition period. The cues available during this period, represented by filled circles, are all conditioned, but those in the unavailable set, S', represented by open circles, are not. Although the probability of the learned response has reached unity in this situation, it does not remain at this level, for during a subsequent rest interval, stimulus elements fluctuate back and forth between S and S', eventually approaching an equilibrium condition in which the proportion of conditioned cues in the available set S is equal to the proportion in the whole population. From our statistical assumptions it is not difficult to derive an equation for the predicted curve of forgetting (Estes[7]). This equation,

$$p_t = J + (1 - J)a^t,$$

where J represents the size of the set S of available cues relative to the total population and a represents the average rate of stimulus fluctuation over time, turns out to be sufficiently similar to the logarithmic function used by Ebbinghaus (1885, cited in Hilgard[14]) so that it would probably be difficult to demonstrate differences in goodness of fit if both were applied to the same empirical forgetting curves. However, the equation used by Ebbinghaus, since the parameters were simply free constants to be fitted from the data, could never fill more than a descriptive function. By contrast, the statistical model, once it has occurred to us to look for them, proves to have interesting implications for type of problems quite different from those we originally had in mind.

Certainly no one will deny that retention and drive have customarily been treated by psychological writers as concepts belonging to quite separate and distinct parts of the textbook. Consequently, it will not be particularly surprising that we had worked with the model in relation to distributional phenomena and the like for quite some time before the idea emerged of considering its implications for problems of motivation and drive. Once the possibility of a theoretical connection between these areas is suggested, however, it immediately seems quite appealing. One of the oldest, and in my view most underestimated, interpretation of the relation between motivation and learning is that of drive stimuli. But the most distinctive property of these stimuli is that the probabilities vary systematically with time during periods of deprivation. What is more natural, then, than that the stimulus fluctuation model should provide a conceptual tool to investigating the consequences of our assumptions about drive stimuli?

To see how such an investigation works out, we may turn to the theoretical schema shown in Figure 4. The assumptions underlying this analysis have been presented in more detail elsewhere (Estes[8]) and I shall summarize them here in rather *simplified* form.

The rectangles in the figure may be taken to represent the set of drive stimuli associated with a given experimental situation; to be concrete, let us say they are all the cues whose sampling probabilities vary systematically with food deprivation. At t_1 the majority of these drive stimuli have been made unavailable as a result of a recent period of satiation. Over a subsequent period of time, stimulus fluctuation occurs; since the stimulus sources that produce satiation are not operative during the deprivation period, elements are more likely to enter than to leave the available set (S in Figure 3) and it increases in size, as we have illustrated in the change from t_1 to t_2. The diagram is intended to represent an experiment in which a series of learning trials is given with t_1 as the deprivation time, then, after a rest interval during which deprivation continues, additional trials are given at the higher deprivation, t_2. Within each series, the proportion of conditioned cues in the available set increases, as indicated by the increasing number of filled circles. Immediately after the shift in deprivation time, however, the proportion of conditioned cues available drops, leading in turn to a drop in expected response probability, before

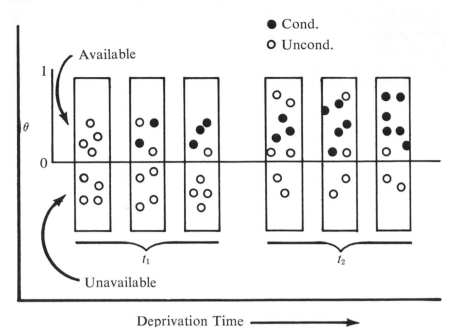

FIGURE 4. Theoretical schema for learning series under a low drive followed by shift to a higher drive. The parameter θ represents sampling probability for elements that are in the available set during a given period.

continuing to increase under the influence of additional reinforced trials. These notions lead to predictive equations for both pre- and postshift phases of an experiment in which deprivation time is abruptly changed either upward or downward, after the learning curve has reached an asymptote under the first condition.

Initial learning:

$$p_{n_1} = \frac{w[1 - (1 - \theta_1)^{n_1-1}]}{w_1 + w_e}$$

Postshift learning:

$$p_{n_1 + n_2} = \frac{f_{12}w_2 + (1 - f_{12})[1 - (1 - \theta_2)^{n_2-1}]}{w_2 + w_e}$$

In these equations, the subscripts 1 and 2 refer to the preshift and post-shift phases, respectively. The parameters w_1 and w_2 represent the weights of the available sets of drive stimuli during the two phases, "weight" of a set being defined as the number of elements multiplied by the average sampling probability; w_e, the weight of any unconditioned extraneous or "background" cues present in the experimental situation; f_{12} is the pro-

portion of elements that the two sets of drive stimuli have in common and
the factor $[1 - (1 - \theta_1)^{n_1-1}]$ is the probability that any available stimulus
element will be conditioned to the reinforced response by the n_1th trial of
phase 1. Some implications of these equations are illustrated in Figure 5.
The first point of interest is the divergence of the learning curves for low
and high drive conditions during phase 1; this picture, which has been
realized in numerous experimental studies (Estes,[8] Spence[22]), has been one

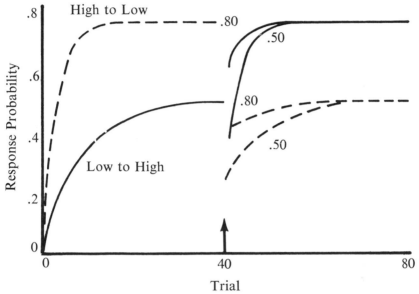

FIGURE 5. Illustrative curves showing predicted course of learning in groups shifted
from high to low, or low to high, drives after reaching asymptote under the first condition. The parameter of the postshift curves is proportion of overlap between the high-
drive and low-drive stimulus sets.

of the chief lines of evidence taken to support the Hullian conception of
drive (D) as an energizing factor. The results of our analysis show clearly,
however, that the divergence of high- and low-drive curves cannot be considered to favor the D concept over the drive-stimulus concept. On the
other hand, the two conceptions differ in their predictions about behavior
following a shift in drive level. Hull's D factor, taken alone, would lead to
the prediction that, under the conditions assumed in this example, response
probability following a shift up or down should change instantaneously to
the new level appropriate to the postshift drive. According to the drive
stimulus theory, a shift from high to low drive should be followed by an
abrupt drop to a point *below* the low-drive asymptote, then a gradual in-

crease with continued reinforcement until the low-drive asymptote is reached. Depending on the amount of overlap between the low-drive and high-drive stimulus sets, a shift from low to high drive may be followed by either a drop or a jump in response probability, in either case followed by a gradual increase to the high-drive asymptote. If, however, additional shifts are given after the subjects have again reached asymptote (so that all of the elements in both sets of drive stimuli have become conditioned to the reinforced response), response probability should change immediately and discontinuously to the appropriate postshift asymptote following each drive shift. Thus we see that, under certain conditions at least, all of the phenomena that have customarily served to support the concept of drive as an energizing factor are predictable from a theory of drive stimuli. Accurate quantitative determinations of response probability as a function of changes in drive level will be required in order to determine whether there are *any* phenomena that require the postulation of a *D* factor.

Here we must leave the story hanging in air, for to my knowledge the extensive literature on drive and learning includes no studies that are suitable for testing our predictions in all details. Perhaps this is not a bad denouement, for my purpose has been not to pass judgment on the *D* concept, but only to illustrate the way in which mathematical models are outgrowing the status of an isolated stepchild and are becoming inextricably bound up with other developments in learning theory. In the case of drive shifts particularly, it would seem discrete to postpone evaluations until someone has gotten around to performing the indicated experiments. What does seem clear at this point is that the mathematical model has at least served the function of setting the stage for sharper differential testing of "drive as stimulus" vs. "drive as energizer." And, on the assumption that incompleted tasks are the best remembered, this may be a strategic point at which to close the present exposition.

REFERENCES

1. Brunswik, E. Probability as a determiner of rat behavior, *J. Exp. Psychol.*, 1939, 25: 175–97.
2. Burke, C. J., and Estes, W. K. A component model for stimulus variables in discriminating learning. *Psychometrika*, 1957, 22: 133–45.
3. Bush, R. R., and Estes, W. K. *Studies in Mathematical Learning Theory*. California: Stanford University Press, 1959.
4. Bush, R. R., and Mosteller, F. *Stochastic Models for Learning*. New York: John Wiley & Sons, Inc., 1955.
5. Chaisson, A. F. An alternative approach to the mathematical study of learning curves. *J. Gen. Psychol.*, 1930, 4: 352–59.

6. Ebbinghaus, H. (1885) *Memory*. Translated by H. A. Ruger and C. E. Busenius. New York: Teachers College, 1913.

7. Estes, W. K. Statistical theory of spontaneous recovery and regression. *Psychol. Rev.*, 1955, 62: 145–54.

8. ——. Stimulus-response theory of drive. In, *Nebraska Symposium on Motivation*. Lincoln: University of Nebraska Press, 1958.

9. ——. The statistical approach to learning theory. In, S. Koch (ed.) *Psychology: A Study of a Science*. Vol. II. New York: McGraw-Hill Book Co., 1959.

10. Frankmann, J. P. Effect of amount of interpolated learning and time interval before test on retention in rats. *J. Exp. Psychol.*, 1957, 54: 462–66.

11. Hebb, D. O. *Organization of Behavior*. New York: John Wiley & Sons, Inc., 1949.

12. Hickson, R. H. "Response Probability in a Two-choice Learning Situation with Varying Probability of Reinforcement." Unpublished doctoral dissertation, University of Indiana, 1959.

13. Hickson, R. H., and Carterette, T. Asymptotic response probability under two conditions of random reinforcement, using a non-correction procedure. Paper given at MPA meetings, 1955.

14. Hilgard, E. R. *Theories of Learning*. (2nd ed.) New York: Appleton-Century-Crofts, Inc., 1956.

15. Homme, L. E. Spontaneous recovery and statistical learning theory. *J. Exp. Psychol.*, 1956, 51: 205–12.

16. Hull, C. L. *Principles of Behavior*. New York: Appleton-Century-Crofts, Inc., 1943.

17. McConnell, D. G. Spontaneous regression and recovery in a sequence of discrimination periods. *J. Exp. Psychol.*, 1959, 57: 121–29.

18. McGeoch, J. A. *The Psychology of Human Learning*. New York: Longmans, Green & Co., Inc., 1942.

19. Parducci, A., and Polt, J. Correction vs. noncorrection with changing reinforcement schedules. *J. Comp. Physiol. Psychol.*, 1958, 51: 492–9.

20. Ramond, C. K. Performance in selective learning as a function of hunger. *J. Exp. Psychol.*, 1954, 48: 265–70.

21. Robertson, T. B. Sur la dynamique chimique de system nerveux central. *Arch. Int. de Physiol.*, 1908, 6: 388–454.

22. Spence, K. W. Behavior theory and selective learning. In, *Nebraska Symposium on Motivation*. Lincoln: University of Nebraska Press, 1958.

23. Thurstone, L. L. The learning function. *J. Gen. Psychol.*, 1930, 3: 469–93.

24. Weinstock, S. W. Resistance to extinction of a running response following partial reinforcement under widely spaced trials. *J. Comp. Physiol. Psychol.*, 1954, 47: 318–22.

Statistical Theory of Distributional Phenomena in Learning[1]

WILLIAM K. ESTES, *Indiana University*

One aspect of distribution of practice that recent reviewers (14, p. 189; 24; 25) seem agreed upon is its persistent refractoriness to any general theoretical interpretation. If *general* is taken to mean *comprehensive,* then I can see no ground for optimism on this point. In all likelihood distributional phenomena are influenced by an extensive set of variables which vary in relative importance from one situation to another. There is no reason, however, why this complexity should be expected to bar progress toward theories which are limited in the sense of dealing with effects of independent variables taken singly or in limited combinations, yet general in the sense of applying to a wide range of situations.

The approach to problems of distribution that will be developed here continues a theoretical program outlined in a recent paper (6). The over-all strategy is to start by analyzing in detail the variables of most ubiquitous influence in order to see how much they account for, leaving for later consideration local variables which are important only in restricted types of experimentation.

As in our previous investigation of spontaneous behavioral changes (6), preliminary analysis of the distributional problem discloses two independent variables associated with intertrial intervals that probably modify the course of learning under all experimental arrangements. These variables are stimulus fluctuation and interpolated learning. In the preceding study, the former was incorporated into a mathematical model in order to permit derivation of its testable consequences. Since experimental arrangements are essentially the same in studies of spacing as in studies of spontaneous changes, we need only make further application of the same model in order to investigate the role of stimulus fluctuation as a determiner of spacing effects in learning.

It will be convenient to consider separately the two principal aspects of learning distinguished in contemporary theories: (*a*) changes in resistance to extinction or resistance to forgetting, and (*b*) changes in momentary probability, rate, or latency of the response. This distinction will be recognized as corresponding in essentials to that between habit strength and momentary reaction potential in Hull's system (10), or that between reflex reserve and reflex strength in Skinner's (21). For brevity I shall use the terms *habit strength* and *response strength* to distinguish the two concepts.

At a common-sense level, we should expect that stimulus fluctuation would affect the two types of learning measure differently. To the extent that fluctuation occurs, the make-up of a stimulating situation will vary from trial to trial or from period to period. Therefore, insofar as the effects of this one variable are concerned, rate of learning in terms of change in response strength should be increased by reducing the intervals between trials or periods. On the other hand, resistance to extinction or forgetting should be expected to de-

[1] This paper was prepared during the author's tenure as a faculty research fellow of the Social Science Research Council.

This article appeared in *Psychol. Rev.*, 1955, **62**, 369–377.

pend on having the response conditioned to as many as possible of the stimuli which might occur during extinction or during a test for retention; therefore, rate of change in habit strength should be directly related to intertrial interval. These notions will be worked out more rigorously in the following pages.

The concepts and assumptions that will be needed for this task have all been presented in a previous paper (6). Only those that are most critical for our present purposes will be reviewed briefly at this point. In order to permit self-selection diets for readers of varying mathematical appetites, I shall again follow the procedure of discussing the model and its applications first at a verbal level and then, in a separate section, in mathematical terms.

CONCEPTS AND ASSUMPTIONS

It is assumed that the stimulus variables associated with any environmental situation undergo constant, random fluctuation. Consequently, of the total population of stimuli available in a given situation over the course of an entire experiment, only a randomly selected subpopulation will be available during any one experimental period. On any one trial, the organism samples the available subpopulation; the probability that any available stimulus element will be sampled on a trial is the parameter θ which has been prominent in other developments of statistical learning theory (7, 19). We shall represent the total stimulus population associated with any experiment by a mathematical set S_*, the subpopulation available on any one period by a set S, and the subpopulation of temporarily unavailable elements by S'.

There is, then, a continuous, random interchange of elements between S and S'. During a given period, all the elements in the available set S may be conditioned or extinguished while those in S' are unaffected. Since probability of a given response is assumed equal to the proportion of conditioned elements in S, it is possible for response probability to go to unity or zero during a period of conditioning or extinction even though there remain in S' many elements, unconditioned or conditioned, respectively, which may reappear in S during some later period and alter the response probability.

INTERPRETATION OF DISTRIBUTIONAL PHENOMENA

Rate of change in habit strength as a function of spacing. According to our assumptions, there will be available for conditioning or extinction during any one period [2] only a limited portion of the total population S of stimulus elements which may appear in the given experimental situation at any time. Consequently, complete extinction of a response can be achieved only if the series of extinction periods is distributed over a long enough interval so that in the course of random fluctuation every previously conditioned element in the population appears in the available set S during at least one period. And in general, the greater the number of conditioned elements present in both parts of the population S_* at the onset of extinction, the longer it will take, in terms of time, trials, or periods, to reach a given criterion of extinction. We have also seen in an earlier paper (6) that, according to the present theory, resistance to forgetting will be directly related to the total density of conditioned elements in S_*.

Since both of the observable symptoms of habit strength vary directly

[2] To avoid circumlocution, the term *period* will be used here to refer to any of the following: (*a*) a period during which conditioning or extinction is carried to a criterion, (*b*) a period of fixed duration, (*c*) a block of trials, or (*d*) even in some circumstances a single trial.

with total density of conditioned elements, we need only consider the relationship between the latter variable and conditions of spacing. The predicted effects of varying the length of the rest interval between successive conditioning periods follow directly from the sampling model. Rate of increase in the proportion $F(m)$ of conditioned elements in S_* will be maximal if the interval is long enough so that the available situation S during each successive period represents a new random sample from the total population. As the interval is reduced, there is less opportunity for elements that are in S, and thus become conditioned, during one period to escape and be replaced by unconditioned ones before the next period, and consequently rate of growth of $F(m)$ is retarded. These considerations give rise to the family of curves illustrated in the lower panel of Fig. 1, which has interperiod interval as a parameter. Following the first period, steepness of the curve is a uniformly increasing function of the interval. The negative acceleration of these curves is due, of course, to the fact that there will be fewer unconditioned elements remaining to be sampled after each successive period. Analogous considerations hold for changes in $F(m)$ during extinction so that, other things equal, the "resistance to reconditioning" will be an increasing function of the interval between successive extinction periods.

Rate of change in response strength as a function of spacing. Changes in response strength during learning may be followed empirically by obtaining measures of response probability, rate, or latency at the beginning of each successive period. For simplicity, we will consider only probability. It can be shown (5) that all arguments that hold for probability carry over directly to the other measures.

Rate of change in response probability during learning will be less simply re-

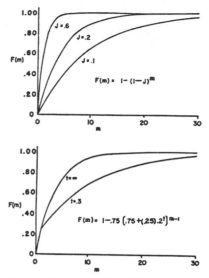

Fig. 1. Proportion of conditioned elements, $F(m)$, in the total population as a function of conditioning periods, m. In the upper panel the parameter is J, the relative size of the available set S during any period; in the lower panel the parameter is t, duration of the interperiod interval.

lated to the interperiod interval than was the rate of change in habit strength. If we compare probability curves for a relatively massed and a relatively spaced group, the former will certainly be expected to show the steeper rise at the outset of conditioning, for between the first and second periods fewer of the newly conditioned elements will escape from S if the interval is short. On the other hand, the gain per period in total number of conditioned elements is greater for the spaced group. From this fact we might guess that as the series goes on, the theoretical curve for the spaced group will overtake and then surpass the curve for the massed group. As a matter of fact this surmise can be proved to be correct, as we shall demonstrate in a later section. The principal characteristics of the family of curves having interperiod interval as a parameter are illustrated in Fig. 2.

According to our assumptions, the course of extinction over a series of extinction periods will be influenced by the length of the interval between periods in precisely the same manner as the course of conditioning. Curves of response probability for massed and spaced extinction groups will be expected to cross, with the latter starting out higher but overtaking the massed curve and running below it during the later extinction periods.

So far we have considered only uniform sequences of conditioning or extinction periods, since these are the cases that have been studied experimentally. Suppose, however, that a group of organisms were administered a mixed series of conditioning and extinction periods. Predictions can be generated from the present theory concerning the course of learning over any specified series. An interesting special case arises if we modify the usual partial reinforcement procedure by taking a block of trials or an experimental period rather than a single trial as the unit relative to which reinforcement is randomized. A theoretical account of this case is given in the following section and illustrated in Fig. 2. An ex-

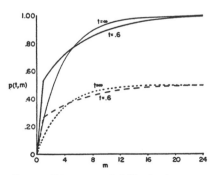

FIG. 2. Response probability in the temporary situation S as a function of number of conditioning or extinction periods, m. The two upper curves represent a sequence of conditioning periods, the two lower curves a random sequence of conditioning and extinction periods with π equal to .5. In each case the parameter is t, the interperiod interval.

periment which provides a preliminary test of the theoretical predictions has recently been reported (12).

MATHEMATICAL DEVELOPMENT OF DISTRIBUTIONAL THEORY

Now it is desirable to show more rigorously how the assumption of random stimulus fluctuation leads to detailed quantitative predictions concerning spacing phenomena. A mathematical model incorporating the fluctuation concept has been presented in a preceding paper (6). Here we shall review briefly a few important terms and relations, and then proceed to apply the same model to problems of spacing.

As before it will facilitate exposition to restrict the formal treatment to highly simplified conditions. We will assume that the behaviors available to the organism in a given situation are categorized into two mutually exclusive and exhaustive classes, A and $\bar{A}$, the former being the response recorded; that each stimulus element in S_{*} is conditioned either to A or to $\bar{A}$; that probability of response A at any time during an experimental period is equal to the proportion of elements in S conditioned to A; and that all elements in S^{*} have equal probabilities of appearing in S.

Let t represent duration of the interperiod interval; N and N' the mean numbers of elements in S and S', respectively; C the probability that an element in S' during period $m - 1$ appears in S during period m; and B the probability that an element in S during period $m - 1$ is still there during period m. Two important relationships derived in the preceding paper (6) are

$$C = J(1 - a^t) \qquad [1]$$

and

$$B = J + (1 - J)a^t, \qquad [2]$$

where J is the ratio of N to $N + N'$, and a is a slope constant depending on rate of stimulus fluctuation.

Now we are ready to derive predictions concerning the course of learning as a function of trial spacing.

Rate of change in habit strength as a function of trial spacing. We require the probability $F(m)$ that an element is conditioned to response A after m learning periods when the interperiod interval is t and all elements present in S during any given period become conditioned to A. The latter assumption implies that the proportion J of the unconditioned elements in S_* will become conditioned during the first period and the proportion C on each subsequent period, yielding the relations

$$F(1) = (1 - J)F(0) + J$$
$$\begin{aligned} F(2) &= F(1) + C[1 - F(1)] \\ &= (1 - J)F(0) + J + C \\ &\quad \times [1 - (1 - J)F(0) - J] \\ &= 1 - (1 - J)[1 - F(0)] \\ &\quad \times (1 - C) \end{aligned}$$

and so on. It can be proved by mathematical induction that in general

$$\begin{aligned} F(m) &= 1 - (1 - J) \\ &\quad \times [1 - F(0)](1 - C)^{m-1}. \end{aligned}$$

Since from equation 1,

$$C = J(1 - a^t)$$

we have finally

$$\begin{aligned} F(m) &= 1 - (1 - J)[1 - F(0)] \\ &\quad \times (1 - J + Ja^t)^{m-1} \quad [3] \end{aligned}$$

and it can be seen that $F(m)$ is an increasing function of the interperiod interval t for all m. This function is illustrated in the lower panel of Fig. 1 with t as a parameter. Under the conditions assumed here, varying the size of the training unit, i.e., the duration of a conditioning period or the number of trials per daily block, will simply result in modifying the value of J, yielding the family of curves illustrated in the upper panel of Fig. 1. Analogous considerations hold for changes in $F(m)$ during extinction.

Comparison of the upper and lower panels of Fig. 1 might lead one to surmise that, beyond a moderate rest interval, the advantage of distribution of practice will come chiefly from dividing a given number of training trials into a larger number of spaced blocks. As a matter of fact this prediction does follow from the theory, not only for the highly restrictive conditions assumed in the derivations of this paper, but quite generally. For any situation in which the learning curve within a daily period is negatively accelerated, the total number of trials needed to attain a criterion of learning will increase with the number of trials per daily period, the function approaching linearity as the number of trials per period becomes large. This relationship is attributable to the fact that fewer elements are conditioned on the second trial of a daily period than would have been conditioned if this trial had been postponed until the next period, and a similar argument holds for each succeeding trial. Once the daily period is made large enough so that nearly all of the available elements are conditioned to the response in question, further increase in the number of trials per period will simply yield a proportionate increase in the total number of trials to a criterion.

Rate of change in response probability as a function of trial spacing. Let us represent by $p(t,m)$ the probability of response A in S at time t following the mth of a series of learning periods, the periods being uniformly spaced with interperiod interval equal to t. First we consider a series of acquisition periods with all elements present in S during a period becoming conditioned to response A. We can write immediately:

$$p(t,m) = \frac{1}{N}[NB + \{(N + N')F(m) - N\}C]$$

where B, C, and $F(m)$ are as defined above. The first term inside the brackets is the number of conditioned elements in S at time t that are held over from the preceding experimental period, while the second term is the number of conditioned elements that were outside S at the end of the preceding period but drifted into S by time t. Simplifying by means of the relation $J = N/N + N'$, and expanding C and B by means of equations 1 and 2, we arrive at the function

$$p(t,m) = B + \left(\frac{F(m)}{J} - 1\right)C$$
$$= 1 - (1 - J)[1 - F(0)](1 - a^t)$$
$$\times (1 - J + Ja^t)^{m-1} \quad [4]$$

which for all its forbidding appearance has only three free parameters and is relatively simple in form, as illustrated in Fig. 2. It will readily be seen that when m equals 1, response probability will be inversely related to the interperiod interval t. For sufficiently large m the derivative of $p(t,m)$ with respect to t will be positive and therefore response probability will be directly related to t. Therefore, as shown in Fig. 2, any pair of otherwise comparable massed and spaced curves will cross exactly once.

The corresponding function for a series of extinction periods during which all elements present in S are unconditioned from A, i.e., conditioned to an opposed response $\bar{A}$, is obtainable in precisely the same way and turns out to be

$$p(t,m) = F(0)(1 - J)$$
$$\times (1 - a^t)(1 - J + Ja^t)^{m-1} \quad [5]$$

Random reinforcement. Finally we consider a series of periods run under the same conditions assumed in the derivation of equations 4 and 5 except that acquisition and extinction periods appear in a random order. It can be verified by substitution from equation 4 that if period $m + 1$ is an acquisition period then

$$p(t,m + 1) = (1 - C)p(t,m) + C$$

whereas if it is an extinction period, it follows from equation 5 that

$$p(t,m + 1) = (1 - C)p(t,m).$$

Again C is being used as an abbreviation for $J(1 - a^t)$. If acquisition and extinction periods occur with relative frequency π and $1 - \pi$ respectively, the expected response probability after period $m + 1$ will be the average of the two expressions preceding:

$$E[p(t,m + 1)] = \pi[(1 - C)$$
$$\times p(t,m) + C] + (1 - \pi)$$
$$\times (1 - C)p(t,m)$$
$$= (1 - C)p(t,m)$$
$$+ \pi C. \quad [6]$$

Solving this difference equation by standard methods we obtain

$$p(t,m) = \pi - K(1 - C)^m$$

where K is an arbitrary constant, and finally

$$p(t,m) = \pi - (1 - J)[\pi - F(0)]$$
$$\times (1 - a^t)(1 - J + Ja^t)^{m-1} \quad [7]$$

when K has been eliminated by setting the expression for $p(t,1)$ obtained from equation 7 equal to the mean value of $p(t,1)$ computed from equations 4 and 5. Since the quantity $(1 - J + Ja^t)$ is a fraction between zero and one, the second term on the right side of equation 7 tends to zero as m increases, and response probability approaches π as an asymptote regardless of the value of J or the duration of the interperiod interval. The dashed curves of Fig. 2 illustrate the effect of varying intertrial interval in a series with $\pi = .5$.

It should be noted that the expressions for response probability derived in this paper refer to expected values for individual organisms or for groups of organisms with like values of the parameters: J and a. However, it is not likely that the errors of approximation involved in applying the derived functions to averaged data from groups of experimental subjects will be large relative to the errors of measurement involved in ordinary learning experiments.

EMPIRICAL RELEVANCE AND ADEQUACY

What I have tried to accomplish in this paper and the one preceding (6) is to work out in systematic fashion the behavioral effects of stimulus fluctuation which is strictly random with respect to experimental variables. To the extent that distributional phenomena prove to be attributable to this source of variation, the burden of explanation upon such constructs as inhibitory potential will be commensurately reduced. To be sure, the conclusions we have reached are not independent of the specific techniques of conceptualization and derivation used, but it seems doubtful that the main features will prove very sensitive to the choice of mathematical techniques.[3]

In applying the theory to learning experiments, we are led to fractionate the empirical material into three main groups: (*a*) experiments involving continuous work or very short rest intervals; (*b*) experiments involving intermediate intervals, ranging from perhaps a minute up to a day or two; and (*c*)

---

[3] As a matter of fact, in an earlier version of the present model, the assumptions were expressed in the form of differential equations and the theorems were derived by means of the calculus. Subsequently I found it desirable for reasons of mathematical rigor and elegance to rework the theory utilizing the method of linear difference equations which has been introduced into learning theory by Bush and Mosteller (2), but none of the testable consequences of the theory were altered. The earlier formulation was presented to a Colloquium at the University of Illinois in May, 1950, and to the SSRC Summer Seminar on Mathematics Models for Behavior in 1951, and I have benefited greatly from the discussion and criticism contributed on those occasions.

experiments involving long intervals. It is in the intermediate range that stimulus fluctuation theory should be expected to play a major role in accounting for experimental phenomena. At very long intervals, or under certain special conditions, such as those of retroactive inhibition experiments, effects of interpolated learning become important; space does not permit discussion of these effects in the present paper. At very short intervals, variables come into play that have not been taken account of in the statistical theory, e.g., response-produced stimulation, physiological changes in effectors; and even if the predicted effects of stimulus fluctuation are present they will be masked by effects of other variables.

Two principal methods are available for assaying the empirical adequacy of the theory. The first is to carry out new experiments especially designed to satisfy the simplifying assumptions made in the theoretical derivations. The second is to review the experimental literature and attempt to provide a unified theoretical account of the already established facts concerning the role of spacing at intermediate intervals.

Only the former method can be entirely free of bias, and consequently publication of the theory has been delayed until several of the indicated experiments could be carried out. One of these was a study of spontaneous recovery of a bar-pressing response in relation to degree of extinction and amount and spacing of reinforcement (8); another was a study of successive acquisitions and extinctions of a jumping habit in relation to schedule of reinforcement (13); a third was a study of successive reversals of a left-right discrimination with varying numbers of trials per daily period (11). Detailed theoretical interpretations of the data of these experiments have been reported elsewhere. It is to researches of this kind that we must look for sharper delimitation of the area of application of the theory and for indications as to desirable lines of revision or supplementation.

A comprehensive review of the literature on distributional phenomena cannot be attempted here, but it will be noted that a variety of rather well-established empirical relationships can be given a uniform and coherent interpretation in terms of theoretical relationships derived in this paper. It may be helpful to bring together at this point a brief summary of these relationships together with appropriate references to the experimental literature.

a. Resistance to extinction is directly related to number and spacing of conditioning periods (**8, 17, 18**).

b. Retention is increased by spacing of learning periods, the advantage of spacing increasing with the retention interval (**14**, pp. 156–158; **16**, p. 508).

c. Retention is increased by overlearning (**9**; **14**, pp. 377–380).

d. Learning tends to be faster at beginning of series with massed practice, later in series with spaced practice: Conditioning (**1, 22**); Extinction (**4, 20, 23**).

e. Number of trials to asymptote of learning is directly related to number of trials per daily period (**3**, pp. 155–156; **15**, p. 320).

f. Retention is directly related to the proportion of common elements in learning and recall situations (**9**; **14**, pp. 449–450; **19**).

The rather surprising prediction that asymptote of response probability under random reinforcement should be independent of trial spacing has not been listed, since only one relevant empirical study (**12**) is so far available.

All the relationships included have been discussed above except for the last, and this is clearly a direct consequence of the basic assumptions of the theory. In all cases, except perhaps for item *d*, there seems to be unequivocal correspondence of fact and theory. In the case of item *d*, the predicted relationship has been obtained more regularly during extinction than during conditioning. Possibly the difference is attributable to the fact that comparisons of massed and spaced trial groups are better controlled during extinction when such extraneous variables as satiation and habituation of UR's are excluded.

Several additional statements derivable from the theory seem to be almost certainly true, although not yet established by experiment. One of these is the prediction that resistance to extinction will be increased by additional training given after the curve of learning in terms of response probability or latency has reached an asymptote; this relationship seems to have been assumed by Skinner in his formulation of the reflex reserve concept (**21**) but has not, to my knowledge, been subjected to a formal check by experiment. A second example is the prediction that resistance to reconditioning will be directly related to spacing of extinction periods.

The principal set of relevant empirical phenomena not handled at all by the present theory concerns certain properties of response decrement under extremely massed trials. In some experiments with very short intertrial intervals or with conditions of continuous work, as in pursuit rotor performance, asymptotes of intraperiod learning are depressed so that it becomes impossible to achieve the simplifying condition, assumed in the derivations of this paper, that all stimuli available during a period become conditioned to a designated response. In the same experiments reminiscence is commonly observed following rest. These effects apparently are not predictable from the fluctuation theory. The question remains open whether they can be accounted for in terms of variables not so far incorporated into the theory, e.g., response-produced stimulation. For the present these phenomena will provide a source of comfort to those who prefer to terminate analysis at the "molar" level of Hull's (**10**) reactive inhibition construct.

SUMMARY

A mathematical model embodying the concept of random stimulus fluctuation has been found to describe in detail numerous phenomena of spontaneous recovery, regression, or short-term forgetting, and effects of trial spacing at intermediate intervals. This information should be of aid in appraising alternative strategies for theoretical development in this area. It can now be seen that if neo-Pavlovian conceptions of inhibitory potential are to be maintained without major revision, it will be necessary to assume that the amount of random variation in standard experimental situations is negligible. On the other hand, if the amount of random variation is assumed to be appreciable, then a substantial class of distributional phenomena can be accounted for without additional hypotheses.

REFERENCES

1. BARON, M. R. The effect of long intertrial intervals on the limit of eyelid conditioning. *J. exp. Psychol.*, 1952, **44**, 438–441.
2. BUSH, R. R., & MOSTELLER, F. A mathematical model for simple learning. *Psychol. Rev.*, 1951, **58**, 313–323.
3. DEESE, J. *The psychology of learning.* New York: McGraw-Hill, 1952.
4. ELLSON, D. G. Successive extinctions of a bar-pressing response in rats. *J. gen. Psychol.*, 1940, **23**, 283–288.
5. ESTES, W. K. Toward a statistical theory of learning. *Psychol. Rev.*, 1950, **57**, 94–107.
6. ESTES, W. K. Statistical theory of spontaneous recovery and regression. *Psychol. Rev.*, 1955, **62**, 145–154.
7. ESTES, W. K., & BURKE, C. J. A theory of stimulus variability in learning. *Psychol. Rev.*, 1953, **60**, 276–286.
8. HOMME, L. E. Spontaneous recovery from extinction in relation to number of reinforcements, spacing of acquisition, and duration of initial extinction period. Unpublished doctor's dissertation, Indiana Univer., 1953.
9. HOVLAND, C. I. Human learning and retention. In S. S. Stevens (Ed.), *Handbook of experimental psychology.* New York: Wiley, 1951. Pp. 613–689.
10. HULL, C. L. *The principles of behavior.* New York: Appleton-Century-Crofts, 1943.
11. LAUER, D. W., & ESTES, W. K. Rate of learning successive discrimination reversals in relation to trial spacing. *Amer. Psychologist*, 1953, **8**, 384. (Abstract)
12. LAUER, D. W., & ESTES, W. K. Observed and predicted terminal distributions of response probability under two conditions of random reinforcement. *Amer. Psychologist*, 1954, **9**, 413. (Abstract)
13. LAUER, D. W., & ESTES, W. K. Successive acquisitions and extinctions of a jumping habit in relation to schedule of reinforcement. *J. comp. physiol. Psychol.*, 1955, **48**, 8–13.
14. McGEOCH, J. A., & IRION, A. L. *The psychology of human learning.* New York: Longmans, Green, 1952.
15. MUNN, N. L. *Handbook of psychological research on the rat.* New York: Houghton Mifflin, 1950.
16. OSGOOD, C. E. *Method and theory in experimental psychology.* New York: Oxford Univer. Press, 1953.
17. REYNOLDS, B. Extinction of trace conditioned responses as a function of the spacing of trials during the acquisition and extinction series. *J. exp. Psychol.*, 1945, **35**, 81–95.
18. ROHRER, J. H. Experimental extinction as a function of the distribution of extinction trials and response strength. *J. exp. Psychol.*, 1947, **37**, 473–493.
19. SCHOEFFLER, M. S. Probability of response to compounds of discriminated stimuli. *J. exp. Psychol.*, 1954, **48**, 323–329.
20. SHEFFIELD, V. F. Resistance to extinction as a function of the distribution of extinction trials. *J. exp. Psychol.*, 1950, **40**, 305–313.
21. SKINNER, B. F. *The behavior of organisms.* New York: Appleton-Century-Crofts, 1938.
22. SPENCE, K. A., & NORRIS, EUGENIA B. Eyelid conditioning as a function of the intertrial interval. *J. exp. Psychol.*, 1950, **40**, 716–720.
23. STANLEY, W. C. Extinction as a function of the spacing of extinction trials. *J. exp. Psychol.*, 1952, **43**, 249–260.
24. TOLMAN, E. C., & POSTMAN, L. Learning. In *Annu. Rev. Psychol.*, 1954, **5**, 27–56.
25. UNDERWOOD, B. J. Studies in distributed practice: XII. Retention following varying degrees of original learning. *J. exp. Psychol.*, 1954, **47**, 294–300.

(Received December 22, 1954)

Nonrandom Stimulus Sampling in Statistical Learning Theory[1]

WILLIAM F. PROKASY, JR.,[2] *Pennsylvania State University*

It generally is assumed in statistical learning theory (Estes, 1950; Estes & Burke, 1953) that the subset, s, of elements selected by the subject on any conditioning trial constitutes a random sample from a larger set of elements which are relevant to the conditioning situation. The purpose of this paper is to investigate the properties of one kind of nonrandom stimulus sampling. Specifically, concern will be accorded the situation wherein the number of elements common to s on Trials n and $n + 1$ varies inversely with the amount of time elapsing between trials.[3] In order that the reader more easily follow the development, background concepts in statistical learning theory will be reviewed briefly.

Associated with an acquisition or extinction session is a finite set of stimulus elements, S, from which the subject samples, on each trial, a random subset, s. Explicitly, each stimulus element in S is assumed to have an independently equal chance of being sampled by the subject on each trial. If the trial is a reinforced one, then the two elements in s become conditioned to the reinforced response; and if it is an extinction trial, the elements become deconditioned (conditioned to another response). Probability of response is defined by the proportion of elements in S that is conditioned to the response. Since s is a random sample from S, the expected proportion of conditioned elements present in the subject's sample is the same as the proportion in S.

Under such assumptions the acquisition of a learned response is described easily. Because few elements will have been conditioned before the conditioning period, the first-trial increment in response probability approximates the ratio s/S. On the second trial, fewer additional elements will become conditioned to the reinforced response because some in s will have been conditioned on Trial 1. Thus, the increment in response probability decreases on each trial, and the performance curve is negatively accelerated.

STIMULUS FLUCTUATION

Estes (1955a; 1955b; 1959, p. 424) introduced and explored the concept of stimulus fluctuation as a supplement to the earlier fixed-population, stimulus sampling model (1950). It was assumed that the composition of the stimulus set from which the subject samples on each trial may be modified from one experimental period to another, due primarily to imprecise control over the environmental context. Such modifications in the composition of S were assumed to be time-dependent, and were, hence, considered to be a source of performance changes labeled spontaneous recovery and spontaneous regression.

Estes (1955a, 1955b) gave his general theory of stimulus fluctuation a mathematical form of expression appropriate for longer time intervals, with special reference to temporal effects between periods rather than between trials.[4] He

---

[1] A grant from the National Science Foundation facilitated this paper.

[2] The author is indebted to Robert Radlow for a critical reading of an earlier version of this manuscript.

[3] Burke and Estes (1957), Witte (1959), and Straughan (1956) developed models incorporating nonrandom stimulus sampling. The former two are discrimination learning models based on fading stimulus traces from prior reinforcing events, but provide no differential time predictions for the conditioning paradigm herein investigated. The latter, although fitting the paradigm, does not address directly the variable of time between trials or between sessions.

[4] This is because the equations derived by Estes (1955a, 1955b) require, for solution, that sufficient time pass between events to insure that the numbers of elements in S and

This article appeared in *Psychol. Rev.*, 1961, **68**, 219–224.

assumed that the total number of elements associated with the entire experimental situation could be partitioned into two components: those, S, available to be sampled during a particular experimental period, and those, S', not available for sampling at that time. Between periods, during discrete time increments, all elements in S possess the same probability, j, of escaping from S into S'; and all elements in S' possess the same probability, j', of escaping from S' into S. Spontaneous recovery and spontaneous regression are thus interpreted to be a result of stimulus fluctuation between two stimulus sets which interact between conditioning periods. For purposes of developing general equations for a series of acquisition and/or extinction periods, it was required, for mathematical simplicity, that p (probability of response) be unity at the end of an acquisition period and zero at the end of an extinction period.[5]

Nonrandom Stimulus Sampling

The present development constitutes an adaptation of stimulus fluctuation theory to the trial-by-trial sampling behavior of the subject. Observe that this is a change in the kind of stimulus fluctuation investigated. Whereas Estes (1955a; 1955b; 1959, p. 424) and McConnell (1957, 1959) posit changes in S to result from stimulus fluctuation in and out of S, emphasis here is upon interchange between s and S, or upon continuous change in the subject's sample.

While it will be evident that the concepts herein investigated are adaptable to complex discrimination contexts which may require sampling from a number of stimulus sets (see, e.g., Anderson, 1960; Burke & Estes, 1957; Restle, 1955), the discussion will be confined to those situations in which the subject is sampling from a single set, S, of fixed size.

S' have stabilized. Tests of this particular model have been confined to periods separated by 24 hours (see, e.g., Estes, 1959, pp. 424f.).

[5] McConnell (1957, 1959) has since extended the model by permitting fluctuations between S and S' to occur during the experimental period.

Consider that s is a random sample of elements from S only on the first conditioning trial. Between trials each element in s has a probability, k, of fluctuating out of s and into the set $S - s$ (i.e., the set composed of those elements of S which were not sampled on the immediately preceding trial). Similarly, those elements in $S - s$ each have a probability, k', of fluctuating into s. Thus, on the next trial, s is composed of that portion of element which has not fluctuated out of the sample, plus a random sample of elements from $S - s$. If time (t) between trials is very short, successive samples will be highly similar in their composition; but, as intertrial interval increases, the number of elements common to successive samples decreases. In the limit, as t increases without bound, the composition of s approaches being a random sample of S.

At the level of the subject, the implication is that the stimulus complex to which a subject responds on Trial n is related in more than a chance fashion to that to which he responded on Trial n-1. As more time elapses between trials, the relationship between stimulus complexes on Trials n and n-1 decreases. Unless there is experimental manipulation, the subject is conceived of as systematically sampling "segments" of S as a function of time, the "segments" overlapping in degree inversely related to the amount of time between trials.

Mathematical Statement

We require the following definitions:

S   = population of stimulus elements present during an experimental period

s   = set of elements sampled by the subject on a trial

$s' = S - s$

N = the number of elements in s

N' = the number of elements in s'

x = the number of conditioned elements in s

x' = the number of conditioned elements in s'

k = probability (instantaneous) that an element in s will fluctuate into s'

k' = probability (instantaneous) that an element in s' will fluctuate into s

P_n = proportion of conditioned elements in s at the end of the nth trial

P_n' = proportion of conditioned elements in s' at the end of the nth trial

The assumptions are generally the same as those made in statistical learning theory, including those of fixed N and N'. However, two simplifying assumptions are added: k is fixed and equal for all elements in s, and k' is fixed and equal for all elements in s'.[6] The additional assumptions provide that $Nk = N'k'$ at all times.[7] Contingent upon presentation of appropriate stimulation, the proportion of conditioned elements in s determines momentary response probability.

Since, in general, the proportions of conditioned elements in s and s' are not the same (e.g., at the termination of the first trial, all elements in s are conditioned, but, most likely, this is not true of s'), the interchange of elements between s and s' results in a modification of the proportion of conditioned elements in s, hence modifying momentary response probability. In any diminishingly small time increment, kx conditioned elements leave s and $k'x'$ enter s from s'. Stated in differential form, the change in the number of conditioned elements may be expressed: $\Delta x = -kx + k'x'$. Dividing through by N yields the incremental change in proportion of conditioned ele-

[6] The assumptions of fixed N, N', k, and k', while more stringent than those of Estes's derivations, do permit application of the present model to short time intervals.

[7] Note that: $Nk = N'k'$; $N/N' = k'/k$; $(N'/N') + 1 = (k'/k) + 1$; $(N + N')/N' = (k' + k)/k$; $k/(k + k') = N/(N + N') = s/S$. The last term represents the growth constant, θ, present in earlier statistical models (Estes, 1950; Estes & Burke, 1953).

ments in s:

$$\Delta(x/N) = -kx/N + k'x'/N$$
$$= -kx/N + k'x'N'/NN'$$

Substituting Nk for $N'k'$:

$$\Delta(x/N) = -kx/N + kx'N/NN'$$
$$= -kx/N + kx'/N'$$

Employing the notation $p = x/N$ and $p' = x'/N'$:

$$\Delta p = -kp + kp' \qquad [1]$$

Similar analysis of the change in number of conditioned elements in s' yields:

$$\Delta p' = k'p - k'p' \qquad [2]$$

Treating stimulus fluctuation between s and s' as a continuous function of time, Equations 1 and 2 become a system of linear, first-order differential equations,[8] and can be expressed:

$$dp/dt = -kp + kp'$$
$$dp'/dt = k'p - k'p'$$

This system of equations can be solved by standard techniques (see, e.g., Leighton, 1952, pp. 105f.) to yield:

$$p = p_n + (p_n' - p_n) \\ \times (1 - K)(1 - e^{-(k+k')t}) \qquad [3]$$
$$p' = p_n + (p_n' - p_n) \\ \times (1 - K + Ke^{-(k+k')t}) \qquad [4]$$

where $K = k'/(k + k')$. Equations 3 and 4 are expressions for p and p' at any time t following a trial or experimental period, and can be solved when p_n and p_n' are known.

Having statements for the modification of p and p' between trials as a function of time, we desire expressions, $p_{n,t}$ and $p_{n,t}'$, for the proportions of conditioned elements in s and s', respectively, t time after the nth trial. Because the mathematical development parallels that of Estes, the reader is referred to his paper (1955a, p. 373) for the method by which

[8] Because it appears plausible to consider a subject as continuously interacting with his environment, the time functions were obtained by solving the differential, rather than the difference, equations.

$p_{n, t}$ and $p_{n, t}'$ were derived. The solutions are:

$$p_{n, t} = 1 - (1 - K)(1 - F(0)) \\ \times (1 - K + Ke^{-(\lambda + k')t})^{n-1} \\ \times (1 - e^{-(\lambda + k')t}) \quad [5]$$

$$p_{n, t}' = 1 - (1 - F(0)) \\ \times (1 - K + Ke^{-(\lambda + k')t})^{n} \quad [6]$$

where $F(0)$ is the proportion of conditioned elements in S at the beginning of the session.

By a similar analysis the equations for extinction trials are:

$$p_{n, t} = F(0)(1 - K) \\ \times (1 - K + Ke^{-(\lambda + k')t})^{n-1} \\ \times (1 - e^{-(\lambda + k')t}) \quad [7]$$

$$p_{n, t}' = F(0) \times (1 - K + Ke^{-(\lambda + k')t})^{n} \quad [8]$$

When t is permitted to grow large, Equations 5 through 8 become the difference equation forms of Estes's original model (1950).

EFFECTS OF NONRANDOM STIMULUS SAMPLING

Some of the predictions yielded by the model are listed below.[9]

Within Acquisition Period

1. Initial massed-trial performance is superior to initial spaced-trial performance. Unless trials are highly massed and the ratio s/S is low, the effect is relatively transient, operating only over the first several trials.

2. Following the brief period of relative depression, distributed-trial performance becomes greater than that of massed-trial. In the limit, however, asymptote is independent of the amount of overlap in s on successive trials.

Between Acquisition and Extinction Periods

1. Unless conditioning is complete, the amount of spontaneous regression is an

[9] Similar qualitative predictions follow from Estes (1955a, 1955b) and McConnell (1957, 1959). Predictions related to the massing of individual trials have a counterpart in the Estes model in the massing of *blocks* of trials.

increasing exponential function of time since the end of acquisition.

2. As the number of acquisition trials increases, the amount of spontaneous regression decreases exponentially with asymptote of zero.

3. As acquisition intertrial interval increases, the amount of spontaneous regression decreases to an asymptote of zero with extreme trial spacing.

Within Extinction Period

1. Unless conditioning is complete, spaced acquisition training yields greater resistance to extinction than does massed acquisition training.

2. Initial resistance to extinction is greater when extinction trials are distributed. As in the case of acquisition trials, this effect will operate only over the first several nonreinforced trials.

3. After the initial extinction trials, resistance to extinction is greater with massed trials.

4. The total number of responses in complete extinction is independent of the amount of time elapsing between acquisition and extinction sessions.

Between Extinction Period and Spontaneous Recovery Test Trials

1. If $p_{n, t} < p_{n, t}'$ at the end of extinction training, spontaneous recovery is an exponential function of time since the end of extinction.

2. If $p_{n, t} > p_{n, t}'$ at the end of acquisition and $p_{n, t} < p_{n, t}'$ at the end of extinction training, the amount of spontaneous recovery is inversely related to the acquisition intertrial interval.

3. If $p_{n, t} < p_{n, t}'$ at the end of extinction, the amount of spontaneous recovery is inversely related to the extent of extinction intertrial interval.

4. The amount of spontaneous recovery is inversely related to both the number of acquisition trials and the number of extinction trials.

DISCUSSION

The model herein developed provides an interpretation of time-related phenomena as the result of nonrandom, time-related stimulus sampling. A survey of the literature for studies which meet the specifications of the model resulted in but a limited number of findings relevant to the predictions made above. While many studies have been reported wherein intertrial interval and/or number of training trials were the independent variables, for two reasons all of them are not referenced. First, it would appear inappropriate to cite as indirect "support" of a model those studies for which inhibition is, at present, satisfactory in accounting for the data. Second, often the predictions of the model hinge upon a single test-trial performance after a rest interval, but data were generally recorded in blocks of 5, 10, or 20 trials, hence confounding the results with effects of further training.

In several instances, however, the model provides predictions in a direction opposite to what might be expected from inhibition. First, Cotton and Lewis (1957) and Howat and Grant (1958) obtained a performance crossover in extinction as a function of intertrial interval. That is, resistance to extinction was greater initially with distributed trials, later with massed trials.

While no tests of significance were made, the data of Baron (1952), Prokasy, Grant, and Myers (1958), and Spence and Norris (1950) suggest a tendency for the initial block of massed training trials to result in relatively superior performance. What appears to be inhibition usually severely depresses performance under massed training conditions, as it did following the initial data points.

Finally, Cotton and Lewis (1957), Howat and Grant (1958), Ellson (1940), Lewis and Cotton (1959), Scott and Wike (1956), Sheffield (1950), Stanley (1952), and Wilson, Weiss, and Amsel (1955) report greater resistance to extinction when extinction trials are massed rather than spaced. Lewis (1956), on the other hand, obtained no difference in resistance to extinction as a function of distribution of extinction trials following training on a 100% reinforcement schedule. Stanley (1952), when employing the number of correct responses as a dependent variable, found greater resistance to extinction with distributed extinction trials.

Experimental tests of the model are not easy. Consider the data of conditioning. The effects of many already discovered variables in the classical conditioning situation would tend to obscure variance attributable to the sampling behavior of the subject. That, for instance, conditioned responses of the all-or-none type do not asymptote at unity may be a combination of many effects not presently addressed by statistical learning models: nonoptimum interstimulus interval, nonoptimum motivation, response produced inhibition, incomplete stimulus control, and the very criteria by which a conditioned response is defined.

Most difficult to control, or eliminate, is inhibition. Its effects appear to be a depression of acquisition asymptote, reminiscence following massed acquisition training and spontaneous recovery following extinction training. The author does not foresee at the present time the implementation of a purely analytic approach to the problems posed by inhibition. Rather, it appears more likely that we shall be required to turn to the organism for a specification of inhibition effects, perhaps incorporating empirically derived functions into present models. One alternative is to treat inhibition as being the result of the addition, to s, of a population of response produced stimulus events having the property of not being conditionable to the response.

Summary

Applying Estes's theory of stimulus fluctuation to the sampling behavior of the subject, a model was developed wherein successive samples from the stimulus population are not independent. Instead of drawing successive random samples from the population, the subject selects samples which overlap in content as a function of the degree of trial massing. Implications of the model for the distribution of trials and experimental sessions were discussed.

REFERENCES

ANDERSON, N. H. Effect of first-order conditional probability in a two-choice learning situation. *J. exp. Psychol.,* 1960, 59, 73–93.

BARON, M. R. The effect of long intertrial intervals on the limit of eyelid conditioning. *J. exp. Psychol.,* 1952, 44, 438–441.

BURKE, C. J., & ESTES, W. K. A component model for stimulus variables in discrimination learning. *Psychometrika,* 1957, 22, 133–145.

COTTON, J. W., & LEWIS, D. J. Effect of intertrial interval on acquisition and extinction of a running response. *J. exp. Psychol.,* 1957, 54, 15–20.

ELLSON, D. G. Successive extinction of a bar-pressing response in rats. *J. gen. Psychol.,* 1940, 23, 283–288.

ESTES, W. K. Toward a statistical theory of learning. *Psychol. Rev.,* 1950, 57, 94–107.

ESTES, W. K. Statistical theory of distributional phenomena in learning. *Psychol. Rev.,* 1955, 62, 369–377. (a)

ESTES, W. K. Statistical theory of spontaneous recovery and regression. *Psychol. Rev.,* 1955, 62, 145–154. (b)

ESTES, W. K. The statistical approach to learning theory. In S. Koch (Ed.), *Psychology: A study of a science.* Vol. II. McGraw-Hill, 1959. Pp. 380–491.

ESTES, W. K., & BURKE, C. J. A theory of stimulus variability in learning. *Psychol. Rev.,* 1953, 60, 276–286.

HOWAT, M. G., & GRANT, D. A. Influence of intertrial interval during extinction on spontaneous recovery of conditioned eyelid responses. *J. exp. Psychol.,* 1958, 56, 11–15.

LEIGHTON, W. *An introduction to the theory of differential equations.* McGraw-Hill, 1952.

LEWIS, D. J. Acquisition, extinction, and spontaneous recovery as a function of percentage of reinforcement and intertrial intervals. *J. exp. Psychol.,* 1956, 51, 45–53.

LEWIS, D. J., & COTTON, J. W. The effect of intertrial interval and number of acquisition trials with partial reinforcement on performance. *J. comp. physiol. Psychol.,* 1959, 52, 598–601.

McCONNELL, D. G. Spontaneous regression and recovery of a bar-pressing response during a sequence of acquisition and extinction periods. Unpublished doctoral dissertation, Indiana University, 1957.

McCONNELL, D. G. An augmented model for spontaneous regression and recovery. *Psychometrika,* 1959, 24, 157–168.

PROKASY, W. F., GRANT, D. A., & MYERS, N. A. Eyelid conditioning as a function of unconditioned stimulus intensity and intertrial interval. *J. exp. Psychol.,* 1958, 55, 242–246.

RESTLE, F. A theory of discrimination learning. *Psychol. Rev.,* 1955, 62, 11–19.

SCOTT, E. D., & WIKE, E. L. The effect of partially delayed reinforcement and trial-distribution on the extinction of an instrumental response. *Amer..J. Psychol.,* 1956, 69, 264–268.

SHEFFIELD, V. F. Resistance to extinction as a function of the distribution of extinction trials. *J. exp. Psychol.,* 1950, 40, 305–313.

SPENCE, K. W., & NORRIS, E. B. Eyelid conditioning as a function of the intertrial interval. *J. exp. Psychol.,* 1950, 40, 716–720.

STANLEY, W. C. Extinction as a function of the spacing of extinction trials. *J. exp. Psychol.,* 1952, 43, 249–260.

STRAUGHAN, J. H. Human escape learning in relation to reinforcement variables and intertrial interval conditions. *J. exp. Psychol.,* 1956, 52, 1–8.

WILSON, W., WEISS, E. J., & AMSEL, A. Two tests of the Sheffield hypothesis concerning resistance to extinction, partial reinforcement, and distribution of practice. *J. exp. Psychol.,* 1955, 50, 51–60.

WITTE, R. S. A stimulus-trace hypothesis for statistical learning theory. *J. exp. Psychol.,* 1959, 57, 273–283.

(Received August 3, 1959)

A Model with Neutral Elements[1]

DAVID LABERGE, *University of Minnesota*

Current stimulus-sampling models [8, 17] assume that each stimulus element in a choice situation is connected to one of the recorded response alternatives. There are a number of well-established empirical relationships, however, which suggest that this simple assumption may be too restrictive. One problem, arising in the case of overlearning, may be considered as part of the broader issue of separating learning from performance. When we continue to present trials to a subject after his performance has stabilized, we may note that this additional training affects behavior under post-training conditions, such as extinction [14] and retention [15]. Therefore some changes in learning are taking place which are not reflected by the typical performance measures. The current models, in their simplest forms, do not provide for the separation of these processes because their performance measure of response probability exhausts the learning information in the population. In these models, the performance measure of response probability is identified with the proportion of stimulus elements in the population set [17] or the sample set [8] connected to that response. The process of learning is represented by a change in the proportion of elements connected to the response, and, under the assumption that elements are connected only to the defined response alternatives, a change in learning will always be revealed by a change in response probability. For example, suppose that a subject has been trained in a two-choice prediction task under a .80 probability of reinforcement (π). At performance asymptote, the two sets of elements in the population are distributed in the proportions .80 and .20. Further training under the same π value may shift elements from one set to another, but the proportions remain the same. Therefore, there is no way to record the amount of further training in the population so as to produce varied behavior in post-training conditions.

One way out of this difficulty, proposed by Estes [6], is to allow elements to fluctuate in and out of the population set in such a way that the conditioning of the set outside the population lags behind the conditioning of the

---

[1] The author is indebted to C. J. Burke and W. K. Estes for very helpful suggestions and criticism.

population set. Performance measures are based solely upon the population set, and after performance has stabilized, further learning may be represented in the model by the continued change of status of elements in the set outside the population. Post-training conditions affect the fluctuation of the elements between the two sets, which in turn affects performance during retention and extinction trials.

While the fluctuation model is quite effective in handling this problem, the present model separates learning from performance by an alternative method, with some notably different consequences. Later in the paper we shall describe an experiment which compares predictions from the fluctuation model with predictions from the present model.

Another problem arises when current models are applied to discrimination learning. There is growing evidence ([13], [21]) for the existence of some sort of orienting or observing response which is distinguishable from the experimentally defined responses in the typical discrimination situation. Presumably there are elements in the situation which elicit these responses, and if we continue to assume that an element can be connected to only one response at a time, then it appears that we must make room in the stimulus population for the stimulus elements which elicit these responses.

Furthermore, current models have not as yet been extended to account for response latencies in choice situations. The reason for this delay may well be the assumption that elements are connected to recorded responses only; whereas it is the occurrence of inappropriate, or unrecorded, responses which appears to be one of the most important variables affecting latency [3].

Now suppose we modify the conditioning assumption so as to allow stimulus elements to be connected to none of the experimentally defined response classes. These "neutral" elements may be connected to responses other than the ones the experimenter chooses to observe or record, and some elements may be connected to no response at all. For clarity, we shall henceforth refer to the recorded or measured responses as *Type R responses*, and to the nonrecorded responses, including the no-response class, as *Type N responses*. The existence of Type N responses and their corresponding stimulus elements does not affect the probability of Type R responses on a trial, so long as we continue the practice of terminating a trial with the occurrence of a Type R response. The organism simply continues sampling and responding until a Type R response occurs and the trial terminates. Thus Type N responses merely postpone the occurrence of a Type R response. And since a Type R response occurs on every trial, the probability of a particular Type R response depends only upon the distribution within the set of elements connected to Type R responses. All other elements are assumed to be neutral with respect to the probability of a Type R response.

In the present modification of stimulus-sampling models, we assume that at the end of a trial in a choice situation, all elements in the sample, neutral and nonneutral, become connected to one of the Type R responses. Since we are assuming that in a choice situation the only reinforcement, or change of connections, occurs in favor of Type R responses,[2] we would presume that during a series of trials the neutral elements would become deneutralized; that is, they would become connected to Type R responses, and Type N responses would drop out. If a sufficient number of trials is allowed in a constant-stimulus situation, then effectively all elements should become connected to Type R responses and learning thereafter should proceed according to the Estes-Burke model. Therefore, for the simple choice experiment, it is only during early trials and on trials when novel stimuli are suddenly introduced that we should expect the proportion of neutral elements to be sufficiently large to generate predictions detectably different from those of other stimulus-sampling models.

In the present development of the model, two aspects of response output will be treated: response frequency and response latency. Along with the formal presentation of the model, we shall describe an experiment which was carried out to test it.

Formal Model for Response Frequency

The experimental situation described by the model consists of a set of Type R response alternatives, A_i $(i = 1, 2, \cdots, k)$, having a one-to-one correspondence with a set of reinforcing events, E_i $(i = 1, 2, \cdots, k)$; and a signal, S. The signal on trial n is associated with a set of stimulus elements which is partitioned into the following $k + 1$ subsets: $C_{0,n}$, the set of neutral elements, all associated with Type N responses; and $C_{i,n}(i = 1, 2, \cdots, k)$, the set of elements associated with the ith Type R response. On a given trial, the subject samples a proportion, θ, of the population of elements, and this sample determines what response, Type R or Type N, will occur on that trial. More specifically, the probability of a response type is identified with the proportion of elements in the sample connected to that response type. If a Type N response occurs, the sample returns to the population unchanged. Then a new sample is drawn and evokes a Type R or Type N response. This successive sampling continues until a Type R response occurs. Following the Type R response, the experimenter determines which reinforcing event shall occur. The elements in the final sample, neutral and nonneutral, then become connected to the response alternative associated with the reinforcing event, and are returned to the population.

For the derivation of the equation for response probability as a function of trials we shall restrict ourselves to "determinate" experimental routines [5], i.e., those in which exactly one of the k reinforcing events occurs on each trial. In addition we assume that $\Pr(E_i) = \pi_i$ is constant over the series of

---

[2] In the discrimination situation, however, it appears that we must permit some of the elements to become connected to observing responses as trials continue, if the organism is to improve. Because it is not yet clear how elements become connected to observing responses, we shall not attempt to describe in further detail the role of these elements in the discrimination situations.

learning trials and is not contingent upon response occurrences. Finally, we assume, for simplicity, that all elements in the population have the same sampling probability, θ.

Taking $c_{0,n}$ for the number of elements in $C_{0,n}$ and $c_{i,n}$ for the number of elements in $C_{i,n}$, the probability of response A_i on trial n is assumed to be

$$(1) \qquad p_{i,n} = \frac{c_{i,n}}{\sum\limits_{i=1}^{k} c_{i,n}} .$$

The proportion of neutral elements in the population on trial n is defined as

$$(2) \qquad u_n = \frac{c_{0,n}}{c_{0,n} + \sum\limits_{i=1}^{k} c_{i,n}} = \frac{c_{0,n}}{N} ,$$

where N is the total number of elements in the population; N is assumed to be constant over all trials. The recursive expressions for response probability may be derived most conveniently by treating separately the numerator and denominator of Equation 1. All the following expressions assume that the sizes of the population and sample sets are large enough so that the variances of sample subset proportions are negligible.

For the numerator, an E_i event on trial n gives

$$(3) \qquad c_{i,n+1} = (1 - \theta)c_{i,n} + \theta N ,$$

and an $E_j (i \neq j)$ event on trial n gives

$$(4) \qquad c_{i,n+1} = (1 - \theta)c_{i,n} .$$

Weighting Equations 3 and 4 by their respective probabilities of occurrence, π_i and $(1 - \pi_i)$, and summing, we obtain the recursive expression for the mean number of elements connected to response A_i on trial n, where the average is taken over the sample space of all possible values of $c_{i,n}$ and all possible reinforcing events on trial n:

$$(5) \qquad c_{i,n+1} = (1 - \theta)c_{i,n} + \pi_i \theta N .$$

The solution of this difference equation gives the mean number of elements connected to A_i:

$$(6) \qquad c_{i,n} = N\pi_i - (N\pi_i - c_{i,1})(1 - \theta)^{n-1} ,$$

where the average is taken over the sample space of all possible sequences of responses and reinforcing events through the first $n - 1$ trials. To obtain the denominator of $p_{i,n}$, we note that summation of both sides of Equation 5 yields

$$(7) \qquad \sum_{i=1}^{k} c_{i,n+1} = \sum_{i=1}^{k} (1 - \theta)c_{i,n} + \theta N \sum_{i=1}^{k} \pi_i = (1 - \theta) \sum_{i=1}^{k} c_{i,n} + \theta N .$$

This is the recursive expression for the mean number of nonneutral elements, where the averaging is defined as in the case of the numerator. Solution of this difference equation yields the mean number of nonneutral elements on trial n:

(8)
$$\sum_{i=1}^{k} c_{i,n} = N - \left(N - \sum_{i=1}^{k} c_{i,1}\right)(1 - \theta)^{n-1} .$$

Having obtained the solutions for the expected values of the numerator and denominator of Equation 1, it is now possible to move directly to the solution of $p_{i,n}$ under the assumption that the population and sample sizes are large enough so that for every n

$$E\left(\frac{c_{i,n}}{\sum\limits_{i=1}^{k} c_{i,n}}\right) \cong \frac{E(c_{i,n})}{E\left(\sum\limits_{i=1}^{k} c_{i,n}\right)} ,$$

where E denotes expectation. Taking the ratio of Equations 6 and 8 and dividing through by N yields the expression for the mean probability of response A_i in terms of $p_{i,1}, \pi_i, u_1, \theta,$ and n:

$$p_{i,n} = \frac{\pi_i - [\pi_i - (1 - u_1)p_{i,1}](1 - \theta)^{n-1}}{1 - u_1(1 - \theta)^{n-1}} ,$$

which, after rearranging terms, may be expressed as

(9)
$$p_{i,n} = \pi_i - [(1 - u_1)(\pi_i - p_{i,1})]\frac{(1 - \theta)^{n-1}}{1 - u_1(1 - \theta)^{n-1}} .$$

If u_1 is zero, Equation 9 reduces to an equation given by Burke and Estes [1],

(10)
$$p_{i,n} = \pi_i - (\pi_i - p_{i,1})(1 - \theta)^{n-1} .$$

A special case of the Bush-Mosteller model [2] with $\alpha_1 = \alpha_2 = 1 - \theta$ is also equivalent to Equation 10. Similarly, the Restle function [17] reduces to Equation 10 when all irrelevant cues have been adapted and when all relevant cues have the same probability of being conditioned to the A_i response.

In order to estimate parameters $\theta, u_1,$ and $p_{i,1}$, and to plot the learning curve in terms of proportion of A_i responses per block of trials, it is useful to express Equation 9 in cumulative form:

(11)
$$\overline{R}_n = \sum_{j=1}^{n} p_{i,j} = n\pi_i - (1 - u_1)(\pi_i - p_{i,1}) \sum_{j=1}^{n} \frac{(1-\theta)^{j-1}}{1 - u_1(1 - \theta)^{j-1}} ,$$

where $\overline{R}_n$ is the expected number of A_i responses in the first n trials. The series term in Equation 11 is a form of the Lambert series [12] and has been tabled by the author for values of u in the range .05 to .95, with values of θ in the range .001 to .100, for successive blocks of 20 trials up to 200 trials. The three parameters, $p_{i,1}, u_1,$ and θ, may be estimated simultaneously from the data of one learning series by successively setting Equation 11 equal to each of the different cumulative proportions, e.g., for n's of 20, 60, and 100. Solutions to these three equations may be obtained by graphic methods although the series term is not in closed form and will not submit to the desired algebraic manipulations.

In the denominator of Equation 9 is the expression for the proportion of neutral elements as a function of trials:

$$(12) \qquad u_n = u_1(1 - \theta)^{n-1} .$$

As n increases, the proportion of neutral elements decreases in a negatively accelerated manner approaching zero asymptotically. After a sufficient number of trials, therefore, virtually all the elements should be connected to Type R responses, and learning should thereafter follow the Estes-Burke model. It is during early trials, then, that we expect Equation 9 to differ from Equation 10.

At this point we may consider possible behavioral consequences of varying the proportion of neutral elements in the stimulus population. We note that when u_1 approaches unity, the A_i probability given by Equation 9 approaches π_i, and the mean performance curve is at asymptote after only one trial. On the other hand, when u_1 is zero, a relatively small amount of change in performance occurs after one trial. It would appear from these two extreme cases that the proportion of neutral elements affects rate of learning. We shall now show that the relationship holds in general. Taking as a measure of rate the cumulative number of A_i responses over n trials for any fixed $n > 1$, and treating u_1 as a continuous variable, we differentiate Equation 11 with respect to u_1:

$$\frac{d\bar{R}_n}{du_1} = (\pi_i - p_{i,1}) \left(\sum_{j=1}^{n} \frac{(1 - \theta)^{j-1}}{1 - u_1(1 - \theta)^{j-1}} - (1 - u_1) \sum_{j=1}^{n} \frac{(1 - \theta)^{2j-2}}{[1 - u_1(1 - \theta)^{j-1}]^2} \right)$$

$$= (\pi_i - p_{i,1}) \sum_{j=1}^{n} \frac{(1 - \theta)^{j-1} - (1 - \theta)^{2j-2}}{[1 - u_1(1 - \theta)^{j-1}]^2} .$$

Since the sum is always positive for admissible values of θ and u_1, the derivative takes the sign of $(\pi_i - p_{i,1})$, and $\bar{R}_n$ is therefore monotonic in u_1 for all $n > 1$. Thus, the greater the proportion of neutral elements in the population, the greater the rate of learning.

An Experimental Test of the Response Frequency Model

The foregoing deduction suggests a simple test of the present model. By increasing the amount of training with a π of .50 in the simple two-choice prediction situation, we should decrease the proportion of neutral elements while maintaining the probability of an A_1 response at .50. Then, if subjects are shifted to a new π value, e.g., .90, their rates of learning under this condition should vary according to the number of preliminary trials they have received. Essentially, this is an overlearning procedure, where learning is presumed to continue while performance remains constant. According to the fluctuation model [6], however, the amount of preliminary training under a π of .50 should have no effect on learning rates, since all elements, inside as well as outside the population, are assumed to be equally distributed between the two responses from the start. Such a test has been carried out [14], giving four groups, 48 undergraduates in each, preliminary training of 0, 20, 60, and 200 trials, respectively, under a π of .50 before shifting them to a π of .90. The obtained rates of learning under the .90 condition were significantly different by an F test and were ordered in magnitude as predicted by the model. Using the data from this study, we shall attempt to evaluate the necessary parameters and write the equations for the mean learning curves. We shall label the groups A, B, C, and D, corresponding to 0, 20, 60, and 200 preliminary trials, respectively.

The value of π is known since it was under the control of the experimenter in the construction of the sequences. Since the side of the E_1 reinforcement was counterbalanced in all subgroups, $p_{i,1}$ is assumed to be .50. The remaining two parameters, u_1 and θ, will be estimated from the data. It should be noted that u_1 refers to the proportion of neutral elements on the first trial of the $\pi = .90$ series. This proportion is expected to decrease as the number of preliminary trials increases.

Since there is evidence [17] that θ is not independent of π, we shall make separate estimates of θ for the $\pi = .50$ and $\pi = .90$ conditions. We shall label these estimated θ's as $\theta_{.50}$ and $\theta_{.90}$, respectively.

The procedure for estimating $\theta_{.90}$ is facilitated considerably by assuming that all neutral elements in the population have been exhausted by trial 200. Thus for Group D, the parameter u_1 in the learning equation vanishes and permits us to estimate $\theta_{.90}$ from the cumulative form of Equation 10:

$$(13) \qquad \overline{R}_n = \sum_{j=1}^{n} p_{1,j} = n\pi - (\pi - p_{1,1}) \sum_{j=1}^{n} (1 - \theta)^{j-1}$$

$$= n\pi - (\pi - p_{1,1}) \frac{[1 - (1 - \theta)_n]}{\theta} \, .$$

To justify the assumption that the proportion of neutral elements is negligible by trial 200, we may use Equation 13 to obtain a measure of learning rates for all groups. Taking the average number of A_1 responses over the first 200 trials of the .90 series for Groups A, B, and C, and over the available 100 trials for Group D, we obtain θ's of .050, .028, .025, and .023, respectively. The learning rates have leveled off by trial 200, and therefore it seems reasonable to assume that the proportion of neutral elements on subsequent trials is very near zero. This finding allows us to take .023 as our estimate of $\theta_{.90}$ and to use it to solve for the u_1 values of the other three groups.

The estimation of u_1 may be accomplished by computing the average number of A_1 responses over the first 200 trials of the .90 series. Using Equation 11, we estimate u_1 directly for Groups A and C, leaving the u_1 of Group B to be predicted. The rationale for choosing A and C for estimation purposes is as follows: Group A is chosen to obtain the best estimate of u_1 at the

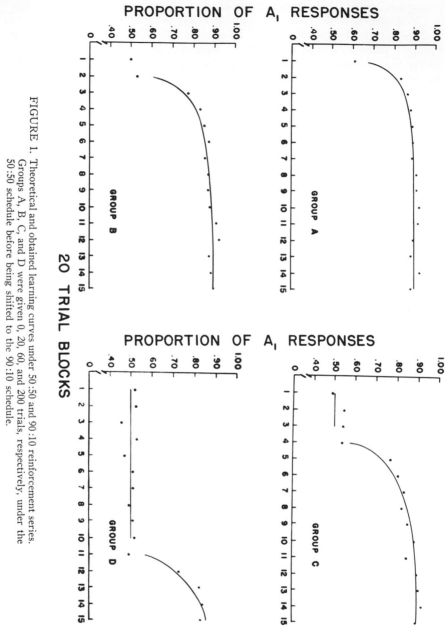

FIGURE 1. Theoretical and obtained learning curves under 50:50 and 90:10 reinforcement series.
Groups A, B, C, and D were given 0, 20, 60, and 200 trials, respectively, under the
50:50 schedule before being shifted to the 90:10 schedule.

beginning of training; and Group C is chosen as the second group because it is farthest removed from Group A in terms of number of preliminary trials.

The u_1 values for Groups A and C at the first trial of the .90 series are .755 and .108, respectively. With these values we may solve for $\theta_{.50}$ by Equation 11, obtaining a value of .032. This estimate cannot be considered to be very reliable because it is based on the ratio of two other estimated quantities, u_1 and u_{60}. Nevertheless, we shall take this rough estimate of $\theta_{.50}$, together with the u_1 of Group A, to write Equation 12 as a function of n alone. This function describes the estimated decrement in the proportion of neutral elements in the population over the series of trials under a π of .50. Entering this function with n's of 20 and 200 yields u values of .394 and .001, respectively, for Groups B and D.

With the necessary parameters evaluated, we may now write the learning equations and draw curves for each of the four groups. In particular, the curve for Group B constitutes a free prediction since no parameters were estimated from the data of Group B. A comparison of the four theoretical curves of Fig. 1 with their corresponding obtained points indicates that the proposed learning function satisfactorily describes the different learning rates. The most noticeable discrepancies occur consistently at the beginning of the .90 series. For each group the proportion for the first block is below and the next few proportions are above the predicted values. Much better predictions for these initial points could have been obtained had we estimated the initial response proportions, $p_{1,1}$, from the data of each group, instead of assuming them to be .50 on a priori grounds. However, it seemed desirable to limit the number of free parameters in the analysis so that we might see how effectively the u parameter alone accounts for the learning rates.

Asymptotic predictions are confirmed for Groups A, B, and C in that the rate of responding levels off at or very near .90 in each case. Similar determination for Group D is not feasible because only 100 trials were run under the .90 condition.

Formal Model for Response Latency

In the remaining section we shall derive the expression for mean latency of a Type R response. The key assumption here is that the drawing of a sample and the execution of a response, Type R or Type N, requires an interval of time. Thus, the larger the proportion of neutral elements present, the more likely it is that the subject will make a series of Type N responses, thereby producing a longer latency for an occurrence of a Type R response.

Let $q_{i,n}(i = 1, 2, \cdots, r)$ be probabilities that drawing a single sample results in the ith of r Type R responses. Then

$$q_{1,n} + q_{2,n} + \cdots + q_{r,n} = 1 - u_n \leqq 1 \,,$$

where the subscript n refers to ordinal trial number, a trial being defined as ending when a Type R response occurs. Let h be the time interval required to select a sample and respond, and let k be a random variable representing the number of samples required to produce a Type R response.   Then

(14) $$\Pr\{L_n = kh\} = \left(1 - \sum_{i=1}^{r} q_{i,n}\right)^{k-1} \sum_{i=1}^{r} q_{i,n} ,$$

where L_n is the latency of a Type R response on trial n.   The mean of this geometric distribution is

(15) $$\bar{L}_n = E(kh) = \frac{h}{\sum_{i=1}^{r} q_{i,n}} = \frac{h}{1 - u_n} ,$$

and the variance is

(16) $$\sigma_{L_n}^2 = \frac{h^2 u_n}{(1 - u_n)^2} .$$

As $n \to \infty$, $u_n \to 0$, and therefore $L_n \to h$; and also $\sigma_{L_n}^2 \to 0$.   In the simple prediction task where u_n is estimated from the mean probability curve, we need only estimate h from the asymptotic latency in order to write the specific expression for mean latency as a function of trials.

We have assumed in the preceding derivation that the response times for Type R and Type N responses are the same.   However, in some situations, Type R responses may require a larger amount of time for execution than Type N responses.   In such cases it will be necessary to introduce another constant, t_0, which is the time required to sample and make a Type R response, while h denotes the time required for each Type N response.   This new latency distribution is merely a translation of the argument of Equation 14 by a quantity $(t_0 - h)$:

(17) $$\Pr\{L_n = (k-1)h + t_0\} = \left(1 - \sum_{i=1}^{r} q_{i,n}\right)^{k-1} \sum_{i=1}^{r} q_{i,n} .$$

The mean latency is

(18) $$\bar{L}_n = E[(k-1)h + t_0] = \frac{h}{1 - u_n} + t_0 - h = \frac{h u_n}{1 - u_n} + t_0 ,$$

and the variance is unchanged from that given by Equation 16.

Estimation of the two parameters, h and t_0, can be carried out by summing over two blocks of trials of convenient length, s, and successively setting the obtained values equal to

(19) $$\sum_{n=m+1}^{m+s} \bar{L}_n = h \sum_{n=m+1}^{m+s} \frac{u_n}{1 - u_n} + s t_0 ,$$

for two values of m.   Assuming that u_n is already known for the required values of n, the resulting two equations can then be solved simultaneously for the two parameters.

In its present form the model yields several rather clear-cut predictions of latency in the choice situation.   First of all, it predicts that the mean latency decreases to some asymptote during training.   Unfortunately there is a sur-prising lack of latency data for the choice situation, but a study by Straughan [20] indicates a small but clear decrease in latency over trials, and the curve is of the predicted exponential form.   The model also predicts that the latency for the Type R responses will be the same regardless of the reinforcement probabilities, since the expected time required to draw an element connected to A_i is the same for all i.   Straughan's data are not clear on this point, and further study of this problem is indicated.   An additional prediction is that after training has progressed sufficiently to bring latency to asymptote, it should remain at that level despite reversals and other shifts in the reinforcement schedule.   Finally, the model indicates that the asymptotic variance of the latencies should be zero.   From the available data on reaction-time experi-ments [22] it appears that this particular prediction will not be confirmed, and further developments of the model will be necessary to bring it in line with variance characteristics of latencies.

Conclusion

In conclusion it appears that, aside from yielding the desired exponential form and asymptotic characteristics of the learning function, the neutral-elements model provides a means of accounting for additional behavioral phenomena:

(1) Level of learning may differ from the level of performance in the model, permitting a parsimonious description of certain phenomena of over-learning.

(2) Stimuli connected to auxiliary responses, such as orienting responses, postural adjustments, etc., are given a place in the population of elements without loss of the successful predictions made by current models.

(3) Changes in the proportion of neutral elements in the population provide a means of predicting changes in response latency during learning in choice situations.

REFERENCES

1.   Burke, C. J., and Estes, W. K. A component model for stimulus variables in discrimination learning. *Psychometrika*, 1957, **22**, 133-45.

2.   Bush, R. R., and Mosteller, F. *Stochastic models for learning*. New York: Wiley, 1955.

3.   Cotton, J. W. Running time as a function of amount of food deprivation. *J. exp. Psychol.*, 1953, **46**, 188-98.

4.   Estes, W. K. Toward a statistical theory of learning. *Psychol. Rev.*, 1950, **57**, 94–107.

5.   Estes, W. K. Theory of learning with constant, variable, or contingent probabili-ties of reinforcement. *Psychometrika*, 1957, **22**, 113-32.

6.   Estes, W. K. Statistical theory of spontaneous recovery and regression. *Psychol. Rev.*, 1955, **62**, 145-54.

7. Estes, W. K. Statistical theory of distributional phenomena in learning. *Psychol. Rev.*, 1955, **62**, 369–77.

8. Estes, W. K., and Burke, C. J. A theory of stimulus variability in learning. *Psychol. Rev.*, 1953, **60**, 276–86.

9. Estes, W. K., and Straughan, J. H. Analysis of a verbal conditioning situation in terms of statistical learning theory. *J. exp. Psychol.*, 1954, **47**, 225–34.

10. Feller, W. *An introduction to probability theory and its applications.* New York: Wiley, 1950.

11. Humphreys, L. G. Acquisition and extinction of verbal expectations in a situation analogous to conditioning. *J. exp. Psychol.*, 1939, **25**, 294–301.

12. Knopp, Konrad. *Theory and application of infinite series.* London and Glasgow: Blackie and Son, Ltd., 1928.

13. LaBerge, D. L., and Smith, A. Selective sampling in discrimination learning. *J. exp. Psychol.*, 1957, **54**, 423–30.

14. LaBerge, D. L. The effect of preliminary trials on rate of conditioning in a simple prediction situation. *J. exp. Psychol.*, 1959, **57**, 20–24.

15. McGeoch, J. A. *The psychology of human learning.* New York: Longmans, 1942.

16. Restle, F. A theory of discrimination learning. *Psychol. Rev.*, 1955, **62**, 11–19.

17. Restle, F. Theory of selective learning with probable reinforcements. *Psychol. Rev.*, 1957, **64**, 182–91.

18. Richardson, C. H. *An introduction to the calculus of finite differences.* New York: Van Nostrand, 1954.

19. Schoeffler, M. S. Probability of responses to compounds of discriminated stimuli. *J. exp. Psychol.*, 1954, **48**, 323–29.

20. Straughan, J. H. An application of statistical learning theory to an escape learning situation using human subjects. Unpublished doctor's dissertation, Indiana University, 1953.

21. Wyckoff, L. B. The role of observing responses in discrimination learning: Part I. *Psychol. Rev.*, 1952, **59**, 431–42.

22. Woodworth, R. S., and Schlosberg, H. *Experimental psychology.* New York: Holt, 1954.

CHAPTER II

Elements of Associative Learning

The conception of the learning process developed in the papers of Chapter I rests heavily upon the assumption that all instances of learning, however complex, can in principle be analyzed into constituent elementary processes. It is further assumed that the elementary processes are basically the same regardless of the particular types of stimuli and responses involved. Initial attempts at gaining empirical evidence relevant to the theory did not bear directly either upon specific assumptions about the nature of the elementary processes or, for that matter, upon any other specific aspects of the theory. The initial strategy was to see whether models including all of the major assumptions in combination led to verifiable predictions concerning rates and limits of learning in a variety of standard situations. Once it had been determined that this type of theory met at least reasonable minimum standards for description and prediction, then attention could be turned to the harder problem of getting more direct evidence concerning specific aspects of the theory. Experimental investigations of the major assumption that elementary learning processes are unitary in character, with changes of state occurring on an all-or-none basis, began to appear in the late 1950's; the present chapter samples a number of them.

If it were the case, as was tacitly assumed in the earliest work on statistical learning theory, that all empirical situations necessarily involve the sampling of considerable numbers of stimulus elements, then there would be no possibility of obtaining direct evidence concerning changes in single associative connections. The possibility of direct attack upon changes in single associative connections was brought closer to attainment by two, by no means independent, developments: (a) elaborations of the one-element model (which was introduced in Chapter I in Estes, 1959), (b) development of special experimental conditions which closely approximated requirements for the idealized pure case in which changes in the state of the single element sampled on a particular trial could be directly determined. Neither development sprang forth fully completed in a single event; rather, both evolved through a process of successive approximations. The evolution is instructive in its own right and will be reviewed in the remainder of this chapter.

Before we trace this evolution, a word of clarification and caution is in order since there has been some misunderstanding of the "all-or-none" assumption. It is *not* asserted that all instances of learning occur on an all-or-none basis regardless of the level of stimulus and response complexity involved, but, rather, that at the level of elementary processes, changes in state occur on an all-or-none basis. Molecules of learning can be analyzed into constituent all-or-none atoms. That is what the "new mental chemistry" is all about.

Early experimental attacks on the all-or-none connection.   Earliest attempts to satisfy the one-element condition (Estes, 1960) led to the use of a free recall task. Almost all subsequent work, however, utilized a paired-associate learning task. Very similar procedures were being used in an independent attack upon the assumption of all-or-none formation of associations (Rock, 1957; Rock and Heimer, 1959).

Rock's mode of attack upon the assumption of all-or-none connection had a simple directness which made it intuitively appealing. The experiment began with serial exposure of eight pairs, each composed of a syllable and a double digit, for the subject to inspect and try to learn. The inspection series was followed by a test trial in which the subject was presented only the stimulus members, one at a time, and was to recall the appropriate response to each; he received no feedback concerning the recall. If recall was correct, the pair was retained and presented again on the inspection series which followed. If a pair had not been learned (as evidenced by incorrect recall or no recall on the test trial), it was removed and replaced in the ensuing inspection trial by a new pair. A control group was run under the usual condition of alternate inspection and test series of the same eight pairs throughout. Rock found no significant difference between the experimental and control groups, either in number of trials to criterion or in total number of errors to criterion. If a given inspection presentation resulted in some increment in the strength of association between the stimulus and response members of a pair, then continued repetition of the same pair should lead to faster learning for the control subjects than for the experimental. It did not, either in Rock's experiment or in a number of careful replications by doubting colleagues (e.g., Clark, Lansford, and Dallenbach, 1960).

The Rock findings were so reliably reproducible that subsequent attacks took the form of search for hidden artifacts. One popular candidate for the role of "artifact most likely to succeed" was covert rehearsal of a pair between presentations. The issue underlying this objection is, of course, the functional definition of a trial. If a subject repeats the pair to himself after it has been presented and removed, it may be argued that he is, in effect, giving himself another trial. How many functional trials he has while the item is being presented is an obviously related question. Attempts to eliminate covert rehearsal took one of three different directions: use of less readily rehearsable stimulus material (Battig, 1962; Neimark, 1963), prevention of opportunity for rehearsal by use of highly massed trials (Lockhead, 1961), or requirement of an activity incompatible with rehearsal, such as spelling out responses at a fixed pace (Postman, 1962). To the extent that the first solution is ever attainable, it seems to have little effect, while the other two both make for significantly faster learning by the control group. In each case, however, rehearsal has been prevented by the addition of new factors which complicate the situation. With massed trials, for example, aftereffects of the immediately preceding condition probably form part of the stimulus situation on the ensuing trial. Clearly, therefore, trials are not independent and cannot be treated as though each involved the sampling of but a single element. Similarly, when responses are spelled out, an additional response integration phase seems to be added (Rock and Steinfeld, 1963). The response integration phase can also be described as an all-or-none process (Kintsch, 1963).

A second quest for artifacts focused upon item selection in the experimental group. If, for example, the list of eight pairs which the experimental group learned were an easier list than the control group list, then it could be learned in fewer trials and with fewer errors. The advantage of learning a simpler list could compensate for the disadvantage resulting from inspecting a larger total number of pairs. There were some very convincing demonstrations that the list finally learned by the experimental group is, in fact, an easier list (Underwood, Rehula, and Keppel, 1963). At this point, as Postman (1963) points out, the issue of all-or-none association would have been stalemated if the Rock technique were the only one available. Alternative courses of research provide yet another demonstration of the role of models in promoting clarification of a problem.

One of the first techniques proposed by Estes (1960) was the use of the so-called "miniature" or RTT experiment which differed from the Rock procedure by adding an additional test trial and by retaining unlearned pairs. A small number of paired associates was presented seriatim for inspection by the subject. The inspection, or R, phase was followed by two unbroken series of presentations of each stimulus member alone, TT; the subject was required to supply a response to each but received no information concerning the correctness or incorrectness of his response. The data of major interest were transition (or conditional) probabilities, frequently presented in the form of a tree diagram. The rationale is, again, straightforward. In order to predict whether the subject will give a correct response on the second trial T_2, all one needs to know, by virtue of the rationale of all Markov models, is what he did on the preceding trial, T_1. With a one-element Markov model, there are only two states in which a given item can be: either the response to it is learned or it is not. If response on the previous trial was incorrect, then presumably the response was not learned and, in the absence of additional opportunity for learning, should remain in that state on the next trial; therefore, an error should be observed. Similarly, under some circumstances, given that a correct response has been observed on T_1; then the item has been learned, and if it is not forgotten (an unlikely contingency over short intervals) or if the probability of correct guessing is zero, it should remain in that state. Thus, denoting a correct response or an error on trial n by C_n or N_n, respectively, $p(C_2|C_1) = 1$ and $p(C_2|N_1) = 0$. The predictions are, however, formulated for *states of conditioning* which are theoretical abstractions, rather than for experimentally observed responses. In an experimental task, by virtue of the requirement that response members should be well learned and readily available, subjects may achieve a correct response by chance. Given the occurrence of a C_1, therefore, we do not know whether the subject has learned the item (and is in the learned state), or has failed to learn it but has guessed correctly. To encompass the experimental realities, it is necessary to correct each prediction for guessing, with the result that $p(C_2|C_1)<1$ and $p(C_2|N_1)>0$. Furthermore, on any given R trial, the probability of transition from unlearned to learned state, customarily denoted by c, is a constant independent of the number of prior pairings. In other words, additional pairings increase the opportunities for occurrence of a transition rather than add increments to an association.

Although initial evidence (Estes, 1960, 1961) was compatible with assumptions of the model, the question arose whether the very act of measuring a response on T_1 might not effect its subsequent probability on T_2 (Estes, Hopkins, and Crothers, 1960). Although such a possibility cannot be ruled out, there is some evidence to indicate that the assumption of no effect is a satisfactory approximation (Izawa and Estes, 1965).

Other investigators (Jones, 1962; Seidel, 1963) questioned whether conditional probabilities would remain unchanged over longer series of test trials. Although the answer proved to be negative under some conditions, the data for long trial series pose additional problems of evaluation. First, there is no technique for assessing the statistical significance of apparent changes, nor is it easy to develop one in view of the fact that (a) each transition probability is based upon a different number of cases, and (b) it is difficult to estimate an appropriate correction for guessing. The first problem may be circumvented by dealing with compound probabilities (Estes, 1961) rather than transition probabilities; the second requires a change in experimental procedure. In earlier studies each stimulus was uniquely paired with a response; that is, number of pairs n was equal to the number of response alternatives k. Prior to learning, it is reasonable to assume that the probability of guessing correctly $p(g)$ is equal to $1/k$; but after the subject has learned j pairs, then $p(g) = 1/(k-j)$; and we have no way of evaluating j empirically (partly because of the problem of correcting for guessing for which we need an estimate of j). The solution adopted in most recent works (e.g., Bower, 1962) has been to employ an experimental task in which $k<n$, usually by a factor of at least 2.

Development of theoretical analyses. The approaches reviewed above have an intuitive reasonableness about them and require almost no mathematical treatment either for derivations or tests of predictions. The price of these advantages is that they leave one confronted with uncomfortable ambiguities in interpreting the data. One trend which has consistently characterized the development of all mathematical theories in psychology is the derivation of more and more specific predictions of properties of the data—for example, not only asymptotes but rates, not only means but variances. In the case of the one-element model, some statistics had been derived by Suppes and Atkinson (1960) and Estes (1961), but full-scale derivation of such details as error distributions, distributions of trials to last error, and so forth, was first accomplished by Bower (1961). To test these predictions, one could use repeated trials of a paired-associate learning task employing the time-honored method of anticipation (with the new restriction of $k<n$). In applying the model to data, parameter estimation requires the assumption that there be no individual differences among (a) items with respect to difficulty or (b) subjects with respect to learning ability. Although both assumptions are obviously indefensible in the vast majority of experimental realizations, it should be noted that both are implicitly accepted by anyone who averages data over subjects and items.

Suppes and Ginsberg (1962) focused upon the two-state property (that is, that an S–R connection either is learned or it is not) and derived statistical tests for a number of data measures which result from the binomial properties of one-element data. One resulting prediction is at once intuitively appealing and seemingly counter to all previous evidence: this is the "stationarity" property. If, with respect to a given item, a subject has either learned it or he has not, then so long as he remains in the initial state, his probability of a correct response should be attributable solely to guessing and should remain constant. An incremental view (and most people's expectations of data), on the other hand, would lead to predictions that the probability of a correct response should increase systematically prior to full learning. Underlying the stationarity test is a subtle shift in focus which has already had such profound consequences that it is worth emphasizing.

The difficulty of connecting a theoretical "learning state" and an objective response of a live subject has already been noted. Most earlier work tended to fix upon the first occurrence of a correct response as an indication that the subject was in the learned state. However, as has already been noted, a correct response can also arise through guessing. On the other hand, if the subject makes an error, it must be the case that he is still in the unlearned state. In other words, we cannot uniquely identify the trial upon which an S–R connection transfers to the learned state, but there is no difficulty in spotting an error. And on all trials up to and including the last trial on which an error occurs, the subject must necessarily be in the unlearned state.

Breaking response protocols into two parts separated by trial of occurrence of the last error is a relatively new procedure; but it has a clear theoretical rationale and it generates some dramatic empirical consequences (as shown in the papers by Suppes and Ginsberg in this chapter). Does this technique also have any deeper psychological consequences and justification? It is too recent a question for final evaluation, but on the basis of some preliminary data the answer appears to be affirmative. Kintsch (1965), for example, has found that GSR activity increases up to and including the trial of last error, whereupon it shows a sharp decrease. Prior to this type of analysis, data on GSR correlates of learning had been quite ambiguous. Similarly, Schlag-Rey, Groen, and Suppes (1965) have found systematic changes in response latency with sharp decrease after the last error. Once again, previous data (e.g., Eimas and Zeaman, 1963; Millward, 1964; Williams, 1962) had shown an apparent lack of correlation between latency and accuracy data, which was often interpreted to mean that one-element Markov models had no relevance to latency data.

Multiprocess models. One review of tests of the stationarity property (Suppes and Ginsberg, 1962) has turned up a number of instances where it is not observed. Such instances constitute a choice point for the theorist: does he abandon his basic assumptions (fear not) or does he modify them, and if so, how? The natural strategy within the general framework of stimulus sampling theory has been to explore the possibility that the failure of stationarity to obtain in any given situation signifies merely that more than one elementary process is involved. This approach is fruitful to the extent that constituent elementary processes can be identified by appropriate analysis of data from relatively complex situations. Some recent efforts in this direction have yielded promising results. For example, Kintsch (1963) has described data which prove interpretable in terms of a response integration process and an association process, each of which is all-or-none in character. In another paper Kintsch and Morris (1965) successfully break the paired-associate acquisition process into a stimulus recognition phase and an association phase. Polson, Restle, and Polson (1965) accurately describe paired-associate data with built-in similarity between some pairs by assuming two all-or-none processes: stimulus discrimination and association. In all cases, the two processes are assumed to proceed concurrently and are, to some extent, directly measurable.

A number of authors (e.g., Atkinson and Crothers, 1964; Bernbach, 1965) have assumed that although learning may be all-or-none, attainment of the state of having learned a response need not be equivalent to perfect retention of that response thereafter. Their solution is to postulate discrete short-term and long-term retention states. Friedman and Gelfand (1963) have achieved a number of accurate predictions of transfer by assuming perfect original learning, with the probability of forgetting depending on the interval between learning and testing. Still another possible complication of the basic model derives from allowing the guessing probability to change by assuming that after making an error, the subject eliminates that particular erroneous response from the pool from which responses are sampled. Thus, on the next trial probability of correct response should increase. The consequences of this assumption have been explored by Millward (1964), and by Binford and Gettys (1965).

For the most part, all such suggested modifications have been developed in order to account for the fact that the probability of correct response prior to the occurrence of last error does not always remain stationary. Recently, Polson and Greeno (1965) have suggested that stationarity need not be observed under all experimental conditions; rather, geometric distribution of total errors is a more general property of all all-or-none models and one which merits testing in future experimentation.

In still other instances, there are a priori reasons to assume that the experimental task comprises a number of "states" which may be hierarchically arranged. Models of hierarchical associative processes are not particularly difficult to develop; the trick lies in finding experimental coordinates for the intervening states. A general approach to this problem has been proposed by Greeno and Steiner (1964). A number of three-state models have already been studied and applied to data with considerable success (e.g., Bower and Theios, 1963). An example of one such application is included at the end of the present chapter.

REFERENCES

Atkinson, R. C., Bower, G. H., and Crothers, E. J. *An introduction to mathematical learning theory*. New York: Wiley, 1965.

Atkinson, R. C. and Crothers, E. J. A comparison of paired-associate learning models having different acquisition and retention axioms. *J. math. Psychol.*, 1964, **1**, 285–315.

Battig, W. F. Paired-associate learning under simultaneous repetition and non-repetition conditions. *J. exp. Psychol.*, 1962, **64**, 87–93.

Bernbach, H. A. A forgetting model for paired-associate learning. *J. math. Psychol.*, 1965, **2**, 128–144.

Binford, J. R. and Gettys, C. Nonstationarity in paired-associate learning as indicated by a second guess procedure. *J. math. Psychol.*, 1965, **2**, 190–195.

Bower, G. H. Application of a model to paired-associate learning. *Psychometrika*, 1961, **26**, 255–280.

Bower, G. H. An association model for response training variables in paired-associate learning. *Psychol. Rev.*, 1962, **69**, 34–53.

Bower, G. H. and Theios, J. A learning model for discrete performance levels. In R. C. Atkinson (Ed.), *Studies in mathematical psychology*. Stanford, California: Stanford Univ. Press, 1963, 1–14, 23–31.

Bush, R. R. and Mosteller, F. *Stochastic models for learning*. New York: Wiley, 1955.

Clark, L. L., Lansford, T. G., and Dallenbach, K. M. Repetition and associative learning. *Amer. J. Psychol.*, 1960, **73**, 22–40.

Eimas, P. D. and Zeaman, D. Response speed changes in an Estes' paired-associate "miniature" experiment. *J. verbal Learn. verbal Behav.*, 1963, **1**, 384–385.

Estes, W. K. Learning theory and the new "mental chemistry." *Psychol. Rev.*, 1960, **67**, 207–223.

Estes, W. K. New developments in statistical behavior theory: Differential tests of axioms for associative learning. *Psychometrika*, 1961, **26**, 73–84.

Estes, W. K. All-or-none processes in learning and retention. *Am. Psychol.*, 1964, **19**, 16–25.

Estes, W. K., Hopkins, B. L., and Crothers, E. J. All-or-none and conservation effects in the learning and retention of paired-associates. *J. exp. Psychol.* 1960, **60**, 329–339.

Friedman, M. P. and Gelfand, H. Transfer effects in discrimination learning. *J. math. Psychol.*, 1964, **1**, 204–214.

Greeno, J. G. and Steiner, T. Markovian processes with identifiable states: General considerations and application to all-or-none learning. *Psychometrika*, 1964, **29**, 309–333.

Izawa, C. and Estes, W. K. Reinforcement-test sequences in paired-associate learning. Tech. Rept. #76, 1965, Stanford Univ. Press, Stanford, Calif.

Jones, J. E. All-or-none vs. incremental learning. *Psychol. Rev.*, 1962, **69**, 156–160.

Kintsch, W. All-or-none learning and the role of repetition in paired-associate learning. *Science*, 1963, **140**, 310–312.

Kintsch, W. Habituation of the GSR component of the orienting reflex during paired-associate learning before and after learning has taken place. *J. math. Psychol.*, 1965, **2**, 330–341.

Kintsch, W. and Morris, C. J. Application of a Markov model to free recall and recognition. *J. exp. Psychol.*, 1965, **69**, 200–206.

Lockhead, B. R. A re-evaluation of evidence of one trial associative learning. *Am. J. Psychol.*, 1961, **74**, 590–595.

Miller, G. A. and McGill, W. J. A statistical description of verbal learning. *Psychometrika*, 1952, **17**, 369–396.

Millward, R. An all-or-none model for noncorrection routines with elimination of incorrect responses. *J. math. Psychol.*, 1964, **1**, 392–404.

Millward, R. Latency in a modified paired-associate learning experiment. *J. verbal Learn. verbal Behav.*, 1964, **3**, 309–316.

Neimark, E. D. Paired-associate learning as a function of amount of material. Paper read at Psychonomic Society, Bryn Mawr, Pa., 1963.

Polson, M. C., Restle, F., and Polson, P. G. Association and discrimination in paired-associate learning. *J. exp. Psychol.*, 1965, **69**, 49–55.

Polson, P. G. and Greeno, J. G. Nonstationarity performance before all-or-none learning. Paper read at Midwest Psychol. Assoc., Chicago, 1965.

Postman, L. Repetition and paired-associate learning. *Am. J. Psychol.*, 1962, **75**, 372–389.

Postman, L. One trial learning. In C. N. Cofer and B. Murgrave (Eds.), *Verbal behavior and learning*. New York: McGraw Hill, 1963, 295–320.

Rock, I. The role of repetition in associative learning. *Am. J. Psychol.*, 1957, **70**, 186–193.

Rock, I. and Heimer, W. Further evidence of one-trial associative learning. *Am. J. Psychol.*, 1959, **72**, 1–16.

Rock, I. and Steinfeld, G. Methodological questions in the study of one-trial learning. *Science*, 1963, **140**, 822–824.

Schlag-Rey, M., Groen, G., and Suppes, P. Latencies in last error in paired-associate learning, *Psychon. Sci.*, 1965, **2**, 15–16.

Seidel, R. J. RTT paradigm: No panacea for theories of associative learning. *Psychol. Rev.*, 1963, **70**, 565–572.

Suppes, P. and Atkinson, R. C. *Markov learning models for multiperson interactions*. Stanford, Calif.: Stanford Univ. Press, 1960.

Suppes, P. and Ginsberg, R. A fundamental property of all-or-none models, binomial distribution of responses prior to conditioning, with application to concept formation in children. *Psychol. Rev.*, 1962, **70**, 139–161.

Underwood, B. J., Rehula, R., and Keppel, G. Item selection in paired-associate learning, *Am. J. Psychol.*, 1962, **75**, 353–371.

Williams, J. P. Supplementary report: A selection artifact in Rock's study of the role of repetition. *J. exp. Psychol.*, 1961, **62**, 627–628.

All-or-None Processes in Learning and Retention[1]

William K. Estes, *Stanford University*

IF I should pull a match from my pocket and strike it, no one in the audience would be surprised at the sudden appearance of fire and smoke. The reason is not simply that we are all accustomed to predicting and controlling the behavior of matches, but rather that we have available a satisfying account of what occurs during the short interval when a bit of sulphur disappears and the air around it bursts into flame. To less civilized individuals, unprepared to visualize what happens during the kindling of a fire in terms of the breakdown of molecules into their constituents and recombination into new molecules, the same phenomenon remains a perpetual source of mystery. But despite all our sophistication concerning molecules and atoms, the situation contains fully as much mystery for us. Although we may feel that we adequately understand the lighting of the match, we can offer no comparable account of the events that occur when an individual is learning to strike one. Eliminating this conceptual blind spot is one of the tasks, indeed to my mind the principal task, of learning theory.

How may we best direct our efforts if we hope to achieve an adequate picture of the processes and events involved in any instance of learning? Simply to the industrious accumulation of parametric data? This seems rather dubious when the mazes and memory drums, the cumulative recorders and variance analyzers already are producing data at a rate well exceeding our capacity to absorb them. When our purpose is to understand a complex system, sheer quantity of information may obstruct more than it illuminates. Suppose we were set the task of comprehending the workings of a metropolitan telephone system. We would make a slow job of it if we proceeded by determining the additive and interactive effects of factorially combined

independent variables upon dollar volume of telephone bills.

Perhaps we could more strategically concentrate attention on particular types and aspects of data that seem likely to be of special diagnostic value. If, as a start in this direction, we consider analogies between properties of the learning organism and those of other organized systems that we know rather more about, such as communication networks and computing machines, we can scarcely fail to be impressed by the fact that it is of the very nature of organized systems to exhibit discontinuities—that is, sharp departures from proportionality of causes and effects. Thus locating discontinuities, despite the fact that they are normally masked by noise, i.e., experimental error, may well be one of our principal objectives. Even in our earliest efforts toward deciphering the organization of the learning process, one clear bit of evidence for a quantal change of state of the system may be of more diagnostic value than a mountain of data exhibiting gradual changes in output as a function of input.

These introductory remarks are intended, not as a prescription or admonition to anyone else, but as a brief reconstruction of the line of thinking that has led some colleagues and me to find special fascination in the uncovering of new sources of evidence for discontinuous changes in the organism's system of behavioral dispositions during learning.

The particular bit of evidence which seemed most compelling to me when I had occasion to address a division of this Association some 4 years ago (Estes, 1960) resulted from detailed analyses of the changes in response probabilities effected by a single reinforced trial in several standard learning situations. The observed pattern of changes uniformly agreed closely with that expected on the assumption of all-or-none association. The experiments were of the RTT design, that is, a single reinforcement followed by two successive unreinforced test trials. The results indicated that a single reinforcement left an item in one or the other of

[1] Preparation of this paper was supported in part by the Personnel and Training Branch, Office of Naval Research, under Contracts 908(16) with Indiana University and 225 (73) with Stanford University, and by a grant from the Carnegie Corporation of New York to Stanford University.

This article appeared in *Am. Psychol.*, 1964, **19**, 16–25.

two quite distinct states: a learned state in which the correct response had a high probability on both tests, or an unlearned state in which the correct response had only chance probability on either test.

This is not to say that the observed pattern of test data could not at the same time agree with any other conception. Alternative interpretations of data can always be produced; consequently, the massive demonstrations (see, e.g., Postman, 1963; Underwood & Keppel, 1962) that such exist in the present instance have impressed me as being useful, but not necessarily of great theoretical import. Certainly we need to find ways of purifying experimental situations: for example, in the case of paired-associate learning, by reducing individual differences in conditioning rates and differences of item difficulty. But no one investigator can do everything, and I have been inclined to leave this purification to individuals expert in the particular areas while I look in other directions that I personally find more congenial.

Sometimes one can make most rapid progress in differentiating among possible theoretical interpretations by looking for many alternative sources of evidence. If the same type of assumption continues to generate simple and satisfying accounts of results within a wide variety of situations, or in the same situation with a wide variety of variations in procedure, we naturally come to believe that the scheme is essentially correct. And long-term scientific experience seems to indicate that this is not a bad strategy even though it cannot be fully justified to the satisfaction of logicians.

When, in particular, we are engaged in analyzing the effect of a single learning trial, we can expect to obtain independent sources of evidence concerning the process involved by looking in different temporal directions from the point of reinforcement. Thus it seemed natural to follow up the studies of response shifts immediately following the reinforcement by examining the effects of events immediately *preceding* the point of reinforcement.

To the extent that the process of learning a response is basically akin to the flipping of a binary switch, we might expect the effect of a single learning trial to be relatively independent of the immediate reinforcement history. This expectation is quite in contrast with that of strong dependence which would, for example, be entailed by an interpretation in terms of thresholds and oscillation distributions of competing responses.

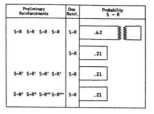

Fig. 1. Effect of a single learning trial in relation to differing reinforcement histories. (Probability of a response R to a stimulus S is assessed following five reinforcements of R, one reinforcement of R, four reinforcements of a single competing response and one of R, or one reinforcement of each of four competing responses and one reinforcement of R.)

One type of experiment designed to yield evidence pertinent to these disparate expectations is schematized in Figure 1. This experiment was conducted at Indiana University with the assistance of Judith Crooks. Forty subjects, undergraduate students, were run on two paired-associate items under each condition (the stimuli being consonant trigrams and the responses English words). The common focus for all conditions was a single reinforcement of a response to a particular stimulus followed by a test to assess the effect of the reinforcement.

For items of the type illustrated in the second row of the figure, neither the stimulus nor the response member of the item had been involved in the experiment in any way prior to this single reinforced trial. In the type shown in the first row, the only difference in procedure was that the given response was reinforced four times in the presence of the same stimulus on preceding trials so that this item had five reinforcements of the correct response prior to the test trial. Inclusion of this condition provides a baseline measure of the effectiveness of additional reinforcements of the same item.

The item type exhibited in the third row of the figure differs from the last described only in that on the four trials preceding the reinforcement of the given response R, some one different response R' was reinforced. Finally, in the fourth row is exhibited an item type for which a different competing response was reinforced on each of the preceding four trials. From the standpoint of an all-or-none conception of the associative process, the items shown in the second, third, and fourth rows are all alike in having a single opportunity for learning of the correct response immediately prior to the test trial; whereas for the type shown in the top row, the correct response has had a larger number of opportunities to become associated with the stimulus present on the test trial.

The results portrayed in the figure speak quite well for themselves. I might add that, being properly impressed with the dangers of accepting null hypotheses, we replicated the second and fourth conditions as part of a later study with a larger number of observations and obtained quite comparable results (correct response probabilities of .25 and .24 based on Ns of 160 and 320, respectively, on the test trial). The charm of these data for me is not that they confirm any one previously formulated model, or even that they raise problems for other extant theories, but that they provide a relatively direct experimental demonstration of an independence-of-path property which has hitherto been assumed in stimulus sampling theories (see, for example, Bush & Mosteller, 1955; Estes, 1959) almost solely on grounds of mathematical simplicity.

It is only natural that new information concerning all-or-none processes should often come from especially contrived experiments, such as the one just discussed. A more surprising, and in some ways even more rewarding, development of the last few years has been the uncovering of previously unsuspected, or at least undemonstrated, evidence for the existence of steady states and discontinuities in the data of standard experiments. The methods of quantitative analysis largely responsible for these findings have grown directly out of attempts to formulate mathematical models of the associative process based on assumptions derived, in part, from the "one-trial" experiments.

Individuals who have been imprinted in the classical tradition of schools and systems of psychology seem to have almost insuperable difficulty in appreciating the function of models in this type of research enterprise. According to the conventional view, a model is chosen to represent a theoretical position; then the representatives of different positions are pitted against each other in crucial experiments, the winner being "accepted" and the losers fading gracefully into oblivion, all much in the spirit of a Miss America contest.

But for those who actually use them in scientific research, the function of models is quite different. The set of theoretical ideas suggested by an array of experimental facts can never be adequately represented by any one formal model. On the contrary, to bring originally vague and incompletely defined theoretical notions to fruition, it is necessary to go through a series of successive approximations. At each stage, a specific, usually highly simplified and idealized realization of the general assumptions, that is, a particular mathematical model, is examined for its theoretical implications, its successes or shortcomings in describing data, its suggestiveness in guiding further experimental and quantitative analysis.

Since standard learning situations characteristically (perhaps universally) include important sources of variation in performance other than the effects of the reinforcing operation, raw data can be expected to reveal the outlines of underlying behavioral processes only if examined on the viewing screen, so to speak, of a model which selectively filters signal from noise. Thus, in the case of all-or-none learning theory, a major step conceptually, though a minor one from a mathematical viewpoint, was the formulation of what has been termed the one-element model.

The mathematical formalism of the one-element model evolved independently in the hands of several different investigators: Bower (1961a), Bush and Mosteller (1959); Estes, Hopkins, and Crothers (1960). But it was Bower who first saw the full potentiality of the model for analyzing verbal learning experiments and spelled out its implications in such detail as to make it a workable tool of analysis.

The assumptions of this model are illustrated in Figure 2. The graph represents probability of correct response versus number of training trials for a number of individual subjects. It is assumed for simplicity that all subjects begin at the same initial level of correct response probability (operant level, or guessing rate), and that on each training trial the subject has some fixed probability of having his correct response probability jump from the initial level to unity. Because of the probabilistic nature of the process, different subjects jump to unity on different trials. Thus if data are pooled for a group of subjects, even though all have identical initial levels and identical probabilities of conditioning on each trial, a curve representing proportion of correct responses per trial should average

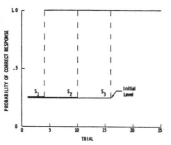

FIG. 2. Illustrative learning functions for individual subjects as conceived in the one-element model.

out to something like the familiar growth curve. In some experiments the initial level of response probability may be expected to be zero; but in many, for example multiple-choice or paired-associate experiments, the initial probability of a correct response by guessing may have some value other than unity, frequently simply the reciprocal of the number of available response alternatives.

Some predictions derivable from this simple model are immediately obvious upon consideration of the assumptions; others are not so obvious until one has done some actual calculations and may even be missed by experts. In Figure 3 we show a sample of predictions derivable from the model. Assuming that all subjects start from an initial response probability of .25 and the probability of forming a correct association is .50 on each trial, we readily derive the mean curve for proportion of correct responses per trial which is shown as the heavy line, and which has the form that we anticipated.

The probability that a correct response will occur on any trial if the given subject made an incorrect response to the same item on the preceding trial is constant, as indicated by the horizontal dashed line toward the bottom of the graph. This prediction follows from the model, of course, only if experimental conditions and previous experience of the subjects are such that there are no learning-to-learn effects which would cause the probability of conditioning to change over trials. In the upper part of the graph is shown the curve representing probability of correct recalls as a function of trials, that is, the probability that a correct response to a given stimulus on one trial will be followed by a correct response to the same stimulus on the next

trial. This result is of special interest because many investigators have believed it intuitively evident that this function should be constant over trials; and, in fact, data which follow quite nicely the trend of the dashed line in the figure have been taken to refute the one-element learning model. Such quaint illogicalities point up quite sharply the need for checking our intuitive ideas as to the consequences of theoretical assumptions by embodying the assumptions in specific models and deriving their implications by exact methods.

Finally, at the top of the graph, is shown the function representing probability of correct response on any trial given that it has been correct on the entire sequence of preceding trials; this function again has sometimes been assumed by the unwary to be constant if the one-element model holds; but that is true only in the special case when the initial level of response probability is zero. In all other cases, one has, following the first reinforced trial, a mixture of subjects who are attaining correct responses by guessing and subjects who have learned; as trials proceed, the balance shifts in the direction of the latter, thus giving rise to the rising curve for probability of correct recalls.

Now, having a model clearly formulated, what should we do with it? Proceed to apply it to various experiments with the plan of retaining it as long as it succeeds and rejecting it upon the first failure? This course would entail an absurd waste of time, for we can be certain in advance that no simple model will fit all sets of data even within a relatively limited area.

It is, however, of interest to see whether the model fits any data at all. Even the laws of mo-

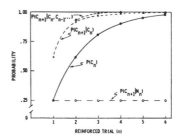

FIG. 3. Theoretical functions derivable from the one-element model, the indicated statistic in each case representing data pooled over subjects on each trial. (The conditioning parameter is taken equal to .50.)

TABLE 1

BOWER VERBAL DISCRIMINATION DATA COMPARED WITH
PREDICTIONS FROM ONE-ELEMENT MODEL

Error distribution

	M	SD
Observed	1.99	1.94
Predicted	($c = .25$)	1.98

Reset on error[a]

n	1	2	3	4	5	Aver.
Observed	1.52	1.40	1.56	1.46	1.48	1.48
Predicted	1.49———(constant)———→1.49					

Constancy of learning parameter[b]

k	1	2	3	4–5
p	.60	.62	.56	.60

Precriterion stationarity[c]

	First half	Second half
Observed	.492	.521
Predicted	.500	.500

[a] Mean errors to criterion after error on trial n.
[b] Proportion correct on trial following k successive errors.
[c] Proportion correct over precriterion sequence.

tion rarely provide highly accurate predictions of the behavior of real objects; but in specially contrived situations, where perfect vacuums and frictionless planes are approximately realized, the Newtonian model comes off well enough to convince us that its abstract properties represent more than figments of our imagination.

In the case of the one-element model the first thorough-going applications were made by Gordon Bower (1961a, 1961b, 1962) and with successes far exceeding any expectations that I, at least, would have considered realistic.

A small sample of data from one of Bower's studies (1961b) is summarized in Table 1. The situation giving rise to the results summarized here was a simple verbal discrimination learning task, in which the materials were cards each containing a pair of nonsense syllables, one of which was arbitrarily designated as correct; and the subject's task on each trial was to guess which member of the pair shown on the given trial was correct. With knowledge of results following each correct or incorrect guess, subjects continued to cycle through the cards until they reached a criterion of correct performance. Estimating the value of the conditioning parameter, c, that is the probability that an association between stimulus and correct response would occur on a given trial for a given item, from the observed mean total errors, Bower proceeded to predict quantitative values for numerous statistics of the data. An example, shown on the top line of Table 1, is the prediction of the standard deviation of total errors per item. Investigators who are familiar by much experience with the difficulties of predicting variances as opposed to means may be somewhat impressed by the correspondence between the predicted and observed values. Similar agreement was found by Bower for a large number of statistics, including distribution of trials before the first success, frequencies of error runs of various lengths, and autocorrelations of errors with various lags.

Some additional results which point up particular aspects of the model are shown in the remainder of this table. The heading "reset on error" refers to the important property of the one-element model that the entire process starts over after each error. That is, the occurrence of an error on any trial signifies that up to that point no learning has occurred for that subject on that item. Consequently it is predicted that such statistics as mean errors to criterion after an error on trial n should be constant over trials. For the present data we can even see readily what the constant value should be. Since mean observed total errors, shown at the top, were 1.99, and the probability of an error on the first trial before the subject had received any reinforcements must have been .50 on the average, we can subtract the .50 from the total of 1.99 and arrive at a prediction of 1.49 for the constant mean errors to criterion following an error on any trial. The observed values seem to vary around this prediction with little indication of any systematic trend. If it is the case not only that learning is occurring on an all-or-none basis but that probability of learning is constant over trials, then the proportion of correct responses on any trial following a sequence of preceding errors should be independent of the number of preceding errors. The next to last row of the table shows the value of this proportion following one, two, three, etc., successive preceding errors (the data for 4 and 5 preceding errors being pooled since the number of cases was falling off).

The remaining type of analysis represented in the table arises from a valuable insight growing out of the reset-on-error property. The gist of the idea, developed fully by Suppes and Ginsberg (1963), is that despite the fact that one cannot observe directly the point at which learning occurs, one can define unequivocally a last point before which learning certainly has not occurred if the one-element model holds. Referring to the illustrative protocols in Figure 4, one can see that this critical point in each protocol is the trial of the last error. If the learning process is correctly described by the model, then on all trials prior to the last error, the subject's responses are in effect being generated by a Bernoulli process with all the properties of coin tossing. Correct responses and errors during this precriterion sequence should occur at random with constant probability (not necessarily one-half except in certain two-choice situations) and independence from trial to trial. Thus cogent evidence concerning the existence of an initial steady state of random responding in any situation may be obtained by analyzing individual protocols, locating the last error in each, and performing various analyses on the data of the precriterion sequence.

One of the coarsest, though at the same time most intuitively appealing, of these analyses is a test for precriterion stationarity, that is, constancy of the probability of correct responding over the precriterion sequence, illustrated in the remaining section of the table for Bower's data. Because learning was rather rapid, the data have been pooled into observed and predicted proportions of correct responses in the first and second halves of

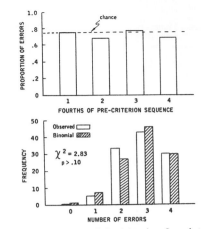

FIG. 5. Precriterion analysis of data from Suppes' study of the learning of mathematical proofs by a group of 50 young children. (The upper diagram exhibits relative constancy of error probability; the lower diagram compares the distribution of error frequencies per four-trial block with the corresponding binomial distribution.)

the precriterion sequence. Departures from the predicted constancy at .5 do not seem great.

Many other results comparable to these have been reported during the last 2 or 3 years. Following are a few illustrations showing some of the situations in which these results arise. Figure 5 shows an analysis of precriterion data from an experiment by Suppes on the learning of mathematical proofs by young school children.[2] The upper portion of the figure shows the constancy of proportion of errors over successive fourths of the precriterion sequence predicted by the one-element model; the lower panel shows close agreement between the data and the binomial distribution of different numbers of errors predicted when data are pooled by four-trial blocks over the entire precriterion sequence. Up to the point when they are able to give several correct responses in a row, the behavior of these children in trying to provide successive steps of proofs in a miniature logical system are much like the data that would be obtained by tossing so many biased pennies.

In Figure 6 are shown data from a study of concept identification (Trabasso, 1963). This figure

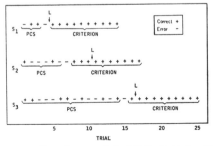

FIG. 4. Illustrative protocols for individual subjects, with the precriterion sequence (PCS), the point of learning (L), and the criterion sequence indicated for each.

[2] I am indebted to Patrick Suppes for making available these unpublished data.

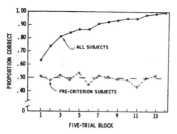

FIG. 6. Learning curve averaged over all subjects and items and curve representing precriterion data only, from Trabasso's (1963) study of concept identification.

shows the dramatic contrast between the curve representing proportion of correct responses per trial block for all subjects over all trials and the plot for the same statistic limited to data from precriterion sequences. Whereas the overall mean curve rises steadily and smoothly, the proportion of correct responses per trial block is about as constant as one could ask for over the precriterion sequences. These data are of especial interest since it has sometimes been suggested that data conforming to predictions from all-or-none models arise only in situations where learning is very rapid; it can be seen that in this situation learning was rather slow, yet precriterion stationarity was nicely realized.

I shall not go on giving examples of all but perfect fits of the one-element model to data because these, although perhaps impressive, cease being particularly instructive.

For an example of a case in which a rather interesting deviation occurs, we may consider Figure 7,

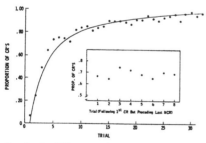

FIG. 7. Acquisition curve for eyelid conditioning data. (The inset shows stationarity of conditioned response proportion on trials following the first CR, but preceding the last non-CR.)

which shows pooled data from a series of eyelid conditioning experiments with human subjects.[3] The curve for proportion of conditioned responses per trial is again nicely negatively accelerated, but this time, when a stationarity analysis is performed, it is found immediately that proportion of correct responses does *not* remain constant over the precriterion sequence; rather the curve exhibits a steady rise, thus showing at once that the one-element model cannot give an adequate representation of the data. However, upon further analysis, stationarity reappears in a rather interesting way. If we truncate the precriterion sequence by considering only trials following the first conditioned response for each subject, then, as shown in the inset, the proportion of correct responses per trial

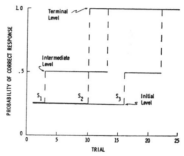

FIG. 8. Illustrative learning functions for individual subjects as conceived in three-state model.

is found to be relatively stationary between the first conditioned response and the last precriterion trial.

A similar observation had been made previously by Theios (1963), working with data from rats in an avoidance situation, and led him to consider the extension of the one-element model illustrated in Figure 8. Here each subject begins at some initial level of response probability and learning occurs by discrete jumps, but subjects may go to an intermediate level before going to the final level of perfect performance. Bower and Theios (1963) investigated the properties of this three-state model and found that predictions from it provided excel-

[3] This analysis was made possible by the cooperation of I. Gormezano, who provided protocols from a series of studies conducted in his laboratory. For the details of apparatus and procedure, see Moore and Gormezano (1961).

lent accounts of the data from the learning of rats in a shuttle box and also of the data on eyelid conditioning from which the preceding illustration was drawn.[4]

Now what is one to conclude from results such as these concerning "one-trial versus incremental learning"? The learning can scarcely be characterized as "one trial," and thus I suppose some will be happy simply to label it as "incremental" and let the matter rest. But if our interest is in understanding the behavior rather than in defending a position, we may wish to pursue the fact that this evidence points to the existence of all-or-none processes even in cases where the structure of the learning process is evidently more complex than that of simple paired-associate or verbal discrimination learning.

From even the brief sketch I have been able to give here, I think it must be evident that the investigators currently working constructively with notions of all-or-none learning have not formed a committee to set down a new theory. Rather they have been largely preoccupied with the always rewarding business of following up some unexpectedly fruitful research leads. At the same time a body of new theory has begun to take form, although only irregularly, and jagged in outline, much like the crystallization of rock candy in a saturated sugar solution. At some stage in this process one begins to raise questions of a broader character than those having to do with the ability of specific models to fit specific data. In particular, one may begin to wonder whether a body of theory based on all-or-none conceptions could ever be extended and elaborated enough to guide research on forms of learning more complex than conditioning and verbal association without becoming unwieldly and unmanageable.

Some recent researches suggest that, to the contrary, theory based on stimulus sampling and all-or-none association may offer some special virtues

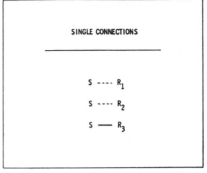

SINGLE CONNECTIONS

S ---- R_1

S ---- R_2

S —— R_3

Fig. 9. Schema for stimulus-response associations according to the one-element pattern model. (Effective reinforcement of response R_3 to pattern S establishes an association—heavy line—supplanting the associations previously existing between S and R_1 or R_2.)

in this respect. The one-element process, abstracted from the original context, may constitute a conceptual pattern which can be identified by similar methods at many different levels of behavioral organization.

The first few published studies involving new techniques for revealing all-or-none acquisition have, understandably, dealt only with simple, unitary responses (usually spoken letters or digits) to discrete stimulus patterns. In Figure 9 is shown the paradigm for individual learned associations assumed in applications of the one-element pattern model at this elementary level of behavioral organization. A stimulus pattern S can be conditioned to one response at a time only. Thus, if first R_1, then R_2, then R_3 were successively reinforced in the presence of S, only the last would remain conditioned. On a test trial at the end of this training sequence, R_3 would be evoked, and no trace of the earlier learned experiences could be detected.

Considered outside the limited context of paired-associate experiments, this last property of the model is not very palatable. We know, for example, that an individual often can recognize a previously learned, correct response to a stimulus even when he can no longer supply the response when presented with the stimulus alone. An earlier suggestion on my part (Estes, 1960) that association theory should allow for the learning and unlearning of recognition and recall responses as

[4] The intermediate state of conditioned response probability has a natural interpretation in stimulus sampling theory (Atkinson & Estes, 1963) on the assumption that the stimulus situation associated with onset of the CS overlaps only in part with the stimulus situation existing at the point of reinforcement (onset of the US). Theios and Bower's analyses bear out the prediction that, although the organism has constant probability of leaving the initial, "unlearned," state on any reinforced trial, it can go from the intermediate to the terminal state only on a trial when the conditioned response occurs at CS onset.

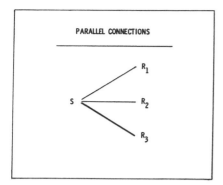

PARALLEL CONNECTIONS

FIG. 10. Schema permitting coexisting associations (light lines) between a stimulus pattern, S, and successively reinforced responses, R_1, R_2, and R_3. (The tendency to recall, or retrieve, a previously learned association—represented by the heavy line—is assumed to be governed by an independent, one-element learning process.)

independent, even though often correlated, processes has met a chorus of complaints about lack of parsimony (see, e.g., Postman, 1963), parsimony being identified with the conception of a unitary underlying construct of associative strength. However, I believe that in this instance the lack of parsimony is in the organism, rather than in the theory.

Numerous considerations [6] suggest modification of the unitary-connection schema to the one illustrated in Figure 10 for the same sequence of events as that of Figure 9. Here the lighter lines represent associations established by earlier reinforcements of R_1 and R_2 (the one to the last reinforced response, R_3, being masked). These associations may be demonstrable by suitable procedures, e.g., recognition tests, even after R_3 has later been learned to the same stimulus. The heavy line represents an association between the stimulus and the response of recalling (selecting, emitting, retrieving) a particular one of the previously reinforced responses upon presentation of the stimulus. In this conception, the formation of each of the associations and the "switching" of the recall, or retrieval tendency, from one response to another are independent one-element processes. A currently ac-

[6] Including recent work on information storage and retrieval in relation to short-term memory (Broadbent, 1958; Sternberg, 1963) and on nonassociative factors in recall (Asch & Ebenholtz, 1962).

tive line of research in my laboratory is concerned with the experimental separation of these processes (DaPolito, Casseday, Kegel, McCollum, & Estes, 1961; Estes, 1964).

Departing in another direction from the elementary schema of Figure 9, we encounter numerous possible levels of response complexity: The behavior segment which is counted as a single "response" in a learning experiment may be a single spoken digit, a multisyllable word in a new or artificial language, a combination of words, a rule or strategy. When a learning situation involves both the development of a relatively complex response unit and the association of this unit with particular cues or stimulus properties, one must expect that, regardless of the nature of the learning process, the probability of "correct responses" will change gradually over learning trials. However, some current researches are yielding encouraging signs of progress toward analyzing such complex forms of learning into simpler constituent processes. For example, the development of response compounds via the chaining of initially distinct component responses has been investigated by Crothers (1962, 1963) and the formation of chains of observing and instrumental responses by Atkinson (1961). In each of these instances, evidence has been forthcoming in support of the notion that the constituent associative processes conform to the one-element, all-or-none model. Once established, even complex response chains, rules, or strategies (Restle, 1962, 1963) may become associated with, or dissociated from, stimulus patterns on an all-or-none basis.

From the general tenor of this report, you might suspect that I think of *all* learning in terms of the pyramiding and branching of simple component all-or-none processes. This would not be far from the truth. But at the same time, I hasten to add, I have no intention of giving up such time tested theoretical devices as linear operator models (Bush & Mosteller, 1955; Estes & Suppes, 1959) even though these are based on different underlying conceptions. However much we might prefer things to be otherwise, learning, as measured by available techniques, appears sometimes to be an essentially continuous, sometimes a sharply discontinuous process. Thus in current research we need models suitable to represent both kinds of data, while we await further evidence to determine which aspect is the more fundamental and which the derivative.

There may turn out to be no basic inconsistencies between what at present appear to be extremely different mathematical models. This will, for example, be the case if we find that in situations involving numerous concurrent one-element processes, the overall functioning of the system should be expected to conform approximately to a continuous model.

While awaiting more definitive clues concerning underlying properties, I myself have come to operate on the working assumption that all instances of apparently incremental changes in behavioral dispositions during learning are simply cases of incomplete analysis. I am well aware that this assumption is untestable in a formal sense. Nonetheless, by following through its implications for a variety of learning situations, we are beginning to evolve quantitative techniques which may even come to rival the scalpel and the electrode as tools for exploring the organization of behavior.

REFERENCES

ASCH, S. E., & EBENHOLTZ, S. M. The process of free recall: Evidence for non-associative factors in acquisition and retention. *J. Psychol.*, 1962, 54, 3–31.

ATKINSON, R. C. The observing response in discrimination learning. *J. exp. Psychol.*, 1961, 62, 253–262.

ATKINSON, R. C., & ESTES, W. K. Stimulus sampling theory. In R. D. Luce, E. Galanter, & R. R. Bush (Eds.), *Handbook of mathematical psychology*. Vol. 2. New York: Wiley, 1963. Pp. 121–268.

BOWER, G. H. Application of a model to paired-associate learning. *Psychometrika*, 1961, 26, 255–280. (a)

BOWER, G. H. All-or-none theory applied to verbal discrimination learning. *Amer. Psychologist*, 1961, 6, 466. (b) (Abstract)

BOWER, G. H. A model for response and training variables in paired-associate learning. *Psychol. Rev.*, 1962, 69, 34–53.

BOWER, G. H., & THEIOS, J. A learning model for discrete performance levels. In R. C. Atkinson (Ed.), *Studies in mathematical psychology*. Stanford: Stanford Univer. Press, 1963. Pp. 1–31.

BROADBENT, D. E. *Perception and communication*. London: Pergamon Press, 1958.

BUSH, R. R., & MOSTELLER, F. *Stochastic models for learning*. New York: Wiley, 1955.

BUSH, R. R., & MOSTELLER, F. A comparison of eight models. In R. R. Bush & W. K. Estes (Eds.), *Studies in mathematical learning theory*. Stanford: Stanford Univer. Press, 1959. Pp. 293–307.

CROTHERS, E. J. Paired-associate learning with compound response. *J. verb. Learn. verb. Behav.*, 1962, 1, 66–70.

CROTHERS, E. J. All-or-none paired-associate learning with compound responses. In R. C. Atkinson (Ed.), *Studies in mathematical psychology*. Stanford: Stanford Univer. Press, 1963. Pp. 95–115.

DAPOLITO, F., CASSEDAY, J., KEGEL, P., McCOLLUM, K., & ESTES, W. K. Acquisition of paired-associates under differential instructions with recall and recognition tests. Paper read at Midwestern Psychological Association, Chicago, May 1961.

ESTES, W. K. Component and pattern models with Markovian interpretations. In R. R. Bush & W. K. Estes (Eds.), *Studies in mathematical learning theory*. Stanford: Stanford Univer. Press, 1959. Pp. 9–52.

ESTES, W. K. Learning theory and the new "mental chemistry." *Psychol. Rev.*, 1960, 67, 207–223.

ESTES, W. K. Information storage in behavior. In R. W. Gerard (Ed.), *Proceedings of symposium on information processing in the nervous system*. Amsterdam: Excerpta Medica Foundation, 1964, in press.

ESTES, W. K., HOPKINS, B. L., & CROTHERS, E. J. All-or-none and conservation effects in the learning and retention of paired-associates. *J. exp. Psychol.*, 1960, 60, 329–339.

ESTES, W. K., & SUPPES, P. Foundations of linear models. In R. R. Bush & W. K. Estes (Eds.), *Studies in mathematical learning theory*. Stanford: Stanford Univer. Press, 1959. Pp. 137–179.

MOORE, J. W., & GORMEZANO, I. Yoked comparisons of instrumental and classical eyelid conditioning. *J. exp. Psychol.*, 1961, 62, 552–559.

POSTMAN, L. One trial learning. In C. N. Cofer & B. S. Musgrave (Eds.), *Verbal behavior and learning*. New York: McGraw-Hill, 1963. Pp. 295–320.

RESTLE, F. The selection of strategies in cue learning. *Psychol. Rev.*, 1962, 69, 329–343.

RESTLE, F. Sources of difficulty in learning paired-associates. In R. C. Atkinson (Ed.), *Studies in mathematical psychology*. Stanford: Stanford Univer. Press, 1963. Pp. 116–172.

THEIOS, J. Simple conditioning as two-stage all-or-none learning. *Psychol. Rev.*, 1963, 70, 403–417.

TRABASSO, T. R. Stimulus emphasis and all-or-none learning in concept identification. *J. exp. Psychol.*, 1963, 65, 398–406.

STERNBERG, S. Retrieval from recent memory: Some reaction-time experiments and a search theory. Paper read at Psychonomic Society, Bryn Mawr, Pennsylvania, August 1963.

SUPPES, P., & GINSBERG, ROSE. A fundamental property of all-or-none models, binomial distribution of responses prior to conditioning, with application to concept formation in children. *Psychol. Rev.*, 1963, 70, 139–161.

UNDERWOOD, B. J., & KEPPEL, G. One-trial learning? *J. verb. Learn. verb. Behav.*, 1962, 1, 1–13.

All-or-None and Conservation Effects in the Learning and Retention of Paired Associates[1]

W. K. Estes, B. L. Hopkins, and E. J. Crothers, *Indiana University*

Tacitly in the functionalist approach (McGeoch & Irion, 1952) and explicitly in the more formalized theories (Estes, 1959a; Gibson, 1940; Hull, 1943; Hull, Hovland, Ross, Hall, Perkins, & Fitch, 1940; Spence, 1955) it has been assumed that simple associative learning proceeds by a gradual increase in the strengths of stimulus-response associations over a series of reinforced trials. This "incremental" assumption, with its implication that the probability of a correct response on the part of an individual S should be increased by each reinforcement, seems to be incorporated almost routinely into each new learning model that appears (e.g., Bourne & Restle, 1959; Bush & Mosteller, 1955; Luce, 1959).

As might be expected in the case of such a widely held conception, the empirical basis of the incremental

assumption does not lack breadth. Nevertheless, it may not be quite solid, for at both the theoretical and experimental levels, small fissures have appeared. Some refractory problems having to do with rates and asymptotes of discrimination learning (Estes, 1959a) led the writer a number of years ago to consider a modified statistical model for learning in which the total pattern of stimulation occurring on a given trial is assumed to become associated with the reinforced response on an all-or-none basis (Estes, 1959b). The purpose of the present study is to provide a differential test of the "pattern model" against the class of models predicated on the incremental assumption.

Working in a different context, Rock (1957) has recently brought forward data which appear to challenge the incremental assumption, at least for paired-associate learning. Rock used a novel procedure in which incorrect items were dropped from the list and replaced with new ones following each presentation cycle. If the missed items were "partially learned," then Ss learning under this

[1] The first author is responsible for the planning and interpretation of the study and for the present report. The second author collaborated in Exp. I and the third author, whose participation was made possible by a grant from the Ford Foundation, collaborated in Exp. II.

This article appeared in *J. exp. Psychol.*, 1960, **60**, 329–339.

167

condition would be handicapped in comparison with conventional controls, but Rock found no difference in rate of learning under the two conditions. However, the interpretation of Rock's findings is complicated by the fact that the items eliminated under his procedure are probably more difficult to learn on the average than the items that replace them. In the hope of clarifying this somewhat perplexing situation, Exp. I of the present study was designed to attack the same problem with a method which would permit simpler controlled comparisons relative to the effects of single reinforced trials upon individual Ss. Once this had been accomplished, it became apparent that the technique contrived to investigate possible all-or-none effects in acquisition could be extended to do the same for retention; Exp. II of this study is addressed to the latter problem.

EXPERIMENT I

The observed result of a single paired-associate trial is to increase the relative frequency of correct responses. With the 8-item list used in this study, the initial probability of a correct response to any item is at most .125. Under the conditions used, the effect of a single reinforcement (paired presentation of stimulus and response members of an item[2]) is to raise the relative frequency of

[2] To avoid confusion in the sequel, it should be emphasized that this definition of "reinforcement" is different from the definition in terms of "correct anticipation" that has been used, e.g., by Underwood (1954). The latter is inapplicable under the conditions of the present study since the test with the stimulus member of an item does not occur in temporal contiguity with the paired stimulus-response presentation, and learning, as measured in terms of frequency of correct responding, increases as a function of paired presentations, not as a function of preceding test trials.

correct responses to approximately .5 for a group of Ss. The first question to be raised is which of the following interpretations is more nearly correct with reference to any given item: (a) the probability of a correct response is now .5 for each S, or (b) the probability of a correct response is now unity for half the Ss and zero (or at least no greater than chance) for the remainder. To distinguish between these alternatives, a single reinforced trial will be followed by a test and then, without intervening reinforcement, a second test. The design may be represented as

$$R \quad T \quad T$$

where R denotes a single exposure of each stimulus-response pair in the list and T an exposure of each stimulus alone. If the first interpretation is correct, then correct and incorrect responses on the first test should be followed about equally often by correct responses on the second test. If the second interpretation is correct, the relative frequency of correct responses on the second test should be greater following correct responses on the first test than following incorrect responses on the first test. In the latter case, if there were no retention loss, the probability of correct following correct should be unity; forgetting would reduce this value by an amount that cannot be specified in advance. The probability of correct following incorrect is critical: according to (a) it must be greater than chance whereas according to (b) it must not.

As a control measure, the design will be completed by giving each S additional items with the paradigm

$$R \quad T \quad R \quad T$$

permitting evaluation of the effect of a second reinforcement upon items which do not yield correct responses on the first test.

Method

Subjects and apparatus.—The Ss were 48 students from introductory psychology classes at Indiana University who served as part of a course requirement.

From S's view the apparatus appeared as an 18 × 18-in. gray panel containing two windows. The windows, each $2\frac{1}{2}$ in. wide by $1\frac{1}{2}$ in. high, were located $8\frac{1}{4}$ in. from the top of the panel and centered 1 in. apart horizontally. Each window was fitted with semisilvered glass, and behind each was a light-tight compartment containing two 110-v., 6-w. lamps which were turned on and off by means of a cam timer. The room was illuminated by a 60-w. lamp so placed above and behind S's chair that S could not see through the windows when the compartment lights were off but could read typewritten material located 1 in. behind a window when its compartment lights were on.

The materials presented for paired-associate learning were two lists of eight consonant syllable-number pairs. The responses were the numbers 1 through 8 for each list. The syllables were randomly drawn sets of three consonants. Each pair was typed in elite type on a 5 × 8-in. white card and spaced so that when the card was in position behind the panel the syllable was centered behind the window on S's left and the number behind the window on S's right.

Procedure.—At the beginning of a session, S was seated before the exposure panel and given instructions to the effect that (*a*) on each practice trial both members of a pair would be shown; (*b*) S's task was to learn to associate the appropriate number with each set of letters; (*c*) every so often, there would be test trials on which only the letters

TABLE 1

FREQUENCIES OF CORRECT (C) AND INCORRECT (N) RESPONSES ON TEST TRIALS 1 AND 2

One Reinforcement		Two Reinforcements	
T_1	T_2	T_1	T_2
C 188	C 133 N 55	C 155	C 134 N 21
N 196	C 18 N 178	N 229	C 106 N 123

TABLE 2

OBSERVED AND THEORETICAL (PATTERN MODEL) PROPORTIONS OF C ON TEST 2 GIVEN C OR N ON TEST 1

	One Reinforcement		Two Reinforcements	
	Observed	Theory	Observed	Theory
$C_2:C_1$	.71	.87	.86	.85
$C_2:N_1$	.09	.12	.46	.40

were shown, and S was to give the numbers from memory if possible; (*d*) on test trials S was to guess if not sure of the correct number.

For each list, S was given two practice trials and two test trials. On the first practice trial, all eight pairs were presented in a random order. Then the first test trial was given, all eight syllables being presented in a new random order. On the second practice trial, only four pairs were shown. Then on the second test trial, all eight syllables were presented in a new random order. The four pairs presented on the second practice trial were randomly selected for pairs of Ss, one S of the pair being presented with the selected four pairs and the other S being presented with the four pairs withheld from his "partner." The same procedure was used for both lists, the order of presentation of the lists being counterbalanced over Ss.

On practice trials, both windows were illuminated for 4 sec., then neither was illuminated during the 4-sec. interpair interval. On test trials, the left window, exposing the syllable alone, was illuminated for 4 sec., then neither window was illuminated during the 4-sec. interpair interval. There was a pause of 1 min. between lists.

Results

Response frequencies pooled over Ss and lists for each test trial are presented in Table 1. The data for the items having only one reinforcement are of principal interest. Nearly 50% of these were correct on the first test and nearly 40% on the second test. Proportions of cases in which items correct (C) or noncorrect, including omissions, (N) on the first test had correct responses on the second test are shown in Table 2. The notation $C_2:C_1$ is to be read "correct on Test 2 given that the item was correct on Test 1," and $C_2:N_1$ "correct on Test 2 given that the item was not correct on Test 1." The observed difference between these two proportions is so large as to make wholly untenable the hypothesis that probabilities of correct responses were raised to approximately .5 by the single reinforcement for all Ss and items. Still more difficult to reconcile with an incremental assumption is the observation that the proportion for $C_2:N_1$ is even smaller than the .125 that could be achieved if Ss guessed at all unlearned items, using all of the response numbers with equal probabilities.

The simplest interpretation of this result would seem to be that in the case of items not correct on Test 1 the reinforcement had had no strengthening effect whatsoever. Several possible objections to this interpretation should be considered. Since Ss may not always have guessed when they did not know the correct answers, the guessing allowance of .125 may be too high. Also, it should be noted that if Ss had a strong tendency to repeat particular errors, the result would be a reduction in the proportion of C following N responses. These points can be taken care of by a new analysis using only items having incorrect responses (excluding omissions) on Test 1 and different responses (again excluding omissions) on Test 2. For these items, a proportion of .14 correct responses would be the chance expectation on Test 2. If it were the case either that the items incorrect on Test 1 were partially learned or that Ss restricted their guesses on Test 2 to the response members of unlearned items, then the proportion correct would be greater than .14. The observed proportion, based on 121 observations, was .13.

Other objections might be based on the possibility that the instances of C responses on Test 1 represent either markedly easier items or Ss of much greater learning ability than instances of N responses on Test 1. The possibility of differential learning rates can be investigated quite directly. The instances of $C_2:N_1$ were scattered over 17 different Ss. Computing the proportion of C responses on Test 1 and also the proportion $C_2:C_1$ for these Ss yields values of .44 and .70, respectively. Comparing these with the corresponding values of .49 and .71 obtained for the full group of 48 Ss, one must conclude that individual differences could have played no significant role in generating the row differences appearing in Table 2. If differences in item difficulty were an important factor, then for the twice reinforced items having N responses on Test 1 we should find that the second reinforcement, given prior to Test 2, would produce only a small increment in probability of correct response as compared to the effect of the first reinforcement upon this probability in the full population of items. However, Table 2 shows the proportion $C_2:N_1$ to be .46 for the twice-reinforced items. Since the same set of items that yielded this proportion of .46 correct after the second reinforcement had manifested no greater than a chance probability of correct response after the first reinforcement, there appears to be no support here for a hypothesis involving important differences in difficulty between the items having C and those having N responses on Test 1.

These analyses having revealed no evidence of any artifact that could account for the observed pattern of response proportions, we are left with no prepossessing alternative to an interpretation in terms of all-or-none acquisition.

In one respect, however, our data do not fit the conventional picture of all-or-none learning; for, once a correct response has occurred to a given item, it does not inevitably recur on the next test trial. This observation of less than perfect retention may mean that an association learned on a reinforced trial does not necessarily stay learned over a subsequent series of rest intervals and unreinforced tests. But before this conclusion can be justified, the contribution of guessing shrinkage must be evaluated. If on both tests, Ss guessed on unlearned items, then apparent forgetting would occur in cases when responses to particular items were correct by chance on the first test but not on the second. To provide a basis for appraising this factor, the theoretical values shown in Table 2 have been calculated from the "pattern model" mentioned above. The pertinent assumptions are simply that on each reinforced trial each unlearned item has some fixed probability c of being learned and that learned items always yield correct responses on subsequent tests. With the boundary condition that unlearned items have probability $\frac{1}{8}$ of yielding correct responses on test trials, for an 8-item list, we can estimate the parameter c from the observed proportions of correct responses on the first test. For the singly reinforced items, for example, this proportion was .49, from which we obtain

$$.49 = c + (1 - c)\tfrac{1}{8}$$
$$c = \frac{.365}{.875} = .42$$

A similar determination for the twice reinforced items yields a value of .31 for c, the difference between the two estimates being presumably attributable to sampling error.

Using these estimates of the conditioning probability, the values shown in Table 2 were calculated for the conditional probabilities of $C_2:C_1$ and $C_2:N_1$ for the once- and twice-reinforced items. It appears that both theoretical values are quite satisfactory for the twice reinforced items, suggesting that the model represents the learning process quite well when further reinforcements following the first test are available to offset any retention losses. For the once reinforced items, the predicted probability of $C_2:N_1$ is close to the mark but that of $C_2:C_1$ is considerably too high. It appears that there must be some retention loss between successive unreinforced

test trials that cannot be accounted for in terms of guessing shrinkage. The theoretical interpretation of this retention loss will be the subject of the next experiment.

EXPERIMENT II

Two principal questions arise concerning the retention losses observed in Exp. I. First, do the retention losses occur on an all-or-none basis, or do they represent reductions in correct response probability to intermediate degrees? Second, in either case, do the observed changes in response probability signify actual forgetting, either partial or complete, of stimulus-response associations established by preceding reinforcement? Information relevant to the first question can be obtained from a simple extension of the design used in Exp. I. It is necessary only to give at least three successive unreinforced test trials following the last reinforcement. The critical datum will be the proportion of instances in which items correct on the first such test but incorrect on the second are again correct on the third. If retention losses are all-or-none in character, this proportion should be no greater than chance. The second question is not so easily answered. An attempt will be made to secure some pertinent evidence by arranging conditions so that there is minimal opportunity for the learning of interfering responses between test trials and determining whether, under these circumstances, there is any progressive loss of information over the test series.

Method

The apparatus, source of Ss, and general procedure were the same as in Exp. I. The design shown in Table 3 was replicated with 12 different 8-item lists for each of 20 Ss, two items in each list being assigned to each

TABLE 3

DESIGN OF EXP. II IN TERMS OF REIN-
FORCEMENTS (R) AND TESTS (T)
FOR EACH ITEM TYPE ON
EACH TRIAL

Item Type	Trial			
	1	2	3	4
$1i$	R T	T	T	T
$1d$	R	T	T	T
$2i$	R T	R T	T	T
$2d$	R	R T	T	T

row of the table. Item types labeled 1 and 2 received one and two reinforcements, respectively. The types labeled i (immediate) were tested immediately following the first reinforced cycle; those labeled d (delayed) were first tested on Trial 2. Thus items of Type $1i$ were reinforced only on Trial 1 but tested on all four trials, and so on.

Besides permitting evaluations of the proportions of items correct on a later trial after being first correct and subsequently not correct (henceforth denoted $C_n:N_{n-1}C_{n-2}$), the design provides for controlled comparisons relative to retention as a function of number of reinforcements and to retention as a function of tests interspersed between reinforcements. Thus it should be possible to differentiate the effects of two variables that have been confounded in standard experimental designs.

The stimuli were again sets of three consonant syllables, randomly drawn except for the elimination of duplicate syllables. For six lists the responses were the numbers 1 to 8; for the remaining six lists the responses were familiar one-syllable words drawn from an articulation test. The two types of responses were used in order to provide a basis for assessing the role of guessing on unlearned items.

Each S was trained and tested on six lists in each of two experimental sessions, number and word lists alternating within each session. Trial 1 on a list began with a reinforced cycle on which all eight stimulus-response pairs were exposed, then there was a test cycle with the stimuli belonging to items of Types $1i$ and $2i$ exposed alone. Trial 2 began with exposure of the stimulus-response pairs for items of Types $2i$ and $2d$; then all eight stimulus members were exposed alone. On Trials 3 and 4, all eight items were retested, in a new random order each time, without intervening reinforcement.

Results

Response shifts.—Perhaps the simplest measure of retention is the probability with which a correct response to a given item on one test trial is followed by a correct response to that item on a later test (by the same S, of course) when no reinforcements have intervened. From the upper portion of Table 4, it is apparent that retention, so measured, was about 90% for adjacent pairs of unreinforced test trials, with no appreciable differences between items with words and items with numbers as responses. There appear to be no differences among item types in amount of retention over the last three test trials. For all types there is a consistent, though small,[3] increase in size of the conditional proportions over successive pairs of trials. Two possible interpretations of this trend im-

TABLE 4

PROPORTIONS OF REPEATED CORRECT RESPONSES ($C_{n+1}:C_n$) AND REPEATED INCORRECT RESPONSES ($I_{n+1}:I_n$) FOR EACH ITEM TYPE IN EXP. II

Item Type	Word Responses			Number Responses		
	$C_2:C_1$	$C_3:C_2$	$C_4:C_3$	$C_2:C_1$	$C_3:C_2$	$C_4:C_3$
$1i$	.74	.93	.93	.83	.90	.91
$1d$		.94	.92		.88	.93
$2i$		.92	.95		.89	.91
$2d$		.89	.93		.88	.95
Item Type	$I_2:I_1$	$I_3:I_2$	$I_4:I_3$	$I_2:I_1$	$I_3:I_2$	$I_4:I_3$
$1i$	.19	.27	.41	.17	.43	.47
$1d$		.30	.58		.41	.41
$2i$		.33	.24		.40	.39
$2d$		.13	.38		.16	.20

[3] The larger increases from $C_2:C_1$ to $C_3:C_2$ and from $I_2:I_1$ to $I_3:I_2$ may be attributable simply to changes in guessing probabilities consequent on the learning of additional Type 2 items on the second reinforced trial.

mediately suggest themselves. The first is that some of the stimulus-response associations established by the reinforced trials are, for some reason, more susceptible to forgetting than others; such differences would permit a selective factor to operate, the items whose responses are more resistant to forgetting being more heavily represented in the proportions for later pairs of trials. The second interpretation is that some learning may have occurred on test trials; other evidence bearing on this possibility will be presented in the next section.

Proportions of instances in which an incorrect response (excluding omissions) to a particular item was repeated from one trial to the next are presented in the lower portion of Table 4. Increases in these proportions from the second to the third pair of test trials[3] are larger, particularly for the items with word responses, than in the case of repeated correct responses. Again, the observed trend is compatible with the hypothesis that some learning occurs on test trials ("learning" being defined in terms of an increase in probability of whatever response actually occurs to a given stimulus), but possible artifacts cannot be entirely ruled out.

Proportions of shifts from incorrect responses on one trial to correct responses on the next (when there has been no intervening reinforcement) are shown in Table 5. The notation I_n has been used for incorrect responses *excluding* omissions on Trial n and is to be distinguished from N_n, used elsewhere for incorrect responses including omissions, and O_n, used in Table 5 to denote omissions. Thus $C_2:I_1$ represents instances in which Ss made incorrect responses to particular items on Trial 1 and then made correct responses to the same items

TABLE 5

PROPORTIONS OF CORRECT RESPONSES FOLLOWING CORRECT RESPONSES $(C_{n+1}:C_n)$, INCORRECT RESPONSES $(C_{n+1}:I_n)$ OR OMISSIONS $(C_{n+1}:O_n)$ AND PROPORTIONS OF REPEATED INCORRECT RESPONSES $(I_{n+1}:I_n)$ POOLED OVER ITEM TYPES FOR TEST TRIALS 2–4 OF EXP. II

	Word Responses	Number Responses
$C_{n+1}:C_n$	.92	.91
$C_{n+1}:I_n$	.13	.23
$C_{n+1}:O_n$	.11	.22
$I_{n+1}:I_n$	.34	.37

on Trial 2. As in Exp. I, the proportions of correct following incorrect are uniformly very much smaller than those of correct following correct responses. The fact that the proportions for both $C_2:C_1$ and $C_2:I_1$ are somewhat higher than in Exp. I is not unexpected. In Exp. II, each S learned 12 different lists; therefore, most of the data come from lists given after the initial period of "learning to learn" and after S has had an opportunity to develop relatively efficient habits of guessing on unlearned items. Allowing for this procedural difference, the results of the two experiments appear quite compatible. All values of $C_n:I_{n-1}$ in Table 4 fall well within the limit of what could be achieved by reasonably efficient guessing on unlearned items. The negligible differences between $C_{n+1}:I_n$ and $C_{n+1}:O_n$, together with the fact that each of these proportions is much larger for numbers than for word responses, would seem to support the interpretation that correct responses to previously noncorrect items are attributable to guessing. It would clearly be desirable to eliminate, or at least drastically reduce, the role of guessing on unlearned items; this is being attempted in experiments now in progress.

In order to determine whether retention losses occur on an all-or-none basis for individual Ss we may examine the proportions for $C_n : N_{n-1}C_{n-2}$. If the occurrence of a noncorrect response to an item that S has responded to correctly on a previous test signifies a total loss of the correct association, then the probability of correct response to the given item on later tests, assuming no intervening reinforcement, should be no greater than that attainable by a random selection from among the unlearned responses. A substantial number of cases can be obtained by including both incorrect responses and omissions on Trial $n - 1$ and pooling over all four item types (using the first three test trials in each case). The proportion of .44, based on 126 observations, thus computed is enough larger than the simple proportions of correct following noncorrect shown in Table 5 to contraindicate the hypothesis of "total forgetting." One might raise the question whether the higher proportions of correct following noncorrect for items that have previously been responded to correctly is interpretable simply as a sequential effect; other things equal, one would expect that a response that has been given to an item on an earlier test would have a greater than chance probability on later tests for the given S even if the response had never been reinforced. As a control for such effects, a computation was made of the proportion of cases in which a particular incorrect response occurred to an item on a given trial after having occurred on the second preceding trial but not on the immediately preceding trial, i.e., $I_n : J_{n-1}I_{n-2}$, where I is a particular incorrect response and J is a different response to the same item. This proportion, based on 270 observations, proved

to be .10. Apparently we must conclude that when a correct response to an item on one trial has been followed by an incorrect response on a later trial in a series of unreinforced tests, the probability of the correct response for the given S has been reduced to a value intermediate between that obtaining immediately after reinforcement and a chance level. In other words, retention losses do not necessarily occur on an all-or-none basis.

Proportion correct per test trial.— At a phenotypic level, partial retention losses clearly occur over a series of unreinforced tests in this situation. But the question remains whether these changes in observed response probability represent forgetting, i.e., weakening of the stimulus-response associations established by reinforcement, or the operation of some extraneous factor which affects performance but not learning. Evidence pertinent to this point is available in the over-all (unconditional) proportions of correct responses per test trial. If a progressive reduction in these proportions is observed, the interpretation will remain uncertain, for a reduction could be produced either by weakening of associations or by extraneous factors. If no reduction occurs, however, then certainly there has been no weakening of associations.

In Table 6 the proportions correct per test trial are given separately for the four item types and for word and number responses, each value being based on 240 observations. If one looks across the row of proportions for the four tests in the case of Type 1i items and the last three tests in the case of the other types, the salient feature is the complete absence of any tendency toward progressive reduction in proportions of correct

TABLE 6

PROPORTION CORRECT PER TEST TRIAL FOR
EACH ITEM AND RESPONSE TYPE
IN EXP. II

Item Type	Word Responses				Number Responses			
	Test Trials				Test Trials			
	1	2	3	4	1	2	3	4
$1i$	.41	.36	.40	.39	.55	.56	.60	.61
$1d$		.28	.32	.31		.49	.53	.58
$2i$	.43	.77	.78	.75	.58	.83	.78	.77
$2d$		.70	.67	.66		.73	.73	.78

responses from test to test. The only systematic trend apparent in the table is the progressive *increase* in proportions of correct responses from test to test in the case of the items with number responses and a single reinforcement. This effect, if significant, is probably attributable to increases in guessing efficiency. The frequency of omissions decreases by nearly 50% from Test 2 to Test 4 for these items, and consequently the contribution from guessing on unlearned items must be expected to increase also. To eliminate this factor, correct response proportions may be recalculated, based only on items which had either correct or incorrect responses, excluding omissions. When this is done the pooled proportions on Tests 2 through 4 run .62, .65, .64 for once-reinforced items and .84, .84, .83 for twice-reinforced items. Clearly there is no loss of information from the response protocols over the series of tests. Since no information is being fed into the system either, the conclusion seems inescapable that there is no progressive weakening of learned associations. The most parsimonious hypothesis as to the source of the response shifts described in the preceding section would seem to be one attributing them to fluctuations in the stimulus context from series to series.

Retention as a function of preceding reinforcements and tests.—Our design provides one fully controlled comparison relative to retention as a function of number of reinforcements, namely that involving item Type $1d$ vs. Type $2d$ on Tests 2 through 4. Examination of the proportions $C_3:C_2$ and $C_4:C_3$ in Table 4 reveals that, with ordinal number of the test trial and number of preceding tests equated, the difference between one and two preceding reinforcements has produced no mean difference whatever between these proportions for the two item types. Contrasting this result with the large difference between corresponding rows in Table 6, we may conclude that the effect of the second reinforcement upon retention was, if not actually zero, at least of a much smaller order of magnitude than its effect upon the amount learned.

Two ways are available to measure the effect of a test trial upon subsequent retention. The first is to compare proportions of correct responses on Test 2 for item Type $1i$ vs. Type $1d$ and for Type $2i$ vs. Type $2d$. In each case, as may be seen in Table 6, there is an advantage of 5 to 10 percentage points for items that had a test immediately after the first, and preceding the second, reinforcement. Application of a rank test for paired replicates shows the differences to be significant at better than the .02 level for both comparisons. The second method, comparing proportions of $C_3:C_2$ and $C_4:C_3$ for Type $1i$ vs. $1d$ and $2i$ vs. $2d$, shows only negligible differences (Table 4).

DISCUSSION

The bearing of our results upon extant theories requires no extended discussion.

The gist of the matter is that no hitherto published theory with which we are familiar gives a reasonable account of our principal findings. Assuming that possible artifacts have been adequately handled by our various control measures, the results on acquisition appear incompatible with any theory which expresses learning in terms of increments in associative strength, excitatory potential, or simply response probability in individual Ss. The "pattern model" (Estes, 1959b) accounts for initial acquisition in this situation, but it is incomplete in that it does not provide for the observed retention losses from training to test trials or the pattern of response shifts occurring over a series of unreinforced test trials.

The shortcomings of the pattern model may be due in part to an unnecessary simplifying assumption. For convenience in calculations, when applying the model to the data of Exp. I, we assumed that with each consonant syllable there was associated a single stimulus pattern which recurred intact from trial to trial. However, there must be some change in the pattern between training and test trials, if only because two windows in the stimulus panel are illuminated in the former instance and only one in the latter. A minimal extension of the pattern model as originally published would include the assumption, common to all stimulus-response learning theories, that probability of a response reinforced on a training trial is reduced on subsequent test trials if components of the training stimulus pattern, including contextual, or "background," cues, have been replaced by novel ones in the test pattern.

An additional factor demonstrated in Exp. II is the occurrence of learning on the unreinforced test trials. It appears that the constancy of mean proportions of correct responses over the test series, the pattern of response shifts, and the increase in stereotypy over the test series would all be predictable on the assumption that the response occurring, whether correct or incorrect, on a test trial becomes conditioned by contiguity

to the full pattern of cues present on the trial.[4] Formal presentation of the augmented pattern model for paired-associate learning suggested by the present findings will be deferred until independent empirical tests have been obtained from studies now in progress.

Summary

In Exp. I, 48 Ss were given a single reinforcement (paired presentation of stimulus and response members) followed by two unreinforced tests on a set of eight paired-associate items. The relative frequency of correct responses on Test 2 for items having correct responses on Test 1 was approximately .7, whereas the relative frequency of correct following noncorrect responses was less than the .125 attainable by chance.

In Exp. II, the following design was replicated with 12 different 8-item lists of paired-associates for each of 20 Ss: equal numbers of items received one and two reinforcements, with and without an interspersed test trial; then all items appeared on three unreinforced test trials. The mean proportion of correct responses remained constant over the series of tests following the last reinforcement; at the same time, significant proportions of shifts from correct to incorrect and vice versa occurred from test to test, but with the degree of stereotypy tending to increase progressively over the series. When other factors were controlled, retention was found to increase with the number of preceding tests but not with the number of preceding reinforcements.

The results were taken to support the view that acquisition occurs on an all-or-none basis, repeated reinforcements simply giving repeated opportunities for the formation of an association between a stimulus pattern and the reinforced response. A provisional interpretation of the data on retention involved two additional assumptions: that decrements in probability of the reinforced response are produced by changes in the stimulus context from training to test trials, and that the response, correct or incorrect, occurring on a test trial has some probability of becoming

[4] Judging by Guthrie's (1959) last publication on learning theory, this assumption comes closer to his intended interpretation of the contiguity principle than earlier formulations of statistical learning theory stated in terms of the independent conditioning of component cues.

conditioned to the stimulus pattern present on the trial.

REFERENCES

BOURNE, L. E., JR., & RESTLE, F. Mathematical theory of concept identification. *Psychol. Rev.*, 1959, **66**, 278–96.

BUSH, R. R., & MOSTELLER, F. *Stochastic models for learning.* New York: Wiley, 1955.

ESTES, W. K. The statistical approach to learning theory. In S. Koch (Ed.), *Psychology: A study of a science.* Vol. 2. New York: McGraw-Hill, 1959. Pp. 380–491. (a)

ESTES, W. K. Component and pattern models with Markovian interpretations. In R. R. Bush & W. K. Estes (Eds.), *Studies in mathematical learning theory.* Stanford: Stanford Univer. Press, 1959. Pp. 9–52. (b)

GIBSON, E. J. A systematic application of the concepts of generalization and differentiation to verbal learning. *Psychol. Rev.*, 1940, **47**, 196–229.

GUTHRIE, E. R. Association by contiguity. In S. Koch (Ed.), *Psychology: A study of a science.* Vol. 2. New York: McGraw-Hill, 1959. Pp. 158–195.

HULL, C. L. *Principles of behavior.* New York: Appleton-Century, 1943.

HULL, C. L., HOVLAND, C. I., ROSS, R. T., HALL, M., PERKINS, D. T., & FITCH, F. B. *Mathematico-deductive theory of rote learning.* New Haven: Yale Univer. Press, 1940.

LUCE, R. D. *Individual choice behavior.* New York: Wiley, 1959.

McGEOCH, J. A., & IRION, A. L. *The psychology of human learning.* (Rev. ed.) New York: Longmans, Green, 1952.

ROCK, I. The role of repetition in associative learning. *Amer. J. Psychol.*, 1957, **70**, 186–93.

SPENCE, K. H. *Behavior theory and conditioning.* New Haven: Yale Univer. Press, 1956.

UNDERWOOD, B. J. Speed of learning and amount retained: A consideration of methodology. *Psychol. Bull.*, 1954, **51**, 276–82.

(Received November 6, 1959)

Application of a Model to Paired-Associate Learning[*]

GORDON H. BOWER, *Stanford University*

The proposal is made to consider a paired-associate item as becoming conditioned to its correct response in all-or-none fashion, and that prior to this conditioning event the subject guesses responses at random to an unlearned item. These simple assumptions enable the derivation of an extensive number of predictions about paired-associate learning. The predictions compare very favorably with the results of an experiment discussed below.

This report describes an elementary model for the stimulus-response association process in paired-associate learning, displays an extensive number of derivations from the axioms of the model, and describes the agreement of the model with some experimental results. Paired-associate learning (PAL) as it is frequently studied involves two, at least conceptually, distinct processes: the learning of relevant responses to the general situation (e.g., as in nonsense syllable-syllable pairs), and the associative "hook-up" of these relevant responses to their appropriate stimulus members. In the belief that fractionating experimental problems leads to quicker understanding of the processes involved, this article is directed to only the second process listed above, the associative hook-up of relevant responses to their respective stimuli. The hope is that once this process is better understood the other problems, having to do with the learning of integrated response units in the situation, will become more amenable to experimental attack.

The way in which the response learning requirement was eliminated in the present experiments was to (i) use responses familiar to the subject, and (ii) inform him of the response alternatives before the experiment began. For these purposes, it was found that the first several integers $(1, 2, \cdots , N)$ worked admirably. Other responses meeting the above requirements could have been used, provided precautions were taken to prevent the subject from forgetting some of the available responses during the course of the experiment. The other procedural peculiarity of these experiments was the requirement that the subject make a relevant response to each stimulus item on each trial. This procedure necessarily involved permitting the subject to control his exposure time to each stimulus.

If there are K items in the list, then a "trial" will be defined as one cycle

*This research was supported by a grant, M-3849, from the National Institutes of Mental Health, United States Public Health Service.

This article appeared in *Psychometrika*, 1961, **26**, 255–280.

of presentation of each of the K items, the order of appearance of the items being randomized over successive trials. Considering only a single stimulus item for a given subject, we may categorize his responses as correct or incorrect (or, 0 or 1, as we shall use later); over successive trials there will be some particular sequence of 1's and 0's to that item. Stripped to its barest essentials, the job for a theory of PAL is to describe and account for the general characteristics of these sequences. The best job of description, of course, would be to reproduce the original sequences. Theories, as economic abstractions, do not perform this task but they can provide general descriptions (e.g., the trial number of the second success) about a sample of sequences allegedly generated under the same process laws. Obviously, models that deliver predictions about many different aspects of such sequences are preferable to less tractable models, since each prediction provides an opportunity to test the adequacy of the model. In turn, the number of predictions derivable in closed form from a model reflects to a large extent the simplicity of the assumptions used to represent the process under consideration. The assumptions of the model to be presented appear to achieve almost maximal simplicity for a model about learning; accordingly, it is possible to derive in closed form an extensive number of predictions (theorems) referring to properties of the response sequences obtained from the learning subject.

The model to be described is derived within the general framework of a stimulus sampling theory of learning [9] but with the assumption that each experimental source of stimulation (i.e., the stimulus member of a paired-associate item) may be represented by a small number of stimulus components or elements. The original investigation of small-element learning models began with a paper by Estes [10] and has been carried on by a number of people. Suppes and Atkinson [15] give an extensive development of such models and show their application to a variety of learning experiments. In the initial development of stimulus sampling theory [8, 9] it was assumed that the population of stimulus components from which the subject sampled on each trial was large. Since conditioning was assumed to take place only with respect to the sampled elements, the model implied relatively gradual changes over trials in the proportion of conditioned elements in the population and hence in response probability. Recent developments with small-element models differ in that the population of stimulus elements is assumed to be small (e.g., one or two elements) so that response probability may take on only a few values over the course of a learning experiment. The common assumption is that only one of these stimulus elements may be sampled on each trial and that the sampled element becomes conditioned to the reinforced response with probability c on every trial. Besides considerable simplification of the mathematics of stimulus sampling theory, the small-element assumptions deliver some predictions which differ markedly from the large-element (i.e., linear) model assumptions; some of these differences are noted and will be compared with data.

The basic notion of the present model is that each stimulus item in the list of paired associates may be represented by exactly one stimulus element within the model and that the correct response to that item becomes associated in all-or-none fashion. Considering only a single item, it can be in either of two "states" on each trial: conditioned or not conditioned to the correct response. The effect of a reinforced trial (i.e., evoking the correct response in the presence of the stimulus item) is to provide an opportunity for the item to become conditioned. The single parameter of the model is c, the probability that an unconditioned item will become conditioned as the result of a reinforced trial. All items begin in the unconditioned state; the effect of continued reinforced trials is to provide repeated opportunities for the item to become conditioned.

If the item has become conditioned, then continued reinforcements of the same correct response will ensure that the item remains conditioned. The probability of the correct response when the item is conditioned is unity. The probability of the correct response when the item is not conditioned depends upon the exact experimental procedure used. In experiments by the writer, the subjects were told the N responses (integers 1, 2, $\cdots$, N) available to them and were told to respond on every trial regardless of whether they knew the correct number. If the N numbers occur equally often as the to-be-learned responses to the items, then the probability that the subject will guess correctly on an unlearned item is $1/N$; correspondingly, his probability of guessing incorrectly is $1 - (1/N)$. Our discussion of the one-element model is oriented specifically towards such an experimental procedure.

Because of the way the model is formulated, there is a partial determinism between the response sequence and the sequence of conditioning states. Specifically, if the subject responds incorrectly to a given item on trial n, then that item was not in the "conditioned" state on trial n. This feature is very helpful in deriving a number of the theorems about errors. If the subject responds correctly, however, then we cannot uniquely specify his state of conditioning, since he may have guessed correctly. Thus, it is not a consequence of the model that the subject's first correct response will be followed with probability one by correct responses on subsequent trials.

After working with the latter model for some time, it came to the writer's attention that Bush and Mosteller [6] had previously published a model for "one-trial learning" that is almost identical to the one stated above. Thus, there can be no pretense to priority in the current formulation of these elementary notions about the learning process. The present account does go beyond the abbreviated discussion by Bush and Mosteller in deriving a large number of predictions from the model and in applying the theory with some success to verbal learning. Although their approach and the present one differ slightly in assumptions about initial conditions, the derivational techniques are sufficiently similar so that theorems can be transposed, with appropriate modifications, from one system to the other. [According to the Bush and Mosteller assumptions, a proportion c of the response sequences (subjects or items) begin in the conditioned state, and this same value of c is assumed to be the learning rate constant.]

Throughout the following sections, the predictions derived from the model will be compared with data from an experiment which now will be described. Twenty-nine subjects learned a list of ten items to a criterion of two consecutive errorless cycles. The stimuli were different pairs of consonant letters; the responses were the integers 1 and 2, each response assigned as correct to a randomly selected five stimuli for each subject. A response was obtained from the subject on each presentation of an item and he was informed of the correct answer following his response. The deck of ten stimulus cards was shuffled between trials to randomize the presentation order of the stimuli.

Axioms and Theorems about Total Errors

Axioms

1. *Each item may be represented by a single stimulus element which is sampled on every trial.*
2. *This element is in either of two conditioning states: C_1 (conditioned to the correct response) or C_0 (not conditioned).*
3. *On each reinforced trial, the probability of a transition from C_0 to C_1 is a constant, c, the probability of a transition from C_1 to C_1 is one.*
4. *If the element is in state C_1 then the probability of a correct response is one; if the element is in state C_0 , then the probability of a correct response is $1/N$, where N is the number of response alternatives.*
5. *The probability c is independent of the trial number and the outcomes of preceding trials.*

The trial to trial sequence of conditioning states forms a Markov chain, with C_1 being an absorbing state. The transition probabilities are given in the following matrix.

(1)
$$P = \begin{array}{c|cc} & C_1 & C_0 \\ \hline C_1 & 1 & 0 \\ C_0 & c & 1-c \end{array}$$

It is easy to show that the nth power of the transition matrix is

(2)
$$P^n = \begin{array}{c|cc} & C_1 & C_0 \\ \hline C_1 & 1 & 0 \\ C_0 & 1 - (1 - c)^n & (1 - c)^n. \end{array}$$

We explicitly assume that all items start out in state C_0 (i.e., are not conditioned initially). Thus, starting out in state C_0, the probability of still being in state C_0 after n reinforced trials is $(1 - c)^n$, which approaches zero as n becomes large. Thus, for $c > 0$, with probability one the process will eventually end in conditioning state C_1 (i.e., will become conditioned).

For each item, define a sequence of response random variables, x_n, which take on the value 1 if an error occurs on trial n, or the value 0 if a success occurs on n. From the axioms, the conditional probabilities of an error given states C_1 or C_0 at the beginning of trial n are

(3) $\quad \mathrm{Pr} \{x_n = 1 \mid C_{1,n}\} = 0 \quad \text{and} \quad \mathrm{Pr} \{x_n = 1 \mid C_{0,n}\} = 1 - \dfrac{1}{N}.$

To obtain the average probability of an error on the nth trial, q_n, multiply these conditional probabilities by the probabilities of being in C_1 or C_0, respectively, at the start of trial n:

(4) $\quad q_n = \mathrm{Pr} \{x_n = 1\} = \mathrm{Pr} \{x_n = 1 \mid C_{1,n}\} \, \mathrm{Pr} \{C_{1,n}\}$

$$+ \mathrm{Pr} \{x_n = 1 \mid C_{0,n}\} \, \mathrm{Pr} \{C_{0,n}\}$$

$$= 0 + \left(1 - \frac{1}{N}\right)(1 - c)^{n-1} = \left(1 - \frac{1}{N}\right)(1 - c)^{n-1}.$$

The expected total number of errors, u_1, before perfect learning is given by

(5) $\quad u_1 = E\left[\displaystyle\sum_{n=1}^{\infty} x_n\right] = \displaystyle\sum_{n=1}^{\infty} \mathrm{Pr} \{x_n = 1\} = \displaystyle\sum_{1}^{\infty} \left(1 - \frac{1}{N}\right)(1 - c)^{n-1} = \dfrac{1 - \dfrac{1}{N}}{c}.$

The expected total errors per item serves as a stable estimator of c. For the experiment described above with $N = 2$, the average number of errors per item was 1.45. Equating u_1 in (5) to 1.45, the c value obtained is .344. This estimate of c will be fixed throughout the remaining discussion of these data. Using this value of c in (4), the predicted learning curve in Fig. 1 is obtained.

In the expression for u_1, all errors are weighted equally. It is also possible to derive expressions for various weighted sums of errors, as Bush and Sternberg [7] have shown for the linear model. The results here are identical with

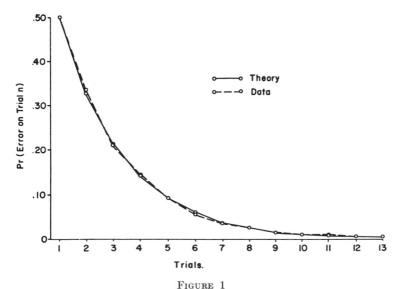

FIGURE 1

q_n, the Probability of an Incorrect Response over Successive Trials of the Experiment

their results. Three examples of the expectation of weighted error sums are given below.

$$(6) \qquad E\left[\sum_{n=1}^{\infty} n x_n\right] = \sum_{n=1}^{\infty} n\left(1 - \frac{1}{N}\right)(1 - c)^{n-1} = \frac{1 - \frac{1}{N}}{c^2} = \frac{u_1}{c} ;$$

$$(7) \qquad E\left[\sum_{n=1}^{\infty} \frac{x_n}{n}\right] = \sum_{n=1}^{\infty} \frac{\left(1 - \frac{1}{N}\right)(1 - c)^{n-1}}{n} = \frac{1 - \frac{1}{N}}{1 - c} \log \frac{1}{c} ;$$

$$(8) \qquad E\left[\sum_{n=1}^{\infty} \frac{x_n}{(n - 1)!}\right] = \left(1 - \frac{1}{N}\right) \sum_{m=0}^{\infty} \frac{(1 - c)^m}{m!} = \left(1 - \frac{1}{N}\right)e^{1-c}.$$

It is possible to obtain the distribution of the total number of errors on each item. This distribution was derived by Bush and Mosteller; their result is readily translated into the terms of the current approach to the theory. If we let T represent the total number of errors (to perfect learning) on a single item, the probability distribution of T is

$$(9) \qquad \Pr \{T = k\} = \begin{cases} b/N & \text{for } k = 0 \\ \dfrac{b(1 - b)^k}{1 - c} & \text{for } k \geq 1, \end{cases}$$

where

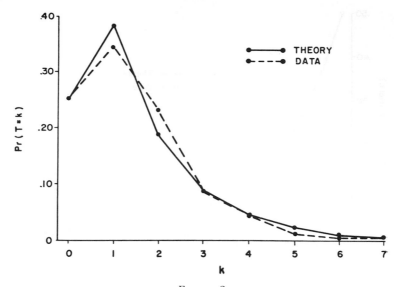

FIGURE 2

Distribution of T, the Total Number of Errors per Item

$$b = \frac{c}{1 - \dfrac{1 - c}{N}}.$$

The mean of T was derived as u_1 in (5); the variance of T is given by

(10) $$\mathrm{Var}\ (T) = u_1 + (1 - 2c)u_1^2 .$$

The predicted and obtained distributions of T are shown in Fig. 2.

Sequential Properties of the Model

Predictions about sequential features of the data may be obtained by considering runs of errors. To date only mean values of the various run distributions have been derived; higher moments will not be discussed. Let r_j represent the number of error runs of length j in an infinite number of trials; we seek the expectation of r_j. For these purposes, it is convenient to define another random variable, u_j, which counts the number of j-tuples of errors that occur in an infinite sequence of trials. Formally, define u_j as

(11) $$u_j = \sum_{n=1}^{\infty} x_n x_{n+1} \cdots x_{n+j-1} \quad \text{for} \quad j = 1, 2, \cdots .$$

The product, $x_n x_{n+1} \cdots x_{n+j-1}$, has the value one only when j consecutive errors occur starting with the error on trial n. It may be seen that u_1 is just the total number of errors.

To make clear how the u_i are being counted and their relation to the r_i, consider the possible sequence

1111100110001101000 $\cdots$ (all the rest zeros).

For this sequence,

$$u_1 = 10, \qquad u_2 = 6, \qquad u_3 = 3, \qquad u_4 = 2, \qquad u_5 = 1;$$

$$r_1 = 1, \qquad r_2 = 2, \qquad r_3 = r_4 = 0, \qquad r_5 = 1, \qquad R = \sum_j r_j = 4.$$

R is the total number of error runs. In an excellent article, Bush [5] has shown that the r_i can be expressed as linear combinations of the u_i. In particular,

$$(12) \qquad\qquad r_j = u_j - 2u_{j+1} + u_{j+2},$$

and

$$(13) \qquad\qquad R = \sum_{j=1}^{\infty} r_j = u_1 - u_2.$$

Having expressed the r_i in terms of the u_i, we now turn to deriving from the model the expected value of u_i. We proceed as follows:

$$(14) \qquad E(u_i) = E\left[\sum_{n=1}^{\infty} x_n \cdot x_{n+1} \cdots \cdot x_{n+i-1} \right] = \sum_{n=1}^{\infty} \Pr\{x_n = 1\}$$

$$\cdot \Pr\{x_{n+1} = 1 \mid x_n = 1\} \Pr\{x_{n+2} = 1 \mid x_n \cdot x_{n+1} = 1\} \cdots$$

$$\cdot \Pr\{x_{n+i-1} = 1 \mid x_n \cdot x_{n+1} \cdots x_{n+i-2} = 1\}.$$

Because of the Markovian properties of the model, the lengthy conditional probabilities on the right-hand side can be simplified, viz.,

$$(15) \qquad \Pr\{x_{n+i} = 1 \mid x_n = 1, x_{n+1} = 1, \cdots, x_{n+i-1} = 1\}$$

$$= \Pr\{x_{n+i} = 1 \mid x_{n+i-1} = 1\}.$$

That is, if the subject made an error on the preceding trial, then that is all the information there is to be extracted from the entire preceding sequence of responses. His error tells us that his conditioning state on the preceding trial was C_0; the probability of an error on the current trial is then

$$(16) \qquad \Pr\{x_{n+1} = 1 \mid x_n = 1\}$$

$$= c \cdot 0 + (1 - c)\left(1 - \frac{1}{N}\right) = (1 - c)\left(1 - \frac{1}{N}\right) = \alpha,$$

and, moreover, this holds for any trial number n. Thus, using relations (15) and (16), the equation for u_j becomes

(17) $\qquad E(u_j) = \sum_{n=1}^{\infty} \text{Pr} \{x_n = 1\} \, \text{Pr} \{x_{n+1} = 1 \mid x_n = 1\} \cdots$

$$\cdot \text{Pr} \{x_{n+j-1} = 1 \mid x_{n+j-2} = 1\}$$

$$= \sum_{n=1}^{\infty} \text{Pr} \{x_n = 1\} \underbrace{\alpha \cdots \alpha}_{(j-1) \text{ times}}.$$

$$E(u_j) = \alpha^{j-1} \sum_{n=1}^{\infty} \text{Pr} \{x_n = 1\} = u_1 \alpha^{j-1}.$$

With these values in hand, now calculate R and r_j , using relations (12) and (13).

(18) $\qquad E(R) = E(u_1) - E(u_2) = u_1(1 - \alpha),$

(19) $\qquad E(r_j) = E(u_j) - 2E(u_{j+1}) + E(u_{j+2}) = u_1(1 - \alpha)^2 \alpha^{j-1}$

$$= R(1 - \alpha)\alpha^{j-1}.$$

Another useful summary of sequential properties in the data is the extent to which an error on trial n tends to be followed by an error k trials later, without regard to what responses intervene between trials n and $n + k$. Define $c_{k,n}$ as $x_n \cdot x_{n+k}$; this expression will have the value 1 only if errors occur on both trials n and $n + k$. It may be noted that $c_{k,n}$ summarizes the same features as does an autocorrelation of lag k. The expectation of $c_{k,n}$ is

(20) $\qquad E(c_{k,n}) = E(x_n \cdot x_{n+k}) = E(x_{n+k} \mid x_n) \cdot E(x_n)$

$$= \text{Pr} \{x_{n+k} = 1 \mid x_n = 1\} \, \text{Pr} \{x_n = 1\}.$$

To find the conditional probability above, note that for an error to occur on trial $n + k$ it must be the case that conditioning has failed to occur during the intervening k trials, and moreover that the subject guesses incorrectly on trial $n + k$. The probability of this joint event is

(21) $\qquad \text{Pr} \{x_{n+k} = 1 \mid x_n = 1\} = (1 - c)^k \left(1 - \frac{1}{N}\right).$

Therefore,

(22) $\qquad E(c_{k,n}) = \left(1 - \frac{1}{N}\right)(1 - c)^k \left(1 - \frac{1}{N}\right)(1 - c)^{n-1}.$

A convenient statistic for comparison with data is obtained by taking the "autocorrelation" of x_n and x_{n+k} over all trials n of the experiment. Defining c_k as the mean value of this random variable,

$$(23) \qquad c_k = E\left[\sum_{n=1}^{\infty} x_n x_{n+k}\right] = \sum_{n=1}^{\infty} E(c_{k,n}) = u_1\left(1 - \frac{1}{N}\right)(1 - c)^k$$

$$\text{for} \quad k = 1, 2, 3, \cdots .$$

Predicted and observed values of c_1, c_2, and c_3 are given in Table 1.

It is a simple matter to construct other statistics which capture various features of the sequential dependencies in the response sequence. Such statistics are expressible as various sums and/or products of the x_n. One illustration will be provided here to demonstrate the general derivational techniques. In order to predict the average number of alternations of successes and failures that occur over the response sequence, define a random variable A_n which will count an alternation between trials n and $n + 1$. Hence,

$$(24) \qquad A_n = (1 - x_n)x_{n+1} + x_n(1 - x_{n+1}).$$

It will be noted that A_n takes on the value 1 either if a success occurs on trial n and a failure on trial $n + 1$ or if a failure occurs on n and a success on $n + 1$. Multiplying out and taking the expectation of A_n yields

$$(25) \qquad E(A_n) = \frac{\alpha}{N}(1 - c)^{n-1} + (1 - \alpha)\left(1 - \frac{1}{N}\right)(1 - c)^{n-1}.$$

The average of the sum of A_n over trials is

$$(26) \qquad A = E[\sum A_n] = u_1\left[c + \frac{2(1 - c)}{N}\right].$$

Errors during Various Parts of Learning

In this section we derive the distribution of the number of errors between the kth and $(k + 1)$st success and also of the number of errors between the kth and $(k + 2)$nd success. As special cases of these general results, for $k = 0$ we obtain the distributions of errors before the first and before the second success. The methods employed in these derivations are general so that the distribution of errors between the kth and $(k + m)$th success could be obtained, the sole limitation being that the expressions get progressively more cumbersome as m is increased.

Consider first the distribution of the number of errors occurring between the kth and $(k + 1)$st success. Let J_k be this random variable; it can take on the values 0, 1, 2, $\cdots$ of the non-negative integers. Errors following the kth success can occur only if the kth success itself came about by guessing (rather than via prior conditioning). Thus, the probability that the kth success occurred by guessing (call it g_k) will play a central role in the expression for the distribution of J_k. To forego for the moment the derivation of g_k, write the distribution of J_k as

$$(27) \qquad \Pr\{J_k = i\} = \begin{cases} 1 - g_k\alpha & \text{for} \quad i = 0 \\ g_k(1 - \alpha)\alpha^i & \text{for} \quad i > 0. \end{cases}$$

For example, the probability of three errors between the kth success and the next one is given by the joint probability of (i) the kth success occurred by guessing, (ii) conditioning failed to occur at the end of trials, k, $k + 1$, and $k + 2$ and incorrect guesses occurred on trials $k + 1$, $k + 2$, and $k + 3$, the probability of this joint event being $(1 - c)^3 (1 - 1/N)^3 = \alpha^3$, and (iii) given that the element was not conditioned at the start of trial $k + 3$, a correct response occurs on trial $k + 4$ with probability $1 - \alpha$. To obtain the term for $J_k = 0$, note that no errors could occur either if the kth success occurred via prior conditioning (with probability $1 - g_k$) or, having guessed the kth success, a success occurs on the next trial with probability $1 - \alpha$. The sum of these two terms, $1 - g_k$ and $g_k(1 - \alpha)$, gives the probability that $J_k = 0$.

From the distribution in (27) one obtains the mean and variance of J_k.

$$(28) \qquad E(J_k) = \frac{ag_k}{1 - \alpha}, \qquad \text{Var}(J_k) = \frac{ag_k}{(1 - \alpha)^2}[1 + \alpha(1 - g_k)].$$

The task now is to derive g_k, the probability that the kth success occurs by guessing. Consider g_1, the probability that the first success occurs by guessing. It is

$$(29) \qquad g_1 = \frac{1}{N} + \left(1 - \frac{1}{N}\right)(1 - c)\frac{1}{N} + \left(1 - \frac{1}{N}\right)^2(1 - c)^2\frac{1}{N} + \cdots$$

$$= \frac{1}{N}\sum_{i=0}^{\infty}\alpha^i = \frac{1}{N(1 - \alpha)}.$$

That is, the subject guesses correctly on the first trial with probability $1/N$; he may fail there so the item does not become conditioned and he guesses correctly on the second trial, and so on. It can be shown for $k > 1$ that a general recursion holds for g_k, viz.,

$$(30) \qquad g_k = g_{k-1}(1 - c)\left[\frac{1}{N} + \alpha\frac{1}{N} + \alpha^2\frac{1}{N} + \cdots\right] = g_{k-1}(1 - c)g_1.$$

That is, for the kth success to occur by guessing, it must be the case that (i) the $(k - 1)$st success occurred by guessing, (ii) conditioning failed to occur on the trial of the $(k - 1)$st success, and (iii) starting out not conditioned on the next trial, the next correct response also occurs by guessing, with probability g_1.

Equation (30) is a standard linear difference equation having the solution

$$(31) \qquad g_k = (1 - c)^{k-1} g_1^k = g_1 \left(1 - \frac{c}{1 - \alpha} \right)^{k-1}$$

Since $c < 1 - \alpha$, it follows that g_k decreases exponentially with k. This result is intuitively clear: the tenth success is less likely to occur by guessing than is, say, the second success. Corresponding to the decrease in g_k, the average errors between the kth and $(k + 1)$st success is decreasing exponentially over k, as (28) shows.

We have been considering J_k for $k > 0$. The interpretation of J_0 is the number of errors before the first success. It is convenient to define g_0 as $1/(1 - c)$, although g_0 itself has no physical interpretation. Defining g_0 in this way, then the distribution of J_0, the errors before the first success, is given by (27). The distribution of J_0 has more intuitive appeal when written as

$$(32) \qquad \Pr \{ J_0 = i \} = \begin{cases} \dfrac{1}{N} & \text{for} \quad i = 0 \\[2mm] \left(1 - \dfrac{1}{N} \right)(1 - \alpha)\alpha^{i-1} & \text{for} \quad i \geq 1, \end{cases}$$

although formally it is the same as (27) with $g_0 = 1/(1 - c)$.

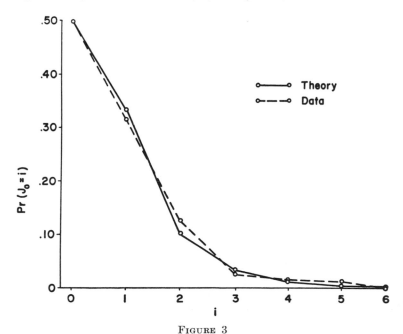

FIGURE 3

Distribution of J_0, the Number of Errors Before the First Success

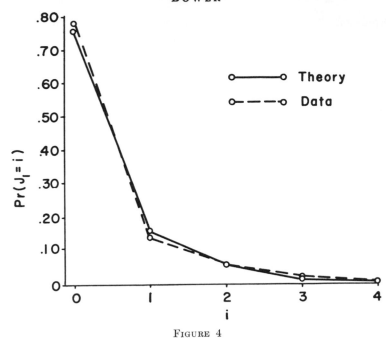

FIGURE 4

Distribution of J_1, the Number of Errors Between the First and Second Success

To illustrate the fit of the model to data, the distribution of the number of errors before the first success is shown in Fig. 3, and the mean and standard error, predicted and observed, are shown in Table 1. Also, the theoretical and observed distributions of J_1, the number of errors between the first and second success, are shown in Fig. 4.

Using the J_k values so calculated, one obtains an expression for the average errors before the kth success. If F_k is defined as the cumulative errors before the kth success, then the obvious recursion on the means is:

$$(33) \qquad E(F_{k+1}) = E(F_k) + E(J_k).$$

The solution of this difference equation is

$$(34) \qquad E(F_k) = \sum_{i=0}^{k-1} E(J_i) = \frac{\alpha}{1 - \alpha} \sum_{i=0}^{k-1} g_i .$$

Substituting the values for g_i, the summation yields

$$(35) \qquad E(F_k) = \frac{1 - \dfrac{1}{N}}{1 - \alpha} + \frac{\alpha g_1}{1 - \alpha} \frac{[1 - (g_1(1 - c))^{k-1}]}{[1 - g_1(1 - c)]}$$

$$= u_1 - \frac{\alpha}{Nc(1 - \alpha)} [g_1(1 - c)]^{k-1},$$

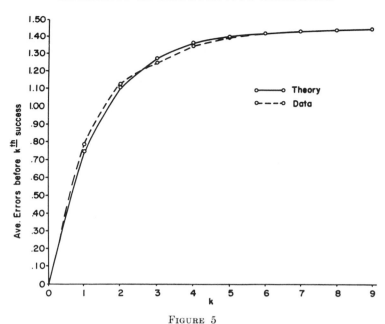

FIGURE 5

$E(F_k)$, the Expected Number of Errors Before the kth Success

where u_1 is the average total errors per item as given in (5). Equation (35) establishes the expected result that, for large k, the average number of errors before the kth success approaches the average total number of errors per item. In Fig. 5, the observed and predicted values of $E(F_k)$ through the ninth success are shown.

The distribution of the number of errors between the kth and $(k + 2)$nd success has been obtained and is presented here for completeness. Define S_k as the number of errors between the kth and $(k + 2)$nd success; it is clear that $S_k = J_k + J_{k+1}$. By specialization for $k = 0$, S_0 gives the distribution of the number of errors before the second success. The distribution of S_k , which is given here without proof (see [3]), is

$$(36) \quad \Pr\{S_k = i\} = \begin{cases} 1 - g_k + g_k\left[c + \dfrac{(1 - c)(1 - \alpha)}{N}\right] & \text{for } i = 0 \\[3mm] g_k\left[c + \dfrac{(1 - c)(1 - \alpha)}{N}(i + 1)\right]\alpha^i & \text{for } i \geq 1, \end{cases}$$

and the first and second raw moments of the distribution are

$$(37) \quad E(S_k) = \frac{\alpha g_k}{(1 - \alpha)^2}\left[c + \frac{2(1 - c)}{N}\right],$$

$$E(S_k^2) = \frac{\alpha g_k}{(1 - \alpha)^3}\left[2(1 - \alpha)(1 + 2\alpha) - c(1 + 3\alpha)\right].$$

The g_k are as given before. Again, defining $g_0 = 1/(1 - c)$, (36) gives the distribution of the number of errors before the second success. The observed and predicted distributions of S_0 are shown in Fig. 6, and the mean and standard error, predicted and observed, are given in Table 1.

The preceding derivations have been carried out for the number of errors before the kth success, etc. The number of *trials* before the kth success is obviously related by a constant. Thus, the trial number of the kth success is the number of errors before the kth success, F_k, plus k. Changing to a "trial" notation shifts the origin (adds a constant) but does not affect the form or variance of the distribution.

The Trial Number of the Last Failure

Our purpose in this section is to derive the distribution of the trial number of the last error in an effectively infinite sequence of trials. However, before proceeding with this derivation, it is helpful to consider another statistic: the proportion of items characterized by having no errors following the first success. In the experimental data, a considerable percentage (62.8 percent, in fact) of the item protocols displayed this characteristic and the question arose whether the model would predict such results. Let p_1 represent the probability that a response sequence will exhibit this property of no errors following the first success. If b represents the probability of no more errors following a correct guess, then an expression for p_1 is

$$(38) \qquad p_1 = 1 - g_1 + g_1 b = 1 - g_1(1 - b).$$

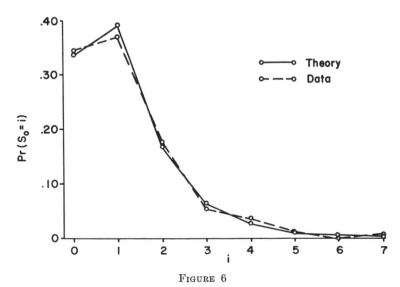

FIGURE 6

Distribution of S_0, the Number of Errors Before the Second Success

That is, a proportion $1 - g_1$ of the first correct responses come about via prior conditioning (so no more errors will occur), while $g_1 b$ represents the probability that the first correct response occurs by guessing but no more errors occur. To complete this derivation, b, the probability that no errors occur following a correct guess is

$$(39) \qquad b = c + (1 - c)\frac{1}{N}c + (1 - c)^2\left(\frac{1}{N}\right)^2 c + \cdots$$

$$= \frac{c}{1 - \dfrac{(1 - c)}{N}} = \frac{c}{\alpha + c}.$$

That is, with probability c the item was conditioned on the trial on which the correct guess occurred; with probability $1 - c$ conditioning failed to occur on that trial, the subject guessed correctly on the next trial with probability $1/N$ and the item became conditioned then with probability c, and so on. This value of b is the same as that used in the distribution of the number of errors given in (9).

Substituting this result for b into (38),

$$(40) \qquad p_1 = 1 - \frac{g_1 \alpha}{\alpha + c}.$$

Using the estimate of c obtained earlier, the predicted p_1 is .638, which is quite close to the observed proportion of .628.

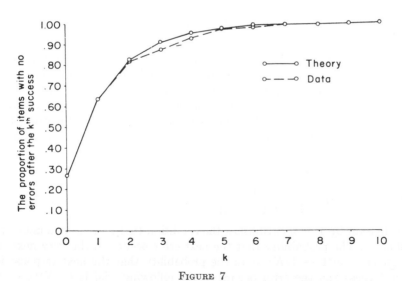

FIGURE 7

p_k, the Probability of Zero Errors Following the kth Success

As (40) suggests, define p_k to be the probability that there are no errors following the kth success. Using our previous result for g_k, one derives

$$(41) \qquad p_k = 1 - \frac{\alpha g_k}{\alpha + c} = 1 - \frac{\alpha g_1}{\alpha + c}[g_1(1-c)]^{k-1}.$$

Observed and predicted values of p_k are shown in Fig. 7.

To determine the position of the last error, define n' as the random variable representing the trial number on which the last error occurs in an infinite sequence of trials. If no errors occur at all, then n' is set equal to zero. The probability distribution of n' is

$$(42) \qquad \Pr\{n' = k\} = \begin{cases} \dfrac{b}{N} & \text{for } k = 0 \\[2ex] b\left(1 - \dfrac{1}{N}\right)(1-c)^{k-1} & \text{for } k \geq 1. \end{cases}$$

The first value is just $\Pr\{T = 0\}$, which was given in (9). If some errors occur, then for the last error to occur on trial k it must be the case that conditioning failed to occur on the preceding $k-1$ trials, an incorrect guess occurred on trial k, but no errors followed that, with probability b. The mean and variance of n' are

$$(43) \qquad E(n') = m = \frac{b\left(1 - \dfrac{1}{N}\right)}{c^2} = \frac{bu_1}{c},$$

$$\text{Var}(n') = m\left[\frac{2}{c} - 1 - m\right].$$

The observed and predicted distributions of n' are shown in Fig. 8; the mean and standard error, observed and predicted, are given in Table 1.

Consider now the distribution of the number of successes that intervene between the kth and $(k+1)$st error, provided that a $(k+1)$st error occurs. Because an error effectively "resets" the process to state C_0, the distribution of this random variable will be independent of k and of the trial number on which the leading error occurs. Let H represent the number of intervening successes. The distribution of H is given by

$$(44) \quad \Pr\{H = j\} = \frac{\alpha}{1-b}\left[\frac{1-c}{N}\right]^j = (\alpha + c)(1 - \alpha - c)^j, \; j = 0, 1, 2, \cdots.$$

The division by $1-b$ establishes the condition that at least one more error will occur. The probability that the next error occurs on the very next trial is just $(1-c)(1 - 1/N) = \alpha$; the probability that the next response is a correct guess and the error occurs on the following trial is $(1/N)(1-c)\alpha$, and so on. Although the derivation of the number of successes before the

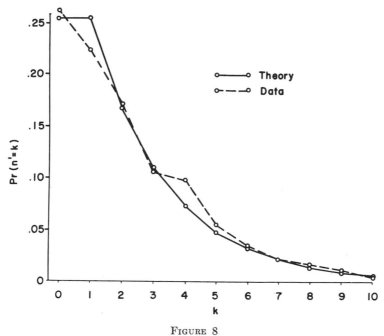

FIGURE 8

Distribution of n', the Trial Number of the Last Failure

first error (provided there is one) proceeds somewhat differently, the resulting distribution is identical to the distribution given in (44). The mean and variance of H are

$$(45) \qquad E(H) = \frac{1 - \alpha - c}{\alpha + c}, \qquad \text{Var } (H) = \frac{1 - \alpha - c}{(\alpha + c)^2}.$$

The observed and predicted distributions of H are shown in Fig. 9, and the means and standard errors are given in Table 1.

The preceding analyses have been carried out for the responses to a single item over trials. If the items can be considered homogeneous in difficulty so that each learning process may be characterized by the same c value, then it is possible to derive a number of predictions about performance across items within a particular trial. If there are K items, then a run through the list (a trial) provides a sequentially ordered sample of size K from a binomial population. With this characterization, one can then derive various quantities of experimental interest, e.g., the probability that a perfect recitation of the list occurs on trial n, the average number of error runs of length j considering the K sequential samples on each trial, and so on. Derivations of such results are relatively easy and are presented in [3].

Comparison with Linear Model

What has been accomplished in the preceding sections is a detailed analysis of the sequence of response random variables. In terms of sheer bulk of predictions derivable from learning axioms, the sole comparable alternative is the single-operator linear model explored extensively by Bush and Sternberg [7]. It would be instructive, therefore, to place on record a detailed quantitative comparison of the fit of these two models to the present data. The basic notion of the linear model is that the associative strength between a stimulus and its correct response increases by a linear transformation following each reinforced trial. Stated differently, the probability of an error is expected to decrease by a constant fraction following each reinforced trial. If the initial error probability is $1 - (1/N)$ then over successive reinforced trials the error probability decreases, taking on a number of values intermediate between $1 - (1/N)$ and 0. In contrast, the one-element model proposed here assumes that the error probability has only two values, $1 - (1/N)$ or 0, and jumps from the first to the second value following the trial on which the all-or-none association is formed.

Although these conceptions differ markedly, the two models predict the same average learning curve. Thus, finer details of the data are required to differentiate these models. Since, according to the linear model, q_n decreases by the same fraction every trial, the response random variables, x_n ,

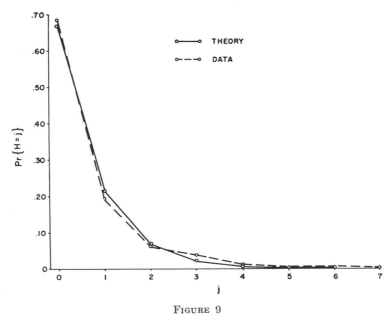

FIGURE 9

Distribution of H, the Number of Successes Intervening Between Adjacent Errors

are statistically independent; that is, the probability of an error on trial n is expected to be the same whether the subject responded correctly or incorrectly on the preceding trial. For the one-element model the x_n are not independent; whether we expect an error on trial n depends heavily on whether or not an error occurred on the preceding trial. Noting these differences, we are led to expect that the two models would be differentiated best by their predictions about sequential aspects of the data. Indeed this is the case, as may be seen in Table 1 which collects 19 comparisons of the one-element and linear models with data. The linear model predictions were obtained by referring to the theorems derived by Bush and Sternberg [7]. Three other

TABLE 1

Comparison of One-Element and Linear Models with Data

	Statistic	One element	Data	Linear
1.	Ave. errors per item	---	1.45	---
2.	S. D.	1.44	1.37	1.00
3.	Ave. errors before first success	.749	.785	.705
4.	S. D.	.98	1.08	.84
5.	Ave. errors between first and second success	.361	.350	.315
6.	S. D.	.76	.72	---
7.	Ave. errors before second success	1.11	1.13	1.02
8.	S. D.	1.10	1.01	.93
9.	Ave. successes between errors	.488	.540	---
10.	S. D.	.72	.83	---
11.	Ave. trial of last error	2.18	2.33	3.08
12.	S. D.	2.40	2.47	3.39
13.	Total error runs	.975	.966	1.162
14.	Error runs of length 1	.655	.645	.949
15.	Error runs of length 2	.215	.221	.144
16.	Error runs of length 3	.070	.058	.064
17.	Error runs of length 4	.023	.024	.005
	Autocorrelation of errors			
18.	--one trial apart (c_1)	.479	.486	.288
19.	--two trials apart (c_2)	.310	.292	.195
20.	--three trials apart (c_3)	.201	.187	.127
21.	Alternations of success and failure	1.45	1.43	1.83
22.	(Fail-Fail runs) — (Success-Fail runs)	.000	.020	-.380
23.	Probability of a success following an error	.672	.666	.730

statistics are shown for which the predictions of the linear model have not been worked out (although stat rats could have been run for these).

The results in Table 1 require little comment. Of the 19 possible comparisons between the one-element and linear models, the one-element model comes closer to the data on 17. The greatest differentiation of the models is seen in sequential statistics, lines 13 through 23, and in the trial number of the last failure (lines 11 and 12). The largest absolute discrepancy from data of the one-element predictions occurs with the average trial number of the last failure, but this statistic also has the largest variance of all those considered. Weighing these considerations along with the excellent fits of the one-element model to the data shown in Figs. 2–9, we may conclude that the one-element model provides a more adequate description of these data than does the linear model.

Other paired-associate data favoring the one-element model have been reported in [4]. One dramatic comparison of the two models is provided by considering the expected number of errors (to perfect learning) following an error that occurs on trial n. According to the linear model, the number of errors expected following an error on trial n should be a decreasing function of n, since associative strength is assumed to increase steadily with the number of preceding reinforced trials. In contrast, from the one-element model the expectation is that the average errors following an error on trial n is a constant, $(1 - c)u_1$, which is independent of the trial number on which the error was observed. The point of the matter is that if we observe an error on trial n, then we know the item was not conditioned prior to that trial; hence, we can assume that our learning process "starts" in conditioning state C_0 at the beginning of trial n and that the state of the subject's associative connection has not effectively changed since he started the experiment. We may, so to speak, reset the clock back to the beginning of the experiment for predicting the subject's future behavior on that item.

To get a stable test of these different predictions, the present data from 29 subjects were pooled with the data of 47 other subjects learning 10 paired-associate items under the same conditions except for 14 of the subjects the number of response alternatives was 3, and for 14 there were 8 responses. The varying N's would not affect the constancy or monotone decreasing aspects of the two predictions. For the 760 learning sequences the average number of errors following an error on trial 1, on trial 2, $\cdots$, on trial 6 were calculated. The data beyond trial 6 were not analyzed since the number of cases involved was dropping off rapidly. The results of these calculations are shown in Fig. 10 where the one-element model prediction (i.e., average of all the data points) and a rough approximation to the linear model's predictions are included for comparative purposes. There is little doubt that the one-element prediction is closer to the data, which show remarkable constancy.

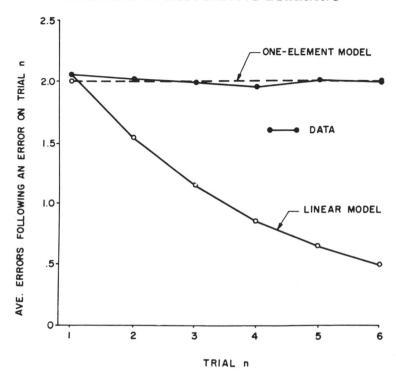

FIGURE 10

Average Number of Errors Following an Error on Trial n
(The one-element and linear predictions are indicated.)

The predicted function for the linear model is not exact since groups with differing N's and c's were pooled in Fig. 10; however, the function does show the relative order of magnitude of differences to be expected from the linear model. The values for the graph were obtained by estimating the average c value across groups (it was .25) and then multiplying successive values on the function by $1 - c$. For example, the average errors observed following an error on trial 1 was 2.05; hence, for trial 2 the linear prediction would be 2.05 (.75) = 1.54, and so on.

Goodness of Fit Considerations

Although the preceding tabulation of various statistics and distributions tells us something about how well the model describes these data, still one legitimately may raise the question of whether there is some summary measure for evaluating the *over-all* goodness of fit of the model to these data. For these purposes a chi-square procedure adapted for stochastic learning models by Suppes and Atkinson [15] from an original paper by Anderson and Goodman [1] may be used. This procedure tests the ability of a model to reproduce the nth order conditional probabilities in the response sequences. Tests involving such quantities have priority in evaluating goodness of fit since the primary reference of stochastic models is to these conditional probabilities. Other statistics of the data (error runs, trial of second success, etc.) are more or less derived from these conditional probabilities and thus should have less priority in deciding over-all goodness of fit. The chi-square test proposed by Anderson and Goodman is most appropriate for those models which assume that the sequence of response random variables is a finite Markov chain (i.e., that current response probability depends upon, say, only one or two prior responses). This happens to be a rather restricted class of learning models; however, the test is practically useful even for chains of infinite order in which current response probability presumably depends upon the entire past history of responses and reinforcements. In practice, such chains can be approximated reasonably well by taking account of only a small number (say 3 or 4) of prior trials when calculating conditional probabilities from the theory.

The chi-square procedure may be illustrated with the present data. The decision was made to look at third-order conditional probabilities using the data from the first six trials of the experiment; beyond trial 6 practically all responses were correct so very little information could be gained by considering the data beyond that point. With two responses (correct and incorrect) there are eight possible sequences of length three. The data were tabulated in an 8×2 table, the entries in each cell corresponding to the frequency with which a given sequence of responses on trials n, $n + 1$, and $n + 2$ was followed by a success (or failure) on trial $n + 3$. For each subject-item sequence, three observations were obtained corresponding to n taking on the values 1, 2, and 3. There were thus $3(290) = 870$ observations in total.

The expected conditional probabilities are readily calculated from the one-element model. For example, four of the eight prior sequences have an error on trial $n + 2$; hence, the expected conditional probability of an error on trial $n + 3$ would be α. The only conditional probability which is troublesome to compute is that of an error given a prior sequence of three successes (with responses prior to trial n being unspecified). This conditional probability is calculated separately for $n = 1, 2, 3$, and then the three results are averaged. Analogous computations from the linear model are extremely simple—in that model the x_n are considered to be statistically independent; hence, one merely averages the response probabilities on trials 4, 5, and 6.

The conditional probabilities calculated above are converted into cell frequencies by multiplying them by the observed frequency of a given prior sequence of three responses (i.e., we multiply by the observed row sums of the table). Chi-square values can then be calculated separately for the one-element model and for the linear model. There are eight rows in the table, each row having one linear constraint (the two entries must sum to the appropriate row total) and for each model we have estimated one parameter (c); hence, each chi square will have seven degrees of freedom. The chi-square values for the observed and expected frequencies were 9.40 for the one-element model and 98.36 for the linear model. Therefore, the test rejects the linear model in its fit to these data but does not reject the one-element model.

Suppes and Chmura [16] have proposed a simple but rigorous procedure for discriminating between the goodness of fit of two models for which the above chi-square values have been calculated. Their statistic, T, is the ratio of the two chi-square values, each divided by its respective degrees of freedom. Under the assumption that one of the models is true, T is distributed as the noncentral F statistic, with a noncentrality parameter equal to the value of an ordinary chi square done on the two sets of expected frequencies (ignoring the data for the moment). For the present case, the value of T is 10.40. This value is so large (an ordinary F table requires only 7.00 for significance at the .01 level) that it would be a mere formality to calculate its exact probability under the assumption that both models fit the data equally well. Hence, we may unequivocally reject the linear model in favor of the one-element model.

Range of Application of the Model

The fact that the one-element model gives an adequate quantitative account of these paired-associate data satisfies one important requisite of a scientific theory, that of being close to the data. If, in addition, the theory is mathematically tractable in that numerous consequences are easily derived in closed form, then indeed we are in a fortunate position. The main task of this paper has been to show that the one-element model is mathematically tractable; those familiar with current work in mathematical learning theory certainly can have no quarrel with this claim. This property of the model is due to the extreme simplicity of its assumptions about the association process. One might effectively argue that the present model nearly achieves the absolute minimum in assumptions for a workable theory of learning.

Once one has demonstrated the predictive validity of a model for a limited class of experimental situations, there remains the task of characterizing more generally those experimental arrangements to which the model may be expected to apply. In the first part of this report, we explicitly restricted the model to the S-R association process and have used simplified experimental situations in which response learning was precluded. Within this restricted domain of PAL, the model has proved extremely useful in investigating the effects on learning of variations in the number of response alternatives and in the reinforcement conditions prevailing during learning [4].

In addition, the model has led us to do experiments in which the guessing probabilities are altered indirectly by varying the proportion of items in the list that have the same correct response (e.g., with 20 items and responses 1 and 2, we have varied the number of items that have 1 as the correct response).

The experimental conditions may differ considerably from those obtaining under paired-associate learning, but still the model may be expected to apply if response learning is precluded. A good example of such an application is to the paradigm that experimenters have called verbal discrimination learning (e.g., Rundquist and Freeman, [14]). In one variant of this experiment, the subject is required to read the correct response from a card on which are printed N alternatives (words, syllables); the subject goes repeatedly through a deck of K such cards until he can give the correct response to all of them. The model has been applied to the results of such an experiment with $N = 2$; its predictive validity proved equally as good as that reported here for the paired-associate task. To cite a further example of work in progress, we are attempting to extend the model to a similar task in which the subject learns to recognize or identify a visual form as one of those that had been shown to him in a "training list" of visual forms.

A further extension of the present work would investigate the modifications in the theory that are required to handle those PAL situations in which the responses per se must be learned. Here again it may prove advantageous to fractionate the problem by utilizing experimental arrangements which primarily involve only response learning. The free verbal recall paradigm [e.g., 2] would appear to serve these purposes. In such experiments the subject is read a number of unrelated words and later is tested for free, unaided recall. With this arrangement, the responses are conditioned presumably to situational and intraverbal cues in a manner analogous to that assumed to occur in PAL response learning. Evidence already exists to indicate that the free verbal recall situation may yield to a simple theoretical analysis. Miller and McGill [12] and Murdock [13] have published quantitative theories which appear to account adequately for their results from free verbal recall experiments. Ultimately, one would like to have a set of combination axioms whereby the assumptions about S-R association and response learning may be combined for predicting results in those experimental situations involving the concurrent operation of these two processes. It may not be presumptuous to suppose that such a development will come about in the next few years.

REFERENCES

[1] Anderson, T. W. and Goodman, L. A. Statistical inference about Markov chains. *Ann. math. Statist.*, 1957, **28**, 89-110.
[2] Bruner, J. S., Miller, G. A., and Zimmerman, C. Discriminative skill and discriminative matching in perceptual recognition. *J. exp. Psychol.*, 1955, **49**, 187-192.
[3] Bower, G. H. Properties of the one-element model as applied to paired-associate

learning. Tech. Rep. No. 31, Psychol. Ser., Inst. for Mathematical Studies in the Social Sciences, Stanford Univ., 1960.

[4] Bower, G. H. A model for response and training variables in paired-associate learning. *Psychol. Rev.*, in press.

[5] Bush, R. R. Sequential properties of linear models. In R. R. Bush and W. K. Estes (Eds.), *Studies in mathematical learning theory*. Stanford: Stanford Univ. Press, 1959. Pp. 215-227.

[6] Bush, R. R. and Mosteller, F. A comparison of eight models. In R. R. Bush and W. K. Estes (Eds.), *Studies in mathematical learning theory*. Stanford: Stanford Univ. Press, 1959. Pp. 293-307.

[7] Bush, R. R. and Sternberg, S. A single-operator model. In R. R. Bush and W. K. Estes (Eds.), *Studies in mathematical learning theory*. Stanford: Stanford Univ. Press, 1959. Pp. 204-214.

[8] Estes, W. K. Toward a statistical theory of learning. *Psychol. Rev.*, 1950, **57**, 94-107.

[9] Estes, W. K. and Burke, C. J. A theory of stimulus variability in learning. *Psychol. Rev.*, 1953, **60**, 276-286.

[10] Estes, W. K. Component and pattern models with Markovian interpretations. In R. R. Bush and W. K. Estes (Eds.), *Studies in mathematical learning theory*. Stanford: Stanford Univ. Press, 1959. Pp. 9-52.

[11] Estes, W. K. Learning theory and the new mental chemistry. *Psychol. Rev.*, 1960, **67**, 207-223.

[12] Miller, G. A. and McGill, W. J. A statistical description of verbal learning. *Psychometrika*, 1952, **17**, 369-396.

[13] Murdock, B. B. The immediate retention of unrelated words. *J. exp. Psychol.*, 1960, **60**, 222-234.

[14] Rundquist, W. N. and Freeman, M. Roles of association value and syllable familiarization in verbal discrimination learning. *J. exp. Psychol.*, 1960, **59**, 396-401.

[15] Suppes, P. and Atkinson, R. C. *Markov learning models for multi-person interactions.* Stanford: Stanford Univ. Press, 1960.

[16] Suppes, P. and Chmura, H. A statistical test for comparative goodness of fit of alternative learning models. Tech. Rep. No. 36, Psychol. Ser., Inst. for Mathematical Studies in the Social Sciences, Stanford Univ., 1961.

Manuscript received 9/1/60

Revised manuscript received 1/11/61

A Fundamental Property of All-or-None Models, Binomial Distribution of Responses Prior to Conditioning, with Application to Concept Formation in Children[1]

PATRICK SUPPES and ROSE GINSBERG, *Stanford University*

A basic assumption of the simple all-or-none conditioning model is that the probability of a correct response remains constant over trials before conditioning. 4 implications of this assumption were tested: (a) prior to the last error there will be no evidence of learning, (b) the sequence of responses prior to the last error forms a sequence of Bernoulli trials, (c) responses prior to the last error exhibit a binomial distribution and (d) specific sequences of errors and successes are distributed in accordance with the binomial hypothesis. These 4 tests were performed on the data from 7 experiments concerned with concept formation in children, paired-associate learning and probability learning in adults, and T maze learning in rats. The statistical evidence from these various experimental groups provided substantial support of the all-or-none model. However, when Vincent curves were constructed for responses prior to the last error, some of the learning curves showed significant departures from stationariness.

In the past year or two there has been extensive application of a single stimulus element conditioning model to paired-associate learning (Bower, 1961; Estes, 1961) and to concept formation in children (Suppes & Ginsberg, 1962). In a paired-associate experiment the single stimulus element represents a stimulus item from a list of paired associates; in a concept formation experiment the stimulus element represents a concept, or some aspect of a concept. The two essential assumptions of the model are the following. First, until the single stimulus element is conditioned, there is a constant guessing probability, p, that the subject responds correctly (the probability of an error on every trial is $q = 1 - p$). Second, on each trial there is a constant probability, c,

that the single stimulus element will be conditioned to the correct response. We consider only those situations in which the subject is always informed of the correct response so that the correct association may be learned on any trial.

This all-or-none conditioning model may be viewed as resulting from imposing special restrictions on more general models of stimulus sampling theory. The statistics of this model have been analyzed in great detail in Bower (1961). Supplementary statistics for a finite number of trials at the end of which not all subjects are conditioned have been given by Estes (1961) and Suppes and Ginsberg (1962).

The point of the present paper is to make explicit a simple but fundamentally important fact about the all-or-none conditioning model: the assumption of a constant guessing probability on each trial before condi-

[1] This research was performed pursuant to a contract with the United States Office of Education, Department of Health, Education, and Welfare.

This article appeared in *Psychol. Rev.*, 1963, **70**, 139–143, 155–161 (abridged).

tioning implies that there is a binomial distribution, with parameter p, of responses prior to the last error.[2] This observation has three important consequences for the analysis of experimental data. First, it implies that the sequence of responses prior to the last error forms a sequence of Bernoulli trials. This null hypothesis admits at once the possibility of applying the many powerful statistics that are not applicable in the usual learning situation for which the theory postulates dependence of responses from trial to trial. Second, the consideration of response sequences prior to the last error makes possible a deeper analysis of response data than do statistics which are averaged over subjects and are a function of the conditioning parameter c. When statistics are expressed as a function of c and the data are analyzed in terms of all subjects regardless of whether or not they are conditioned, then it is often the case that the large number of correct responses occurring after conditioning bias the statistics very favorably in terms of the model. Third, the observation that the distribution of responses prior to the last error should be binomial permits generalization of the model to admit individual differences in the conditioning parameter c, while retaining a uniform guessing parameter p.

These points may be emphasized by considering just one example of a familiar statistic for the model. Let $P_n(11)$ be the joint probability of a success on Trial n and on Trial $n + 1$. It is easily shown that

$$P_n(11)$$
$$= 1 - [1 - p^2(1 - c) - pc]$$
$$\times (1 - c)^{n-1} \quad [1]$$

Consider now how much simpler this quantity is if we know whether or not the subject is conditioned. Let U_n stand for the unconditioned state on Trial n and C_n for the conditioned state on that trial, etc. Then the conditional probabilities are simply[3]

$$P_n(11 \mid U_{n+1}) = p^2 \quad [2]$$
$$P_n(11 \mid U_n C_{n+1}) = p \quad [3]$$
$$P_n(11 \mid C_n) = 1 \quad [4]$$

Moreover, except for a few trials after the last error when the subject may be unconditioned but guessing correctly, we know what state he is in. In particular, on all trials prior to the last error we know he is in the unconditioned state and thus that the probability of two successes in a row should be p^2. Relative to the third point above, it may be noted that if the data are summed over subjects, test of Equation 1 requires the assumption that all subjects have the same conditioning parameter c, whereas test of Equation 2 does not, and is compatible with the assumption of individual differences in conditioning "propensity."

STATISTICAL TESTS OF THE MODEL

Once the observation has been made that according to the model responses prior to the last error have a binomial distribution, it is possible to consider a variety of goodness of fit tests for this assumption. The virtue of these goodness of fit tests is that in contradistinction to the many statistics considered by Bower they permit a genuine statistical evaluation of the null hypothesis that the model fits the data. There are four goodness of fit

[2] It is easy to demonstrate that it is statistically incorrect actually to include the last error in the analysis of response data.

[3] There are only three cases to consider, namely, U_{n+1}, $U_n C_{n+1}$, and C_n, because U_{n+1} implies U_n with probability one and C_n implies C_{n+1} with probability one.

tests we believe to be of particular importance. In introducing these four tests, we want to emphasize that we are not suggesting they are the only tests or that they are the only interesting ones. It seems to us, however, that they do ask the four most important questions suggested by the "guessing" assumption of the model. The statistical properties of these four tests are well known in the literature and do not need to be discussed here. A good reference for the first two on stationarity and order is Anderson and Goodman (1957).

Stationarity. Perhaps the most striking feature predicted is that if data summed only over responses made prior to the last error are considered, then there will be *no* evidence of learning over trials. Statistically this means the model predicts a binomial distribution of responses with the constant parameter p. From the standpoint of learning theory this is a particularly interesting prediction because of the classical emphasis on the mean learning curve. If the binomial assumption holds, the mean learning curve, when estimated over responses prior to the last error for each subject, will be a horizontal line. Empirical tests of this prediction in experiments concerned with children's concept formation, animal learning, probability learning, and paired-associate learning in human adults, are given below. The appropriate statistical test for stationarity may be formulated in terms of the null hypothesis that there is no change in the proportion of correct responses over trials. In order to obtain adequate data it is necessary to consider blocks of trials. Letting, then, the variable t run over blocks of trials the appropriate χ^2 test is as follows:

$$\chi^2 = \sum_{t,i} n(t) \left(\frac{n_i(t)}{n(t)} - \frac{n_i}{N} \right)^2 \bigg/ \frac{n_i}{N}$$

where $i = 0, 1$; $n_i(t)$ is the number of correct $(i = 1)$ or incorrect $(i = 0)$ responses in Block t; $n(t)$ is the total number of responses in Block t; n_i is the number of correct (or incorrect) responses summed over all blocks; and N is the total number of responses summed over all blocks. The χ^2 statistic has the usual limiting distribution with $T - 1$ degrees of freedom, where T is the number of blocks of trials. If there are $m > 2$ responses, the number of degrees of freedom is $(m - 1)(T - 1)$. Under the restriction to two responses, the expression for χ^2 may be simplified to

$$\chi^2 = \sum_t [Nn_1(t) - n_1 n(t)]^2 / n_1 n_2 n(t)$$

thus eliminating the summation over i.

Order. The second property following from the guessing assumption which it is critical and significant to test is that the sequence of responses prior to the last error does indeed form a sequence of Bernoulli trials, that is, that there is statistical independence in the responses made from trial to trial. There are various ways of testing this assumption but it seems to us that the simplest and most direct is to test the null hypothesis that the dependence is zero order versus the hypothesis that the dependence is first order. Acceptance of the null hypothesis has the strong implication that we cannot predict responses better if we know whether the preceding response was correct or incorrect. The application of this test to many other sets of learning data has led to rejection of the null hypothesis at extremely high levels of significance (often $p < 10^{-5}$). Many results of this sort are to be found in Suppes and Atkinson (1960). In terms of other experimental evidence this must be regarded as a sensitive test of the assumption of the statistical independence of responses.

The appropriate formulation of the χ^2 test is as follows.

$$\chi^2 = \sum_{i,j} n_i \left(\frac{n_{ij}}{n_i} - \frac{n_j}{N} \right)^2 \bigg/ \frac{n_j}{N}$$

where j as well as i is 0 or 1; n_{ij} is the number of transitions from State i to State j; $n_i = \sum_j n_{ij}$; $n_j = \sum_i n_{ij}$; and N is the total number of responses, as before. Again, χ^2 has the usual limiting distribution with $(m - 1)^2$ degrees of freedom, where m is the number of states: here, $m = 2$.

Distribution of responses. Granted the assumption that responses prior to the last error are binomially distributed, it is natural to ask if these responses do indeed exhibit a binomial distribution. Because the number of responses prior to the last error varies from subject to subject and because, unless the number of subjects is very large, insufficient data will be obtained by grouping subjects according to the number whose last error occurs on the same trial, the natural and practical way to test the hypothesis that the distribution is binomial seems to be the following. For each subject consider blocks of, say four, trials taken up to the highest multiple of four equal to or less than the total number of responses prior to the last error. So that, for example, if the last error for a subject occurred on Trial 28, we would include in this analysis the first six blocks of four trials. Over the total of such blocks, summed for all subjects, the frequency of occurrence of k errors, where $k = 0, 1, 2, 3, 4$, provides our obtained frequencies. The proportion of correct responses over the blocks of trials included in this analysis is the maximum likelihood estimate of p. Using this estimate we may obtain from the binomial distribution the predicted frequencies. On the null hypothesis that responses are statistically independent a standard χ^2 test for goodness of fit of the obtained and predicted frequencies is appropriate.

Distribution of sequences of responses. In addition to considering the distribution of responses, we may analyze the data in a still more refined way by considering the distribution of sequences of responses. As in the case of the distribution of responses, the practical approach is to consider blocks of trials of relatively small length and look at the sequence of responses within those blocks. For example, if we look at blocks of four trials, then 0111 would represent a sequence on which the first response was incorrect and the subsequent three responses were correct. In four trials there are, of course, 16 different possible sequences of errors and successes. If we consider the relative frequency of every possible sequence of responses of this length, a χ^2 test of goodness of fit may then be applied in exactly the manner appropriate to the distribution of responses themselves. In connection with this test, it is important to remark that the goodness of fit of the distribution of these sequences provides a goodness-of-fit test for the kind of run statistics much studied in the literature of learning theory. The difficulty with the usual statistics derived for runs is that they occur in the context of statistical dependence in response sequences and, therefore, a simple goodness of fit test is not valid.

Homogeneity of individual conditioning parameters. On the assumption that all subjects have the same conditioning parameter c, Bower (1961) derived the following distribution for the trial n' on which the last error occurs (essentially this distribution was derived earlier by Bush &

Mosteller, 1959).

$$Pr(n' = k)$$

$$= \begin{cases} bp & \text{for } k = 0 \\ b(1 - p)(1 - c)^{k-1} & \text{for } k > 0 \end{cases}$$

where

$$b = \frac{c}{1 - p(1 - c)}$$

The test of the null hypothesis is simply a test of the goodness of fit of this predicted distribution. Because of the relative complexity of the expressions for this distribution we have found it convenient to estimate c by a minimum χ^2 method. The obtained minimum enables us to evaluate at once the goodness of fit of the assumption of homogeneity. When the number of subjects is small, a more sensitive test of significance needs to be used.

The empirical distribution of the trial of the last error is a sufficient statistic for estimating c and is the only statistic that needs to be considered in which the conditioning parameter c enters. For sequences of trials after conditioning, where the probability of a correct response is unity, statistics such as the expected errors before the first success, the variance of this random variable, the expected number of success runs, the expected number of alternations of errors and successes, etc., are totally trivial and uninteresting and are therefore best evaluated on the data prior to the last error where they do not depend upon c. In itself the goodness of fit test for the distribution of last errors is a test of the null hypothesis that subjects have a homogeneous conditioning propensity.

PRELIMINARY DISCUSSION

We initiated the extensive analyses of the preceding pages to investigate two basic assumptions of the simple all-or-none conditioning model: first, the assumption that correct responses before the final error are binomially distributed, and second, that all subjects have the same conditioning parameter. To examine the first hypothesis we suggested four goodness of fit tests to be applied to responses before the final error; these were for stationarity, order—a test of statistical independence of responses from one trial to the next—binomial distribution of responses, and finally the distribution of specific sequences of responses over small blocks of trials. To test the second assumption, that conditioning parameters are homogeneous, we proposed a goodness of fit test for the distribution of trials on which the last error occurs.

We applied the above tests to the data from seven experiments in various areas—three in children's concept formation, two in adult human learning, and two in animal learning. Six of the experiments were two response situations, one—in children's concept formation—involved three responses. Because there were not in every case sufficient observations, we were not able to apply all the tests to the data from every experiment. In general we were able to analyze the animal and children's concept learning experiments quite thoroughly, and the adult learning experiments rather more superficially. Two of the children's concept formation experiments involved subgroups, and wherever possible the tests listed above were applied to the data of each subgroup separately.

The test for stationarity was applied to the data from every experimental group and subgroup. In all we performed 16 such tests—3 of which were on combined data of subgroups which were also tested individually.

In no case was the result of the goodness of fit test significant. In so far as this test is concerned, the evidence that there is no change in the proportion of correct responses over trials— that the process before the final error is in fact stationary—appears to be substantial. We shall return to these results later.

We were able to perform the goodness of fit test for order in 11 cases, none of which were on data from combined groups. Of these test results, 10 were not significant and 1 was highly significant ($.01 > p > .001$). The latter result was from a subgroup of the children's three response concept formation experiment (Geometric Forms). The foregoing results in general provide quite good evidence to support the hypothesis that responses are independent over trials before the final error. However, we earlier pointed out a systematic tendency in the data of at least one of the experiments reported which was not in accord with the statistical evidence of trial independence. In the six subgroups of the Stoll experiment (see Table 1), the probability of a success following a success was in every case slightly greater than the probability of a success following an error. The same slight tendency is shown in the concept learning subgroup of the Binary Numbers experiment and in both animal learning experiments. On the other hand the inequality was reversed for the paired-associate group of the Binary Numbers and the Identity of Sets experiments. For the latter the probability of a success following a success was .81, the probability of a success following an error .85. All the other probabilities referred to are given earlier in the paper. We do not have available the two conditional probabilities for the Goodnow Two-Armed Bandit or the Bower Paired-Associate experiments.

The binomial goodness of fit tests were applied to 10 groups and of the 10 test results 9 were not significant and 1—from a subgroup of a children's concept formation experiment (Geometric Forms)—was again highly significant. Insofar as the test for distribution of specific sequences of responses is concerned, we were able to apply this test in only four cases, of which three gave nonsignificant results and one, again from a subgroup of one of the children's concept formation experiment (Binary Numbers), approached significance ($.05 > p > .02$). From these tests it appears that the assumption of a constant probability of a correct response over responses before the final error, with the consequent implication of independence of trials and a binomial distribution of responses, is not unreasonable.

As far as the test for homogeneity of learning parameters is concerned, the results are by no means unequivocal. We were able to consider this test for only three of the experimental groups—with each of the groups from a different area; one involving animals; one adult human subjects; and the third, young children.

TABLE 1

PROBABILITY OF A SUCCESS FOLLOWING A SUCCESS AND OF A SUCCESS FOLLOWING AN ERROR FOR RESPONSES PRIOR TO THE LAST ERROR

Concept	Problem of success following:	
	Success	Error
Quadrilateral	.63	.58
Pentagon	.63	.55
Acute angle	.70	.61
Right angle	.55	.46
Obtuse angle	.77	.60

Note.—Stoll's experiment on Geometric Forms.

Bower reports that the fit of the observed and predicted distribution of trials on which the last error occurred was very good for the adult humans in the paired-associate learning experiment. On the other hand, we found the fit to be very poor for the animal learning experiment ($p < .001$) and for the children's concept formation experiment (Identity of Sets) it was highly significant when we estimated the conditioning parameter value from the total errors, ($p < .001$) and only just significant at the .02 level when the parameter was estimated by a minimum χ^2 method.

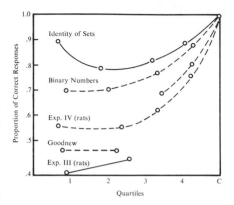

Fig. 10   Vincent learning curves in quartiles for proportion of correct responses prior to last error for five experiments.

Stationarity Reconsidered

The data from the seven experiments we have examined indicate that the simple all-or-none conditioning model is a good first approximation to the actual response behavior in a reasonably wide class of situations. Of the various properties of the model we have statistically examined above, the property of stationarity of response probability prior to the last error is the most crucial for supporting the basic assumption that conditioning occurs on an all-or-none rather than incremental basis.

A rather consistent phenomenon in respect to the stationary learning curves we present above is that of a persistent, though not statistically significant, tendency for the probability of a correct response prior to the last error to increase over trials. This observation naturally gives rise to the question of whether the method of statistical analysis used may not have been such as to miss what is, in fact, a genuine change of probability over trials. One possibility is the following. The individual subject may actually be making a higher proportion of correct responses towards the end of the sequence of trials prior to his last error. At the same time, as the data indicate, individual subjects are becoming conditioned at different rates. When the mean stationarity curve is constructed by averaging over a fixed block of trials for all subjects no account is taken of this individual difference. The result may be that the subjects who meet criterion early—and are therefore making more correct responses—favorably weight the total proportion of correct responses in the early trials and thus appreciably support the null hypothesis of stationarity, in spite of the actual fact of individual change over trials before the last error.

To avoid this possible bias therefore, and to take into account individual differences in trial numbers of last errors we have constructed Vincent-type learning curves for trials prior to the last error. In Figures 1 and 2 the proportion of correct responses is presented over percentiles of trials prior to the last error, instead of the usual blocks of trials. Five of the experiments are shown in

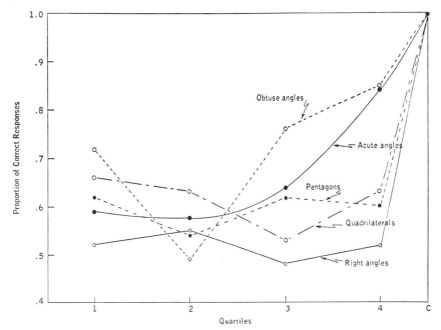

FIG. 2.   Vincent learning curves in quartiles for proportion of correct
responses prior to last error for Stoll's experiment.

Figure 1 and 5 of the subgroups from the Stoll experiment are presented in Figure 2. (The raw data from the Bower experiment were not available for this analysis.) To construct these curves the responses made by each subject, prior to his final error, were divided into quartiles. The first data point on each curve represents the proportion of correct responses in the first 25% of the responses of all subjects. The second, third, and fourth data points similarly represent the further quartiles. At the far right of each figure is shown the criterion point C, where the response proportion is of course, one. As the mean percentile of each of the four quartiles is 12.5%, 37.5%, 62.5%, and 87.5%, respectively, and C represents the 100% point, the distance between Points 4 and C on the abscissa is one half of that between the quartiles themselves.

In the case of the Identity of Sets experiment the curve in Figure 1 is for the 38 subjects in the group who reached criterion, and in the case of the Binary Numbers experiment the curve is for those subjects who achieved concept mastery as defined in the earlier discussion of this experiment.

Nonstationarity and concavity are the two striking characteristics of all five curves in Figure 1. Two of the five curves in Figure 2 also exhibit these properties, whereas the other three are approximately stationary.

The actual frequencies of correct responses in each quartile for all experiments are shown in Table 2, together with the results of the χ^2 test of stationarity—the test being performed with the quartiles as the newly defined trial blocks, so that each test has three degrees of freedom. The

TABLE 2

RAW DATA AND STATIONARY TESTS FOR VINCENT LEARNING CURVES PRIOR TO LAST ERROR,
WHERE N = TOTAL OBSERVATIONS, $n(t)$ = TOTAL OBSERVATIONS IN EACH BLOCK t,
$n_1(t)$ = SUCCESSES IN BLOCK t FOR t = 1, 2, 3, 4

Experiment	N	$n(t)$	$n_1(1)$	$n_1(2)$	$n_1(3)$	$n_1(4)$	x^2
Identity of sets	564	141	117	110	113	126	7.66
Binary numbers	416	104	64	69	71	85	11.01
Goodnow	436	109	49	49	59	86	34.09
Galanter-Bush III	396	99	41	43	56	71	23.40
Galanter-Bush IV	408	102	52	51	58	73	12.39
Quadrilaterals	260	65	43	41	36	41	1.75
Pentagon	260	65	40	35	41	39	1.33
Right angles	320	80	42	44	38	42	.95
Obtuse angles	252	63	45	34	48	51	12.63
Acute angles	340	85	50	49	54	71	16.43

results exactly support the qualitative summary of the curves just given with the single exception of the Identity of Sets experiment, for which the initial guessing probability in the first quartile is already close to one. The Vincent curve for this latter group is in appearance like the rest of the curves in Figure 1, that is concave upward. The statistical significance of the nonstationarity test for six of the curves is in sharp contrast to the nonsignificant results presented earlier for the same experiments. In the earlier case the stationarity test was performed on an initial segment of trials and in that segment responses from the last quartile of subjects who conditioned in the early trials were averaged with responses from those who conditioned after a relatively large number of trials. It will be noted from Figures 1 and 2 that the nonstationary curves are relatively stationary for the first two or three quartiles, which we suggest explains the excellent statistical results for the one-element model considered earlier. A rough but intuitive way of putting it is that the one-element all-or-none conditioning model seems to be accounting for about two-thirds to three-fourths of the data.

On the other hand it is equally evident that the nonstationary concave curves of Figures 1 and 2 cannot be accounted for by the simple all-or-none conditioning model, which predicts a horizontal straight line. It is not immediately clear what kind of model will fit these curves with any accuracy. The problem is complicated by the fact that a percentile scale on the abscissa is not the kind of scale ordinarily used in plotting learning curves. The remainder of this paper is devoted to a brief examination of this problem in which we show that a certain sort of two-element stimulus sampling model can account for the obtained empirical cures.

The two-element model we consider may be psychologically conceptualized as follows.[4] There are two stimulus elements or patterns associated with each experimental situation. With equal probability exactly one of the two elements is sampled on every trial. Let us call the elements σ and τ. When either element is unconditioned there is associated with it a guessing

[4] The intuitive idea of this model originated in a conversation between the first author, Gordon Bower, and Frank Restle.

probability g_σ or g_τ, as the case may be, that the correct response will be made when that unconditioned stimulus is sampled. The assumption of particular importance to the present model—and one that is not familiar in the literature—is that the probability of the sampled stimulus element becoming conditioned is not necessarily the same when both elements are unconditioned as it is when the nonsampled element is already conditioned. We call the first probability a and the second b' (the reason for the prime will become evident in a moment).

Under these assumptions, together with appropriate general independence of path assumptions as given, for example, in Suppes and Atkinson (1960, p. 5), the basic learning process may be represented by the following four state Markov process, where the four states (σ, τ), σ, τ, and 0 represent the possible states of conditioning of the two stimulus elements.

(σ, τ)	σ	τ	0
(σ, τ)	1	0	0	0
σ	$b'/2$	$1 - b'/2$	0	0
τ	$b'/2$	0	$1 - b'/2$	0
0	0	$a/2$	$a/2$	$1 - a$

Because we do not attempt experimentally to identify the stimuli σ and τ, this Markov process may be collapsed into a three-state process, whose states are simply the *number* of stimuli conditioned to the correct response. Here it is convenient to replace $b'/2$ by b and we obtain the transition matrix

	2	1	0
2	1	0	0
1	b	$1 - b$	0
0	0	a	$1 - a$

[5]

Moreover, accompanying the states 0 and 1 we have the guessing probabilities g_0 and g_1 defined in the obvious manner in terms of the sampling probability $\frac{1}{2}$ and the guessing probabilities g_σ and g_τ

$$g_0 = \tfrac{1}{2}g_\sigma + \tfrac{1}{2}g_\tau$$

$$g_1 = \tfrac{1}{4}g_\sigma + \tfrac{1}{4}g_\tau + \tfrac{1}{2} = \tfrac{1}{2}g_0 + \tfrac{1}{2}$$

The probabilities g_σ and g_τ are not observable, but g_0 is, and g_1 is a simple function of it. This means that we have a process with three free parameters, the conditioning parameters a and b, and the guessing probability g_0.

To obtain a simple expression roughly corresponding to the concave curves of Figures 1 and 11, we give here the probability of a correct response on Trial j (Event $A_{1,j}$) *given* that State 2—both stimuli conditioned —was entered on Trial N (Event $2*_N$, $j < N$).

$$P(A_{1,j}|2*_N)$$

$$= (g_1 - g_0)\left[\frac{\alpha^{j-1} - 1}{\alpha^{N-2} - 1} \right] + g_0 \quad [6]$$

where $\alpha = \dfrac{1 - a}{1 - b}$. It is easily shown that the learning curve derived from Equation 6 is concave upward when $b > a$, and convex upward—the standard result—when $b < a$.

The expression for the probability of a correct response on Trial j given that the last error occurred on Trial N is considerably more complicated than Equation 6, but it yields the same concavity results for $b > a$, with convexity for $b < a$. On the other hand, it is not difficult to prove that at least for the simplest incremental model, the one-parameter linear model in which the increment is constant independent of the response made, no such concavity results can be obtained.

Further detailed analysis of data will be required to determine the adequacy of the two-element model proposed here. It is unfortunately not easy to make a good estimate of the three parameters. Moreover, the detailed statistical tests reported for the one-element model are not valid for the two-element model. Evaluation of the goodness of fit of the two-element model is consequently a difficult matter, and is not pursued in this paper.

If a two-element model does turn out to give a good account of the kind of experimental data analyzed in this paper, it may be thought of as a conceptual compromise between incremental and all-or-none conditioning models. The conditioning is all-or-none for each of the two stimulus elements, but the probability of a correct response prior to the last error will be at two different levels, g_0 and g_1, during the sequence of trials prior to criterion.

SUMMARY

A basic assumption of the simple all-or-none conditioning model is that the probability of a correct response remains constant over trials before conditioning. In this paper we have examined that assumption and some of its implications, in some detail. The implications we have specifically tested—using data from a number of different experimental areas to do so—are, over data prior to the last error there will be *no* evidence of learning over trials, responses prior to the last form a sequence of Bernoulli trials, responses prior to the last error exhibit a binomial distribution, and specific sequences of errors and successes are distributed in accordance with the binomial hypothesis. Four goodness of fit tests were used to evaluate the above implications and these are described in detail in the preceding pages. The four tests were performed on the data from seven experiments concerned with concept formation in children, paired-associate learning and probability learning in adults, and T maze learning in rats. The statistical evidence from these various experimental groups provided substantial support of the above predictions. In particular, insofar as the prediction of stationarity over trials before the final error is concerned, in no case was the goodness of fit test significant.

As the statistical method used does not take into account individual differences in the trial number of the last error, and may therefore have biased the data in favor of the null hypothesis, a more refined test of the stationarity process was performed by constructing Vincent-type learning curves. These curves were, for the most part, concave upwards and significantly nonstationary, although a few of the curves remained stationary. Neither the all-or-none single-element conditioning model discussed here, nor a simple incremental model accounts for concave upwards Vincent learning curves, but a simple two-element model was sketched which does predict such results.

REFERENCES

ANDERSON, T. W., & GOODMAN, L. A. Statistical inference about Markov chains. *Ann. math. Statist*, 1957, **28**, 89–110.

BOWER, G. H. Application of a model to paired-associate learning. *Psychometrika*, 1961, **26**, 255–280.

BUSH, R. R., & MOSTELLER, F. A comparison of eight models. In R. R. Bush & W. K. Estes (Eds.), *Studies in mathematical learning theory*. Stanford: Stanford Univer. Press, 1959. Pp. 293–307.

ESTES, W. K.   New developments in statistical behavior theory: Differential tests of axioms for associative learning.   *Psychometrika*, 1961, 26, 73–84.

GALANTER, E., & BUSH, R. R.   Some T-maze experiments.   In R. R. Bush & W. K. Estes (Eds.), *Studies in mathematical learning theory.*   Stanford: Stanford Univer. Press, 1959.   Pp. 265–289.

GOODNOW, J. J.   Determinants of choice distributions in two-choice probability situations.   *Amer. J. Psychol.*, 1955, 68, 106–116.

GOODNOW, J. J., & PETTIGREW, T. F.   Effect of prior patterns of experience upon strategies and learning sets.   *J. exp. Psychol.*, 1955, 49, 381–389.

STERNBERG, S. H.   Application of four models.   In R. R. Bush & W. K. Estes (Eds.), *Studies in mathematical learning theory.*   Stanford: Stanford Univer. Press, 1959.   Pp. 340–381.

STOLL, E. A.   Geometrical concept formation in kindergarten children.   Unpublished doctoral dissertation, Stanford University, 1962.

SUPPES, P., & ATKINSON, R. C.   *Markov learning models for multiperson interactions.*   Stanford: Stanford Univer. Press, 1960.

SUPPES, P., & GINSBERG, R.   Application of a stimulus sampling model to children's concept formation with and without overt correction responses.   *J. exp. Psychol.*, 1962, 63, 330–336.

(Received November 2, 1961)

Experimental Studies of Mathematical Concept Formation in Young Children*

PATRICK SUPPES and ROSE GINSBERG, *Stanford University*

DURING the last three years we have performed a series of experiments in the area of children's mathematical concept formation, a number of which we present in this report. One of our most urgent concerns during this period and one which will probably be of close interest to our readers, has been to try to bring to this somewhat amorphous area precise quantative analysis. To achieve this we have made use of a quantitative theory of psychology, mathematical learning theory [1], which in one form or another has had considerable success in dealing with other behavioral areas [2].

To familiarize the reader with this approach we present, in the following pages, an intuitive description of the assumptions, implications and outcomes of the particular mathematical model employed and have tried to give enough of the theoretical analysis to give the reader some feeling for the possibilities of this kind of approach.

At the same time the empirical variables introduced in these experiments have not been arbitrarily chosen. This experimental project has been run concurrently with the development of a program of primary grade mathematics "Sets and Numbers" [3] which makes use of simple set theoretical notions to introduce the child at the outset to concepts and operations in arithmetic. Consequently the concepts to be learned in each experiment and the experimental variables introduced have some bearing on problems which have arisen through the development of the *Sets and Numbers* program. Because of shortness of space

these experiments are presented only in summarized form and for the same reason we have limited ourselves strictly to rigorous experimental studies. Other studies involving whole classes of children, which have been run to answer some specific problem encountered in developing the *Sets and Numbers* program are not reported here.

THE MODEL

The situation for which the model was developed is one in which a subject is presented on each trial with some stimulus display to which he is required to make a specific response. The subject is always told whether he was correct or incorrect on that trial.

The basic assumption of the model is that in such a situation the correct response will with some probability become associated with, or conditioned to, the stimulus display. If it is conditioned the subject will then, as long as the situation remains unchanged, continue to respond correctly whenever the same stimulus is presented. On the other hand where the correct response is not conditioned to a stimulus display the probability of a correct response is at some chance level which remains constant until the association between stimulus and appropriate response has been established.

To make the theoretical assumptions perfectly clear, consider a paired-associate situation. In this case the subject must learn the correct response to each of a list of stimuli. For example let us say that he must give a specific number response each time we present him with one of a list of nonsense syllables. He must respond with

* Based on paper presented at meeting of Section Q, American Association for the Advancement of Science, Denver, Colorado, December 29, 1961.

This article appeared in *Science Ed.*, 1962, **46**, 230–240.

"2" to the stimulus "tux," with "9" to "fax," and so on. According to our theory, if we consider the responses over trials to some particular item in the list of nonsense syllables, the probability of a correct response will be at some chance level, in other words, the subject will simply be guessing, until on a particular trial conditioning is effected, after which the subject will make no further errors.

Each time therefore, we present the stimulus "tux" the subject makes his guess and is told that the correct response is "2." On some specific trial the association between "tux" and "2" is made and after that, whenever we present "tux" the subject responds correctly. An interesting feature of these very simple assumptions is that if we look only at the responses made by each subject before his final error we know that at least up to that trial the subject has not learned the correct response but has been guessing. The implications of this particular aspect of our theory will be discussed later in this paper.

From the above assumptions, given mathematical expression, it is possible to derive a large number of specific quantitative predictions. For example, statistics for the number of errors such as number of errors before the first success, error runs of length k, number of alternations of success and error can all be estimated as can such sequential statistics as errors on trial n and on trial $n + k$.

Such theoretical predictions provide a sound quantitative basis for comparison with observations taken directly from the data. The advantage of a quantitative rather than the qualitative approach usual to this area is that on the one hand it ensures a more rigorous analysis and on the other permits detailed evaluation of the empirical adequacy of the theory of concept formation used.

THE EXPERIMENTS

Of the experiments summarized below all except the first have in common both the kind of concepts to be acquired and certain experimental methods. Much of the description therefore will be common to these experiments. Experiment I on the other hand, representing a more or less classical type of concept formation experiment is presented by itself.

EXPERIMENT I

This experiment has been presented in considerable detail elsewhere [4]. In essence equal numbers of kindergarden and first grade children were required to learn the binary equivalents of the arabic numerals 4 and 5 (100 and 101). Using different symbols for the binary digits 0 and 1 (such as π, σ, etc.) six completely different stimuli were presented one at a time in random order. The child was required to respond by placing a large 4 or 5 directly upon the stimulus. All the children were told on each trial whether they had made the correct or incorrect response and half of them were also required to correct their responses following an error.

Our main interests in this experiment were firstly, to examine the effect upon learning of requiring the subject to correct overtly a wrong response and secondly, to determine if the simple model described above which had been so successful with paired-associate learning, would account equally well for concept learning.

Our results indicated that the children who do make the immediate correction response after an error perform significantly better than those who do not. This result, in a situation where there are only two possible responses, is contrary to that obtained with adult subjects [5], but is similar to results obtained with lower organisms [6].

The fit of the model described above to the data of this experiment was good. A large number of predicted and observed statistics have been presented for these data and as an example a few of the typical results are presented in Table I.

TABLE I

Predicted and Observed Statistics for Group (N=24) Making Overt Correction Response. Experiment I (Binary Number)

Statistic	Predicted	Observed
1. Expected errors per item per subject	....	4.38*
2. Standard deviation of errors per item per S	3.13	3.00
3. Expected errors before first success	0.92	0.94
4. Standard deviation of errors before 1st success	1.30	1.29
5. Expected number of success runs	2.82	2.83
6. Expected number of error runs	2.44	2.48
7. Expected error runs of length 1	1.36	1.48
8. Expected errors on trial n and on trial $n+1$	1.94	1.86
9. Net difference between success following error and error following error	0.38	0.48

* Used to estimate the single parameter of this model.

In the experimental situation described, as with most concept formation situations, particularly those involving young children, each concept was represented by a small number of different stimuli. In this situation it is possible that the child simply acquires associations between specific stimuli and their appropriate responses, in which case we have essentially a paired-associate situation, which in itself might account for the good fit obtained with the theory employed. In all subsequent experiments summarized in this report therefore, the stimulus displays representing each concept are different on each trial. In such a situation with no stimulus display ever repeated, the question of whether the child can acquire the concepts involved, by recognizing a common property of a number of different displays, is of great empirical interest. Moreover if the data of such an experiment can be adequately described by the simple theory outlined above, quantitative predictions will be possible in an area which has not hitherto lent itself to precise description of this kind.

As our basic interest is in the formation of mathematical concepts, the concept of number is of fundamental importance and in all further experiments this concept was the primary learning task. Explicitly we presented to a child on each trial pictures of two sets of objects. If the number of objects in each set was the same, that is if the sets were equipollent, one of two available answers was experimentally defined as "correct"—if the sets were non-equipollent the alternative response was correct. As a further point of empirical interest, in no single set was there any duplication of objects—a set for example, might consist of a ball and a box—but never of two balls or two boxes. Following our findings in Experiment I—that learning was more rapid when the child was required to make an overt correction response after an error—we included this requirement in all the experiments reported below.

For the following experiments, no attempt will be made to give details of the experimental situation or methodology. Some of the experiments have been reported elsewhere in very considerable detail and where these are available the references will be given. In this report only a very general description of experimental situations and empirical results is offered. In a final theoretical section we will attempt to indicate a few of the interesting quantitative results which are more or less typical of the various situations examined. As indicated earlier in this paper, some interesting implications of the theory used will be discussed and evaluated in terms of the empirical evidence available.

EXPERIMENT II

The learning tasks involved in this experiment were equipollence and non-equipollence of sets and the two related concepts of identity of sets (sets consisting of the same objects regardless of the order of those objects) and ordered sets (sets consisting of the same objects in the same order).

Ninety-six first grade subjects were run, in four groups of 24 each. In one group the subjects were required to learn identity of sets for 56 trials and then equipollence for a further 56 trials. In a second group this order of presentation was reversed. In a third group the subjects learned first ordered sets and then identity and in the fourth group, order followed by identity. Our empirical aim was to establish the most adequate sequence (in terms of efficient learning) of these concepts. More specifically we were asking this kind of a question, "Is it easier for six year old children to learn to match sets, in the sense of matching the number of objects in those sets, after they have learned to match the actual objects in those sets, or vice versa?" At the same time we were specifically interested in the level of acquisition of each of those concepts in children at the beginning of the first grade. And, finally, as discussed earlier, we wished to determine whether children of this age can acquire this kind of concept when every stimulus display representing the concept is different. Our theoretical aims were as before, to examine the adequacy of the simple quantitative model described, in a concept formation situation. In this present situation of course, the test of the model was more rigorous in that any analogy to a paired associate situation was ruled out by the use of different stimulus presentations on each trial.

From our experimental results it is clear that first grade children can learn a common property, or a concept, even in a situation where every stimulus representing that concept is unique. It is true that in this situation with a severe restriction of verbal instruction the concept of equipollence proved to be quite difficult.

A particularly interesting, and unexpected empirical finding was that in no case did prior learning on one of the concepts—order, identity or equipollence—appreciably facilitate learning on a second of these concepts. This is intuitively surprising when one recollects the overlap between these concepts—for example ordered sets are always identical and identical sets are of course, always equipollent. In this experiment, if the learning task was, for example, equipollence of sets one-third of the equipollent sets were ordered and one-third were identical. Hence one would expect that prior learning on identity would have a facilitating effect on learning equipollence. Despite this, prior training on identity of sets did not increase the level of achievement or rate of learning on equipollence. Similarly neither prior training on equipollence nor on order improved learning on identity of sets.

EXPERIMENT III

In this study we compared the rate of learning in two experimental situations—one in which stimulus displays were presented individually in the usual way and the other in which the same stimulus displays were presented by means of colored slides to groups of four children. The concept to be learned was identity of sets and in both situations the children were required to respond by pressing one of two buttons, depending upon whether the stimulus display on that trial was identical or nonidentical. Of the 64 subjects 32 were from first grade, 32 from kindergarten classes.

The results of this investigation suggest that presentation by slides is a less effective learning situation and the younger the child the more this finding seems to apply. At all levels of difficulty of stimulus displays the kindergarten children learned more efficiently when the stimuli were presented to them in individual sessions. On the basis of experimental evidence "difficulty" of a stimulus display is defined here in terms of the number of objects in each of the pairs of sets of objects displayed and the reader will recall that this varied from one to a maximum of three objects in a set.

With one or two element sets displayed on a trial Grade 1 subjects learned only slightly better in the individual session situation than in the slide situation, but when the task was more difficult (stimulus displays of three element sets) the individual learning situation was clearly the most adequate. It should be emphasized that the individual session was strictly experimental so that the amount of interaction between subject and experimenter was paralleled in both individual and slide situation.

Why these two experimental situations should produce different results in terms of efficiency of learning is not yet clear to us. One possibility is the following. It has been shown, both with lower organisms [7] and with young children [8] that the ideal situation for learning is when stimulus, response and reinforcement are contiguous. In the individual session situation these requirements were met, the response buttons were 1½" below the stimulus displays, the reinforcement (colored lights, one for a correct response and one for an incorrect response) were 1" from the stimuli. In the slide presentation situation whereas the stimulus displays and reinforcements were immediately adjacent to each other, the response button which was at the child's hand, was about 3 feet from the screen onto which the stimulus display was projected. Experimentally it has been shown [8] that with children of this age group a separation of 6 inches is sufficient to interfere with efficient learning.

EXPERIMENT IV

Thirty-six kindergarten children in three groups of twelve each were run for sixty trials a day on two successive days in individual experimental sessions during which they were required to learn equipollence of sets.

On Day 1 the stimulus displays presented to the subjects on each trial differed in color between the three groups but were otherwise the same. In Group I all displays were in one color, black. In Group II equipollent sets were presented in red and non-equipollent sets in yellow. For the first twelve trials in Group III equipollent sets were presented in red and non-equipollent sets in yellow, for the remaining 48 trials on that day the two colors were gradually fused until discrimination between them was not possible. On Day 2 all sets were presented to all three Groups in one color, black.

In Group I then, we simply have a situation in which the subject has two days practice under the same conditions with the concept of equipollence. In Group II the child does not need to learn equipollence on Day I, if he simply responds to the *color* difference between equipollent and non-equipollent sets (a very simple discrimination) he will be correct on every trial. If he learns anything about equipollence of sets on the first day therefore, we assume this to be a function of incidental learning. If incidental learning is effective his performance on Day II when the color cue is dropped should at the least, be better than the performance of children in Group I on the first day. In Group III where we give the child the discriminative cue of color difference in the first trials and then very slowly withdraw that cue, the child continues to search the stimulus displays very closely for the color difference, and is thus obliged to pay very close attention to the stimuli.

Of the three groups only Group II approached perfect learning on Day I. In this Group only color discrimination was necessary. Both the other groups did not improve over the first 60 trials, although Group III showed initial improvement over those trials where the color cues remained discriminable. On the second day Group I showed no improvement and the learning curves for this group and for Group II were practically identical. In Group III on the other hand, the results were conspicuously better on the second day than were those of any other group. Apparently the task we had chosen was very difficult—in view of the fact that no improvement was shown by Group I over a total of 120 trials—but even in this case the conditions of Group III, where the children were forced to pay very close attention to the stimuli, significantly enhanced learned.

EXPERIMENT V

In the experiments described up to this point, we have been concerned with the effect upon learning of variations in the stimulus displays, in the present experiment we introduce variations in the methods of response. Specifically three groups, each composed of 20 kindergarten children, were taken individually through a sequence of 60 trials on each of two successive days for a total of 120 trials.

In Group I the child was presented with pictures of two sets of objects and indicated, by pressing one of two buttons, whether the sets "went together" or did not "go together" (were equipollent or non-equipollent).

In Group II the child was presented with one display set and *two* "answer" sets and was required to choose the "answer" which "went together" with the display set.

In Group III the child was presented with one display set and *three* "answer" sets and made his choice from the three possible answers.

This situation has immediate reference to teaching methodology in the sense that Group II and Group III represent a multiple choice situation. In Group I where the child is required to identify either the presence of the concept or its absence on each trial, the situation is comparable to one in which the child must indicate whether an equation or statement is correct or incorrect.

On the first day each group of children learned the task as described above. On the second day they were run on an alternative method. Specifically Group I was run under Group III conditions and Groups II and III were run in the Group I situation.

Although we intend to run a further group of children in the present experimental situation before we attempt a fine analysis of these results, some clear and interesting empirical results have become apparent. In Group II—where the subjects were required to choose from one of two available responses—the subjects learned slightly more quickly and to a slightly better level of achievement on Day 1 than in the other Groups but, on the second day, when the experimental conditions were shifted, Group II subjects did considerably less well than the subjects in the other two Groups.

When we examined, separately, the data from subjects achieving criterion of 12 successive correct responses on the first day and those who did not achieve that criterion, the more successful method was clearly that used in Group I. The subjects in this Group were conspicuously more successful than the other Groups in dealing with the new situation on the second day, making in fact, no errors on that day from trial 30 to trial 60. Group III achieved perfect scores on the second day only in the last six trials, and Group II never reached that level on Day 2, although they, like the other criterion subjects, had achieved perfect learning on the first day.

It appears that the method used with Group I, where subjects were required to recognize the presence or absence of some property on each trial is the more successful method in establishing understanding of a concept well enough to permit transfer to a different situation.

If we assume, as seems reasonable, that in concept learning transfer from one situation to another is a good indication of the level of understanding of the concept learned, then a multiple choice method of response with only two available responses, seems a particularly ineffective method of acquisition. Of the three response methods compared in this experiment, that requiring the child to identify the presence or absence of the concept to be learned on each trial was considerably the most successful.

THEORETICAL ANALYSIS

The mathematical model described at the beginning of this paper was intended for a paired associate situation. We applied it to our first experimental concept formation data (Experiment I) where six stimulus displays represented two concepts, by assuming that each of the stimulus displays involved could be treated as if it were an independent item. In effect we treated the situation as if it were a paired-associate situation with a list of six independent items to be learned. In subsequent experiments however, where every stimulus display representing a concept was different so that no stimulus display was ever repeated for any one subject, this would have been analogous to assuming a "paired associate list" with as many items in it as there were trials in the experiment.

This, therefore, required some interpretation of our situation which would enable us to define a "stimulus item" in some other way than as identified with any specific stimulus display. There are several methods of analysis which may be used in this situation, most of which we examined but we mention here only two of these.

In each case the specific stimulus to be learned is defined as some property of the stimulus display, in other words it is identical with the concept itself. Consider, for example, experimental trials where the subject must learn equipollence of sets. We may here consider all equipollent stimulus displays as representing the one concept, equipollence, and all non-equipollent sets as representing the concept of non-equipollence. So that we have two concepts to be learned, or in a paired-associate sense we have a list of two items. If we wish to do so we could, in fact, consider all stimulus

displays, equipollent and non-equipollent, as representing the one concept of equipollence and analyze our data as if we had a single concept item to be learned.

The detailed analysis which we performed for Experiment I, as instanced by the statistics listed in Table I, were performed in Experiment II for two of our groups combined. In this case we had sufficient subjects (48) to make predicted and observed comparisons of some of the sequential statistics that would not otherwise, with fewer observations, have been possible. We analyzed these data from a "two item list" point of view and the results were good. In view of the wide assumptions we made in this situation that 2 abstract concepts could be treated exactly as if they were specific stimulus displays in themselves, we feel almost inclined to say that the results were surprisingly good! Again, as an example of these results, we present below in Table II some of the obtained and predicted statistics for these data.

TABLE II

PREDICTED AND OBSERVED STATISTICS FOR CONCEPT FORMATION EXPERIMENT II (N=48) WITH NON-REPEATED STIMULUS DISPLAYS

Statistic	Predicted	Observed
1. Expected errors per item per S	....	2.64
2. s.d. of errors per item per S	2.38	2.61
3. Expected errors before first success	.27	.25
4. s.d. of errors before first successes	.58	.50
5. Expected number of success runs	2.88	2.91
6. Expected number of alternations of success and failure	3.99	4.07
7. Net difference between success following error and error following error	1.55	1.66
8. Net difference between error following error and error following success	−1.36	−1.48

SOME IMPLICATIONS OF THE MODEL

We indicated earlier that certain implications are implicit in the assumptions of the quantitative theory we have used to analyze the present concept formation experiments. These implications we feel, provide a more rigorous test of the model than do the numerous statistics we have previously calculated, examples of which are given in Table I and II.

To illustrate these implications we would remind the reader that a basic assumption of the theory employed is that, over trials before the correct association is made between stimulus display and its appropriate response, the probability of a correct response is at chance level, which is to say that the subject is simply guessing. Moreover the "guessing level" is assumed to remain constant over these trials. Immediately after the correct association is made, the probability of a correct response is one. This model is in fact, one of the class known as "all-or-none" models [6] in the sense that it is assumed that learning occurs, not in an incremental fashion over trials, but immediately and completely on one trial (hence the "all-or-none" description). If therefore, we look only at the trials before the final error occurs for each subject (an event directly observable in the subject's protocol) according to our model the probability of a correct response over these trials remains constant at some "guessing" level. Hence over these trials, instead of the traditional negatively accelerated learning curve, our theory would predict a horizontal line. This prediction can be immediately tested by a simple χ^2 goodness-of-fit test for stationarity. The precise statistic employed is described in Suppes and Atkinson [10].

At the same time the reader will recollect that repeated independent trials with a fixed set of possible outcomes for each trial and with constant probabilities throughout the trials exactly defines Bernoulli trials. A test for independent trials

is immediately possible—again the appropriate statistic is described in Suppes and Atkinson [10]. For the experiments with more than two responses it is simplest to apply the test in terms of the two categories of correct and incorrect responses. The probability of k successes in n Bernoulli trials has the binomial distribution

$$\binom{n}{k} p^k q^{n-k}$$

If therefore, we divide our data into blocks of, say 4, trials making the best estimate of p by using the mean probability of a correct response over all trials before the final error, our n in this case would be 4. As from 0 to 4 errors are possible in a block of 4 trials we can estimate the predicted frequencies of successes for each value of k ($k=0, 1, 2, 3, 4$) and compare by means of a χ^2 goodness-of-fit test with the frequencies obtained from the data. Or we may make an even more stringent test by considering the frequencies of specific sequences of successes and failures in every block of four responses. There are 16 combinations of successes and failures possible in four trials and we can predict a frequency of occurrence for each of these combinations. These predicted frequencies can again be compared with the empirical frequencies.

Not all the experimental data from the experiment mentioned in this report have yet been analyzed by the methods indicated above but the tests enumerated have been applied to the data from both groups in Experiment I and all 8 subgroups in Experiment II. In all ten cases the tests for stationarity and independence of trials were non significant so that these assumptions were well confirmed.

As further examples of some of our theoretical and empirical results we present below in Figure 1 the empirical and predicted histogram for the binomial distribution of correct responses in blocks of 4

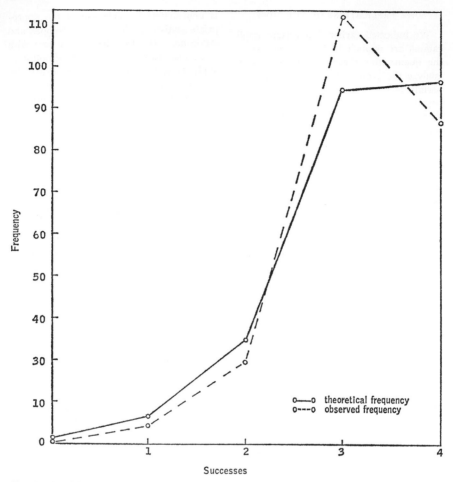

FIG. 1. Empirical and predicted histogram for binomial distribution of correct responses in blocks of 4 trials (Identity of sets experiment).

trials for the 48 subjects in Exp. 2 whose learning task was identity of sets. In Table III we present a frequency distribution for predicted and obtained number of specific sequences of errors and successes in blocks of 4 trials for the group of 24 subjects who learned equipollence of sets *after* having learned identity of sets first. These examples provide fairly typical results of this kind of analysis as far as it is completed to date, and supply quite encouraging

confirmation of the present theoretical position.

SUMMARY

A series of experiments in children's concept formation has been presented and some of the empirical and theoretical results listed. Some of our findings which would seem to have immediate import to the pedagogical situation are:

1. Learning is more efficient if the child

TABLE III

Frequency Distribution of Sequences of Errors and Successes Over Blocks of 4 Trials (Exp. II. Learning Task- Equipollence of Sets *after* Identify of Sets. N=24)

	Obtained Frequency	Predicted Frequency
0000	0	1.37
1000	1	1.40
0100	3	1.40
0010	3	1.40
0001	0	1.40
1100	4	5.37
0110	8	5.37
0011	4	5.37
1001	5	5.37
1010	2	5.37
0101	2	5.37
1110	21	20.55
1101	23	20.55
1011	16	20.55
0111	34	20.55
1111	73	78.58

who makes an error is required to make the correct response in the presence of the stimulus to be learned (Exp. I).

2. Incidental learning does not appear to be an effective method of acquisition for young children. In Exp. IV the group of children who responded to a color discrimination in a concept formation situation, did not subsequently give any indication of having learned the underlying concept.

3. A condition which focuses the child's attention upon the stimuli to be learned, enhances learning (Exp. IV).

4. Transfer of a concept is more effective if the learning situation has required the subject to recognize the presence or absence of a concept in a number of stimulus displays than if learning has involved matching from a number of possible responses. At the same time a multiple answer situation involving three responses is more effective than one involving only two possible responses (Exp. V).

5. A young child's learning tends to be very specific. In Exp. II prior training on one concept did not improve learning on a related concept.

Some of these results are unexpected. For example in Exp. IV we found incidental learning to be quite inefficient although much reliance has been placed on its effectiveness in the teaching situation, especially in the case of younger children.

Moreover, the reader will recall that at least two of our experiments achieved results not typical of adult behavior but confirming experimental results with lower organisms. We believe this to be an important point to hold in mind. At the same time the small child can, of course, be taught quite complex concepts. For example in the *Sets and Numbers* program we find that the average first grader can solve simple equations which involve the use of letters as variables, can alternate between set operations and arithmetic operations as required by the problem at hand or can deal with problems in which numbers are represented by two different kinds of notation. But the intellectual capacity of the child is one which the adult, as he himself shares it, can readily take into account. On the other hand it is difficult to appreciate that variables not generally important in adult learning behavior—such as slight variations in the response required, or the immediate overt correction of an incorrect response—may enhance or seriously interfere with learning in the young child.

In this report we have also presented a verbal description of a mathematical model of learning and in our minds of equal importance with the empirical conclusions discussed above is the success we have achieved in making detailed quantitative behavior predictions, based on this theory.

REFERENCES

1. Estes, W. K. *The Statistical Approach to Learning Theory.* In S. Koch (Ed.), *Psychology: A Study of a Science.* Vol. 2. McGraw-Hill Book Company, Inc. (1959), pp. 380–491.
2. Bower, G. H. "Application of a Model to Paired Associate Learning," *Psychometrika* (1961), 26:3, 255–280.
3. Suppes, P. *Sets and Numbers.* Stanford, California, 1961.
4. Suppes, P. and Ginsberg, R. "Application

of a Stimulus Sampling Model to Childrens Concept Formation of Binary Numbers, with and without an Overt Correction Response," *J. Exp. Psychol.* (In press.)

5. Burke, C. J., Estes, W. K. and Hellyer, S. "Rate of Verbal Conditioning in Relation to Stimulus Variability," *J. Exp. Psychol.* (1954), 48:153–161.

6. Hull, C. C. and Spence, K. W. " 'Correction' vs. 'Non-Correction' Method of Trial-and-Error Learning in Rats," *J. Comp. Psychol.* (1938), 25:127–145.

7. Murphy, J. V. and Miller, R. E. "The Effect of Spatial Contiguity of Cue and Reward in the Object-Quality Learning of Rhesus Mon-

keys," *J. Comp. Physiol. Psychol.* (1955), 48: 221–229.

8. Murphy, J. V. and Miller, R. E. "Spatial Contiguity of Cue, Reward, and Response in Discrimination Learning by Children," *J. Exp. Psychol.* (1959), 58:485–489.

9. Suppes, P. and Ginsberg, R. "A Fundamental Property of All-or-None Models, Binomial Distribution of Responses Prior to Conditioning, with Application to Concept Formation in Children," *Psychol. Rev.* (In press.)

10. Suppes, P. and Atkinson, R. C. *Markov Learning Models for Multiperson Interactions.* Stanford University Press, 1960, p. 56.

11. *Ibid.,* p. 57.

All-or-None Learning and the Role of Repetition in Paired-Associate Learning

WALTER KINTSCH, *University of Missouri*

The learning of a list of stimulus-response items is a two-stage process involving response learning and association. It is assumed that both stages are learned in an all-or-none fashion. Subjects were trained to learn a list of paired-associate items with Rock's substitution procedure. Their performance could be predicted from the all-or-none theory with parameter estimates based upon the performance of a different group of subjects who learned the same items under normal conditions.

In paired-associate learning the learning material is arranged in pairs consisting of a stimulus item and a response item. The stimulus-response pairs are first presented together and then the stimulus item is shown alone and the subject is asked to give the response item. Normally item pairs are repeated until the subject always gives the correct response. With the substitution procedure, however, an item pair is replaced with a new one whenever the subject fails to give the correct response.

Rock (1) found that this procedure did not retard learning when compared to the usual procedure of repeated presentation of all items. From this finding he concluded that learning was not gradual but an all-or-none phenomenon, since replacing "wrong" items should lead to slower learning if learning were incremental. The idea of all-or-none learning has achieved a certain popularity in the meantime, but Rock's initial evidence has been questioned by recent investigators. A process of item selection confounded the results obtained with the substitution procedure. Difficult items were not learned and were therefore replaced by new items in the substitution condition, but in the control group subjects had to master all associations. Thus the subjects in the substitution group learned, in effect, an easier list than subjects in the control group.

It now appears that the substitution procedure retards learning whenever proper control groups are used to account for the effects of item selection (2) or when these effects are minimized by the use of items which are very homogeneous in difficulty (3). The present report attempts to show that this result not only does not contradict an all-or-none theory of learning, but can be quantitatively predicted from such a theory. The model proposed here uses the finding that the learning of a stimulus-response pair is a two-stage task (see, for example, 4). First, the response must be learned and then it can be associated with the proper stimulus. It is assumed here that both of these processes occur in an all-or-none fashion. Such a model will, of course, predict impairment of learning under the substitution procedure because items will sometimes be discarded after the response has already been acquired though not yet hooked up to the correct stimulus.

Consider a three-state Markov process. The two stages, response learning and association, correspond to two transitions, first from a state C_0 of no learning to a state C_1 where the response is learned but not yet connected to the right stimulus, and then from state C_1 to state C_2 when the association occurs. Let p represent the probability of a correct response to an item for which only response learning has occurred. Then the probability that the correct response will be given to a stimulus will be 0, p, or 1 in states C_0, C_1, and C_2, respectively. These assumptions are expressed in transition matrix Q, where for reasons of mathematical convenience the state C_1 has been subdivided, depending upon whether the subject makes an error (with probability $1 - p = q$) or a success (with probability p).

$$Q = \begin{array}{c} \\ C_0 \\ C_{1e} \\ C_{1s} \\ C_2 \end{array} \begin{array}{cccc} C_0 & C_{1e} & C_{1s} & C_2 \\ \left[\begin{array}{cccc} (1-c) & cq & cp & 0 \\ 0 & (1-e)q & (1-e)p & e \\ 0 & (1-s)q & (1-s)p & s \\ 0 & 0 & 0 & 1 \end{array}\right] \end{array}$$

The four parameters of the model are c, the probability of response learning, e, the probability of association after the subject has made an error in state C_1, s, the same probability after a success, and p, as defined above (5). This model is based upon Estes' "two element pattern model" and was first employed and described in detail by Bower and Theios (6). The model implies that as long as a subject is in state C_1 successes will occur with probability p, independent of what happened on the previous trial. A great number of predictions concerning various statistics of the data are also implied. For instance, the first row of the matrix Q^n contains the probabilities of being in each one of the states C_0, C_{1e}, C_{1s}, and C_2 on trial n, since the process always begins in C_0. The predicted proportion of errors on that trial will then be the sum of the first two of these terms, since errors can only be made in C_0 and C_{1e}.

All predictions will be expressions involving some or all of the parameters of the model. By setting three of these theoretical expressions equal to their observed values and solving the resulting equations simultaneously for c, e, and s, estimates for these parameters can be obtained (7). Since p is the probability of success after the response has been learned but not yet connected to the right stimulus, the observed proportion of successes on the trials between the first success and the last failure serves as an estimate for it. No desirable statistical properties of these estimates are known, but they are acceptable in the sense that a fairly good fit of the model is achieved with them.

When the substitution procedure described above is used, Q will no longer be a correct representation because with probability 1 the subject returns from state C_{1e} to C_0. These two states therefore become indistinguishable and the

Table 1. Predictions and data for the control group.

Item	Predicted	Observed
Mean number of errors per item	3.79*	3.79
Standard deviation	2.45	2.15
Mean number of trials before the first success	3.40*	3.40
Standard deviation	2.42	2.01
Mean trial of last error	4.15	4.29
Standard deviation	2.92	2.76
Mean number of error runs per item	1.26	1.27
Number of error runs of length 1	.40	.32
Number of error runs of length 2	.27	.30
Number of error runs of length 3	.20	.26
Number of error runs of length 4	.13	.16
Number of error runs of length 5	.09	.07
Number of error runs of length 6	.06	.07
Number of error runs of length 7	.04	.05

* Used for estimation.

transition matrix characterizing the substitution condition can be written as

$$Q^* = \begin{array}{c} C_0, C_{1e} \\ C_{1s} \\ C_2 \end{array} \begin{array}{ccc} C_0, C_{1e} & C_{1s} & C_2 \\ \left[\begin{array}{ccc} (1-c)+cq & cp & 0 \\ (1-s)q & (1-s)p & s \\ 0 & 0 & 1 \end{array} \right] \end{array}$$

Several predictions about subjects' behavior under the substitution procedure can be derived from Q^*. For example the mean proportion of errors on trial n will be given by the upper left-hand entry in the matrix Q^{*n}. These predictions are made without using any of the data for parameter estimation. Instead, estimates for c, s, and p were obtained from matrix Q, that is, from the behavior of a separate control group which learned the same material under normal conditions. These estimates should predict the behavior of the experimental group when inserted into Q^* if the two transition matrices given above correctly represent the situation.

In order to test these predictions two groups of 23 subjects each were given a list of paired-associate items to learn. The items were two-place numbers paired with nonsense syllables. The syllables were of about 55-percent association value and pairs were selected for homogeneity on the basis of a rating procedure (8). Each subject learned a list of eight randomly selected pairs. A trial consisted of a presentation of the eight pairs, each for 4 seconds, during which the subject read the number-nonsense syllable pair aloud. Immediately afterwards each stimulus number was presented alone for 4 seconds and the subject was asked to give the proper response. The order of items was randomized for each presentation. Learning in the control group was continued to a criterion of three successive correct trials. For the experimental group the substitution procedure was used, that is, whenever a subject did not give the correct response on a test trial the item was replaced by a randomly selected new number-syllable pair. Ten trials were given. In order to acquaint the subjects in both groups with the experimental procedure they were given practice trials with a six-syllable list until they reached a criterion of one errorless trial.

The most important results of this experiment are presented in Fig. 1. The substitution procedure retarded learning in the amount predicted by the two-stage model. The theoretical curves in Fig. 1 were obtained by estimating the parameters of the model from the

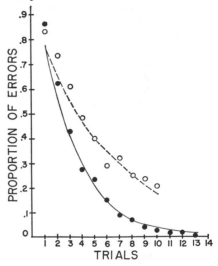

Fig. 1. Proportion of errors made by experimental subjects (open circles) and controls (solid circles). The smooth curves are the predictions derived from the two-stage model.

data of the control group ($c = .35$, $s = .55$, $e = .17$, $p = .61$). The predicted mean learning curve for the experimental group was then computed by inserting these values into Q^{*n}. Considering that no data from the experimental group were used for this prediction, the fit is quite good. The occurrence of more errors than predicted during the first few trials in both the control and experimental groups might possibly be due to a warm-up effect in the experiment because of insufficient pretraining.

The probability of an item being replaced after one or more correct responses was .29; predicted was .24.

Apart from predictions concerning the experimental group, the model can also be used to describe the behavior of the control group. The crucial point here is the prediction that successes in state C_1 will be independent events, emitted with a stationary probability p. On trials between the first success and the last error subjects must be in state C_1. A Vincentized learning curve based upon responses on these trials reveals that the proportion of errors decreases from .39 in the first half of the trials to .36 in the second, which is far from being statistically significant ($\chi^2 = .12$). A test for independence also led to a nonsignificant χ^2 value ($\chi^2 = 1.47$, one degree of freedom). These results are in good agreement with the model but they are based upon too small a portion of the data, since, owing to the generally fast learning, many items did not have any responses between the first success and last error. Statistics which are based upon all items with their predictions derived from the two-stage model are given in Table 1.

The results of the present experiment were completely confirmed in a second experiment. The two-stage model predicted 5.09 errors per item during the first 10 trials in the substitution condition; 5.16 were observed. Again, this is a true prediction, since no data of the experimental group were used for parameter estimation. The only difference between the two experiments was that in the second experiment subjects were not required to read all items aloud. This experiment was therefore more open to the criticism that any observed all-or-none behavior simply reflected the fact that subjects could concentrate upon a few items at a time.

In spite of the successful predictions derived from the present model, a major problem remains. What has proved its usefulness here is a two-stage Markov model. The interpretation given to the two stages in terms of response learning and associative stages has not been tested directly. In order to do this, it would be necessary to show that the parameters of the model are differentially affected by experimental manipulations of the amount of response learning required and the difficulty of association (9).

REFERENCES AND NOTES

1. I. Rock, *Am. J. Psychol.* **70,** 186 (1957).
2. B. J. Underwood, R. Rehula, G. Keppel, *ibid.* **75,** 353 (1962); L. Postman, *ibid.* **75,** 372 (1962).
3. W. F. Battig, *J. Exptl. Psychol.* **64,** 87 (1962).
4. B. J. Underwood and R. W. Schulz, *Meaningfulness and Verbal Learning* (Lippincott, Chicago, 1962).
5. A similar model was also tried in which one-step transitions from C_0 to C_2 were allowed, but it predicted poorly the results obtained with the substitution procedure.
6. W. K. Estes, in *Studies in Mathematical Learning Theory*, R. R. Bush and W. K. Estes, Eds. (Stanford Univ. Press, Stanford, Calif., 1959), p. 9; G. H. Bower and J. Theios, in *Studies in Mathematical Psychology*, R. C. Atkinson, Ed. (Stanford Univ. Press, Stanford, Calif., in press).
7. The expressions used are the mean number of errors, the mean trials before the first success, and the mean number of times a success is followed by an error. For details of the estimation procedure as well as for the derivation of other predictions see Bower and Theios (6).
8. This procedure resulted in quite a homogeneous item pool. Only very little evidence of item selection due to differential difficulty was found in the present experiment.
9. The assistance of Jacqueline Bragg and Don McCoy in collecting part of the data is acknowledged. This research was supported by NSF grant GB–195.

February 11, 1963

Association and Discrimination in Paired-Associate Learning[1]

Martha C. Polson, Frank Restle, and Peter G. Polson,
Indiana University

A paired-associates list with 8 unique items and 8 confusable twinned stimuli, was administered to 50 Ss by the anticipation method. Responses were 5 common nouns, highly integrated and discriminable, and prelearned by Ss. Unique items were learned in an all-or-nothing fashion, but twin items were learned in 2 steps, association and stimulus discrimination, each of which was all-or-nothing. A discontinuous multiple-process model, based on strategy-selection theory, was shown to fit the data.

One branch of the theory of paired-associates (PA) learning, stemming from E. J. Gibson's (1940) work on stimulus differentiation, says that a PA may be learned through several processes. Underwood and others (Underwood, Runquist, & Schulz, 1959; Underwood & Schulz, 1960) have extended the idea, and shown that along with stimulus discrimination there are separable processes of response discrimination and response integration. McGuire (1961) has partitioned errors into those caused by confusions between stimuli, those caused by lack of response integration, and associative failures. If S gives the response that belongs with a similar stimulus, then the error is attributable to stimulus confusion. If the response S makes is part of, or similar to, the correct answer, then the error is a failure of response integration or discrimination (Shep-

[1] Preparation of this report was supported in part by National Science Foundation Grant No. GB 319 to the second author. The authors wish to thank Garry Flint and Gary Holstrom who helped in collecting, handling, and analyzing data; and David Kern for writing the program for generating the random orders and experimental procedures. The Indiana University Research Computing Center made a grant of machine time for these purposes, and it is gratefully acknowledged.

ard, 1957). Omission or any other error is probably caused by lack of the correct association. This analysis of errors gives a picture of the processes involved in learning a PA list.

A second diverging branch of paired-associate theory begins with Rock (1957) followed by Estes (1959, 1960), Estes, Hopkins, and Crothers, (1960), and Bower (1961). These authors assert that ordinary PA learning occurs as an all-or-nothing process, and show that if stimuli are easily discriminated, responses are discrete and well known to S, and training proceeds at a leisurely pace, all-or-nothing (discontinuous) data may be observed.

Three main experimental methods have been used to test the all-or-nothing hypothesis; Rock's item-replacement method (Rock, 1957), Estes' miniature experiment (Estes, 1960; Estes et al., 1960), and the method of teaching a PA list by anticipation and then analyzing the data in detail (Bower, 1961; Bush & Mosteller, 1959). We employ the third method, using level of performance before the last error, the learning curve, $P(\mathcal{E}_n)$, the distribution of total errors (T), and the distribution of trial of last error (n'), as summary descriptions of the data.

This article appeared in *J. exp. Psychol.*, 1965, **69,** 47–55.

In Bower's all-or-none PA model S with respect to a given item begins in State S_0. His responses in S_0 are correct or wrong with probabilities p and q. On any trial with probability c he shifts to State S_1 on that item, and makes no more errors.

Before the last error, performance is stationary with a probability p of giving a correct response. The learning curve, probability of an error on Trial n, is given by

$$P(\mathcal{E}_n) = q(1 - c)^{n-1} \quad [1]$$

Distribution of Total Errors per Item (T_0):

$$P(T_0 = 0) = bp \quad [2]$$

$$P(T_0 = k) = (1 - bp)b(1 - b)^{k-1}$$
$$\text{for any } k > 0.$$

Here b is the probability of no more errors following a given error, and is

$$b = \frac{c}{q + pc}$$

The distribution of total errors per item has mean

$$E(T_0) = q/c = u_0$$

and variance

$$\text{Var}(T_0) = u_0 + (1 - 2c)u^2_0$$

Trial of Last Error (n'_0)

$$P(n'_0 = 0) = bp \quad [3]$$

$$P(n'_0 = k) = qb(1 - c)^{k-1}$$
$$\text{for all } k > 0.$$

The mean trial of the last error is

$$E(n'_0) = m_0 = bu_0/c$$

$$\text{Var}(n'_0) = m_0 \left(\frac{2}{c} - 1 - m_0 \right).$$

An older all-or-nothing learning theory (called the "noncontinuity" or "insight" theory) has been applied to discrimination learning (Lashley, 1929). Several recent papers have revived this theory as a mathematical model (Bower & Trabasso, 1963; Restle, 1961, 1962; Trabasso, 1961, 1963). Assume that S begins with some strategy on which he bases responses. When a strategy fails, S resamples with replacement from his set of strategies. Suppose that strategies can be partitioned into irrelevant ones, which lead to success and failure with probabilities P and Q, and correct strategies which always lead to success. Let S_I be the presolution state of using an irrelevant strategy and S_L be the solution state of using a correct strategy. Let d be the proportion of correct strategies. The S will go from S_I to S_L only when his strategy fails, and then only with probability d. This model has the properties,

Learning Curve:

$$P(\mathcal{E}_n) = Q(1 - Qd)^{n-1}(1 - d), \quad [4]$$

Distribution of Total Errors:

$$P(T_1 = k) = (1 - d)^k d,$$
$$E(T_1) = (1 - d)/d \quad [5]$$
$$\text{Var}(T_1) = (1 - d)/d^2$$

Distribution of Trial of Last Error:

$$P(n'_1 = 0) = d \quad [6]$$

$$P(n'_1 = k) = (1 - Qd)^{k-1}Qd(1 - d)$$
$$\text{for all } k > 0.$$
$$E(n'_1) = (1 - d)/Qd = m_1$$
$$\text{Var}(n'_1) = m_1(2 + Qd - m_1).$$

The Bower association model and the noncontinuity theory of discrimination learning can be combined into a more comprehensive theory of PA learning. To obtain all-or-none PA data, Es eliminate all sources of difficulty except simple association. In particular, both stimulus discrimination and response integration are made very easy. However, PA experiments may involve several processes other than association. To account for the results of such experiments we propose a *Discontinuous Multiprocess* theory in which each process is an all-or-nothing event. This idea has been developed and given detailed support by analysis of some existing data (Restle, 1963). A more definite test is made herein by first showing the distinctive mathematical properties of a discontinuous two-process model, then performing a detailed experimental test.

The model is as follows: Initially, in State S_0, S does not know the correct response and guesses among the response alternatives, having a constant probability p of being correct and distributing his errors among various responses. With probability c on any trial he learns the response to that item. If the stimulus is unique, S has mastered the item. If there is a confusable twin stimulus, then S may enter an intermediate State S_I in which he knows the response but cannot differentiate between stimuli. He therefore, with probability Q, makes a stimulus confusion error. On any error S resamples and may, with probability d, choose a discriminating strategy and stop confusing the twin stimuli. At that time he enters State S_L and since he has both formed the association and the discrimination, he performs correctly. Both steps of learning can occur on the same trial. The arrangement of states is as shown in Fig. 1.

The following statistical properties can be derived by elementary, though somewhat laborious methods:

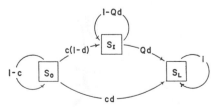

FIG. 1. Arrangement of states in the two-process model.

Learning Curve:

$$P(\mathscr{E}_n) = q(1 - c)^{n-1} + \frac{Qc(1 - d)}{c - dQ}$$
$$\times [(1 - dQ)^{n-1} - (1 - c)^{n-1}] \quad [7]$$

Distribution of Total Errors:

$$P(T = k) = \frac{bd}{b - d}$$
$$\times [(1 - dp)(1 - d)^n$$
$$- (1 - bp)(1 - b)^n] \quad [8]$$

$$E(T) = E(T_0) + E(T_1)$$
from Equations 2 and 5.
$$\mathrm{Var}(T) = \mathrm{Var}(T_0) + \mathrm{Var}(T_1).$$

These results follow because total errors is the convolution (Feller, 1957) of the distributions of errors in States S_0 and S_I.

Trial of last error is dealt with in two parts. If no errors are made in State S_I (with probability d), then the last error is made in S_0, as given in Equation 3. If an error is made in S_I (probability $1 - d$), then the trial of the last error is the convolution of the distribution of trials in State S_0 (not trial of last error in that state) with the distribution of trial of last error in S_I. This gives Trial of Last Error:

$$P(n' = k) = dbp \quad \text{for } k = 0 \quad [9]$$
$$= dqb(1 - c)^{k-1} + \frac{c(1 - d)dQ}{dQ - c}$$
$$[(1 - c)^{k-1} - (1 - dQ)^{k-1}]$$
$$\text{for } k > 0.$$
$$E(n') = dm_0 + (1 - d)\left[\frac{1}{c} + \frac{1}{dQ}\right]$$

For mathematical details and several related applications see Restle (1963).

This discontinuous two-process theory agrees in substance with McGuire's position that PA learning may involve separate processes, and that the processes can be separated experimentally and also by analysis of errors. The learning curves of the separate types of errors are fit well by both theories.

The discontinuous theory is like McGuire's, but goes beyond. First, by defining specific states, it makes possible the use of ordinary discrete probability theory. Second, the discontinuous theory generates not only mean group effects, but distributions of statistics. An extra advantage of the discontinuous multiple-process theory is that it gives a definition of an irreducible process. The analysis of PA learning into separate processes is terminated whenever all processes yield geometric distributions. This prevents an infinite regress of subdivisions which might occur with continuous models and a determined theorist. To test the discrete two-stage theory, we performed a direct experimental analysis of the effect of stimulus similarity in PA learning, to see if it produces a separate and unitary stage of learning.

METHOD

A mixed-list design was used. Every S learned a list composed half of PAs with unique stimuli and half of PAs with confusable twinned stimuli.

Subjects.—In fulfillment of course requirements, 52 introductory psychology students served as Ss. Two failed to learn in 30 trials, were found not to have understood instructions, and were discarded, leaving 50 Ss in the analysis.

Apparatus and materials.—The Ss sat at a table across from E and were shown flash cards over the top of an 18-in. screen. Stimuli were symbols and outline pictures; all 16 are shown in Fig. 2. As can be seen there were 8 unique and 8 twinned stimuli. Responses were the words COST, HOPE, PART, RUSH, and ONLY, which are among the most frequent 1,000 words (Thorndike & Lorge, 1944). Responses were assigned randomly to stimuli, separately for each S, with the restriction that twinned stimuli never both had the same response. Also no two pair of twinned stimuli had the same pair of responses for a given S.

Procedure.—Before beginning the PA task S was taught the five responses by having to repeat them in an order said by E. Five different orders were given until all were recited perfectly, and then S was required to repeat the words in any order. All Ss succeeded.

In instructions, S was informed that some stimuli would be very similar to others; that each stimulus had one and only one correct response which would not change; and that each response would be the answer to more than one stimulus.

The stimulus card was shown until S responded, after which E gave the correct answer orally. Next was a 3-sec. delay while E recorded the response and selected the next

FIG. 2. Stimuli used in the experiment, showing twinned stimuli on the right.

stimulus. Training continued with no inter-trial interval until S went twice through the list without error or completed 30 trials. Items were presented in a different permutation for each trial for each S, with the restrictions that twinned stimuli ·were not presented successively, and if a stimulus appeared in the fifteenth or sixteenth position on one trial it would not appear first or second on the following trial. Orders, subject to these restrictions, were generated randomly on an IBM 709 computer. The motivation behind most of these procedures is to produce all-or-nothing learning of the unique items. The use of short common words as responses, and slow flash-card training with face-to-face contact of S and E, were intended to replicate some of Bower's (1962) technique. The use of five responses for 16 stimuli, and the elaborate randomizing procedures, were intended to prevent efficient guessing. Five responses rather than, say, only two, were used so that confusions of twin stimuli could be distinguished from mere guesses.

Results

Items with twin confusable stimuli (twinned items) were much more difficult than items with unique stimuli (unique items). Mean errors were 5.96 and 2.80, respectively. Of the 5.96 errors, 3.81 were stimulus-confusion and 2.15 were nonconfusion errors.

Unique stimulus items.—These data closely approximate the all-or-nothing assumptions with $p = .30$, $c = .25$. Figure 3A shows the learning curve,

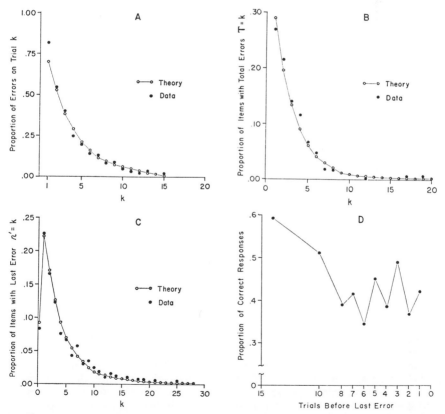

Fig. 3. Total errors on unique items: (A) as a function of trials (learning curve); (B) distribution of total errors; (C) distribution of trial of last error; (D) backwards learning curve.

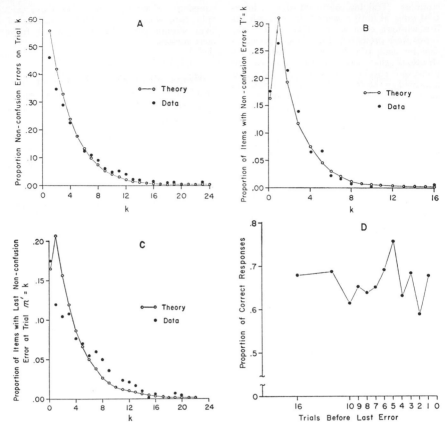

FIG. 4. Nonconfusion errors on twinned items: (A) as a function of trials (learning curve); (B) distribution of nonconfusion errors; (C) distribution of trial of last nonconfusion error; (D) backwards learning curve.

3B shows the distribution of total errors per item, 3C the distribution of trials of the last error per item. Theory and data are very close, comparable to Bower's (1961) results. There was some gradual improvement on trials before the last error, as shown by the backward learning curve in Fig. 3D.

Twin stimulus items.—Of the five responses available to S, one is correct, one is the confusion response, and the other three are scored as nonconfusion errors. Recall that on the average, Ss responded erroneously with probability $1 - p = .70$ to the

unique items which had four wrong answers. Since just three of these answers are scored as nonconfusion errors for twinned stimulus items, the probability of a nonconfusion error in State S_0 should be .70 × .75 = .525. Theoretical predictions for $c = .25$ and $p = .475$, using the simple one-process model, were calculated. These are the appropriate parameters for twin items in State S_0, if we count only nonconfusion errors. Results are shown in Fig. 4, in which the four panels correspond to the four main statistical results. The predictions in Fig. 4 are made without any estimated parameters; the value of c is from the unique items, and the predicted p depends upon a priori considerations and the results on unique items. Panel 4B, the distribution of total nonconfusion errors, shows an almost perfect correspondence. Panels 4A and 4C show that the errors are made on somewhat later trials than is predicted. The backwards learning curve (4D) shows stationarity but at a surprisingly high level, a mean of .625 correct, as contrasted with the calculated value of .475.

Now consider confusion and non-

confusion errors together. The mean total errors on twinned items is 5.96. Mean total errors on unique items was 2.80, and the difference, 3.16, is presumed to be the mean errors made in the intermediate state. By the strategy-selection theory (Restle, 1961) one can estimate the probability of learning, on an error, at $1/(1 + \bar{T})$ where $\bar{T}$ is mean errors. Taking account of the fact that some items were not mastered in 30 trials, $d \triangleq .225$. Since exactly two items are twinned in the list, it is assumed that the intermediate stage is one of two-choice discrimination. We set $Q = .50$. From

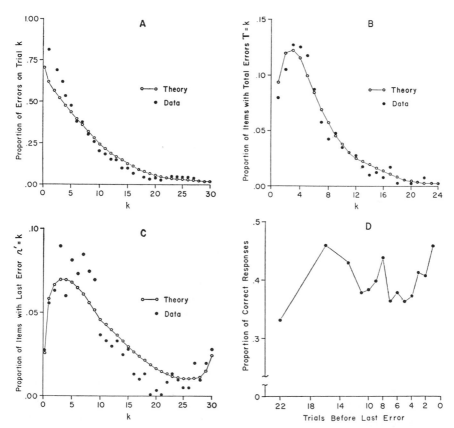

FIG. 5. Total errors on twinned items: (A) as a function of trials (learning curve); (B) distribution of total errors; (C) distribution of trial of last error; (D) backwards learning curve.

the unique items, $c \doteq .25$, $p \doteq .30$, and $b = c/(q + pc) = .33$. These values were inserted in Equations 7, 8, and 9 to compute predictions of total errors on twinned items. The calculations are compared with observations in Fig. 5. The theoretical curves in Fig. 5A, 5B, and 5C are calculated from Equations 7, 8, and 9.[2] The agreement is close, showing that total errors could arise from a two-stage process. A one-stage model will not fit these data.

DISCUSSION

This experiment has demonstrated why there can be no answer to the question, "Is learning (especially PA learning) an all-or-nothing event?" In one list, with one set of Ss, we obtained all-or-nothing data on half the items and two-process data on the other half. Each process is all-or-nothing and the times of the several processes are independent random variables. The several processes are identified as separate learning processes; in this we distinguish the present results from typical applications of Estes' "N-Pattern" theory (Estes, 1959).

Kintsch (1963) has recently shown that a two-process model fits the learning of PA items in which the responses require integration. He also shows the connection between these results and Rock's experimental method. Rock and

[2] With the parameters estimated, we calculate that about 15 items would be left unsolved in the 30 trials, probably all in the intermediate discrimination State S_I. In Fig. 5B the total errors from Equation 8 are modified by adding in the distribution of 15 items unlearned for 30 trials. This is approximated by a binomial distribution of 30 random responses with $P = .5$. Figure 5C is modified by noting that of these 15 items, a fraction Q have last error at Trial 30, QP have last error at Trial 29, etc. This geometric distribution is added to the distribution calculated from Equation 9. These corrections for termination of the experiment are only approximate, for they do not take account of the possible effects of trials in State S_0.

Steinfeld (1963), using Rock's method, observed all-or-nothing performance when Ss pronounced nonsense-syllable responses. Other Ss who had to spell the responses, learned slower and showed multiple-stage learning, presumably because the spelled responses required integration and the pronounced words did not.

Above we have tested a simple additive model of the two processes of association learning and stimulus discrimination. In our model, each item is considered separately. A deeper analysis shows that twin stimuli are more intimately entangled than is said in that theory, and some of the consequences are seen in Fig. 4C and 4D. Figure 4C shows that the last nonconfusion (random) error was made on a later trial than predicted by the theory. What happens is that some items show initial guessing errors, then a string of confusion errors, then one or more guessing errors. The presolution curve, Fig. 4D, plots the proportion of correct responses on trials before the last random error. For this plot confusion errors are considered correct responses and only random errors are scored as errors. The blocks of confusion responses before a late random error have served to elevate this curve. It seems that items get into the stimulus discrimination state (State S_1) and then return to the original State S_0.

What may actually happen is this. Suppose that S-R_1 and S'-R_2 are two items and S and S' are twinned. The S finds some strategy for remembering S-R_1 but then generalizes, and to S' he says R_1. He knows no separate response to S'. Now he finds a discriminating strategy and no longer confuses S with S'. He makes R_1 to S, correctly, but he has no response at all to S'. He now makes random responses to S' until he finds a strategy for remembering S'-R_2. Discrimination may occur before association on some items. Item-by-item inspection of protocols gives some support to this conjecture, in that if one item shows confusion followed by random errors, the twin item usually shows a string of correct responses throughout. This is consistent with the idea that one name was learned for both stimuli, and then the stimuli were discriminated, before S ever learned the second name for the other stimulus.

A correct theoretical analysis requires at least that the pair of twin items be treated together, in a fairly complicated Markov chain analysis. We have not reduced such an analysis to manageable calculations thus far. Furthermore, a whole list of items may be learned by interconnected systems of strategies. The Ss may use sentences or other compound strategies to learn several items at once, or may classify stimuli, or use other techniques to master a list. Such strategies can be discovered by studying interconnections between learning of the various items in a list. We attempt no such analysis in this paper.

If the present theoretical position is correct, then (a) unitary learning is an all-or-nothing process, (b) many typical learning experiments require multiple processes to solution, and (c) these processes are each all-or-nothing, and with sufficient controls and proper experimental design can be separated.

REFERENCES

BOWER, G. H. Application of a model to paired-associate learning. *Psychometrika*, 1961, **26**, 255–280.

BOWER, G. H. An association model for response and training variables in paired-associate learning. *Psychol. Rev.*, 1962, **69**, 34–53.

BOWER, G. H., & TRABASSO, T. R. Concept identification. In R. C. Atkinson (Ed.), *Studies in mathematical psychology.* Stanford: Stanford Univer. Press, 1963.

BUSH, R. R., & MOSTELLER, F. A comparison of eight models. In R. R. Bush & W. K. Estes (Eds.), *Studies in mathematical learning theory.* Stanford: Stanford Univer. Press, 1959.

ESTES, W. K. Component and pattern models with Markovian interpretations. In R. R. Bush & W. K. Estes (Eds.), *Studies in mathematical learning theory.* Stanford: Stanford Univer. Press, 1959.

ESTES, W. K. Learning theory and the new "mental chemistry." *Psychol. Rev.*, 1960, **67**, 207–223.

ESTES, W. K., HOPKINS, B. L., & CROTHERS, E. J. All-or-none and conservation effects in the learning and retention of paired associates. *J. exp. Psychol.*, 1960, **60**, 329–339.

FELLER, W. *Introduction to probability theory and its applications.* (2nd ed.) New York: Wiley, 1957.

GIBSON, E. J. A systematic application of the concepts of generalization and differentiation to verbal learning. *Psychol. Rev.*, 1940, **47**, 196–229.

KINTSCH, W. All-or-none learning and the role of repetition in paired-associate learning. *Science*, 1963, **140**, 310–312.

LASHLEY, K. S. *Brain mechanisms and intelligence.* Chicago: Univer. Chicago Press, 1929.

MCGUIRE, W. J. A multiprocess model for paired-associate learning. *J. exp. Psychol.*, 1961, **62**, 335–347.

RESTLE, F. Statistical methods for a theory of cue learning. *Psychometrika*, 1961, **26**, 291–306.

RESTLE, F. The selection of strategies in cue learning. *Psychol. Rev.*, 1962, **69**, 329–343.

RESTLE, F. Sources of difficulty in learning paired associates. In R. C. Atkinson (Ed.), *Studies in mathematical psychology.* Stanford: Stanford Univer. Press, 1963.

ROCK, I. The role of repetition in associative learning. *Amer. J. Psychol.*, 1957, **70**, 186–193.

ROCK, I., & STEINFELD, G. Methodological questions in the study of one-trial learning. *Science*, 1963, **140**, 822–824.

SHEPARD, R. N. Stimulus and response generalization: A stochastic model relating generalization to distance in psychological space. *Psychometrika*, 1957, **22**, 325–345.

THORNDIKE, E. L., & LORGE, I. *The teacher's word book of 30,000 words.* New York: Teachers College, Columbia University, Bureau of Publications, 1944.

TRABASSO, T. R. The effect of stimulus emphasis on strategy selection in the acquisition and transfer of concepts. Unpublished doctoral dissertation, Michigan State University, 1961.

TRABASSO, T. R. Stimulus emphasis and all-or-none learning in concept identification. *J. exp. Psychol.*, 1963, **65**, 398–406.

UNDERWOOD, B. J., RUNQUIST, W. N., & SCHULZ, R. W. Response learning in paired-associate lists as a function of intra-list similarity. *J. exp. Psychol.*, 1959, **58**, 70–78.

UNDERWOOD, B. J., & SCHULZ, R. W. *Meaningfulness and verbal learning.* Chicago: Lippincott, 1960.

(Received December 7, 1963)

Simple Conditioning as Two-Stage All-or-None Learning[1]

JOHN THEIOS, *University of Texas*

A theoretical model which postulates learning to take place in 2 discrete steps is developed and applied to avoidance conditioning. According to the model, conditioning is interpreted as an absorbing Markov process with three distinct states of conditioning. Among other things, the model predicts that the probability of a successful conditioned response should be constant on trials between the first success and the last error. Data are reported which support the constancy prediction as well as the model's other quantitative predictions. The model was generalized to apply to other learning situations, and relevant data were summarized. It would be quite difficult for a linear operator or habit-strength model to account for these data which support the constancy prediction.

In many learning situations, the response under study has initially a zero probability of occurring, but as the experiment progresses, the response probability approaches an asymptote of unity. A few situations of this type are instrumental avoidance conditioning, classical defense and appetitive conditioning, and reversal learning. These situations will be referred to as simple conditioning. In the past, simple conditioning has been analyzed in terms of response strength or linear operator models (Bush & Mosteller, 1955; Estes, 1950; Hull, 1943), which assume that the strength or probability of a learned response increases gradually during the course of learning. Recently, it has been found that Markov models, which assume that learning takes place on single trials in

[1] I am indebted to Gordon H. Bower for deriving a number of the theoretical predictions and for his valuable advice during the development of this paper. Appreciation is also expressed to Patrick Suppes, William K. Estes, Frank Restle, and Robert R. Bush for their interest and encouragement. Much of this research was conducted during the author's tenure on a National Science Foundation Cooperative Graduate Fellowship at Stanford University during the academic year 1960–61.

an all-or-none fashion, more adequately describe some types of verbal learning than do the linear models (Bower, 1962; Estes, 1960). It is quite possible that simple conditioning is also characterized by some sort of discrete learning as opposed to gradual learning. This possibility is further enhanced by the fact that the "zero to unity" changes in response probabilities, characteristic of simple conditioning, should lend themselves nicely to discrete conditioning states, which an absorbing Markov model would require (cf. Suppes & Atkinson, 1960). The present paper presents a three-state absorbing Markov model for simple conditioning, and then compares the theoretical predictions to actual data collected in an extensive experiment on avoidance conditioning of rats.

THE TWO-PATTERN STIMULUS SAMPLING MODEL

The basic learning theory assumed in this paper is that proposed by Suppes and Atkinson (1960). They suggest that any learning situation can be represented by a finite set of stimulus patterns and that each com-

This article appeared in *Psychol. Rev.*, 1963, **70**, 403–417.

ponent pattern of the stimulus set is conditioned to exactly one response from a set of mutually exclusive responses available to the subject. On each trial the subject samples only one stimulus pattern and makes that response to which the sampled pattern is conditioned. If the subject makes an incorrect response, reinforcement occurs and elicits or forces the correct response, which becomes conditioned to the sampled pattern with a fixed probability, c.

In simple conditioning only one response is reinforced consistently on every trial. The particular model to be proposed assumes that simple conditioning situations can be represented by exactly two stimulus patterns and that on any given trial each pattern has probability .5 of being sampled by the subject. The fundamental axioms of the model are as follows:

Identification Axioms

I1. A simple conditioning situation may be represented by exactly two stimulus patterns.

I2. At the start of conditioning, neither of the two patterns is conditioned to the correct, A_1, response.

Conditioning Axioms

C1. A stimulus pattern is conditioned to only one response at a given time.

C2. The stimulus pattern that is sampled on a trial becomes conditioned to the reinforced response with a fixed probability, c. If the pattern is already conditioned to the reinforced response, it remains so conditioned.

C3. The stimulus pattern that is not sampled on a given trial cannot become conditioned to the correct response on that trial.

C4. The probability, c, that the

sampled pattern will become conditioned to the reinforced response is independent of the trial number and preceding sequence of events.

Sampling Axioms

S1. Exactly one pattern is sampled on each trial.

S2. Each of the two patterns has probability .5 of being sampled on a given trial.

S3. On any trial, the probability of sampling a given pattern is independent of the trial number and preceding sequence of events.

Response Axiom

R1. On any trial, that response is made to which the sampled pattern is conditioned.

According to the axioms, the learning process in simple conditioning may be described as an absorbing Markov process with three states. At the start of the experiment, when neither of the two stimulus patterns is conditioned to the correct response, the process is in conditioning state S_0. After one of the patterns becomes conditioned to the correct response, the process is in conditioning state S_1, where the probability of a correct response is .5. Finally, when both patterns are conditioned to the correct response, the process is in the absorbing state, S_2, where the probability of a correct response is unity. The trees of the Markov process are given in Figure 1. The matrix of transition probabilities, P, in canonical form is

$$
P = \begin{array}{c|ccc}
 & S_2 & S_1 & S_0 \\
\hline
S_2 & 1 & 0 & 0 \\
S_1 & \dfrac{c}{2} & 1 - \dfrac{c}{2} & 0 \\
S_0 & 0 & c & 1 - c
\end{array} \qquad [1]
$$

PREDICTIONS AND DATA

A large number of predictions which follow from the model will be derived in this section. As a test of the adequacy of the model, the predictions will be compared to data collected in an avoidance learning experiment where 50 rats served as subjects. The apparatus was a modified Miller-Mowrer electric shock box, consisting of a black and a white compartment separated by a guillotine door. The correct response (A_1) was to run from one compartment to the other within 3 seconds after a buzzer sounded and a light came on in the white compartment. Special care was taken to reduce the stimulus situation drastically so that the situation could be represented by only two stimulus patterns. The reduction was achieved, for example, by reducing the external distractions for the rat, using a high intensity shock (255 volts), running the rats only one way (e.g., always black to white) rather than having them shuttle, and giving all trials in one experimental session at 20 second intertrial intervals. The procedure was to place the subject in one compartment and turn on the buzzer and light as the door between the compartments was opened. If the subject did not run into the other compartment within 3 seconds, he was shocked until he escaped into the other compartment. The buzzer, light, and shock terminated when the other compartment was entered. If the rat's response was an escape from the shock, it was designated an error (A_2). If the response occurred before the onset of the shock it was designated a success (A_1). After 20 seconds the subject was returned to the first compartment, and another trial was given. A rat was run until he met a criterion of 20 consecutive successful avoidance responses. When the subject met the criterion he was given reversal learning (e.g., if he had originally learned to run from black to white, during reversal learning, he learned to run from white to black). Since there were no significant differences between the data of original and reversal learning (e.g., mean total errors were 4.8 and 4.6, respectively), the data from the two series were pooled, yielding 100 response sequences to test the model.

Bernoulli Properties of the Model

One cannot observe on what trial a transition from Conditioning States S_0 to S_1 occurs. However, if there are some trials between the first success and the last error, we can be sure that the subject is in State S_1 on these trials. For surely, if the subject has made one success, at least one of the stimulus patterns is conditioned to the A_1 response; and if on a later trial the subject makes an error, then at least one of the patterns is not conditioned to the A_1 response. Since unconditioning does not occur in the present model, the above two patterns must be distinct, and, by

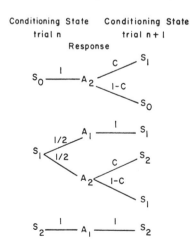

Conditioning State trial n Conditioning State trial $n+1$

FIG. 1. The trees of the Markov process.

definition, the subject must be in conditioning State S_1. According to the model, the probability of a success in State S_1 is a constant, $\frac{1}{2}$. Also, the conditional probability of a success on Trial $n + 1$ given a success on Trial n is a constant, $\frac{1}{2}$, since conditioning cannot occur on success trials:

$$P(A_{1,n+1}|A_{1,n} \cap S_{1,n}) = \tfrac{1}{2}. \quad [2]$$

Thus, according to the model, the sequence of responses between the first success and the last error should be an independent Bernoulli sequence with $p = q = \frac{1}{2}$, and all statistics relevant to coin tossing experiments should be applicable to the response sequences during these trials.

For example, defining h as the length of a run of successes between the first success and the last error, the probability distribution of h will be equal to the expected probability distribution of obtaining a run of heads in a coin tossing experiment, which is

$$P(h = j) = p^{j-1}q = (\tfrac{1}{2})^j,$$
$$\text{For } j = 1, 2, 3, \cdots. \quad [3]$$

The mean and variance of the distribution of h will be

$$E(h) = \sum_{j=1}^{\infty} j(\tfrac{1}{2})^j = 2, \quad [4]$$

and

$$\text{Var } (h) = \sum_{j=1}^{n} (j - 2)^2 (\tfrac{1}{2})^j = 2. \quad [5]$$

The obtained and predicted expectation and standard deviation of the mean length of runs of successes between the first success and the last error are given in Table 2.

According to the linear models (Bush & Mosteller, 1955; Estes, 1950; Hull, 1943), as n increases, the conditional probability of a success on

Trial n following a success on Trial $n - 1$ should also increase. But, the two-pattern sampling model predicts that on trials between the first success and the last error, the conditional probability of a success on Trial n given a success on Trial $n - 1$ should have a constant value of $\frac{1}{2}$. The obtained conditional probabilities, given in Figure 2, are approximating a constant value near $\frac{1}{2}$, rather than increasing with trials as the linear model would predict. This relationship is, by far, the strongest evidence for the two-pattern sampling model.

Another exacting test of the Bernoulli property of the model is that the response sequences during the trials between the first success and the last error should satisfy the binomial distribution. To provide this test, the data were divided into blocks of four trials, and the number of successes in each block was counted. This sum can take on the values 0, 1, 2, 3, or 4. If the model fits the data, the obtained frequency distribution should not differ significantly from what would be expected from performing a large number of coin tossing

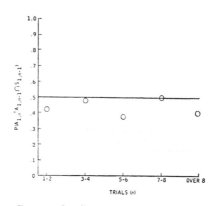

FIG. 2. Conditional probability of a success on Trial n given a success on Trial $n - 1$ on trials between the first success and the last error, $P(A_{1,n}|A_{1,n-1} \cap S_{1,n-1})$.

TABLE 1

NUMBER OF SUCCESSES IN BLOCKS OF FOUR
BINOMIAL TRIALS BETWEEN THE FIRST
SUCCESS AND THE LAST ERROR

Number of successes	Obtained frequency	Predicted frequency
0	2	3.1
1	12	12.5
2	17	18.8
3	15	12.5
4	4	3.1

Note.—Chi square = 1.47, $df = 4$.

experiments in which a coin was tossed four times in each experiment and the distribution of the number of heads in each experiment was tabulated. The obtained and predicted frequencies of successes are given in Table 1. A test of goodness of fit yielded a chi square of 1.47, which, with 4 degrees of freedom indicates that the predictions fit the obtained data very well.

If sampling of the two patterns is random, then the outcomes of trials between the first success and the last error should be statistically independent (a zero-order Markov process). This hypothesis can be tested against the alternative hypothesis that the process is a first-order Markov chain by a chi square test of homogeneity (cf., Suppes & Atkinson, 1960). The obtained chi square of .07 with one degree of freedom indicates that we cannot reject the hypothesis that the response sequence between the first success and the last error is a zero-order Markov chain.

Total Errors

Suppose we let t_i represent the number of errors made in transient Conditioning State S_i, where $i = (0, 1)$. By the axioms, t_i has the geometric distribution given by

$$P(t_i = j) = c(1 - c)^{j-1}, \quad [6]$$

with mean and variance

$$E(t_i) = \frac{1}{c}, \quad \mathrm{Var}(t_i) = \frac{(1 - c)}{c^2}. \quad [7]$$

We let T represent the total number of errors before absorption, i.e.,

$$T = t_0 + t_1. \quad [8]$$

The variable T is the sum of two independent, identically distributed random variables. The probability that T takes on an arbitrary value k is given by the negative binomial distribution

$$P(T = k) =$$
$$\begin{cases} 0 & \text{for } k < 2 \\ (k-1)c^2(1-c)^{k-2} & \text{for } k \geq 2 \end{cases}, \quad [9]$$

which has mean and variance

$$E(T) = \frac{2}{c}, \mathrm{Var}(T) = \frac{2(1 - c)}{c^2}. \quad [10]$$

It should be noted from Equation 9 that the model makes the very strong prediction that the number of errors in any learning sequence must be equal to or larger than two, the number of stimulus patterns representing the situation. This prediction follows from the assumption that conditioning can occur only on trials on which an error has been made.

The expected total errors can serve as a stable estimator of the model's single parameter, c. In the avoidance experiment described above, the mean total errors was 4.68. Equating $E(T)$ in Equation 10 to 4.68, the resulting c value is .427. This estimate of c will be fixed throughout the remaining discussion and will be used in the calculations of all the following theoretical predictions.

The obtained distribution of total errors is given in Figure 3, along with the theoretical predictions. It can

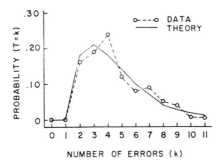

FIG. 3.   Probability distribution of total errors, $P(T = k)$.

be seen that the model predicts the data quite well.

In deriving further predictions it is useful to have the probabilities, $w_{i,n}$, that the subject is in Conditioning State $S_i (i = 0, 1, 2)$ on Trial n of the experiment $(n = 1, 2, 3, \cdots)$. The result for $w_{0,n}$ is

$$w_{0,n} = (1 - c)^{n-1}. \qquad [11]$$

For a subject to be in State S_1 on Trial n we note that he must have remained in State S_0 for k trials $(k = 1, 2, \cdots, n - 1)$ before moving to S_1 and then have remained in State S_1 for $(n - k - 1)$ trials. Thus, the probability of being in State S_1 on Trial n will be given by

$$w_{1,n} = \sum_{k=1}^{n-1} (1-c)^{k-1} c \left(1 - \frac{c}{2}\right)^{n-k-1}, \qquad [12]$$

which has the solution

$$w_{1,n} = 2 \left[\left(1 - \frac{c}{2}\right)^{n-1} - (1 - c)^{n-1}\right]. \qquad [13]$$

Having obtained the probabilities of being in conditioning States S_0 and S_1 on Trial n, the probability of being in S_2 may be obtained by subtraction:

$$w_{2,n} = 1 - w_{0,n} - w_{1,n}, \qquad [14]$$

$$w_{2,n} = 1 - 2 \left(1 - \frac{c}{2}\right)^{n-1} + (1 - c)^{n-1}.$$

Once the subject has arrived at Conditioning State S_2 there can be no more errors. Hence, $w_{2,n}$ gives the probability of no more errors after Trial $n - 1$. The observed and theoretical proportions of response sequences having no errors following Trial $n - 1$ are given in Figure 4. The c value used in the predictions is .427, which was estimated from the mean total errors.

Trial Number of the Last Error

A subject's last error can occur on Trial n only if he is in Conditioning State S_1, samples the unconditioned pattern, and conditioning of that pattern is effective. Thus, the probability distribution of the trial number of the last error, $P(L = n)$ for $n = 1, 2, 3, \cdots$, is

$$P(L = n) = w_{1,n} \cdot \frac{c}{2}$$

$$= c \left[\left(1 - \frac{c}{2}\right)^{n-1} - (1 - c)^{n-1}\right], \qquad [15]$$

which has mean and variance

$$E(L) = \frac{3}{c}, \quad \text{Var}(L) = \frac{(5 - 3c)}{c^2}. \qquad [16]$$

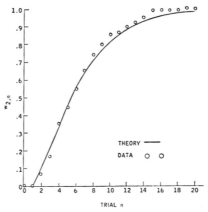

FIG. 4.   Proportion of sequences with no errors following Trial $n - 1$, $(w_{2,n})$. (These curves also represent the cumulant of the distribution of the trial number of the last error.)

The obtained and predicted means and standard deviations of the trial number of the last error are given in Table 2. The cumulant of the distribution of the trial number of the last error is just $w_{2,n}$, the probability of no errors following Trial $n - 1$, which was given in Figure 4.

The average probability of an error on Trial n will be equal to the probability of being in State S_0 on Trial n times the probability of an error in S_0 plus the probability of being in State S_1 on trial n times the probability of an error in S_1. Thus,

$$P(A_{2,n}) = 1 \cdot w_{0,n} + \tfrac{1}{2} \cdot w_{1,n},$$

$$P(A_{2,n}) = (1-c)^{n-1}$$

$$+ \tfrac{1}{2} \cdot 2\left[\left(1 - \frac{c}{2}\right)^{n-1}\right. \quad [17]$$

$$\left. - (1-c)^{n-1}\right],$$

$$P(A_{2,n}) = \left(1 - \frac{c}{2}\right)^{n-1}.$$

The probability of a success on Trial n is given by

$$P(A_{1,n}) = 1 - P(A_{2,n}),$$

$$P(A_{1,n}) = 1 - \left(1 - \frac{c}{2}\right)^{n-1}. \quad [18]$$

The obtained and predicted mean learning curves are given in Figure 5.

Although many more predictions follow from the model, further exposition of specific predictions would run the risk of unduly burdening the reader with mathematical material. However, for those readers interested in using the model in further research, sequential statistics and other predictions are given in the Appendix, with only brief explanations. The complete deviations of these predictions and the corresponding obtained

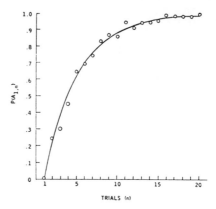

FIG. 5. Probability of an avoidance response, $P(A_{1,n})$, on successive trials of the experiment.

data can be found in a technical report (Theios, 1961). Sequential data for individual rats are presented in Table 4 of the Appendix for readers interested in checking other predictions or alternative models.

To summarize this section on the two-pattern model, a number of predictions are compared with obtained

TABLE 2

OBSERVED AND PREDICTED VALUES FOR VARIOUS RESPONSE MEASURES

Response measure	Observed	Predicted
Total errors		
$E(T)$	4.68	
$\sigma(T)$	2.34	2.48
Trial number of last error		
$E(L)$	6.56	7.02
$\sigma(L)$	3.40	4.52
Errors before the first success		
$E(J_0)$	2.96	3.03
$\sigma(J_0)$	1.83	2.14
Probability of no reversals		
$P(NR)$	.26	.30
Mean number of runs of errors		
R	2.18	2.18
Runs of errors, r_j, of Length j		
r_1	1.05	1.05
r_2	.46	.51
r_3	.30	.27
Autocorrelation of errors, c_k, k trials apart		
c_1	2.50	2.62
c_2	2.06	2.06
c_3	1.47	1.61
c_4	1.18	1.27
Mean length of runs of successes in State S_1		
$E(h)$	1.77	2.00
$\sigma(h)$	1.14	1.41

data in Table 2. In general, the predictions approximate the obtained data quite well.

General N-Pattern Models

Any experiment in which the initial probability of a correct response is zero, but asymptotically becomes unity can be analyzed in terms of an absorbing Markov model. However, it would be premature to suggest that all learning situations of this type could be represented by two stimulus patterns, i.e., a two-stage learning process. It would be wiser to assume that the complexity of the individual learning situation determines the number of stimulus patterns or stages of learning. In other words, more stimulus patterns would be necessary to represent complex learning situations than would be necessary for simple situations. Thus, a general N-pattern stimulus sampling model where the number of patterns (N) is a parameter which must be estimated from the data, would be of greater scientific value than the simple two-pattern model.

An N-pattern model can be represented by a Markov chain that has N transient states and one terminal absorbing state. Suppose we let t_i represent the number of errors in transient State S_i, for $i = (0, 1, 2, \cdots, N - 1)$. It can be shown that t_i has the geometric distribution given earlier in Equation 6

$$P(t_i = j) = c(1 - c)^{j-1}.$$

We let T represent the total number of errors before absorption, i.e.,

$$T = t_0 + t_1 + t_2 + \cdots + t_{N-1}. \quad [19]$$

The variable T is the sum of N independent, identically distributed random variables. The probability that T takes on an arbitrary value k is given by the negative binomial distribution

$$P(T = k) = \begin{cases} 0 & \text{for } k < N \\ \binom{k-1}{N-1} c^N (1 - c)^{k-N} & \text{for } k \geq N \end{cases}, \quad [20]$$

which has mean and variance

$$E(T) = \frac{N}{c}, \quad \text{Var}(T) = \frac{N(1-c)}{c^2}. \quad [21]$$

It should be noted from Equation 20 that the stimulus sampling models of the type we have been considering make the very strong prediction that the number of errors in any learning sequence must be equal to or larger than the number of stimulus patterns representing the situation.

It is quite easy to obtain an estimate of the number of stimulus patterns for an N-pattern model which assumes all of the axioms given earlier, except Axioms I1 and S2. For any experiment in which the probability of a correct response increases from zero to unity, one can compute the mean and variance of the total number of errors before perfect learning. The obtained mean and variance can be set equal to the general theoretical equations for the mean and variance of the total errors (Equation 20), and the two equations can be solved simultaneously for the conditioning parameter, c, and the number of stimulus patterns, N. For the present data on avoidance conditioning in rats, this estimate of N is 2.019, indicating that the two-pattern model is most applicable for these data.

Solomon and Wynne Data and the N-Pattern Model

To demonstrate its generality, the N-pattern model will now be applied to the data of an experiment by Solomon and Wynne (1953) in which 30 dogs learned an avoidance response. This application of the model is of great interest since Bush and Mosteller (1959) have already fitted eight models to these data, with varying degrees of success. The procedure used by Solomon and Wynne differed from that of the rat avoidance study already considered in that they used the more difficult shuttle response which requires the subject to jump to a place where he has been previously shocked. It might be expected that the shuttle procedure would result in a stimulus situation which was more complex than the nonshuttle situation. If so, the estimate of the number of stimulus patterns should be greater for the shuttle situation.

For the Solomon and Wynne data, the estimate of the conditioning parameter, c, is .538 and the estimated number of stimulus patterns, N, is 4.2. Rounding 4.2 to the nearest integer, it follows that some four-pattern model may describe these data better than Bush and Mosteller's (1955) two-operator linear model which for so long has been assumed to give the best description of these data. The obtained probability distribution of total errors for the Solomon and Wynne data is given in Figure 6, along with the predictions from the two-pattern and four-pattern models. The predictions from the four-pattern model approximate the data very well, while the predictions from the two-pattern model are quite discrepant. It should be noted that the very strong prediction that the total number of errors for any subject cannot be less than the number of

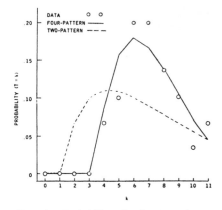

FIG. 6. Probability distribution of total errors for the Solomon and Wynne dogs, and the predictions from the two-pattern and four-pattern Markov models.

stimulus patterns was upheld in the data of the dogs as it was in the data of the rats.

The mean and variance of the trial number of the last error, L, predicted by the four-pattern model are

$$E(L) = \frac{25}{3c} \qquad [22]$$

and

$$\mathrm{Var}(L) = \frac{96 - 75c}{9c^2}. \qquad [23]$$

For a general N-pattern model, the expected trial number of the last error will be given by

$E(L \mid N\text{-patterns})$

$$= \frac{N}{c} \sum_{i=0}^{N-1} \frac{1}{N-i}. \qquad [24]$$

Because of the tedious algebra involved, other predictions for the four-pattern and N-pattern models are not yet available in closed form.

In Table 3, the obtained means and standard deviations of total errors and trial number of the last error are compared with the predictions from

TABLE 3

A COMPARISON OF AVOIDANCE CONDITIONING
DATA OF REAL DOGS WITH LINEAR
STAT-DOGS AND FOUR-PATTERN
MARKOV PREDICTIONS

Response measure	4-Pattern	Data	Linear
Total errors			
E(T)	7.43	7.80	7.60
$\sigma(T)$	2.53	2.52	2.27
Trial of last error			
E(L)	15.47	12.33	13.53
$\sigma(L)$	4.62	4.36	4.78

the four-pattern model and the linear model (Bush & Mosteller, 1955).

DISCUSSION

A two-pattern stimulus sampling model, which can be represented as a three-state, absorbing Markov chain, has been presented to account for simple conditioning. A large number of predictions about sequences of response random variables were derived in closed form and were compared to actual data obtained in an avoidance conditioning experiment with rats. The theoretical predictions fit the data extremely well. In particular, the predicted Bernoulli properties of the response sequences between the first success and the last error were upheld surprisingly well by the data. This characteristic of the data is sufficient to question the adequacy of any linear model as a description of the present data. It should be noted, also, that no estimated parameters entered into the predictions about the response sequences during trials between the first success and the last error, since the Bernoulli properties of the model are parameter-free.

The predictions about various response measures over the entire learning sequence involved only a single parameter, c. Although c was estimated from an arbitrarily selected response measure, mean total errors, the predictions for the numerous other response measures fit the data very well. It should be noted that entire distributions of response variables and not just mean values were fitted to the data.

To demonstrate the generality of the present approach to conditioning, an N-pattern model was developed and applied to the data of Solomon and Wynne (1953) on avoidance conditioning of dogs. Although the avoidance situation for rats (unidirectional response) could be represented by two stimulus patterns, it was found that four stimulus patterns were necessary to represent the avoidance situation for dogs (shuttle response). This result is in line with the expectation that the shuttle situation is more complex than the unidirectional situation.

The two-pattern and N-pattern Markov models have been presented as applying to simple conditioning situations where the response probabilities increase from zero to unity. However, to date the models have been applied only to avoidance learning data. The axioms assume that learning occurs only on trials on which an error is made, and, in fact, in avoidance conditioning an experimenter-controlled reinforcement (shock) occurs only on these error trials. Therefore, it is of interest whether this assumption of learning only on error trials will be upheld by, say, classical conditioning or T maze reversal data, where an experimenter-controlled reinforcement occurs on both error and success trials.

Another question which remains to be answered is why the probability of a correct response on trials between the first success and the last error is .5 in the data from the rats. Of course this prediction follows from the two-pattern model, but it is difficult to find intuitive reasons why this should be the case. More reasonably, it might be expected that the probability of a correct response on these trials should be determined, at least partly, by variables such as the CS-UCS interval. For example, one would logically expect the response probability to decrease as the CS-UCS interval is decreased, and vice versa. Working on the assumption that specific situational factors may affect various parameters in the two-pattern stimulus sampling model, Bower (1961) has developed a general two-pattern model, of which the model presented in this paper may be thought of as a special case. Instead of each stimulus pattern having an equal sampling probability of .5, in the Bower model one pattern has probability a of being sampled on a given trial, while the other pattern can be sampled with probability $1 - a$. This model, too, predicts stationarity of the response probabilities on trials between the first success and last error. However, the response probability on these trials does not have to be exactly .5, but can take on any arbitrary value between zero and unity. Thus, if stationarity of the response probabilities between the first success and the last error were found in a learning situation, but not at .5, some variation of the general Bower model would probably be most appropriate.

The learning of individual paired-associate response shifts by humans has been found to satisfy the restrictions of the Bower model (Theios & Hakes, 1962). Using color names as stimuli and numbers as responses, the correct response for a stimulus was shifted to one of the alternate responses when the subject reached a criterion. As predicted by the Bower model, the relative frequency of a correct response on each trial between the first success and the last error was constant (about .7), and errors on these trials were distributed binomially. In general, the fit of the Bower model to the data is good.

Since the model developed in this paper is very abstract, it might be interesting to assume a reductionist point of view and attempt to relate the present formulation to more traditional interpretations of avoidance conditioning. The notion of avoidance conditioning as a two-stage process in which the subject starts in one state and moves through an intermediate state to a third, terminal state is not new. Solomon and Wynne (1954) and Wynne and Solomon (1955) proposed an avoidance conditioning process with three states of conditioning. They suggest that autonomic nervous system responses are important in the initial state, but play at most a minor role in the terminal state.

To speculate now about identification of the states in the present model, we may view the organism as being naive when the experiment starts. In this initial, naive state the organism will get shocked on every trial. The UCS (e.g., shock) will cause autonomic nervous system responses in the organism as well as skeletal responses. It has been customary to designate autonomic responses produced by shock as "emotional" responses. The first stage of learning may consist of conditioning the "emotional" responses to the CS. After this, the organism may be viewed as being in the intermediate state, where the presentation of the CS will cause the organism to become "emotionally" aroused. The autonomic or emotional arousal, which may be considered as an increase in drive level, results in an increase in the probability that the subject makes an avoidance response by chance. Because of the symmetry of the situation and the CS-UCS timing in the present experiment with rats, the probability of crossing before the onset of shock happened to be .5. The second stage of learning may consist of conditioning the instrumental, skeletal escape response to the CS, to the stimuli from the "emotional" responses, or both. Since the axioms of the model as well as the data from the rats indicate that conditioning of the instrumental response can occur only on shock trials and cannot occur on avoidance trials in the intermediate state, the reinforcement for the conditioning of the instrumental avoidance response must be shock reduction and not emotion or fear reduction. This follows since avoidance responses in the intermediate state would reduce emotional responses, yet conditioning of the instrumental response does not occur following these avoidance trials. Thus, the subject cannot avoid the shock until he becomes emotional in the situation. Following conditioning of the emotional responses, he has some fixed probability of avoiding by chance, until finally the instrumental avoidance response becomes learned. After this, the subject avoids the shock on every trial.

This speculative interpretation gains some merit when latency data are considered. Wynne and Solomon (1955) have published curves of response latency for individual dogs which look like step functions with two jumps. The response latency initially is quite long, but constant, for the first few trials of the conditioning experiment. Then the latencies shorten to just about the CS-UCS interval (10 seconds) and remain constant there for a few trials.

Finally, the latencies become quite short, about 2 seconds, and the subject avoids the shock on every trial. The first jump in the curves could be interpreted as the conditioning of emotional responses to the CS and the second jump interpreted as the conditioning of the instrumental response.

However, in spite of the intuitive appeal of a reductionist type of interpretation over a purely abstract mathematical approach, it should be remembered that the real test of the appropriateness of a psychological model is how well it predicts behavior. The two-pattern stimulus sampling model predicts avoidance conditioning data of rats extremely well. The predictive ability of the model should be the main consideration in evaluating the model. How well the model approximates intuition or traditional theoretical conceptualizations should be of lesser concern.

REFERENCES

BOWER, G. H.   General three-state Markov learning models.   Technical Report No. 41, 1961, Stanford University, Institute for Mathematical Studies in the Social Sciences.

BOWER, G. H.   An association model for response and training variables in paired-associate learning.   *Psychol. Rev.*, 1962, 69, 34–53.

BUSH, R. R.   Sequential properties of linear models.   In R. R. Bush and W. K. Estes (Eds.), *Studies in mathematical learning theory.*   Stanford: Stanford University Press, 1959.   Pp. 215–227.

BUSH, R. R., & MOSTELLER, F.   *Stochastic models for learning.*   New York: Wiley, 1955.

BUSH, R. R., & MOSTELLER, F.   A comparison of eight models.   In R. R. Bush and W. K. Estes (Eds.), *Studies in mathematical learning theory.*   Stanford: Stanford Univer. Press, 1959.   Pp. 293–307.

ESTES, W. K.   Toward a statistical theory of learning.   *Psychol. Rev.*, 1950, 57, 94–104.

ESTES, W. K.   Learning theory and the new mental chemistry.   *Psychol. Rev.*, 1960, 67, 207–223.

HULL, C. L.   *Principles of behavior.*   New Haven: Yale Univer. Press, 1943.

SOLOMON, R. L., & WYNNE, L. C. Traumatic avoidance learning: Acquisition in normal dogs. *Psychol. Monogr.*, 1953, **67**(4, Whole No. 354).

SOLOMON, R. L., & WYNNE, L. C. Traumatic avoidance learning: The principles of anxiety conservation and partial irreversibility. *Psychol. Rev.*, 1954, **61**, 353–385.

SUPPES, P., & ATKINSON, R. C. *Markov learning models for multiperson interactions.* Stanford: Stanford Univer. Press, 1960.

THEIOS, J. A three-state Markov model for learning. Technical Report No. 40, 1961,

Stanford University, Institute for Mathematical Studies in the Social Sciences.

THEIOS, J., & HAKES, D. T. Paired-associate response shifts as two-stage all-or-none learning. Paper read at Midwestern Psychological Association, Chicago, May 4, 1962.

WYNNE, L. C., & SOLOMON, R. L. Traumatic avoidance learning: Acquisition and extinction in dogs deprived of normal peripheral autonomic function. *Genet. Psychol. Monogr.*, 1955, **52**, 241–284.

(Received March 13, 1962)

APPENDIX

SEQUENTIAL STATISTICS AND OTHER PREDICTIONS FROM THE TWO-PATTERN MODEL

Defining J_0 as the number of errors before the subject's first success, the probability that J_0 takes on an arbitrary value, k, will be given by

$$P(J_0 = k) = \begin{cases} \frac{1}{2}c & \text{for } k=1 \\ c(1-c)^{k-2}[1-(1+c)(\frac{1}{2})^k] & \text{for } k \geq 2. \end{cases} \quad [25]$$

This probability distribution has a mean equal to

$$E(J_0) = \frac{1}{c} + \frac{1}{1+c}. \quad [26]$$

A response sequence with no reversals can be defined as a sequence in which no errors occur after the first success. Sequences with no reversals can occur only if there have been at least two initial errors. This prediction follows from the model because conditioning can occur only after an error has been made and there are two stimulus patterns which must become conditioned before perfect learning is attained. The probability of obtaining a sequence without any reversals is

$$P(NR) = \frac{c}{1+c}. \quad [27]$$

In the avoidance experiment with rats the obtained proportion of nonreversal sequences was .26, while the predicted value was .30.

Letting J_k represent the number of errors between the kth and $(k+1)^{st}$ successes, the expectation of J_k is

$$E(J_k) = \left(\frac{1}{1+c}\right)^{k+1} \quad \text{for } k \geq 1. \quad [28]$$

The cumulative number of errors before the kth success, F_k, can be obtained by adding the values of J_i from $i = 0$ up to $i = (k-1)$. The expectation of F_k will be

$$E(F_k) = \sum_{i=0}^{k-1} E(J_i)$$
$$= \frac{2}{c} - \frac{1}{c}\left(\frac{1}{1+c}\right)^k. \quad [29]$$

The limit of $E(F_k)$ as k approaches infinity is the expected mean total errors $(2/c)$ as it should be.

Consider the number of successes before a subject's last error. If we let Z represent this sum, then Z can take on the values $0, 1, 2, 3, \cdots$. It can be shown that the probability distribution of Z will be given by

$$P(Z = k) = c\left(\frac{1}{1+c}\right)^{k+1}$$
$$\text{for } k = 0, 1, 2, \cdots. \quad [30]$$

The distribution of Z has a mean and variance equal to

$$E(Z) = \frac{1}{c}, \quad \text{Var}(Z) = \frac{1+c}{c^2}. \quad [31]$$

TABLE 4

SEQUENTIAL DATA FOR INDIVIDUAL RATS

Rat	Original learning							Reversal learning								
	1	0	1	0	1	0	1	1	0	1	0	1	0	1	0	1
1	4	1	1	1	1			6	3	3						
2	4	1	3					2								
3	3	4	1					2	1	1						
4	4	5	1					3	1	1	1	1	1	1		
5	6	2	2					2	1	3						
6	2	1	1	1	1			1	1	1						
7	4							3								
8	2	1	1					1	1	1						
9	1	1	2					4	1	2	3	1				
10	4	2	2	1	1			3								
11	3	1	2					1	2	1						
12	3	1	1					1	1	1	4	1				
13	5	1	1					4								
14	4							3	1	2						
15	4							1	1	1	1	1	1	1		
16	3	2	1					2	1	1						
17	2							1	1	1						
18	1	1	1	2	1	3	1	4	2	1	1	1				
19	2	1	4	1	1			7								
20	5							9	1	1	1	1				
21	2	1	4	2	1			1	1	2	1	1	3	2	2	1
22	2	5	1					2								
23	5	1	3	2	2			2	1	1	2	1				
24	2	1	1					4	3	1	1	1	1	2		
25	4	4	2					3	2	1	2	1	2	1	1	1
26	3							3								
27	1	1	3					2	3	1						
28	2	1	1					1	1	1	1	1				
29	3	1	1					2								
30	5	2	1					1	3	1	1	1				
31	5							1	1	1	1	2				
32	3	1	1	1	2			7	3	2						
33	4	1	1					3	5	1						
34	1	1	1					4								
35	3	1	1					1	1	3						
36	1	2	1					2	3	1						
37	1	1	1	1	3			2								
38	1	3	2					1	2	1						
39	4							4	2	4						
40	5							10	1	2	3	3				
41	1	2	1					3	2	3	1	1	1	1	2	1
42	2							1	1	1	3	2				
43	1	1	3	4	1	1	1	4								
44	3	1	2	2	1	4	2	1	3	1	1	1				
45	6	1	1	5	2			3								
46	4							2								
47	2	3	2	5	3			2	1	1	4	2				
48	8							1	1	1						
49	4							2	1	2	1	1				
50	3	2	1					4	2	1						

Note.—The columns represent consecutive runs of failures to avoid (errors) and runs of avoidance responses (successes). (The columns labeled 1 designate runs of errors. The columns labeled 0 designate runs of successes. The entries of the table give the length of the runs in number of trials. The final criterion run of 20 successes has not been indicated, but it follows the last entry for each rat.)

Sequential Statistics

In deriving sequential statistics it is useful to define a sequence of response random variables, X_n, which take on the value 1 if an error occurred on Trial n or the value 0 if a success occurred on Trial n. From the axioms, the conditional probabilities of an error given State S_i are

$$P(X_n = 1 \mid S_{0,n}) = 1,$$
$$P(X_n = 1 \mid S_{1,n}) = \tfrac{1}{2}, \qquad [32]$$
$$P(X_n = 1 \mid S_{2,n}) = 0.$$

Using the notation of Bush (1959), a j tuple of errors will be defined as u_j, where

$$u_{j,n} = X_n \cdot X_{n+1} \cdots \cdots X_{n+j-1}$$
$$\text{for } j = 1, 2, \cdots. \quad [33]$$

and

$$E(u_{j,n}) = w_{0,n}\Big\{ (1-c)^{j-1} + \sum_{k=1}^{j-1} (1-c)^{k-1}\tfrac{1}{2}c[\tfrac{1}{2}(1-c)]^{j-1-k}\Big\} \quad [34]$$
$$+ w_{1,n}[(\tfrac{1}{2})^j (1-c)^{j-1}].$$

The expected number of j tuples of errors will have the solution

$$E(u_j) = E \sum_{n=1}^{\infty} u_{j,n}$$
$$= \frac{(1-c)^{j-2}}{c} [1 + (1-2c)(\tfrac{1}{2})^{j-1}]$$
$$\text{for } j \geq 2. \quad [35]$$

The value of u_1 will be given by mean total errors, which has expectation $2/c$. Bush (1959) has shown that predictions about runs of errors can be obtained once the expected u_j are known. Defining total error runs as R, the expectation of R is

$$E(R) = E(u_1) - E(u_2) = 1 + \frac{1}{2c}. \quad [36]$$

Letting r_j be the number of error runs of Length j, for $j = 1, 2, 3, \cdots$, the expectation of r_j is

$$E(r_j) = E(u_j) - 2E(u_{j+1}) + E(u_{j+2}),$$

$$E(r_j) = \begin{cases} \frac{1}{4}c(1 + c + 2c^2), & \text{for } j = 1 \\ c(1 - c)^{j-2} + \dfrac{(1 - c)(1 + c)^2 \left(\dfrac{1 - c}{2}\right)^{j-2}}{8c} & \text{for } j \geq 2. \end{cases} \qquad [37]$$

The number of alternations of errors and successes, A, over the entire learning sequence will be twice the number of error runs minus one. Thus, the expectation of A will be

$$E(A) = 2 \cdot E(R) - 1 = 1 + \frac{1}{c}. \qquad [38]$$

The obtained and predicted values for runs of errors are given in Table 2.

Another useful summary of sequential characteristics in the response data is the extent to which an error on Trial n tends to be followed by an error k trials later, irrespective of the intervening responses. Define the autocorrelation, $c_{k,n}$, as the product $X_n \cdot X_{n+k}$, which will have the value 1 if errors occurred on both Trials n and $n + k$ and the value 0 otherwise. The expectation of $c_{k,n}$ is

$$E(c_{k,n}) = [w_{0,n}(w_{0,k+1} + \tfrac{1}{2}w_{1,k+1})] + [w_{1,n}\tfrac{1}{4}(1 - \tfrac{1}{2}c)^{k-1}(1 - c)]. \qquad [39]$$

The expectation of $c_{k,n}$ over all trials will be

$$c_k = E \sum_{n=1}^{\infty} c_{k,n} = \frac{(3 - 2c)}{2c}(1 - \tfrac{1}{2}c)^{k-1}, \qquad [40]$$

for $k = 1, 2, 3, \cdots$. The obtained and predicted autocorrelations of errors for the first few values of k are given in Table 2.

CHAPTER III

Probability Learning

The material of the present chapter is concerned with changes in the probability of a choice response over repeated trials in an experimental procedure which has come to be known as the *probability learning* task. In structure the probability learning task consists of a large number of trials which are run off automatically at a rapid rate. Each trial begins with the presentation of a signal (which presumably is constant throughout the task) upon whose appearance a subject is to predict, by means of a simple choice response, which of a number of experimental events, E_i ($i = 1$, $2, \ldots, r$) will occur. The number r of choice responses available to the subject is fixed (generally $r = 2$) and he is required to make exactly one of them on each signal onset. The scheduling of the events may be varied in a number of ways; in the simplest procedure, the noncontingent case, exactly one of the events appears on each trial, independent of the subject's choice, with event E_i having preassigned relative frequency, π_i. This procedure is characterized by a number of features which distinguish it from the experimental tasks discussed in the first two chapters. First, interest is focused upon the effect of a variety of experimental events (sometimes referred to as reinforcing operations) which follow a choice response, rather than upon the stimulus situation at the outset of a trial. Second, the mathematical technique most commonly employed in the derivation of predictions is that of linear operators (Bush and Mosteller, 1955).

To introduce the so-called *linear model* for probability learning, we consider the probability of any one of the choice responses $A_i (i = 1, \ldots, r)$ on an arbitrary trial n of an experiment. The learning axioms of the model take the form of linear functions describing the way in which probability of a given choice changes on trials in which it is, and on trials in which it is not, followed by its corresponding reinforcing event. Since it is immaterial which member of the set of response alternatives is taken as a reference, we shall fix attention upon response A_1. When an A_1 choice is followed by an E_1 event (that is, the reinforcing event appropriate to it), the resulting change in the probability of an A_1 response at the start of the next trial is described by the linear function:

$$p(A_{1,n+1}) = (1 - \theta)p(A_{1,n}) + \theta \qquad (1)$$

where θ is a learning rate parameter. When, on the other hand, A_1 is followed by some other reinforcing event, E_i ($i \neq 1$), then the resulting change in probability of an A_1 response is described by

$$p(A_{1,n+1}) = (1 - \theta)p(A_{1,n}) . \qquad (2)$$

Considered simply from a mathematical viewpoint, these equations state that (a) when response A_1 is reinforced, its probability is increased by a constant fraction of the difference between its current probability and unity; and (b) that when some competing response is reinforced, the probability of response A_1 is decreased by a constant fraction of the difference between its current probability and zero. The significance of the parameter θ, on the other hand, depends upon the theoretical interpretation from which the linear function derives. When equations (1) and (2) arise in a special case of Bush and Mosteller's stochastic model, θ is defined simply as a constant whose value (limited to the interval 0, 1) may depend upon properties of the organism and the reinforcing operations. Within stimulus sampling theory, on the other hand, θ represents the fraction of the stimulus population which is sampled by the organism on any one trial (for elucidation of this point, see Estes, 1959, in Chapter I, or Estes and Straughan, 1954, in the present chapter). In the latter interpretation, the two equations state, in effect, that the state of learning of unsampled elements does not change, while sampled elements become connected to the reinforced response. The effect upon change in the probability of an A_1 response of a trial in which no reinforcing event occurs is a bit more difficult to describe. A number of alternative descriptions of the effect of such "blank" trials will be considered later in this chapter.

The importance of the two "reinforcement operators" represented by equations (1) and (2), in the context of probability learning, lies in the possibility of deducing predictions about the course of learning to be expected under an innumerable variety of reinforcement schedules. The method of deriving expected learning curves is most simply illustrated for the case of noncontingent, random reinforcement. Each operator is weighted by its appropriate relative frequency of application, and the weighted operators are summed to obtain an expected operator which describes the mean, or expected, change in probability of an A_1 response from any trial to the next. For the case of two responses, A_1 and A_2, and corresponding events E_1 and E_2 occurring with relative frequencies of π and $(1 - \pi)$, respectively, operator (1) would be multiplied by π, operator (2) would be multiplied by $(1 - \pi)$, yielding the weighted mean

$$p(A_{1,n+1}) = (1 - \theta)p(A_{1,n}) + \theta\pi. \qquad (3)$$

This difference equation is then solved for response probability as a function of n,

$$p(A_{1,n}) = \pi - [\pi - p(A_{1,0})](1 - \theta)^n. \tag{4}$$

The resulting expression describes a negatively accelerated change from some initial value $p(A_{1,0})$ to an asymptote π. A variety of alternative theoretical formulations lead to somewhat different descriptions of some properties of the distribution of response probabilities, for example, the variance (see Estes, 1959, in Chapter I); but they all lead to the same predicted asymptote of π for the two-alternative noncontingent case. This predicted relationship between response and reinforcement probability is commonly referred to as the *probability matching law* which has been supported, although not consistently, by a great variety of experimental data. Actually, as noted by Estes (1957b), it is more properly a theorem in the sense that it is a consequence of assumptions of the theory rather than a basic assumption.

It is also possible to derive predictions concerning the variance of the distribution of response probabilities and a great variety of sequential statistics: e.g., $p(A_{j,n+1}|E_{i,n})$, the probability of an A_j response on trial $n + 1$ given the occurrence of an E_i on trial n, etc. For details on the derivation of these descriptive statistics, the reader should consult Atkinson, Bower, and Crothers (1965), Atkinson and Estes (1964), or Estes and Suppes (1959).

In the remainder of this chapter we shall consider two topics: questions as to the tenability of basic assumptions, and extensions of the basic model to a great variety of experimental situations.

EXAMINATION OF BASIC ASSUMPTIONS

The trial operators introduced in the preceding section imply a number of assumptions about the nature of the learning process in this situation; some of the assumptions are related and most of them are not independently testable. We shall consider them under two general categories: parameter invariance and independence of path.

Parameter invariance. The trial operators (1) and (2) and the general expression for $p(A_{1,n})$ which is derived from them, (4), contain only one free parameter θ which is to be evaluated from the data. This parameter has no identifying subscript, which means that its value is not a function of trial number n (that is, it should remain constant throughout the course of the experiment), or of the schedule of reinforcing events. To the extent that the value of θ reflects properties of the stimulus situation at the beginning of a trial, both assumptions would seem justifiable on psychological grounds, if trials are independent, since the same signal characterizes the start of a trial for all trials and for all experimental conditions. It should, therefore, be possible to evaluate θ for one experimental group and then apply that value to obtain predictions for other experimental groups run under the same experimental conditions with, for example, different π values. Such a prediction constitutes an extremely strong test of the theory since it employs none of the data being predicted to estimate parameters. This strategy was employed by Estes and Straughan (1954) with partial success. Their data suggested that the value of θ is an increasing function of the difference between asymptote and initial value; practically every subsequent experiment which examined the value of θ for different noncontingent groups has also found θ to be a function of π (with a contingent procedure, Woods (1959) found θ to be invariant over a variety of π values, whereas Neimark (1953) did not). One possible explanation for the relationship of θ and π assumes that with highly massed trials (as is usually the case), aftereffects of the preceding trial constitute part of the stimulus situation at the outset of the ensuing trial; when π is close to unity (or zero), successive trials are more similar than when π approaches .50. In effect, then, the theory assumes that trials are independent, whereas in practice this may not be the case. Straughan (1956) attempted to achieve independent trials by introducing a distracting task between trials. Although his data indicate that the procedure was not entirely successful in eliminating the relationship between θ and π, he could account for the change in θ values by assuming a carryover of stimulus aftereffects. A different attack was employed by Ginsberg (1964), who directly manipulated the degree of stimulus overlap between successive trials. A modified model which took stimulus overlap into account described her data quite accurately. A more recent examination of the invariance of θ (Friedman et al., 1965) suggests that following a shift in π values the value of θ on early trials of the post-shift series reflects the magnitude of the shift, but that the value of θ stabilizes over later trials under the shifted values.

Two techniques are commonly employed in estimating the value of θ: the more commonly used procedure utilizes the total number of A_1 responses over trials; the second employs the difference between two sequential statistics. Studies which have compared estimates obtained with the two procedures (e.g., Ginsberg, 1964; Friedman et al., 1964) typically find that the second procedure yields much higher estimates than the first. Although these discrepancies naturally provide some ground for uneasiness, they do not necessarily justify rejecting the basic assumptions of the theory; they may, for example, be accounted for by the modified sampling scheme proposed by Straughan (1956) and Ginsberg (1964).

Independence of path. The trial operators (1) and (2) indicate that change in probability of an A_1 response is a function solely of the response probability at the start of a trial, and of the outcome on that trial. This property, commonly described as *independence of path*, implies that accuracy in predicting A_1 probability is not improved substantially by taking into account the responses or experimental outcomes of earlier trials in the series. It will be noted that this property is also a characteristic of Markov chains (see Chapter I). Tenability of the assumption of independence of path may be tested directly by analysis of the appropriate sequential probabilities by either an uncertainty analysis (Attneave, 1959) or by a χ^2 test (Suppes and Atkinson, 1960). Although the results of such analyses are often compatible with an independence of path assumption (Edwards, 1961; Feldman, 1959; Hake and Hyman, 1953; Friedman et al., 1964), even in more complicated experimental tasks involving two persons (Suppes and Atkinson, 1960), there is also a good deal of evidence which indicates dependence of A_1 response probability upon responses and outcomes farther back in the sequence than the immediately preceding trial (Anderson, 1960; Engler, 1958; Goodnow, Rubenstein, and Lubin, 1960; Jarvik, 1951; Nicks, 1959). One explanation commonly invoked to account for the finding of dependence of response probability upon experimental outcomes of the preceding sequence of trials, assumes that subjects approach the experimental task with a tendency to look for sequences, and with guessing habits resulting from prior learning. For example, the "gambler's fallacy" (the tendency after a run of E_1 to expect that E_2 is "due" and, therefore, to predict it) would lead to a decrease in the tendency to make an A_1 response after a sequence of E_1 events (negative recency); whereas the trial operator (1) states that each E_1 increases the probability of an A_1 on the following trial (positive recency). A number of early experiments did, in fact, report evidence of negative recency (Jarvik, 1951; Nicks, 1959). There is, however, later evidence (Edwards, 1961; Friedman et al., 1964) which indicates that although negative recency may occur on early trials, it disappears over the course of training and, on later trials, positive recency obtains—as it should according to the theory. It is, of course, possible to construct models to describe the effect upon response probability when sequences or patterns of reinforcing events are in some sense treated as units by the subject (e.g., Estes and Suppes, 1959, pp. 150–153; Sternberg, 1959). Also, some investigators have used modifications of the probability learning task to study the learning of sequences (Galanter and Smith, 1948; Bruner, Wallach, and Galanter, 1959; Weir, 1965) or to demonstrate that some sequences—

usually those involving runs of a single outcome—are easier to learn than others (Restle, 1966; Wolin et al., 1965). The problem of learning of sequences is, however, beyond the scope of the simple models to be considered in this chapter.

EFFECTS OF ADDITIONAL EXPERIMENTAL VARIABLES

Much of the work on probability learning tasks has been concerned with the extension of models for a simple noncontingent two-choice task to description of the effect of additional experimental variables such as: (a) number of response alternatives, (b) relation of reinforcement to response (contingency), (c) schedules in which π changes systematically over trials, (d) removal of the restriction that the reinforcing events are mutually exclusive and exhaustive, (e) variation in the amount of reinforcement, (f) effects of prior training, (g) two-person interactions, (h) continuous response tasks, and (i) manipulation of trial rate, instructions, etc. We shall not attempt to review findings with respect to each of these variables since an extensive review is already available (Estes, 1964). Rather, we shall consider recent developments with respect to questions which have received a good deal of experimental attention, although such attention often fails to provide a clearcut answer to the problem.

Varying probability of reinforcement. Although practically every one of the many reported studies of probability learning has been run with constant reinforcement probabilities throughout an experimental session, this procedural simplification is not theoretically dictated. In principle, the relative frequency of E_i could vary as any arbitrary function of trial number. Predictions for this general case have been derived by Estes (1957a) for both the noncontingent and contingent procedures with any number of response alternatives. Although specific prediction is not obtainable for all cases, it is generally true that $p(A_{1,n})$ should follow, or "track," $\pi_1(n)$. An experiment in which $\pi_1(n)$ is a linear function has been briefly described by Estes (1957b), and one in which it is an exponential function by Hickson (1961). However, the major experimental tests of the general model reported to date come from studies of learning in situations involving two-person interactions (e.g., Suppes and Atkinson, 1960).

There are a few experiments (e.g., Hake and Hyman, 1953) in which not only first-order probability of E_1, i.e., π_1, but also second-order probability, i.e., $\pi_{ij} = p(E_{i,n+1}|E_{j,n})$, have been varied experimentally. In these instances, "probability matching" seems roughly to obtain with respect to conditional probabilities of reinforcing events as well as to first-order probabilities, although deviations from matching do occur and may prove to be of major significance with regard to revision or extension of present models (Anderson, 1960; Engler, 1958). Probability matching has also been obtained with other dependent variables, for example judgments (Estes and Johns, 1958) or estimates (Neimark and Shuford, 1959), rather than predictions.

Transfer effects. If a subject is given a series of trials with constant π and then shifted to a series with a different, but still constant, π value, is the course of learning on the second series affected in any way by prior experiences with the first? If the stimulus situation characterizing the start of a trial does not change in any way, then one would not expect a priori to observe any systematic transfer effect (other than upon the initial level of response probability at the start of the transfer series). As we have seen in examination of the Estes and Straughan (1954) experiment, tests of transfer effects are complicated by the fact θ values change with change in π. Despite results of at least one study (Anderson, 1960) which suggested long-lasting transfer effects, data for transfer experiments are accurately predicted by the model under some conditions (Anderson and Grant, 1957; Friedman et al., 1964).

Early analogies of the noncontingent procedure to Pavlovian conditioning (and of the contingent procedure to instrumental) suggested the use of a probability learning procedure to investigate differential resistance to extinction following partial reinforcement (Humphreys, 1939). As Detambel (1950) showed, the analogy was inappropriate; a later series with different π values is not equivalent to extinction as the term is traditionally used. A more appropriate analogue of extinction is a series in which no reinforcing events even appear (that is, the subject's response is followed by no signal indicating correctness or incorrectness). Neimark (1953) employed such an extinction series and did get evidence of differential resistance following partial reinforcement ($\pi = .66$) as compared with continuous reinforcement ($\pi = 1.0$). As was noted in Chapter I, LaBerge's neutral element model provides a theoretical basis for predicting these differential transfer effects.

Number of response alternatives. Extension of existing models for the two-choice noncontingent case to experimental tasks involving more than two response alternatives requires no additional theoretical considerations and no change in the equation for predicted frequency of A_1 responses over trial blocks. Although early evidence (Detambel, 1955; Neimark, 1956) supported that prediction, subsequent work with longer trial series (Gardner, 1957; Cotton and Rechtshaffen, 1958) showed that, with three response alternatives, the asymptotic probability of A_1 responding exceeds π_1. Moreover, there is evidence (Gardner, 1958) that the degree of "overshoot" is an increasing function of the number of response alternatives.

When reinforcing events are contingent upon responses, the limited evidence available (Detambel, 1955; Neimark, 1956) suggests that the effect of increasing the number of response alternatives may be dependent upon a number of additional variables, some of which will be treated in the remainder of this chapter.

As the number of available response alternatives increases indefinitely, one approximates the class of experimental tasks involving a response continuum (as contrasted with some finite number r of mutually exclusive discrete classes). One example of this procedure is the task employed by Suppes and Frankmann (1961) in which the subject is instructed to position a lever to indicate where on the circumference of a circle a light will occur. Recently, there have been a number of theoretical considerations of tasks involving a response continuum (Anderson, 1959, 1961, 1964; Rosenberg, 1962, 1963; Rouanet and Rosenberg, 1964; Suppes, 1959, 1960; Suppes and Rouanet, 1964; Suppes, Rouanet, Levine, and Frankmann, 1964; Suppes and Zinnes, 1961) and experimental results are generally in accord with predictions. These findings suggest that the function relating deviation of observed from predicted asymptote $\pi - p(A_1, \infty)$ to number of response alternatives r does not continue to increase as r increases, but, rather, that it may be an inverted U-shaped function. At present we know of no data adequate to test this speculation rigorously.

Although models for a response continuum have potential application to an impressive variety of problems, from attitude change (Anderson, 1959) to team performance (Rosenberg, 1962), extended consideration of such models is beyond the scope of the present chapter.

Variation in amount of reward. Most applications of stimulus sampling theory to the effect of reinforcement discussed so far have been concerned with the experimental variation of relative frequency of occurrence of a variety of reinforcing events. The events themselves have generally been alike in kind (for example, lighting of one of a number of lamps differing in spatial location). An important question in the psychological consideration of effects of reinforcement variables concerns the effect of quantitative variation of amount of reinforcement (Pubols, 1960). Within the context of the probability learning experiment, amount of reinforcement is generally manipulated in terms of a "pay-off matrix," that is, the amount of reward, usually monetary, associated with certain experimental events or correct predictions, and penalties associated with other events or incorrect predictions.

Generally (e.g., Suppes and Atkinson, 1960), asymptotic response probability has been found to increase with increase in magnitude of reward. None of the models discussed thus far can describe the effect of variation in *amount* of reward without the use of an additional parameter; the extensions proposed differ with respect to their interpretation of the amount of reward parameter and, to a certain extent, to the variable assumed to affect the value of that parameter or parameters.

A natural extension of existing models to the description of the effect of amount of reinforcement involves the introduction of an amount of reward parameter c whose value is an increasing function of amount of reward. The modified trial operators are then:

$$\text{if } E_1 \qquad p(A_{1,n+1}) = (1 - \theta)p(A_{1,n}) + \theta c_1$$

and   (6)

$$\text{if } E_2 \qquad p(A_{1,n+1}) = (1 - \theta)p(A_{1,n}) + \theta(1 - c_2).$$

Resulting predictions do not provide a particularly accurate description of some of the data to which they have been applied (Estes, 1962) despite the additional flexibility of two more parameters to be estimated from the data.

Siegel (1965) introduces an amount of reward parameter α_i which is interpreted in terms of the concept of utility. It is the ratio of the marginal utility of reward a_i and the disutility of boredom b: $\alpha_i = a_i/b$. Thus, α_i should increase with an increase in a_i or with a decrease in b. Variation in a_i is obvious; the value of b is assumed to be lowered by introducing variation into the experimental task, for example by including trials on which S confronts a mirror image of the apparatus, or by increasing the number of response alternatives r. If the assumption that b is a decreasing function of r is correct, then Siegel's model should provide accurate description of response probabilities for experiments with more than two responses—and it does describe Gardner's (1958) data for asymptotic response probabilities, although Messick (1965) has failed to confirm predictions on the effect of increasing the number of alternative responses. Unfortunately, although the amount of reward parameter of this model has considerable intuitive appeal, the model itself has not been elaborated to account for more than asymptotic probabilities of response.

A generalization of stimulus sampling theory proposed by Atkinson (1961) provides a description of the effect of amount of reinforcement by allowing the strength of conditioning of the ith stimulus element to vary along an integer-valued scale. As a consequence of this assumption, probability matching is predicted only for the special case in which s, the scale value, is unity. As the value of s increases, the function relating $p(A_{1,\infty})$ and π becomes negatively accelerated and as $s \to \infty$, $p(A_{1,\infty}) \to 1$ for all $\pi > .50$. Like Siegel's model, this model describes the effect of number of response alternatives as well as the manipulation of amount of reward.

For example, Gardner's (1957) data for three-choice groups are described by assuming $s = 2$, whereas data for the comparable two-choice groups are described by $s = 1$.

By restricting the possible states of conditioning to two, strong or weak, Atkinson (1962) develops a Markov model with simpler mathematical properties. An element which is strongly conditioned to response A_i will remain strongly conditioned if it is sampled and response A_i is reinforced; if A_i is not reinforced, it will become weakly conditioned to an alternative response with probability δ. If a stimulus element which is weakly conditioned to A_i is sampled and A_i is reinforced, the element will become strongly conditioned to A_i with probability μ; if A_i is not reinforced, the element will become weakly conditioned to $A_j (j \neq i)$ with probability δ. Although both δ and μ are functions of amount of reinforcement and must be evaluated from the data, predictions of asymptotic response probabilities involve only one parameter, the ratio of δ/μ. Myers and Atkinson (1964) have shown that the strong–weak model provides good prediction of data from a variety of experiments; in addition, they have suggested extensions of the model to other response measures such as response time. Although the relationship of theoretical parameters to experimental manipulation of amount of reward remains to be explored, at the present time the strong–weak model is elaborated in greater detail and offers greater potential generality than any other model available.

Still another approach to the description of the effect of amount of reinforcement is the scanning model (Estes, 1962) included in this chapter, which is related in important respects to the random-walk model for choice behavior (Estes, 1960) given in Chapter V. Although it is always gratifying to find that the effect of an experimental variable can be described by a more general theory, at present the scanning model has not been elaborated in great detail nor sufficiently tested to predict its future role. It has, however, been useful in describing results of a number of experiments (Cole, 1965; Friedman, Padilla, and Gelfand, 1964).

Effects of nonreinforcement. Most experimental tests of reinforcement models have utilized a noncontingent procedure; that is, on each trial, exactly one reinforcing event occurs, independent of the subject's response. Thus, on each trial a response appropriate to the event which occurred is strengthened and the increase in response probability is described by the trial operator (1). With modified experimental procedures, on the other hand, it is possible to have a trial on which none of the alternative reinforcing events occurs (for example, no panel lamp is lighted); this state of affairs will be called nonreinforcement. Nonreinforcement, so defined, may occur in a number of ways: in a noncontingent procedure one may introduce E_0 trials (trials on which none of the events $E_1, E_2, \ldots, E_r$ is presented), so that $\pi_1 + \pi_2 + \cdots + \pi_r < 1$; in a contingent procedure (where the occurrence of an event is dependent upon the response which occurs), if the subject does not predict correctly, he receives no information as to which, if any, of the events would have occurred had he chosen a different response. For such trial outcomes, a new trial operator is required, and a number of alternatives have been suggested. Before going into the effect of nonreinforcement in a contingent procedure, however, we shall consider the effect of a blank trial in the noncontingent procedure.

Most investigators (e.g., Bush and Mosteller, 1955; Estes and Suppes, 1959; Neimark, 1956) have introduced a third trial operator to account for the effect of a blank trial upon response probability:

$$p(A_{1,n+1}) = p(A_{1,n}) . \tag{7}$$

In other words, it is assumed that a blank trial leaves response probability unchanged; hence, Bush and Mosteller's description of (7) as the *identity operator*. As a consequence of this assumption, one can predict that $p(A_{1,n})$ for groups receiving some proportion, π_0, of E_0 trials will approach an asymptote of $\pi_1/(\pi_1 + \pi_2)$, but will do so at a more gradual rate than for "traditional" noncontingent groups with the same relative frequencies of E_1 and E_2. Results of the first experiment examining the effect of blank trials (Neimark, 1956) were in accord with this prediction. Moreover, Anderson and Grant (1957), using longer series of trials, showed that the result obtains not only for E_0 trials, but also for trials on which both E_1 and E_2 may occur simultaneously. In the analysis of their data, however, Anderson and Grant (1958) introduced a new technique for evaluating the effect of both these types of trials, on the basis of which they concluded that elements sampled are, in effect, shared among the response alternatives with the lion's share ($\alpha = .88$) going to the response which occurred on that trial.

There are two more complications in evaluating the adequacy of an identity operator in describing the effect of E_0 trials: one a theoretical consideration and one an empirical one. Bush and Mosteller (1955) had derived the identity operator by assuming that the effect of an E_0 trial is, in fact, to leave conditioning status unchanged. Neimark (1953), on the other hand, had assumed that on E_0 trials all sampled elements are conditioned to the response which occurred on that trial. Thus, for any given trial, the effect of an E_0 trial is to increase the probability of the response which occurs, although over a series of trials the net or expected effect of E_0 is to leave response probability unchanged. Thus two different sets of assumptions generally lead to the same testable prediction. Atkinson (1956) derived differential predictions for the two assumptions by using an experimental procedure in which the occurrence of an E_0 is contingent upon the occurrence of an A_1 response and occurs with probability $\pi_0 = (1 - \beta)$. For the values of π_i and β which Atkinson employed, the contiguity assumption (Neimark, 1953) leads to higher predicted asymptotic response probabilities than the identity assumption (Bush and Mosteller, 1955). Obtained asymptotic response probabilities were best described by the identity operator. A third assumption, that the sampled elements are shared, with a proportion σ of the elements going to A_1 and the remainder to A_2 (where σ corresponds to the α of Anderson and Grant), leads to predicted asymptotes which are significantly below the observed values.

Although the early evidence on the effect of E_0 trials seemed to be consonant with the assumption that E_0 events leave response probability unchanged, the data of LaBerge and his associates (LaBerge, Greeno, and Peterson, 1962; Greeno and LaBerge, 1963; Greeno, 1962) indicate that not only learning rates, but also asymptotic response probabilities are reduced with the addition of large numbers of E_0 trials—a finding which is not in accord with the assumption that E_0 trials leave response probability unchanged. They suggest that E_0 trials may serve to neutralize some of the elements, that is, may result in the elements being conditioned to neither of the response alternatives. In addition, their analysis of the effects of events preceding an E_0 trial shows that the effect of an E_0 depends on the events of the preceding trial. Thus, it would appear that although equation (7) provides a fairly accurate description of the effect of E_0 trials in many experimental situations, the process or mechanics involved may be more complex and more dependent upon other experimental operations than is implied by the simple identity operator.

For experiments involving a noncontingent procedure, description of the consequences of an experimental trial is straightforward since, when E_0 trials are not involved, one of the events $E_1, E_2, \ldots, E_r$ occurs on each trial regardless of the nature of the subject's response, and the appropriate trial operator is applicable. In other experimental tasks, for example in a T-maze with noncorrection or in a multiple choice situation in which human subjects are instructed to turn on a light rather than to predict it, the occurrence of a reinforcing event is contingent upon the nature of the subject's response, and it is not generally the case that he receives full information on all trials. When the event signifying a correct response does occur, its effects on the response which occurred, and on any alternative response, should be described by the appropriate trial operator (1) or (2), respectively. When no such event occurs following a response, one may assume (a) that an alternative response is reinforced and operator (2) applies, (b) that the identity operator (7) applies, or (c) that there is some sharing of elements among responses. A model for the two-choice situation based upon the first assumption (Estes, 1954) leads to predicted asymptotic response probabilities of

$$p(A_{1,\infty}) = (1 - \pi_2)/(2 - \pi_1 - \pi_2) , \qquad (8)$$

where π_1 and π_2 denote the probabilities of reinforcement (that is, a "correct" signal) following A_1 and A_2 responses, respectively. Some comparisons of the contingent and noncontingent procedures for the special case where $\pi_1 = 1 - \pi_2$, so that equation (8) reduces to $p(A_{1,\infty}) = \pi_1$ (e.g., Neimark, 1956), have found similar learning curves under both procedures, whereas others (e.g., Uhl, 1963; Parducci and Polt, 1958; Stanley, 1950) have not. With a contingent procedure, it is often found that observed response probabilities exceed the predicted asymptotic response probabilities (Brand, Sakoda, and Woods, 1957; Woods, 1959; Koehler, 1961), especially with animal subjects (Bush and Wilson, 1956; Parducci and Polt, 1958; Uhl, 1963; Weinstock, North, Brody, and LoGiudice, 1965; Brody, 1965). Such results would seem to indicate that contingent nonreinforcement is not generally equivalent to reinforcement of an alternative response.

In some of these instances (Bush and Wilson, 1956; Weinstock et al., 1965), the use of an identity operator for nonreinforced trials appears to provide fairly accurate description of the data and, in general, it appears that nonreward-noncorrection trials, when imbedded in probabilistic schedules with animal subjects, have virtually no effect on response probability.

With human subjects, on the other hand, although observed response probabilities occasionally exceed the predicted asymptotes of equation (8), they rarely approach the unity asymptote which would be expected if contingent nonreinforcement were accurately described by an identity operator. Existing evidence strongly suggests that with human subjects the effect of a contingent nonreinforcement is a function of relationships among the reinforcement probabilities (Brand, Sakoda, and Woods, 1957) and of instructions to the subject concerning the interpretation of nonreinforced trials (Koehler, 1961). To date, no one has proposed a formal theory for the contingent procedure which takes these variables into account.

EVALUATION OF MODELS FOR PROBABILITY LEARNING

In the relatively short time since its first introduction, the probability learning experiment has become extremely popular among experimental psychologists, both as a test of theoretical descriptions of the task itself, and also as a simple paradigm of more complex processes such as decision, judgment, and discrimination (see Chapters IV and V for some applications to judgment and discrimination). Of more immediate relevance to the present chapter, the probability learning situation proved admirably suited for the first large-scale deployment in learning theory of a strategy with a long record of success in the physical sciences. From relatively primitive assumptions concerning processes of stimulus sampling and associative learning, operators were derived expressing the predicted effects of learning trials involving particular types of reinforcing events. Then, by taking this set of operators, together with the particular boundary conditions of individual experiments, one could deduce predictions concerning the course of learning under virtually any reinforcement schedule an experimenter might prescribe. Over the years, more and more detailed predictions have been tested for an increasing variety of reinforcement schedules.

In general, one can conclude that the strategy has proven useful, even though theoretical predictions have not been supported uniformly by experimental findings. For example, the prediction of probability matching and related phenomena in a great variety of situations may be regarded as a major achievement for the theory despite the fact that (a) continued experimentation has uncovered a number of conditions under which matching relationships no longer obtain, and (b) continued theoretical work revealed alternative sets of primitive assumptions which could lead to essentially the same predictions.

Close scrutiny of the fairly sizable body of available experimental evidence in relation to the theory suggests some meaningful patterning of successes and failures. One can conclude, with fair assurance, that the mathematical operators of stimulus sampling theory accurately describe the effect of a reinforced trial under a wide variety of experimental conditions. Treatment of nonreinforcement, on the other hand, presents some problems. The effect of an omission of reinforcement (that is, a noninformative trial outcome) does not generally prove constant over a sequence of trials, the most common trend being a shift from a decremental effect of nonreinforcement early in a learning series to a negligible effect (described by the identity operator) late in the series. Furthermore, the rationale for operators describing effects of nonreinforcement is not as well grounded in more primitive assumptions as is the case for reinforcement operators. Problems in dealing with nonreinforcement seem to be confounded when more than two responses are available, or when reinforcing events are contingent upon response. Finally, it is clear that the independent sampling assumption of the simplest cases of stimulus sampling theory does not hold for more than a very limited class of experimental situations.

Development of a theory which will provide more accurate description of this problem area, at least for the behavior of human subjects, may require that assumptions concerning elementary learning mechanisms, of the sort discussed in the present chapter, be augmented by higher order verbal processes of the kinds customarily described in terms of hypothesis testing and selection of strategies. Future research will doubtless be directed toward development of theoretical machinery to handle cases in which (a) stimulus sampling is not independent from trial to trial, and (b) the manner of stimulus sampling changes systematically as a result of the learning and unlearning of observing or perceptual behaviors. Some research pointing in this direction will be discussed in later chapters; but most of it remains for the future.

REFERENCES

Anderson, N. H. Test of a model for opinion change. *J. abnorm. soc. Psychol.*, 1959, **59**, 371–381.

Anderson, N. H. Effect of first-order conditional probability in a two-choice learning situation. *J. exp. Psychol.*, 1960, **59**, 73–93.

Anderson, N. H. Two learning models for responses measured on a continous scale. *Psychometrika*, 1961, **26**, 391–403.

Anderson, N. H. Linear models for responses measured on a continuous scale. *J. math. Psychol.*, 1964, **1**, 121–142.

Anderson, N. H. and Grant, D. A. A test of a statistical learning theory model for two-choice behavior with double stimulus events. *J. exp. Psychol.*, 1957, **54**, 305–317.

Anderson, N. H. and Grant, D. A. A correction and reanalysis. *J. exp. Psychol.*, 1958, **56**, 453–454.

Atkinson, R. C. An analysis of the effect of non-reinforced trials in terms of statistical learning theory. *J. exp. Psychol.*, 1956, **52**, 28–32.

Atkinson, R. C. A generalization of stimulus sampling theory. *Psychometrika*, 1961, **26**, 281–290.

Atkinson, R. C. Choice behavior and monetary payoff: Strong and weak conditioning. In J. H. Criswell, H. Solomon, and P. Suppes (Eds.), *Mathematical methods in small group processes*. Stanford, Calif.: Stanford Univ. Press, 1962, 23–34.

Atkinson, R. C., Bower, G. H., and Crothers, E. J. *An introduction to mathematical learning theory*. New York: Wiley, 1965.

Atkinson, R. C. and Estes, W. K. Stimulus sampling theory. In R. D. Luce, R. R. Bush, and E. Galanter (Eds.), *Handbook of mathematical psychology*. New York: Wiley, 1963, 206–239.

Brand, H., Sakoda, J. M., and Woods, P. J. Contingent partial reinforcement and the anticipation of correct alternatives. *J. exp. Psychol.*, 1957, **53**, 417–424.

Brody, A. L. Nonreinforcement in a noncorrection T–maze. *J. comp. physiol. Psychol.*, 1965, **60**, 428–431.

Bruner, J. S., Wallach, M. A., and Galanter, E. H. The identification of recurrent regularity. *Am. J. Psychol.*, 1959, **72**, 200–209.

Burke, C. J. Applications of a linear model to two-person interactions. In R. R. Bush & W. K. Estes (Eds.), *Studies in mathematical learning theory*. Stanford, Calif.: Stanford Univ. Press, 1959, 180–203.

Burke, C. J. Two-person interactive learning. In J. H. Criswell, H. Solomon, and P. Suppes (Eds.), *Mathematical methods in small group processes*. Stanford, Calif.: Stanford Univ. Press, 1962, 49–68.

Bush, R. R. and Mosteller, F. *Stochastic models for learning*. New York: Wiley, 1955.

Bush, R. R. and Wilson, T. R. Two-choice behavior of paradise fish. *J. exp. Psychol.*, 1956, **51,** 315–322.

Cole, M. Search behavior: A correction procedure for three-choice probability learning. *J. math. Psychol.*, 1965, **2,** 145–170.

Cole, M., Belinky, G. L., Boucher, R., Fernandez, R. N., and Myers, D. L. Probability learning to escape from shock. *Psychon. Sci.*, 1965, **3,** 127–128.

Cotton, J. W. and Rechtschaffen, A. Replication report: Two- and three-choice verbal conditioning phenomena. *J. exp. Psychol.*, 1958, **56,** 96.

Detambel, M. H. A re-analysis of Humphreys' "Acquisition and extinction of verbal expectations." Unpublished master's thesis, Indiana Univ., 1950.

Detambel, M. H. A test of a model for multiple-choice behavior. *J. exp. Psychol.*, 1955, **49,** 97–104.

Edwards, W. D. Probability learning in 1000 trials. *J. exp. Psychol.*, 1961, **62,** 385–394.

Engler, J. Marginal and conditional stimulus and response probabilities in verbal conditioning. *J. exp. Psychol.*, 1958, **55,** 303–317.

Estes, W. K. Individual behavior in uncertain situations. In R. M. Thrall, C. H. Coombs, and R. L. Davis (Eds.), *Decision processes*. New York: Wiley, 1954, 127–138.

Estes, W. K. Theory of learning with constant, variable, or contingent probability of reinforcement. *Psychometrika*, 1957, **22,** 113–132. (a)

Estes, W. K. Of models and men. *Am. Psychol.*, 1957, **12,** 609–617. (b)

Estes, W. K. Component and pattern models with Markovian interpretations. In R. R. Bush and W. K. Estes (Eds.), *Studies in mathematical learning theory*. Stanford, Calif.: Stanford Univ. Press, 1959, 9–53.

Estes, W. K. Theoretical treatment of differential reward in multiple-choice learning and two-person interactions. In J. H. Criswell, H. Solomon, and P. Suppes (Eds.), *Mathematical methods in small group processes*. Stanford, Calif.: Stanford Univ. Press, 1962, 133–149.

Estes, W. K. Probability learning. In A. W. Melton (Ed.), *Categories of human learning*. New York: Academic Press, 1964, 89–128.

Estes, W. K., and Burke, C. J. A theory of stimulus variability in learning. *Psychol. Rev.*, 1953, **60,** 276–286.

Estes, W. K. and Johns, M. D. Probability learning with ambiguity in the reinforcing stimulus. *Am. J. Psychol.*, 1958, **71,** 219–228.

Estes, W. K. and Straughan, J. H. Analysis of a verbal conditioning situation in terms of statistical learning theory. *J. exp. Psychol.*, 1954, **47,** 225–234.

Estes, W. K. and Suppes, P. Foundations of linear models. In R. R. Bush and

W. K. Estes (Eds.), *Studies in mathematical learning theory*. Stanford, Calif.: Stanford Univ. Press, 1959, 137–179.

Feldman, J. On the negative recency hypothesis in prediction of a series of binary symbols. *Am. J. Psychol.*, 1959, **72,** 597–599.

Friedman, M. P., Burke, C. J., Cole, M., Keller, L., Millward, R. B., and Estes, W. K. Two-choice behavior under extended training with shifting probabilities of reinforcement. In R. C. Atkinson (Ed.), *Studies in mathematical psychology*. Stanford, Calif.: Stanford Univ. Press, 1964, 250–316.

Friedman, M. P., Padilla, G., and Gelfand, H. The learning of choices between bets. *J. math. Psychol.*, 1964, **1,** 375–385.

Galanter, E. and Smith, W. A. S. Some experiments on a simple thought-problem. *Am. J. Psychol.*, 1958, **71,** 359–366.

Gardner, R. A. Probability learning with two and three choices. *Am. J. Psychol.*, 1957, **70,** 174–185.

Gardner, R. A. Multiple-choice decision behavior. *Am. J. Psychol.*, 1958, **71,** 710–717.

Ginsberg, R. Stimulus overlap in a massed-trial situation. *J. exp. Psychol.*, 1964, **67,** 553–559.

Goodnow, J. J., Rubinstein, J., and Lubin, A. Response to changing patterns of events. *Am. J. Psychol.*, 1960, **73,** 56–67.

Grant, D. A., Hake, H. W., and Hornseth, J. P. Acquisition and extinction of a verbal conditioned response with differing percentages of reinforcement. *J. exp. Psychol.*, 1951, **42,** 1–5.

Greeno, J. G. Effects of nonreinforced trials in two-choice learning with noncontingent reinforcement. *J. exp. Psychol.*, 1962, **64,** 373–379.

Greeno, J. G. and LaBerge, D. Sequential dependencies and nonreinforcement in probability learning. *J. exp. Psychol.*, 1963, **66,** 547–552.

Hake, H. W. and Hyman, R. Perception of the statistical structure of a random series of binary symbols. *J. exp. Psychol.*, 1953, **45,** 64–74.

Hall, R. L. Group performance under feedback that confounds responses of group members. *Sociometry*, 1957, **20,** 297–305.

Hickson, R. H. Response probability in a two-choice learning situation with varying probability of reinforcement. *J. exp. Psychol.*, 1961, **62,** 138–144.

Humphreys, L. G. Acquisition and extinction of verbal expectations in a situation analogous to conditioning. *J. exp. Psychol.*, 1939, **25,** 294–301.

Jarvik, M. E. Probability learning and negative recency effect in the serial anticipation of alternative symbols. *J. exp. Psychol.*, 1951, **41,** 291–297.

Keller, L., Burke, C. J., and Schneider, A. M. Probability learning and nonreinforced trials. Paper read at Midwest Psychol. Assoc., Chicago, 1961.

Koehler, J., Jr. Role of instructions in two-choice verbal conditioning with contingent partial reinforcement. *J. exp. Psychol.*, 1961, **62,** 122–125.

LaBerge, D. A model with neutral elements. In R. R. Bush and W. K. Estes (Eds.), *Studies in mathematical learning theory*. Stanford, Calif.: Stanford Univ. Press, 1959, 53–64. (a)

LaBerge, D. The effect of preliminary trials on rate of conditioning in a simple prediction situation. *J. exp. Psychol.*, 1959, **57,** 20–24. (b)

LaBerge, D., Greeno, J. G., and Peterson, O. F. Nonreinforcement and neutralization of stimuli. *J. exp. Psychol.*, 1962, **63**, 207–213.

Levine, M. Mediating processes in humans at the outset of discrimination learning. *Psychol. Rev.*, 1963, **70**, 254–276.

Levine, M., Leitenberg, H., and Richter, M. The blank trials law: The equivalence of positive reinforcement and nonreinforcement. *Psychol. Rev.*, 1964, **71**, 94–103.

Melton, A. W. (Ed.) *Categories of human learning.* New York: Academic Press, 1964.

Messick, D. M. The utility of variability in probability learning. *Psychon. Sci.*, 1965, **3**, 355–356.

Myers, J. L. and Atkinson, R. C. Choice behavior and reward structure. *J. math. Psychol.*, 1964, **1**, 170–203.

Neimark, E. D. Effects of type of non-reinforcement and number of alternative responses in two verbal conditioning situations. Unpublished doctor's dissertation, Indiana Univ., 1953.

Neimark, E. D. Effects of type of non-reinforcement and number of alternative responses in two verbal conditioning situations. *J. exp. Psychol.*, 1956, **52**, 209–211.

Neimark, E. D. and Shuford, E. H., Jr. Comparison of predictions and estimates in a probability learning situation. *J. exp. Psychol.*, 1959, **57**, 294–298.

Nicks, D. C. Prediction of sequential two-choice decisions from event runs. *J. exp. Psychol.*, 1959, **57**, 105–114.

Parducci, A. and Polt, J. Correction vs. non-correction with changing reinforcement schedules. *J. comp. physiol. Psychol.*, 1958, **51**, 492–499.

Pubols, B. H., Jr. Incentive magnitude, learning and performance in animals. *Psychol. Bull.*, 1960, **57**, 89–115.

Restle, F. Grammatical analysis of the prediction of binary events. *J. verbal Learn. Verbal Behav.*, 1966, **5**.

Rosenberg, S. Two-person interactions in a continuous-response task. In J. Criswell, J. Solomon, and P. Suppes (Eds.), *Mathematical methods in small group processes.* Stanford, Calif.: Stanford Univ. Press, 1962, 282–304.

Rosenberg, S. Behavior in a continuous-response task with noncontingent reinforcement. *J. exp. Psychol.*, 1963, **66**, 168–176.

Rouanet, H. and Rosenberg, S. Stochastic models for the response continuum in a determinate situation: Comparisons and extensions. *J. math. Psychol.*, 1964, **1**, 215–232.

Siegel, S., Siegel, A. E., and Andrews, J. M. *Choice, strategy and utility.* New York: McGraw Hill, 1964.

Stanley, J. C., Jr. The differential effects of partial and continuous reward upon the acquisition and elimination of a running response in a two-choice situation. Unpublished Ed.D. thesis, Harvard Univ., 1950.

Sternberg, S. H. A path-dependent linear model. In R. R. Bush and W. K. Estes (Eds.), *Studies in mathematical learning theory.* Stanford, Calif.: Stanford Univ. Press, 1959, 308–339.

Straughan, J. H. Human escape learning in relation to reinforcement variables and intertrial conditions. *J. exp. Psychol.*, 1956, **52**, 1–8.

Suppes, P. A linear model for a continuum of responses. In R. R. Bush and W. K. Estes (Eds.), *Studies in mathematical learning theory*. Stanford, Calif.: Stanford Univ. Press, 1959, 400–414.

Suppes, P. Stimulus sampling theory for a continuum of responses. In K. J. Arrow, S. Karlin, and P. Suppes (Eds.), *Mathematical methods in the social sciences*. Stanford, Calif.: Stanford Univ. Press, 1960, 348–365.

Suppes, P. and Atkinson, R. C. *Markov learning models for multi-person interactions*. Stanford, Calif.: Stanford Univ. Press, 1960.

Suppes, P. and Carlsmith, J. M. Experimental analysis of a duopoly situation from the standpoint of mathematical learning theory. *International economic Rev.*, 1962, **3**, 60–78.

Suppes, P. and Frankmann, R. W. Test of stimulus sampling theory for a continuum of responses with unimodal noncontingent determinate reinforcement. *J. exp. Psychol.*, 1961, **61**, 122–132.

Suppes, P. and Krasne, F. Application of stimulus sampling theory to a situation involving social pressure. *Psychol. Rev.*, 1961, **68**, 46–59.

Suppes, P., Rouanet, H., Levine, M., and Frankmann, R. W. Empirical comparison of models for a continuum of responses with noncontingent bimodal reinforcement. In R. C. Atkinson (Ed.), *Studies in mathematical psychology*. Stanford, Calif.: Stanford Univ. Press, 1964, 358–379.

Suppes, P. and Rouanet, H. A simple discrimination experiment with a continuum of responses. In R. C. Atkinson (Ed.), *Studies in mathematical psychology*. Stanford, Calif.: Stanford Univ. Press, 1964, 317–357.

Suppes, P. and Zinnes, J. L. Stochastic learning theories for a response continuum with non-determinate reinforcement. *Psychometrika*, 1961, **26**, 373–390.

Uhl, C. N. Two-choice probability learning in the rat as a function of incentive, probability of reinforcement, and training procedure. *J. exp. Psychol.*, 1963, **66**, 443–449.

Weinstock, S., North, A. J., Brody, A. L., and LoGiudice, J. Probability learning in the T–maze with noncorrection. *J. comp. physiol. Psychol.*, 1965, **68**, 76–81.

Weir, M. W. Developmental changes in problem-solving strategies. *Psychol. Rev.*, 1964, **71**, 473–490.

Wilson, W. A., Jr. and Rollin, A. R. Two-choice behavior of rhesus monkeys in a non-contingent situation. *J. exp. Psychol.*, 1959, **58**, 74–80.

Wolin, B. R., Weichel, R., Terebinski, S. J., and Hansford, E. A. Performance on complexly patterned binary event sequences. *Psychol. Monog.*, 1965, **79**, No. 7 (Whole No. 600).

Woods, P. J. The relationship between probability differences ($\pi_1 - \pi_2$) and learning rate in a contingent partial reinforcement situation. *J. exp. Psychol.*, 1959, **58**, 27–30.

Analysis of a Verbal Conditioning Situation in Terms of Statistical Learning Theory[1]

W. K. ESTES and J. H. STRAUGHAN, *Indiana University*

It is the purpose of this study to investigate the theoretical significance of a rather striking coincidence between an experimental fact and a mathematical fact. The experimental fact has been established in the Humphreys-type "verbal conditioning" situation. In this situation S is asked to predict on each of a series of trials whether some designated event, e.g., the flash of a light, will occur; this event, the analogue of the US in a conditioning experiment, is presented in accordance with a predetermined schedule, usually random with some fixed probability. Several recent investigators (3, 5) have noted that S tends to match his response rate to the rate of occurrence of the predicted event so that if the probability of the latter is, say, .75, the mean response curve for a group of Ss tends over a series of trials toward an apparently stable final level at which the event is predicted on approximately 75% of the trials. This behavior has seemed puzzling to most investigators since it does not maximize the proportion of successful predictions and thus does

[1] This research was facilitated by the senior author's tenure as a faculty research fellow of the Social Science Research Council.

not conform to conventional law of effect doctrine. The mathematical fact which will concern us appeared in the course of developing the formal consequences of statistical association theory (1, 2); in a simple associative learning situation satisfying certain conditions of symmetry, the theoretical asymptote of response probability turns out to be equal to the probability of reinforcement. The reasoning involved may be sketched briefly as follows.

We consider a situation in which each trial begins with presentation of a signal, or CS; following the signal, one or the other of two reinforcing stimuli, E_1 or E_2, occurs, the probability of E_1 and E_2 during a given series being π and $1-\pi$, respectively. The behaviors available to S are categorized into two classes, A_1 and A_2, by experimental criteria. In the verbal conditioning situation, A_1 is a prediction that E_1 will occur, and A_2 a prediction that E_2 will occur on the given trial. We assume that the CS determines a population, S_c, of stimulus elements which is sampled by S on each trial, the proportion θ of the elements in this population constituting the effective sample on any one

This article appeared in *J. exp. Psychol.*, 1954, **47**, 225–234.

trial. The dependence of S's responses upon the stimulating situation is expressed in the theory by defining a conditional relationship such that each element in S_c is conditioned to (tends to evoke) either A_1 or A_2. In order to interpret the formal model in terms of a verbal conditioning experiment, we assume that when an E_1 occurs it evokes from S a response belonging to class A_1, i.e., one which is compatible with the response of predicting E_1 but which interferes with the response of predicting E_2, and that when an E_2 occurs it evokes a response of class A_2. Then on a trial on which E_1 occurs we expect on the basis of association principles (1) that all elements sampled from S_c on the trial will become conditioned to A_1 while on an E_2 trial the sample will be conditioned to A_2. Now if successive trials are sufficiently discrete so that samples from S_c are statistically independent, the probability of an A_1 after Trial n, abbreviated $p(n)$, is defined in the model as the proportion of elements in S_c that are conditioned to A_1, and similarly for the probability of an A_2, $[1-p(n)]$. With these definitions the rule for calculating the change in response probability on an E_1 trial may be stated formally as

$$p(n + 1) = (1-\theta)p(n) + \theta \quad (1)$$

and on an E_2 trial as

$$p(n + 1) = (1-\theta)p(n). \quad (2)$$

The genesis of these equations will be fairly obvious. The proportion $(1-\theta)$ of stimulus elements is not sampled, and the status of elements that are not sampled on a trial does not change; the proportion θ is sampled and these elements are all conditioned either to A_1 or to A_2 accordingly as an E_1 or an E_2 occurs.[2] Now in a random rein-

[2] Consequently the functions derived in this paper should be expected to apply only to learn-

forcement situation, Equation 1 will be applicable on the proportion π of trials and Equation 2 on the proportion $(1-\pi)$; then the average probability of A_1 after Trial $n + 1$ will be given by the relation

$$\begin{aligned} \bar{p}(n + 1) &= \pi[(1-\theta)\,\bar{p}(n) + \theta] \\ &\quad + (1 - \pi)(1 - \theta)\,\bar{p}(n) \quad (3) \\ &= (1 - \theta)\,\bar{p}(n) + \theta\pi. \end{aligned}$$

If a group of Ss begins an experiment with the value $\bar{p}(0)$, then at the end of Trial 1 we would have

$$\bar{p}(1) = (1 - \theta)\,\bar{p}(0) + \theta\pi,$$

at the end of Trial 2

$$\begin{aligned} \bar{p}(2) &= (1 - \theta)[(1 - \theta)\,\bar{p}(0) \\ &\quad\quad\quad\quad\quad + \theta\pi] + \theta\pi \\ &= \pi - [\pi - \bar{p}(0)](1 - \theta)^2, \end{aligned}$$

and so on for successive trials; in general it can be shown by induction that at the end of the nth trial

$$\bar{p}(n) = \pi - [\pi - \bar{p}(0)](1 - \theta)^n. \quad (4)$$

Since $(1 - \theta)$ must be a fraction between zero and one, it will be seen that Equation 4 must be a negatively accelerated curve running from the initial value $\bar{p}(0)$ to the asymptotic value π.

This outcome of the statistical learning model is rather surprising at first since it makes asymptotic response probability depend solely upon the probability of reinforcement. It seems, however, to be in excellent agreement with the experimental results of Grant, Hake, and Hornseth (3) and Jarvik (5). The question that interests us

ing situations which are symmetrical in the following sense. To each response class there must correspond a reinforcing condition which, if present on any trial, ensures that a response belonging to the class will terminate the trial. These functions should, for example, be applicable to learning of a simple left-right discrimination with correction; but not to a left-right discrimination without correction, to free responding in the Skinner box, or to Pavlovian conditioning.

now is whether this agreement is to be regarded as a remarkable coincidence or as a confirmation of the theory. We cannot estimate a confidence level for the latter conclusion since the experiments were not conducted specifically to test the theory, and we cannot guarantee that we would be as alert to notice results contrary to the theory which might appear in the literature as we have been in the case of these decidedly positive instances. It has seemed to us that the least objectionable way out of this impasse is to carry out some new experiments, making use of one of the convenient features of a mathematical theory, namely, that if it will generate one testable prediction for a given experimental situation, it can generally be made to yield many more. In the experiment to be reported we have tried to set up a situation similar in essentials to that used by Humphreys, Grant, and others with an experimental design which would permit testing of a variety of consequences of the theory. Each S was run through two successive series of 120 trials in an individualized modification of the Humphreys situation with the schedule of π values shown in Table 1. Within the first series we will be able to compare learning rates and asymptotes of groups starting from similar initial values but exposed to different probabilities of reinforcement; within the second series we will be able to compare groups starting at different initial values but exposed to the same probabilities of reinforcement. Comparison of Group I with the other groups over both series will permit evaluation of the stability of learning rate (θ value) from series to series when the π value does or does not change. Series I_A and series II_B will provide a comparison in which initial response probabilities and π values are the same but the amount of

TABLE 1

EXPERIMENTAL DESIGN IN TERMS OF PROBABILITY OF REINFORCEMENT (π VALUE) DURING EACH SERIES

Group	N	Trials 1–120 Series A	Trials 121–240 Series B
I	16	.30	.30
II	16	.50	.30
III	16	.85	.30

preceding reinforcement differs. In order to separate the effect of over-all π value from that of particular orders of event occurrences, each of the three groups indicated in Table 1 has been subdivided into four subgroups of four Ss each; within a treatment group, say Group I, all subgroups have the same π value but each receives a separate randomly drawn sequence of E_1's and E_2's.

METHOD

Apparatus.—The experiment was run in a room containing a 2-ft. square signal board and four booths. Upon the signal board were mounted 12 12-v., .25-amp. light bulbs spaced evenly in a circle 18 in. in diameter. The bulbs occupied the half-hour positions of a clock face. Only the top two lights on the board were used as signals in this experiment. The signal board was mounted vertically on a table 40 in. high and was about 5 ft. in front of Ss' booths.

The booths were made from two 30 × 60 in. tables, 30 in. high, placed end to end but meeting at an angle so that Ss sitting behind them would be facing almost directly toward the signal board, about 7 ft. in front of Ss' eyes. Two Ss sat at each table. The four Ss were separated from one another by panels 2 ft. high and 32 in. wide. These panels were mounted vertically on the table tops so as to extend 14½ in. beyond the edge of the table between the seated Ss.

In each booth, 18 in. back from S's edge of the table, was a wooden panel 12 in. high mounted vertically on the table top and extending across the width of the booth. On the side of this panel facing S were two reinforcing lights of the same size as those on the signal board but covered by white, translucent lenses. These lights were directly in front of S, 4 in. apart and 8 in. above the table top. On the table below each reinforcing light was a telegraph key.

The orders of presentation and the durations of the signal lights and reinforcing lights were controlled by a modified Esterline-Angus recorder using a punched tape and a system of electrical pick-up brushes. The recorder was placed on the table behind the signal board. Recorder pens which were activated by depression of the telegraph keys in Ss' booths were mounted between the brushes. Thus, the presentations of the lights and Ss' responses were recorded on the same tape. A panel light was mounted above the Esterline-Angus recorder so that E, seated behind the signal board, could watch the operation of brushes and pens during the experiment.

Windows in the experimental room were covered with opaque material and the experiment was run in darkness except for light that came from the apparatus.

Subjects.—The Ss were 48 students obtained from beginning lecture courses in psychology during the fall semester of 1952 and assigned at random to experimental groups.

Procedure.—At the beginning of a session, Ss were brought into the room, asked to be seated, and read the following instructions:

"Be sure you are seated comfortably; it will be necessary to keep one hand resting lightly beside each of the telegraph keys throughout the experiment and to watch both the large board in the front of the room and the two small lights in your own compartment. Your task in this experiment will be to outguess the experimenter on each trial, or at least as often as you can. The ready signal on each trial will be a flash from the two top lights on the big board. About a second later either the left or the right lamp in your compartment will light for a moment. As soon as the ready signal flashes you are to guess whether the left or the right lamp will light on that trial and indicate your choice by pressing the proper key. If you expect the left lamp to light, press the left key; if you expect the right lamp to light, press the right key; if you are not sure, guess. Be sure to make your choice as soon as the ready signal appears, press the proper key down firmly, then release the key before the ready signal goes off. It is important that you press either the left or the right key, never both, on each trial, and that you make your decision and indicate your choice while the signal light is on.

"Now we will give you four practice trials."

At this point the overhead lights were extinguished and the recorder started. If any obvious mistakes were made by S during the four practice trials, they were pointed out by E. During the four practice trials the reinforcing lights were always given in the order: E_1, E_1, E_2, E_2. After the practice trials the following instructions were read:

"Are you sure you understand all of the instructions so far? The rest of the trials will have to be run off without any conversation or other interruptions. Please make a choice on every trial even if it seems difficult. Make a guess on the first trial, then try to improve your guesses as you go along and make as many correct choices as possible."

Questions were answered by rereading or paraphrasing the appropriate part of the instructions. If there were any questions about tricks the following additional paragraph was read.

"We have told you everything that will happen. There are no tricks or catches in this experiment. We simply want to see how well you can profit from experience in a rather difficult problem-solving situation while working under time pressure."

The recorder was now started again and the 240 experimental trials were run off in a continuous sequence with no break or other indication to S at the transition from Series A to Series B. On each trial, the signal lamps were lighted for approximately 2 sec.; 1 sec. later the appropriate reinforcing light in each S's booth lighted for .8 sec.; then after an interval of .4 sec. the next ready signal appeared; and so on. The high rate of stimulus presentation was used in order to minimize verbalization on the part of Ss.

RESULTS AND DISCUSSION

Terminal response probabilities.—It will be clear from our discussion of Equation 4 that the predicted asymptote for each series will be the value of π obtaining during the series. We have taken the mean proportion of A_1 responses during the last 40 trials of each series as an estimate of terminal response probability, and these values are summarized for all groups and both series in Table 2.

TABLE 2

TERMINAL MEAN RESPONSE PROBABILITIES FOR EACH SERIES

Group	Series A			Series B		
	$\bar{P}$	π	t	$\bar{P}$	π	t
I	.37	.30	2.35	.28	.30	0.77
II	.48	.50	0.55	.37	.30	2.56
III	.87	.85	0.55	.30	.30	0.05
F	69.31			2.98		

For the first series a simple analysis of variance yields an F significant beyond the .001 level for differences among means. From the within-groups variance estimate we obtain a value for the standard error of a group mean, and this is used in the t test between each group mean and the appropriate theoretical mean. For the second series the between-groups F has a probability between the .05 and .10 levels. In neither series were differences among subgroup means significant at the .05 level.

The interpretation seems straightforward. Group III approximates the theoretical asymptote in both series. Group I falls significantly short of the theoretical asymptote in the first series but approximates it in the second series. Group II falls significantly short of the theoretical asymptote in the second series, but reaches the same probability level as had Group I in the first series. Of the t tests computed for differences between the last two blocks of 20 trials in each series, all yielded probabilities greater than .10 except the t for Series II$_B$ which was significant at the .02 level. Evidently the predictions concerning mean asymptotic values are correct, but the rate of approach to asymptote is faster with Group III than under the other conditions.

According to theory, not only group means, but also individual curves should approach π asymptotically. To obtain evidence as to the tenability of this aspect of the theory we have examined the distributions of individual A$_1$ response proportions for the last 40 trials of Series III$_A$, III$_B$, and I$_B$. If all individual p values approximate the theoretical asymptotes over these trials, then for each of the series the individual response proportions should cluster around the mean value, π, with an approximately binomial

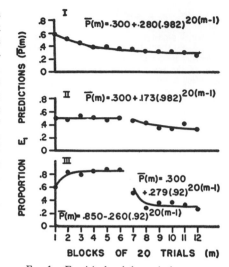

Fig. 1. Empirical and theoretical curves representing mean proportion of E$_1$ predictions (A$_1$ responses) per 20-trial block for each series

distribution. Taking the theoretical σ equal to $\sqrt{40\pi(1-\pi)}$, which is actually a slight underestimate of the true value, we find that approximately half of the scores in each series fall within one σ of the theoretical asymptote and only one score in each series deviates by more than three σ. It appears, then, that except for a few widely deviant cases the p values of individual Ss approach the theoretical asymptote.

One might raise a question as to just what is meant by the asymptote of an empirical curve in a situation of this kind. Naturally one would not expect the Ss to perform at constant rates indefinitely. It does not seem that any sort of breaking point was approached in the present study, however; one subgroup of Group I was run for an additional 60 trials beyond Trial 240 and maintained an average proportion of .304 A$_1$ responses over these trials.

Mean learning curves.—In Fig. 1 mean data are plotted in terms of the proportion of A$_1$ responses per block of

20 trials. The theoretical function which should describe these empirical curves is readily obtained from Equation 4. Letting m be the ordinal number of a block of 20 trials running from Trial $n + 1$ to Trial $n + 20$ inclusive, and $\bar{P}(m)$ the expected proportion of A_1 responses in the block, we can write

$$\bar{P}(m) = \pi$$
$$- \frac{[\pi - \bar{p}(0)](1 - \theta)^{20(m-1)}}{20\,\theta}$$
$$[1 - (1 - \theta)^{20}] \qquad (5)$$

this expression being simply the mean value of $p(n)$ over the mth block of 20 trials. According to theory, Equation 5 should describe each of the mean curves of Fig. 1 once numerical values are substituted for the parameters π, $\bar{p}(0)$, and θ; furthermore, the value of θ required should not differ among groups within either series and should be constant from series to series for each group. The values of π are of course fixed by the experimental procedure. The values of $\bar{p}(0)$ in the first series should be in the neighborhood of .50, but for groups of size 16 sampling deviations could be quite large so it will be best to get rid of $\bar{p}(0)$ in favor of $\bar{P}(1)$ which can be measured more accurately. To do this we write Equation 5 for $m = 1$

$$\bar{P}(1) = \pi$$
$$- \frac{[\pi - \bar{p}(0)]}{20\,\theta}[1 - (1 - \theta)^{20}]$$

then solve for $[\pi - \bar{p}(0)]$

$$[\pi - \bar{p}(0)] = \frac{20\,\theta\,[\pi - \bar{P}(1)]}{1 - (1 - \theta)^{20}}$$

and substitute this result into Equation 5 giving

$$\bar{P}(m) = \pi$$
$$- [\pi - \bar{P}(1)](1 - \theta)^{20(m-1)}. \qquad (6)$$

Observed values of $\bar{P}(1)$ turn out to be .58 and .59 for Series I_A and III_A,

respectively. Now we lack only empirical estimates of θ and these can be obtained by a simple statistical procedure. The method we have used is to sum Equation 6 over all values of m, obtaining for K blocks of trials

$$\sum_{m=1}^{K} \pi - [\pi - \bar{P}(1)](1 - \theta)^{20(m-1)}$$
$$= K\,\pi - [\pi - \bar{P}(1)]$$
$$\frac{[1 - (1 - \theta)^{20K}]}{1 - (1 - \theta)^{20}} \qquad (7)$$

then equate Equation 7 to the sum of the observed proportions for a given series and solve for θ. For Group I we obtain the estimate $\theta = .018$ and for III_A, $\theta = .08$. Using these parameter values we have computed the theoretical curves for Group I and for the first series of Group III, which may be seen in Fig. 1. In this analysis we find agreement between data and theory in one respect but not in another. The theoretical curves provide reasonably good descriptions of the observed points, especially in the case of Group I, but the θ values for the two groups are by no means equal. The latter finding does not come as a surprise inasmuch as we had found in the previous section that Group I was significantly short of its theoretical asymptote in the first series, while Group III was not.

We did not try to estimate a θ value for the first series of Group II since the empirical curve is virtually horizontal and closely approximates the line $\bar{P}(m) = \pi = .50$. We could proceed to estimate θ values for Series II_B and III_B by the method used above, but it will be of more interest to construct predicted curves for these series without using any additional information from the data. According to the theory, it should be possible to compute those curves from information already at our disposal. The $\bar{p}(0)$ values in the second series should be

TABLE 3

PREDICTED AND OBSERVED MEAN FREQUENCIES
OF THE A_1 RESPONSE IN THE
SECOND SERIES

Group	Observed	Predicted	t
I	37.19	37.74	0.22
II	46.00	45.94	0.02
III	42.75	42.86	0.04
F	3.16 $(p > .05)$		

the theoretical asymptotes of the first series, or .50 and .85 for Groups II and III, respectively. The only procedural difference between I_A and II_B lies in the number of preceding reinforcements; according to the statistical model, however, this variable will be expected to have no effect except insofar as it leads to a change in $\bar{p}(0)$, so except for sampling error the θ value estimated for Group I should be applicable to II_B. Using .50, .30, and .018 as the values of $\bar{p}(0)$, π, and θ, respectively, we have computed a theoretical curve for Series II_B, and this is plotted in Fig. 1. Similarly, the θ value estimated for Series III_A should apply also to III_B, and we have used this value, .08, together with .30 for π and .85 for $\bar{p}(0)$ to compute the predicted curve for III_B shown in Fig. 1. Considering that no degrees of freedom in the Series B data have been utilized in curve fitting, the correspondence between the theoretical and

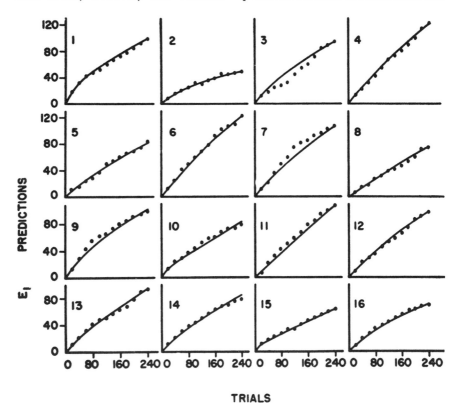

FIG. 2. Empirical and theoretical cumulative response curves for individual Ss of Group I

empirical curves does not seem bad. The reason for some of the irregularities will be brought out in the next section. A statistical test of one aspect of the correspondence can be obtained by calculating for each theoretical curve a predicted mean total of A_1 responses in the second series, by means of Equation 5, and comparing these values with the observed mean totals. This has been done and the comparison is given in Table 3. The t values for differences between observed and theoretical values seem satisfactorily low.

In order to give an idea of the extent to which the behavior of individual Ss conforms to the theoretical function, we have plotted in Fig. 2 the individual cumulative response curves for all Ss of Group I. The cumulative form was chosen for the smoothing effect, some of the noncumulative curves being too irregular for curve-fitting purposes. The theoretical curves in Fig. 2 represent Equation 7 with θ values obtained by a method of approximation. Ten of the curves are fitted quite well by this function with $\pi = .30$ as the asymptote parameter. Four curves, Numbers 2, 11, 15, 16, require other values for this parameter, viz., .075, .45, .24, and .18, respectively. Curves 3 and 4 deviate considerably from the theoretical form. In general, it appears that the empirical curves for most individual Ss can be described quite satisfactorily by the theoretical function, and this fact gives us some basis for inferring that in this situation mean learning curves for groups of Ss reflect the trend of individual learning uncomplicated by any gross artifacts of averaging.

The effect of 120 reinforcements at a π value of .50 may be evaluated by comparing curve forms and mean A_1 response totals for Series I_A and II_B. We find that the reinforcements lead

to no increase in resistance to change. Slopes of the two curves are very similar and the response totals do not differ significantly. This result is in line with predictions from the statistical model, but a little surprising, perhaps, from the viewpoint of Thorndikian or Hullian reinforcement theory since partial reinforcement has generally (6) been held to increase resistance to extinction in this situation.

The conclusions from our study of the mean learning curves would seem to be (a) that under some circumstances at least it is possible to evaluate theoretical parameters from the data of one series of learning trials and then to predict the course of learning in a new series; and (b) that the rate at which the mean learning curve approaches its asymptote depends, in an as yet incompletely specified manner, upon the difference between initial response probability and the probability of reinforcement obtaining during the series.

Sequence effects.—The mean curves studied in the preceding section may not reflect adequately all of the learning that went on during the experiment. The irregularities in some of the mean curves of Fig. 1 might be accounted for if there is a significant tendency for Ss' response sequences to follow the vagaries of the sequences of E_1's and E_2's. To check on this possibility we have plotted in Fig. 3 the mean proportions of A_1 responses vs. frequencies of E_1 occurrences per 10-trial block for all groups in Series B. In preparing this graph, the 120 trials of Series B were divided into 12 successive blocks of 10. Since there were 48 Ss, there were 576 of these trial blocks and they were classified according to the number of E_1 occurrences in a block. Then for the set of all blocks in which no E_1's occurred, the mean proportion of A_1 responses was computed and entered as the first point in Fig. 3, and so on for the remaining points. It seems clear that Ss were responding to the particular sequences of E_1's and E_2's, and not simply to the over-all rate. Corresponding graphs for the three groups in the first series had somewhat shallower slopes; they have not been reported since some of the individual points were based on too few cases to be reliable and the groups could not be averaged together in the first series owing to the different π values.

In order to deal statistically with this apparent dependence of response tendency upon the density of E_1 occurrences in the immediately preceding sequence, we have computed for each series the average probability, $\bar{p}_{A_1|E_1}$, that an A_1 occurs on Trial n given that an E_1 occurs on Trial $n - 1$ and the average probability, $\bar{p}_{A_1|E_2}$, that an A_1 occurs on Trial n given that an E_2 occurs on Trial $n - 1$. The difference between these two quantities can be shown to be proportional to the point correlation (7) between $A(n)$ and $E(n - 1)$ for a given series. Furthermore our Equations 1 and 2 may be regarded as theoretical expressions for the two conditional probabilities, $p_{A_1|E_1}$ and $p_{A_1|E_2}$, respectively, and it will be seen that if these expressions are averaged over all values of n in a series and the second subtracted from the first, the difference is equal to the parameter θ, i.e.,

$$(1 - \theta)\bar{p}(n) + \theta - (1 - \theta)\bar{p}(n) = \theta.$$

Thus from the statistical model we must predict that the difference between empirical estimates of these conditional probabilities for any series should be positive and, if successive trials are independent, this difference should be equal to the value of θ estimated from the mean response curve. The conditional probabilities have been computed from the data for each S and mean differences by groups are summarized in Table 4.

All of the differences are positive and significant at better than the .001 level of confidence. The differences among group means are insignificant for both series (F's equal to .45 and .73, respectively) as are differences among subgroup means. The increases from the first series to the second are, however, significant beyond the .005 level. The latter effect was not anticipated on theoretical grounds; the most plausible explanation that has occurred to us is that alternation tendencies associated with previously established guessing habits extinguished during the early part of the experiment. This hypothesis would also account for the high $\bar{P}(1)$ value observed for Group I in Fig. 1.

Although all of the quantities in Table 4 are positive and apparently

TABLE 4

MEAN DIFFERENCES BETWEEN OBSERVED VALUES OF $\bar{p}_{A_1 E_1}$ AND $\bar{p}_{A_1 E_2}$ FOR EACH SERIES

Series	Group I	Group II	Group III
A	.128	.199	.153
B	.214	.294	.231

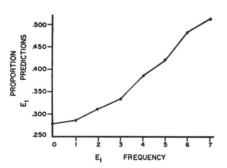

FIG. 3. Mean proportion of E_1 predictions (A_1 responses) in a block of ten trials plotted against the actual number of E_1 occurrences in the block; data averaged for all groups in Series B

independent of π, as required by the theory, the numerical values are all larger than the θ estimates obtained from mean response curves. The most straightforward interpretation of this disparity would be that, owing to the short intertrial interval, successive trials are not independent in the sense required by the theoretical model. Nonindependence would have at least two immediate consequences in so far as the present experiment is concerned. First, stimulus samples drawn on successive trials would overlap, and the learning that occurred on one trial would affect behavior on the next to a greater extent than random sampling would allow for, thus increasing $\bar{p}_{A_1E_1}$, and decreasing $\bar{p}_{A_1E_2}$. Second, the reinforcing stimulus of one trial, E_1 or E_2, would be part of the stimulus complex effective at the beginning of the next trial. If this interpretation is correct, then more widely spaced trials should result in better agreement between the alternative estimates of θ and also in reduction of the dependence of mean learning rate upon probability of reinforcement.

SUMMARY

Learning rates, asymptotic behavior, and sequential properties of response in a verbal conditioning situation were studied in relation to predictions from statistical learning theory.

Forty-eight college students were run in an individualized modification of the "verbal conditioning" experiment originated by Humphreys (4). Each trial consisted in presentation of a signal followed by a left-hand or right-hand "reinforcing" light; S operated an appropriate key to indicate his prediction as to which light would appear on each trial. For each S one of the lights, selected randomly, was designated as E_1, the other as E_2. On the first series of 120 trials, E_1 occurred with probability .30, .50, and .85 for Groups I, II, and III, respectively. On the second 120 trials, E_1 occurred with probability .30 for all groups.

Theoretical predictions were that mean probability of predicting E_1 should tend asymptotically to the actual probability of E_1, both during original learning and following a shift in probability of reinforcement; and that response probabilities should change in accordance with exponential functions, learning rates (as measured by slope parameters) being independent of both initial condition and probability of reinforcement.

The statistical criterion for approach to theoretical asymptote was met by Group I by the end of the second series and by Group III in both first and second series. In the second series, Group II was short of theoretical asymptote but reached the same response probability as had Group I during the first series.

Learning rates were virtually identical for Group I, first series, and Group II, second series, indicating that resistance of response probability to change is not altered by 50% random reinforcement in this situation. Learning rates differed significantly among groups within both series. In general, learning rate was directly related to difference between initial response probability and probability of reinforcement during a series. It was suggested that this relationship may depend upon temporal massing of trials. Not only group means, but individual learning curves could be described satisfactorily by theoretical functions.

No tendency was observed for Ss to respond to a series as a whole. On the contrary, sensitivity to effects of individual reinforcements and nonreinforcements (E_1 and E_2 occurrences) increased significantly as a function of trials.

REFERENCES

1. ESTES, W. K. Toward a statistical theory of learning. *Psychol. Rev.*, 1950, **57,** 94–107.
2. ESTES, W. K., & BURKE, C. J. A theory of stimulus variability in learning. *Psychol. Rev.*, 1953, **60,** 276–286.
3. GRANT, D. A., HAKE, H. W., & HORNSETH, J. P. Acquisition and extinction of a verbal conditioned response with differing percentages of reinforcement. *J. exp. Psychol.*, 1951, **42,** 1–5.
4. HUMPHREYS, L. G. Acquisition and extinction of verbal expectations in a situation analogous to conditioning. *J. exp. Psychol.*, 1939, **25,** 294–301.
5. JARVIK, M. E. Probability learning and a negative recency effect in the serial anticipation of alternative symbols. *J. exp. Psychol.*, 1951, **41,** 291–297.
6. JENKINS, W. O., & STANLEY, J. C. Partial reinforcement: a review and critique. *Psychol. Bull.*, 1950, **47,** 193–234.
7. McNEMAR, Q. *Psychological statistics.* New York: Wiley, 1949.

(Received July 10, 1953)

Theory of Learning with Constant, Variable, or Contingent Probabilities of Reinforcement*

WILLIAM K. ESTES, *Indiana University*

The methods used in recent probabilistic learning models to generate mean curves of learning under random reinforcement are extended to the general case in which probability of reinforcement may vary in any specified manner as a function of trials and to cases in which probability of reinforcement on a given trial is contingent upon responses or outcomes of preceding trials.

Our purpose is to develop a general model for mean curves of learning under random reinforcement in "determinate" situations. By "determinate" we signify the following restrictions. In these situations the subject is confronted with the same stimulating situation, e.g., a ready signal, at the beginning of each trial. The subject responds with one of a specified set of alternative responses, $(A_1 , A_2 , \cdots , A_r)$, and following his response is presented with one of a specified set of reinforcing events, $(E_1 , E_2 , \cdots , E_r)$, exactly one reinforcing event E_i corresponding to each possible response A_i . In a T-maze experiment (with correction procedure), A_1 and A_2 correspond to left and right turns; E_1 and E_2 correspond to "food obtained on left" and "food obtained on right", respectively. In a simple prediction experiment with human subjects [3, 8, 9, 10, 11, 13], the responses $(A_1 , A_2 , \cdots , A_r)$ correspond to the subject's predictions as to which of a set of "reinforcing lights" $(E_1 , E_2 , \cdots , E_r)$ will appear on each trial; instructions are such that the subject interprets the appearance of E_i to mean that response A_i was correct. It is further assumed that one can specify in advance of any trial the probability that any given response will be followed by any given reinforcing event.

From the set-theoretical model of Estes and Burke [4, 6] plus an assumption of association of contiguity, it is possible (see [1, 8]) to derive the following quantitative law describing the change in the probability of response A_i on any trial:

If E_i occurs on trial n

(1a) $$p_{i,n+1} = (1 - \theta)p_{i,n} + \theta.$$

*This paper was prepared while the writer was in residence at the Center for Advanced Study in the Behavioral Sciences, Stanford, California. The research on which it is based was supported by a faculty research grant from the Social Science Research Council.

This article appeared in *Psychometrika*, 1957, **22**, 113–132.

If E_k ($k \neq j$) occurs on trial n

(1b) $$p_{i,n+1} = (1 - \theta)p_{i,n}.$$

The quantity $p_{i,n}$ represents the probability of response A_i on trial n, and θ is a parameter satisfying the restriction $0 \leq \theta \leq 1$. The parameter θ may vary in value from one organism to another, and for a given organism from one situation to another, but is assumed to remain constant during any given experiment. Functional equations of the form (1a) and (1b) may also be obtained from the stochastic learning model of Bush and Mosteller [2] by imposing suitable restrictions on the parameters.

Now if we can specify the probabilities with which each of the events [E_j] will occur on each trial of a learning experiment, then, given the initial probability of A_i, it becomes a purely mathematical problem to deduce the expected value of $p_{i,n}$ on any trial and thus to generate a predicted learning curve which can be compared with experimental curves. For two special cases, the mathematical problem has already been solved and the desired theoretical curves have been computed and fitted to data [1, 2, 8, 13]. In the first of these, which we shall call the simple non-contingent case, the probability of E_i, hereafter designated π_i, has the same value on all trials of the series regardless of the subject's response. In the second of these, which we shall call the simple contingent case, the probability of E_j on any trial depends upon which response is made by the subject. Thus if the subject makes response A_1, the probability of E_j is π_{1j}; if the subject makes response A_2, the probability of E_j is π_{2j}; and so on; but the values of π_{ij}, remain fixed throughout the series of trials. Now we wish to obtain a more general solution which will yield predicted curves for experiments in which the constancy requirement is removed and the π_i are permitted to vary over a series of trials.

General Solution and Asymptotic Matching Theorem

Let $\pi_{j,n}$ represent the probability that reinforcing event E_j will occur on trial n, with $\sum_j \pi_{j,n} = 1$ for all n. Then given that a subject's probability of making response A_j on trial n is $p_{j,n}$, the expected, or mean, value of the probability* on trial $n + 1$ must be

*Throughout the paper, the quantity p_j should be interpreted as follows. (a) In equations dealing with learning on a particular trial, e.g., (1a) and (1b), $p_{j,n+1}$ represents the new probability on trial $n + 1$ for a subject who had the value $p_{j,n}$ on trial n. (b) In equations dealing with the expected change on a trial, e.g., (2), (2a), $p_{j,n+1}$ represents the expected value of p_j on trial $n + 1$, where the average is taken over all possible values of $p_{j,n}$ and all possible outcomes of trial n; the term "all possible" is defined for any given situation by the initial values of p_j and the possible sequences of responses and reinforcing events over the first n trials. (c) In solutions giving p_j as a function of n, e.g., (3), (3a), $p_{j,n}$ is the expected value p_j on trial n, where the average is taken over all initial values of p_j and all possible sequences of responses and reinforcing events over the first $n - 1$ trials.

(2)
$$p_{j,n+1} = (1 - \theta)p_{j,n} + \theta\pi_{j,n} .$$

To obtain (2) average the right hand sides of (1a) and (1b), weighting them by the probabilities $\pi_{j,n}$ and $[1 - \pi_{j,n}]$, respectively, that E_j will and will not occur.

Some general asymptotic properties of the model can be clearly displayed if we consider, not simply $p_{j,n}$, the probability of a response on a particular trial, but the expected proportion of response occurrences over a series of trials. The latter quantity, which we shall designate $\bar{p}_i(n)$, must of course satisfy the relation

$$\bar{p}_i(n) = \frac{1}{n} \sum_{v=1}^{n} p_{i,v} .$$

Substituting into the right side of this expression from (2), we obtain

$$\bar{p}_i(n) = \frac{1}{n} \left\{ p_{j,1} + \sum_{v=1}^{n-1} [(1 - \theta)p_{i,v} + \theta\pi_{i,v}] \right\}$$

$$= \frac{1}{n} [p_{j,1} + (n - 1)(1 - \theta)\bar{p}_i(n - 1) + \theta(n - 1)\bar{\pi}_i(n - 1)]$$

where $\bar{\pi}_i (n - 1)$ represents the expected proportion of E_i reinforcing events over the first $n - 1$ trials. For large n, the right side of the last expression approaches the limit

$$(1 - \theta)\bar{p}_i(n - 1) + \theta\bar{\pi}_i(n - 1).$$

Further, since $\bar{p}_i(n - 1)$ always differs from $\bar{p}_i(n)$ by a term of the order of $1/n$, we can write, for sufficiently large n, the approximate equality

$$\bar{p}_i(n) \cong (1 - \theta)\bar{p}_i(n) + \theta\bar{\pi}_i(n - 1),$$

or

$$\bar{p}_i(n) \cong \bar{\pi}_i(n - 1).$$

Thus we find that no matter how π_j varies over a series of trials, the cumulative proportions of A_j and E_j occurrences tend to equality as n becomes large. It can be expected that this remarkably general "matching law" will play a central role in empirical tests of the theory.

To study the pre-asymptotic course of learning, we proceed as follows. Suppose that a subject begins an experiment with the probability $p_{j,1}$ of making an A_j ; then his expected probability on trial 2 will be, applying (2),

$$p_{j,2} = (1 - \theta)p_{j,1} + \theta\pi_{j,1} ;$$

on trial 3,

$$p_{j,3} = (1 - \theta)p_{j,2} + \theta\pi_{j,2} ;$$

$$= (1 - \theta)^2 p_{j,1} + \theta(1 - \theta)\pi_{j,1} + \theta\pi_{j,2} ;$$

and, in general, on trial n

(3) $\quad p_{i,n} = (1 - \theta)^{n-1} p_{i,1} + \theta[(1 - \theta)^{n-2} \pi_{i,1} + (1 - \theta)^{n-3} \pi_{i,2} + \cdots$

$$+ (1 - \theta)^{n-n} \pi_{i,n-1}]$$

$$= (1 - \theta)^{n-1} p_{i,1} + \theta \sum_{v=1}^{n-1} (1 - \theta)^{n-v-1} \pi_{i,v} .$$

A number of important features that will characterize the mean learning curve regardless of the nature of the function $\pi_{i,n}$ can be ascertained by inspection of (2) and (3). If the value of θ is zero, no learning will occur; in the remainder of the paper this case will be excluded from all derivations. If the value of θ is greater than zero then learning will occur. By rewriting (2) in the form

$$p_{i,n+1} = p_{i,n} + \theta(\pi_{i,n} - p_{i,n}),$$

we see that on the average, response probability on any trial changes in the direction of the current value of π_i . As n becomes large, the term $(1 - \theta)^{n-1} p_{i,1}$ in (3) tends to zero. After n is large enough so that $(1 - \theta)^{n-1} p_{i,1}$ is negligible, $p_{i,n}$ is essentially a weighted mean of the π_i values which obtained on preceding trials, with $\pi_{i,n-1}$ having most weight, $\pi_{i,n-2}$ less weight, and so on. If $\pi_{i,n}$ is some orderly function of n, as for example a straight line or a growth function, then the curve for $p_{i,n}$ tends to approach this function as n increases, but always "follows it with a lag." If rate of learning is maximal, i.e., θ is equal to one, then $p_{i,n}$ is simply equal to $\pi_{i,n-1}$ throughout the series of trials; the more θ deviates from one, the more the curve for $p_{i,n}$ lags behind that for $\pi_{i,n}$.

We may gain further insight into this learning process and at the same time develop functions that will be useful in experimental applications by considering some special cases in which $\pi_{i,n}$ can be represented by familiar functions with simple properties.

Non-Contingent Case

a. The special case of $\pi_{i,n}$ constant

If π_i is constant, then as one might expect, (2) and (3) reduce to the simple expressions

(2a) $$p_{i,n+1} = (1 - \theta) p_{i,n} + \theta \pi_i ,$$

and

(3a) $$p_{i,n} = \pi_i - (\pi_i - p_{i,1})(1 - \theta)^{n-1},$$

derived by Estes and Straughan [8] from the set-theoretical model [4, 6] and, with slightly different notation, by Bush and Mosteller [2] from their "linear operator" model. In this case the predicted learning curve is given by a negatively accelerated function tending to π_i asymptotically. Experimental applications of (3a) are described in references [2, 3, 5, 6, 13].

b. The special case of $\pi_{i,n}$ linear

We shall treat this case in some detail since it has a number of properties that will be especially convenient for experimental tests of the theory. The linear function

$$\pi_{i,n} = a_i + b_i n,$$

a_i and b_i being constants, is not in general bounded between zero and one for all n; for experimental purposes, however, one need only choose values of a_i and b_i which, for the number of trials to be given, keep the value of $\pi_{i,n}$ within the required range. Subject to this restriction, we may substitute into (2) and (3) to obtain the expected response probability on any trial,

(2b)
$$p_{i,n+1} = (1 - \theta)p_{i,n} + \theta(a_i + b_i n),$$

and

(3b)
$$p_{i,n} = a_i + b_i n - \frac{b_i}{\theta} - \left(a_i + b_i - \frac{b_i}{\theta} - p_{i,1}\right)(1 - \theta)^{n-1}.$$

In the interest of brevity we have omitted the detailed steps involved in summing the series in (3); the method of performing the summation in this case, and in others to be considered in following sections, is given in standard sources [12, 14]. The reader can verify that (3b) is the correct solution to (2b) by substituting the former into the latter. The main properties of (3b) are illustrated in Fig. 1. Regardless of the initial value $p_{i,1}$, after a sufficiently large number of trials the curve for $p_{i,n}$ approaches a straight line,

$$p_{i,n} = a_i - \frac{b_i}{\theta} + b_i n,$$

which has the same slope as the straight line representing $\pi_{i,n}$. If the initial value of $p_{i,n}$ is greater than $\pi_{i,1}$ and the slope of $\pi_{i,n}$ is positive, $p_{i,n}$ will decrease until its curve crosses the line $\pi_{i,n}$, following which it will increase; if b_i is small, the point of crossing will be approximately at the minimum value of $p_{i,n}$. To prove the last statement, we replace n by a continuous variable t, then set the derivative of $p_{i,t}$ with respect to t equal to zero and find that $p_{i,t}$ has as its minimum value

$$p_{i,t_m} = a_i - \frac{b_i}{\theta} + b_i t_m - \frac{b_i}{\log (1 - \theta)},$$

where

$$t_m = \frac{\log b_i - \log \log (1 - \theta)^K}{\log (1 - \theta)}$$

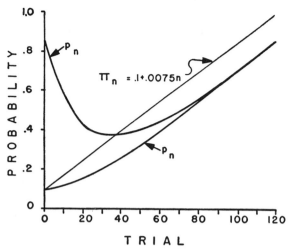

FIGURE 1

Curves describing changes in response probability when probability of reinforcement varies linearly with trials. The parameter θ has been taken equal to .05.

and

$$K = \frac{a_i - \dfrac{(1 - \theta)b_i}{\theta} - p_{i,1}}{(1 - \theta)}.$$

Subtracting π_{i,t_m} from the minimum value of p_i, we find that the difference is equal to

$$-\frac{b_i}{\theta} - \frac{b_i}{\log (1 - \theta)} = b_i\left[-\frac{1}{\theta} + \frac{1}{\theta + \dfrac{\theta^2}{2} + \dfrac{\theta^3}{3} + \cdots} \right]$$

$$= -b_i\left[\frac{\dfrac{1}{2} + \dfrac{\theta}{3} + \dfrac{\theta^2}{4} + \cdots}{1 + \dfrac{\theta}{2} + \dfrac{\theta^2}{3} + \cdots} \right],$$

which is negative and does not exceed b_i in absolute value for any value of θ.

To obtain an expression for $R_i(n)$, the cumulative number of A_i responses expected in n trials, we need only sum (3b):

(4)
$$R_i(n) = \sum_{v=1}^{n} p_{i,v}$$

$$= \left[a_i - \frac{b_i}{\theta} \right]n + \frac{b_i n(n + 1)}{2}$$

$$- \left[a_i + b_i - \frac{b_i}{\theta} - p_{i,1} \right] \frac{[1 - (1 - \theta)^n]}{\theta}.$$

Similarly, by summing (3b) over the mth block of k trials and dividing by k, we obtain the expected proportion of A_i responses in the block:

(5)
$$\bar{p}_i(k, m) = a_i - \frac{b_i}{\theta} + \frac{b_i}{2}(2mk - k + 1)$$
$$- \frac{\left[a_i + b_i - \frac{b_i}{\theta} - p_{i,1} \right]}{k\theta} [1 - (1 - \theta)^k](1 - \theta)^{k(m-1)}.$$

Equation (5), despite its cumbersome appearance, has essentially the same properties as (3b) and can readily be fitted to experimental data. For a block of k trials beginning with a value of n large enough so that $(1 - \theta)^{k(m-1)}$ is near zero, we have the approximation

$$\bar{p}_i(k, m) \cong a_i - \frac{b_i}{\theta} + \frac{b_i}{2}(2mk - k + 1).$$

By substituting the observed value of $p_i(k, m)$ from a set of experimental data and solving for θ, we obtain an estimate of this parameter which, although not unbiased, will be adequate for many experimental purposes.

c. *The special case* $\pi_{i,n} = a_i + c_i b_i^n$

Among the possible monotone relations between π_i and n, the second main type of interest is that in which $\pi_{i,n}$ approaches an asymptote. This type will be represented by the function $\pi_{i,n} = a_i + c_i b_i^n$, the values of the constants a_i , b_i , and c_i being so restricted that $\pi_{i,n}$ is properly bounded between zero and one for all n.

Equations (2) and (3) now take the forms

(2c) $$p_{i,n+1} = (1 - \theta)p_{i,n} + \theta(a_i + c_i b_i^n);$$

and, if $b_i \neq 1 - \theta$,

$$p_{i,n} = a_i + \frac{\theta c_i b_i^n}{b_i - 1 + \theta} - \left(a_i + \frac{\theta c_i b_i}{b_i - 1 + \theta} - p_{i,1} \right)(1 - \theta)^{n-1};$$

or, if $b_i = 1 - \theta$,

(3c) $$p_{i,n} = a_i + c_i \theta(n - 1)(1 - \theta)^{n-1} - (a_i - p_{i,1})(1 - \theta)^{n-1}.$$

Some properties of (3c) are illustrated in Fig. 2. In the upper panel, a_i has been taken equal to .50, c_i to 1.0, and b_i to .98 so that $\pi_{i,n}$ describes a negatively accelerated decreasing curve approaching .50 asymptotically. The effect of changing the sign of b_i from positive to negative can be seen by comparing the lower panel of Fig. 2, which has $b_i = -.98$, $a_i = .50$, and $c_i = 1.0$, with the upper panel. Now the values of π_i oscillate from trial to trial between a pair of curves, the upper envelope being identical with the $\pi_{i,n}$ curve in the upper panel and the lower envelope curve the mirror image of

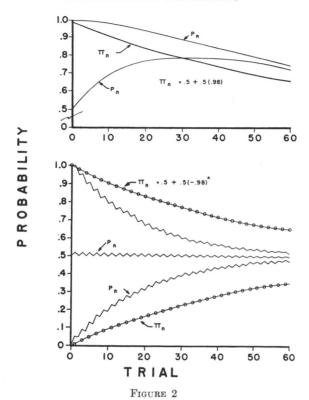

FIGURE 2

Curves describing changes in response probability when probability of reinforcement varies exponentially with trials. The parameter θ has been taken equal to .05.

it. The values of $p_{i,n}$ describe a damped oscillation around an exponential function; for any given set of parameter values, the values of $p_{i,n}$ will be alternately above and below those of the curve

$$p_{i,n} = a_i - \left(a_i + \frac{\theta c_i b_i}{b_i - 1 + \theta} - p_{i,1}\right)(1 - \theta)^{n-1},$$

with the deviation from the smooth curve decreasing progressively in magnitude toward zero as n increases.

A formula for the expected number of A_i responses in n trials can be obtained and utilized for estimation of θ as in case (c).

d. A periodic case

From an analysis of the general solution in section (a) above, we can predict that if π_i varies in accordance with a periodic function, then asymptotically the curve for $p_{i,n}$ will be described by a periodic function having the same period. A simple case with convenient properties for experimental purposes is the following: π_i is constant within any one block of k trials, but alternates between two values, say $a_i + b_i$ and $a_i - b_i$, on successive blocks so that the value of π_i on each trial of the mth block is given by

$$\pi_i = a_i + b_i(-1)^m.$$

The value of p_i at the end of the mth block can be taken directly from section (a) above:

$$p_{i,mk+1} = a_i + b_i(-1)^m - [a_i + b_i(-1)^m - p_{i,(m-1)k+1}](1 - \theta)^k.$$

Treating blocks of k trials as units, this expression may be viewed as a difference equation of the same form as (2). Substituting $a_i + b_i(-1)^m$, $(1 - \theta)^k$, and mk for the corresponding terms $\pi_{i,n}$, $(1 - \theta)$, and n of (2) and (3), we obtain the solution

$$(3d) \qquad p_{i,mk+1} = a_i + b_i(-1)^m \frac{[1 - (1 - \theta)^k]}{[1 + (1 - \theta)^k]}$$

$$- \left\{ a_i + b_i \frac{[1 - (1 - \theta)^k]}{[1 + (1 - \theta)^k]} - p_{i,1} \right\}(1 - \theta)^{mk}.$$

Equation (3d) gives us the expected value of p_i at the end of the mth trial block. Using (3a) of section (a) again, we have for the expected value of p_i on the n'th trial of the $(m + 1)$st block

$$(3e) \quad p_{i,mk+n'} = a_i + b_i(-1)^{m+1} - [a_i + b_i(-1)^{m+1} - p_{i,mk+1}](1 - \theta)^{n'-1}.$$

Properties of this solution are illustrated in Fig. 3. It can be seen that regardless of its initial value, p_i settles down to a periodic function with period k.

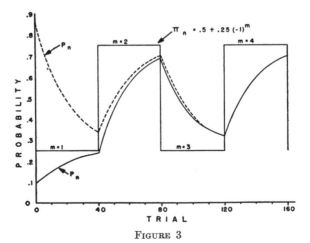

FIGURE 3

Curves describing changes in response probability when probability of reinforcement varies periodically with trials. The parameter θ has been taken equal to .05.

e. Outcome contingencies

Many cases in which the probability of a given reinforcing event on any trial depends on the outcome (reinforcing event) of some preceding trial can be reduced to cases already considered. Suppose, for example, that we set the probability of E_1 on any trial equal to π_{11} if an E_1 occurred on the vth preceding trial and to π_{21} if an E_2 occurred on the vth preceding trial. Then we can write the following difference equation for $\pi_{1,n}$, the expected probability of E_1 on trial n,

$$\pi_{1,n} = \pi_{1,n-v}\pi_{11} + (1 - \pi_{1,n-v})\pi_{21}$$

$$= (\pi_{11} - \pi_{21})\pi_{1,n-v} + \pi_{21} ,$$

which has the general solution

$$\pi_{1,n} = \pi_1 + C_1 r_1^n + C_2 r_2^n + \cdots + C_v r_v^n .$$

The C_i are constants to be evaluated from the initial conditions of the experiment; the r_i are roots of the characteristic equation

$$r^v - \pi_{11} + \pi_{21} = 0;$$

and π_1, the asymptotic value of $\pi_{1,n}$, is given by

$$\pi_1 = \frac{\pi_{21}}{1 - \pi_{11} + \pi_{21}}.$$

If $v = 1$, i.e., the probability of a given outcome depends on the outcome of the preceding trial, the formula for $\pi_{1,n}$ reduces to

$$\pi_{1,n} = \pi_1 - (\pi_1 - \pi_{1,1})(\pi_{11} - \pi_{21})^{n-1}.$$

Once a formula for $\pi_{i,n}$ has been deduced, it may be substituted into (2), and the machinery already developed for non-contingent cases with varying probabilities of reinforcement can be applied to generate predictions about the course of learning. In the case $v = 1$, the difference equation for $p_{1,n}$ and its solution will be given by (2c) and (3c), respectively, with $a = \pi_1$ and $b = \pi_{11} - \pi_{21}$; this case has been discussed in some detail by Bush and Mosteller [2].

It should be emphasized that functions derived from the present model for outcome contingencies with $v = 1$ will generally provide satisfactory descriptions of empirical relationships only if the experiments are conducted with well-spaced trials. According to this model, the asymptotic conditional probabilities of A_1 on trials following E_1 and E_2 occurrences, respectively, are given by

$$p_{11} = \pi_1 + \theta(1 - \pi_1)$$

and

$$p_{21} = \pi_1 - \theta\pi_1 .$$

When trials are adequately spaced, these relations may prove to be empirically confirmable, but if intertrial intervals are small enough so that the subject can form a discrimination based on the differential stimulus after-effects of E_1 and E_2 trials, then the asymptotic conditional probabilities will certainly approach π_{11} and π_{21}. A model for the massed-trial case can be derived from a set-theoretical model for discrimination learning [1, 7]. Although a detailed presentation of the discrimination model would be beyond the scope of this paper, it is interesting to note that the discrimination model yields the same asymptotic value for the over all mean value of p_1 as the present model, but yields asymptotic means for p_{11} and p_{21} which differ from π_{11} and π_{21}, respectively, only by terms which are smaller than θ.

Contingent Case

Let $\pi_{ij,n}$ represent the probability that reinforcing event E_j will occur on trial n of a series given that the subject makes response A_i on this trial, and assume that $\sum_j \pi_{ij,n} = 1$ for all i and n. Then to obtain the expected value of $p_{i,n+1}$ as a function of the value on trial n, we again average the right-hand sides of (1a) and (1b), weighting each of the possible outcomes by its probability of occurrence, viz.,

$$(6) \qquad p_{i,n+1} = (1 - \theta)p_{i,n} + \theta \sum_i p_{i,n}\pi_{ij,n} .$$

a. General solution for the case of two response classes

If there are only two response classes, A_1 and A_2, with corresponding reinforcing events, E_1 and E_2, defined for a given situation, then we have for the expected probability of A_1 on the second trial of a series,

$$p_{1,2} = (1 - \theta)p_{1,1} + \theta[p_{1,1}\pi_{11,1} + (1 - p_{1,1})\pi_{21,1}]$$
$$= (1 - \theta + \theta\pi_{11,1} - \theta\pi_{21,1})p_{1,1} + \theta\pi_{21,1} ,$$

on the third trial

$$p_{1,3} = (1 - \theta)p_{1,2} + \theta[p_{1,2}\pi_{11,2} + (1 - p_{1,2})\pi_{21,2}]$$
$$= \alpha_2\alpha_1 p_{1,1} + \alpha_2\theta\pi_{21,1} + \theta\pi_{21,2} ,$$

when we have introduced the abbreviation

$$\alpha_v = 1 - \theta + \theta\pi_{11,v} - \theta\pi_{21,v} .$$

In general on the nth trial,

$$(7) \qquad p_{1,n} = p_{1,1}\alpha_1\alpha_2 \cdots \alpha_{n-1} + \theta\alpha_1\alpha_2 \cdots \alpha_{n-1} \sum_{u=1}^{n-1} \frac{\pi_{21,u}}{\alpha_1\alpha_2 \cdots \alpha_u}$$
$$= p_{1,1} \prod_{v=1}^{n-1} \alpha_v + \theta \prod_{v=1}^{n-1} \alpha_v \sum_{u=1}^{n-1} \frac{\pi_{21,u}}{\prod_{v'=1}^{u} \alpha_{v'}} .$$

Since each of the α_v is a fraction between zero and one, we can see by inspection of (7) that $p_{1,n}$ becomes independent of its initial value, $p_{1,1}$, as n becomes large; on later trials it is essentially equal to a weighted mean of the π_{21} values which obtained on preceding trials, with $\pi_{21,n-1}$ having most weight, $\pi_{21,n-2}$ less weight, and so on. [If $\pi_{11} = 1$ and $\pi_{21} = 0$, then $\alpha = 1$ and (6) reduces to

$$p_{1,n+1} = p_{1,n},$$

i.e., on the average no learning occurs. In all derivations presented, we shall assume this case to be excluded.] The smaller the average difference between $\pi_{11,v}$ and $\pi_{21,v}$, the more completely is the value of $p_{1,n}$ determined by the π_{ij} values of a few immediately preceding trials. As in the non-contingent case, the dependence of $p_{1,n}$ on the sequence of π_{ij} values, might be described as "tracking with a lag," but in this instance it will be necessary to study some special cases in order to see just what is being "tracked." For convenience in exposition we shall limit ourselves to situations involving two response classes while describing the special cases. In a later section we shall indicate how all of the results can be extended to situations involving more than two response classes.

b. The special case of π_{ij} constant

If $\pi_{11,n}$ and $\pi_{21,n}$ are both constant, then (6) and (7) reduce to the expressions

(6a)
$$p_{j,n+1} = (1 - \theta)p_{j,n} + \theta \sum_{i=1}^{2} p_{i,n}\pi_{ij},$$

and

(7a)
$$p_{1,n} = \frac{\pi_{21}}{1 - \pi_{11} + \pi_{21}}$$
$$- \left(\frac{\pi_{21}}{1 - \pi_{11} + \pi_{21}} - p_{1,1}\right)(1 - \theta + \theta\pi_{11} - \theta\pi_{21})^{n-1},$$

previously derived by Estes [5] from the set-theoretical model and by Bush and Mosteller [2] from their "linear operator" model. Experimental applications of (7a) are described in references [2, 5, 13].

c. Special cases leading to linear difference equations with constant coefficients

Examination of (6) reveals that it will take the form of a linear difference equation with constant coefficients whenever $\pi_{11,n}$ and $\pi_{21,n}$ differ only by a constant. Thus, if

$$\pi_{11,n} = a_{11} + g_n$$

and

$$\pi_{21,n} = a_{21} + g_n,$$

where g_n is any function that keeps $\pi_{ij,n}$ properly bounded for the range of n under consideration, then (7) has the form

(7b)
$$p_{1,n} = p_{1,1}\alpha^{n-1} + \theta\alpha^{n-1} \sum_{u=1}^{n-1} \frac{a_{21} + g_u}{\alpha^u}$$

$$= p_{1,1}\alpha^{n-1} + \frac{a_{21}}{1 - a_{11} + a_{21}}(1 - \alpha^{n-1}) + \theta\alpha^{n-1} \sum_{u=1}^{n-1} \frac{g_u}{\alpha^u},$$

where $\alpha = (1 - \theta + \theta a_{11} - \theta a_{21})$. For experimental purposes, it will usually be most convenient to make g_n a linear function of n, say $g_n = bn$, in which case we can perform the summation in (7b) and obtain a simple closed formula for $p_{1,n}$, viz.,

(7c)
$$p_{1,n} = \frac{a_{21} + bn}{1 - a_{11} + a_{21}} - \frac{b}{\theta(1 - a_{11} + a_{21})^2}$$

$$- \left(\frac{a_{21} + b}{1 - a_{11} + a_{21}} - \frac{b}{\theta(1 - a_{11} + a_{21})^2} - p_{1,1} \right)$$

$$\cdot (1 - \theta + \theta a_{11} - \theta a_{21})^{n-1}.$$

The properties of (7c) are very similar to those of (3b), the corresponding solution for the non-contingent case. Regardless of the initial value $p_{1,1}$, after a sufficiently large number of trials, the curve for $p_{1,n}$ approaches the straight line

$$p_{1,n} = \frac{a_{21} + bn}{1 - a_{11} + a_{21}} - \frac{b}{\theta(1 - a_{11} + a_{21})^2}.$$

Since θ is the only free parameter in the latter expression, its value can be estimated by fitting the straight line to data obtained from a block of trials relatively late in the learning series. It becomes apparent now, incidentally, what it is that the $p_{1,n}$ curve "tracks with a lag." The first term on the right-hand side of (7c) is simply $\pi_{21,n}/(1 - \pi_{11,n} + \pi_{21,n})$. Thus at any moment, the slope of the $p_{1,n}$ curve is such that it would approach $\pi_{21}/(1 - \pi_{11} + \pi_{21})$, the asymptote of the constant π_{ij} solution, (7a), if $\pi_{11,n}$ and $\pi_{21,n}$ were to remain constant from that moment on. Since the $\pi_{ij,n}$ do not remain constant, the subject's curve tracks the "moving asymptote" with a lag which depends inversely on θ. As in the corresponding non-contingent case, the slope of the terminal linear portion of the $p_{1,n}$ curve can be predicted in advance of an experiment since it depends only on the values of a_{11}, a_{21}, and b, which are assigned by the experimenter.

d. Contingent case with more than two response classes

The results of the preceding section can be extended without difficulty to situations involving more than two response classes. If $\pi_{ij,n} = a_{ij} + g_n$

for all i ($i = 1, 2, \cdots, r$), then for a situation involving r response classes, we obtain by application of (6) the system of r difference equations

$$p_{1,n+1} = (1 - \theta + \theta a_{11})p_{1,n} + \theta a_{21}p_{2,n} + \cdots + \theta a_{r1}p_{r,n} + \theta g_n$$

(8) $\qquad p_{2,n+1} = \theta a_{12}p_{1,n} + (1 - \theta + \theta a_{22})p_{2,n} + \cdots + \theta a_{r2}p_{r,n} + \theta g_n$

$$\cdots\cdots\cdots\cdots\cdots\cdots\cdots\cdots\cdots\cdots\cdots\cdots\cdots\cdots\cdots\cdots\cdots\cdots$$

$$p_{r,n+1} = \theta a_{1r}p_{1,n} + \theta a_{2r}p_{2,n} + \cdots + (1 - \theta + \theta a_{rr})p_{r,n} + \theta g_n,$$

which must be solved simultaneously in order to obtain the desired formulas for $p_{i,n}$. To facilitate the solution, we define an operator $\mathbf{E}$ as follows:

$$\mathbf{E}p_{i,n} = p_{i,n+1}.$$

Then the system (8) can be rewritten in the form:

$$(\mathbf{E} - 1 + \theta - \theta a_{11})p_{1,n} - \theta a_{21}p_{2,n} - \cdots - \theta a_{r1}p_{r,n} = \theta g_n$$

$$- \theta a_{12}p_{1,n} + (\mathbf{E} - 1 + \theta - \theta a_{22})p_{2,n} - \cdots - \theta a_{r2}p_{r,n} = \theta g_n$$

$$\cdots\cdots\cdots\cdots\cdots\cdots\cdots\cdots\cdots\cdots\cdots\cdots\cdots\cdots\cdots\cdots$$

$$- \theta a_{1r}p_{1,n} - \theta a_{2r}p_{2,n} - \cdots + (\mathbf{E} - 1 + \theta - \theta a_{rr})p_{r,n} = \theta g_n.$$

Now the symbol $\mathbf{E}$ may be treated as a number while we proceed to solve the system of equations by standard methods. The solution will express each of the $p_{i,n}$ as a polynomial in powers of $\mathbf{E}$. Then to obtain a formula expressing $p_{i,n}$ as an explicit function of n, we will have only to solve a linear difference equation with constant coefficients.

If the form of the function g_n is such that $a_{ii} + g_n$ approaches an asymptotic value, π_{ii}, as n increases, then the asymptotic values, call them λ_i, of the $p_{i,n}$ can be obtained by solving simultaneously the system of r linear equations in the r unknowns λ_j, ($j = 1, 2, \cdots, r$):

$$-(1 - \pi_{11})\lambda_1 + \pi_{21}\lambda_2 + \cdots + \pi_{r1}\lambda_r = 0$$

$$\pi_{12}\lambda_1 - (1 - \pi_{22})\lambda_2 + \cdots + \pi_{r2}\lambda_r = 0$$

$$\cdots\cdots\cdots\cdots\cdots\cdots\cdots\cdots\cdots\cdots\cdots\cdots\cdots$$

$$\pi_{1r}\lambda_1 + \pi_{2r}\lambda_2 + \cdots - (1 - \pi_{rr})\lambda_r = 0$$

This system of equations has two properties of special interest, First, the asymptotic response probabilities λ_i are completely determined by the parameters π_{ij}. Second, the mean asymptotic probabilities of the reinforcing events are determined by the same system of equations. If we let π_j represent the mean asymptotic probability of E_j, then clearly

$$\pi_j = \lambda_1\pi_{1j} + \lambda_2\pi_{2j} + \cdots + \lambda_r\pi_{rj}.$$

But inspecting the jth row in the equation system above, we see that

$$\lambda_j = \lambda_1 \pi_{1j} + \lambda_2 \pi_{2j} + \cdots + \lambda_r \pi_{rj} \, .$$

Therefore, $\pi_j = \lambda_j$, i.e., asymptotically the mean probability of a response is equal to the mean probability of the corresponding reinforcing event. We have another example of the "probability matching" which has frequently been noted in studies of probability learning with simple, non-contingent reinforcement [3, 5, 8, 9, 13]. In the contingent case, there are no fixed environmental probabilities to be matched by the subject, but the matching property again obtains when the stimulus-response system arrives at a state of statistical equilibrium.

In the special case when $g_n = 0$ for all n and $a_{ij} = \pi_{ij}$, the value of $p_{i,n}$ will be given by an expression of the form

$$(9) \qquad p_{i,n} = \lambda_i + C_1 x_1^n + C_2 x_2^n + \cdots + C_{r-1} x_{r-1}^n \, ,$$

where the absolute value of each of the x_i is in the range $0 \leq x_i \leq 1$, and the C_i are constants whose values depend on the initial p_i values and on the π_{ij} . It may be noted that all of the C_i need not have the same sign, and consequently the curve of $p_{i,n}$ will not always be a monotone function of n. Some of the curve forms which arise are illustrated in Fig. 4; the curves in the upper and lower panels represent the same value of θ but different combinations of π_{ij} , viz.,

	Upper panel			*Lower panel*		
	E_1	E_2	E_3	E_1	E_2	E_3
A_1	.33	.33	.33	.33	.33	.33
A_2	.50	.50	.00	.50	.50	.00
A_3	.17	.00	.83	.83	.00	.17

It will be apparent from inspection of Fig. 4 that in this case, unlike the non-contingent case, not only the asymptotes of the learning curves but also the relative rates at which the curves approach their asymptotes depend upon the probabilities of reinforcement.

e. Contingency with a lag

The contingent cases discussed above cover the common types of experiments in which the probabilities of such reinforcing events as rewards or knowledge of results on any trial depend on the subject's response on that trial. Now we wish to extend the theory to include the more remote contingencies which arise in games or similar two-person situations. In this type of situation it is a common strategy to make one's choice of moves, or plays, on a given trial depend upon the choices made by one's adversary on preceding trials. Regarding the first player as the experimenter and the

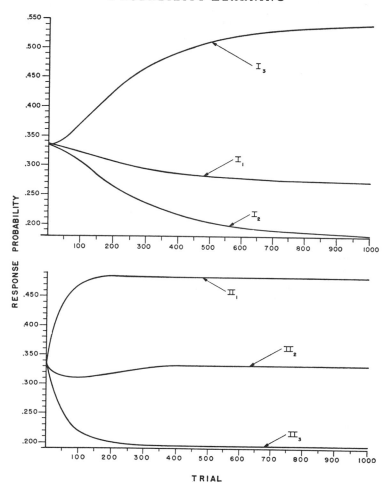

FIGURE 4

Curves describing changes in response probability under simple, contingent reinforcement. Probabilities of reinforcement following responses A_1 ane A_2 are the same under Schedules I and II, but probabilities following A_3 differ. The parameter θ has been taken equal to .015.

second as the subject, we can represent this kind of strategy in the present model by letting the probability of reinforcement of a given response on trial n depend upon the subject's response on some preceding trial, say $n - v$. By the same reasoning used in the case of (2) and (6), we can write a difference equation for mean probability of response A_i on any given trial:

$$(10) \qquad p_{i,n+1} = (1 - \theta)p_{i,n} + \theta \sum_i p_{i,n-v}\pi_{ij,n}^{(v)} ,$$

where $\pi_{ij,n}^{(v)}$ represents the probability of reinforcement of A_j on trial $n + 1$ given that A_i occurred on trial $n - v$. (10) is difficult to handle unless the functions $\pi_{ij,n}^{(v)}$ differ only by constant terms [i.e., $\pi_{11} = a_{11} + g_n(v)$, $\pi_{21} = a_{21} + g_n(v)$, etc.]; for this case, (10) reduces to a linear difference equation with constant coefficients

(10a)
$$p_{j,n+1} = (1 - \theta)p_{j,n} + \theta \sum_i p_{i,n-v}a_{ij} + \theta g_n^{(v)} ,$$

which can be solved explicitly. In order to exhibit some of the most readily testable implications of this model for experiments involving remote contingencies, let us consider the special case of two response classes and $\pi_{ij,n}^{(v)}$ independent of n. Then for a given contingency lag v, the $\pi_{ij,n}^{(v)}$ can be treated as constants, and (10) reduces to

(10b)
$$p_{1,n+1} = (1 - \theta)p_{1,n} + \theta[p_{1,n-v}\pi_{11} + (1 - p_{1,n-v})\pi_{21}]$$
$$= (1 - \theta)p_{1,n} + \theta(\pi_{11} - \pi_{21})p_{1,n-v} + \theta\pi_{21} .$$

Now [excluding, as before, the case ($\pi_{11} = 1$ and $\pi_{21} = 0$) for which $p_{1,\infty} = p_{1,1}$] we can obtain the asymptotic probability of response A_1 by setting $p_{1,n+1} = p_{1,n} = p_{1,n-v} = p_{1,\infty}$ in (10b) and solving, viz.,

$$p_{1,\infty} = \frac{\pi_{21}}{1 - \pi_{11} + \pi_{21}}.$$

We obtain the interesting prediction that asymptotic probability is independent of the contingency lag v. The complete solution of (10b) is (cf. [12] for the detailed method of derivation and for the treatment of cases in which the characteristic roots are not all distinct)

(10c)
$$p_{1,n} = C_1x_1^n + C_2x_2^n + \cdots + C_{v+1}x_{v+1}^n + \frac{\pi_{21}}{1 - \pi_{11} + \pi_{21}} ,$$

where the C_i are constants which can be evaluated from the initial conditions of the experiment and the x_i are the roots of the characteristic equation

$$x^{v+1} - (1 - \theta)x^v - \theta(\pi_{11} - \pi_{21}) = 0.$$

Except for the degenerate case ($\pi_{11} = 1$ and $\pi_{21} = 0$), the characteristic roots will have absolute values in the range $0 \leq x < 1$, and therefore x^n will tend to zero as n increases. If the lag v is zero, then the characteristic equation is simply

$$x - (1 - \theta) - \theta(\pi_{11} - \pi_{21}) = 0$$

which has the single root

$$x = 1 - \theta + \theta\pi_{11} - \theta\pi_{21} ,$$

and (10c) reduces to (7a) as it should.

If the lag v is 1, i.e., probability of reinforcement on a given trial depends on the response of the immediately preceding trial, the characteristic equation is

$$x^2 - (1 - \theta)x - \theta(\pi_{11} - \pi_{21}) = 0,$$

which has the two roots

$$x_1 = \frac{1 - \theta + \sqrt{(1 - \theta)^2 + 4\theta(\pi_{11} - \pi_{21})}}{2}$$

and

$$x_2 = \frac{1 - \theta - \sqrt{(1 - \theta)^2 + 4\theta(\pi_{11} - \pi_{21})}}{2}.$$

The properties of the solution will depend on the relative magnitudes of π_{11} and π_{21} as follows:

1. If $\pi_{11} = \pi_{21}$, then x_1 and x_2 are equal to $1 - \theta$ and 0, respectively, and (10c) reduces to the (3a) of the simple non-contingent case.

2. If $\pi_{11} > \pi_{21}$, then x_1 and x_2 are real numbers, positive and negative, respectively, with absolute values between 0 and 1. Comparing the larger root, x_1, with the characteristic root for the case of lag 0, we find that the difference between the former and the latter is always non-negative when $\pi_{11} > \pi_{21}$; i.e.,

$$\frac{1 - \theta + \sqrt{(1 - \theta)^2 + 4\theta(\pi_{11} - \pi_{21})}}{2}$$
$$- (1 - \theta + \theta\pi_{11} - \theta\pi_{21}) \geqq 0,$$

and the equality holds only in the degenerate cases ($\theta = 0$; $\pi_{11} = 1$ and $\pi_{21} = 0$) for which (10c) is inapplicable. Thus it can be predicted that when $\pi_{11} > \pi_{21}$, the mean learning curve will approach its asymptote more slowly for the case of lag 1 than for the case of lag 0.

3. If $\pi_{11} < \pi_{21}$, then neither x_1 nor x_2 is negative. Both x_1 and x_2 are real numbers in the interval $0 < x < (1 - \theta)$ if the quantity

$$[(1 - \theta)^2 + 4\theta(\pi_{11} - \pi_{21})]$$

is positive; otherwise they are complex numbers with moduli in the interval $0 < |x| < 1$.

In general the estimation of parameters from data will be difficult when there is a contingency lag. Tests of this aspect of the theory can be achieved most conveniently by obtaining estimates of θ from data obtained under conditions of simple non-contingent or contingent reinforcement and then computing predicted relationships for experiments run under similar conditions except for the introduction of contingency lags. Predictions about asymptotic probabilities are, of course, independent of θ and thus can be made in advance of any experiment.

Interpretation of the Model

The theory of reinforcement developed here might be characterized as descriptive, rather than explanatory. The concept of reinforcing event represents an abstraction from a considerable body of experimental data on conditioning and simple motor and verbal learning. In a number of standard experimental situations used to study these elementary forms of learning, it is possible to identify experimentally defined events or operations whose effects upon response probability appear to satisfy the quantitative laws expressed by (1a) and (1b). The first task of our quantitative theory is simply to describe how learning should proceed under various experimental arrangements when these particular experimental operations are assigned the role of reinforcing events. A second task, which becomes important once the theory has survived preliminary tests, is to facilitate the identification of reinforcing operations in new empirical situations. We can test hypotheses concerning a class of events termed reinforcers only if we can state detailed testable consequences of class membership. To the extent that the model elaborated here acquires standing as a descriptive theory, it will serve also to specify the quantitative properties which define membership in the class of reinforcers. Although a quantitative theory of this kind does not contribute immediately to an intensive definition, or interpretive account, of reinforcement, it does provide an additional research tool which may contribute to the construction and testing of explanatory theories.

REFERENCES

[1] Burke, C. J. and Estes, W. K. A component model for stimulus variables in discrimination learning. *Psychometrika*, 1957, **22**, 133-145.
[2] Bush, R. R. and Mosteller, F. Stochastic models for learning. New York: Wiley, 1955.
[3] Detambel, M. H. A test of a model for multiple-choice behavior. *J. exp. Psychol.*, 1955, **49**, 97-104.
[4] Estes, W. K. Toward a statistical theory of learning. *Psychol. Rev.*, 1950, **57**, 94-107.
[5] Estes, W. K. Individual behavior in uncertain situations. In R. M. Thrall, C. H. Coombs, and R. L. Davis (Eds.), Decision processes. New York: Wiley, 1954, pp. 127-137.
[6] Estes, W. K. and Burke, C. J. A theory of stimulus variability in learning. *Psychol. Rev.*, 1953, **60**, 276-286.
[7] Estes, W. K. and Burke, C. J. Application of a statistical model to simple discrimination learning in human subjects. *J. exp. Psychol.*, 1955, **50**, 81-88.
[8] Estes, W. K. and Straughan, J. H. Analysis of a verbal conditioning situation in terms of statistical learning theory. *J. exp. Psychol.*, 1954, **47**, 225-234.

[9] Grant, D. A., Hake, H. W., and Hornseth, J. P. Acquisition and extinction of a verbal conditioned response with differing percentages of reinforcement. *J. exp. Psychol.*, 1951, **42**, 1-5.

[10] Hake, H. W. and Hyman, R. Perception of the statistical structure of a random series of binary symbols. *J. exp. Psychol.*, 1953, **45**, 64-74.

[11] Humphreys, L. G. Acquisition and extinction of verbal expectations in a situation analogous to conditioning. *J. exp. Psychol.*, 1939, **25**, 294-301.

[12] Jordan, C. Calculus of finite differences. New York: Chelsea, 1950.

[13] Neimark, E. D. Effects of type of non-reinforcement and number of alternative responses in two verbal conditioning situations. *J. exp. Psychol.*, 1956, **52**, 209-220.

[14] Richardson, C. H. An introduction to the calculus of finite differences. New York: Van Nostrand, 1954.

Manuscript received 8/27/56

Two-Choice Behavior under Extended Training with Shifting Probabilities of Reinforcement

M. P. FRIEDMAN, *University of California, Los Angeles;* C. J. BURKE, *Indiana University;* M. COLE, *University of Moscow;* L. KELLER, *Indiana University;* R. B. MILLWARD, *Brown University;* and W. K. ESTES, *Stanford University*

This study is concerned with the detailed quantitative description of behavior at various stages of learning in a two-choice situation with random, non-contingent reinforcement. Since the first published report by Humphreys (1939), numerous investigations of simple predictive behavior, or "verbal conditioning," have appeared in the literature. These studies provide considerable information about the effects of various parameters of the experimental situation (see Estes, 1962, for a review of this literature). They do not, however, provide satisfactory material for quantitative analysis. Typically, groups of subjects run under like conditions have been too small (N's being usually in the neighborhood of 20) to make possible reliable estimates of any statistics except perhaps terminal mean-response proportions. Also, previous experiments have generally been limited to series of no more than a few hundred trials, all run under a single reinforcement schedule. It has become clear that some characteristics of the subjects' predictive behavior, especially recency phenomena, change significantly over the early portion of a series. Consequently, one can assess the properties of the behavior that develops under random reinforcement (as distinguished from properties of the behavior of naive subjects newly confronted with the situation) only if reasonably well-practiced subjects are studied.

The particular variant of the two-choice experiment utilized in this investigation is the one introduced by Estes and Straughan (1954). Each trial of the experiment begins with the presentation of a visual signal; the subject responds to the signal by pressing one of two keys to indicate which of two reinforcing lights he expects to follow; finally, one of the two lights appears. For any given series, the reinforcing lights are programed according to an

This research was conducted in the Psychological Laboratories of Indiana University with support from Grant G-5525 from the National Science Foundation.

unrestricted random schedule in which one light appears with probability π and the other with probability $1 - \pi$. To provide an adequate sample of data for certain analyses, we have run a group of 80 subjects, all under essentially the same conditions. Each subject was run for three daily sessions, each of which comprised a series of 384 trials. During the first two sessions, the subject was rotated through a variety of reinforcement schedules, i.e., trial blocks programed with different π values. During the third session, the subject, who now had had experience with a wide range of reinforcement probabilities, was given a series of nearly 300 trials on a single schedule. Although data for all parts of the experiment will be reported, those for the third session are of primary interest. In addition to the usual record of choices, latencies of the key-pressing response were recorded during all sessions. Thus we will be able to provide latency distributions at different stages of learning and to relate these to several parameters of the experimental situation.

Much recent work on two-choice learning has been conducted in conjunction with the development of a family of probabilistic learning models which, depending upon the particular assumptions involved in different cases, have been termed *linear* models, or *stimulus-sampling* models. For presentations and comparisons of these models, the reader is referred to Bush and Estes (1959). One of our main purposes in this investigation is to provide a substantial body of data that will be useful in the testing and extension of these and related models. In order to make our empirical results available without excessive delay, we shall present a variety of data that have been found useful for theoretical purposes, but we shall give them without making intensive analyses in terms of particular models.

To facilitate the inclusion of this data, we have adopted the following compromise relative to theoretical analysis. Whenever possible, we present analyses that show the degree to which the data can be handled by theoretical expressions that are common to the family of linear and stimulus-sampling models. This presentation is possible because of the fact that for all of these models (see, e.g., Bush and Estes, 1959, chaps. 1 and 8), the expected change in probability of a response that is reinforced on trial n of a noncontingent series is given by the linear difference equation

$$(1) \qquad\qquad p_{n+1} = (1 - \theta)p_n + \theta,$$

where p_n denotes probability of the response on trial n and θ is a parameter that has different interpretations in different models but in all cases is assumed to be a constant with a value between 0 and 1. The fact that this "trial operator," representing the effect of any one reinforcement, is the same for all of the models in the noncontingent case, means that all predictions based on successive applications of this trial operator are likewise the same for all of the models. Thus, for example, the curve relating response probability to trials is in all instances described by the function

$$(2) \qquad\qquad p_n = \pi - (\pi - p_1)(1 - \theta)^{n-1},$$

which generates the familiar prediction of asymptotic probability matching. Similarly, in all of these models, "recency curves" relating the probability of a response on a given trial to the number of consecutive immediately preceding reinforcements should be described by negatively accelerated increasing functions, of the same form as the curve for p_n but going asymptotically to unity. Some published studies, e.g., Jarvik (1951), have reported bowed recency curves that increase to a maximum and then decrease as the run of consecutive reinforcements continues. We have, however, proceeded on the assumption that "negative recency" phenomena may represent a peculiarity of naive subjects, accentuated in some studies by restrictions on the randomization of reinforcing events, and that an analysis of recency effects in well-practiced subjects may be of more theoretical import.

Some statistics, for example variances of response proportions over trial blocks, and frequencies of particular sequences of reinforcing events and responses, yield different predictions for different members of the family of models. We shall illustrate some of these differences without going into a systematic analysis. Latency measures have received almost no attention in the literature of two-choice theory to date; consequently we shall present descriptive statistics of the latency data without theoretical analyses. Some of these empirical results on the latency measure may prove useful in indicating properties that will be needed to formulate an adequate theory of latencies of choice responses.

1. Method

Subjects. Eighty undergraduates recruited from introductory psychology classes at Indiana University served for each of three experimental sessions. All introductory psychology students were required to serve as subjects for at least three hours, but were allowed to select from sign-up sheets distributed during class hours the experiments in which they wished to participate. The experiment under discussion was called "Prediction I."

Apparatus. The experimental room is shown in Fig. 1. A tripod-mounted 60 × 60 inch projection screen was located at one end of the room. The booths were placed at the opposite end of the room facing the screen. The bottom of the screen was 2 feet from the floor. The distance from the subject to the screen was about 7 feet.

The booths were constructed using a 2 × 4 frame, and the top, lower front, and sides of the booths were covered with $\frac{3}{4}$-inch plywood. The booths were lined with acoustic tile and painted gray. As shown in Fig. 1, the booths were trapezoidal-shaped. They were 75 inches high and were 40 inches wide at the back and 44 inches wide in front. Only one booth was used in the present study.

Inside the booth, a platform was mounted 30 inches from the floor. A $31\frac{1}{2}$ × 15 inch panel was placed on the platform at a 45-degree angle to the horizontal plane. Two push-button switches, mounted $6\frac{1}{2}$ inches apart, were

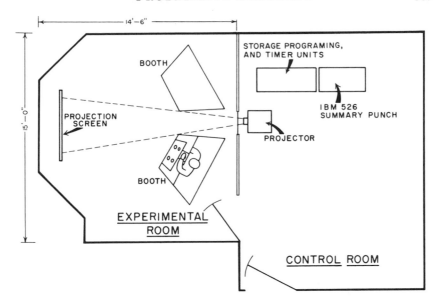

FIG. 1. Floor plan of experimental room and control room.

centrally located on the panel. Above each of these response buttons was a red jeweled pilot lamp, which served as the reinforcing light. A flat wooden plate, placed on the platform in front of the response panel, served as a handrest. The subject was instructed to keep his hand on the handrest except when making a response. A contact in the handrest was wired to a pilot lamp in the experimental room and enabled the experimenter to monitor this aspect of the procedure.

The set of slides that served as stimuli in the experiment was prepared by punching IBM cards and cutting them to a 2 × 2 inch size. On each trial of the experiment, a rectangle of light $4\frac{3}{4}$ inches high by 2 inches wide was projected on the screen at one of nine positions in a square array.

The experimental room was dimly illuminated, and an air-conditioner in continuous operation provided masking noise. As shown in Fig. 1, all programing and recording equipment was located in the adjoining control room.

Figure 2 is a block diagram of the programing and recording system. The setup was designed to allow for a variety of experimental procedures. The principal advantages of this system over other automatic setups are derived from the use of the IBM 526 Summary Punch. The 526 allows for controlled column-by-column readout of data from standard IBM cards, and for column-by-column punching of data into the same cards. Fairly complex stimulus-presentation and stimulus-reinforcement routines can be set up easily by employing the IBM 650 or 700 series computers to prepunch the cards used for the trial-by-trial programing. The output of the system (trial-

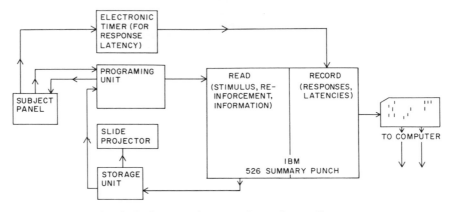

FIG. 2. Block diagram of programing and recording system.

by-trial stimulus, reinforcement, and response information on IBM cards) is in a form suitable for direct analysis by IBM computers. For example, in the present experiment, the card format was set up as follows: The standard 80-column IBM card was divided into eight 10-digit "words." Words 1 and 5 of the card contained coding information, including subject number, group number, card number, etc. The other six words of the card were data words, each of which contained complete stimulus, reinforcement, and response information for a single trial. The first two digits of the data word were blank. The slide number (00–49) was prepunched into the third and fourth digits, and the reinforcing event (1 or 2) was prepunched into the fifth digit of the data word. Digits 6 through 10 of each data word contained the response event (1 or 2) and four columns of response latency recorded to the nearest millisecond.

When the system is operating, events occur in the following sequence: Prepunched cards containing stimulus and reinforcement information are placed in the IBM 526. A programing unit consisting of commercial clip-in relay and timer assemblies controls all experimentally timed intervals and the readout and punching of information for the IBM 526. In the present experiment, Grason-Stadler Model E1100H electronic timers were used to control intra-trial intervals, and ATC Model 350 mechanical timers were used to control the inter-trial interval. At a signal from the programing unit, stimulus and reinforcement information are read into the storage unit. The storage unit consists of three banks of relays, which correspond to the three columns in the data words of the IBM cards into which stimulus and reinforcement information have been prepunched. The relays in the programing unit are wired so that a particular digit punched in one of these columns causes a relay to be energized in the bank corresponding to that column. In this way, slides are set up and reinforcing contingencies are arranged. The slide projector is a Sarkes Tarzian Model TSP-6A, which allows random access to any of 50 slides on any trial. The programing unit controls the stimulus exposure by means of an electromechanical shutter. An electronic timer, constructed by the electronics department at Indiana University, measures response latency to the nearest millisecond and stores both the response event and the response latency in a series of cold cathode tubes. When the programing unit gives the signal, the electronic timer transfers the response information to the IBM 526, where the information is punched into cards. The storage unit is cleared, the timer is reset, and cards in the 526 are advanced so that stimulus and reinforcement information punched in the next data word are ready to be read into storage.

All components of the system are rack-mounted, all are activated by a common switching voltage, and, insofar as possible, all connections are brought out to Nu-way studs.

Design. The main concern was the varying of the probability of reinforcement, π, of the A_1 response. A noncontingent reinforcement procedure was used. Therefore the programed sequence of reinforcing events occurred independently of the subject's responses, the E_1 reinforcing event appearing with probability π and the E_2 event with probability $1 - \pi$. During the first two sessions, for all subjects, each even-numbered block of 48 trials was assigned one of the π-values .1 through .9, excluding .5; and each odd-numbered block was assigned a π-value of .5. Eight 48-trial blocks were administered during each of these two sessions. Thus, each subject received a series of shifts of reinforcement from .5 to some higher or lower value, then back to .5 again, and so on. During the third session, eight 48-trial blocks were also administered; the first and last blocks were assigned π-values of .5, and the middle six blocks were assigned π-values of .8. Each subject received 1,152 trials in all.

The experiment can be regarded as a 2 by 2 by 10 factorial design, with two subjects in each of the 40 cells, and the variables being signal, reinforcement sequence, and order of administration of the 8 π-values used in sessions 1 and 2 (block order).

Signal condition. Half of the subjects were run under a constant-signal condition, in which the same signal was used to initiate each trial, and half were run under a variable-signal condition, in which one of nine different signals appeared on each trial. All variable-signal subjects received the same sequence of signals for the 1,152 trials, independent of reinforcement sequence and block order. For the constant-signal condition, the signal light appeared in the center of the screen on each trial; for the variable-signal condition, the signal appeared in one of nine positions arranged in a square array (the position of the constant signal being the middle member of this array). In the variable condition, the nine positions had equal probabilities of selection on all trials.

Reinforcement sequence. Half of the subjects were run under each sequence condition. For each of the two sequence conditions, one strictly

TABLE 1
SUMMARY OF BLOCK-ORDER CONDITIONS
48-TRIAL BLOCK

Block Order	Session 1								Session 2								Session 3							
	1	2	3	4	5	6	7	8	9	10	11	12	13	14	15	16	17	18	19	20	21	22	23	24
1	.5e	.4	.5h	.6	.5d	.2	.5a	.1	.5j	.7	.5b	.9	.5i	.3	.5c	.8	.5g	.8a	.8d	.8f	.8c	.8e	.8b	.8f
2	.5c	.6	.5a	.2	.5h	.4	.5j	.1	.5i	.7	.5h	.9	.5g	.8	.5d	.3	.5e	.8e	.8a	.8f	.8c	.8d	.8b	.8f
3	.5h	.9	.5j	.8	.5g	.2	.5b	.4	.5d	.3	.5i	.6	.5e	.7	.5c	.1	.5a	.8d	.8c	.8e	.8b	.8a	.8f	.8f
4	.5b	.3	.5i	.8	.5f	.4	.5e	.9	.5g	.6	.5d	.7	.5a	.1	.5h	.2	.5c	.8d	.8a	.8c	.8b	.8f	.8e	.8j
5	.5f	.9	.5b	.6	.5g	.3	.5i	.7	.5e	.2	.5c	.4	.5j	.8	.5d	.1	.5a	.8b	.8c	.8f	.8e	.8d	.8a	.8h
6	.5j	.8	.5d	.2	.5f	.9	.5b	.3	.5i	.1	.5h	.6	.5c	.7	.5g	.4	.5e	.8c	.8b	.8a	.8e	.8d	.8f	.8a
7	.5d	.9	.5f	.3	.5e	.4	.5j	.8	.5g	.2	.5h	.1	.5a	.6	.5c	.7	.5i	.8d	.8e	.8b	.8c	.8a	.8f	.8b
8	.5f	.4	.5j	.9	.5b	.8	.5h	.7	.5c	.1	.5d	.6	.5a	.3	.5e	.2	.5g	.8b	.8c	.8e	.8a	.8f	.8d	.8i
9	.5h	.2	.5i	.4	.5g	.8	.5c	.7	.5e	.3	.5b	.1	.5a	.6	.5j	.9	.5f	.8f	.8h	.8d	.8e	.8f	.8c	.8d
10	.5a	.7	.5d	.2	.5c	.9	.5j	.3	.5h	.8	.5f	.6	.5i	.4	.5e	.1	.5g	.8d	.8a	.8e	.8f	.8c	.8b	.8b

Letters a–j indicate different 48-trial sequences generated for those π values.

random 48-trial sequence was constructed for each of the π-values .1 through .9, excluding .5, which was administered on the even-numbered blocks in sessions 1 and 2. In addition, ten strictly random sequences with π-values of .5, and six strictly random sequences with π-values of .8 (for the third session) were constructed for each sequence condition.

Block order. Ten block orders were constructed, and eight subjects were run under each order. For each block order, the order in which the eight different π-value blocks were administered in sessions 1 and 2 was randomly determined. Also, for each block order, the order of administration of the ten different .5-blocks and of the six .8-blocks in the third session was randomly determined. Table 1 summarizes the block-order conditions used in the experiment. The columns in Table 1 indicate successive 48-trial blocks, and the rows indicate the ten block orders. The entries are π-values for each block. The letters attached to the .5 π-values and to the .8 π-values in session 3 indicate the different 48-trial sequences generated for those π-values. For each block order, two subjects received the same signal (variable or constant) and the same sequence of reinforcements (sequence 1 or sequence 2) for the 1,152 trials. Within each of these signal-sequence block-order cells, the left button and light on the response panel were assigned the roles of A_1 and E_1, respectively, for one subject, and the right button and light were A_1 and E_1 for the other subject.

Procedure. The subject was seated in the booth and was read the following instructions:

This is a very simple experiment. It consists of a series of repeated trials. On each trial, one of the two red lights in your booth will go on, and you are to guess which one it will be. If you think the right light will go on, push the right button. If you think the left light will go on, press the left button. Will you now please push the left button, then the right button.

At the beginning of each trial, a slide will be shown on the screen. This is your signal to make a guess. As soon as the slide appears on the screen, take a quick glance at it, and then, if you think the right light in your booth will go on, press the right button; if you think the left light will go on, press the left button. As soon as the slide goes off, the correct light—the one you should have guessed—will go on in your booth. A few seconds later, a slide will again be presented on the screen, and you are to make a guess again. You must make your guess while the slide is on the screen. If you press a button too early or too late, a tone will sound, reminding you to make your guess while the slide is being shown on the screen, but before the correct light comes on.

After you have made your guess by pressing either the right or the left button, put your hand on this handrest and press down lightly on it. Keep your hand there except when you are making a guess. You may use either hand, but be sure to use the same hand throughout the experiment. Keep your other hand in your lap. Be sure to look at the slide before you make your guess. Any questions?

Before the second and third sessions, shorter instructions were given:

This session will be just like the first one. You will receive a series of repeated trials; at the beginning of the trial, a slide will be shown on the screen, and you are to guess which of the two red lights in your booth will go on. You are to press the right button if you think the right light will flash on, the left button if you think the left light will go on. As soon as the slide goes off, the correct light—the one you should have guessed—will go on. A few seconds later, a slide will again be presented, and you are to make a guess again. You must make your guess while the slide is on the screen. If you press a button too early or too late, a tone will sound, reminding you to make your guess while the slide is being shown on the screen.

Remember to keep your hand on this handrest and press down lightly on it, except when you are making a guess. Use the same hand you used in the last session; keep your other hand in your lap. Be sure to look at the slide before you make your guess. Any questions?

All questions were answered by paraphrasing relevant parts of the instructions.

Following the reading of instructions, the 384 trials comprising a session were conducted without breaks.

On each trial, the signal appeared on the screen for 2 seconds. One of the two reinforcing lights came on for 2 seconds following the signal period. The inter-trial interval, from the offset of the reinforcer to the onset of the signal for the next trial, was $2\frac{1}{4}$ seconds. Each experimental session lasted about 35 minutes. Two sessions for a given subject were never run on the same day, and insofar as possible, each subject completed his three sessions within a seven-day period.

2. Results

Effects of experimental variables. In all analyses it will be convenient to group the data into three main segments, to be denoted the *variable π series*, the *.5 series*, and the *.8 series*. During sessions 1 and 2, it will be recalled, the probability of reinforcement of the A_1 response (π-value) was shifted at the end of every 48-trial block; odd-numbered blocks were assigned π-values of .5, and even-numbered blocks were assigned π-values of .1, .2, $\cdots$ .9, excluding .5. The data from the even-numbered blocks of the first two sessions comprise the variable π series; the data from the eight .5 blocks of the first two sessions together with the .5 blocks that began and ended the third session comprise the .5 series. Data from the six successive

48-trial blocks run under a π-value of .8 in the third session comprise the .8 series. Analyses of variance for total A_1 frequencies are presented in Tables 2–4 for the variable π series, .5 series, and .8 series, respectively.

Table 2 is self-explanatory, except, perhaps, for the sequence variable. In programing the experiment, two 48-trial sequences of E_1 and E_2 events

TABLE 2

ANALYSIS OF VARIANCE OF A_1 RESPONSE FREQUENCY FOR THE VARIABLE π SERIES IN SESSIONS 1 AND 2

Source	df	MS	F
Between subjects	79	85.65	
Sequence	1	972.69	12.84*
Signal	1	14.70	.19
Sequence × signal	1	23.64	.31
Error (*b*)	76	75.73	
Within subjects	560	113.15	
π value	7	5984.23	162.37*
π × sequence	7	166.78	4.52*
π × signal	7	65.84	1.79
π × sequence × signal	7	34.04	.92
Error (*w*)	532	36.86	
Total	608		

* $P < .01$.

TABLE 3

ANALYSIS OF VARIANCE OF A_1 RESPONSE FREQUENCY FOR THE .5-BLOCKS IN ALL THREE SESSIONS

Source	df	MS	F
Between subjects	79	128.70	
Sequence	1	1526.28	13.49*
Signal	1	40.05	.35
Sequence × signal	1	.06	.01
Error (*b*)	76	113.17	
Within subjects	720	31.09	
Blocks	9	438.49	17.63*
Block × sequence	9	88.73	3.57
Block × signal	9	45.58	1.83
Block × sequence × signal	9	23.83	.96
Error (*w*)	684	24.88	
Total	799		

* $P < .01$.

TABLE 4

ANALYSIS OF VARIANCE OF A_1 RESPONSE FREQUENCY FOR THE .8 SERIES IN SESSION 3

Source	df	MS	F
Between subjects	79	218.50	
Sequence	1	1062.08	4.96
Signal	1	9.08	.04
Sequence × signal	1	8.01	.04
Error (b)	76	214.24	
Within subjects	400	25.45	
Blocks	5	416.12	20.02*
Block × sequence	5	20.77	1.00
Block × signal	5	10.27	.49
Block × sequence × signal	5	8.78	.42
Error (w)	380	20.79	
Total	479		

* $P < .01$.

were drawn for each of the eight π-values in the variable π series; one of the resulting sets of eight 48-trial sequences was used for 40 subjects and the other set for the remaining 40 subjects. The difference between these two subgroups constitutes the sequence effect in Table 2. Analogously, in Table 3, *sequence* refers to the two sets of ten 48-trial sequences drawn for π of .5, and in Table 4, *sequence* refers to the two sets of six 48-trial sequences drawn with a π of .8 for the third session. The *blocks* in Table 3 refer to the first and last 48-trial blocks of the experiment, and to the remaining eight 48-trial .5 blocks, each of which is identified by the variable π-value that it followed for a given subject. The *blocks* in Table 4 are chronologically ordered.

Of the two between-subject treatment variables, that of sequence was included simply to provide for some assessment of its importance in relation to the various empirical relationships of primary interest. It is apparent from Tables 2–4 that the sequence effect is uniformly highly significant. This fact severely limits the analyses that can usefully be accomplished with the data of the variable π series. In the case of the .5 and the .8 series, the sequence effect is much less because different subgroups of subjects within each sequence group received the blocks in different orders (see Table 1).

In our original planning, the difference between constant and variable signal conditions was a major point of interest. But it is apparent from the analyses of variance that the contribution of this factor to the total variation in the frequency data was negligible. Consequently, data for the two signal conditions will be pooled in all further analyses of response frequencies. These results, together with those of the preceding studies by Burke, Estes, and Hellyer (1954), and Kalman (1961), suggest that the contribution of the experimentally controlled signal to the stimulus complex influencing the subject at the beginning of any trial is small relative to that of stimulus after-effects of preceding trials. This conclusion might not hold for the early trials,

TABLE 5

MEAN E_1 FREQUENCY, MEAN A_1 FREQUENCY, AND VARIANCE OF A_1 FREQUENCY FOR 12-TRIAL BLOCKS IN THE VARIABLE π SERIES IN SESSIONS 1 AND 2

π Value	12-Trial Sub-Block	Mean E_1 Frequency	Mean A_1 Frequency	Variance of A_1 Frequency
.1	1	1.00	4.02	3.65
	2	1.00	2.72	4.50
	3	1.00	2.11	5.52
	4	1.00	1.79	5.09
.2	1	2.00	4.40	4.46
	2	0.50	3.14	5.39
	3	3.48	3.49	5.30
	4	3.00	3.75	3.61
.3	1	5.00	5.82	3.94
	2	3.00	4.90	5.16
	3	4.50	5.22	4.22
	4	3.50	4.14	5.52
.4	1	6.00	5.50	2.92
	2	5.00	5.30	4.61
	3	4.00	4.61	5.49
	4	3.88	4.61	5.86
.6	1	7.93	6.66	4.82
	2	7.47	6.17	4.67
	3	6.48	6.19	4.48
	4	7.00	6.20	4.49
.7	1	8.00	6.02	3.77
	2	8.50	6.36	5.73
	3	9.00	7.01	5.54
	4	9.50	7.45	7.57
.8	1	7.97	6.04	4.66
	2	11.46	9.09	6.60
	3	9.47	8.84	7.59
	4	9.50	8.72	4.02
.9	1	11.50	7.95	6.05
	2	10.97	9.38	4.63
	3	11.00	9.41	3.97
	4	9.50	9.42	4.47

but since each subject began the present experiment with a .5 series, we are not in a position to explore the possibility of a shift in the relative weights of the two types of stimulation over the initial portion of the experiment. Evidence concerning the effect of signal variability upon response times will be presented in a later section.

TABLE 6

MEAN E_1 FREQUENCY, MEAN A_1 FREQUENCY, AND VARIANCE OF
A_1 FREQUENCY FOR 48-TRIAL VARIABLE π
BLOCKS IN SESSIONS 1 AND 2

π Value	Mean E_1 Frequency	Mean A_1 Frequency	Variance of A_1 Frequency
.1	4.00	10.65	50.90
.2	8.98	14.77	44.05
.3	16.00	20.09	36.88
.4	18.88	20.02	37.62
.6	28.90	25.22	33.75
.7	35.00	26.85	57.30
.8	38.41	32.69	45.64
.9	42.97	36.16	46.86

Frequency of A_1 response over trial blocks. Means and variances of A_1 frequencies are presented for the variable π, .5, and .8 series, respectively, in Tables 5, 7, and 9, by 12-trial blocks, and in Tables 6, 8, and 10, by 48-trial blocks. In the case of the variable π series, there is no reason to study the detailed course of change in response frequency over 12-trial blocks, since there were only two sequences of events for each π-value and the differential effect of sequence is known to be considerable. Consequently, for this series we shall examine only the relation between mean A_1 frequency per block and the associated π-value. It can readily be shown that according to the linear model, this relation should be linear, with the intercept of the function depending jointly on learning rate and initial response probability, and the slope constant depending only on learning rate.

The theoretical probability, p_i, of the A_1 response on trial i is given by Eq. (2) above, i.e.,

$$p_i = \pi - (\pi - p_1)(1 - \theta)^{i-1}$$

[see, e.g., Bush and Estes, 1959, Ch. 1, Eq. (51), or Ch. 8, Eq. (8.3)]. The expected number, $R(n)$, of A_1 responses in a block of n trials is obtained by summing the formula for p_i over trials,

TABLE 7

MEAN E_1 FREQUENCY, MEAN A_1 FREQUENCY, AND VARIANCE OF A_1 FREQUENCY FOR 12-TRIAL .5-BLOCKS IN ALL THREE SESSIONS

Block	12-Trial Sub-Block	Mean E_1 Frequency	Mean A_1 Frequency	Variance of A_1 Frequency
Initial .5	1	6.02	5.39	3.99
	2	6.55	5.90	3.61
	3	5.61	5.82	2.67
	4	4.83	5.87	3.56
.5 following .1	1	6.35	5.55	4.75
	2	6.15	5.94	4.18
	3	6.00	5.80	3.96
	4	5.95	5.76	5.50
.5 following .2	1	6.15	5.02	5.22
	2	6.58	5.79	5.04
	3	5.80	5.51	4.17
	4	4.93	5.42	4.49
.5 following .3	1	4.55	5.05	5.10
	2	7.00	5.36	3.43
	3	5.60	5.79	4.79
	4	5.30	5.46	5.10
.5 following .4	1	5.20	4.81	4.28
	2	5.93	5.65	4.43
	3	5.78	5.52	4.52
	4	5.55	5.11	4.32
.5 following .6	1	5.43	5.99	4.59
	2	6.38	5.77	4.78
	3	5.45	5.81	5.10
	4	5.33	5.72	5.32
.5 following .7	1	5.10	6.19	5.70
	2	6.40	5.91	5.03
	3	5.43	5.80	3.56
	4	5.20	6.17	5.14
.5 following .8	1	6.25	6.74	3.72
	2	7.00	6.69	5.21
	3	5.35	6.10	4.36
	4	4.65	5.49	5.90
.5 following .9	1	5.73	6.64	4.18
	2	6.10	6.05	5.97
	3	5.20	5.84	4.39
	4	5.55	5.68	4.44
Final .5	1	6.00	8.38	4.21
	2	6.70	7.77	8.00
	3	5.20	6.99	7.14
	4	5.01	6.05	7.75

TABLE 8

MEAN E_1 FREQUENCY, MEAN A_1 FREQUENCY, AND VARIANCE OF
A_1 FREQUENCY FOR 48-TRIAL .5-BLOCKS
IN ALL THREE SESSIONS

Block	Mean E_1 Frequency	Mean A_1 Frequency	Variance of A_1 Frequency
Initial .5	23.02	22.99	22.36
.5 following .1	24.45	23.05	32.65
.5 following .2	23.47	21.75	32.71
.5 following .3	22.45	21.66	38.80
.5 following .4	22.47	21.10	31.61
.5 following .6	22.61	23.30	37.43
.5 following .7	22.13	24.07	41.22
.5 following .8	23.25	25.01	34.14
.5 following .9	22.58	24.20	31.86
Final .5	22.91	29.19	50.95

(3)
$$R(n) = \sum_{i=1}^{n} p_i = n\pi - (\pi - p_1) \frac{[1 - (1 - \theta)^n]}{\theta}$$
$$= Ap_1 + (n - A)\pi,$$

where

$$A = \frac{[1 - (1 - \theta)^n]}{\theta}.$$

Similarly, considering successive blocks of n trials, we obtain

$$R(2n) = 2n\pi - (\pi - p_1) \frac{[1 - (1 - \theta)^{2n}]}{\theta},$$

and, for the expected number of A_1's in the second block,

$$R(2n) - R(n) = (1 - \theta)^n \frac{[1 - (1 - \theta)^n]}{\theta} + \left\{ n - (1 - \theta)^n \frac{[1 - (1 - \theta)^n]}{\theta} \right\} \pi$$
$$= (1 - \theta)^n Ap_1 + [n - (1 - \theta)^n A]\pi.$$

More generally, for the expected number of A_1's in the mth block of n trials, we have

(4) $$R(m, n) = (1 - \theta)^{(m-1)n} Ap_1 + [n - (1 - \theta)^{(m-1)n} A]\pi.$$

In the analysis of our variable π series, $n = 12$, and $m = 1, 2, 3, 4$, for the four successive 12-trial blocks at each π value. The corresponding empirical values have been plotted in the four panels of Fig. 3, together with fitted lines representing Eq. (4), with p_1 taken to be .5 and θ estimated by a least-squares technique. In these graphs, the data for all 80 subjects have been pooled, and A_2 responses for π-values above .5 have been combined with A_1 responses for π-values below .5.

TABLE 9
Mean E_1 Frequency, Mean A_1 Frequency, and Variance of A_1 Frequency for 12-Trial Blocks of the .8-Series in Session 3

Trials	Mean E_1 Frequency	Mean A_1 Frequency	Variance of A_1 Frequency
1–12	9.55	7.57	3.89
13–24	9.00	7.67	5.77
25–36	10.35	9.17	5.24
37–48	9.80	9.02	6.55
49–60	8.95	8.88	6.31
61–72	8.82	8.55	6.07
73–84	10.42	9.61	4.29
85–96	9.90	9.92	4.67
97–108	9.47	9.54	4.97
109–120	9.50	9.36	4.63
121–132	10.30	10.15	4.60
133–144	9.10	9.36	5.31
145–156	9.05	9.62	5.08
157–168	9.20	9.30	5.51
169–180	10.45	9.84	6.51
181–192	9.50	9.71	5.40
193–204	9.75	9.60	4.94
205–216	9.35	9.41	4.99
217–228	10.35	10.37	3.78
229–240	9.60	10.27	4.52
241–252	9.20	9.59	4.62
253–264	9.10	9.40	6.46
265–276	10.10	10.27	3.87
277–288	9.10	9.94	4.43

TABLE 10
Mean E_1 Frequency, Mean A_1 Frequency, and Variance of A_1 Frequency for 48-Trial .8-Blocks in Session 3

Block	Mean E_1 Frequency	Mean A_1 Frequency	Variance of A_1 Frequency
1	38.70	33.45	53.37
2	38.10	36.96	59.04
3	38.37	38.41	47.74
4	38.20	38.47	59.05
5	39.05	39.66	49.27
6	37.50	39.20	48.11

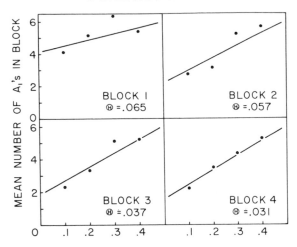

FIG. 3. Frequency of A_1 responses at each π value during variable π series by successive 12-trial blocks. Values are pooled for $\pi = .9$ and $\pi = .1$, $\pi = .8$ and $\pi = .2$, $\pi = .7$ and $\pi = .3$, $\pi = .6$ and $\pi = .4$, as described in text. Fitted linear functions are derived from linear model.

The empirical functions are somewhat irregular for the early blocks but approach linearity in the later blocks. The more general implications of Eq. (4) are borne out reasonably well: over successive blocks, the intercept decreases toward zero and the slope increases toward n (which is the "probability-matching" value). The estimated values of θ are not as constant over blocks as might be wished; however, there is no way to determine whether this indicates a shortcoming of the model or merely instability of the estimates owing to the small number of event sequences represented.

For the .5 blocks following the variable π blocks in sessions 1 and 2, the expectation is that response probabilities should approach a common asymptote of .5. The theoretical function in each case should be Eq. (2) with $\pi = .5$, p_1 now being the terminal A_1 probability for the preceding variable π block. Theoretical expressions for the expected frequency of A_1's per 12-trial block over the .5 block following each variable π condition can be obtained as they were in the case of Eq. (4). For our present purpose, however, it is convenient to divide Eq. (4) through by n, thereby converting the dependent variable to proportions. In Fig. 4 we have plotted the empirical and theoretical functions for all of the .5 blocks in sessions 1 and 2. The initial points in the last four panels represent the terminal proportion for the preceding variable π block. The .5 blocks that follow a given π-value are pooled, and A_2 responses for blocks with initial A_1 response probabilities greater than .5 have been combined with A_1 responses for blocks with initial A_1 probabilities symmetrically below .5 (i.e., the panel labeled ".1 to .5" represents proportions of A_1 responses for .5 blocks following

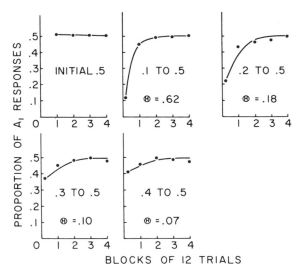

FIG. 4. Observed and theoretical (linear model) proportions of A_1 responses per 12-trial block during .5 series following various variable π conditions.

$\pi = .1$ pooled with A_2 responses for .5 blocks following $\pi = .9$, and so on). The estimates of θ were obtained by setting the observed mean total number of A_1's in a given 48-trial block equal to the corresponding theoretical expression derived from Eq. (4) and solving for θ.

On the whole, the theoretical curves graduate the observed values quite satisfactorily. However, the θ estimates vary systematically as a function of the difference between .5 and the preceding π-value (in agreement with previous findings, e.g., Estes and Straughan, 1954, although not with the simple form of stimulus-sampling theory that is here being applied). It will be noted that this variation in estimated learning rate is entirely a function of the change from the response proportion on the terminal twelve trials of the preceding variable π block to the proportion on the first twelve trials of the .5 block. The rate of change from the first to the fourth 12-trial block under .5 is very similar in all cases. If we rewrite Eq. (4) in terms of the observed frequency in the first twelve trials of each block as the origin, i.e.,

(5) $$R(m,12) = 12\pi - [12\pi - R(1,12)](1 - \theta)^{12(m-1)}$$

(cf. Estes and Straughan, 1954, p. 230), we find that a single value of θ, $\theta = .08$, generates quite satisfactory predictions for the empirical points of Fig. 4. When we consider the last three points for each of the .5 blocks following a variable π series, we see that Eq. (5) with the common θ-value yields a mean difference of $-.04$ between observed and predicted frequencies, as compared to a mean of $-.02$ for Eq. (4) with a different θ estimate for each curve.

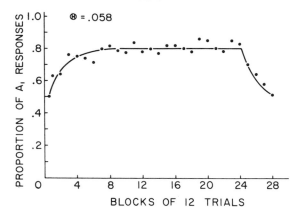

FIG. 5. Observed and theoretical (linear model) proportions of A_1 responses per 12-trial block during .8 series and following .5 series.

This result is about what would be expected if the effective stimulus complex for the subject at the beginning of any trial were comprised largely of the aftereffects of the immediately preceding sequence of reinforcing events. The abrupt shift in response probability at the beginning of each .5 series would, then, represent the effect of the sudden change in prevailing stimulus conditions, the change being larger the greater the disparity between the preceding π-value and the current value of .5. Once the subject has been returned to the stimulation prevailing under a π of .5, further learning would be expected to proceed at a rate independent of the conditions of the preceding series.

The 288-trial .8 series included in session 3 should provide a relatively stable picture of the course of learning for a group of relatively well-practiced subjects. Figure 5 exhibits the mean A_1 response proportions for all 80 subjects by 12-trial blocks for this extended .8 series and the subsequent .5 series.[1] With the relatively large number of cases and event sequences, the empirical curve should be expected to provide a more detailed and stable

---

[1] The theoretical curve in Fig. 5 represents Eq. (4), converted from response frequencies to proportions, with $n = 12$ and with the value of θ chosen to equate theoretical and observed mean A_1 totals for the .8 series. The larger deviations of observed points from theoretical points can be shown to be the result of the particular event sequences used. Consider, for example, the S-shape of the empirical curve over the first four blocks. By applying the trial operators $p_{n+1} = (1-\theta)p_n + \theta$ for each E_1 and $p_{n+1} = (1-\theta)p_n$ for each E_2, and by following the actual sequence of events for each sub-group and then averaging over subgroups, a theoretical curve with the same θ estimate used in computing the curve from Eq. (4) is obtained. This curve shows that the sum of squared deviations of observed from theoretical values is reduced by one-fourth from .0061 to .0046. The sequence-specific theoretical curve, unlike the curve from Eq. (4), is S-shaped, with the largest increase in probability occurring between blocks 2 and 3 (the A_1 proportions for blocks 1–4 are .585, .657, .765, and .801). The increase in goodness of fit would doubtless be even greater if θ were re-estimated for the sequence-specific functions.

picture of the average course of learning than has been available in previous studies of the two-choice, noncontingent situation. One aspect of the curve that is of theoretical significance is the close probability matching that it exhibits over a considerable portion of the series. In particular, the function appears to be closely described by a horizontal straight line over about the middle hundred trials, with the A_1 response proportions averaging almost

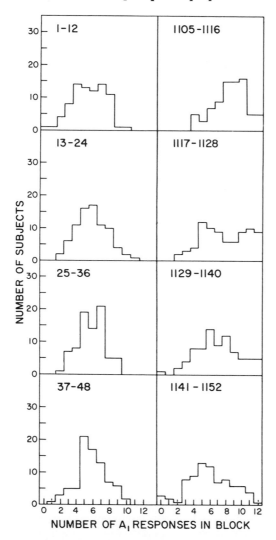

FIG. 6. Frequency distributions of A_1 responses by 12-trial blocks for initial and terminal .5 series.

exactly .80. A slight drift of the empirical values above the matching value appears during the final portion of the .8 series (however, the deviation of .02 for the last 48-trial block does not approach significance; regardless of whether the sample variance or the error mean square from the analysis of variance, given in Tables 6 and 4, respectively, is used as a basis for estimation, 10 per cent confidence limits around the mean A_1 proportion for the final .8 block contain the matching value). The rate of return of the A_1 proportion to .5 during the terminal .5 block appears to be well described by the same parameter ($\theta = .058$) as the learning curve under a π-value of .8. This θ value agrees reasonably well with those obtained for the variable π data by the functions exhibited in Fig. 3. It is smaller than any of the θ estimates obtained for return to .5 after variable π blocks (Fig. 4), but not far from the θ value that was found to permit description of the last three blocks in each curve of Fig. 4 by means of Eq. (5).

The picture of changes in mean response frequencies is supplemented by frequency distributions of A_1 frequencies per 12-trial block for the total group of 80 subjects in Figs. 6 and 7. The initial and terminal .5 blocks of the experiment are represented in the left- and right-hand columns, respectively, of Fig. 6. For the initial .5 series, the distributions appear roughly binomial in form; the variances (given in Table 7) do not deviate greatly from theoretical expectation. Using the θ estimate of .058, the linear model [Bush and Estes, 1959, p. 168, Eq. (8.20)] predicts a variance of 3.24 for the initial 12-trial block and a variance of 3.76 for an asymptotic 12-trial block. All four sample variances for the initial series are satisfactorily close to expectation. (Neither, of course, are they far from the value of 3.0 associated with a binomial distribution for blocks of 12 trials with a p of .5.)

The situation is somewhat different for the terminal .5 blocks, shown on the right side of Fig. 6. The distribution shifts back toward symmetry over the four blocks as expected, but the variance of 7.75 (Table 7) for the final 12 trials is just about twice the value prescribed by the linear model. Had we known this, we would doubtless have continued the final .5 series longer; but, unfortunately, our computing facilities are not yet up to the task of turning out sample variances while the subjects are being run.

Distributions of A_1 responses by 12-trial blocks over the .8 series, presented in Figs. 7a and 7b, are roughly binomial in form over the first couple of hundred trials, but late in the series the mode shifts to the right so that in each of the last eight blocks about one-fourth of the subjects are making 100 per cent A_1 responses. Unfortunately, the form of the frequency distribution specified by the linear model is not known, but certainly a shift in the mode as great as that we observed could not be predicted. The variances for the .8 series are larger than can be accommodated by the linear model with any reasonable choice of parameter values. Consider, for example, the

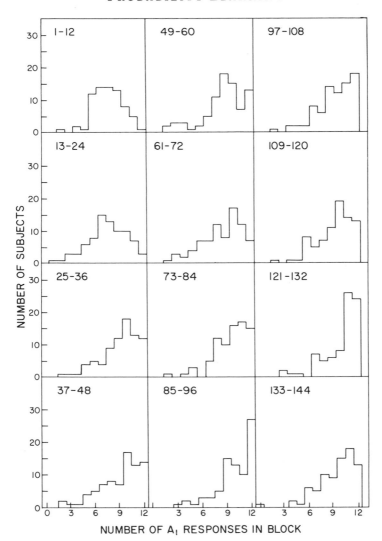

FIG. 7a. Frequency distributions of A_1 responses by 12-trial blocks for first half of .8 series.

asymptotic portion of the series. Using the estimate of .17 for θ, which, as will be shown below, is optimal for predicting various sequential statistics of the .8 data, we obtain a predicted variance of 13.99 for A_1 frequency in a 48-trial block [for the computational formula, see Estes and Suppes, 1959, p. 168, Eq. (8.19)]. This value does not compare well with the observed value of 48.20 for the terminal 48-trial block of the .8 series. It may be noted that the

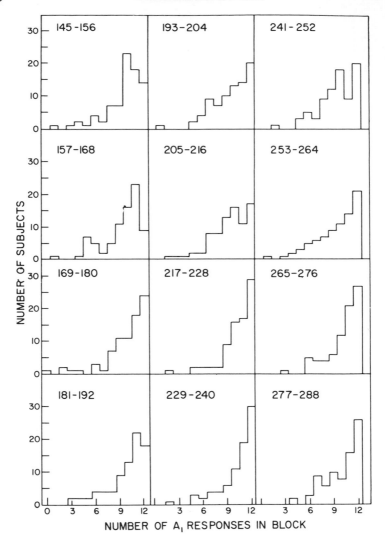

FIG. 7*b*. Frequency distributions of A_1 responses by 12-trial blocks for last half of .8 series.

variance of 37.45 predicted from the special case of stimulus-sampling theory known as the pattern model (see Atkinson and Estes, 1963) comes considerably closer to the mark.

The dependence of response frequencies upon preceding relative frequencies of reinforcement is portrayed in a somewhat different manner in Fig. 8. A general theorem of statistical learning theory (see, e.g., Estes and Suppes, 1959, pp. 157–160) states that, regardless of variation in probability

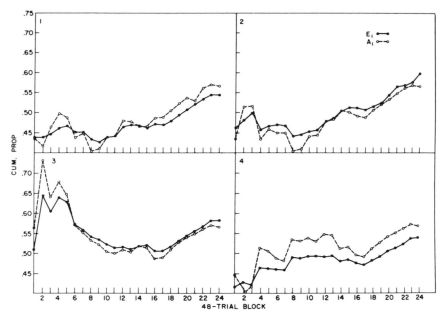

FIG. 8a. Proportions of A_1 and E_1 occurrences cumulated over successive 48-trial blocks for all three sessions for first four block-order subgroups.

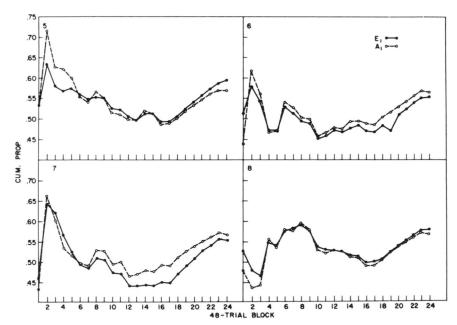

FIG. 8b. Proportions of A_1 and E_1 occurrences cumulated over 48-trial blocks for all three sessions for second four block-order subgroups.

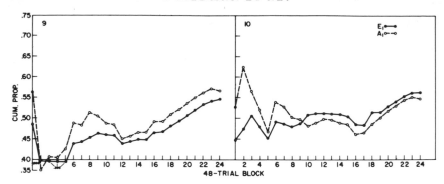

FIG. 8c. Proportions of A_1 and E_1 occurrences cumulated over 48-trial blocks for all three sessions for the last two subgroups.

of reinforcement, and regardless of the θ value for a given subject or group of subjects, over a long series of trials the relative frequency of a given response should approximate the relative frequency of the corresponding reinforcing event. Figures 8a, 8b, and 8c were prepared with this prediction in mind. Each panel represents one of the subgroups of eight subjects, all of whom had the same order of π-values and the same sequence of events within blocks (see Table 1). Each plotted point on the curve labeled A_1 represents the proportion of A_1 responses made by the eight subjects from the beginning of the experiment through the block indicated on the abscissa. Similarly, each point on the curve labeled E_1 represents the proportion of E_1 events experienced by subjects of that subgroup from the beginning of the experiment through the given block. According to the linear model, or to any of the other published variants of stimulus-sampling theory, these two curves, for each subgroup, should converge (though not necessarily in any smooth or regular manner) over the first few trial blocks and then run together throughout the remainder of the series. Despite the small sizes of these subgroups, it is apparent that the response curves follow the wanderings of the event curves with considerable fidelity throughout most of the three sessions. In no case are there discrepancies as large as .05 between corresponding points on response and event curves by the end of the second session, and in some instances, notably subgroups 2, 3, 5 and, especially, subgroup 8, the matching is impressively close.

The frequency distribution of A_1 response proportions for individual subjects over the whole experiment is graphed in Fig. 9. It is apparent that a great majority of subjects yield total A_1 response proportions very close to the over-all proportion of E_1 events. A comparison of the observed and theoretical variances of this distribution would be of considerable interest, but computing the theoretical variance is a more laborious task than we have been able to undertake.

Recency functions. As we mentioned earlier, one of our principal goals in this investigation has been to obtain empirical recency functions for well-practiced subjects. In order to avoid the complications associated with systematic changes in mean response probability over trials, we have taken for this purpose the data from the last half (trials 145–288) of the .8 series. Proportions, pooled over all 80 subjects and over 144 trials, of occurrences of response A_1 following runs of 0 to 4 successive E_1 events, and of response A_2 following runs of 0 to 2 consecutive E_2 events, are plotted in Fig. 10. Fewer points are given for A_2 because, with the E_2 event having a probability of only .2, runs of more than two consecutive E_2's are too rare to permit reliable estimates of conditional response proportions.

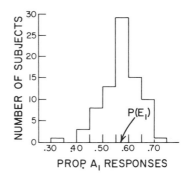

Fig. 9. Frequency distribution of A_1 responses over all three sessions for total group of 80 subjects.

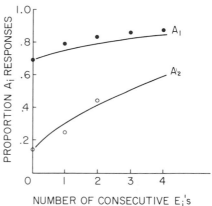

Fig. 10. Recency curves (proportions of A_i responses following runs of immediately preceding E_i events) for last half of .8 series. Theoretical curves computed from linear model.

The first point to be noted about the empirical functions in Fig. 10 is that there is no sign of a negative recency effect; the curves for A_1 and A_2 both increase uniformly with increasing numbers of preceding reinforcements. Although we have not plotted the obtained proportions because the numbers of observations on which they are based becomes too small for stability, we have computed the function for A_1 to runs of 20, still without finding any evidence of a decrease in A_1 probability. None of the obtained conditional proportions fall appreciably below the last point shown in Fig. 10, and the observed proportion of A_1's following 17 to 20 consecutive E_1's is greater than .90. The stability of the positive recency effect at all stages of the .8 series is apparent in Table 11, which includes frequencies of each response following runs of the corresponding reinforcing event for each third of the series.

According to the linear model, the function giving proportion of A_1's following a run of v E_1's, over an asymptotic trial block, should be expressed by the formula (see Atkinson and Estes, 1963)

(6) $P(A_{1,n+v} : E_{1,n+v-1} E_{1,n+v-2} \cdots E_{1,n} E_{2,n-1})$
$$= 1 - [1 - (1 - \theta)\pi](1 - \theta)^v,$$

and the expression for A_2 following a run of E_2's is the same but with π
replaced by $1 - \pi$ on the right-hand side. Curves computed for these·func-
tions with $\theta = .17$, given in Fig. 10, appear to predict the trends of the
observed values reasonably well.

TABLE 11

RECENCY DATA FOR .8 SERIES: A_i FREQUENCIES
FOLLOWING RUNS OF E_i's

Number of Preceding Events	Blocks 1 and 2		Blocks 3 and 4		Blocks 5 and 6	
	A_1	A_2	A_1	A_2	A_1	A_2
E_1's						
1	846	384	981	278	934	261
2	746	274	857	188	820	159
3	616	165	682	134	659	115
4	529	107	533	98	567	70
5	429	91	463	73	488	43
6	352	59	333	51	387	49
7	289	62	308	38	356	35
8	222	46	231	32	259	39
9	183	41	171	28	197	26
10	87	21	110	22	127	13
11	83	17	95	12	100	12
12	71	9	69	11	64	11
13	71	9	64	12	65	11
14	41	7	28	8	43	5
15	42	6	30	6	44	4
16	41	7	30	6	35	5
17	40	4	29	7	39	1
18	41	3	29	6	38	2
19	20	4	30	2	23	1
20	15	1	8	0	15	1
	4764	1317	5081	1012	5260	863
E_2's						
1	707	471	925	338	895	297
2	99	137	130	88	120	91
3	24	48	14	34	27	61
4	3	17	2	21	7	29
	833	673	1071	481	1049	478

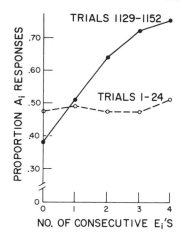

FIG. 11. Recency curves for initial and terminal .5 blocks.

The analysis illustrated in Fig. 11 was conducted in order to provide evidence concerning any changes over the course of the experiment in the subjects' mode of response to runs of reinforcing events. It will be recalled that the experiment began and ended with blocks run under probabilities of .5 for each reinforcing event. Thus estimates of the initial and terminal states of the recency function can conveniently be obtained from these blocks. It is apparent from the empirical function for the first 24 trials that initially the subjects' response tendencies were virtually independent of the length of run of preceding reinforcing events. The negative recency effect that has often been observed with naïve subjects under other reinforcement schedules evidently does not appear at all under our .5 condition. But neither is the positive recency effect predicted by the learning models in evidence at the beginning of the experiment. Perhaps the most parsimonious interpretation of the striking change from a horizontal function during the initial .5 block to a clear positive recency function during the terminal .5 block is that at the beginning of the experiment the subjects' behavior is influenced to an appreciable extent by guessing habits carried over from other situations. Since in all parts of the present experiment random sequences of reinforcing events were generated with no restrictions upon the frequencies of either event within trial blocks, most of these pre-existing response tendencies could not have been reinforced, and thus might be expected to extinguish. To obtain a more direct check on this interpretation, it will evidently be necessary to conduct similar experiments following controlled periods of experience with other types of guessing situations.

Response-reinforcement dependence with lag. All of the models under consideration embody the basic notion of reinforcement theory that the probability of a given response should increase after each reinforcement. However, in the stimulus-sampling theory, reinforcement is defined in terms of occurrence of a particular event, regardless of the response that occurs on the given trial. Thus it is predicted that, other things being equal, the mean probability of an A_i response should be higher on trials following occurrences of the E_i event than following occurrences of the other event. Similarly, probability of A_i on any trial should be higher, other things being equal, if event E_i occurred r trials earlier than if it did not. Specifically, the asymptotic dependence of response probability upon the reinforcing event of an earlier trial should be expected to fall off as the number of intervening trials increases according to the function

(7) $$P(A_{i,n} : E_{i,n-r}) = \pi_i + (1 - \pi_i)\theta(1 - \theta)^{r-1},$$

where π_i denotes probability of E_i [Estes and Suppes, 1959, p. 169, Eq. (8.22)].

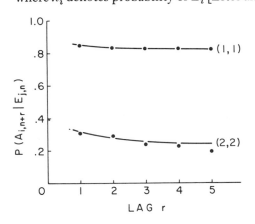

FIG. 12. Proportion of A_1 or A_2 responses on a trial given that an E_1 or E_2 event, respectively, occurred on the rth preceding trial. Data averaged over last half of .8 series.

In Fig. 12 are plotted proportions of A_1 and A_2 responses following E_1 and E_2 events, respectively, at lags of 1 to 5 trials, averaged over the last half of the .8 series. The curves computed from Eq. (7) with the same θ estimate used in Fig. 10 provide reasonable graduations of the observed points, although the A_2 curve declines slightly faster than predicted at the longer lags.

Joint response-event combinations. In this report, we limit ourselves to illustrating two types of analyses, one utilizing standard informational measures and the other utilizing the linear model.

It is appropriate first to raise the question of whether the degree to which the response of a given trial depends on immediately preceding events remains relatively constant over the course of the experiment or whether it is influenced to an important extent by experience in the experimental situation. Evidence on this point is conveniently provided by a comparison of behavior during the initial .5 block with behavior during the .5 block which terminated the third session. The reinforcement schedule is the same in both cases, so any difference in response dependencies may be attributed to the intervening learning experience on other schedules. A suitable measure of dependence for our present purpose is the conditional uncertainty, $H_X(Y)$, of the event Y on any given trial, given the occurrence of the event sequence X on the immediately preceding trials (cf. Attneave, 1959, chap. 2). For the data of Table B-3, Y will be the response on trial n, and X will be the response and reinforcing event of the preceding trial. If Y and X are independent, the value of this measure of conditional uncertainty will be 1.0; if information about X enables us to improve our prediction of Y, the value of $H_X(Y)$ will be reduced below 1.0. For the pooled triplet frequencies of the initial and terminal .5 blocks, the obtained values of the information measure prove to be as follows:

Information Measure	Initial .5 Block	Terminal .5 Block
$H_A(A)$	.9997	.9210
$H_E(A)$	.9965	.9140
$H_{AE}(A)$	.9969	.8721

For the initial block, we observe a rather striking degree of independence. Knowledge of the previous response or event or both simply does not perceptibly enhance our ability to predict the response of a given trial. By contrast, a strong dependence of responses upon previous responses and events is manifest in the terminal .5 block. Prediction of the response on trial n is considerably improved given knowledge of the previous response, slightly more by knowledge of the previous event, and still more by knowledge of both. The pattern of dependence is of the type to be expected on the basis of learning theory (although the relative degree of dependence on the preceding response as opposed to the preceding event could not be predicted without information about the value of the learning parameter θ, in the linear model, or a similar parameter in other models). The lack of similar dependencies in the initial block could be rationalized within the framework of stimulus-sampling theory if we knew that the population of cues sampled by the subjects was much larger, and the learning rate therefore much smaller, on early trials of a series than on later trials. Another line of evidence relevant to this interpretation will be discussed below.

To give a sample of the results obtainable by applying the linear model to local response dependencies, we may consider the triplets $A_{n-1}E_{n-1}A_n$. Theoretical expressions for these quantities are available in the literature (see, e.g., Estes and Suppes, 1959) and take the following form:

$$(8) \quad P(A_{1,n-1}E_{1,n-1}A_{1,n}) = \pi[(1-\theta)V_{2,n} + \theta p_n],$$
$$P(A_{1,n-1}E_{1,n-1}A_{2,n}) = \pi(1-\theta)(p_n - V_{2,n}),$$
$$P(A_{1,n-1}E_{2,n-1}A_{1,n}) = (1-\pi)(1-\theta)V_{2,n},$$
$$P(A_{1,n-1}E_{2,n-1}A_{2,n}) = (1-\pi)[p_n - (1-\theta)V_{2,n}],$$
$$P(A_{2,n-1}E_{1,n-1}A_{1,n}) = \pi[(1-\theta)(p_n - V_{2,n}) + \theta(1-p_n)],$$
$$P(A_{2,n-1}E_{1,n-1}A_{2,n}) = \pi(1-\theta)(1 - 2p_n + V_{2,n}),$$
$$P(A_{2,n-1}E_{2,n-1}A_{1,n}) = (1-\pi)(1-\theta)(p_n - V_{2,n}),$$
$$P(A_{2,n-1}E_{2,n-1}A_{2,n}) = (1-\pi)[1 - (2-\theta)p_n + (1-\theta)V_{2,n}],$$

where p_n denotes probability of A_1 on trial n; $V_{2,n}$ the second moment (mean square) of the A_1 probabilities on trial n; and θ, as before, the learning parameter. For application to asymptotic data, the expressions for proportions of triplets averaged over a given trial block can be assumed to have the same form as Eq. (7), with p_n replaced by π and $V_{2,n}$ replaced by its asymptotic equivalent in terms of other parameters, viz.,

$$V_2 = \frac{\pi(2\pi - 20\pi + \theta)}{2 - \theta}.$$

In Table 12, we present a comparison of the mean triplet proportions over the last 192 trials of the .8 series with predicted values from Eq. (7), with θ taken equal to .17, the value used in the applications of the linear model to recency functions in the preceding section.

The goodness of fit is somewhat difficult to evaluate for this analysis taken by itself. Judged by eye, the correspondence of predicted and observed values is not bad, considering that only one parameter has been evaluated from the data. On the other hand, the fit is by no means as good as can be

TABLE 12

PROPORTIONS OF RESPONSE–EVENT TRIPLETS OVER
LAST 192 TRIALS OF .8 SERIES COMPARED WITH VALUES
PREDICTED FROM LINEAR MODEL

$A_{n-1}E_{n-1}A_n$			Observed	Predicted
1	1	1	.5770	.5437
1	1	2	.0758	.0963
1	2	1	.1176	.1087
1	2	2	.0422	.0513
2	1	1	.1002	.1235
2	1	2	.0489	.0365
2	2	1	.0179	.0241
2	2	2	.0206	.0159

obtained with other stimulus-sampling models (see, e.g., results for the pattern model given in Atkinson and Estes, 1963 or in Estes, 1961). A point that, at least on first inspection, seems to raise considerable difficulty for the model is the lack of agreement between the θ value required to fit the mean curve for the .8 series (Fig. 5) and the value giving best fit to the triplet proportions of Table 12. The θ estimate for the mean curve is approximately .06, whereas the best estimate for the triplet proportions is in the neighborhood of .17 (perhaps slightly larger; the sum of absolute deviations of observed from predicted values is decreased in the third decimal place if we go from $\theta = .17$ to $\theta = .20$). Use of the θ estimate of .06 to compute predicted triplet proportions yields a distinctly poorer fit, the theoretical value for $P(A_{1,n-1}E_{1,n-1}A_{1,n})$, for example, being .5232, and the theoretical value for $P(A_{1,n-1}E_{1,n-1}A_{2,n})$ being .1168, both yielding deviations substantially larger than any of those present in Table 12.

TABLE 13

PROPORTIONS OF RESPONSE–EVENT TRIPLETS OVER
FIRST 12 TRIALS OF .8 SERIES COMPARED WITH LINEAR MODEL
PREDICTIONS FOR TWO θ-VALUES

$A_{n-1}E_{n-1}A_n$			Observed	$\theta = .17$	$\theta = .06$
1	1	1	.379	.378	.376
1	1	2	.168	.126	.128
1	2	1	.061	.073	.086
1	2	2	.035	.053	.040
2	1	1	.128	.177	.146
2	1	2	.121	.120	.152
2	2	1	.062	.032	.032
2	2	2	.045	.042	.042

A possible basis for this discrepancy in θ estimates would be a change in learning rate over trials, as might, for example, result from a progressive change in size of the stimulus population from which the subjects are sampling. Some evidence regarding the plausibility of this hypothesis can be obtained from an analysis of sequential dependencies on the early learning trials. To this end, proportions of response–event triplets averaged over the first 12 trials of the .8 series are presented in Table 13, together with values calculated from the linear model with $\theta = .17$ and $\theta = .06$. Equations (8) are again the basis for the predictions, but in this instance, the quantity $V_{2'n}$, or rather its average value over the block of 12 trials, is simply treated as a free parameter and estimated from the data. In Table 13, unlike the corresponding comparison for asymptotic data, the fit of theoretical to observed values is no worse, and perhaps a bit better, for $\theta = .06$ than for $\theta = .17$. From this result it appears that the possibility of some systematic change in learning rate over trials will merit more intensive investigation.

3. Discussion

Comparisons with related studies. In the matter of experimental procedure, this study was very similar to a number of others that have been reported from the Indiana University laboratory (e.g., Burke, Estes, and Hellyer, 1954; Estes and Straughan, 1954; Neimark, 1956), and in most essentials it appears comparable to many investigations of two-choice learning under simple noncontingent schedules that have been reported from other laboratories (for reviews see Estes, 1961, 1964). A subject in the present experiment could see the rather formidable programing and recording apparatus while he was on his way into the experimental chamber, but once in the booth he was exposed only to the response buttons, the reinforcing lights, and the projection screen. Instructions simply emphasized that the subject was to indicate his expectations concerning the reinforcing event on each trial, and gave no hint whether or not he might learn to always predict correctly. Although response times were recorded, the subjects were not so informed.

The chief qualitative difference between the results of this study and those of related ones is the absence of any sign of a negative recency effect in the present case, even in the early portion of the experimental series. Unfortunately the importance of the fact that we began with a .5 series cannot be assessed, for this condition has not been included in any of the preceding studies that have reported recency functions. Concerning changes in the recency function over trials, previous investigators (Anderson, 1960; Edwards, 1961) have noted a tendency for the negative recency effect to "adapt out" during a prolonged series under a single schedule. In the present study, a comparison of the initial and terminal .5 series shows that the intervening exposure to a variety of reinforcement probabilities produced a marked shift from the initial lack of correlation between responses and preceding events to a uniformly positive recency function. All of these results are consonant with the assumption that, regardless of the particular reinforcement probabilities employed, the subject's behavior tends to come increasingly under the control of the reinforcing events as a function of experience in the experimental situation.

A novel feature of this study was the securing of a substantial quantity of data for a single reinforcement schedule after the subjects had had extensive training under a variety of π values. Comparison of results for this .8 series with results reported from previous studies using similar schedules but relatively unpracticed subjects reveals only a few noteworthy differences. The form of the learning curve, and in fact even the value of the slope constant for the fitted theoretical function, did not differ appreciably from those of earlier studies (e.g., Estes and Straughan, 1954, obtained a θ estimate of .08 for the acquisition curve of an .85 series, and LaBerge, 1959, a θ estimate of .05 for an initial .9 series). Probability matching was unusually precise over the middle third of the 288-trial series, and the deviation from matching was only about two percentage points over the final third, with no significant increasing trend over the terminal trial blocks. Unlike the usual result with less-practiced subjects, recency functions for the .8 series were uniformly positive, even for response probabilities following runs of up to 20 consecutive preceding reinforcements.

Assessment of the linear model. One of our main goals was to assess the adequacy of the linear model for two-choice learning. Predictions from the model proved generally satisfactory for the relationship between response frequency and reinforcement probability in the variable π series, for curve forms and asymptotes in the .5 and .8 series, and for sequential relationships, including recency functions and local dependencies of responses upon combinations of preceding responses and reinforcing events, in the .8 series.

Two weaknesses of the simple linear model that have appeared in previous studies were especially clear in the present case against the background of otherwise relatively accurate prediction. The first weakness is the lack of invariance of the learning parameter θ across various aspects of the data. The value required to fit the learning curves was significantly smaller than the value that provided the best account of local sequential dependencies in the asymptotic data. Also, attempts to fit the trial-by-trial learning functions for groups of subjects who learned under particular sequences of reinforcing events yielded evidence that the optimal value of θ varies during a trial series as a function of characteristics, as yet incompletely specified, of the event sequence. This difficulty can perhaps be overcome as more information concerning the manner in which the value of θ depends upon experimental conditions is accumulated. A second important weakness of the linear model appears to be more fundamental, namely that it does not allow for sufficient variability in the data. Our results concerning the variances of response frequencies suggest that another form of stimulus-sampling theory, perhaps some variant of the pattern model (Estes, 1959, 1961; Suppes and Atkinson, 1960), which yields predictions similar to those of the linear model for mean curves but allows for more variance, may provide a more nearly adequate account of probability learning data.

REFERENCES

ANDERSON, N. H. Effect of first-order conditional probability in a two-choice learning situation. *J. exp. Psychol.*, 1960, **59**, 73–93.

ATKINSON, R. C., and ESTES, W. K. Stimulus sampling theory. In R. D. Luce, R. R. Bush, and E. Galanter (Eds.), *Handbook of mathematical psychology*. Vol. 2. New York: Wiley, 1963. Pp. 121–268.

ATTNEAVE, F. *Application of information theory in psychology*. New York: Holt, Rinehart, and Winston, 1959.

BURKE, C. J., ESTES, W. K., and HELLYER, S. Rate of verbal conditioning in relation to stimulus variability. *J. exp. Psychol.*, 1954, **48**, 153–161.

BUSH, R. R., and ESTES, W. K. (Eds.), *Studies in mathematical learning theory*. Stanford, Calif.: Stanford Univer. Press, 1959.

EDWARDS, W. Probability learning in 1000 trials. *J. exp. Psychol.*, 1961, **62**, 385–394.

ESTES, W. K. Component and pattern models with Markovian interpretations. In R. R. Bush and W. K. Estes (Eds.), *Studies in mathematical learning theory*. Stanford Univer. Press, Stanford, Calif., 1959. Pp. 9–52.

ESTES, W. K. A descriptive approach to the dynamics of choice behavior. *Behavioral Science*, 1961, **6**, 177–184.

ESTES, W. K. Probability learning. In A. W. Melton (Ed.), *Categories of human learning*. New York: Academic Press, in press.

ESTES, W. K., and STRAUGHAN, J. H. Analysis of a verbal conditioning situation in terms of statistical learning theory. *J. exp. Psychol.*, 1954, **47**, 225–234.

ESTES, W. K., and SUPPES, P. Foundations of linear models. In R. R. Bush and W.K. Estes (Eds.), *Studies in mathematical learning theory*. Stanford, Calif.: Stanford Univer. Press, 1959. Pp. 137–179.

HULL, C. L. *Principles of behavior*. New York: Appleton-Century, 1943.

HUMPHREYS, L. G. Acquisition and extinction of verbal expectations in a situation analogous to conditioning. *J. exp. Psychol.*, 1939, **25**, 294–301.

JARVIK, M. E. Probability learning and a negative recency effect in the serial anticipation of alternative symbols. *J. exp. Psychol.*, 1951, **41**, 291–297.

KALMAN, D. The effects of intertrial spacing and stimulus variability on verbal conditioning. *J. gen. Psychol.*, 1961, **65**, 243–260.

LaBERGE, D. A model with neutral elements. In R. R. Bush and W. K. Estes (Eds.), *Studies in mathematical learning theory*. Stanford, Calif.: Stanford Univer. Press, 1959. Pp. 53–64.

NEIMARK, E. D. Effects of type of non-reinforcement and number of available responses in two verbal conditioning situations. *J. exp. Psychol.*, 1956, **52**, 209–220.

SUPPES, P., and ATKINSON, R. C. *Markov learning models for multiperson interactions.* Stanford, Calif.: Stanford Univer. Press, 1960.

Effects of Type of Nonreinforcement and Number of Alternative Responses in Two Verbal Conditioning Situations[1]

EDITH D. NEIMARK,[2] *Indiana University*

In his original experiment on the conditioning of "verbal expectations" Humphreys (10) provided the procedural paradigm for a good deal of subsequent research (7, 8, 11). The procedure may be summarized briefly as follows: (*a*) a series of discrete trials is given in which the start of each trial is signaled by the presentation of a brief stimulus; (*b*) upon the appearance of the stimulus S is to predict the occurrence of a random event by making one of two available responses, A_1 or A_2; (*c*) following S's prediction and independently of it, E presents one of the to-be-predicted events, E_1 or E_2, according to a predetermined random sequence in which each event has a fixed probability of occurrence, π_1 and π_2. The dependent variable is the proportion of A_1 responses in successive trial blocks.

The major concern of most studies in this area has been the effect of proportion and arrangement of E_1 and E_2 and development of a quantitative formulation for this experimental situation. With the exception of the first group of studies there have been few attempts to investigate the variables affecting behavior in this situation or to extend the available quantitative theories of verbal conditioning to encompass the effects of these additional variables. The present study attempts to fill both these gaps. Specifically, the effects of two variables have been investigated: (*a*) the number of available response alternatives, two or three; and (*b*) event sequences in which exactly one of the E_i need not occur on each trial, i.e., some of the trials are blank in the sense that none of the E_i occur. In addition, the verbal conditioning model developed by Estes and Burke (6, 7) has been extended to cover the effects of these variables.

An additional purpose of the present study has been to compare learning under the traditional procedure with that under a procedure in which

[1] This article is based on a dissertation submitted to the faculty of the Department of Psychology of Indiana University in partial fulfillment of the requirements for the Ph.D. degree, September, 1953. The author wishes to express her appreciation to Dr. W. K. Estes for his unfailing suggestions, criticisms, advice, and patience.

[2] Now at AFP & TRC, Lackland A.F.B.

This article appeared in *J. exp. Psychol.*, 1956, **52**, 209–220.

the occurrence of the E_i is contingent upon S's response. Such a procedure is achieved when S is instructed to produce one of the E_i rather than to predict its appearance. The results of this procedure will be presented in Exp. II.

EXPERIMENT I

Method

Apparatus.—The S was seated facing a large black screen (36 × 30 in.) at the base of which three telegraph keys were mounted. Three milk-glass panel lamps, E_1, E_2, and E_3, were mounted upon the screen, one above each of the telegraph keys. A fourth lamp, the signal, was centered at S's eye level.

The durations of the signal, the E_i, and the interval between signal and E_i were automatically controlled by means of a mechanical timer. The timer and two sets of three knife switches, each wired in circuit with one of the E_i, were located on E's side of the screen. The E side of the screen also contained three 6-w. bulbs each of which corresponded to one of the telegraph keys. Recording of responses and programing of E_i were done manually by E.

The experiment was run in a light-tight sound-shielded room under conditions of low illumination.

Procedure.—The Ss were 160 volunteers from Introductory Psychology classes at Indiana University. The S was seated facing the screen and given the following instructions: "This is going to be like a guessing game. First this top light comes on as a signal to guess and then one of these lower lights may follow it. You are to guess which of the lower lights will go on following the signal. Your object is to guess correctly as many times as you can.

"Now here is what you are to do. Be sure you are seated comfortably with the index finger of each hand resting on one of the outside keys (with one finger resting on each of the three keys). When this top light goes on you are to press the key above which you think the light will appear. Sometimes no light may appear—that is all right—you are to keep on guessing. You may not, however, guess that no light will appear. You must always press one and only one key when the top light goes on."

Following the instructions S was given a series of six practice trials in which the order of occurrence of the E_i was RLLRRL for Ss with two responses available, and LCRRLC for Ss with three responses available. After questioning to ensure his understanding of the procedure, S was given a series of training trials in which the

TABLE 1

SUMMARY OF NUMBER OF TRAINING TRIALS AND RELATIVE FREQUENCIES OF OCCURRENCE, π_i, OF E_1, E_2, AND E_3 FOR EACH OF THE NONCONTINGENT GROUPS

Group		No. of Trials	Relative Frequency		
			π_1	π_2	π_3
2-Key	A	66	1.00	0	
	B	100	.66	0	
	C	100	.66	.34	
	D	100	.66	.17	
3-Key	A	66	1.00	0	0
	B	100	.66	0	0
	C	100	.66	.17	.17
	D	100	.66	.085	.085

signal was presented for 2 sec. immediately followed by presentation of the appropriate E_i for 2 sec. Following a 2-sec. intertrial interval the signal reappeared.

The training procedures for each of the groups differed with respect to the number of training trials, 66 or 100; the number of available responses, two or three keys; and the relative frequencies, π_i, with which each of the E_i was presented. Details of the treatment of each of the eight groups are summarized in Table 1. Assignment to groups was random within restrictions to be outlined in the next section. For Ss in the two-key groups the center key was covered by a metal shield and only the two outer keys were available. The position of each of the E_i and its corresponding A_i was counterbalanced within each group.

Immediately following the training series and with no break in the procedure, each S received a series of 50 extinction trials in which none of the E_i ever appeared. The results of the extinction series are presented elsewhere (12).

Preparation of random sequences of E_i.—Since evidence (7, 11) indicates that the response sequence for a given S is influenced by the preceding E_i sequence, it was decided to evaluate the effect of this dependence by using ten different E_i sequences in each group. For Groups A in which only one light, E_1, was presented on all 66 training trials all 20 Ss in each group obviously received the same sequence. For the remaining groups the sequences were prepared as follows: (a) a column of 100 two-digit numbers was selected from a table of random numbers. For $n \leq 65$ E_1 was entered for the corresponding trial. For Groups 2B and 3B the remaining trials were blank, i.e., no other E appeared; while for Group 2C E_2 was presented on the remaining trials. (*b*) The non-E_1 trials were divided by means of the table of random numbers into E_2 and E_3 trials in the case of Group 3C, or E_2 and blank trials in the case of Group 2D. (*c*) For Group 3D all E_2 trials of the corresponding 2D sequence were divided into E_2 and E_3 trials. Thus the sequence of E_1's was the same for the B, C, and D groups, training sequences for these groups differing only with respect to the treatment on non-E_1 trials (see Table 1). Ten separate random sequences were prepared in this fashion. Essentially, then, Exp. I consists of 10 replications of the 4×2 factorial design. The *S*s were assigned to groups randomly with the restriction that a replication must be completed before the next could be begun.

Results

Theoretical considerations.—In a recent paper by Estes and Straughan (7) a statistical learning theory (4, 6) has been successfully applied to a verbal conditioning situation of the Humphreys type by the use of several relatively simple assumptions. The signal marking the start of each trial is conceptualized as a population of stimulus elements which is sampled by *S* on each trial. The symbol θ is introduced to refer to the proportion of the population of elements which constitutes the effective sample on a given trial. Each time the signal is presented *S* must predict the occurrence of one of two random events, E_1 or E_2, by making the appropriate response, A_1 or A_2. On a fixed proportion, π_1, of the trial series E_1 is presented; on the remaining proportion, $1 - \pi_1$, E_2 is presented. It is assumed that on E_1 trials the stimulus elements sampled will become associated with response class A_1 and on E_2 trials the elements sampled will become associated with response class A_2. The probability of a response of class A_1 on any given trial is determined by the proportion of the population of stimulus elements associated with that response class. For a group of *S*s the mean probability (relative frequency) of a response of class A_1 on the *n*th trial, $\bar{p}_1(n)$, has been shown to be

$$\bar{p}_1(n) = \pi_1 - (\pi_1 - \bar{p}_1(0))(1 - \theta)^n \quad (1)$$

where $\bar{p}_1(0)$ refers to the group mean initial probability of A_1 at the start of training.

As *n* becomes large the value of the second term in Equation 1 becomes smaller and approaches 0, leaving π_1, the proportion of trials on which E_1 occurs, as the final probability of responses of class A_1. This prediction has been supported by the results of a number of experiments (7, 8, 10). Moreover, since the asymptotic value of $\bar{p}_1(n)$ is a function of π_1 alone, it follows that if exactly one E_i is presented on each trial and E_1 is presented on π_1 of the trial series, then Equation 1 should apply regardless of the number of response alternatives, A_i, and corresponding E_i available. In the present study, then, there should be no difference in final level of A_1 responding between two- and three-key groups trained under comparable E_i treatments. A difference between two- and three-key groups will be reflected, however, by a steeper slope in the learning curve for the three-key groups since $\bar{p}_1(0)$ should become lower in value as more responses are available.

The extension of Equation 1 to multiple response groups has assumed—as is usually the case in verbal conditioning—that exactly one E_i is presented on each trial. In the case of Groups B and D of the present study this is not the case. Each of the E_i is presented on a proportion π_i of the trials but since $\Sigma_i \pi_i < 1$, the remaining $1 - \Sigma_i \pi_i$ trials are blank. To account for the effect of blank trials we assume that the stimulus elements sampled on a blank trial will become associated with the response class of which a member occurs on that trial. Given that no E_i is presented on the *n*th trial the probability of response A_1 on the $n + 1$ trial will be

$$p_1(n + 1) = (1 - \theta)p_1(n) + \theta_{p_1}(n) = p_1(n). \quad (2)$$

It can then be shown that for any number, α, of available response classes and corresponding E_i each of which occurs with relative frequency π_i the group mean probability of response A_1

on the nth trial is

$$\bar{p}_1(n) = \frac{\pi_1}{\Sigma_i \pi_i} - \left[\frac{\pi_1}{\Sigma_i \pi_i} - \bar{p}_1(0) \right]$$
$$\times (1 - \theta \sum_{i=1}^{\alpha} \pi_i)^n. \quad (3)$$

Whenever $\sum_{i=1}^{\alpha} \pi_i = 1$ Equation 3 reduces

to Equation 1. However, for $\sum_{i=1}^{\alpha} \pi_i < 1$ the final probability of A_1 will exceed π_1 and the slope of the learning curve will be more gradual than in the traditional verbal conditioning situation.

In the following section we shall be concerned with the group mean proportion of A_1 responses on successive 10-trial blocks; and more specifically with the group mean curves of these proportions and the final level of responding at the end of training. An expression appropriate for the consideration of group data in 10-trial blocks may be obtained by a method outlined elsewhere (7). The group mean proportion of A_1 responses on the mth block of 10 trials turns out to be

$$\bar{P}_1(m) = \frac{\pi_1}{\Sigma_i \pi_i} - \left[\frac{\pi_1}{\Sigma_i \pi_i} - \bar{P}_1(1) \right]$$
$$\times (1 - \theta \Sigma_i \pi_i)^{10(m-1)}. \quad (4)$$

Final level of A_1 responding.—As an estimate of asymptotic group mean proportion of A_1 responses, $\bar{P}_1(\infty)$, we have taken the group mean total of A_1 responses on the last 20 trials of the training series. The mean total and SD of A_1 responses for each of the eight groups are summarized in Table 2. In order to determine whether this measure represents a stable final level of responding, a t for paired measures was computed between A_1 totals for the first and last halves of the block of 20 trials. In all cases the obtained values of t fall short of significance at the .05 level (Table 2). It appears reasonable to assume that

TABLE 2

GROUP MEANS AND STANDARD DEVIATIONS OF FINAL LEVEL OF A_1 RESPONDING AND t TESTS OF STABILITY OF RESPONSE

(All t values based on 19 df; $N = 20$)

Grou		Mean	SD	$t_{diff.}$ (Last 10-First 10)
2-Key	A	19.90	.300	0
	B	19.60	1.158	− .809
	C	12.40	2.245	− 1.182
	D	15.85	1.905	1.239
3-Key	A	19.70	.781	0
	B	19.70	.714	− 1.000
	C	13.10	2.700	.880
	D	15.50	3.668	− 1.703

a stable level of responding has been reached.

Although the study was designed to enable over-all group comparisons of final response levels by means of analysis of variance, failure to fulfill the assumption of homogeneity of variance makes the use of this procedure questionable. In the case of Groups A and B the final levels of A_1 responding are so stable and so similar that further comparison was deemed to be gratuitous. In the case of Groups C and D an analysis of variance was run despite failure to fulfill the assumption of homogeneity of variance (Table 3). The obtained F values for differences due to the 10 random sequences of E_i, and for differences due to training treatment (C vs. D) are significant at better than the .001 level. The F values for differences due to number of response alternatives and for all interactions fall short of significance at the .05 level. These findings suggest that when only E_1 is presented during training (Groups A and B) the asymptote of A_1 responding approaches unity whether or not blank trials are included in the training sequence. In the case of groups receiving 100

TABLE 3

ANALYSIS OF VARIANCE OF FINAL LEVEL OF A_1
RESPONDING FOR THE C AND D
NONCONTINGENT GROUPS

Source	df	MS	F
Sequence (S)	9	24.946	4.90***
No. of keys (K)	1	.613	
C vs. D group (G)	1	171.113	33.63***
S × K	9	6.168	
S × G	9	5.113	
K × G	1	5.515	
S × K × G	9	5.401	
Within sequence	40	5.088	
Total	79		

*** Significant at $P \leq .001$.

trials, approximately 66 of which are E_1 trials, (B, C, D) the asymptotic probability of A_1 approaches .66 only under the traditional procedure, Group C. The greater the proportion of blank trials in the training series the greater the amount by which the asymptotic response probability exceeds π_1.

The differences in final level of A_1 responding among two- and three-key groups given comparable training treatments were further tested by means of t tests for independent groups (Table 4). None of the obtained t values is significant at the .05 level. The prediction that the

asymptotic level of A_1 responding should be independent of the number of response alternatives available appears to be amply supported.

As an additional test of the accuracy of theoretical predictions of asymptotic level of A_1 responding, theoretical and observed asymptotes were compared by means of t tests (with the variance of each group taken as an estimate of population variance). With the exception of Group 3B, all obtained t values fall short of significance at the .05 level (Table 5). In view of the apparently slight mean difference of .3 responses in Group 3B, a significant t is somewhat surprising. Possibly the slight variance of this group, .51, is an underestimate of the population variance. In general, however, the extended model for verbal conditioning appears to provide a satisfactory description of final level of A_1 responding for all groups.

Mean learning curves.—The mean proportions of A_1 responses in successive 10-trial blocks have been plotted in Fig. 1 where the small black dots refer to the two-key groups and the large white dots to the three-key groups. Theoretical curves through the observed points have

TABLE 4

VALUES OF t FOR DIFFERENCES BETWEEN GROUP MEAN TOTALS OF A_1 RESPONSES
IN THE LAST 20 TRAINING TRIALS

Group	I2A	I2B	I2C	I2D	II3A	II3B	II3C	II3D
II2A	.650				.769			
II2B		5.915***				.183		
II2C			.483				.591	
II2D				.488				2.210*
I3A	1.047				.118			
I3B		.303				4.460***		
I3C			.745				1.614	
I3D				.369				1.944

Note.—I refers to Non-contingent groups; II to the Contingent groups.
* Significant at $P = .05$.
*** Significant at $P = .001$.

TABLE 5

PREDICTED AND OBSERVED PROPORTIONS OF A_1
RESPONSES FOR THE LAST 20 TRIALS FOR
THE NONCONTINGENT GROUPS AND
t TESTS OF ACCURACY OF
PREDICTION

Group		Observed Proportion	Predicted Proportion	$t_{\text{diff.}}$ (Pred.-Obs.)
2-Key	A	.995	1.000	1.453
	B	.980	1.000	1.504
	C	.620	.660	1.553
	D	.793	.795	.011
3-Key	A	.985	1.000	1.676
	B	.985	1.000	2.424*
	C	.655	.660	.016
	D	.775	.795	.476

* Significant at $P \le .05$; $df = 19$.

been derived from Equation 4.. In obtaining each theoretical curve three parameters must be evaluated: π_i, $\bar{P}_1(1)$, and θ. The values of π_i are fixed by the experimental procedure (Table 1); values for $\bar{P}_1(1)$ have been obtained from the observed group mean proportion of A_1 responses during the first 10 trials; θ has been evaluated for each group by means of a statistical device outlined in detail elsewhere (7).

Although the theoretical curves appear to describe the data adequately the question of goodness of fit is largely academic. Each point represents the mean of 20 Ss for 10 trials and undoubtedly reflects artifacts due to averaging. Secondly, each point represents the mean of 10 separate sequences of E_i, a variable whose effect upon responding has been demonstrated in this experiment as well as others (7, 11).

Comparisons among group curves are complicated by differences in both

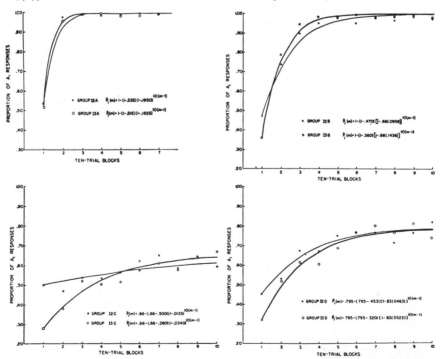

FIG. 1. Observed and theoretical mean proportions of A_1 responses in successive 10-trial blocks for the two- and three-key subgroups trained under each of the noncontingent treatments.

asymptote and initial value. However, in the case of Groups A and B, both of which have a unity asymptote, it is possible to test the prediction that the curves of the B groups should have a more gradual slope than those of the A groups (the prediction follows from the fact that the slope term for the A group contains the term $(1 - \theta)$ while the comparable term for the B groups is $(1 - .66\theta)$). Inspection of the curves for Groups A and B in Fig. 1 supports the prediction. Although the inclusion of blank trials in a training series of E_1 trials—a procedure somewhat analogous to partial reinforcement—does not affect the unity asymptote it does retard the rate of approach to that asymptote. The analogy to partial reinforcement is further strengthened by the finding of superior resistance to extinction for Group B (12).

Another assumption which follows from theoretical considerations is that the same value of θ should apply for all groups since the signal at the start of each trial is the same for all groups. An inspection of the θ values in Fig. 1 fails to support the prediction. Rather, the value of θ appears to be a decreasing function of the proportion of E_2 and E_3 trials. Similar results have been reported by Estes and Straughan (7) and our θ values are very similar to theirs for comparable groups. The only immediately apparent explanation for this finding has been suggested by Estes and Straughan: because of the massing of trials the stimulus elements present on successive trials cannot be assumed to constitute independent samples from the population of stimulus elements.

EXPERIMENT II

It has been noted above that in the traditional verbal conditioning situation S is required to predict the occurrence of random events which are presented with some fixed probability by E independently of S's response. A few Es (2, 3, 9) have deviated from this procedure by making the occurrence of the random event dependent upon the appropriateness of S's response; e.g., S is instructed to press the key which will "pay off" in poker chips, or turn on a light, etc. We shall refer to this procedure as the contingent case in order to distinguish it from the non-contingent or traditional procedure. Studies employing the contingent procedure with two available response classes, one of which is followed by E on approximately π_1 of the trial series while the other is followed by E on $1 - \pi_1$ of the trials, have obtained results very similar to those for the comparable noncontingent procedure (2). Assuming that trials on which E follows A_1 or no E follows A_2 function as E_1 trials, and that trials on which E follows A_2 or no E follows A_1 function as E_2 trials, then it is obvious that the contingent and non-contingent procedures should be equivalent. Whether the equivalence still obtains with the inclusion of blank trials or of more than two available response classes is open to question.

Starting from the assumptions outlined in Exp. I and making use of the additional assumption above that both E following A_1 and no E following A_2 are equivalent to an E_1 trial, it is possible to derive an expression for the probability of an A_1 response of the nth trial, $\bar{p}_1(n)$

$$\bar{p}_1(n) = \frac{1 - \pi_2}{2 - \pi_1 - \pi_2}$$

$$- \left[\frac{1 - \pi_2}{2 - \pi_1 - \pi_2} - \bar{p}_1(0) \right]$$

$$\times (1 - \theta(2 - \pi_1 - \pi_2))^n. \quad (5)$$

Essentially the same expression has been derived by Bush and Mosteller (1), as a special case of their linear operator model, and by Estes (5).

It will be noted that when $\pi_2 = 1 - \pi_1$ Equation 5 reduces to Equation 1, the expression for the noncontingent case. With the inclusion of blank trials, however, the equivalence will not generally be expected to hold.

Method

Apparatus.—The apparatus was the same as that in Exp. I; both experiments were run concurrently.

Subjects.—The Ss were 160 volunteers from Introductory Psychology classes at Indiana University and were randomly assigned to one of eight groups (analogous to the groups of Exp. I) within the restrictions which applied in Exp. I.

Procedure.—The Ss were run individually under a procedure identical with that of Exp. I except for necessary differences in instructions and in the presentation of E_1, E_2, E_3 or blank trials. Instructions for the contingent groups were similar to those of the noncontingent groups with the exception that S was told to press the key which he thought would light the lamp above it rather than to press the key below the light he thought would follow. After the recitation of the instructions, S received the series of six practice trials. In this instance S was told which key to press on each of the practice trials, but the series was otherwise identical to that used for the noncontingent groups. Following the correction of any mistake S made during practice, the training series was begun. The number of trials and treatments for each of the eight groups are summarized in Table 6. In this table π_1 refers to the proportion of trials on which the light above Key A_1 can be turned on if S presses that key; similarly for π_2 and π_3. Immediately upon the completion of the training series S received 50 extinction trials in which no key would light the lamp above it. The results of the extinction series are reported elsewhere (12).

Preparation of random sequences.—As was noted above, E_1 refers to trials on which the lamp above Key A_1 can be lighted if S presses Key A_1 and the relative frequency of such trials is denoted by π_1. Ten different sequences of E_i were prepared for each group in a manner similar to that employed in Exp. I. For the A groups only one lamp could be lighted on each of the 66 training trials. In the case of the 2B and 3B groups the same sequences were employed as for the comparable noncontingent groups. For the

TABLE 6

SUMMARY OF NUMBER OF TRAINING TRIALS AND RELATIVE FREQUENCIES OF OCCURRENCE, π_1, OF THE E APPROPRIATE TO EACH RESPONSE CLASS, A_i, FOR EACH OF THE CONTINGENT GROUPS

Group		No. of Trials	Relative Frequency		
			π_1	π_2	π_3
2-Key	A	66	1.00	0	
	B	100	.66	0	
	C	100	.66	.34	
	D	100	.66	.17	
3-Key	A	66	1.00	0	0
	B	100	.66	0	0
	C	100	.66	.34	.34
	D	100	.66	.17	.17

C and D groups, the sequences of E_1 trials were identical to those of the comparable noncontingent groups but E_2 and E_3 trials were independently assigned, each with its appropriate probability, in the same manner as E_1 trials had been assigned. Thus, in Group 2C, e.g., over the entire series of trials the lamp above Key A_1 could be lighted about 66% of the time and the lamp above Key A_2 could be lighted about 34% of the trials; but on any given trial, either E_1, E_2, both or neither might be set to light.

Results and Discussion

Final level of A_1 responding.—As in the case of the noncontingent groups, the group mean proportion of A_1 responses in the last 20 trials of the training series was taken as an estimate of the final probability of A_1 responding for each group. The mean totals and SDs of A_1 responses in the last 20 trials for each group are summarized in Table 7. The stability of the estimates has been tested for each group by means of a t for paired measures comparing A_1 totals in the first and second halves of the block of 20 trials. All resulting t values fall short of significance at the .05 level with the exception of that for Group 3D in which the A_1 total during the second half is significantly lower than during the first half of the 20-trial block.

TABLE 7

GROUP MEANS AND STANDARD DEVIATIONS OF
FINAL LEVEL OF A_1 RESPONDING AND
t TESTS OF STABILITY OF RESPONSE

(All t values based on 19 df; $N = 20$)

Group		Mean	SD	$t_{diff.}$ (Last 10- First 10)
2-Key	A	19.70	1.308	− 1.0
	B	16.45	2.012	− 1.926
	C	12.00	2.828	.212
	D	15.50	2.480	− .112
3-Key	A	19.80	.276	0
	B	16.60	2.939	0
	C	11.35	3.877	1.715
	D	13.00	4.242	− 2.269*

* Significant at $P \leq .05$.

Final probability of A_1 responding approaches unity only in the case of the continuously reinforced A groups. The differences among group mean A_1 totals of the B, C, and D groups were tested by means of analysis of variance (Table 8). Only the F for treatments reaches significance ($P < .001$) whereas F ratios for E_i sequences, number of alternative responses, and all interactions fall short of significance at the .05 level. The differences between final A_1 levels for two- and three-key groups trained under comparable conditions were further tested by means of t tests (Table 4). All values of t fall short of significance at the .05 level except that for the D groups. However, since it is questionable whether Group 3D has reached a stable asymptote, the meaning of the significant t is not clear. In general, it would appear that the final level of A_1 responding is a decreasing function of the proportion of trials on which an alternative response is reinforced. Furthermore, final level of responding is independent of the number of response alternatives—at least at the level of two vs. three. These two findings are similar to those for the noncontingent procedure. Under the contingent procedure, however, responding seems to be less dependent upon E_i sequence. This is not too surprising since the exact E_i sequence for any given S is dependent upon his responses. Thus, 20 E_i sequences rather than 10 have been compared and the resulting statistical test loses in sensitivity through inflation of the error term.

For additional comparisons of the two procedures the final levels of A_1 responding for contingent and noncontingent groups given comparable training treatments have been tested by t tests (Table 4). The nonsignificant t values for both two- and three-key A and C groups support Detambel's (2) finding that under the contingent analogue of the traditional procedure in which an E_i occurs on each trial the final proportion of A_1 responses approaches π_1 just as it does under the noncontingent procedure. Moreover, it suggests that the equivalence of the contingent and noncontingent procedures, in the traditional type of situation, still holds when more than two responses are available. When blank trials are substituted for E_2 (or E_3) trials, the similarity of the contingent and non-

TABLE 8

ANALYSIS OF VARIANCE OF FINAL LEVEL OF A_1
RESPONDING FOR THE B, C, AND D
CONTINGENT GROUPS

Source	df	MS	F
Sequences (S)	9	12.530	1.20
No of keys (K)	1	30.000	2.88
B vs C vs D group (G)	2	235.525	22.58***
S × K	9	5.500	
S × G	18	12.497	1.20
K × G	2	18.475	1.77
S × K × G	18	10.225	
Within sequences	60	10.433	
Total	119		

*** Significant at $P \leq .001$.

contingent procedures breaks down, as is indicated by the significant (.001) t values for all B groups. In the mixed series, Groups D, containing E_2 (E_3) and blank trials the nonsignificant t leaves the role of the blank trials in doubt. In general, however, the blank trial does not appear to play the same role in the contingent procedure that it does in the noncontingent.

Theoretical predictions of final level of A_1 responding for each of the two-key contingent groups have been computed from Equation 5 and are summarized in Table 9. Theoretical and observed final levels for each group were compared by means of t tests. In the case of the A and C groups the resulting t values fall short of significance at the .05 level; the t values for the B and D groups are significant at the .05 and .01 levels, respectively. It appears that the model for the contingent case is adequate for the traditional procedure in which one E_i appears on each trial. For this procedure predictions of no difference between comparable contingent and noncontingent asymptotes are also supported by the data. However, with the inclusion of blank trials, the predicted asymptotes are significantly too low. This finding seems to challenge the assumption that the blank trials function as reinforcements of an alternative response. The rejection of this assumption, however, raises the question as to how S discriminates a blank trial from, e.g., a trial on which no light appears following an A_1 but light would have appeared following A_2. Since S is instructed that no light may appear on some trials it is possible that he develops the seemingly impossible discrimination, especially in the case of the B groups for whom A_2 (A_3) never produces its E. Conceivably

the asymptotic A_1 probability for the B groups might approach unity after a very long training series, although there is no indication that it will do so in the data of this study. Clearly the development of an extended model for the contingent case will be more complex than was true of the noncontingent case. However, since the series containing blank trials in this experiment are more closely analogous to partial reinforcement in other types of experimental situations the problem merits further investigation.

Mean learning curves.—The mean proportions of A_1 responses in successive 10-trial blocks for the 2A, 2B and 2C contingent and noncontingent groups have been plotted in Fig. 2. Theoretical curves through the observed points of the noncontingent groups (solid curves and white points) have been computed from Equation 4; theoretical curves for the A and C contingent groups (broken lines and black points) have been computed from Equation 5. In comparing the contingent and noncontingent procedures for both A and C groups, not only the asymptotes but also the course of the learning curves appear to be almost identical. These findings further support theoretical predic-

TABLE 9

PREDICTED AND OBSERVED PROPORTIONS OF A_1 RESPONSES FOR THE LAST 20 TRIALS OF THE 2-KEY CONTINGENT GROUPS AND t TESTS OF ACCURACY OF PREDICTION

Group	Observed Proportion	Predicted Proportion	$t_{diff.}$ (Pred.-Obs.)
A	.985	1.000	1.000
B	.823	.746	2.324*
C	.600	.660	1.849
D	.775	.709	3.312**

* Significant at $P \leq .05$; $df = 19$.
** Significant at $P \leq .01$.

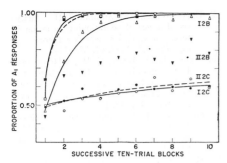

FIG. 2. Comparison of the learning curves of the two-key A, B, and C noncontingent groups (I) with curves of groups trained under the comparable contingent (II) procedure.

tions. An additional similarity among the contingent and noncontingent curves is reflected in the obtained values of the parameter θ: .1415 and .0183 for the A and C contingent groups, respectively, as compared with .1950 and .0135 for the noncontingent groups. Again the higher θ values for the A groups accords with previous findings.

Although no theoretical curve was plotted through the observed points of the contingent B group because of the failure of Equation 5 to describe the asymptote for this group, a comparison of the empirical curves suggests the possibility of a steeper slope for the contingent group than for the noncontingent group. This comparison is complicated, however, by a lower asymptote for the curve of the contingent group and by doubts as to the eventual final level for this group after a much longer series of trials. If the preceding analysis of behavior in this group is correct, a more or less sudden jump toward a unity asymptote would be expected in the contingent B curve with a prolonged training series.

Although a comparison of the curves of the three-key contingent and noncontingent groups has not

been included, it is in general similar to that of the two-key groups in Fig. 2. With the exception of a lower initial level of A_1 responding the curves of the three-key contingent groups are very similar to those for the comparable two-key contingent groups. Similarities of the contingent three-key A and C groups' curves to their noncontingent counterparts are, however, somewhat obscured by chance differences in initial level of A_1 responding.

SUMMARY

Sixteen groups of 20 Ss each were run in an individualized modification of Humphreys' (10) verbal conditioning situation in which one response class, A_1, was most frequently "reinforced." Treatment of the groups differed with respect to: (a) number of response alternatives, two or three; (b) proportion of trials in which responses other than A_1 were "reinforced"; (c) whether "reinforcement" of a given response class was independent of or contingent upon S's response. The purpose of the two experiments reported was to investigate the effects of the above variables upon relative frequency of A_1 responding and to test predictions from a mathematical model for a wider variety of verbal conditioning situations.

Results for the noncontingent groups indicate: (a) final level of A_1 responding is a decreasing function of the proportion of trials on which an alternative response is "reinforced" and is (b) independent of the number of alternative responses. (c) Inclusion of blank trials on which no response is "reinforced" depresses the slope of the learning curve. (d) Theoretical predictions concerning asymptotic levels of A_1 responding and learning rates were supported, but (e) predictions concerning parameters of the learning curves were not completely supported.

For the contingent groups: (a) final level of A_1 responding is a decreasing function of the proportion of trials on which an alternative response is reinforced and is (b) independent of the number of response alternatives. (c) Performance is equivalent to that under the noncontingent procedure only for groups in which some response is reinforced on each trial, while (d) the inclusion of blank trials results in lower final levels than under the comparable noncontingent procedure. (e) A mathematical model for the two-choice groups yielded accurate predictions of asymptotes only for groups receiving no blank trials; (*f*) predictions concerning groups receiving blank trials were not supported.

REFERENCES

1. BUSH, R. R., & MOSTELLER, F. A mathematical model for simple learning. *Psychol. Rev.*, 1951, **58**, 313–323.

2. DETAMBEL, M. H. A reanalysis of Humphreys' "Acquisition and extinction of verbal expectations." Unpublished master's thesis, Indiana Univer., 1950.

3. DETAMBEL, M. H. A test of a model for multiple-choice behavior. *J. exp. Psychol.*, 1955, **49**, 97–105.

4. ESTES, W. K. Toward a statistical theory of learning. *Psychol. Rev.*, 1950, **57**, 94–107.

5. ESTES, W. K. Individual behavior in uncertain situations. In C. L. Coombs, R. M. Thrall, and R. L. Davis (Eds.), *Decision processes.* New York: Wiley, 1954.

6. ESTES, W. K., & BURKE, C. J. A theory of stimulus variability in learning. *Psychol. Rev.*, 1953, **60**, 276–286.

7. ESTES, W. K., & STRAUGHAN, J. H. Analysis of a verbal conditioning situation in terms of statistical learning theory. *J. exp. Psychol.*, 1954, **47**, 225–234.

8. GRANT, D. A., HAKE, H. W., & HORNSETH, J. P. Acquisition and extinction of a verbal conditioned response with differing percentages of reinforcement. *J. exp. Psychol.*, 1951, **42**, 1–5.

9. GOODNOW, J. J. Determinants of choice distributions in two-choice probability situations. *Amer. J. Psychol.*, 1955, **68**, 106–116.

10. HUMPHREYS, L. G. Acquisition and extinction of verbal expectations in a situation analogous to conditioning. *J. exp. Psychol.*, 1939, **25**, 294–301.

11. JARVIK, M. E. Probability learning and a negative recency effect in the serial anticipation of alternative symbols. *J. exp. Psychol.*, 1951, **41**, 291–297.

12. NEIMARK, E. D. Effects of type of non-reinforcement and number of alternative responses in two verbal conditioning situations. Unpublished doctor's dissertation, Indiana Univer., 1953.

(Received September 12, 1955)

An Analysis of the Effect of Nonreinforced Trials in Terms of Statistical Learning Theory[1]

RICHARD C. ATKINSON, *Indiana University*

It is the purpose of this study to investigate the effect of nonreinforced trials in a Humphreys-type "verbal conditioning" situation. Before specifying the problem, however, a synopsis of both the situation and the theoretical orientation to be employed will be presented by referring to an article by Estes and Straughan.

We consider a situation in which each trial begins with presentation of a signal, or CS; following the signal, one or the other of two reinforcing stimuli, E_1 or E_2, occurs, the probability of E_1 and E_2 during a given series being π and $1 - \pi$, respectively. The behaviors available to S are categorized into two classes, A_1 and A_2, by experimental criteria. In the verbal conditioning situation, A_1 is a prediction that E_1 will occur, and A_2 a prediction that E_2 will occur on the given trial. We assume that the CS determines a population, S_c, of stimulus elements which is sampled by S on each trial, the proportion θ of the elements in this population constituting the effective sample on any one trial. The dependence of S's responses upon the stimulating situation is expressed in the theory by defining a conditional relationship such that each element in S_c is conditioned to (tends to evoke) either A_1 or A_2. In order to interpret the formal model in terms of a verbal conditioning experiment, we assume that when an E_1 occurs it evokes from S a response

belonging to class A_1, i.e., one which is compatible with the response of predicting E_1 but which interferes with the response of prediction E_2, and that when an E_2 occurs it evokes a response of class A_2. Then on a trial on which E_1 occurs we expect on the basis of association principles that all elements sampled from S_c on the trial will become conditioned to A_1, while on an E_2 trial the sample will be conditioned to A_2. Now if successive trials are sufficiently discrete so that samples from S_c are statistically independent, the probability of an A_1 after Trial n, abbreviated $p(n)$, is defined in the model as the proportion of elements in S_c that are conditioned to A_1, and similarly for the probability of an A_2, $[1 - p(n)]$ (**2**, p. 225).

An interesting problem arises when one modifies this situation by introducing trials on which neither E_1 nor E_2 occurs, that is, trials on which S is given no information as to whether or not his predictive response (A_1 or A_2) was correct. What prediction would one venture concerning the effect of such nonreinforced trials on the probability of an A_1 or A_2 response on subsequent trials? This paper proposes and examines the following three hypotheses which are stated in terms of statistical association concepts (**1**).

Hypothesis I, (H-I).—Nonreinforced trials have no effect on the hypothetical connection between stimulus elements and response classes. Elements sampled from the S_c population on such trials are returned to the population at the end

[1] The author wishes to thank Professor W. K. Estes for advice and assistance in carrying out this research.

This article appeared in *J. exp. Psychol.*, 1956, **52**, 28–32.

351

of the trial with their conditional status unchanged. That is to say, if an element is sampled on a nonreinforced trial, it will remain connected to the same response class that it was connected to before the start of the trial.

Hypothesis II, (H-II).—In the absence of the E_1 and E_2 events, S's overt predictive A_1 or A_2 response is viewed as a terminal response for the trial, and it is posited that elements sampled on such nonreinforced trials are conditioned to the A_1 or A_2 response emitted on the trial. This notion is similar to Guthrie's assumption (**3**) that the last response emitted in the presence of a stimulus pattern is the one which will tend to be produced when the stimulus pattern recurs.

Hypothesis III, (H-III).—Elements sampled on a nonreinforced trial are connected to the A_1 response class with probability σ, and to the A_2 response class with probability $1 - \sigma$. We shall only consider the case where $\sigma = 1 - \sigma = .5$. Here we assume that, in the absence of information as to which response was correct, there exists an equal likelihood that sampled elements will be connected to either response class.

In order to evaluate these hypotheses we shall use an approach similar to that employed by Estes and Straughan (**2**). For any schedule of E_1 and E_2 trials they were able, by means of statistical learning theory, to predict asymptotic response probability. Similarly, for any schedule of E_1, E_2, and nonreinforced trials we can predict asymptotic response probability under the conditions of each of the hypotheses stated above. The problem then of defining the effect of nonreinforced trials on behavior can be formulated in terms of the long run effect of schedules of reinforced and nonreinforced trials on asymptotic response probability.

There is, however, the problem that not all schedules of E_1, E_2, and nonreinforced trials will yield differential predictions for the three hypotheses. For example, in the situation employed by Estes and Straughan (**2**), it can be shown that the inclusion of nonreinforced trials with any fixed probability in the schedule of E_1's and E_2's would yield identical asymptote and slope predictions (*a*) for H-I and H-II for all values of π and (*b*) for H-I, H-II, and H-III for $\pi = .5$.

Consequently, a schedule of events is required which will yield differential predictions for the three hypotheses. We have selected the following schedule which, with the substitution of appropriate experimental parameter values, meets this requirement:

1. If an A_1 occurs on Trial n, there is: (*a*) a probability $\beta\pi$ that an E_1 will occur, (*b*) a probability $\beta(1 - \pi)$ that an E_2 will occur, (*c*) a probability $(1 - \beta)$ that neither an E_1 nor E_2 will occur.

2. If an A_2 occurs on Trial n, there is: (*a*) a probability π that an E_1 will occur, (*b*) a probability $(1 - \pi)$ that an E_2 will occur.

By methods of finite calculus we can describe the expected asymptotic probability of an A_1 response, denoted by $\overline{p(\infty)}$, for the above schedule under the conditions of each hypothesis.

By H-I, $\overline{p(\infty)}$ is bounded by

$$\pi \quad \text{and} \quad \frac{\pi}{\pi + \beta(1 - \pi)}. \quad (1)$$

By H-II,

$$\overline{p(\infty)} = \frac{\pi}{1 - (1 - \beta)(1 - \pi)}. \quad (2)$$

By H-III,

$$\overline{p(\infty)} = \frac{\pi}{1 - (1 - \beta)(.5 - \pi)}. \quad (3)$$

The derivations of these results are given in the next section.

MATHEMATICAL FORMULATION

For the schedule specified above, the probability of an A_1 response after Trial n, $p(n + 1)$, is:

By H-I,

$$p(n + 1) = (1 - \theta)p(n) + \theta\{[1 - p(n)]$$
$$\times [\pi(1) + (1 - \pi)(0)]$$
$$+ p(n)\beta[\pi(1) + (1 - \pi)(0)]$$
$$+ p(n)(1 - \beta)p(n)\}. \quad (4)$$

The proportion $(1 - \theta)$ of the elements is not sampled and remains unchanged. The proportion θ of the elements is sampled and conditioned as follows: (a) If an A_2 occurs, with probability $[1 - p(n)]$, there is a probability π that all sampled elements will be connected to A_1, and a probability $(1 - \pi)$ that the elements will be connected to A_2; (b) If an A_1 occurs, with probability $p(n)$, there is a probability $\beta\pi$ that all sampled elements will be conditioned to A_1, a probability $\beta(1 - \pi)$ that the elements will be conditioned to A_2, and a probability $(1 - \beta)$ that the conditional status of the elements will remain unchanged.

Rewrite Equation 4

$$p(n + 1) = (1 - \theta)p(n) + \theta[\lambda(n)$$
$$+ p(n)^2(1 - \beta)] \quad (5)$$

where

$$\lambda(n) = [1 - p(n)]\pi + p(n)\beta\pi. \quad (6)$$

By H-II,

$$p(n + 1) = (1 - \theta)p(n) + \theta[\lambda(n)$$
$$+ p(n)(1 - \beta)]. \quad (7)$$

This equation is isomorphic with Equation 5 except for the final product of the last term. If an A_1 occurs and is not followed by an E_1 or E_2, this joint event having probability $p(n)(1 - \beta)$, then all elements will be conditioned to the response emitted on the trial, namely, A_1.

By H-III,

$$p(n + 1) = (1 - \theta)p(n) + \theta[\lambda(n)$$
$$+ p(n)(1 - \beta)(.5)]. \quad (8)$$

This equation is also isomorphic with Equation 5 except for the final product of the last term. If an A_1 event occurs and is not followed by an E_1 or E_2, then there is a probability .5 that sampled elements will be connected to A_1.

Taking the expected value of Equation 7 and solving the resulting equation (4) we obtain

$$\overline{p(n)} = \overline{p(\infty)} - [\overline{p(\infty)} - \overline{p(0)}]$$
$$\times [1 - \theta + \theta(1 - \beta)(1 - \pi)]^n, \quad (9)$$

where $\overline{p(\infty)}$ is given by Equation 2.

Similarly for Equation 8

$$\overline{p(n)} = \overline{p(\infty)} - [\overline{p(\infty)} - \overline{p(0)}]$$
$$\times [1 - \theta + \theta(1 - \beta)(.5 - \pi)]^n, \quad (10)$$

where $\overline{p(\infty)}$ is given by Equation 3.

Equation 5 is a second-order difference equation, and no method is known for effecting a solution. However, by taking the expected value and letting $n \to \infty$ we obtain

$$\overline{p(\infty)} = \frac{\pi + (1 - \beta)\overline{p(\infty)}^2}{1 + \pi(1 - \beta)}. \quad (11)$$

An upper and lower bound can now be calculated for $\overline{p(\infty)}$ by letting the variance of $\overline{p(\infty)}$ assume a minimum value of zero and a maximum of $\bar{p}(1 - \bar{p})$. When variance is minimal $\bar{p}^2 = \overline{p^2}$, when maximal $\bar{p} = \overline{p^2}$. These substitutions in Equation 11 yield boundary conditions on $\overline{p(\infty)}$ given by Equation 1.

METHOD

Design.—Two groups, A and B, were necessary for good differentiation between the hypotheses. For Group A the value of π was .8125; for Group B the value of π was .1875. The value of β was .25 for both groups.

Apparatus.—The E and S sat on opposite sides of a table with a large opaque screen separating them. The apparatus, as viewed from S's side, consisted of two telegraph keys mounted 24 in. apart at right angles to the base of the screen; upon the screen were mounted three milk-glass panel lights. One of these lights, which served as the signal for S to guess, was centered between the telegraph keys at S's eye level. Each of the two remaining lights, the reinforcing signals, was mounted directly above one of the telegraph keys. The presentation and duration of the lights were automatically controlled, and on any trial the reinforcing signal could be withheld.

Subjects.—The Ss, 52 students obtained from beginning courses in psychology during the fall semester of 1954, were assigned at random to experimental groups.

Procedure.—After being seated in front of the screen S was read instructions, similar to those reported by Estes and Straughan (2), requesting that he respond to the signal light on each trial by operating the telegraph key corresponding to the reinforcing light that he expected to follow. For each S, one of the two reinforcing lights was randomly designated as E_1, and the other as E_2. After the instructions were read, four practice trials were given with the lights presented in the order E_2, E_1, E_1, E_2. After these trials E corrected any apparent errors in procedure and reviewed the instructions.

Following the practice trials, 144 trials were given each S. These trials were run off in continuous sequence. For each S a sequence of E_1, E_2, and nonreinforced trials was generated in accordance with the assigned values of π and β.

On each trial the signal light was lighted for 2.5 sec.; the time between successive signal exposures was 7.5 sec. On reinforced trials the reinforcing light followed the cessation of the signal light by 2 sec. and remained on for 1 sec.

RESULTS AND DISCUSSION

Substituting values of π and β in Equations 1, 2, and 3, $\overline{p(\infty)}$ can be described under the conditions of each hypothesis.

Predictions for Group A are

1. By H-I, $\overline{p(\infty)}$ is bounded by .8125 and .9455.
2. By H-II, $\overline{p(\infty)} = .9455$.
3. By H-III, $\overline{p(\infty)} = .6582$.

Predictions for Group B are

1. By H-I, $\overline{p(\infty)}$ is bounded by .1875 and .4800.
2. By H-II, $\overline{p(\infty)} = .4800$.
3. By H-III, $\overline{p(\infty)} = .2449$.

Taking the proportion of A_1 responses over the last two blocks of 16 trials as an estimate of $\overline{p(\infty)}$ we can compare these values with the above set of predictions. By inspection of Fig. 1 we see that for Group A the proportions for the last two trial blocks are .828 and .842,

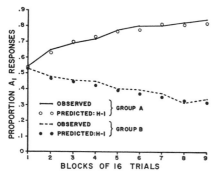

FIG. 1. Empirical and theoretical curves representing mean proportion of A_1 responses per 16-trial blocks.

with a mean of .835. To determine how well this value approximated the predictions of H-II and H-III, t tests were run between the predicted value and the proportions computed for individual Ss over the last 32 trials. The σ_m was .017. The difference between the predicted value and the mean of the observed values was .110 for H-II and .175 for H-III; both differences are significant at the .05 level. By inspection of Fig. 1 we see that for Group B the proportions for the last two trial blocks are .315 and .337 with a mean of .326. The σ_m was .021. The differences between predicted and observed values were .154 and .081 for H-II and H-III, respectively; both are significant at the .05 level.

In view of these results, it is clear that neither H-II nor H-III accounts for the obtained data. What then can be said concerning H-I? First of all, the proportions computed over the last 32 trials for both groups fall within the bounds for $\overline{p(\infty)}$ specified by H-I. However, more important is the fact that we can generate curves by H-I which closely approximate the observed results. By employing a Monte Carlo method (5) 10 individual learning curves were generated under the conditions of Equation 4, five using the experimental parameter values of Group A, and five using those of Group B. The θ and $p(0)$ values employed for Group A were .063 and .480; respective values for Group B were .010 and .550. The averages by blocks of 16 trials for each group of five curves are presented in Fig. 1. As can be seen, there is close agreement between these values and the observed values.

We conclude that, of the three hypotheses presented, only H-I can account for the findings of this study.

SUMMARY

This study employs a modified Estes-Straughan "verbal conditioning" situation. Each trial consists in the presentation of a signal followed by an E_1 or E_2 reinforcing light; S operates an appropriate key to indicate his prediction as to which light will appear on each trial. The present study deals with the effect of introducing trials on which neither reinforcing light is presented, that is, trials on which S is given no information as to which of the two alternative predictions is correct.

Three hypotheses are developed, in terms of statistical learning theory, concerning the effect of such trials. Since some schedules of E_1, E_2, and nonreinforced trials provide identical predictions from the three hypotheses, it was necessary to employ a schedule which yielded differential prediction. The one selected was such that on any trial (*a*) if S predicted E_1 then E_1, E_2, or no reinforcement would occur with probability $\beta\pi, \beta(1 - \pi)$ and $1 - \beta$, respectively, while (*b*) if S predicted E_2 either E_1 or E_2 would occur with probability π and $1 - \pi$.

The set of quantitative predictions generated by each hypothesis was checked against experimental results. It was concluded that the hypothesis requiring zero change in response probability on trials on which no information is given best accounts for the findings.

REFERENCES

1. ESTES, W. K., & BURKE, C. J. A theory of stimulus variability in learning. *Psychol. Rev.*, 1953, **60**, 276–286.
2. ESTES, W. K., & STRAUGHAN, J. H. Analysis of a verbal conditioning situation in terms of statistical learning theory. *J. exp. Psychol.*, 1954, **47**, 225–234.
3. GUTHRIE, E. R. Psychological facts and psychological theory. *Psychol. Bull.*, 1946, **43**, 1–20.
4. JORDAN, C. *Calculus of finite differences.* New York: Chelsea, 1950.
5. MCCRACKEN, D. D. The Monte Carlo method. *Scientific Amer.*, May 1955, 90–96.

(Received June 30, 1955)

Test of Stimulus Sampling Theory for a Continuum of Responses with Unimodal Noncontingent Determinate Reinforcement[1]

PATRICK SUPPES and RAYMOND W. FRANKMANN,[2] *Stanford University*

In the last decade a large number of quantitative experimental studies of simple learning have been made for cases in which the reinforcement schedule is probabilistic and the number of possible responses is finite. Both stimulus sampling and linear models have been used extensively to analyze these studies. There have been, as far as we know, no previous attempts to extend these models to situations which permit a continuum of possible responses. Such is the aim of the present study, which may be briefly described as follows.

The S is told that his task on each trial is to predict by means of a pointer where a spot of light will appear on the circumference of a circle; S's responses are his pointer predictions. At the end of each trial the "correct" position of the spot is shown to S; this is the reinforcing event for the trial. The response x and the reinforcement y vary continuously along a circle from 0 to 2π. The most important variable controlled by E is choice of a particular probability distribution of reinforcement. In the present study reinforcement is noncontingent, i.e., the probability distribution of reinforcements is independent of S's responses and the same distribution is used on every trial. Moreover, the reinforcement is determinate because

[1] This research was supported by the Rockefeller Foundation and the Group Psychology Branch of the Office of Naval Research.

[2] Now at the University of Illinois.

exactly one reinforcement y occurs on each trial. The purpose of a model is to predict the probability distribution of responses.

To analyze this situation we shall apply the stimulus sampling and linear models developed in Suppes (1959, 1960). Because the stimulus sampling model provides a more deatiled account of the psychological process of learning than does the linear model, and because its mathematical development is somewhat simpler, we shall concentrate mainly on it. However, the theoretical results considered here also hold in the linear model.

Stimulus sampling model.—The basic theory derives from Estes (1950). Roughly speaking, this theory runs as follows. On each trial S samples a set of stimuli each of which is conditioned to exactly one response. The probability that S will make a given response is the proportion of sampled stimuli conditioned to that response, and all the sampled stimuli become conditioned to the response which is reinforced. Thus, theoretically the learning process is described in terms of the states of the conditioning of the stimuli, these states not being directly observable. For many experiments it has proved desirable to assume that exactly one stimulus is sampled on each trial and that the probability is not necessarily one that the sampled stimulus becomes conditioned to the reinforced response. We shall designate as θ the probability that reinforcement is *effective* and shall postulate the usual independence of path assumptions for this probability. In our context θ plays

This article appeared in *J. exp. Psychol.*, 1961, **61**, 122–132.

the role of the learning parameter. To simplify considerably the mathematics we assume there is exactly one stimulus element that is available for sampling on every trial and is therefore sampled with probability 1.0. Most of the theoretical results given here actually do not depend on this one-element assumption.

For a continuum of responses, one fundamental modification in the theory just described seems called for. The assumption that each stimulus is conditioned to exactly one response seems unsound, and we replace it with the assumption (Suppes, 1960) that the conditioning of each stimulus is *smeared* over a certain interval of responses, possibly the whole continuum. We represent the conditioning of any stimulus by a *smearing distribution*, $K(x; y)$. It is postulated that parameter y, the mean of the distribution, takes on the value of the point of reinforcement when the stimulus is sampled and reinforcement is effective. In mathematical language, the basic learning process is a continuous-state discrete-trial Markov process in parameter y. On each trial, with probability θ, y moves to the new point of reinforcement, and with probability $1 - \theta$ it stays in the same place.

Various intuitive arguments can be given to support the representation of conditioning by a smearing distribution. It might seem that the best one would be based on well-known psychophysical facts about the impossibility of making exact discriminations among a continuum of choices. From this standpoint the smearing distribution would arise from the perceptual inability of the organism to distinguish exactly a given point on the continuum. However, the empirical estimates of the smearing distribution, which are discussed in detail later, yield a variance for the distribution which is far in excess of that which can be justified on purely psychophysical grounds. It seems likely that a better argument can be put together in terms of ideas of response generalization, but to make these ideas precise would require theoretical developments beyond the scope of the present paper.

We now summarize the results which are proved in Suppes (1960) and which we shall use in the analysis of data. In the form given, the equations hold only for a noncontingent reinforcement distribution, $F(y)$.[3] Let $[a, b]$ be the interval of possible responses; let $r_n(x)$ be the mean response density averaged over Ss on trial n; and let $k(x; y)$ be the smearing density of the single stimulus. Then we have the recursion

$$r_{n+1}(x) = (1 - \theta)r_n(x)$$
$$+ \theta \int_a^b k(x; y)f(y)dy \quad [1]$$

and thus for $r(x) = \lim_{n \to \infty} r_n(x)$, the important asymptotic relation

$$r(x) = \int_a^b k(x; y)f(y)dy \quad [2]$$

Multiplying both sides of Equation 1 by x^r, using Equation 2 and integrating with respect to x, we obtain as the recursion for the rth raw moment $\mu_{r,n}$ of $r_n(x)$

$$\mu_{r,n+1} = (1 - \theta)\mu_{r,n} + \theta\mu_r \quad [3]$$

and this difference equation may be solved explicitly to yield

$$\mu_{r,n} = \mu_r - [\mu_r - \mu_{r,1}](1 - \theta)^{n-1} \quad [4]$$

where $\mu_r = \lim_{n \to \infty} \mu_{r,n}$. Let $\mathcal{E}_n$ and σ_n^2 be the mean and variance of $r_n(x)$; and $\mathcal{E}$ and σ^2 the mean and variance of the asymptotic distribution $r(x)$. Then the recursion for σ_n^2 is as follows:

$$\sigma_{n+1}^2 = (1 - \theta)\sigma_n^2 + \theta\sigma^2$$
$$+ \theta(1 - \theta)(\mathcal{E}_n - \mathcal{E})^2 \quad [5]$$

We use these last two equations to estimate θ. It is important to note that if the initial and asymptotic mean response densities are estimated directly from the data, then Equations 3–5 may be used independently of any particular choice of a smearing distribution $K(x; y)$.

Also independent of the choice of a smearing distribution is the prediction from Equation 2 that for a unimodal re-

[3] We use capital letters for distributions and lower case letters for the corresponding densities.

inforcement distribution the dispersion of the response distribution is greater than that of the reinforcement distribution. This particular prediction is an excellent gross test of the theory, for the rational strategy in terms of statistical decision theory is to make all responses at the mean of the reinforcement distribution and thus to have an asymptotic response distribution with zero variance.

It may also be shown that the variance of the asymptotic mean response distribution is approximately the variance of any long sequence of an individual S's responses. This means that the prediction about the dispersion of responses is a prediction about individual behavior, not simply that of the group of Ss.

In like fashion it follows from Equation 2 that if the reinforcement and smearing distributions are symmetric, then the response distribution is also symmetric. Again this is a prediction that should hold for individual Ss as well as for group averages.

The method used for estimating the smearing distribution is discussed below.

METHOD

Subjects.—Twenty-three male and thirty-seven female Stanford undergraduates, obtained from the student employment bureau and through personal contact, were employed as Ss. Each S was paid $1.25 for the 1-hr. experimental session.

Apparatus.—From S's side the apparatus appeared as a vertical blue plastic screen 6-ft. square mounted 8 in. above the floor. At either side hung heavy white curtains which blocked S's view of the area beyond the screen. A small amount of indirect illumination came from behind the curtains.

The translucent plastic was stretched across a 4-in.-deep wooden box. A ⅜-in. steel shaft supported horizontally in a bearing mounted on the back of the box projected 21 in. on S's side of the screen. Within the enclosure, light sources supported on a counterbalanced arm affixed to the shaft were arranged to project a ⅛ × ¾-in. bar of red light onto the screen at either 1.25 ft. or 2.5 ft. from the shaft. Light sources were 6.3-v. pilot lights (RCA No. 47) covered by red plastic domes. The short dimension of the bars of light was perpendicular to the supporting arms.

By turning a knob on the end of the shaft

S could make his prediction by positioning the light bar at any point on the 2.5-ft.-diameter circle about the axis of the shaft (or 5.0-ft.-diameter circle, depending on S's group). The S was seated at a classroom desk chair so that the shaft was about at eye level. An optional arm rest was mounted on the chair arm and S was instructed to use either hand and to change hands or position whenever he wished.

A 23-in.-diameter scale with 400 equally spaced divisions was mounted behind the enclosure to indicate the location of the light. The entire scale could be rotated to change the physical location of the zero point. By turning a knob on his end of the shaft, E could position the light bar to indicate reinforcement location.

A 40-w. fluorescent light tube mounted over the scale furnished the only illumination in the experimental room.

Procedure.—After acquainting S with the method of operating the equipment, E read the following instructions.

In various military situations the most effective operators of radar fire-control and target-locating devices are those who most frequently anticipate the approximate location of the next target. We are studying how this skill is developed.

If you are holding the knob, please release it and I will show the target. Do you see the bar of red light that is moving around the screen? The target may be anywhere on the circle that the light is moving in. (Stop light at top of circle.) You will use the knob in front of you to move the light to where you think the target will be. Try it. O.K.? Now, when you have the light where you want it, release the knob and say, "Mark!" Then I will move the light to the target position and say, "Target!" As soon as you see where the target is take the knob again and move the light to where you think the next target will be, release the knob, and say, "Mark!" Then I will show you the target position as before. Because time is limited, you will only have 5 sec. to make your decision each time. You will seldom need this much time, but when you exceed the limit I will say, "Time!" and you will then have 1 sec. to position the light.

At first, you will have to guess about the target location, but, with practice, your predictions should improve. The factors which determine target location are very complex, and you will find that target position changes quite erratically. You will seldom be able to make an exact prediction but errors should reduce so that much of the time your predictions are close to the vicinity of the target.

As soon as questions had been answered by paraphrasing the instructions 300 trials were run without interruption. The average rate was 6 trials per minute.

Design.—There were two groups of 20 Ss, one group using the 2.5-ft. circle and the other the 5.0-ft. circle.

Thirty 300-trial reinforcement sequences were computed using the triangular density shown in Fig. 2 below. By random choice 30 equally spaced divisions of the circle, starting from arbitrary fixed physical zero, were assigned without repetition as scale zero points for the separate reinforcement sequences. Each reinforcement sequence was employed for one S using the 2.5-ft. circle and one S using the 5.0-ft. circle. The Ss were assigned to circle sizes randomly with the restriction that matched reinforcement sequences were run successively.

RESULTS AND DISCUSSION

Response histogram variances over trials.—Table 1 shows the means and variances of the response histograms averaged over Ss in each group in blocks of 50 trials. The closeness of the means in the first block of trials to the mean, π, of the reinforcement distribution is due to the randomly selected scale origin for each S. The randomization of the physical position of the scale origin guarantees a uniform distribution on Trial 1 as the number of Ss becomes large, and the mean of the uniform distribution on the interval 0 to 2π is π. Consequently we have used the change in variance of the response histogram to estimate learning parameter θ.

The rates of decrease in the variances indicate both groups were close to their asymptotic variances at the end of the first 100 trials, if we take the variances of the last two blocks of trials as an estimate of the asymptotic variances. In Fig. 1 are plotted the variances of the response histograms averaged over Ss in each group in

TABLE 1

OBSERVED MEANS AND VARIANCES OF RESPONSE DENSITY FOR BLOCKS OF 50 TRIALS

Block	2.5-Ft. Circle		5.0-Ft. Circle	
	Mean	Var.	Mean	Var.
1	.990	.258	1.037	.260
2	.991	.223	.998	.229
3	.991	.228	.998	.219
4	.996	.224	.990	.210
5	1.011	.225	.984	.215
6	.990	.219	1.001	.197

Note. All table entries are observed values divided by π for means and π^2 for variances.

blocks of 10 trials for the initial 100 trials. Because of its small magnitude, the term $\theta(1 - \theta)(\mathcal{E}_n - \mathcal{E})^2$ in Equation 5 was omitted, yielding the recursion

$$\sigma_{n+1}{}^2 = (1 - \theta)\sigma_n{}^2 + \theta\sigma^2$$

which has the solution

$$\sigma_n{}^2 = \sigma^2 - (\sigma^2 - \sigma_1{}^2)(1 - \theta)^{n-1}$$

Averaging over blocks of 10 trials, we have, for $i = 1, 2, \cdots, 10$

$$\sigma_i{}^2(\theta) = \tfrac{1}{10} \sum_{\nu=10i-9}^{10i} \sigma_\nu{}^2$$

$$= \sigma^2 - \frac{1 - (1-\theta)^{10}}{10\theta}$$

$$\times (\sigma^2 - \sigma_1{}^2)(1-\theta)^{10(i-1)} \quad [6]$$

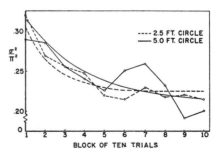

FIG. 1. Observed variances of $r_n(x)$ in blocks of 10 trials for initial 100 trials and variance curves fitted by least squares.

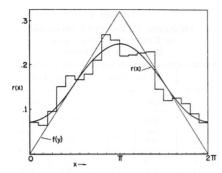

FIG. 2. Response histogram for 2.5-ft. circle and fitted response density for last 200 trials.

Equation 6 and the observed variances $\sigma_i{}^2(\text{obs})$ were used to find by the method of least squares the value of θ which yields a curve which best fits, for each circle, the observed variances plotted in Fig. 1. That is,

$$L(\theta) = \sum_{i=1}^{10} \left[\sigma_i{}^2(\text{obs}) - \sigma_i{}^2(\theta)\right]^2$$

was minimized. Because the derivative of $L(\theta)$ with respect to θ is a complicated function, the minimum was not found by analytical methods but $L(\theta)$ was computed for each circle and the minimum θ approximated to four decimal places. For the 2.5-ft. circle, the estimated θ is .0650, and for the 5.0-ft. circle the estimated θ is .0325. The fitted curves based on the estimated θ's are shown in Fig. 1. These computations were based on the assumption that $\sigma_1{}^2 = \dfrac{\pi^2}{3}$, the variance of the uniform distribution on the interval $[0, 2\pi]$. The fit to the data from the 2.5-ft. circle is the better of the two. This is because of the unexpected increase in variance following Block 5 for the 5.0-ft. circle. The increase is contrary to the theory and seems to be too large to be due to sampling error. The estimates of θ

are surprisingly close to those obtained by Estes and Straughan (1954) from the mean learning curve for two-choice noncontingent data.

Asymptotic response histograms.— Figures 2 and 3 present for the two groups of Ss response histograms in class intervals of $.1\pi$ for the last 200 trials. The triangular reinforcement density $f(y)$ is also shown in both figures.

The reinforcement density $f(y)$ has a mean of π and a variance of $.167\pi^2$. The response histogram for the group of Ss using the 2.5-ft. circle has a mean of $.997\pi$ and a variance of $.224\pi^2$. The response histogram for the group using the 5.0-ft. circle has a mean of $.993\pi$ and a variance of $.210\pi^2$.

Individual data are presented in Table 2. The mean, variance, and third central moment are given for each individual histogram for the last 200 trials. These moments for the 200 reinforcements are also tabled. Note that for each pair of Ss, one for the 2.5-ft. circle and one for the 5.0-ft. circle, the moments of only one reinforcement histogram are tabulated because the two members of the pair received exactly the same sequence of reinforcements.

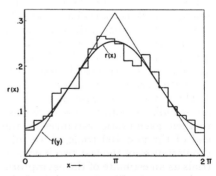

FIG. 3. Response histogram for 5.0-ft. circle and fitted response density for last 200 trials.

TABLE 2

INDIVIDUAL OBSERVED MEANS, VARIANCES, AND THIRD MOMENTS
FOR LAST 200 TRIALS

S	Reinforcement Distribution			2.5-Ft. Circle			5.0-Ft. Circle		
	Mean	Var.	Third Moment	Mean	Var.	Third Moment	Mean	Var.	Third Moment
1	.95	.163	.000	1.01	.277	.006	1.00	.209	.003
2	1.03	.159	.002	1.03	.180	.000	.99	.253	.004
3	.98	.155	.002	1.08	.185	.007	1.02	.131	.005
4	.97	.173	.010	.97	.304	.016	1.03	.240	.004
5	.98	.164	.004	.96	.167	.000	1.07	.178	.011
6	1.04	.147	.000	1.01	.184	.013	.95	.128	.003
7	.98	.176	.005	1.10	.220	.001	1.10	.152	.015
8	1.03	.179	.002	.99	.149	.005	1.01	.197	.012
9	.97	.163	.000	.93	.240	.016	.96	.224	.001
10	.94	.170	.007	.97	.268	.031	.92	.221	.034
11	1.00	.156	.006	1.03	.305	.013	1.05	.210	.001
12	.98	.157	.001	1.04	.250	.019	1.01	.222	.005
13	1.00	.174	.008	.89	.138	.008	.97	.337	.021
14	.99	.175	.004	1.02	.202	.003	.96	.169	.002
15	1.01	.157	.003	.94	.160	.011	.91	.301	.006
16	1.01	.179	.002	.97	.209	.032	.92	.248	.020
17	.97	.181	.010	.96	.297	.003	.94	.256	.022
18	1.03	.214	.004	1.03	.228	.000	1.13	.262	.050
19	.95	.185	.009	.95	.225	.031	.86	.219	.040
20	.99	.152	.004	.94	.223	.009	.99	.146	.004
21	.97	.150	.006	1.02	.240	.006	.99	.188	.000
22	1.00	.166	.006	1.01	.172	.011	.96	.130	.006
23	1.01	.149	.007	.95	.204	.007	.97	.230	.007
24	1.01	.179	.002	.97	.203	.016	1.00	.291	.017
25	1.08	.149	.001	1.05	.168	.009	1.02	.089	.005
26	1.01	.171	.016	1.01	.291	.005	.99	.230	.001
27	1.02	.148	.008	1.08	.231	.017	.99	.170	.010
28	1.00	.169	.000	.95	.381	.018	1.04	.270	.003
29	1.00	.127	.006	1.00	.256	.002	1.01	.177	.003
30	1.02	.159	.003	1.09	.083	.004	1.04	.136	.012

Note. All table entries are observed values divided by π for means, π^2 for variances, and π^3 for third central moments.

Putting aside for the moment detailed quantitative questions, these individual data qualitatively support the fundamental theory in three important respects.

First, the means of the individual histograms are all quite close to the mean of the reinforcement distribution, as is predicted by the theory. In the case of the 2.5-ft. circle, only 3 Ss deviate from the theoretical mean of 1.0π by more than does the most deviant reinforcement histogram (that for S 25). In the case of the 5.0-ft. circle there are only 5 such Ss. The deviation from the theoretical mean of no S in either group is more than twice that of this most deviant reinforcement histogram (whose deviation is 15°). These results would seem to show that the reinforcement conditions obtaining in the experiment easily dominated any a priori positioning habits.

Secondly, the variances of the individual histograms are generally larger than those of the corresponding reinforcement histograms. In particular, this is true for 27 of the 30 Ss on the 2.5-ft. circle and 22 of the 30 Ss on the 5.0-ft. circle. This result shows rather clearly that there was no general tendency for individual Ss to adopt the rational strategy of statistical decision theory, i.e., asymptotically to respond very close to the mean of the reinforcement distribution.

Thirdly, the relatively small magnitudes of the individual third central moments indicate a high degree of symmetry in the individual histograms. The third moments for 21 Ss on the 2.5-ft. circle and 23 on the 5.0-ft. circle are larger than those of the corresponding reinforcement histograms, but none seems excessive; only 3 of the 60 Ss have a third moment more than twice the largest third moment of the 30 reinforcement histograms.

It seems to us that these results for individual Ss are sufficiently encouraging to warrant quantitative investigations of the extent to which individual Ss are satisfying the model. Such investigations will require many more trials than were obtained in the present study. For this reason the remainder of the analysis in this paper is restricted to group data.

Estimation of smearing distributions. —The noncontingent triangular reinforcement distribution shown in Fig. 2 and 3 is analytically defined by the density

$$f(y) = \begin{cases} \dfrac{y}{\pi^2} & 0 < y \le \pi \\ \dfrac{1}{\pi^2}(2\pi - y) & \pi < y \le 2\pi \end{cases} \qquad [7]$$

For the circular display it is reasonable to assume that the smearing distribution about a point of reinforcement, y, is symmetric, and therefore $k(x;y) = k(t)$, where $t = x - y$. For detailed analysis of data we restrict ourselves to two general forms for the smearing distribution—*uniform* distributions and *symmetric beta* distributions, with the free parameter of the distribution to be estimated from the data by use of Equation 2. Two things have motivated this choice, namely, the mathematical simplicity of both distributions and the fact that as m increases the symmetric beta distribution closely resembles the normal distribution, and thus has the bell shape which seems intuitively appropriate for a smearing phenomenon.

The *uniform smearing* density with parameter a is defined by

$$k(t) = \begin{cases} \dfrac{1}{2a} & |t| \le a \\ 0 & a < |t| \le \pi \end{cases} \qquad [8]$$

where $-\pi \le t \le \pi$ and $0 < a < \dfrac{\pi}{2}$. Combining Equations 2, 7, and 8, and integrating, we have for the asymptotic response density:

$$r(x) = \begin{cases} \dfrac{1}{2a\pi^2}(a^2 + x^2) & 0 < x \le a \\ \dfrac{x}{\pi^2} & a < x \le \pi - a \\ \dfrac{1}{2a\pi^2}(2a\pi - a^2 - (x-\pi)^2) & \pi - a < x \le \pi \end{cases} \qquad [9]$$

for $0 < x \le \pi$, and because $r(x)$ is symmetric about π, it is sufficient to know its values for $0 < x \le \pi$. For estimation of a, it is desirable to compute the variance of $r(x)$ as defined by Equation 9, which is:

$$\sigma_{U(a)}{}^2(r(x)) = \frac{\pi^2}{6}\left[1 + \left(\frac{a}{\pi}\right)^2\left(2 - \frac{a}{\pi}\right)\right] \qquad [10]$$

where the subscript $U(a)$ denotes the uniform smearing distribution with parameter a.

The *symmetric beta smearing* density with parameter m is defined by:

$$k(t) = \frac{1}{\pi B(m, \frac{1}{2})} \left(1 - \frac{t^2}{\pi^2}\right)^{m-1} \quad [11]$$

for $-\pi < t < \pi$ and $B(m, \frac{1}{2})$ the usual beta coefficient. (Because of the form of the reinforcement density $f(y)$, Equation 2 must be written as

$$r(x) = \frac{1}{\pi^2} \left\{ \int_{-\pi}^{x-\pi} k(t)(2\pi - x + t)dt \right.$$

$$\left. + \int_{x-\pi}^{x} k(t)(x - t)dt + \int_{x}^{\pi} k(t)(t - x)dt \right\} \quad [12]$$

and thus in considering the beta smearing density it is necessary to restrict the exponent $m - 1$ to integer values in order to integrate Equation 11, which restriction turns out not to be serious.) Combining now Equations 2, 7, and 11, and again integrating, we obtain for $0 < x < \pi$:

$$r(x) = \frac{1}{\pi} \left\{ \frac{(\pi^2 - x^2)^m - (\pi^2 - (x - \pi)^2)^m}{m\pi^{2m}B(m, \frac{1}{2})} + 1 - \frac{x}{\pi} \right.$$

$$\left. + \frac{2}{B(m, \frac{1}{2})} \sum_{\nu=0}^{m-1} \binom{m-1}{\nu} (-1)^\nu \frac{x^{2\nu+2} - (x - \pi)^{2\nu+2}}{(2\nu + 1)\pi^{2\nu+1}} \right\} \quad [13]$$

For the variance of $r(x)$ as defined by Equation 13, we have:

$$\sigma_{\beta(m)}^2(r(x)) = \pi^2 \left\{ \frac{2}{2m + 1} + \frac{3}{2(2m + 3)(2m + 1)} \right.$$

$$\left. - \frac{2}{B(m, \frac{1}{2})} \left[\frac{1}{m(m + 1)} - 2 \sum_{\nu=0}^{m-1} \binom{m-1}{\nu} (-1)^\nu \frac{B(2\nu + 3, 3)}{2\nu + 1} \right] \right\} \quad [14]$$

Asymptotic response densities, as given by Equation 9 for the uniform smearing density and Equation 13 for the beta smearing density, were fitted by the method of moments to the response histograms shown in Fig. 2 and 3. In the present situation this amounted to estimating the values of parameters a and m, respectively, which determine asymptotic response densities whose variances (Equations 10 and 14) are equal to the variances of the histograms. The variances of the response histograms were computed from the individual observations and not from the frequency functions for the class intervals. The histograms and the fitted response densities both show the smoothing and spreading effects which are to be ex-

pected if the notion is correct of a distribution which smears the conditioning of the sampled stimulus.

As already stated, the response histogram for the group of Ss using the 2.5-ft. circle has a mean of $.997\pi$ and a variance of $.224\pi^2$. In order to fit this response histogram, if we take a uniform smearing density with $a = .475\pi$, we obtain an asymptotic response density with mean of π and variance of $.224\pi^2$. And if we take $m = 6$, we obtain for the beta smearing density, an asymptotic response density with mean of π and variance of $.222\pi^2$. The two response densities resulting from the two smearing densities are so nearly identical, it was possible to plot only one response density in Fig. 2; the one selected is that arising from the beta smearing density. For numerical comparison, the maximum difference between the two response densities occurs at $x = 0$, for which $r_U(x) = .076$ and $r_\beta(x) = .071$. Goodness of fit tests for the response densities are given below.

The response histogram for the 5.0-ft. circle has a mean of $.993\pi$ and a variance of $.210\pi^2$. In order to fit this histogram, if we take a uniform smearing density with $a = .405\pi$, we obtain an asymptotic response density with mean of π and variance of $.210\pi^2$. And if we take a beta smearing distribution with $m = 8$, we get an asymptotic smearing density with mean of π and variance of $.211\pi^2$. Again the two response densities are so similar it was possible to plot only $r_\beta(x)$ in Fig. 3. At $x = 0$, $r_U(x) = .064$ and $r_\beta(x) = .063$.

Because of its greater circumference the larger circle permits finer discrimination; thus, when measurements are made in radians, the variance of the response density and that of the corresponding smearing density are less for the larger of the two circles. The four fitted smearing densities are plotted in Fig. 4.

Figure 5 presents the theoretical variance of the asymptotic response density as a function of parameter a of the uniform smearing density and also as a function of parameter m of

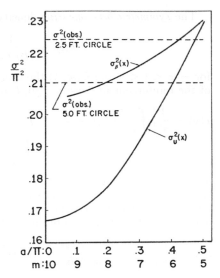

FIG. 5. Theoretical variance of $r(x)$ for uniform smearing density with parameter a and beta smearing density with parameter m.

the beta smearing distribution. The empirical variances of the response histograms for the two circles appear as horizontal lines in the figure. The figure shows that the use of integer values for parameter m of the beta smearing density is sufficiently sensitive for good estimation of the asymptotic response density. It should be noted that when the variance of the smearing distribution goes to zero, the asymptotic response density is identical with the noncontingent reinforcement density.

Prior to detailed calculations it was not anticipated that the exact form of the smearing distribution would affect so slightly the form of the asymptotic response distribution. This is a highly encouraging result for the investigation of more complicated reinforcement distributions which pose increasingly difficult mathematical problems, for in most cases the possibility of assuming a uniform smearing distribution leads to considerable formal simplifications.

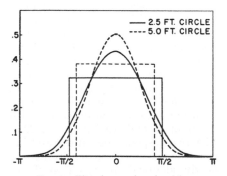

FIG. 4. Fitted smearing densities.

On the other hand, the near identity of the response distributions arising from the two different smearing distributions implies that there is little possibility of identifying from response histograms the general form of the smearing distribution. Theoretically Equation 2 may be regarded as an integral equation, and when $k(x; y)$ is taken to be symmetric, Equation 2 may be easily transformed into a standard integral equation of Fredholm type with the reinforcement density $f(y)$ as the kernel. Given $f(y)$ and an analytical function $r(x)$ it is then possible to determine the class of functions $k(x; y)$ which satisfy the integral equation. However, as the discussion of Fig. 1 and 2 has indicated, response densities of quite different analytical form fit the empirical response histograms equally well and the choice between them is empirically arbitrary. It remains to be seen whether other properties of the model, which have not been considered here, will yield a practical method for identifying the form of the smearing distribution.

Goodness of fit of response densities. —Inspection of Fig. 2 and 3 suggests that the response densities fit the response histograms better than the triangular reinforcement distribution does, and that the over-all fit is reasonably good. Because of the importance of this goodness of fit for evaluating the validity of the theory, it is pertinent to examine it more closely. The obvious procedure is to apply a χ^2 test, but the difficulty is that the 6,000 observations on which each histogram and fitted response density are based are not statistically independent, as is required for a χ^2 test. However, it is known that for stationary stochastic processes observations sufficiently spaced in trials are statistically independent. Following this line of thought, we considered responses on every fifth trial for each S starting with Trial 102. To test the statistical independence of these responses, we divided the circumference

of the circle into six class intervals with approximately equal relative frequencies for the 2.5-ft. circle data. In terms of these six class intervals we then tested the null hypothesis that the 1200 responses were drawn from a zero-order Markov process (i.e., are statistically independent) against the alternative hypothesis that they were drawn from a first order Markov process. The appropriate χ^2 test is given in Anderson and Goodman (1957) and has been used repeatedly on learning data by Suppes and Atkinson (1960). For the 2.5-ft. circle, $\chi^2 = 32.97$, which with $(6 - 1)^2 = 25$ df has a significance level of $P = .20$. For the 5.0-ft. circle $\chi^2 = 30.66$, which with the same number of df has $P = .24$. For purpose of comparison the same test was run on the reinforcements occurring on the immediately preceding trial, i.e., Trials 101, 106, etc. Here $\chi^2 = 24.95$ which has $P = .49$. With 1,200 observations the power of this χ^2 test is high, so that with the obtained significance levels it is reasonable to accept the null hypothesis that the responses are statistically independent.

Using then the 1,200 statistically independent responses on each circle, the following results were obtained. First, the null hypothesis that the response data fit the reinforcement distribution was tested. On the basis of dividing the circle into 30 class intervals of approximately equal frequency for the 2.5-ft. circle data, the rejection of the null hypothesis was decisive. For the 2.5-ft. circle $\chi^2 = 154.21$ with 29 df, and for the 5.0-ft. circle $\chi^2 = 74.02$ with 29 df; both results are highly significant. In this instance, an aspect of the continuum theory is confirmed in which it differs from the discrete response theory. Numerous two-choice experiments have confirmed the matching law that asymptotically the number of A_1 responses in any large block of trials is essentially equal to the number of E_1 reinforcements. Because of the smearing distribution in the continuum case, no such matching of response and reinforcement distributions is predicted, nor was it obtained.

Secondly, we tested for each circle the null hypothesis that the response distributions (Equation 9) with the estimated parameter a fit the response data. For the 2.5-ft. circle $\chi^2 = 47.56$ with 28 df, for which $P = .02$. For the 5.0-ft. circle $\chi^2 = 30.09$, also with 28 df for which $P > .30$. The somewhat disappointing result for the 2.5-ft. circle is entirely due to one cell which has an observed frequency of 66, whereas a frequency of 40.68 is predicted. The contribution of this one cell of the 30 to the χ^2 total is 16.15. Examination of the data for individual Ss indicates that this large figure cannot really be explained by unusual behavior of one or two Ss. The maximum contribution to the 66 total of any one S is 9. The fit of the remaining 29 cells is quite good, and, of course, the fit of the data from the 5.0-ft. circle is very satisfactory. The encouraging character of these results suggests a deeper analysis of sequential data in subsequent experiments; unfortunately, analytical computation of detailed sequential statistics is rather forbidding, although possible.

SUMMARY

The study tests a formulation of stimulus sampling theory for a continuum of responses when reinforcement is determinate and the probability distribution of reinforcements is noncontingent, unimodal, and symmetric. Sixty college students were run for 300 trials on a circular display apparatus. The Ss' responses consisted of predicting the location of a spot of light on the circumference of a circle. At the end of each trial S was shown the "correct" location, which constituted the reinforcing event for that trial. The Ss were divided into two groups, one of which used a circle with a diameter of 2.5 ft. and the other a circle with a diameter of 5.0 ft. The means, variances and third central moments of the last 200 responses for individual Ss were tabulated. The results are in good qualitative agreement with the theory. In particular, the means matched closely that of the reinforcement distributions, but the variances were generally larger, as predicted by the theory, in contrast to the zero variance of the rational strategy of statistical decision theory. The learning parameter θ and the smearing distribution which represents the conditioning of the single stimulus were estimated from the data. Asymptotic response densities were computed by use of the estimated smearing distributions and were found to be highly similar for both assumed forms of the smearing distribution and to agree well with the observed histograms for both groups.

REFERENCES

ANDERSON, T. W., & GOODMAN, L. A. Statistical inference about Markov chains. *Ann. math. Statist.*, 1957, **28**, 89–110.

ESTES, W. K. Toward a statistical theory of learning. *Psychol. Rev.*, 1950, **57**, 94–107.

ESTES, W. K., & STRAUGHAN, J. H. Analysis of a verbal conditioning situation in terms of statistical learning theory. *J. exp. Psychol.*, 1954, **47**, 225–234.

SUPPES, P. A linear model for a continuum of responses. In R. R. Bush & W. K. Estes (Eds.), *Studies in mathematical learning theory*. Stanford: Stanford Univer. Press, 1959.

SUPPES, P. Stimulus sampling theory for a continuum of responses. In K. J. Arrow, S. Karlin, & P. Suppes (Eds.), *Mathematical methods in the social sciences*. Stanford: Stanford Univer. Press, 1960.

SUPPES, P., & ATKINSON, R. C. *Markov learning models for multiperson interactions*. Stanford: Stanford Univer. Press, 1960.

(Early publication received October 6, 1960)

Theoretical Treatments of Differential Reward in Multiple-Choice Learning and Two-Person Interactions

WILLIAM K. ESTES, *University of Michigan*

Mathematical theories for human learning in two-choice situations have been developed primarily in relation to simple verbal conditioning experiments in which reinforcing events are simply informational signals indicating to the subject whether his response was correct or incorrect on each trial [7]. Thus when interest arose in extending learning theory to the treatment of two-person interactions, it was natural to use essentially the same experimental conditions, except that the reinforcing signals for each of two interacting subjects should be made contingent upon the other's responses. With experimental situations so contrived, a considerable quantity of research has been accomplished during the past five years, and on the whole, applications of statistical learning theory have yielded satisfactory accounts of long-term response proportions [2], [4], [12].[1] Although there is reason to doubt that comparable success in theoretical interpretation can readily be attained, an equally interesting problem is that of a two-person interaction in which the amount of reward associated with each response for each subject, rather than the probability of being right or wrong, depends jointly upon his own response and the response of the other subject. This varying payoff situation is closer to those dealt with explicitly by game theory, but it poses greater difficulty for learning theory, for little work has been done on the basic problem of reward as a parameter of the learning process for a single human subject. Only one stratagem has occurred to me that might enable us to bypass this difficulty without major theoretical effort; it will be discussed in connection with an exploratory study now to be described.

Preparation of this paper was supported by Contract Nonr-908(16) between the Office of Naval Research and Indiana University, and Contract Nonr-225(17) between the Office of Naval Research and Stanford University.

[1] In some instances, detailed statistics of learning data for interacting subjects have been treated [12], but in this paper attention will be confined to the prediction of asymptotic choice probabilities.

1. Experimental Comparison of Game Theory and Statistical Learning Theory

In this section we shall first summarize an experiment designed to explore the course and limits of learning in an experiment concerning two-person interactions with varying payoffs. Terminal response proportions for both players in each of two experimental games will be compared, first with the response probabilities specified by game theory (as we interpret the theory in this situation), and then with predictions generated by an extension of the statistical learning model that has been successfully applied to simpler experimental games not involving varying payoffs.

1.1 Design and Procedure of the Exploratory Experiment. This experiment was conducted by Michael Cole, Alfred Bruner, Jane Bond, and Suchoon Mo as a project in my advanced laboratory psychology course at Indiana University in the fall, 1959–60 semester. The initial interest of the group was partly in developing an experimental situation suitable for evaluating the degree to which human subjects competing in simple games of strategy approximate the strategies prescribed by von Neumann and Morgenstern's theory of games.

During an experimental session, two subjects confronted each other across a table. On each subject's side of the table, out of sight of the other, were two response keys. In the center of the table top, visible to both subjects, was a double row of windows. When any pair of windows was illuminated, numerals became visible, indicating the payoff, in "points," to each subject on the given trial. A pair of signal lamps on each subject's side of the table top was so wired that after both subjects had operated their response keys on a trial, the lights indicated to each subject the choice made by the other.

The subjects, Indiana University undergraduates who were serving to fulfill part of a course requirement, were told that they were participating in a "reasoning game" and that the object of the game was to score as many points as possible on each play of the game (i.e., on each trial). Each trial began with the sounding of a signal buzzer; then, during a $2\frac{1}{2}$-sec response interval, each subject operated one of his response keys; finally, during the $3\frac{1}{2}$-sec information interval, the response lamp and the payoff windows were illuminated. Each pair of subjects was run for 200 of these trials in a continuous session with no communication permitted between them except for that mediated by the apparatus.

Two payoff conditions were investigated, each with 20 pairs of subjects; one (Game 1) represented a strictly determined game in the sense of game theory, and the other (Game 2) a nondetermined game requiring mixed strategies. The payoff matrices for the two games were as follows: For Game 1,

$$
\begin{array}{cc}
 & \begin{array}{cc} B_1 & B_2 \end{array} \\
\begin{array}{c} A_1 \\ A_2 \end{array} & \begin{bmatrix} 0,\ 4 & 2,\ 2 \\ 1,\ 3 & 4,\ 0 \end{bmatrix},
\end{array}
$$

and for Game 2,

$$A_1 \quad \begin{matrix} B_1 & B_2 \end{matrix} \\ A_2 \quad \begin{bmatrix} 1,\ 3 & 3,\ 1 \\ 2,\ 2 & 0,\ 4 \end{bmatrix},$$

where A and B, with appropriate subscripts, represent the choices available to the row and column players, respectively, and the pair of numbers in cell ij represents the payoffs to the row and column player, respectively, when their combination of choices on a given trial is A_iB_j.

It will be seen that the matrix for Game 1 has a saddle point at A_2B_1, whereas the matrix for Game 2 has no saddle point and its game-theoretic solution requires the row player to choose A_1 with probability .50 and the column player to choose B_1 with probability .75.

1.2 Comparison of Experimental Results with Game-Theoretic Strategies. Proportions of A_1 and B_1 choices during the final 20 trials of the experiment for each group are compared with the values prescribed by game theory in table 1.

TABLE 1

PROPORTION OF A_1 AND B_1 CHOICES DURING THE FINAL 20 TRIALS FOR EACH GROUP COMPARED WITH VALUES PRESCRIBED BY GAME THEORY AND BOUNDS PREDICTED BY A LINEAR LEARNING MODEL

	Observed Proportions	Game Theory	Bounds
Game 1			
Row player (A_1)	.13	0	.38–.50
Column player (B_1)	.92	1	.75–.88
Game 2			
Row player (A_1)	.50	.50	.54–.62
Column player (B_1)	.69	.75	.46–.64

In contrast to the results reported for the type of game with right–wrong payoffs [4], [12], all four groups in this experiment clearly tended to approach terminal response probabilities corresponding to the appropriate game-theoretic strategies. A considerable proportion of the subject pairs in Game 1 were following the minimax strategy $(0, 1)$ during the last part of the experiment, and it seems not unlikely that nearly all would have arrived at this state if the series had continued long enough. In the sense of decision theory, these subjects could be said to be approximating rational behavior. Since the subjects had no knowledge of game or decision theory, this result poses an interesting problem for the psychology of learning. Can we account, in terms of principles of individual learning, for the manner in which these pairs of interacting subjects have used the information gained solely by experience in the experimental situation to progress toward "rational" strategies?

1.3 Comparison of Experimental Results with Predictions from a Learning Model. Before we can apply contemporary theories of individual two-choice learning to the present experiment, we must be able to specify the probability that each combination of payoffs will constitute an effective reward, or *reinforcement*, for each of the two subjects. The only simple way of accomplishing this specification that has occurred to me is to assume that the probabilities of effective reinforcement are proportional to the payoff values. If we apply this assumption, the payoff matrices for the two games studied can be transformed into matrices of effective reward probabilities: for Game 1,

$$\begin{array}{cc} & \begin{array}{cc} B_1 & {}^{\text{-}}B_2 \end{array} \\ \begin{array}{c} A_1 \\ A_2 \end{array} & \left[\begin{array}{cc} 0,\ 1 & \frac{1}{2},\ \frac{1}{2} \\ \frac{1}{4},\ \frac{3}{4} & 1,\ 0 \end{array} \right] \end{array},$$

and for Game 2,

$$\begin{array}{cc} & \begin{array}{cc} B_1 & B_2 \end{array} \\ \begin{array}{c} A_1 \\ A_2 \end{array} & \left[\begin{array}{cc} \frac{1}{4},\ \frac{3}{4} & \frac{3}{4},\ \frac{1}{4} \\ \frac{1}{2},\ \frac{1}{2} & 0,\ 1 \end{array} \right] \end{array},$$

where the entries in cell ij now represent the probabilities that the obtained payoff will serve to reward the responses made by the row and column player, respectively, when the response combination is A_iB_j.

We can now readily apply either the linear model, as previously extended to the two-person, right–wrong situation by Burke [2] and Estes and Suppes [8], or the Markovian, stimulus-sampling model extensively studied by Suppes and Atkinson [12]. In order to avoid the necessity of discussing the differences between the two models, I shall here make use only of the *matching theorem* that holds for both models (proved for the linear model in [5] and [8], and for the stimulus-sampling model in [9]). According to this theorem, over a sufficiently long series of trials, the proportion of choices of a given response by a subject should tend to match the proportion of instances in which that response has been reinforced. Application of the theorem enables us to make *a priori* predictions (i.e., predictions which do not require knowledge about the values of learning parameters) of the ranges of values within which the terminal response proportions should fall for each group of subjects. These predicted values are presented in table 1, and the method of derivation is described in Appendix A. Considering that in none of the four cases does the observed terminal response proportion fall within the predicted range, and noting especially the very large disparity for the group of row players in Game 1, we must conclude that the learning models, as interpreted, do not offer a satisfactory account of the observed behavior.

The one possibility for "saving" the simple learning models in this situation would be to revise the assumption of proportionality between payoffs and reinforcement probabilities. It seems apparent from inspection of the payoff matrix for Game 1, together with the corresponding data in table 1, that under this condition the row players are tending to avoid the zero payoff more strongly than allowed for by the assumption of proportionality. The theoretical bounds for this group can be brought into line with the observed response proportion by means of a scaling function of the "diminishing returns" type, i.e., one which generates a larger difference in effective reinforcement probability for the increment from 2 to 3 payoff units than for the increment from 3 to 4 units, and a still larger difference for the increment from 0 to 1 unit. Unhappily, this scaling function simultaneously increases the disparity between theory and observation when applied to Game 2.

Prospects do not seem to be promising that we will find a single scaling function that will enable the learning theory to provide a reasonable account of asymptotic choice proportions for *both* games studied in this experiment, as well as comparable data from such related studies as that of Lieberman (see chapter 14 of this volume) in which the subjects played against a mixed strategy followed by the experimenter. Nonetheless, it is important from a theoretical standpoint to decide between two principal interpretations of our results: (1) the learning models are sound but the relationship between payoff values and reinforcement probabilities depends upon particular combinations of conditions in too complex a way to be captured by any simple scaling function; or (2) revision or augmentation of the basic assumptions of the learning models is required. To gain further information relevant to this decision, we turn now to a more detailed examination of one of the learning models.

2. Analysis of a Linear Model for Individual Learning as a Function of Reward Magnitude

For convenience of exposition, this analysis will be limited to the linear model for individual learning in two-choice situations; however, it can be assumed that strictly analogous conclusions hold for any of the stimulus-sampling models that have been applied to human binary-choice learning.

During an earlier period of concentration on learning under right–wrong reinforcing conditions, I, at least, had assumed that variation in amount of reward could be readily handled simply by lifting certain restrictions on parameter values in the linear model. The appropriate generalization of the model that was developed in connection with analyses of simple probability learning was outlined in the following manner by Estes and Suppes [8]. A distinction was made between the observable outcome of a trial and the conditioning event assumed to be produced by the conjunction of this outcome with the stimulus and response conditions obtaining on the trial. In a two-choice situation, there might be any number of experimenter-defined trial outcomes O_j, $j = 1, 2, \cdots, M$ (which might, for example, be different amounts of reward), but only three reinforcing events. These events are:

E_1: the event that the first response alternative, A_1, is effectively re-inforced by the trial outcome, in which case probability p_1 of the first response receives the increment specified by the linear transform

$$p_{1,n+1} = (1 - \theta)p_{1,n} + \theta , \tag{1}$$

where n is the ordinal number of the rewarded trial and θ is the learning parameter, restricted in value to the interval $0 < \theta \leq 1$;

E_2: the event that the second response, A_2, is effectively reinforced, in which case probability of the *first* response receives the decrement described by

$$p_{1,n+1} = (1 - \theta)p_{1,n} ; \tag{2}$$

and

E_0: the event that the trial outcome has no effect on either response, that is,

$$p_{1,n+1} = p_{1,n} . \tag{3}$$

It was assumed that a given combination of outcome, O_j, and response, A_i, might generate any of the three reinforcing events, although in general with different probabilities. These probabilities may be represented by a set of parameters,

$$c_{ijk} = P(E_k \mid O_j A_i) .$$

One would naturally expect that when O_j is a reward and $O_{j'}$ is a non-reward, c_{iji} will be relatively large and $c_{ij'i}$ will be relatively small.

Now, over a series of trials on each of which response A_1 occurs and is rewarded with outcome O_1, the expected change in response probability on any one trial may readily be computed by weighting the right sides of equations (1), (2), and (3) by these probabilities of the corresponding re-inforcing events. Dropping the i and j subscripts on the c parameters, we obtain[2]

$$p_{1,n} = c_1[(1 - \theta)p_{1,n-1} + \theta] + c_2(1 - \theta)p_{1,n-1} + c_0 p_{1,n-1} \\ = (1 - \theta + \theta c_0)p_{1,n-1} + \theta c_1 . \tag{4}$$

As n approaches infinity we can obtain the limiting value of $p_{1,n}$ in the usual manner by setting $p_{1,n} = p_{1,n-1} = p_1$ in equation (4) and solving for p_1, obtaining

$$p_1 = \frac{c_1}{1 - c_0} = \frac{c_1}{c_1 + c_2} . \tag{5}$$

It is apparent that under the conditions described, probability of the

[2] It should be noted that, whereas in equations (1), (2), and (3), $p_{1,n}$ denoted the response probability for some one arbitrarily selected subject on trial n, in equation (4) and henceforth through the remainder of the paper, $p_{1,n}$ denotes the response proba-bility for a population of subjects whose learning through the first n trials has been governed by the specified set of parameters; for a full discussion of this distinction, see [8].

continuously rewarded response will go to an asymptote of unity over a series of trials if and only if the probability is zero that administration of the reward represented by O_1 following occurrences of A_1 will ever lead to strengthening of A_2, i.e., if $c_2 = 0$. If O_1 represents anything that would normally be considered a reward, human subjects will certainly be almost always found to approximate an asymptote of unity for the rewarded response over a series of trials. In this case, setting $c_2 = 0$, we note that the learning curve obtained by solving equation (4) takes the form

$$(6) \qquad p_{1,n} = 1 - (1 - p_{1,1})(1 - \theta c_1)^{n-1} .$$

The experimental interpretation of $p_{1,n}$ in this context is that it represents the probability of A_1 when trial n is a free-choice trial, with response alternatives A_1 and A_2, following $n - 1$ trials on which A_1 has been the only available response. Under the usual conditions of human learning experiments with, say, monetary rewards, a set of experimental groups (each run for a series of trials on which response A_1 always occurs and is rewarded, but with different amounts of reward assigned to different groups), would be predicted to generate a family of learning curves all going to a common asymptote of unity, but at different rates depending on the magnitudes of reward.

To proceed in the direction of the experimental situations of primary concern in this paper, we consider next an experimental routine in which response A_1, whenever it occurs, is followed by outcome O_1 and response A_2 is followed by outcome O_2. Letting $c_{jk} = P(E_k \mid O_j A_j)$, we have for the effect of an $A_1 O_1$ trial

$$(7) \qquad p_{1,n+1} = (1 - \theta + \theta c_{10}) p_{1,n} + \theta c_{11} ,$$

and for the effect of an $A_2 O_2$ trial (upon probability of A_1)

$$(8) \qquad p_{1,n+1} = (1 - \theta + \theta c_{20}) p_{1,n} + \theta c_{21} .$$

Treatment of a series of free-choice trials run under these conditions involves mathematical difficulties which have been extensively investigated by Bush and Mosteller [3], Estes and Suppes [8], Karlin [10], and Tatsuoka and Mosteller [13], among others. We can bring out the points of immediate interest while bypassing these difficulties if we consider an experimental routine in which the experimenter has insured by means of a forcing procedure that $A_1 O_1$ and $A_2 O_2$ trials occur with equal probabilities over the first n trials and in which we wish to predict the result of a free choice on trial $n + 1$. Under these circumstances, equations (7) and (8) can be weighted by their probabilities (1/2 in each case) and combined to yield the desired probability of an A_1 response on trial $n + 1$:

$$(9) \qquad p_{1,n+1} = \left[1 - \theta + \frac{\theta}{2}(c_{10} + c_{20}) \right] p_{1,n} + \frac{\theta}{2}(c_{11} + c_{21}) ,$$

which, as $n \to \infty$, tends to the asymptote

(10) $$p_1 = \frac{c_{11} + c_{21}}{2 - c_{10} - c_{20}} = \frac{c_{11} + c_{21}}{c_{11} + c_{12} + c_{21} + c_{22}} .$$

Now, if O_1 is a reward such that $c_{11} > 0$ and O_2 is nonreward, so that $c_{22} = 0$, the asymptotic probability of A_1 will vary from near zero to unity, depending on the values of c_{11} and c_{12}. If $c_{12} > 0$, then the asymptote must be intermediate between zero and unity. If $c_{12} = 0$, we again obtain a family of curves all going to a common asymptote of unity, but at different rates, depending now on the values of c_{11} and c_{21}.

So far, our results with the linear model seem quite reasonable. A less satisfactory state of affairs arises, however, if we consider the following conditions.

Suppose two rewards, O_1 and O_2, are selected such that over a series of A_1O_1 trials p_1 would go to unity and over a series of A_2O_2 trials p_2 would go to unity (and therefore p_1 to zero), but the former at the faster rate. This means, in terms of the model under consideration, that $c_{11} > c_{22} > 0$, but $c_{12} = c_{21} = 0$. Now, over a series of trials in which A_1O_1 and A_2O_2 occur with equal probabilities, equation (10) reduces to

(11) $$p_1 = \frac{c_{11}}{c_{11} + c_{22}} ,$$

and we have the prediction that the asymptotic probability of an A_1 response by the subject on a free-choice trial following a series reinforced under the conditions stated must have a value intermediate between zero and unity. Although I cannot cite specific experiments bearing on the prediction,[3] I cannot believe that it would generally hold for human subjects. Suppose, for example, that O_1 and O_2 were payoffs of different amounts of money, O_1 being the larger. It seems almost certain that the conditions given at the beginning of the paragraph could be satisfied, but it is even more certain that under any ordinary circumstances, p_1 would go to unity when the larger and smaller rewards were pitted against each other in the two-choice situation. The only important case in which I would expect to obtain asymptotes intermediate between zero and unity in this type of experiment is that in which the rewards given following A_1 and A_2 responses are not entirely discriminable, so that the subject sometimes believes he has received the larger reward when in fact he has been given the smaller (for some evidence bearing on this assumption, see [6]).

In the light of this analysis, I can see little promise in the notion of accounting for human learning as a function of reward (in one-person situations, let alone in two-person interactions) by any of the models hitherto utilized in the interpretation of simple probability learning with only informative feedback. It appears that some revision of the basic assumptions will be required. One direction these revisions might take is alteration of

---

[3] A study meeting these specifications closely has, however, been conducted by Bower [1] with rats as subjects and different amounts of food as rewards; his results agree with those that I am conjecturing would hold for human subjects (see section 3).

the learning axioms, done, for example, in Atkinson's extension of the Markovian pattern model (see chapter 2 of this volume). Another direction is to leave the learning axioms unchanged but to introduce some modification of the response rule (in the terminology of the statistician or economist, the decision rule) relating the state of learning to the overt choice response. The latter possibility will be explored in the following section.

3. A Provisional Model for Human Learning as a Function of Reward Magnitude

A frequently useful strategy is to assume that relationships between variables established in simpler situations continue to hold when the same variables are imbedded in a more complex situation, even though it may not be possible to make the same observations or measurements in the more complex case. Considering experiments on learning in relation to reward magnitude with this idea in mind, one may note that the simpler experiment on probability learning is, in a sense, imbedded in the reward situation. In the typical experiment on probability learning, the task set for the subject is to predict on each trial which of two reinforcing lights will appear; if these lights have been programmed by the experimenter to appear with fixed probabilities, the usual result is that over a series of trials the subject's probability of predicting a given light comes to match its actual probability of occurrence. If the reinforcing lights were replaced by two magnitudes of monetary payoff, again programmed to occur with fixed probabilities independently of the subject's behavior, there is little doubt that the subject's probability of predicting a given reward would approach the actual probability of occurrence of that reward, with the course of learning described by the same models that have been applied to the standard experiment on prediction of lights. The key assumption now to be proposed for a theory of human learning under differential reward is that this type of probability learning does in fact occur whenever different responses are followed by different rewards with fixed probabilities, even though it is not explicitly called for by instructions to the subject. Whenever each member of a set of response alternatives, $\{A_i\}$, $i = 1, 2, \cdots, r$, is followed by different magnitudes of reward, $\{O_j\}$, $j = 1, \cdots, M$, with probabilities π_{ij}, the subject's tendency to expect reward O_j following response A_i is assumed to change from trial to trial in accord with the usual reinforcement axioms for simple probability learning, approaching π_{ij} as the number of A_i occurrences becomes large. On each free-choice trial, the subject is considered to scan the set of available response alternatives, generating for each alternative a prediction of the reward that will be received if the response is made, and then to make the response which he predicts will yield the largest reward.

A full presentation of this theory must include exact specifications of (1) the random-walk process whereby the subject considers the various response alternatives and arrives at an overt choice on any given trial; (2) learning axioms for the implicit responses of predicting the outcomes that will follow different responses; and (3) learning axioms for the responses of choosing or rejecting the response leading to a given predicted outcome (or, in other terms, for developing a scale of reward values for different outcomes). In the present paper, we shall present only the aspects of the model relevant to our immediate purpose of accounting for asymptotic choice probabilities in human learning experiments involving exactly two different reward magnitudes. Further, we shall limit the present discussion to situations in which the two possible rewards, O_1 and O_2, are clearly discriminable, with one being uniformly preferred over the other, as, for example, would certainly be the case with monetary payoffs to adult subjects.

Subject to the simplifying assumptions mentioned above, asymptotic performance in a two-choice situation can be analyzed as follows: On each trial, the subject considers both responses and predicts the reward that will follow each. On denoting predictions of the more and less preferred rewards by 1 and 0, respectively, and true probabilities that the more preferred reward will follow responses A_1 and A_2 by π_1 and π_2, respectively, application of the probability matching theorem (discussed in section 1.3) yields the following probabilities that the subject will predict each of the four possible combinations of outcomes following responses:

A_1	A_2	Probability
1	1	$\pi_1\pi_2$
1	0	$\pi_1(1 - \pi_2)$
0	1	$(1 - \pi_1)\pi_2$
0	0	$(1 - \pi_1)(1 - \pi_2)$

The subject's "decision rule" in this situation is to make response A_1 with probability 1 when he predicts the outcome combination $(1, 0)$, and with probability 0 when he predicts $(0, 1)$. When the subject predicts either of the outcome combinations $(1, 1)$ or $(0, 0)$, he makes whichever response he first considers on the given trial. The probability that A_1 will be the first response considered differs depending on whether the response alternatives are presented to the subject in a randomized or a fixed arrangement. In the first case, each response has probability $1/2$ of being considered first, and therefore response A_1 is made with probability $1/2$ on trials when $(1, 1)$ or $(0, 0)$ are predicted. In the second case, the probability that A_1 will be considered first on these trials is equal to the current choice probability $P(1)$ for the A_1 response on all types of trials.

With these assumptions, the asymptotic probability of an A_1 choice can readily be computed for either of the two experimental conditions: For the case of randomized presentation order,

$$(12) \quad P(1) = \frac{1}{2}[\pi_1\pi_2 + \pi_1(1 - \pi_2) + (1 - \pi_1)(1 - \pi_2)] + \frac{1}{2}[\pi_1(1 - \pi_2)]$$

$$= \frac{1}{2}(1 + \pi_1 - \pi_2) ;$$

and for the case of fixed presentation order,

$$P(1) = P(1)[\pi_1\pi_2 + \pi_1(1 - \pi_2) + (1 - \pi_1)(1 - \pi_2)] + [1 - P(1)][\pi_1(1 - \pi_2)],$$

which, solved for $P(1)$, yields

$$(13) \qquad P(1) = \frac{\pi_1(1 - \pi_2)}{\pi_1 + \pi_2 - 2\pi_1\pi_2}.$$

It may readily be shown that if $\pi_1 > \pi_2$, then the expression for $P(1)$ given by equation (13) is always greater than that given by equation (12) (except for the special case of $\pi_1 = 1$, $\pi_2 = 0$, where the two are equal). This relation is just what would be expected on psychological grounds. When the presentation arrangement of the response alternatives is fixed, as in the standard key-pressing situation (see [7] and [12, ch. 3]), the subject can learn to consider the more preferred alternative first on each trial; but when the arrangement of alternatives is randomly varied from trial to trial, as in Suppes and Atkinson's "paired-comparison" learning experiment ([12, ch. 11]), it is a matter of chance which alternative first comes to the subject's attention on any trial.

As an illustrative application of the model to the case of randomized alternatives, we may conveniently take the experiment of Suppes and Atkinson, just mentioned. On each trial of this experiment, the experimenter presented orally some combination of two or all three of the letters A, B, and C (all combinations occurring equally often, and order of presentation of the letters within a presentation set being randomized) and the subject chose one of the proffered alternatives. Probabilities that choices of each alternative would be "correct" were A: .67, B: .40, and C: .20. For one group of 48 subjects each correct choice received a payoff of one cent, and for a second group of 48 subjects a payoff of five cents. The choice proportions for the two groups differed very little; consequently, we shall pool their data for our present purposes. Predicted asymptotic proportions of choices of A from A, B; A from A, C; and B from B, C may be computed simply by substituting the appropriate pairs of values of π_i in equation (12), and prove to be .64, .74, and .60, respectively. To predict the probability of a choice of A from A, B, C, we require an extension of the model to the case of three alternatives. No new assumptions are needed, and the same method of derivation used in the case of equation (12) yields

$$(14a) \qquad P(1) = \pi_1(1 - \pi_2)(1 - \pi_3) + \frac{1}{2}[\pi_1\pi_2(1 - \pi_3) + \pi_1\pi_3(1 - \pi_2)]$$

$$+ \frac{1}{3}[\pi_1\pi_2\pi_3 + (1 - \pi_1)(1 - \pi_2)(1 - \pi_3)]$$

$$= \frac{1 + 2\pi_1 - \pi_1 - \pi_3}{3} - \frac{\pi_1\pi_2 + \pi_1\pi_3 - 2\pi_2\pi_3}{6},$$

and similarly,

$$(14b) \qquad P(2) = \frac{1 + 2\pi_2 - \pi_1 - \pi_3}{3} - \frac{\pi_2\pi_3 + \pi_1\pi_2 - 2\pi_1\pi_3}{6},$$

$$(14c) \qquad P(3) = \frac{1 + 2\pi_3 - \pi_1 - \pi_2}{3} - \frac{\pi_2\pi_3 + \pi_1\pi_3 - 2\pi_1\pi_2}{6}.$$

When the appropriate values of π_i are inserted, equations (14) yield .54, .30, and .16 for the probabilities of choice of A, B, and C, respectively, from A, B, C. Weighting the choice probabilities by the relative frequencies of occurrence of the various combinations of alternatives, we obtain the predicted values which are compared in table 2 with the observed values reported

TABLE 2

PREDICTED AND OBSERVED ASYMPTOTIC CHOICE PROPORTIONS FOR THE THREE ALTERNATIVES IN A PAIRED-COMPARISON LEARNING EXPERIMENT

Alternative	Observed Proportion	Predicted Proportion
A	.475	.476
B	.290	.316
C	.235	.207

by Suppes and Atkinson [12, p. 254] for choices on the last 100 trials of a 400-trial series. The predictions do not come quite as close to the data as those of two other models that have been applied to the same experiment (see chapter 2 of this volume and [12, ch. 11]), but, on the other hand, the present model is in the comfortable position of allowing for the possibility that the subjects' choice proportions might not have quite reached asymptote by the end of the experimental session.

To illustrate application of the present model to an experiment with a fixed arrangement of alternatives, it will be of interest to consider a study described by Atkinson (see chapter 2 of this volume). In Atkinson's experiment, the subject's task on each trial of a 340-trial series was simply to operate one or the other of two keys; when the choice was correct the subject was paid five cents and when it was incorrect he was fined five cents. Three groups of 20 subjects each were run on three simple contingent reinforcement schedules. In table 3 are presented the combination of π_i values for each group, the asymptotic probabilities of the A_1 response

TABLE 3

PREDICTED AND OBSERVED ASYMPTOTIC A_1 CHOICE PROPORTIONS FOR ATKINSON'S EXPERIMENT ON SIMPLE CONTINGENT REINFORCEMENT WITH TWO PAYOFF VALUES

Probability of Higher Payoff		Observed Proportion	Predicted Proportion
π_1	π_2		
.6	.5	.601	.600
.7	.5	.685	.700
.8	.5	.832	.800

predicted from equation (13), and the corresponding observed response proportions over the last 100 trials of the experiment. The fit of calculated to observed values is not quite as good as that reported by Atkinson for his "strong and weak conditioning" model, but it should be noted in this regard that the predictions from the present model require no evaluation of parameters from the data.

An important limitation of the present model in the simplified form presented above is that no means are provided for handling different absolute payoff values. Suppose, for example, that we attempted application to an experiment reported by Siegel and Goldstein [11] in which conditions were similar to those of the study by Atkinson represented in table 3 except that the three groups had the same reinforcement probabilities, $\pi_1 = 1 - \pi_2 = .75$, but different payoff combinations: Group I, simply information as to correctness of the subject's prediction; Group II, five cent payoff for correct responses and zero for errors; and Group III, five cent payoff for correct responses and five cent fine for errors. Both Group II and Group III represent cases for which equation (13) should hold, and there is no way within the present formulation of distinguishing between the two conditions. Applying equation (13), we obtain a prediction of .90 for asymptotic probability of the A_1 choice, which may be compared with the observed estimates of .86 and .95 for Groups II and III, respectively. The predicted value is not far off in either case; but it would be desirable to account also for the difference in outcomes for the two payoff combinations. Alternative ways of achieving this desideratum within the theory outlined in this section are currently under investigation.

Application of the present model to the prediction of asymptotic choice proportions in two-person situations such as those discussed in section 1.1 above is straightforward (see Appendix B) but wholly satisfactory results cannot be expected until a suitable way of handling different absolute payoff values has been incorporated into the theory. In the case of Game 1, the predicted outcome is an asymptotic A_1 probability of 0 for the row player and a B_1 probability of 1 for the column player, which is distinctly more promising than the prediction from the simple linear model (see table 1). But for Game 2, the theoretical asymptotic probabilities are .62 both for response A_1 of the row player and B_1 of the column player; the model comes close to the average for the two players, but fails to predict the observed difference between them. In the case of another similar experimental game studied in the Indiana laboratory,[4] again with 20 pairs of subjects and "points" as payoffs, and with the same payoff matrix as that of Game 2, the prediction of .62 for the asymptotic probability of both A_1 and B_1 agrees quite well with the observed terminal proportions of .58 and .62, respectively. This experiment differed procedurally from the one described in section 1.1 only in that the subjects were not permitted to see their opponents' payoffs. Thus the suggestion arises that a fully adequate theory will have to take explicit account of this variable.

---

[4] This study, conducted by Michael Cole and Allen Schneider, was reported at the fall 1961 meetings of the American Psychological Association.

Another two-person experiment to which the present model can readily be applied has been reported by Lieberman . With the matrix

$$
\begin{array}{cc}
 & B_1 \quad B_2 \\
\begin{array}{c} A_1 \\ A_2 \end{array} & \begin{bmatrix} 3 & -1 \\ -9 & 3 \end{bmatrix}
\end{array}
$$

of payoffs to the row player, two groups of ten subjects played for 300 trials against the experimenter who made his choices of B_1 and B_2 in accordance with a random "mixed strategy" of .25–.75 for one group and .50–.50 for the other. Payoffs were in chips, exchangeable for money. Predicted asymptotic probabilities of the A_1 choice are .31 and .67 for the .25–.75 and .50–.50 groups, respectively, and may be compared to observed proportions over the last 50 trials of .38 and .67.

On the whole, the "scanning model," even in the highly simplified form presented in this paper, appears to represent a distinct advance over the simple linear or stimulus-sampling models for the interpretation both of individual learning as a function of reward and of two-person interactions with varying payoffs. It should be emphasized, however, that scarcely a start has been made toward solving the mathematical problems of deriving statistics of learning data for the scanning model or toward handling the differential effects of different absolute magnitudes of reward.

APPENDIX A

Derivation of Asymptotic Choice Proportions for a Two-Person Game by Application of the Matching Theorem

We consider a two-person situation described by the matrix

$$
\begin{array}{cc}
 & B_1 \quad B_2 \\
\begin{array}{c} A_1 \\ A_2 \end{array} & \begin{bmatrix} a_{11} & a_{12} \\ a_{21} & a_{22} \end{bmatrix},
\end{array}
$$

where a_{ij} represents the probability that player A is effectively rewarded on a trial when the choices of players A and B are A_i and B_j, respectively; and the corresponding reward probability for player B is $1 - a_{ij}$. We shall denote by α and β the asymptotic probabilities of an A_1 choice by player A and a B_1 choice by player B, respectively. According to the matching theorem, the long-term proportion of occurrences of a given choice should equal its long-term proportion of reinforcements. To simplify the exposition, we shall here make use of the fact that in the case of both the linear model [8] and the stimulus-sampling model [9], the asymptotic probabilities α and β are known to exist. Noting also that in a two-choice situation a response is assumed to be reinforced either when it occurs and is rewarded or when the alternative response occurs and is not rewarded, we can write the "matching equations,"

(A1) $\alpha = u_{11} + u_{12} = u_{11}a_{11} + u_{12}a_{12} + u_{21}(1 - a_{21}) + u_{22}(1 - a_{22})$,

and

(A2) $\beta = u_{11} + u_{21} = u_{11}(1 - a_{11}) + u_{21}(1 - a_{21}) + u_{12}a_{12} + u_{22}a_{22}$,

where u_{ij} denotes asymptotic probability of the joint choice A_iB_j. Once the reward probabilities are specified for any particular experiment, we can solve the system consisting of equations (A1) and (A2) together with $\sum_{i,j}u_{ij} = 1$, obtaining, in general, expressions for any three of the u_{ij} in terms of the fourth and the reward parameter.

In the case of the matrix for Game 1 given in section 1.3, we have, substituting the a_{ij} values into equations (A1) and (A2), respectively,

$$u_{11} + u_{12} = \frac{1}{2}u_{12} + \frac{3}{4}u_{21} ,$$

and

$$u_{11} + u_{21} = u_{11} + \frac{3}{4}u_{21} + \frac{1}{2}u_{12} + u_{22} ,$$

which yield the solutions

$$u_{12} = \frac{3}{4} - 2u_{11} , \qquad u_{21} = \frac{1}{2} , \quad \text{and} \quad u_{22} = u_{11} - \frac{1}{4} .$$

Since u_{11} is a probability, its value must obviously fall in the range $.25 \leq u_{11} \leq .375$, and, using these bounds on u_{11}, we can in turn generate bounds on α and β:

$$.375 \leq \alpha = u_{11} + u_{12} \leq .500 \quad \text{and} \quad .750 \leq \beta = u_{11} + u_{21} \leq .875 .$$

The same procedure applied to the second game matrix of section 1.3 leads to the bounds given for that game in table 1.

APPENDIX B

Derivation of Asymptotic Choice Proportions for a Two-Person Game by Application of the Scanning Model

The technique of deriving asymptotic choice probabilities (assuming that they exist) for the type of situation discussed in this paper can conveniently be illustrated in terms of the two experimental games discussed in sections 1.1 and 1.2. For Game 1, the possible combination of outcomes with their associated conditional probabilities are as follows:

PLAYER A				PLAYER B		
A_1	A_2	Probability		B_1	B_2	Probability
0	1	β^2		4	2	α^2
2	1	$(1 - \beta)\beta$		4	0	$\alpha(1 - \alpha)$
0	4	$\beta(1 - \beta)$		3	2	$(1 - \alpha)\alpha$
2	4	$(1 - \beta)^2$		3	0	$(1 - \alpha)^2$

If we consider the first row for player A, and refer to the appropriate payoff matrix of section 1.1, the true asymptotic conditional probability that an A_1 choice will eventuate in the outcome of 0 payoff is β, and the probability that an A_2 choice will eventuate in a payoff of 1 is also β. Thus, according to the theory, the probability that player A (when he considers his two possible responses on any given trial) will expect this combination of outcomes should asymptotically equal β^2. The other probabilities are obtained similarly. Now the theoretical probability that player A will choose A_1 is equal to the probability that he will expect A_1 to yield the greater payoff, and the same holds for player B's probability of choosing B_1. Therefore, we have

$$\alpha = (1 - \beta)\beta \ ,$$

and

$$\beta = \alpha^2 + \alpha(1 - \alpha) + (1 - \alpha)\alpha + (1 - \alpha)^2 = 1 \ ,$$

whence $\alpha = 0$.

For Game 2, the combinations of outcomes and conditional probabilities are as follows:

PLAYER A				PLAYER B		
A_1	A_2	Probability		B_1	B_2	Probability
1	2	β^2		3	1	α^2
1	0	$\beta(1 - \beta)$		3	4	$\alpha(1 - \alpha)$
3	2	$(1 - \beta)\beta$		2	1	$(1 - \alpha)\alpha$
3	0	$(1 - \beta)^2$		2	4	$(1 - \alpha)^2$

These yield

$$\alpha = \beta(1 - \beta) + (1 - \beta)\beta + (1 - \beta)^2 = 1 - \beta^2 \ ,$$
$$\beta = \alpha^2 + \alpha(1 - \alpha) = \alpha \ ,$$

whence $\alpha = \beta = .618$.

REFERENCES

[1]   BOWER, G. H., Response strengths and choice probability: a consideration of two combination rules, in *Logic, Methodology and Philosophy of Science, Proceedings of the 1960 International Congress*, E. Nagel, P. Suppes, and A. Tarski, eds., Stanford, Calif: Stanford Univ. Press, 1962.

[2]   BURKE, C. J., Applications of a linear model to two-person interactions, chap. 9 in *Studies in Mathematical Learning Theory*, R. R. Bush and W. K. Estes, eds., Stanford, Calif.: Stanford Univ. Press, 1959.

[3]   BUSH, R. R., and F. MOSTELLER, *Stochastic Models for Learning*, New York: Wiley, 1955.

[4]   ESTES, W. K., Of models and men, *Amer. Psychologist*, 1957, **12**, 609-17.

[5]   ESTES, W. K., Theory of learning with constant, variable, or contingent schedules of reinforcement, *Psychometrika*, 1957, **22**, 113-32.

[6]   ESTES, W. K., and M. JOHNS, Probability learning with ambiguity in the reinforcing stimulus, *Amer. J. Psychol.*, 1958, **71**, 219-28.

[7] ESTES, W. K., and J. H. STRAUGHAN, Analysis of a verbal conditioning situation in terms of statistical learning theory, *J. Exptl. Psychol.*, 1954, **47**, 225–34.

[8] ESTES, W. K., and P. SUPPES, Foundations of linear models, chap. 8 in *Studies in Mathematical Learning Theory*, R. R. Bush and W. K. Estes, eds., Stanford, Calif.: Stanford Univ. Press, 1959.

[9] ESTES, W. K., and P. SUPPES, "Foundations of statistical learning theory, II: The stimulus sampling model for simple learning," Technical Report No. 26, Contract Nonr-225(17), Institute for Mathematical Studies in the Social Sciences, Stanford University, Stanford, Calif., 1959.

[10] KARLIN, S., Some random walks arising in learning models, *Pac. J. Math.*, 1953, **3**, 725–56.

[11] SIEGEL, S., and D. A. GOLDSTEIN, Decision-making behavior in a two-choice uncertain outcome situation, *J. Exptl. Psychol.*, 1959, **57**, 37–42.

[12] SUPPES, P., and R. C. ATKINSON, *Markov Learning Models for Multiperson Interactions*, Stanford, Calif.: Stanford Univ. Press, 1960.

[13] TATSUOKA, M., and F. MOSTELLER, A commuting-operator model, chap. 12 in *Studies in Mathematical Learning Theory*, R. R. Bush and W. K. Estes, eds., Stanford, Calif.: Stanford Univ. Press, 1959.

The Learning of Choices Between Bets[1]

Morton P. Friedman, Gilbert Padilla, and Harold Gelfand,[2]
University of California, Los Angeles

A "choice between bets" situation was analyzed in terms of Estes's scanning model. On each trial, the subject was offered a choice between two alternative bets. He was asked to choose the bet which was most likely to win on that trial. Following his choice, feedback was given for both bets. Wins and losses on both bets were programmed independently according to simple noncontingent random schedules. The principal independent variables were the values of the probabilities of wins and losses on the two bets. All pairwise combinations of .8, .5, and .2 were employed, yielding six main experimental conditions. An additional condition was run in which subjects received feedback only for the choice made on each trial. Twenty-four subjects were assigned to each experimental condition. The scanning model adequately predicted final choice proportions for all conditions. A linear learning model in conjunction with the scanning model was applied to the sequential statistics with some success.

Many of the experimental studies dealing with decision theory (see Edwards, 1961, for an extensive review) have employed a test situation in which the subject is offered a choice among alternative bets. In this paper, we present an analysis of this type of experiment in terms of mathematical learning theory.

Before considering the decision task used in the experiment, it will be helpful to review the simple probability learning task which has been the focus of much research in mathematical learning theory. A typical experimental paradigm for binary choice probability learning is the following: On each trial, the subject is asked to predict whether a bet, say A, will win or lose. Following his choice he is presented with one of two outcomes: A wins, or A loses. In the simple "noncontingent" experiment, the sequence of wins and losses is programmed according to a random schedule independent of the subject's predictions; on every trial, a win occurs with probability π_A and a loss occurs with probability $1 - \pi_A$. It is the noncontingent situation that "probability matching" obtains; that is, after a sufficiently long series of trials, the relative frequency with which a win is predicted tends to match the relative frequency

[1] This research was supported in part by a grant from the University Research Committee, University of California, Los Angeles, and in part by the Office of Naval Research (Nonr 233(58)).

[2] Present address: University of Michigan, Ann Arbor, Michigan.

This article appeared in *J. math. Psychol.*, 1964, **1**, 375–385.

with which a win actually occurs. (See Estes, 1964, for a discussion of conditions under which probability matching is generally obtained.)

We will be concerned with a more complex choice situation which contains elements of the simple experiment just described. The paradigm for the experimental procedure is shown in Fig. 1. On each trial, the subject is offered a choice between two bets, Bet A and Bet B. He is asked to choose the bet which is most likely to win on that trial. The wins and losses on both bets are programmed independently according to simple non-contingent schedules. Therefore, on each trial, Bet A wins with probability π_A and loses with probability $1 - \pi_A$ and Bet B wins with probability π_B and loses with probability $1 - \pi_B$. Following his choice, the subject is shown one of the four combined outcomes in Fig. 1: Both A and B win, A wins and B loses, B wins and A loses, or both A and B lose. The probabilities of these various outcomes are obtained by multiplying the probabilities of the separate outcomes on A and B.

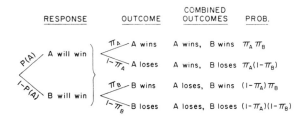

FIG. 1.   Experimental paradigm for choice between bets.

The experimental paradigm just described for choosing between bets is similar to situations frequently employed in experimental studies of decision theory. The concern in these studies has been whether the subjects' choices are consistent with a theory of rational choice. Research in mathematical learning theory has, on the other hand, generally emphasized the relation between psychological processes of choice and particular experimental procedures. For example, in analyzing the paradigm for choosing between bets in terms of mathematical learning theory, we begin by noting that Bets A and B separately might be regarded as simple noncontingent binary choice experiments. And generalizing from the binary choice experiment, subjects should come to predict or expect A to win with probability π_A and to lose with probability $1 - \pi_A$, and expect B to win with probability π_B and to lose with probability $1 - \pi_B$. Another way of stating this is to say that our training procedure has had the effect of building up separate and independent response strengths toward choosing A and choosing B. Thus, the situation involves two competing responses, and the question of primary theoretical interest is simply this: How do these response strengths combine to determine the overt choice of the subject?

The particular model we will apply to the results was suggested by Estes's (1962) analysis of choice experiments with differential reward. The gist of the model, termed the "scanning model," is that before an overt choice is made on a given trial, the subject scans the response alternatives and generates a covert win or loss prediction for each alternative. The overt response is determined by the pattern of covert predictions.

TABLE 1

ASYMPTOTIC PROBABILITIES OF COVERT PREDICTIONS AND RESPONSE PROBABILITIES GIVEN THE COVERT PREDICTIONS FOR THE SCANNING MODEL

Covert prediction	Asymptotic probability	Pr (A choice | covert predict.)
A will win, B will win	$\pi_A \pi_B$	$P(A)$
A will win, B will lose	$\pi_A(1 - \pi_B)$	1
A will lose, B will win	$(1 - \pi_A) \pi_B$	0
A will lose, B will lose	$(1 - \pi_A)(1 - \pi_B)$	$P(A)$

The essentials of the model are outlined in Table 1. It is assumed that before an overt choice is made on a given trial, the subject scans the response alternatives and generates for each alternative a covert win or loss prediction for each response. The possible covert predictions and the asymptotic probabilities of their occurrence are shown in Table 1. The covert predictions mirror directly the possible trial outcomes. The asymptotic probabilities follow from the assumption that probability matching obtains on the two independent covert response processes. Table 1 also shows the probabilities of an overt choice of Bet A for each pattern of covert predictions. These probabilities derive from the following response rule: "Always choose the response with the preferred predicted outcome. When both responses are equally preferred, choose the response which was first considered on that trial." It is assumed that a win is always preferred over a loss and that the probability that the A response is considered first is equal to the current choice probability of the A response, $P(A)$. Summing the overt response probabilities weighted by the probabilities of the corresponding covert predictions and solving for $P(A)$, we obtain the following expression for the asymptotic probability of choosing Bet A:

$$P(A) = \frac{\pi_A(1 - \pi_B)}{\pi_A + \pi_B - 2\pi_A\pi_B} . \tag{1}$$

In the experiment reported here, we tested predictions arising from Eq. 1 by running groups of subjects using different combinations of values of π_A and π_B.

METHOD

Subjects

The subjects were 168 introductory psychology students at the University of California, Los Angeles. Participation in experiments was a course requirement.

Apparatus

The subjects' panel was 12 inches high and 18 inches wide. It was set at a 45 degree angle and placed on a small table. A blue pilot lamp centered on the upper part of the panel was used to indicate the start of a trial. On the lower part of the panel were two pushbutton response switches set 9 in. apart. The left and right response switches were labeled "*A*" and "*B*" respectively. Two pilot lamps arranged vertically above each response switch were used to indicate the trial outcomes. The upper lamp was green and the lower lamp was red. The green lamps were labeled "win" and the red lamps were labeled "lose." All programming and recording equipment was located in a control room which adjoined the experimental room.

Procedure

Subjects were run individually. They were seated before the response panel and read the following instructions:

"This is a very simple experiment. It consists of a series of repeated trials. On each trial, you are to bet on one of the events *A* or *B*. You indicate your bet by pressing either the button marked *A* or the button marked *B*. If you think *A* will win on that trial, press the button marked *A*; if you think that *B* will win on that trial, press the button marked *B*. Will you now please press the button marked *A*, then the button marked *B*.

First of all, at the beginning of each trial, this blue lamp will go on. This is your signal to make your bet. If you think that *A* is most likely to win, press the button marked *A*. If you think that *B* is most likely to win, press the button marked *B*. After you have made your choice, either the win or lose lamp will light above *A*, and at the same time, either the win or lose lamp will light above *B*. Note that it is possible for both *A* and *B* to win on a trial, and it is possible for both *A* and *B* to lose on a trial. A short time after the outcome lamps go out the blue lamp will light again indicating the start of another trial.

After you have made your bet by pressing either button *A* or *B*, place your hand on this black cross mark, and keep it there until the blue lamp goes on again, indicating the start of another trial.

Are there any questions?"

Questions about the procedure were answered by paraphrasing relevant parts of the instructions. After the reading of instructions, the 300 experimental trials were run off without interruption.

On each trial, the blue signal light remained on until the subject pressed one of the response switches. Unlimited response time was allowed. The outcome lamps came on as soon as the subject responded. One of four outcomes occurred on each trial: the lighting of the "win" or "lose" lamp above response A coupled with the lighting of the "win" or "lose" lamp above response B. The outcome lamps remained on for 1.5 seconds. Following a 1.5 second intertial interval, the blue lamp came on again indicating the start of the next trial.

DESIGN

The principal independent variable was the combination of values of π_A and π_B, the probabilities of win outcomes on A and B respectively. All pairwise combinations of the values .8, .5, and .2 were used as π_A and π_B, so there were six main π-value conditions in all. Twenty-four subjects were randomly assigned to each condition.

For each π-value condition, four sequences of outcomes were constructed using a random procedure without any restriction on the obtained number of wins and losses on the two bets. Each sequence was 300 trials long. Six subjects were run on each sequence in each π-value condition. For each sequence, the designation of the outcomes as A or B on the subject's panel was counterbalanced.

In addition to the main experimental conditions just described, a group of 24 subjects was run with a partial feedback procedure. Subjects in this condition were run with π_A and π_B equal to .5 for the first 20 trials. They were then instructed that on all further trials, they would receive the outcomes only for the bet they chose on that trial. Thus, the win or lose lamps came on only above the button they pressed on each trial. Following these additional instructions, subjects were run for 300 trials with $\pi_A = .8$, and $\pi_B = .5$ using the same sequences as were used in the $\pi_A = .8$, $\pi_B = .5$ condition described earlier. The partial feedback condition was included to assess the generality of the scanning model in the present experimental situation. The 20 preliminary trials before partial feedback was introduced served to make it clear to the subjects that there were four outcomes on each trial. From the probability matching considerations discussed earlier subjects should tend to expect A to win with probability .8, and expect B to win with probability .5.[3] It was expected that the asymptotic choice probabilities would be the same for the partial feedback condition as for the $\pi_A = .8$, $\pi_B = .5$ condition which received complete feedback.

---

[3] In order for the expectancies to approach π_a and π_b, it must be assumed that the overt probability of an A choice does not approach 1 or 0 too quickly. This is based on the notion that subject must receive a number of win and loss outcomes on each alternative before the expectancies match the objective probabilities.

RESULTS AND DISCUSSION

MEAN CHOICE RESPONDING

Mean learning curves are shown in Fig. 2. Proportion of choices of the A response averaged over all subjects are shown in successive 25-trial blocks for each π-value condition. The experimental conditions are labeled so that the first number denotes the value of π_A and the second number denotes the value of π_B. The experimental condition labeled 80-50(P) refers to the group which was run with partial feedback. The first 20 trials for the 80-50(P) condition which were run with a 50-50 schedule are not shown in Fig. 2.

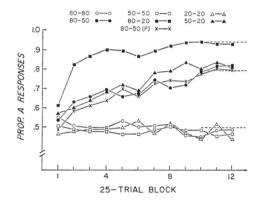

FIG. 2. Proportion of A responses in blocks of 25 trials over the 300-trial experimental session for the seven experimental conditions. The dotted lines indicate asymptotic predictions of the scanning model.

Figure 2 shows that the proportion of A choices for the three equal π-value conditions, 80-80, 50-50, and 20-20, stay close to .50 chance level. For all the other conditions, in which π_A was greater than π_B, the final proportion of A choices was greater than .5. For the 80-50, 80-50(P) and 50-20 conditions, the final proportion of A choices was slightly above .80. For the 80-20 condition, in which the discrepancy between π_A and π_B was the greatest, the final proportion of A choices was above .90. Also the rate of learning appeared to be the fastest in the 80-20 condition.

Final performance levels for the experimental conditions were compared using a Scheffé analysis for multiple comparisons with an .05 significance level. The score used in this analysis was the total number of A responses over the final 75 trials. The results of the Scheffé analysis may be summarized as follows: (1) The 80-20 condition was significantly different from all other conditions; (2) the 80-50, 80-50(P), and 50-20 conditions were not significantly different from each other, but were reliably different from all other conditions; (3) similarly, the 80-80, 50-50, and 20-20 conditions were not significantly different from each other, but were reliably different from all other conditions.

The means and standard deviations of the proportion of choices of the A response over the last 75 trials are shown in Table 2. Using (1), predicted asymptotic probabilities of A choices were computed for each experimental condition. These values are also shown in Table 2. The fit of obtained to predicted proportions appears to be very good, especially in view of the fact that the predictions involved no quantities estimated from the data. Judging from these data, the scanning model appears to offer a good description of mean choice responding in this experimental situation.

TABLE 2

PREDICTED AND OBTAINED PROPORTIONS OF A RESPONSES, AND STANDARD DEVIATION OF THE PROPORTION OF A RESPONSES OVER THE LAST 75 TRIALS (TRIALS 226-300)

Condition	Proportion of A responses		Obtained S.D.
	Predicted	Obtained	
80-80	.500	.474	.108
80-50	.800	.813	.163
80-50(P)	.800	.801	.133
80-20	.941	.937	.084
50-50	.500	.476	.085
50-20	.800	.821	.142
20-20	.500	.468	.121

It should be pointed out, however, that there is at least one other response rule for the scanning model which also yields (1). It will be recalled that the response rule discussed earlier assumed an overt response for each possible pattern of covert predictions. Alternatively, it could be assumed that when wins or losses on both bets were predicted, these predictions are discarded and a new set of predictions are made. Stated more formally, the alternative response rule is: "Always choose the response with the preferred predicted outcome. When both covert predicted outcomes are equally preferred, make a new set of predictions until an unambiguous prediction obtains."[4]

The kernel of the scanning model is the notion that overt choices are based on the *pattern* of covert predictions. Because only informational signals were used as out-

[4] The alternate response rule was suggested by Gordon Bower. He also has shown that under quite reasonable conditions, (1) could be derived from both of his random walk choice models A and B (Bower, 1960).

comes in the experiment, a simple response rule and utility scale (a preference of a win over a loss) sufficed. In experiments involving monetary costs and rewards as outcomes, we would not expect the same rules to work. We would, however, expect that as costs and rewards were introduced, these would affect only the response rule and not the process of scanning the response alternatives and generating predictions. The reader is referred to Estes's (1962) paper for a discussion of reward in connection with the scanning model.

SEQUENTIAL STATISTICS

Although the experiment was designed primarily to test the over-all choice predictions of the scanning model, some information was obtained regarding the sequential aspects of responding. Table 3 shows proportions of A responses conditional on the outcomes of the preceding trial for the six main experimental conditions. The proportions were obtained by tabulating the corresponding conditional response frequencies for all subjects over the last 75 trials of the experiment, and dividing by the total frequency of each outcome. In computing proportions for the three equal π-value conditions, the B response frequencies following "lose on A, win on B" outcomes were combined with A response frequencies following "win on A, lose on B" outcomes; similarly, A response frequencies following "lose on A, win on B" outcomes were combined with B response frequencies following "win on A, lose on B" outcomes. This combining was done to improve the estimates of the response proportions.

TABLE 3

OBTAINED AND PREDICTED PROPORTIONS OF A RESPONSES FOLLOWING
VARIOUS TRIAL OUTCOMES OVER THE LAST 75 TRIALS OF THE EXPERIMENT

Trial outcome	80-80		80-50		80-20		50-50		50-20		20-20	
	Obt.	Pred.	Obt.	Pred.	Obt.	Pred.	Obt.	Pred.	Obt.	Pred.	Obt.	Pred.
A wins, B wins	.495	.500	.791	.793	.920	.929	.501	.500	.790	.774	.471	.500
A wins, B loses	.586	.587	.845	.830	.951	.949	.572	.560	.880	.830	.463	.588
A loses, B wins	.414	.413	.737	.730	.851	.902	.428	.440	.768	.730	.537	.412
A loses, B loses	.480	.500	.741	.774	.873	.929	.461	.500	.778	.794	.462	.500

Some evaluative comments about these results can be made by comparing the conditional proportions in Table 3 with the over-all mean response proportions in Table 1. First, the response proportions following the two unambiguous outcomes, "win on A, lose on B" and "lose on A, win on B" show the "positive recency" behavior which is typically obtained in simple probability learning experiments. For example, in the 80-80 condition, the proportion of A responses following a "win on A, lose on B" outcome is .586, which is above the over-all mean proportion of .474. Similarly, following a "lose on A, win on B" outcome, the proportion of A responses drops below the mean response level. This general result for the unambiguous outcomes holds for all conditions except the 20-20 condition. A second point about the results in Table 3 is that for the unequal π-value conditions, the proportion of A responses following the two ambiguous outcomes—wins or losses on both bets, are below the over-all response proportions. Further, there is more regression following a "lose on A, lose on B" outcome than a "win on A, win on B" outcome.

As an illustration of how a learning model might be applied to this data, we have derived predictions from a linear learning model in conjunction with the scanning model. In order to understand how the model was applied, we will need a more general statement of the scanning model. Let $p_{A,n}$ denote the probability that a win on A is expected on the nth trial, and $p_{B,n}$ the probability that a win on B is expected on the nth trial. Substituting $p_{A,n}$ for π_A and $p_{B,n}$ for π_B in Table 1 we obtain a more general statement of the scanning model. The probability of a choice of A on trial n is

$$P(A)_n = \frac{p_{A,n}(1 - p_{B,n})}{p_{A,n} + p_{B,n} - 2p_{A,n}p_{B,n}} . \qquad (2)$$

The learning model employs the same leraning assumptions which have proved useful in the analysis of the simple noncontingent probability learning experiment. We assume that if a win outcome on A occurs on trial n, then the probability of expecting A to win, $p_{A,n}$, is increased in a linear fashion; a loss outcome is assumed to decrease $p_{A,n}$. More specifically:

$$p_{A,n+1} = \begin{cases} (1 - \theta) p_{A,n} + \theta & \text{if } A \text{ wins on trial } n \\ (1 - \theta) p_{A,n} & \text{if } A \text{ loses on trial } n \end{cases} \qquad (3)$$

We assume the same process for the probability of expecting a win on B on trial n, $p_{B,n}$. One of the consequences of these assumptions is probability matching—$p_{A,n}$ approaches π_A and $p_{B,n}$ approaches π_B as the number of trials gets large. We already have indirect evidence for matching from the asymptotic mean choice proportions. But the adequacy of these learning assumptions is best evaluated by considering the local dependencies between outcomes and responses such as those shown in Table 3. The theoretical expressions for these dependencies involve expectations of ratios of linear operators, and we are unable to derive explicit prediction equations. As an approximation, expressions for the probabilities of the covert responses contingent on win and loss outcomes were substituted for $p_{A,n}$ and $p_{B,n}$ in (2). Thus, the approximation essentially involves substitution of a ratio of expected values for the expected value of a ratio.[5] The expressions for the covert responses are those derived for the simple linear model described above as applied to the noncontingent probability learning experiment. (See, for example, Anderson, 1959.)

The predicted probabilities shown in Table 3 were computed assuming $p_{A,n}$ and $p_{B,n}$ equal to their theoretical asymptotes. The same value of the learning parameter θ was used for the learning processes associated with covert predictions of both A and B. An estimate of θ equal to .06 was derived by fitting the predicted to the obtained conditional proportions in the 80-80 condition using a minimum least squares criterion. The same θ value of .06 was used to obtain the predicted proportions in the other experimental conditions.

Considering Table 3 as a whole, the qualitative agreement is quite good, in that the predicted ordering of proportions for each condition (excepting the 20-20 condition) agrees with the obtained values. It is interesting that the learning model correctly predicts the regression of response probability following "win on A and B" and "loss on both A and B" outcomes which we have previously noted in the data for the unequal π-value conditions. In fact, the learning model makes the interesting prediction that, asymptotically, choice probability in the unequal π-value conditions should continue to drop towards chance responding in a run of successive wins or losses on both bets. Unfortunately, the asymptotic or near-asymptotic data on this point are too scanty to check out the prediction.

In some cases, the quantitative fits in Table 3 can be improved by employing different parameter values for the two learning processes. However, in our explorations of various parameter values, we have found no clear relation between θ values and π-value conditions. The results in Table 3 indicate that the learning assumptions employed here have some merit, but it is clear that more data is needed for a proper evaluation of these assumptions as well as other reasonable learning models.

The most deviant predictions are for the 20-20 condition, in which negative recency, rather than the predicted positive recency, occurred following the unambiguous outcomes. This result was investigated further by calculating the proportion of A responses following the unambiguous outcomes in successive 50-trial blocks of the session for the 80-80, 50-50, and 20-20 conditions. In the 80-80 and 50-50 conditions, positive recency developed within the first 100 trials and remained stable over the rest of the session. In the 20-20 condition, there was no consistent pattern of either positive or negative recency. We are unable to account for this result, except to point out the obvious: The over-all level of reinforcement is very low for the 20-20 condition.

---

[5] In terms of the learning model, (1) represents the same sort of approximation for the asymptotic value of $P(A)$. A better approximation for the asymptotic value of $P(A)$ has been worked out by Raphael Hanson of Long Beach State College. For values of θ which seem appropriate for our sequential results, Hanson's approximation yields values for $P(A)$ which are within .01 of those given by (1).

In such situations, win and loss outcomes appear to have different consequences for choice behavior. This finding deserves further investigation.

Another shortcoming of the learning model shows up when the θ-value of .06 estimated from the sequential statistics is used to predict learning curves using an expected-operator approximation. The predicted learning curves for the unequal π-value conditions approach asymptote faster than obtained functions. A similar effect is found in the noncontingent probability learning situation when the θ-value estimated from the sequential statistics is used to predict rates of learning.

REFERENCES

ANDERSON, N. H. An analysis of sequential dependencies. In R. R. Bush and W. K. Estes (Eds.), *Studies in mathematical learning theory*. Stanford, Calif.: Stanford Univ. Press, 1959.

BOWER, G. H. Response strengths and choice probability: a consideration of two combination rules. In E. Nagle, P. Suppes and A. Tarski (Eds.), *Methodology and Philosophy of Science, Proceedings of the 1960 International Congress*. Stanford, Calif.: Stanford Univ. Press, 1960.

EDWARDS, W. Behavioral decision theory. *Ann. Rev. Psychol.*, 1961, **12**.

ESTES, W. K. Theoretical treatments of differential reward in multiple choice learning and two-person interactions. In J. Criswell, H. Solomon, and P. Suppes (Eds.), *Mathematical methods in small group processes*. Stanford, Calif.: Stanford Univ. Press, 1962.

ESTES, W. K. Probability Learning. In A. Melton (Ed.) *Categories of human learning*. New York: Academic Press, 1964.

RECEIVED: November 18, 1963

Choice Behavior and Reward Structure[1]

JEROME L. MYERS, *University of Massachusetts*, and RICHARD C. ATKINSON, *Stanford University*

A model for choice behavior under conditions of variable payoff is presented. Predictions of choice probabilities are evaluated for an array of experiments involving different event probabilities, differential-payoff structures, two and three choices, and contingent and noncontingent reinforcement. An extension of the model to the prediction of response time is also considered.

A growing body of data, from both animal and human experimentation, reflects the importance of magnitude of reinforcement in choice behavior. In this paper we attempt a quantitative description of the role of this variable. The model under consideration was originally proposed by Atkinson (1962), who showed that it was applicable to both contingent and noncontingent reinforcement and to any number of response alternatives. We have extended this work by deriving predictions of response times, and of conditional statistics that were not previously presented. We have also considered ways of formulating the model to yield predictions for more general reward-punishment combinations than those previously considered. In addition, the observed and predicted values of a number of measures obtained from several different experiments are displayed in this paper. We hope that the data presented will provide an impetus to the development of alternative models, and that the description of the data by our model will provide a criterion against which to judge other models.

The model that we will consider assumes a population of stimulus elements, each of which is conditioned to one and only one response. It is further assumed that a

[1] Support for this research was in part provided by NIMH grant M-3803 and NSF grant G-11228 to the first author and by NIMH grant M-5184 to the second author. Computer time and programming assistance for the analyses reported in this paper were paid for by NIMH grant M-6154. Additional support was provided by a special fellowship awarded by the U. S. Public Health Service to the first author.

This article appeared in *J. math. Psychol.*, 1964, **1**, 170–203.

single element is randomly sampled from the stimulus population on each trial, and
that the subject's response depends upon the state of conditioning of the sampled
element. These assumptions are common to other stimulus sampling models (Atkinson
and Estes, 1963); however, the present model differs from its predecessors, for it
is assumed that an element may be at one of two stages of conditioning, either weakly
or strongly conditioned to a response. This modification of stimulus sampling theory
provides the basis for a fairly general analysis of reinforcement variables.

AXIOMS

Consider an experiment in which on each trial the subject must select one of r
mutually exclusive and exhaustive responses $(A_1, \cdots, A_i, \cdots, A_r)$. The ith response
corresponds to the prediction of the ith member of a set of r mutually exclusive and
exhaustive events $(E_1, \cdots, E_i, \cdots, E_r)$. Associated with each response-event combination is some outcome such as the gain or loss of an amount of money. In the experiments
that we examine the $r \times r$ set of outcomes is constant over trials. We will first consider
axioms for the special case in which each $A_i - E_i$ combination is followed by the
same gain, and all other response-event combinations are followed by the same loss.
This situation may be represented by the following payoff matrix

$$
\begin{array}{c}
\begin{array}{cccc} E_1 & E_2 & \cdots & E_r \end{array} \\
\begin{array}{c} A_1 \\ A_2 \\ \vdots \\ A_r \end{array}
\left[\begin{array}{cccc}
w & -x & \cdots & -x \\
-x & w & \cdots & -x \\
\cdot & \cdot & \cdot & \cdot \\
-x & -x & \cdots & w
\end{array} \right]
\end{array}
$$

where w is the gain associated with a correct prediction, and x is the loss associated
with an incorrect prediction. We shall henceforth refer to this case as the symmetric
payoff condition. We will later consider modifications of the axioms appropriate to
the more general nonsymmetric case in which the amount of gain or loss varies as a
function of the particular response-event combinations.

STIMULUS AXIOM. *The stimulus situation associated with the onset of each trial is
represented by a set of N stimulus elements. On each trial exactly one element is randomly
sampled from this set.*

CONDITIONING-STATE AXIOM. *On every trial each stimulus element is conditioned to
exactly one response; furthermore, the element is either strongly or weakly conditioned
to that response. (The strong conditioning state for the A_i response is denoted by S_i,
the weak state by W_i.)*

RESPONSE AXIOM. *If the sampled element is conditioned to the A_i response (either weakly or strongly) then that response will occur with probability 1.*

CONDITIONING AXIOMS:

C1. Stimulus elements that are not sampled on a trial do not change their conditioning state.

C2. If event E_i occurs, then (a) if the sampled element is strongly conditioned to the A_i response it remains so, and (b) if the sampled element is weakly conditioned to the A_i response there is a probability μ that it becomes strongly conditioned.

C3. If event E_j occurs $(i \neq j)$, then (a) if the sampled element is strongly conditioned to the A_i response there is a probability δ that it becomes weakly conditioned to A_i, and (b) if the sampled element is weakly conditioned to the A_i response there is a probability δ that it becomes weakly conditioned to the A_j response.

Figure 1 illustrates the transitions that are possible under the conditions of Axioms C2 and C3 for the two-response case. Note that an element can transit only to a directly adjoining conditioning state.

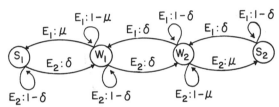

FIG. 1. Possible transitions among conditioning states for the weak-strong model.

MATHEMATICAL DEVELOPMENT

ASYMPTOTIC CHOICE PROPORTIONS IN THE TWO-RESPONSE CASE

We begin by considering the two-response case in which the matrix of outcomes is symmetric. The event probabilities are specified by π_i, the probability of event E_1 on trial n, given that response A_i was made on that trial. Thus

$$\pi_1 = P(E_{1,n} \mid A_{1,n}) \qquad \pi_2 = P(E_{1,n} \mid A_{2,n})$$
$$1 - \pi_1 = P(E_{2,n} \mid A_{1,n}) \qquad 1 - \pi_2 = P(E_{2,n} \mid A_{2,n}) \qquad (1)$$

Now assume that the kth element is sampled on some trial n. The tree diagrams of Fig. 2 illustrate how the conditioning states of that element may change. For example, suppose that the sampled element is in state S_1. By the Response Axiom, the subject will make an A_1 response, which will be reinforced with probability π_1 and not reinforced with probability $1 - \pi_1$. By Axiom C2, if the response is reinforced, the conditioning state will not change. If the response is not reinforced, then (by Axiom C3) with probability δ the conditioning state becomes W_1. Similar applications of the axioms permit us to completely specify the possible ways in which each conditioning state may change.

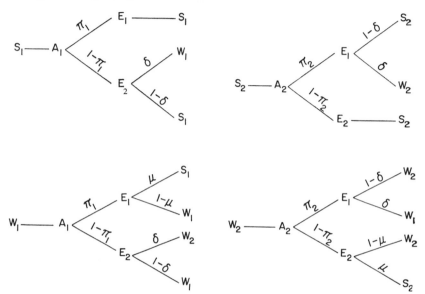

FIG. 2. Transitions among conditioning states for the subset of trials on which an element is sampled.

We will denote the subsequence of trials on which the kth stimulus element is sampled by ω_k. We next define a random variable associated with the kth element that takes the conditioning states S_1, W_1, W_2, and S_2 as its values. It can be shown that over the subsequence of trials, ω_k, the random variable forms a Markov chain.

$$
\begin{array}{c}
\quad\quad\quad S_1 \quad\quad\quad\quad\quad W_1 \quad\quad\quad\quad\quad\quad W_2 \quad\quad\quad\quad S_2 \\
\begin{array}{c} S_1 \\ W_1 \\ W_2 \\ S_2 \end{array}
\left[
\begin{array}{cccc}
1 - \delta(1 - \pi_1) & \delta(1 - \pi_1) & 0 & 0 \\
\mu\pi_1 & 1 - \mu\pi_1 - \delta(1 - \pi_1) & \delta(1 - \pi_1) & 0 \\
0 & \delta\pi_2 & 1 - \delta\pi_2 - \mu(1 - \pi_2) & \mu(1 - \pi_2) \\
0 & 0 & \delta\pi_2 & 1 - \delta\pi_2
\end{array}
\right]
\end{array}
$$

$$(2)$$

For simplicity the states will be numbered as follows: $1 = S_1$, $2 = W_1$, $3 = W_2$, and $4 = S_2$. Next, consider the quantity $p_{ij}^{(m)}$, the probability of the kth element being in state j on the mth trial of subsequence ω_k, given that on trial 1 the element was in state i. Since the four-state Markov chain defined by Eq. 2 is irreducible and aperiodic, the quantity u_j exists, where

$$u_j = \lim_{m \to \infty} p_{ij}^{(m)}. \tag{3}$$

The u_j's may be computed by

$$u_j = \frac{D_j}{D_1 + D_2 + D_3 + D_4},$$

where

$$D_1 = \pi_1 \pi_2^2, \qquad\qquad D_3 = (1 - \pi_1)^2 \pi_2 \varphi,$$

$$D_2 = (1 - \pi_1) \pi_2^2 \varphi, \qquad D_4 = (1 - \pi_2)(1 - \pi_1)^2, \tag{5}$$

and $\varphi = \delta/\mu$.

Atkinson (1962) has shown that at asymptote, the probability of an A_1 response for the complete N-element process is a simple function of the u_j's. Specifically,

$$\lim_{n \to \infty} P(A_{1,n}) = u_1 + u_2$$

$$= \frac{\pi_1 \pi_2^2 + (1 - \pi_1) \pi_2^2 \varphi}{\pi_1 \pi_2^2 + (1 - \pi_2)(1 - \pi_1)^2 + [(1 - \pi_1) \pi_2^2 + (1 - \pi_1)^2 \pi_2] \varphi}. \tag{6}$$

Note that the expression is independent of N, the number of stimulus elements. Henceforth, to simplify notation the trial subscripts will be omitted when asymptotic expressions are referred to; i.e.,

$$\lim_{n \to \infty} P(A_{1,n}) = P(A_1).$$

Experiments in which noncontingent reinforcement is employed are frequently encountered; reinforcement is said to be noncontingent if the occurrence of an E_i event on trial n is independent of the response made on that trial. In such instances $\pi_1 = \pi_2 = \pi$, and Eq. 6 simplifies to

$$P(A_1) = \frac{\pi^3 + \pi^2(1 - \pi) \varphi}{\pi^3 + (1 - \pi)^3 + \pi(1 - \pi) \varphi}. \tag{7}$$

If

$$0 \leqslant \mu \leqslant 1, \qquad 0 < \delta \leqslant 1, \tag{8}$$

then $P(A_1)$ is a monotonically decreasing function of φ and has the bounds

$$\pi \leqslant P(A_1) < \frac{\pi^3}{\pi^3 + (1 - \pi)^3}. \tag{9}$$

If μ equals 0, then the transition matrix for each element is reduced to two states, W_1 and W_2. In this case we have a one-stage, N-element model with a single conditioning parameter δ, and the limit of $P(A_{1,n})$ is π. This special case of our model is precisely that described by Estes (1959) and Atkinson and Estes (1963) as the "pattern" model. The more general formulation presented in this paper has the advantage over the pattern model of being able to account for observed values of $P(A_1)$ greater than π. Such values are generally obtained in choice experiments involving animals, choice experiments involving human subjects playing for monetary payoffs, and frequently in human choice experiments not involving payoff when run for several hundred trials.

When δ equals μ then

$$P(A_1) = \frac{\pi^2}{\pi^2 + (1 - \pi)^2} . \tag{10}$$

This last result is of special interest, since it is predicted by the "scanning" model developed by Estes (1962), and has been shown to give a fairly good account of several sets of data obtained in monetary payoff experiments.

Sequential Statistics for the Noncontingent Two-Response Case

Statistics that reflect the sequences of responses and events are of special interest. Such statistics may discriminate among models when the statistic $P(A_1)$ does not; furthermore, for our model they provide a basis for the estimation of the full array of parameters. In this paper, we will apply the model to first-order conditional probabilities of the form

$$P(A_{i,n+1} \mid E_{j,n}A_{k,n}),$$

and, when the number of observations permits, to second-order conditional probabilities of the form

$$P(A_{i,n+1} \mid E_{j,n}A_{k,n}E_{l,n-1}A_{m,n-1}),$$

for $i, j, k, l, m, = 1,2$. The presentation will be restricted to asymptotic predictions for the noncontingent two-response case, though extensions to more complex situations and to preasymptotic data can be obtained. In referring to the asymptotic statistics, we will drop the trial subscripts with the order in time from right to left being understood; thus

$$\lim_{n \to \infty} P(A_{i,n+1} \mid E_{j,n}A_{k,n}) = P(A_i \mid E_jA_k)$$

$$\lim_{n \to \infty} P(A_{i,n+1} \mid E_{j,n}A_{k,n}E_{l,n-1}A_{m,n-1}) = P(A_i \mid E_jA_kE_lA_m). \tag{11}$$

The derivation of these statistics is lengthy and will not be presented here. However, the general approach is developed in several sources, notably Suppes and Atkinson (1960) and Atkinson and Estes (1963). The first-order conditional probabilities are as follows:

$$P(A_1 \mid E_1A_1) = \frac{N-1}{N}(u_1 + u_2) + \frac{1}{N},$$

$$P(A_1 \mid E_2A_1) = \frac{N-1}{N}(u_1 + u_2) + \frac{1}{N}\left[\frac{u_1 + u_2(1-\delta)}{u_1 + u_2}\right],$$

$$P(A_1 \mid E_1A_2) = \frac{N-1}{N}(u_1 + u_2) + \frac{1}{N}\left(\frac{u_3\delta}{u_3 + u_4}\right),$$

$$P(A_1 \mid E_2A_2) = \frac{N-1}{N}(u_1 + u_2), \tag{12}$$

where u_i is defined by Eq. 4. The next four equations are representative of the second-order conditional probabilities. (The complete set of equations appear in Appendix A.)

$$P(A_1 \mid E_1A_1E_1A_1) = \frac{1 + (N-1)(u_1 + u_2)[3 + (N-2)(u_1 + u_2)]}{N[(N-1)(u_1 + u_2) + 1]},$$

$$P(A_1 \mid E_1A_2E_1A_1) = \frac{(u_3 + u_4)[1 + (N-3)(u_1 + u_2)] + u_3}{N(u_3 + u_4)},$$

$$P(A_1 \mid E_2A_1E_1A_1) =$$

$$\frac{(u_1 + u_2) - u_2\delta(1-\mu) + (N-1)(u_1 + u_2)\{(u_1 + u_2)[3 + (N-2)(u_1 + u_2)] - u_2\delta\}}{N[(N-1)(u_1 + u_2) + 1]}$$

$$P(A_1 \mid E_2A_2E_1A_1) = \frac{1 + (N-2)(u_3 + u_4)}{N}. \tag{13}$$

Note that predictions of $P(A_1)$ depend only on estimates of φ; the predictions of the conditional statistics require estimates of N, δ, and μ.

ESTIMATION OF PARAMETERS AND EVALUATION

The estimates of N, δ, and μ that we shall use to make predictions for the first-order conditional probabilities are those that yield a minimum value for the function

$$\chi^2 = \sum_{i,j,k} \frac{n_{jk}[\hat{P}(A_i \mid E_jA_k) - P(A_i \mid E_jA_k)]^2}{P(A_i \mid E_jA_k)}. \tag{14}$$

In this equation $\hat{P}(A_i \mid E_jA_k)$ is the observed asymptotic conditional probability; $P(A_i \mid E_jA_k)$ is a predicted conditional probability based on Eq. 12 and is a function of N, μ, and δ; and n_{jk} is the observed number of E_jA_k occurrences, i.e., the denomina- tor of the observed conditional probabilities. The minimum χ^2 estimates cannot be obtained analytically; however, a high-speed computer can be used to scan a grid of possible values, until estimates of N, μ, and δ are obtained that minimize χ^2 to the desired degree of accuracy.

If the theory postulated that the probability distribution on trial n depends only upon the responses and reinforcing events of trial $n - 1$, then the statistic described by Eq. 14 would indeed be distributed as χ^2 (Anderson and Goodman, 1957). Under these conditions the statistic would serve as a rigorous test of the ability of the model to describe the conditional sequential data. Furthermore, the estimates of the para- meters would have several desirable properties common to minimum χ^2 estimates. Such estimates are consistent (as the sample size increases the estimates converge stochastically to the parameter) and asymptotically efficient (as the sample size increases, the variance of the estimates approaches the minimal variance attainable for any consistent estimate of the parameter, and the distribution of the estimate approaches the normal distribution). In the model that we have proposed, the distribu- tion on trial n in fact depends upon the reinforcement events of all preceding trials. Therefore, the statistic defined by Eq. 14 is only approximately χ^2-distributed. Its validity as a test of goodness-of-fit is not absolute, and we cannot be certain of the properties of our estimates. However, this "pseudo-χ^2" is useful as a rough index of the fit of the model and as a means of discriminating among alternative models. Furthermore, the approximation to the χ^2 distribution improves rapidly as the number of trial outcomes upon which we are conditioning increases. With the above qualifica- tions in mind, we will continue to refer to the statistic of Eq. 14, and to similar statistics, as χ^2. In assessing the significance level of the χ^2 of Eq. 14, we shall assume that it is distributed on one degree of freedom (df) when based on the data of a single experi- mental group. There are initially 8 df, one for each observed conditional probability. However, only four of these observations are independently distributed since $P(A_1 \mid E_jA_k) + P(A_2 \mid E_jA_k) = 1$. An additional degree of freedom is then subtracted for each parameter estimate, leaving 1 df.

The minimum χ^2 procedure may also be used to obtain parameter estimates from the second-order conditional data. In this case, it is necessary to obtain the set of estimates that minimize

$$\chi^2 = \sum_{i,j,k,l,m} \frac{n_{jklm}[\hat{P}(A_i \mid E_jA_kE_lA_m) - P(A_i \mid E_jA_kE_lA_m)]^2}{P(A_i \mid E_jA_kE_lA_m)}. \tag{15}$$

Here n_{jklm} is the observed number of $E_jA_kE_lA_m$ occurrences. As a test of the data from a single experimental group this χ^2 would be distributed on 13 df; i.e., there are initially $2 \times 2 \times 2 \times 2 = 16$ degrees of freedom but three parameters are estimated from the data and χ^2 is therefore interpreted with $16 - 3 = 13$ df.

DATA ANALYSES IN THE TWO-RESPONSE CASE

Suppes and Atkinson Study

Suppes and Atkinson (1960, Ch. 10) ran 3 groups of 30 subjects each for 240 trials in a noncontingent two-choice situation. The groups differed with respect to the amount of payoff. Group Z had no monetary gains or losses; Group F gained 5¢ for each correct response and lost 5¢ for each incorrect response; and Group T gained or lost 10¢. The values of π was 0.6 for all groups. Table 1 contains predicted and

TABLE 1

Observed and Predicted Values, Parameter Estimates, and
Minimum χ^2 for the Suppes and Atkinson Experiment

	Group		
	Z	F	T
$P(A_1)$	0.600	0.648	0.695
	$(0.600)^a$	(0.649)	(0.700)
$P(A_1 \mid E_1 A_1)$	0.705	0.792	0.855
	(0.709)	(0.794)	(0.855)
$P(A_1 \mid E_2 A_1)$	0.538	0.603	0.660
	(0.534)	(0.601)	(0.670)
$P(A_1 \mid E_1 A_2)$	0.610	0.615	0.624
	(0.606)	(0.613)	(0.638)
$P(A_1 \mid E_2 A^2)$	0.452	0.382	0.329
	(0.449)	(0.388)	(0.323)
χ^2	0.18	0.09	0.68
μ	0.00	0.23	1.00
δ	0.64	0.69	0.95
N	3.80	2.44	1.90

^{a} Observed values are given in parantheses.

observed values of $P(A_1)$ and of the first-order conditional probabilities, the minimum χ^2 estimates of N, δ, and μ, and the values of the minimum χ^2. All observations are based on the last block of 80 trials.[2] The model describes the conditional probabilities exceedingly well, whether we merely compare the observed and predicted values or

---

[2] Values of n_{jk} are tabled in Appendix B for all experimental groups discussed in this section. Thus the data on which our analyses have been based can be completely reproduced, and the interested reader may use the data to analyze alternative models.

look at the values of the minimum χ^2. The mean absolute difference between observed and predicted values is approximately 0.005 and the sum of χ^2 over the three experimental groups is 1.85, which is not significant at even the 50% level with 3 df.

The parameter estimates indicate that, under zero payoff, an incorrect response is far more likely to result in a change of conditioning state than is a correct response. Since μ exhibits a more rapid increase than δ does over groups, the discrepancy between the effects of gains and losses decreases as payoff increases. Further, the decrease in N, the number of stimulus elements, with increased payoff suggests that the subjects attend to fewer cues as motivation is increased. These conclusions, that follow from the values of the estimated parameters, suggest how the model may provide an interpretation of the effects of gains and losses.

MYERS, FORT, KATZ, AND SUYDAM'S STUDY

Myers et al. (1963) ran 9 groups of 20 subjects for 400 trials in a noncontingent two-choice experiment. Levels of π of 0.6, 0.7, and 0.8 were employed and subjects gained or lost 0, 1, or 10¢. The data analysis reported here is based on trials 301–400. (Due to an error in recording during one experimental session, the data of only 16 subjects are available for the 0.6-0¢ group.)

The minimum χ^2 procedure described in the previous section was applied to the first-order conditional probabilities of the Myers et al. study with one modification. The estimates reported for each payoff level in Table 2 are those that minimized a

TABLE 2

VALUES OF THE PARAMETER AND MINIMUM CHI-SQUARES FOR
THE MYERS et al. STUDY

	Payoffs		
	0¢	1¢	10¢
N	5.05	2.21	2.19
δ	0.82	1.00	1.00
μ	0.13	0.83	1.00
χ^2	52.27	48.06	24.98

sum of χ^2 over the three levels of π. Thus there are 9 df associated with each χ^2 value in Table 2, i.e., twelve predictions were made on the basis of three parameters at each payoff level. As in the Suppes and Atkinson study μ increases more rapidly than does δ, and N decreases with increasing payoff; unlike the results of that study, the statistics for the 1¢ and 10¢ groups are not widely disparate, and this is reflected in the closeness of the estimates for those groups. The minimum χ^2 are fairly large and it appears that the model does not adequately describe the data. We will consider this point further when we look at the actual observations and predictions.

Table 3 presents observed and predicted values of $P(A_1)$, obtained by inserting the minimum estimates of δ and μ into Eq. 7. With the exception of the 0.6-1¢ and 0.7-1¢ groups, the fit appears quite good; the over-all mean deviation of observed and predicted values is 1.6%. At least for the 0 and 10¢ groups, single values of φ give a reasonably good account of the data at three different levels of π. Despite the large χ^2 values reported above, this is an important result. That adequate predictions of $P(A_1)$ under payoff is not trivial is suggested by the fact that several theories (Edwards, 1956; Siegel, 1959; Estes, 1962) have been developed for this purpose alone.[3]

TABLE 3

PREDICTED AND OBSERVED VALUES OF $P(A_1)$ FOR THE
MYERS *et. al.* STUDY

| | π | | |
Payoffs	0.6	0.7	0.8
0¢	0.627 (0.624)[a]	0.749 (0.753)	0.863 (0.869)
1¢	0.684 (0.653)	0.835 (0.871)	0.934 (0.925)
10¢	0.692 (0.714)	0.845 (0.866)	0.941 (0.951)

[a] Observed values are given in parentheses.

Table 4 presents the observed and predicted first-order conditional probabilities. The most notable aspect of the table is the fact that, excluding the 0.6-0¢ group, statistics of the form $P(A_1 \mid E_jA_1)$ are accurately predicted; the major source of the large values of χ^2 appears to be the failure to predict statistics of the form $P(A_1 \mid E_jA_2)$. This conclusion is supported by the fact that a χ^2 computed for the 16 E_jA_1 statistics is 13.23 which is not significant at the 0.05 level on 7 df. There are at least two obvious explanations for the poor fit of the E_jA_2 statistics: (a) it is possible that these statistics are unreliable since they are generally based on fewer observations than the E_jA_1 statistics (this argument might also be applied to the data of the 0.6-0¢ group which are based on 20% fewer observations than those of the other groups); and (b) the model may require some modification to describe adequately the statistics that are

[3] If the investigator is only interested in predicting $P(A_1)$, estimates of φ can be obtained by direct solution of Eq. 7. The procedure, and the resulting fit (which is better than that reported in Table 3) are reported by Myers et al. (1963).

poorly fit in Table 4. One argument against the second conclusion is the fact that the relationship between observations and predictions is not consistent; if the defect was in the theory rather than in the data, the predictions might be expected to be consistently too high, or consistently too low. However, additional experimentation involving more trials and subjects is required to decide between these two alternatives.

TABLE 4

PREDICTED AND OBSERVED VALUES OF $P(A_1 \mid E_i A_j)$ FOR THE MYERS *et al.* STUDY

Payoffs	π	$P(A_1 \mid E_1 A_1)$	$P(A_1 \mid E_2 A_1)$	$P(A_1 \mid E_1 A_2)$	$P(A_1 \mid E_2 A_2)$
0¢	0.6	0.701	0.569	0.649	0.503
		(0.668)[a]	(0.484)	(0.726)	(0.593)
	0.7	0.799	0.680	0.753	0.601
		(0.816)	(0.666)	(0.747)	(0.571)
	0.8	0.890	0.790	0.848	0.692
		(0.901)	(0.824)	(0.746)	(0.803)
1¢	0.6	0.810	0.614	0.643	0.356
		(0.818)	(0.609)	(0.613)	(0.336)
	0.7	0.930	0.780	0.806	0.475
		(0.939)	(0.789)	(0.825)	(0.415)
	0.8	0.959	0.858	0.878	0.505
		(0.947)	(0.856)	(0.974)	(0.588)
10¢	0.6	0.837	0.655	0.674	0.406
		(0.849)	(0.674)	(0.653)	(0.407)
	0.7	0.924	0.786	0.803	0.492
		(0.923)	(0.786)	(0.865)	(0.471)
	0.8	0.972	0.879	0.892	0.540
		(0.974)	(0.873)	(0.906)	(0.923)

[a] Observed values are given in parentheses.

FRIEDMAN *et al.* STUDY

Friedman *et al.* (1963) ran 80 subjects for three sessions of 384 trials each in a noncontingent two-choice experiment. No monetary payoff was involved. During the first two sessions, π was varied among blocks of 48 trials. In the third session (following 48 trials at a π value of 0.5) subjects were tested for 288 trials at a π value of 0.8. The analyses of Tables 5 and 6 are based on trials 193-288 of the 0.8 series. Parameter estimates were obtained from the first-order statistics by minimizing the χ^2

of Eq. 14. These estimates are the basis for both the predictions of the first-order conditional probabilities of Table 5 and the second-order conditional probabilities of Table 6. We have also investigated the possibility of obtaining parameter estimates from the second-order data by minimizing the χ^2 of Eq. 15; the results of the two procedures differ very little, and consequently we present only the results based on parameter estimates for the first-order data.

TABLE 5

PREDICTED AND OBSERVED VALUES OF $P(A_1 \mid E_j A_k)$, PARAMETER ESTIMATES, AND MINIMUM χ^2 VALUE FOR THE FRIEDMAN *et al.* STUDY

	Observed	Predicted
$P(A_1 \mid E_1 A_1)$	0.894	0.899
$P(A_1 \mid E_2 A_1)$	0.744	0.730
$P(A_1 \mid E_1 A_2)$	0.692	0.693
$P(A_1 \mid E_2 A_2)$	0.407	0.489
δ		0.50
μ		0.03
N		2.44
χ^2		9.68

TABLE 6

OBSERVED AND PREDICTED VALUES OF $P(A_1 \mid E_j A_k A_1 A_m)$ FOR THE FRIEDMAN *et al.* STUDY

$P(A_1 \mid E_j A_k E_1 A_m)$	Observed	Predicted
$P(A_1 \mid E_1 A_1 E_1 A_1)$	0.925	0.937
$P(A_1 \mid E_1 A_1 E_1 A_2)$	0.817	0.803
$P(A_1 \mid E_1 A_1 E_2 A_1)$	0.848	0.833
$P(A_1 \mid E_1 A_1 E_2 A_2)$	0.610	0.559
$P(A_1 \mid E_1 A_2 E_1 A_1)$	0.747	0.763
$P(A_1 \mid E_1 A_2 E_1 A_2)$	0.606	0.648
$P(A_1 \mid E_1 A_2 E_2 A_1)$	0.769	0.657
$P(A_1 \mid E_1 A_2 E_2 A_2)$	0.523	0.621
$P(A_1 \mid E_2 A_1 E_1 A_1)$	0.801	0.770
$P(A_1 \mid E_2 A_1 E_1 A_2)$	0.603	0.623
$P(A_1 \mid E_2 A_1 E_2 A_1)$	0.595	0.662
$P(A_1 \mid E_2 A_1 E_2 A_2)$	0.519	0.390
$P(A_1 \mid E_2 A_2 E_1 A_1)$	0.600	0.559
$P(A_1 \mid E_2 A_2 E_1 A_2)$	0.483	0.444
$P(A_1 \mid E_2 A_2 E_2 A_1)$	0.257	0.452
$P(A_1 \mid E_2 A_1 E_2 A_2)$	0.220	0.421

The first-order conditional statistics are fairly well fit; the second-order statistics appear to present a problem. The χ^2 defined by Eq. 15 is 60.48 on 13 df and several predictions clearly deviate from the observations. The fit is particularly poor for those statistics that are based on the fewest observations whereas the description of the more reliably based $P(A_1 \mid E_1 A_1 E_1 A_m)$ is quite reasonable.

CALFEE'S STUDY

Other fits to second-order statistics have been reported by Calfee (1963). He ran rats on noncontingent two-choice problems for 3680 trials under π values of either 0.65 or 0.80. In view of the large variability among subjects, and the presence of marked position preferences, Calfee selected four subsets of subjects; each subset contained subjects who were fairly similar with respect to the observed values of $P(A_1)$. The weak-strong model was then applied to the second-order conditional statistics for each subgroup for the last 1520 trials. For six subjects in the 0.80 group with $P(A_1)$ between 0.81 and 0.91, the average absolute weighted deviation of observed from predicted was 1%, and χ^2 was 25.46. For six subjects in the 0.80 group, with $P(A_1)$ between 0.91 and 0.98, the deviation was 0.35%, and χ^2 was 14.18. For three subjects in the 0.65 group with $P(A_1)$ between 0.65 and 0.75, the deviation was 4.74% and χ^2 was 71.53. For five subjects in the 0.65 group, with $P(A_1)$ between 0.85 and 0.92, the deviation was 2.64% and χ^2 was 85.48. While it is difficult to account for the relatively poor fit to the 0.65 data, the extremely good fit to the 0.80 data is encouraging. (A detailed account of these analyses is given by Calfee, 1963.)

More experiments are required before firm conclusions can be drawn about the ability of the model to describe higher order conditional statistics. However, the above results are encouraging in view of the poor fits obtained from similar analyses for other models. This problem has been discussed in greater detail by Anderson (1963).

A CONTINGENT REINFORCEMENT STUDY

Thus far, all the studies considered in this section have involved a noncontingent reinforcement procedure. Experiments using the contingent reinforcement procedure are relatively rare, and we know only one such study in which monetary payoff was involved. Since only three values of $P(A_1)$ are involved, our analysis hardly constitutes a test of the model for contingent experiments. However, the results are encouraging. Atkinson (1962) ran 3 groups of 20 subjects each for 340 trials, with each correct response resulting in a gain of 5¢ and each incorrect response resulting in a loss of 5¢. The groups differed with respect to π_1, which took the values 0.6, 0.7, and 0.8; for all groups π_2 equalled 0.5. Table 7 presents the observed proportions of A_1 responses for the last 80 trials. The predicted values were obtained by inserting a least-squares estimate of φ into Eq. 6. The estimate $\varphi = 2.1$ results in a good acount of the values of $P(A_1)$; the mean absolute deviation of observed from predicted is about 1%.

TABLE 7

OBSERVED AND PREDICTED VALUES OF $P(A_1)$ FOR
A CONTINGENT REINFORCEMENT EXPERIMENT

π_1	Observed	Predicted
0.6	0.601	0.592
0.7	0.685	0.704
0.8	0.832	0.831

ANALYSES OF THE THREE-RESPONSE CASE

We will now consider an extension of the model to experiments involving three responses. Since the only available data have been obtained for noncontingent procedures, equations will be presented only for that case. However, a more general statement is easily obtained following the approach of the previous section. For the noncontingent case, the axioms presented earlier result in the following transition matrix for element k over a subsequence w_k of trials.

$$
\begin{array}{c@{\quad}c@{\quad}c@{\quad}c}
 & S_1 & S_2 & S_3 \\
S_1 & 1 - \delta(1 - \gamma_1) & 0 & 0 \\
S_2 & 0 & 1 - \delta(1 - \gamma_2) & 0 \\
S_3 & 0 & 0 & 1 - \delta(1 - \gamma_3) \\
W_1 & \mu\gamma_1 & 0 & 0 \\
W_2 & 0 & \mu\gamma_2 & 0 \\
W_3 & 0 & 0 & \mu\gamma_3
\end{array}
$$

$$
\begin{array}{c@{\quad}c@{\quad}c@{\quad}c}
 & W_1 & W_2 & W_3 \\
S_1 & \delta(1 - \gamma_1) & 0 & 0 \\
S_2 & 0 & \delta(1 - \gamma_2) & 0 \\
S_3 & 0 & 0 & \delta(1 - \gamma_3) \\
W_1 & 1 - \mu\gamma_1 - \delta(1 - \gamma_1) & \delta\gamma_2 & \delta\gamma_3 \\
W_2 & \delta\gamma_1 & 1 - \mu\gamma_2 - \delta(1 - \gamma_2) & \delta\gamma_3 \\
W_3 & \delta\gamma_1 & \delta\gamma_2 & 1 - \mu\gamma_3 - \delta(1 - \gamma_3)
\end{array} \tag{16}
$$

For this case we let γ_i denote the probability of event E_i, where $\gamma_1 + \gamma_2 + \gamma_3 = 1$. The states will be designated by numbers corresponding to the ordering in the matrix, i.e., $S_1 = 1$, etc. From Eq. 16 we obtain the u_j defined previously by Eq. 3:

$$
u_j = \frac{D_j}{D_1 + D_2 + D_3 + D_4 + D_5 + D_6}, \tag{17}
$$

where

$$D_1 = \gamma_1^2(1 - \gamma_2)(1 - \gamma_3), \quad D_4 = \gamma_1(1 - \gamma_1)(1 - \gamma_2)(1 - \gamma_3)\,\varphi,$$

$$D_2 = \gamma_2^2(1 - \gamma_1)(1 - \gamma_3), \quad D_5 = \gamma_2(1 - \gamma_1)(1 - \gamma_2)(1 - \gamma_3)\,\varphi,$$

$$D_3 = \gamma_3^2(1 - \gamma_1)(1 - \gamma_2), \quad D_6 = \gamma_3(1 - \gamma_1)(1 - \gamma_2)(1 - \gamma_3)\,\varphi, \qquad (18)$$

and again $\varphi = \delta/\mu$. Following the procedure for the two-response case we may derive expressions for $\lim_{n\to\infty} P(A_{i,n}) = P(A_i)$, specifically

$$P(A_1) = u_1 + u_4 ,$$

$$P(A_2) = u_2 + u_5 ,$$

$$P(A_3) = u_3 + u_6 . \qquad (19)$$

COTTON AND RECHTSHAFFEN'S STUDY

Cotton and Rechtshaffen (1958) report values of $P(A_1)$ for six groups, two having two responses available, and four having three responses available. Values of $P(A_1)$ and standard deviations of proportions for trials 286-450 are presented in Table 8,

TABLE 8

OBSERVED AND PREDICTED $P(A_1)$ FOR THE COTTON-RECHTSCHAFFEN EXPERIMENT

Condition	Predicted $P(A_1)$	Observed $P(A_1)$	s_p
60-40	0.641	0.614	0.118
60-30-10	0.658	0.658	0.112
60-20-20	0.671	0.660	0.096
70-30	0.773	0.741	0.099
70-20-10	0.783	0.801	0.137
70-15-15	0.784	0.805	0.091

together with predictions derived from the model. A least-squares estimation procedure yielded a value of φ of 3.7; this was then substituted into Eq. 19 with the appropriate γ_i values to generate the six predictions. The average absolute deviation of observed from predicted values is less than 1.4%, which is quite small in view of the variability in the proportions. It is particularly interesting to note that the finding that $P(A_1)$ increases as the number of choices increases (see also Gardner, 1957) is accounted for by the present model.

Cole's Study

Cole (1962) ran three groups of human subjects under a noncontingent reinforcement procedure. Two of the groups had three responses available, with γ_i's of 2/3, 2/9, and 1/9 for one group, and γ_i's of 4/9, 1/3, and 2/9 for the second group; the third group had two responses available with γ equal to 2/3. Table 9 presents the observed and predicted values of $P(A_1)$ and values of φ for each group and response. The values of φ were computed by solving Eq. 19, and the observations were based on trials 501-1000.

TABLE 9

Observed and Predicted $P(A_i)$ for the Cole Experiment

Condition	Response	Predicted $P(A_i)$	Observed $P(A_i)$	φ
$\frac{2}{3} - \frac{2}{9} - \frac{1}{9}$	A_1	0.844	0.881	0.45
	A_2	0.109	0.087	0.43
	A_3	0.047	0.029	0.41
$\frac{4}{9} - \frac{1}{3} - \frac{2}{9}$	A_1	0.512	0.531	0.52
	A_2	0.313	0.304	0.40
	A_3	0.174	0.165	0.55
$\frac{2}{3} - \frac{1}{3}$	A_1	0.812	0.779	1.50
	A_2	0.188	0.221	1.50

Averaging over responses and then over groups, a value of φ of 0.81 was obtained; substitution in Eq. 19 resulted in the predicted $P(A_i)$ of Table 9. The model again correctly predicts an increase in the value of $P(A_1)$ as the number of response alternatives increases from two to three, but the discrepancies between observations and predictions are somewhat greater than they were for the Cotton and Rechtshaffen data. This is due to the difference in the average values of φ for two- and three-choice data. If predictions are made just for the data from the three-choice groups (using a value of φ based only on the observations for those groups) the average difference between the observed and predicted values of $P(A_i)$ is only 0.5%. It is possible that different values of φ are required for each number of response alternatives. However, the fit for the Cotton and Rechtshaffen data could argue against this assumption. Additional experimentation involving varying numbers of response alternatives is required for clarification of this problem.

EXTENSION OF THE MODEL TO RESPONSE TIMES

Despite recurrent attempts to develop an adequate theory of response times (Estes, 1951; Bush and Mosteller, 1955, LaBerge, 1959; Luce, 1960) this dependent variable has proven more elusive than response probability. One attractive feature of the weak-strong model is that it can be extended to treat response times with the addition of only one assumption. Furthermore, derivations of a variety of statistics are extremely simple, and estimates of response time parameters can be easily obtained. To facilitate the presentation, we will limit the discussion to the asymptotic case for the two-response noncontingent situation. Extensions to more complex situations and to preasymptotic data follow readily from the developments of this section.

The set of axioms previously presented for choice behavior are assumed to hold. Thus, we postulate that exactly one element is sampled on each trial, that the element is either weakly or strongly conditioned to one of the response alternatives, and that the conditioning state may change in accord with the previously presented conditioning axioms. In addition, we require the following axiom:

Response Time Axiom. The random variable T_n denotes the response time on trial n of the experiment and depends on the conditioning state of the sampled stimulus element. If the sampled element is in a strong state of conditioning, then the response-time distribution has probability density $S(t)$ with mean s. If the sampled element is in a weak state of conditioning, then the response-time distribution has probability density $W(t)$ with mean w.

On the basis of the response time axiom and our choice model, a number of predictions may be derived. We will next consider some of these. Since all equations will be for the asymptotic case, the subscript n with be omitted.

MEAN RESPONSE TIMES

The mean asymptotic response time obtained by averaging over both A_1 and A_2 responses, $E(T)$, is simply the weighted sum of s and w, where the weights are the probabilities of sampling from the two hypothesized distributions. Accordingly, we have

$$E(T) = (u_1 + u_4)\, s + (u_2 + u_3)\, w$$

$$= \frac{s[\pi^3 + (1 - \pi)^3] + w[\pi(1 - \pi)\, \varphi]}{\pi^3 + (1 - \pi)^3 + \pi(1 - \pi)\, \varphi} . \tag{20}$$

If we assume that $s < w$, which appears reasonable, then it is easily proven that the mean response time is greatest when $\pi = 0.5$, and monotonically decreases as π approaches one.

We next consider $E(T \mid A_i)$, the mean response time for an A_i response. This quantity is derived as the weighted sum of s and w, where the weights are the probabilities of sampling from the two hypothesized distributions, given that an A_i response has occurred. The appropriate equations are

$$E(T \mid A_1) = \frac{su_1 + wu_2}{u_1 + u_2} = \frac{s\pi + w(1 - \pi)\,\varphi}{\pi + (1 - \pi)\,\varphi}\,. \tag{21}$$

$$E(T \mid A_2) = \frac{s(1 - \pi) + w\pi\varphi}{1 - \pi + \pi\varphi}\,. \tag{22}$$

Once φ has been estimated from the choice data, the parameters s and w may be simultaneously solved for in Eqs. 21 and 22. Predictions of $E(T)$, $E(T \mid A_1)$, and $E(T \mid A_2)$ can then be made for any value of π.

If $s < w$, it can be shown that the mean time required for a response to occur is a monotone decreasing function of the probability of the predicted event. Response time data from the Friedman *et al.* study are ambiguous with regard to this prediction. For $\pi > 1/2$ response times for the A_1 response were slightly (but significantly) less than A_2 response times, as predicted; however, response time did not vary as a function of π.[4] Data that are more clearly consistent with the predictions of this model are reported by Calfee (1963) who found that response times for rats decreased as π increased, and that the preferred response was made more quickly than the less preferred response. These data support the weak-strong model, and suggest that LaBerge's (1959) neutral elements model requires revision. That model predicts no differences in average A_1 and A_2 response times, or in response times as a function of π.

We conclude this section by presenting equations for statistics of the form $E(T \mid A_i E_j A_k)$, the expected response time of an A_i response on trial $n + 1$, given that it was preceded by event E_j and response A_k on trial n. The general form of the expression for this statistic is

$$E(T \mid A_i E_j A_k) = \frac{sP(S_i \mid E_j A_k) + wP(W_i \mid E_j A_k)}{P(A_i \mid E_j A_k)}\,. \tag{23}$$

In the above expression $P(S_i \mid E_j A_k)$ denotes the asymptotic probability that an element is strongly conditioned to A_i on trial $n + 1$ given that $E_j A_k$ occurred on trial n;

---

[4] It is possible that in the typical experimental situation the subject decides on his response prior to the signal to respond. Under these conditions response time, measured from the onset of the signal, would reflect the speed of reaction to the trial signal, and not choice time. A more sensitive test of response time predictions might be made if subjects were permitted to pace themselves; latency would be measured from the onset of the event on trial n to the occurrence of the response on trial $n + 1$.

$P(W_i \mid E_j A_k)$ has a similar interpretation. Substituting in Eq. 23, we obtain the following expressions:

$$E(T \mid A_1 E_1 A_1) = \frac{(N-1)(su_1 + wu_2) + \left(\dfrac{1}{u_1 + u_2}\right)\lceil s(u_1 + u_2\mu) + wu_2(1-\mu)\rceil}{(N-1)(u_1 + u_2) + 1}$$

$$E(T \mid A_1 E_2 A_1) =$$

$$\frac{(N-1)(su_1 + wu_2) + \left(\dfrac{1}{u_1 + u_2}\right)\{su_1(1-\delta) + w[u_1\delta + u_2(1-\delta)]\}}{(N-1)(u_1 + u_2) + \left(\dfrac{1}{u_1 + u_2}\right)[u_1 + u_2(1-\delta)]}$$

$$E(T \mid A_1 E_1 A_2) = \frac{(N-1)(su_1 + wu_2) + \dfrac{wu_3\delta}{u_3 + u_4}}{(N-1)(u_1 + u_2) + \dfrac{u_3\delta}{u_3 + u_4}}$$

$$E(T \mid A_1 E_2 A_2) = \frac{su_1 + wu_2}{u_1 + u_2}. \tag{24}$$

The expressions for the $E(T \mid A_2 E_j A_k)$ are obtained by substituting u_4 for u_1, u_3 for u_2, and vice versa, in Eq. 24; e.g.,

$$E(T \mid A_2 E_1 A_1) = \frac{su_4 + wu_3}{u_1 + u_3}.$$

EXTENSION OF THE MODEL TO THE DIFFERENTIAL PAYOFF CASE

Thus far we have considered a model that is applicable only to the symmetric payoff case, in which the amount gained is the same for all correct responses, and the amount lost is the same for all incorrect responses. We next consider an extension of the model to the nonsymmetric payoff case. For the two-response situation this payoff scheme may be represented by the matrix

$$\begin{array}{cc} & \begin{array}{cc} E_1 & E_2 \end{array} \\ \begin{array}{c} A_1 \\ A_2 \end{array} & \left[\begin{array}{cc} w & -x \\ -y & z \end{array}\right], \end{array}$$

where the amount gained or lost is a function of the response-event combination. Although an adequate description of data obtained under such conditions would seem to be a prerequisite for a general theory of motivational variables, to date little progress has been made on the problem. Bush and Mosteller's "experimenter-subject-controlled events" model (1955, p. 286) is applicable, but this approach leads to severe mathematical difficulties. Estes' "scanning" model (1962) involves simple computations, but only yields predictions of $P(A_1)$. The same objection may be raised to Edwards' "RELM" model (1956). The generalization of the weak-strong model that we will present is mathematically tractable; the only complication beyond the original model is the need to estimate one additional parameter. The variety of predictions that follow from the original model can also be derived for the extended model. For these reasons, the generalized weak-strong model merits consideration. However, it should be noted that the developments of this section are extremely tentative. A detailed empirical evaluation of the model is excluded at this time since there have been few experiments involving differential payoffs. These studies, while theoretically suggestive, have involved too few trials and subjects to permit a rigorous test of the model.

We might extend the weak-strong model by postulating two values of μ (μ_w and μ_z), corresponding to the two gains, and the two values of δ (δ_x and δ_y), corresponding to the two losses. That this identification of parameters has limited applicability is suggested by data obtained from a matrix such as

$$\begin{array}{cc} & E_1 \quad E_2 \\ \begin{array}{c} A_1 \\ A_2 \end{array} & \begin{bmatrix} 5 & -5 \\ 1 & 1 \end{bmatrix} \end{array}.$$

For the parameter identification proposed above, E_1 and E_2 should have identical effects upon the conditioning-state whenever the subject makes an A_2 response. Furthermore, if a 1¢ gain is assumed to be reinforcing, the subject should absorb on A_2. Both inferences are contradicted by experimental data (Myers and Sadler, 1960; Myers and Fort, 1961). A mechanism is required which permits the A_2 response to be strengthened or weakened following a 1¢ gain, depending on which event occurred.

The concept of regret (Simon, 1956; Savage, 1957) provides one approach to the problem just posed. Regret is the difference between the obtained payoff and the maximum possible payoff, given that event E_i occurs. Thus, for the last payoff matrix presented, we have the regret matrix

$$\begin{array}{cc} & E_1 \quad E_2 \\ \begin{array}{c} A_1 \\ A_2 \end{array} & \begin{bmatrix} 0 & 6 \\ 4 & 0 \end{bmatrix} \end{array}.$$

In general, corresponding to the payoff matrix

$$\begin{array}{cc} & E_1 \quad E_2 \\ \begin{array}{c} A_1 \\ A_2 \end{array} & \begin{bmatrix} w & x \\ y & z \end{bmatrix} \end{array},$$

where $y < w$ and $x < z$ (note that x and y are not necessarily negative), we have

$$\begin{array}{cc} & E_1 \quad E_2 \\ \begin{array}{c} A_1 \\ A_2 \end{array} & \begin{bmatrix} 0 & r_1 \\ r_2 & 0 \end{bmatrix}, \end{array}$$

where the regret associated with an incorrect A_1 response is

$$r_1 = z - x, \tag{25}$$

and the regret associated with an incorrect A_2 response is

$$r_2 = w - y. \tag{26}$$

Here, we define an incorrect response as one that yields a payoff less than the maximum possible payoff, given the occurrence of E_i.

The notion of regret provides a basis for modifying the weak-strong model in the following manner. We identify μ with the probability that zero regret results in the strengthening of a correct response, δ_1 with the probability that r_1 results in the weakening of an incorrect A_1 response, and δ_2 with the probability that r_2 results in the weakening of an incorrect A_2 response. A minor change in our system of axioms now suffices in order to derive equations for choice behavior under differential payoffs, Axiom C3 is rewritten as follows:

AXIOM C3'. *If event E_j occurs $(i \neq j)$, then (a) if the sampled element is strongly conditioned to A_i there is a probability δ_i that it becomes weakly conditioned to A_i, and (b) if the sampled element is weakly conditioned to A_i there is a probability δ_i that it becomes weakly conditioned to A_j.*

For the revised axioms we may now obtain the following results in the noncontingent two-choice situation:

$$D_1 = \pi^2 \varphi_2^2 \qquad\qquad D_3 = \pi(1-\pi)^2 \, \varphi_2 \varphi_1^2,$$

$$D_2 = \pi^2(1-\pi) \, \varphi_2^2 \varphi_1 \qquad D_4 = (1-\pi)^3 \, \varphi_1^2, \tag{27}$$

where

$$\varphi_i = \frac{\delta_i}{\mu}. \tag{28}$$

Substituting in Eq. 4 we have

$$P(A_1) = \frac{\pi^3 + \pi^2(1-\pi)\,\varphi_1}{\pi^3 + \pi^2(1-\pi)\,\varphi_1 + \pi(1-\pi)^2\,\varepsilon\varphi_1 + (1-\pi)^3\,\varepsilon^2}, \tag{29}$$

where $\varepsilon = \varphi_1/\varphi_2$. Note that $P(A_1)$ is independent of N. Furthermore, for the symmetric case $r_1 = r_2$ and therefore $\varphi_1 = \varphi_2$; hence under this condition Eq. 29 reduces to Eq. 7. Also, the following results can be easily proved:

(i) $P(A_1)$ is bounded by zero and one. Specifically,

$$\lim_{\varepsilon \to 0} P(A_1) = 1 \qquad \lim_{\varepsilon \to \infty} P(A_1) = 0. \tag{30}$$

(ii) For constant π and φ_2, $P(A_1)$ is a decreasing monotonic function of φ_1. As the regret associated with an incorrect A_1 response increases, the probability of making an A_1 decreases.

(iii) For constant π and φ_1, $P(A_1)$ is an increasing monotonic function of φ_2. As the regret associated with an incorrect A_2 response increases, the probability of making an A_1 increases.

Several experiments have recently been performed (Royden, Suppes, and Walsh, 1959; Myers and Sadler, 1960; Myers and Katz, 1962; Katz, 1962) involving the choice between a "sure thing" and a risky option. The payoff matrices are of the form

$$\begin{array}{c} \\ A_1 \\ A_2 \end{array} \begin{array}{cc} E_1 & E_2 \\ \left[\begin{array}{cc} w & -w \\ 1 & 1 \end{array} \right], \end{array} \quad \text{and} \quad \begin{array}{c} \\ A_1 \\ A_2 \end{array} \begin{array}{cc} E_1 & E_2 \\ \left[\begin{array}{cc} w & -w \\ -1 & -1 \end{array} \right], \end{array}$$

where E_1 and E_2 are equiprobable, i.e., $\pi = 0.5$. The major findings are that (a) $P(A_1)$ is always greater when the payoff associated with an A_2 response is -1 than when the payoff is $+1$, and (b) as the absolute value of w increases, $P(A_1)$ increases when the A_2 payoff is $+1$, and decreases when the A_2 payoff is -1. These results are schematically represented in Fig. 3. The convergence effect exhibited in Fig. 3 is not consistent with the results for the symmetric payoff case, in which subjects approach

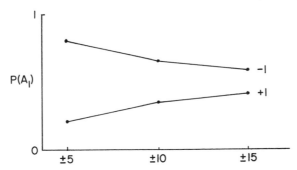

FIG. 3.   The proportion of risky responses as a function of the amount of risk, with the values of the "sure thing" alternative as the parameter.

the optimal strategy (always predict the more frequent event) as payoffs increase. In the studies under discussion, the optimal strategy is to always make the A_1 response when the A_2 payoff is $+ 1$; subjects increasingly deviate from this strategy as the amount risked increases.

Since the convergence effect displayed in Fig. 3 does not seem to be easily explained by existing theories of decision behavior, it is of interest to consider it in terms of the weak-strong model. Upon converting the above payoff matrices to regret matrices, it becomes apparent that r_2 is less than r_1 when the A_2 payoff is $+ 1$; and r_2 is greater than r_1 when the A_2 payoff is $- 1$. Assuming that δ_i is a monotonically increasing function of r_i, ε will be greater when the A_2 payoff is $+ 1$ than when it is $- 1$. Consequently, the $- 1$ curve should lie above the $+ 1$ curve, as it does.

We next attempt to account for the convergence depicted in Fig. 3. As w increases, both r_1 and r_2 increase, but the ratio r_1/r_2 monotonically approaches an asymptote of 1. If δ_i is a negatively accelerated function of r_i then (a) if the A_2 payoff is $+ 1$, ε will decrease to an asymptote of 1, and (b) if the A_2 payoff is $- 1$, ε will increase to an asymptote of 1. Consequently, the curves converge as they both approach an asymptote of 0.5.

To conclude our discussion of differential-payoff experiments, we present an analysis of first-order joint probabilities. The data were taken from trials 301 to 400 for three groups of 20 subjects run by Katz (1963). All groups were run on a noncontingent schedule with $\pi = 0.5$; the groups differed with respect to the payoff matrices:

$$
\begin{array}{ccc}
\text{Group 1} & \text{Group 2} & \text{Group 3} \\[6pt]
\begin{array}{cc} E_1 & E_2 \end{array} & \begin{array}{cc} E_1 & E_2 \end{array} & \begin{array}{cc} E_1 & E_2 \end{array} \\[2pt]
\begin{array}{c} A_1 \\ A_2 \end{array}\!\begin{bmatrix} 1 & -4 \\ -1 & 1 \end{bmatrix} &
\begin{array}{c} A_1 \\ A_2 \end{array}\!\begin{bmatrix} 2 & -4 \\ -1 & 1 \end{bmatrix} &
\begin{array}{c} A_1 \\ A_2 \end{array}\!\begin{bmatrix} 4 & -4 \\ -1 & 1 \end{bmatrix}
\end{array}
$$

The regret transforms of these matrices are

$$
\begin{array}{ccc}
\begin{array}{cc} E_1 & E_2 \end{array} & \begin{array}{cc} E_1 & E_2 \end{array} & \begin{array}{cc} E_1 & E_2 \end{array} \\[2pt]
\begin{array}{c} A_1 \\ A_2 \end{array}\!\begin{bmatrix} 0 & 5 \\ 2 & 0 \end{bmatrix} &
\begin{array}{c} A_1 \\ A_2 \end{array}\!\begin{bmatrix} 0 & 5 \\ 3 & 0 \end{bmatrix} &
\begin{array}{c} A_1 \\ A_2 \end{array}\!\begin{bmatrix} 0 & 5 \\ 5 & 0 \end{bmatrix}
\end{array}
$$

The minimum χ^2 procedure was applied to the first-order joint probabilities under the restrictions that μ and δ_1 be constant across games, as a literal interpretation of the theory would demand. In addition, N was held constant across games to simplify the numerical search procedure. Despite these restrictions on parameter estimates, the fits exhibited in Table 10 are remarkably good. Further support for the theory comes from the estimates of δ_2; these values increase in a negatively accelerated manner as previously hypothesized. Furthermore, the values of δ_1 and δ_2 are virtually identical for Group 3 as the theory would predict.

TABLE 10

Observed and Predicted Values and Parameter Estimates for the Katz Study

	Group 1	Group 2	Group 3
$P(A_1E_1A_1)$	0.074 (0.079)[a]	0.124 (0.119)	0.190 (0.194)
$P(A_1E_1A_2)$	0.083 (0.070)	0.111 (0.124)	0.133 (0.126)
$P(A_1E_2A_1)$	0.043 (0.054)	0.077 (0.060)	0.125 (0.120)
$P(A_1E_2A_2)$	0.051 (0.047)	0.064 (0.063)	0.068 (0.075)
$P(A_2E_1A_1)$	0.051 (0.047)	0.064 (0.062)	0.068 (0.072)
$P(A_2E_1A_2)$	0.292 (0.311)	0.202 (0.200)	0.110 (0.115)
$P(A_2E_2A_1)$	0.083 (0.074)	0.111 (0.125)	0.133 (0.129)
$P(A_2E_2A_2)$	0.324 (0.322)	0.249 (0.247)	0.174 (0.169)
$P(A_1)$	0.251 (0.250)	0.376 (0.366)	0.516 (0.515)
μ	0.516	0.516	0.516
δ_1	0.875	0.875	0.875
δ_2	0.414	0.609	0.914
N	2.19	2.19	2.19
χ^2	18.34	14.38	4.09

[a] Observed values are in parentheses.

Although the results described in this section are encouraging, additional quantitative analyses are required to provide an adequate evaluation. When such analyses are available, the relations between parameter and regret values may be more complicated than we have suggested. For example, as indicated above a literal interpretation of our model would require that μ be invariant over different payoff matrices. This assumption may be satisfactory when the range of payoffs under analysis is small, but it seems doubtful that it would hold for all possible sets of payoff matrices. With the collection of additional data, it may be necessary to assume that μ is a function of some measure of the payoff structure. However, in view of the reasonable fits obtained, we consider the present theory a promising starting point.

A MULTI-STAGE MODEL

As indicated earlier the "pattern" model of stimulus sampling theory would be regarded as a one-stage model. Similarly the model discussed in this paper is a two-stage model. In this section, we investigate the consequences of generalizing the model so than an element may be in one of k stages of conditioning to a response. The generalized model follows logically from the weak-strong model. The Stimulus Axiom and the Response Axiom remain unchanged; the other axioms require only the obvious modifications.

CONDITIONING-STATE AXIOM. *On every trial each stimulus element is conditioned to exactly one response; furthermore, the element is in one of k stages of conditioning to that response. (An element in conditioning state C_{im} is in stage m of conditioning to response A_i where m = 1, 2, $\cdots$, k and k denotes the strongest stage.)*

CONDITIONING AXIOMS

C2'. If event E_i occurs, then (a) *if the sampled element is in state C_{ik} it remains so, and* (b) *if the sampled element is in state C_{im} (m $\neq$ k) there is a probability μ that it enters state $C_{i,m+1}$.*

C3'. If event E_j occurs (i $\neq$ j), then (a) *if the sampled element is in state C_{im} (m $\neq$ 1), there is a probability δ that it enters state $C_{i,m-1}$, and* (b) *if the sampled element is in state C_{i1} there is a probability δ that it enters state C_{j1} .*

Expressions can be derived for those statistics previously treated in the $k = 2$ case. For the noncontingent two-response case, it can be shown that

$$P(A_i) = \sum_m u_{im} , \tag{31}$$

where

$$u_i = \frac{D_{im}}{\sum\limits_{i,m} D_{im}}, \tag{32}$$

and

$$D_{1m} = \pi^{k+m-1}[(1 - \pi)\,\varphi]^{k-m}$$
$$D_{2m} = (\pi\varphi)^{k-m}\,(1 - \pi)^{k+m-1}. \tag{33}$$

These expressions can be evaluated to yield the following equation:

$$P(A_1) = \frac{\alpha}{\alpha + \beta}, \tag{34}$$

where

$$\alpha = \pi^k\{\pi^k + [(1 - \pi)\,\varphi]^k\}\,(1 - \pi - \pi\varphi)$$
$$\beta = (1 - \pi)^k\,[(1 - \pi)^k + (\pi\varphi)^k]\,[\pi - (1 - \pi)\,\varphi]. \tag{35}$$

Note that

$$\lim_{\varphi \to \infty} P(A_1) = \pi$$

$$\lim_{\varphi \to 0} P(A_1) = \frac{\pi^{2k-1}}{\pi^{2k-1} + (1 - \pi)^{2k-1}}. \tag{36}$$

Thus, one consequence of introducing k is to increase the upper asymptotic bound on $P(A_1)$ and place it as close to 1 as desired for $\pi > 1/2$.

The form of the conditional statistics is also simple; the first order statistics are as follows:

$$P(A_1 \mid E_1 A_1) = \left(\frac{N - 1}{N}\right)\left(\frac{\alpha}{\alpha + \beta}\right) + \frac{1}{N}$$

$$P(A_1 \mid E_2 A_1) = \left(\frac{N - 1}{N}\right)\left(\frac{\alpha}{\alpha + \beta}\right) + \frac{1}{N}\left[\frac{\alpha - u_{11}\delta(\alpha + \beta)}{\alpha}\right]$$

$$P(A_1 \mid E_1 A_2) = \left(\frac{N - 1}{N}\right)\left(\frac{\alpha}{\alpha + \beta}\right) + \frac{1}{N}\left[\frac{u_{21}\delta(\alpha + \beta)}{\beta}\right]$$

$$P(A_1 \mid E_2 A_2) = \left(\frac{N - 1}{N}\right)\left(\frac{\alpha}{\alpha + \beta}\right).$$

We have applied the minimum χ^2 estimation procedure to the first order conditional data presented previously for $k = 2, 3, 4, 5,$ and 10. Generally, the minimum χ^2

was smallest at $k = 2$ though there were a few instances for which it was slightly less at $k = 3$. In most instances the goodness of fit showed fairly rapid deterioration as k increased. For example, when the models were applied to the Friedman et al data, the minimum χ^2 was at a low of 9.37 for $k = 2$, increased to 38.51 for $k = 5$, and then increased to 42,784 for $k = 10$. The increase in χ^2 appears to be due to the fact that for large k, the model predicts more response perserveration, following a correct response, than actually occurs. In view of these analyses we are prone to conclude that significant improvements in goodness of fit will not follow as a result of increases in k, and that two-stages generally will best describe the data. Assuming that this conclusion holds for future analyses of data, it, of course, applies only to our particular statement of the model. For example, a k-stage model involving different response axioms leads to quite different results (Atkinson, 1961).

AN OBSERVING RESPONSE INTERPRETATION

Several articles (Bower, 1959; Atkinson, 1960, 1961a, b; Estes, 1960, 1962) have recently demonstrated that a more molecular analysis of the subject's preresponse behavior may prove fruitful in formulating a choice model. It is therefore interesting to note that at least one such analysis of choice behavior results in the same equations derived for the weak-strong model. Specifically, consider a model which postulates that associated with each response alternative is a tendency to approach or avoid that alternative. Further assume that the set of approach tendencies, and the order in which response alternatives are considered (or observed) determine the subject's choice on any trial, and are themselves determined by the outcomes of preceding trials.

To formalize these notions let the function v_k be the approach tendency associated with response A_k. When the subject observes the kth alternative, he will make that response if $v_k = 1$, or move on to observe some other alternative if $v_k = 0$. The values of v_k for the r-response alternatives will be represented by a vector $V = \langle v_1, v_2, \cdots, v_r \rangle$. For example, $V = \langle 001 \rangle$ indicates that the subject will approach A_3 when he observes it; all other alternatives will be avoided. We further assume that, in the time period immediately preceding his choice, the subject orients towards each response alternative in some sequence, until he observes an alternative for which v_k is one, or, if all v_k's are zero, until he has observed each alternative. In either case, the alternative chosen is the one last observed by the subject. Thus, the subject will choose the first observed alternative for which v_k is one, or, if all values are zero, the last alternative observed. The sequence in which the alternatives are observed on any given trial will be represented by the vector $0 = \langle o_1, o_2, \cdots, o_r \rangle$. The value of o_i indicates which response will be observed at position i in the observing sequence.

With these concepts in mind we can define the conditioning state of the subject on any trial n of an experiment as the vector $C_n = \langle 0, V \rangle$. For example, if $C_n = \langle \langle 12 \rangle, \langle 10 \rangle \rangle$, then the subject initiatives the trial by observing response A_1 and then makes that response. If $C_n = \langle \langle 12 \rangle, \langle 00 \rangle \rangle$ the subject first observes A_1, then A_2 and terminates the trial by choosing A_2 since both v_1 and v_2 equal 0.

To complete the analysis we need some rule for describing changes in C_n over trials. The following assumption seems reasonable: If response A_k occurs on a trial and is reinforced, then with probability μ the function v_k takes on the value one and that response moves to the top of the observing sequence. If the response is not reinforced, then with probability δ the v_k function for that response becomes zero and the observing sequence is reordered.

Given these assumptions it can be shown that for large n this model and the weak-strong model are equivalent. For example, in the two-response noncontingent case, if we let

$$S_1 = \langle \langle 12 \rangle, \langle 10 \rangle \rangle \qquad S_2 = \langle \langle 21 \rangle, \langle 01 \rangle \rangle$$
$$W_1 = \langle \langle 21 \rangle, \langle 00 \rangle \rangle \qquad W_2 = \langle \langle 21 \rangle, \langle 01 \rangle \rangle, \tag{37}$$

then the transitions among states is that given by Eq. 2 and at asymptote the predictions for the weak-strong model are precisely those of the model outlined in this section.

The implications of the approach that we have just considered are broader than the fact that we achieve results identical to those derivable from weak-strong axioms. A number of models may be generated, starting with the notions of approach tendencies and observing vectors, if one examines various natural modifications of the conditioning and responding assumptions that were sketched above. In view of the possibility that some of these models will provide further insights into choice behavior, this frame of reference merits further investigation.

CONCLUDING REMARKS

In this paper we have attempted to present more than an analysis and extension of the weak-strong model. We have presented data that we hope will be useful in evaluating other theories of choice behavior and we have provided goodness-of-fit results that we hope will serve as criteria against which to evaluate the success of other models. Furthermore, there are at least two aspects of our work that might profitably be incorporated into other models. The approach to the prediction of response times can be appended to any behavior theory formulated as a finite-state Markov process. It has the advantage over previous approaches of simplicity; there is no recourse to unobservable responses and predictions do not depend upon an explicit statement of the form of the response-time distribution. Identifying conditioning parameters with the concept of regret also has implications that go beyond the present model. This approach can be readily incorporated into any theory dealing with situations in which different response-event combinations have recognizably distinct consequences.

APPENDIX A

Listed below are the expressions for the asymptotic joint probabilities of the form $P(A_{1,n}E_{j,n-1}A_{k,n-1}E_{l,n-2}A_{m,n-2})$ for the weak-strong model ($j, k, l, m = 1, 2$). The conditional statistics may be obtained by noting that in the noncontingent case.

$$P(A_i \mid E_j A_k E_l A_m) = \frac{P(A_i E_j A_k E_l A_m)}{Pr(E_j)\,Pr(E_l)\,P(A_k \mid E_l A_m)\,P(A_m)}$$

where $P(E_1) = \pi$ and $P(E_2) = (1 - \pi)$.

$$P(A_1E_1A_1E_1A_1) = \frac{\pi^2}{N^2}\{A + 3\,(n - 1)\,A^2 + (N - 1)\,(N - 2)\,A^3\}$$

$$P(A_1E_1A_1E_1A_2) = \frac{\pi^2}{N^2}\,[u_3\delta + (N - 1)\,A(B + 2u_3\delta) + (N - 1)\,(N - 2)\,A^2B]$$

$$P(A_1E_1A_1E_2A_1) = \frac{\pi(1 - \pi)}{N^2}\,[C + (N - 1)\,A(A + 2C) + (N - 1)\,(N - 2)\,A^3]$$

$$P(A_1E_1A_1E_2A_2) = \frac{\pi(1 - \pi)}{N^2}\,\{(N - 1)\,AB[1 + (N - 2)\,A]\}$$

$$P(A_1E_1A_2E_1A_1) = \frac{\pi^2}{N^2}\,\{(N - 1)\,A[u_3\delta + B + (N - 2)\,AB]\}$$

$$P(A_1E_1A_2E_1A_2) = \frac{\pi^2}{N^2}\,\{u_3\delta(1 - \delta) + u_4\delta^2 + (N - 1)\,[2Bu,\delta + AD] \\ + (N - 1)\,(N - 2)\,AB^2\}$$

$$P(A_1E_1A_2E_2A_1) = \frac{\pi(1 - \pi)}{N^2}\,\{u_2\delta^2 + (N - 1)\,[A\delta(u_2 + u_3) + BC] \\ + (N - 1)\,(N - 2)\,A^2B\}$$

$$P(A_1E_1A_2E_2A_2) = \frac{\pi(1 - \pi)}{N^2}\,[u_3\delta(1 - \mu_3) + (N - 1)\,B(u_3\delta + A) \\ + (N - 1)\,(N - 2)\,AB^2]$$

$$P(A_1E_2A_1E_1A_1) = \frac{\pi(1-\pi)}{N^2} \{u_1 + u_2[1 - \delta(1 - \mu)] + (N-1) A(2A + C)$$
$$+ (N-1)(N-2) A^3\}$$

$$P(A_1E_2A_1E_1A_2) = \frac{\pi(1-\pi)}{N^2} [u_3\delta(1 - \delta) + (N-1)(BC + 2Au_3\delta)$$
$$+ (N-1)(N-2) A^2B]$$

$$P(A_1E_2A_1E_2A_1) = \frac{(1-\pi)^2}{N^2} [u_1(1 - \delta^2) + u_2(1 - \delta^2 + 3(N-1) AC$$
$$+ (N-1)(N-2) A^3]$$

$$P(A_1E_2A_1E_2A_2) = \frac{(1-\pi)^2}{N^2} (N-1) B[C + (N-2) A^2]$$

$$P(A_1E_2A_2E_1A_1) = \frac{\pi(1-\pi)}{N^2} (N-1) AB[1 + (N-2) A]$$

$$P(A_1E_2A_2E_1A_2) = \frac{\pi(1-\pi)}{N^2} (N-1) [Bu_3\delta + AD + (N-2) AB]$$

$$P(A_1E_2A_2E_2A_1) = \frac{(1-\pi)^2}{N^2} (N-1) [BC + Au_2\delta + (N-2) A^2B]$$

$$P(A_1E_2A_2E_2A_2) = \frac{(1-\pi)^2}{N^2} (N-1) AB[1 + (N-2) B]$$

where

$$A = u_1 + u_2$$
$$B = u_3 + u_4$$
$$C = u_1 + u_2(1 - \delta)$$
$$D = u_3(1 - \delta) + u_4$$

APPENDIX B

The values of n_{jk} presented in Table 10 are the total numbers of asymptotic trials on which E_j and A_k both occurred, pooling over all subjects in each group. These values are the denominators for the first-order conditional statistics presented in the paper. Values of n_{jklm} in Table 11 are the numbers of pairs of asymptotic trials containing E_j and A_k on trial n and E_l and A_m on trial $n - 1$. These values are the denominators of the second-order conditional statistics analyzed for the Friedman *et al.* study.

TABLE 11

VALUES OF n_{jk} FOR SEVERAL STUDIES

Experiment	Group	n_{11}	n_{21}	n_{12}	n_{22}
Suppes and Atkinson	Z	1238	595	602	365
	F	900	656	537	307
	T	1008	673	428	291
Myers *et al.*	0.6-0¢	590	395	358	241
	0.7-0¢	1042	449	356	133
	0.8-0¢	1382	340	197	61
	0.6-1¢	771	516	413	280
	0.7-1¢	1204	517	194	65
	0.8-1¢	1463	368	115	34
	0.6-10¢	828	582	349	221
	0.7-10¢	1202	515	193	70
	0.8-10¢	1489	393	85	13
Friedman *et al.*		4815	1166	1028	268

TABLE 12

VALUES OF n_{jklm} FOR THE FRIEDMAN *et al.* STUDY

jklm	n_{jklm}	jklm	n_{jklm}
1111	3435	2211	868
1112	585	2112	126
1121	699	2121	168
1122	82	2122	27
1211	427	2211	85
1212	259	2212	58
1221	225	2221	74
1222	109	2222	50

REFERENCES

ANDERSON, N. H. Comments on Professor Estes' paper. In A. W. Melton (Ed.), *Categories of human learning.* New York: Academic Press, 1963.

ANDERSON, T. W., AND GOODMAN, L. A. Statistical inference about Markov chains. *Ann. Math. Statist.*, 1957, **28**, 89-110.

ATKINSON, R. C. The use of models in experimental psychology. *Synthese*, 1960, **12**, 162-171.

ATKINSON, R. C. A generalization of stimulus sampling theory. *Psychometrika*, 1961, **26**, 281-290. (a)

ATKINSON, R. C. The observing response in discrimination learning. *J. exp. Psychol.*, 1961, **62**, 253-262. (b)

ATKINSON, R. C. Choice behavior and monetary payoff: strong and weak conditioning. In J. H. Criswell, H. Solomon, and P. Suppes (Eds.), *Mathematical methods in small group processes.* Stanford, Calif.: Stanford Univer. Press, 1962. Pp. 23-34.

ATKINSON, R. C., AND ESTES, W. K. Stimulus sampling theory. In R. D. Luce, R. R. Bush, and E. Galanter (Eds.), *Handbook of mathematical psychology.* Vol. 2. New York: Wiley, 1963. Pp. 121-268.

BOWER, G. H. Choice-point behavior. In R. R. Bush and W. K. Estes (Eds.), *Studies in mathematical learning theory.* Stanford, Calif.: Stanford Univer. Press, 1959. Pp. 109-124.

BUSH, R. R., AND MOSTELLER, F. *Stochastic models for learning.* New York: Wiley, 1955.

CALFEE, R. Extended training under probabilistic reinforcement schedules with rats. Univ. of Calif., Los Angeles, Ph. D. thesis, 1963.

COLE, M. Search behavior: A correction procedure for three-choice probability learning. Indiana Univer., Ph.D. thesis, 1962.

COTTON, J. W., AND RECHSCHAFFEN, A. Replication reports: Two and three choice verbal conditioning phenomena. *J. exp. Psychol.*, 1958, **56**, 96.

EDWARDS, W. Reward probability, amount, and information as determiners of sequential two-alternative decisions. *J. exp. Psychol.*, 1956, **52**, 177-188.

ESTES, W. K. Toward a statistical theory of learning. *Psychol. Rev.*, 1950, **57**, 94-107.

ESTES, W. K. Component and pattern models with Markovian interpretations. In R. R. Bush and W. K. Estes (Eds.), *Studies in mathematical learning theory.* Stanford, Calif. : Stanford Univer. Press, 1959.

ESTES, W. K. A random-walk model for choice behavior. In K. J. Arrow, S. Jarlin, and P. Suppes (Eds.), *Mathematical methods in the social sciences.* Stanford, Calif.: Stanford Univer. Press, 1960.

ESTES, W. K. Theoretical treatments of differential reward in multiplechoice learning and two-person interactions. In J. H. Criswell, H. Solomon, and P. Suppes (Eds.), *Mathematical models in small group processes.* Stanford, Calif.: Stanford Univer. Press, 1962.

FRIEDMAN, M. P., BURKE, C. J., COLE, M., ESTES, W. K., KELLER, L., AND MILLWARD, R. B. Two-choice behavior under extended training with shifting probabilities of reinforcement. In R. C. Atkinson (Ed.), *Studies in mathematical psychology.* Stanford, Calif. : Stanford Univer. Press, 1963.

GARDNER, R. A. Probability-learning with two and three choices. *Amer. J. Psychol.*, 1957, **70**, 174-185.

KATZ, L. Monetary incentive and range of payoffs as determiners of risk-taking. *J. exp. Psychol.*, 1962, **64**, 541-544.

KATZ, L. Manipulation of payoff parameters in a two-choice situation. *J. exp. Psychol.,* in press.

LA BERGE, D. A model with neutral elements. In R. R. Bush and W. K. Estes (Eds.), *Studies in mathematical learning theory.* Stanford, Calif.: Stanford Univer. Press, 1959.

LUCE, R. D. *Individual choice behavior.* New York: Wiley, 1960.

MYERS, J. L., AND FORT, J. G. A sequential analysis of gambling behavior. Paper presented at meeting of Psychonomic Society, New York, 1962.

MYERS, J. L., AND KATZ, L. Range of payoffs and feedback in risk taking. *Psychol. Rep.*, 1962. **10**, 483-486.

MYERS, J. L., AND SADLER, E. Effects of range of payoffs as a variable in risk taking. *J. exp. Psychol.*, 1960. **60**, 306-309.

MYERS, J. L., FORT, J. G., KATZ, L., AND SUYDAM, M. M. Supplementary report: Differential monetary gains and losses and event probabilities in a two-choice situation. *J. exp. Psychol.*, 1963, in press.

ROYDEN, H. L., SUPPES, P., AND WALSH, K. A model for the experimental measurement of the utility of gambling. *Behav. Sci.*, 1959, **4**, 11-18.

SAVAGE, L. J. The theory of statistical decision. *J. Amer. Statist. Assoc.* 1957. **48**, 238-248.

SIEGEL, S. Theoretical models of choice and strategy behavior-stable state behavior in the two-choice uncertain outcome situation. *Psychometrika*, 1959, **24**, 203-216.

SIMON, H. A. A comparison of game theory and learning theory. *Psychometrika*, 1956. **21**, 267-272.

SUPPES, P., AND ATKINSON, R. C. *Markov learning models for multiperson interactions.* Stanford, Calif.: Stanford Univer. Press, 1960.

RECEIVED: May 24, 1963

CHAPTER IV

Single Process Models for Generalization
and Discrimination

Some of the earliest systematic attempts to develop a theory of stimulus generalization and discrimination (for example, Hull, 1952; Spence, 1936) utilized a strategy of accounting for these phenomena wholly in terms of the same principles employed in describing elementary acquisition and extinction. Early applications of stimulus sampling theory to discrimination and generalization (which are represented in the first five papers of this chapter) adopted the same strategy; response probabilities were described in terms of the sampling and conditioning of stimulus elements from populations representing the different discriminative stimuli involved in a situation. The limits of this approach were quickly reached. Revisions and extensions of the initial approach have ensued in several major directions, all of which involve the basic concepts of stimulus sampling theory in some form. One group of models results from employing the same basic assumptions and the same mathematical formulation of the assumptions, while changing the interpretation of the unit involved. In one instance it is assumed that strategies, or hypotheses, rather than stimulus elements, are sampled and differentially conditioned; in another case, stimulus patterns are treated as the basic unit. Examples of both these reinterpretations of a single process theory are included in the present chapter. Chapter V deals with discrimination models which introduce an additional process at the stage of stimulus selection and, by so doing, generally introduce greater mathematical complexity.

The classification of discrimination theories imposed in this and the ensuing chapter is based upon the number of elementary processes invoked: one or more than one, with finer classification in terms of interpretation of the processes and the elements, or units, on which they operate. For a more detailed comparison of discrimination theories based upon a similar classification scheme, see Bush (1965).

DIRECT EXTENSION OF MODELS FOR SIMPLE LEARNING

Generalization. Although most attempts at theoretical descriptions of the learning process have been concerned with simple learning, there is general agreement that any comprehensive account of learning must provide an adequate account of stimulus generalization and discrimination. In studies of stimulus generalization, a subject is trained to make some response A_1 in the presence of a stimulus S_1, and is then tested with a variety of stimuli in order to determine whether the probability of response A_1 varies systematically with the similarity of other stimuli to S_1. In discrimination training, on the other hand, over a series of trials the subject is rewarded for A_1 in the presence of one stimulus configuration S_1, but not in the presence of some other stimulus configuration S_2; learning is defined in terms of concurrent increases in probability of A_1 to S_1 and decreases in probability of A_1 to S_2.

The methods of Chapter I may be directly extended to account for the process of stimulus generalization. One of the first direct extensions was proposed by Bush and Mosteller (1951), who approached the problem from the standpoint of relations between sets of stimulus elements. Two discriminative stimuli, for example a black card and a white card, are treated as sets, S and S', of elements. Associated with each element is a number characterizing its "weight," or measure of potential importance, in influencing behavior. The integral of the density function of the numbers associated with each set defines a measure of the set: $m(S)$ and $m(S')$. Furthermore, some elements are common to both sets: $I = S \cap S'$. Bush and Mosteller then show that, following training in which some proportion, $m(c)/m(S) = p$, of elements in set S is conditioned to the response in question, the probability p' of response to stimuli of S' will be the product of the probability p of response to S and the similarity, $\eta(S' \text{ to } S)$, of S' to S:

$$p' = \eta(S' \text{ to } S)p = m(I)/m(S') \cdot m(C)/m(S).$$

In this context the numerical value of η provides an index of similarity.

Similar assumptions, but with different notation, have been employed by Atkinson and Estes (1963) in the derivation of the generalization gradient for response to S' (S_b in their notation) following varying amounts of training of A_1 to S (S_a in their notation). Experimental tests of this model applied to the problem of summated generalization (Carterette, 1961; LaBerge & Martin, 1964) provide some support to the model.

Discrimination. As was noted in Chapter I, within the general conception of representing the stimulus situation on any given trial as a random sample of stimulus elements drawn from a larger population, there are two possible assumptions concerning the sampling process. One assumes *fixed sample size*, that is, that the number of elements drawn from the population on any given trial is a constant number s throughout the experiment; the second assumes that each element s_i has a fixed sampling probability θ_i throughout the experiment, and, therefore, the precise number sampled on each trial is a random variable. Models reflecting the fixed probability assumption are called *independent-sampling* models. The fixed sample size assumption was employed in the initial development of statistical learning theory (Estes, 1950), whereas the fixed probability assumption was employed by Estes and Burke (1953) (see Chapter I).

The treatment of simple learning (Estes and Burke, 1953) was extended to discrimination learning by Burke and Estes (1957). The experimental situation to which the model applies is one in which there are two types of trials, T_1 and T_2, differing with respect to the stimulus situation presented, which are presented with relative frequencies of β and $(1 - \beta)$, respectively. For example, a white card might be presented at the outset of a trial on 40% of the series of trials, and a black card on the remaining 60% of the series. The subject on each trial may make one of two mutually exclusive responses, A_1 or A_2 (pressing the left or the right key), following which he observes a reinforcing event E_j. The event E_j is not contingent upon the subject's response but occurs with fixed probability π_{hj} (the double subscript on π is required to specify the probability of E_j on a trial of type T_h, $h = 1$ or 2). When only one trial type, for example T_1, is given ($\beta = 1$), then the model reduces to the earlier model of simple learning. In the classical discrimination procedure at least two different stimuli are presented ($\beta \neq 1$) and each stimulus may be treated as composed of a set of unique elements, S_1 or S_2, along with components associated with the experimental context S_c, which are common to both T_1 and T_2 trials. In these situations the asymptotic probability of correct response on T_1 and T_2 trials will be a function of the relative weights of the unique and common elements. An experimental test of this prediction (Estes and Burke, 1955), while generally in accord with the prediction, suggested that common elements had less effect on responding than expected and, furthermore, that the effect of common elements might decrease over training.

Another feature of the Estes and Burke (1955) experiment to be noted is the introduction of π_{hj}. In classical discrimination training, it is generally the case that one response A_1 is always correct on T_1 trials, whereas another response A_2 is correct on T_2 trials. More generally, however, the probability of an event E_j on a trial of type T_h may assume any value from 0 to 1. Thus one might expect to find something like probability matching in probabilistic discrimination; results of relevant experimental tests (e.g., Neimark and Rosenberg, 1959) provide fair support of this prediction.

Probabilistic relations may be introduced not only in the correlation of reinforcing events with trial types, but also with respect to the relative frequency with which a given stimulus element occurs on a trial of type T_h in relation to an event schedule. As a first approximation to experimental manipulation of the probability of occurrence of each stimulus element, Estes, Burke, Atkinson, and Frankmann (1957) used a stimulus display of 12 lights arranged in a circle. Each light was randomly assigned a number from $i = 1, 2, \ldots, 12$, and the probability of occurrence of light i on T_1 trials was $5i/78$, while on T_2 trials it was $5(13 - i)/78$. Two groups, differing with respect to the relative frequency β of T_1 trials and the conditional probability of E_1, were given two daily sessions of 240 training trials per day. On the third day they received additional training along with test trials (involving neither E_1 nor E_2 events) on which single lights, successive triads, or one of two mixed triads were presented. In deriving theoretical predictions, only one parameter θ was estimated from the data. While there was some suggestion that the observed proportion of correct responses on the second day of training exceeded prediction (which would suggest that subjects, in effect, gave greater weight to cues of greater validity), in general, test results were in fair agreement with predicted values.

Pattern models. Another possible approach to theoretical description of discrimination derives from the methods of Chapter II. Within this framework, the stimulus situation on a given trial is viewed as a unique pattern rather than as a sample from a subset of elements; hence, the description *pattern model* as contrasted with *component models* described above. In general, pattern models will have one desirable property which component models lack, that is, it will be possible to predict the occurrence of perfect discrimination between two stimulus patterns S_1 and S_2, despite the presence of common elements in the two stimulus configurations. On the other hand, pattern models do not provide as simple and straightforward a mechanism for describing stimulus generalization, or even of dealing with the scaling of stimulus similarity, as do component models. One obvious solution lies in incorporating the desirable features of both approaches in a "mixed model." One possible mixed model is discussed by Atkinson and Estes (1964). In essence, this approach assumes that (a) once a response has been conditioned to a pattern, it will be evoked by that pattern on subsequent trials (barring later change in reinforcement contingencies) and (b) response to a pattern which has not yet been conditioned but which contains components that have been conditioned as parts of other patterns, will be determined by the relative weights of the conditioned components. Of course, one cannot directly observe the conditioning status of patterns and components; nevertheless, it is possible to predict bounds on the probability of response over the presolution trial sequence. To the extent that predictions from the pattern model have been tested experimentally (Estes and Hopkins, 1961; Johns, 1965; Friedman, 1966), they seem to be in fair accord with the data.

Another possible combination of the properties of the pattern and component models has been proposed by Atkinson (1959). He distinguished two possible "perceptual states": P, in which on a given trial a subject responds to the stimulus situation as a pattern, and C, in which the subject responds to the stimulus situation on the basis of its components. Which state the subject is in on any given trial will depend upon his previous reinforcement history. Two states of conditioning are defined: one in which each *element* is conditioned to one of the available responses, and one in which each *pattern* is conditioned to one of the available responses. Response probabilities, then, are dependent upon conditioning state and perceptual state. As to the relationship of conditioning states and perceptual states, two alternative assumptions are considered: that perceptual and conditioning states are completely dependent upon each other, or that they are independent. Although the theoretical distinction between perceptual and conditioning states cannot be coordinated to direct experimental observations, it is possible to derive a number of experimentally testable predictions when the two cases are applied to a variety of experimental situations.

Mediational models. In discussing pattern and component interpretations of discriminative stimuli, no explicit consideration was given to the operational definition of "component" or "pattern" but, rather, it was implied that the operational definitions—when formulated—would be based upon physical properties of stimulus events. In one sense all specifications of the stimulus must be *based* upon physical properties; what is at issue is the transformation of physical properties introduced by their action upon the receptors and nervous sytem of a subject. In the case of human subjects it is reasonable to assume that they pay attention to some properties rather than to others, and that their responses are determined by, in effect, things they say to themselves about the nature of the stimulus and the purpose of the experiment. For example, in a concept attainment study humans typically respond to a variety of physically different stimuli as members of a single concept class identified by a common label. In this experimental situation it is commonly assumed that correct responding is mediated by subject-generated activity: hypothesizing, labeling, or selective attending to the common property which characterizes members of a concept class.

A number of investigators have developed models based upon an assumed mediation process (Restle, 1961, 1962, 1964; Bower and Trabasso, 1964; Suppes and Atkinson, 1960; Levine, 1963a). Although the models differ in some details, they are highly similar in general properties. On each experimental trial the subject is assumed to sample from a set of mediators (hypotheses in the case of Restle's model, or properties of stimulus dimensions in the case of Bower and Trabasso); if the resulting response is correct, he uses the same mediator subsequently; if not, he changes to a different one. For any given experimental task, the very large number of potential mediators may be classified into subsets on the basis of the outcome to which they lead, that is, classes of correct or irrelevant (Restle also includes the category of wrong) mediators. Each class corresponds to a hypothetical subject state and experimental procedures insure that one state, correct mediator, is absorbing, whereas the others are transitory. Thus, simple concept identification experiments may be described by a Markov process of the sort discussed in Chapter II. Most of the methods and many of the predictions derived for paired-associate learning are directly applicable to concept attainment tasks; the difference lies in the identification of the elements and of corresponding subject states. Once again, the process is all-or-none, but in concept attainment, transitions from one state to another are assumed to occur only on trials on which the subject's response is incorrect (an assumption which is not altogether supported by recent evidence, e.g., Suppes and Schlag-Rey, 1965; Levine, 1963b).

Statistics for a number of aspects of the data have been derived not only for simple concept attainment tasks, but also for transfer tasks such as concept reversal. For the most part, available data are well described by theoretical predictions (Trabasso, 1963; Bower and Trabasso, 1963; Trabasso and Bower, 1964). Interestingly enough, in concept reversal studies both the experimental designs and the theoretical predictions are reminiscent of the earlier continuity vs. discontinuity controversy with respect to discrimination. In the case of concept attainment studies, performance is well described by assuming an all-or-none process of hypothesis selection which resembles the earlier noncontinuity view of discrimination. This finding suggests that the noncontinuity theorists had a good idea but an inappropriate organism.

Hypothesis, or strategy, selection models have been applied primarily to data of concept identification experiments. In this context the distinction between discrimination and generalization is obscured. It would appear, therefore, that pattern interpretations of a single process model provide the most natural interpretation for traditional discrimination experiments, whereas strategy selection models are their logical counterpart for concept identification studies. At first blush, such a state of affairs might seem to violate preferences for theoretical parsimony. On the other hand, there is a good deal of parsimony with respect to the formal structure of the theory. The fact that the level of interpretation of the unit of the theory changes has some interesting implications for research on human thought processes and their development.

REFERENCES

Atkinson, R. C. A theory of stimulus discrimination learning. In K. J. Arrow, S. Karlin, and P. Suppes (Eds.), *Mathematical methods in the social sciences.* Stanford, Calif.: Stanford Univ. Press, 1959, 221–241.

Atkinson, R. C. and Estes, W. K. Stimulus sampling theory. In R. D. Luce, R. R. Bush, and E. Galanter (Eds.), *Handbook of mathematical psychology.* New York: Wiley, 1963, 121–268.

Bower, G. H. and Trabasso, T. Reversals prior to solution in concept identification. *J. exp. Psychol.*, 1963, **66**, 409–418.

Bower, G. H. and Trabasso, T. Concept identification. In R. C. Atkinson (Ed.), *Studies in mathematical psychology.* Stanford, Calif.: Stanford Univ. Press, 1964, 32–94.

Burke, C. J. and Estes, W. K. A component model for stimulus variables in discrimination learning. *Psychometrika*, 1957, **22**, 133–145.

Bush, R. R. Identification learning. In R. D. Luce, R. R. Bush, and E. Galanter (Eds.), *Handbook of mathematical psychology*, Vol. III, New York: Wiley, 1965, 161–203.

Bush, R. R. and Mosteller, F. A model for stimulus generalization and discrimination. *Psychol. Rev.*, 1951, **58**, 413–423.

Carterette, T. S. An application of stimulus sampling theory to summated generalization. *J. exp. Psychol.*, 1961, **62**, 448–455.

Estes, W. K. Toward a statistical theory of learning. *Psychol. Rev.*, 1950, **57**, 94–107.

Estes, W. K. and Burke, C. J. A theory of stimulus variability in learning. *Psychol. Rev.*, 1953, **60**, 276–286.

Estes, W. K. and Burke, C. J. Application of a statistical model to simple discrimination learning in human subjects. *J. exp. Psychol.*, 1955, **50**, 81–88.

Estes, W. K., Burke, C. J., Atkinson, R. C., and Frankmann, J. P. Probabilistic discrimination learning. *J. exp. Psychol.*, 1957, **54**, 233–239.

Estes, W. K. and Hopkins, B. L. Acquisition and transfer in pattern vs. component discrimination learning. *J. exp. Psychol.*, 1961, **61**, 322–328.

Friedman, M. P. Transfer effects and response strategies in pattern vs. component discrimination learning. *J. exp. Psychol.*, 1966, **71**, 420–428.

Hull, C. L. *A Behavior System.* New Haven: Yale Univ. Press, 1952.

Johns, M. D. Supplementary report: Transfer of a pattern vs. component discrimination following training in a probabilistic situation. *J. exp. Psychol.*, 1965, **70**, 506–509.

LaBerge, D. and Martin, D. R. An analysis of summated generalization. *J. exp. Psychol.*, 1964, **68,** 71–79.

Levine, M. Mediating processes in humans at the outset of discrimination learning. *Psychol. Rev.*, 1963, **70,** 254–276. (a)

Levine, M. The assumption concerning "wrongs" in Restle's model of strategies in cue learning. *Psychol. Rev.*, 1963, **70,** 559–561. (b)

Neimark, E. D. and Rosenberg, S. The effect of "social" discriminative cues on probability learning. *J. exp. Psychol.*, 1959, **58,** 302–311.

Restle, F. Statistical methods for a theory of cue learning. *Psychometrika*, 1961, **26,** 291–306.

Restle, F. The selection of strategies in cue learning. *Psychol. Rev.*, 1962, **69,** 329–343.

Restle, F. Sources of difficulty in learning paired associates. In R. C. Atkinson (Ed.), *Studies in mathematical psychology.* Stanford, Calif.: Stanford Univ. Press, 1964, 116–125.

Spence, K. W. The nature of discrimination learning in animals. *Psychol. Rev.*, 1936, **43,** 427–449.

Suppes, P. and Atkinson, R. C. *Markov learning models for multiperson interactions.* Stanford, Calif.: Stanford Univ. Press, 1960, 247–252.

Suppes, P. and Schlag-Rey, M. Observable changes of hypotheses under positive reinforcement. *Science*, 1965, **148,** 661–662.

Trabasso, T. R. Stimulus emphasis and all-or-none learning in concept identification. *J. exp. Psychol.*, 1963, **65,** 398–406.

Trabasso, T. R. and Bower, G. H. Component learning in the four-category concept problem. *J. math. Psychol.*, 1964, **1,** 143–170.

A Model for Stimulus Generalization and Discrimination

ROBERT R. BUSH[1] and FREDERICK MOSTELLER, *Harvard University*[2]

INTRODUCTION

The processes of stimulus generalization and discrimination seem as fundamental to behavior theory as the simple mechanisms of reinforcement and extinction are to learning theory. Whether or not this distinction between learning and behavior is a useful one, there can be little doubt that few if any applications of behavior theory to practical problems can be made without a clear exposition of the phenomena of generalization and discrimination. It is our impression that few crucial experiments in this area have been reported compared with the number of important experiments on simple conditioning and extinction. Perhaps part of the reason for this is that there are too few theoretical formulations available. That is to say, we conceive that explicit and quantitative theoretical structures are useful in guiding the direction of experimental research and in suggesting the type of data which are needed.

In this paper we describe a model, based upon elementary concepts of mathematical set theory. This model provides one possible framework for analyzing problems in stimulus generalization and discrimination. Further, we shall show how this model generates the basic postulates of our previous work on acquisition and extinction (1), where the stimulus situation as defined by the experimenter was assumed constant.

Stated in the simplest terms, generalization is the phenomenon in which an increase in strength of a response learned in one stimulus situation implies an increase in strength of response in a somewhat different stimulus situation. When this occurs, the two situations are said to be similar. Although there are several intuitive notions as to what is meant by "similarity," one usually means the properties which give rise to generalization. We see no alternative to using the amount of generalization as an operational definition of degree of "similarity." In the model, however, we shall give another definition of the degree of similarity, but this definition will be entirely consistent with the above-mentioned operational definition.

We also wish to clarify what we mean by stimulus discrimination. In one sense of the term, all learning is a process of discrimination. Our usage of the term is a more restricted one, however. We refer specifically to the process by which an animal learns to make response A in one stimulus situation and response B (or response A with different "strength") in a different stimulus situation. We are not at the moment concerned with, for example, the process by which an animal learns to discriminate between

[1] SSRC-NRC Post-doctoral Fellow in the Natural and Social Sciences.

[2] This research was supported by the Laboratory of Social Relations, Harvard University, as part of a program of the Laboratory's Project on Mathematical Models.

We are indebted to many persons for assistance and encouragement, but in particular to F. R. Brush, C. I. Hovland, K. C. Montgomery, F. D. Sheffield, and R. L. Solomon. We are also grateful to W. K. Estes for sending us a pre-publication copy of his paper(2).

This article appeared in *Psychol. Rev.*, 1951, **58**, 413–423.

various possible responses in a fixed stimulus situation.

As prototypes of the more general problems of stimulus generalization and discrimination, we shall consider the following two kinds of experiments:

(i) An animal is trained to make a particular response, by the usual reinforcement procedure, in an experimentally defined stimulus situation. At the end of training, the response has a certain strength or probability of occurrence. The animal is then "tested" in a new stimulus situation similar to the training one and in which the same response, insofar as it is experimentally defined, is possible. One then asks about the strength or probability of occurrence of the response in this new stimulus situation and how it depends on the degree of similarity of the new situation to the old stimulus situation.

(ii) An animal is presented alternately with two stimulus situations which are similar. In one, an experimentally defined response is rewarded, and in the other that response is either not rewarded or rewarded less than in the first. Through the process of generalization, the effects of rewards and non-rewards in one stimulus situation influence the response strength in the other, but eventually the animal learns to respond in one but not in the other, or at least to respond with different probabilities (rates or strengths). One then asks how the probability of the response in each situation varies with the number of training trials, with the degree of similarity of the two situations, and with the amount of reward.

We do not consider that these two kinds of experiments come close to exhausting the problems classified under the heading of generalization and discrimination, but we do believe that they are fundamental. Thus, the model to be described has been designed to permit analysis of these experiments. In the next section we will present the major features of the model, and in later sections we shall apply it to the above described experiments.

THE MODEL

We shall employ some of the elementary notions of mathematical set theory to define our model. A particular stimulus situation, such as an experimental box with specific properties (geometrical, optical, acoustical, etc.) is regarded as separate and distinct from the rest of the universe. Thus, we shall denote this situation by a set of stimuli which is part of the entire universe of stimuli. The elements of this set are undefined and we place no restriction on their number. This lack of definition of the stimulus elements does not give rise to any serious difficulties since our final results involve neither properties of individual elements nor numbers of such elements. We next introduce the notion of the *measure* of a set. If the set consists of a finite number of elements, we may associate with each element a positive number to denote its "weight"; the measure of such a set is the sum of all these numbers. Intuitively, the weight associated with an element is the measure of the potential importance of that element in influencing the organism's behavior. More generally, we can define a density function over the set; the measure is the integral of that function over the set.

To bridge the gap between stimuli and responses, we shall borrow some of the basic notions of Estes (2). (The concept of reinforcement will play an integral role, however.) It is assumed that stimulus elements exist in one of two states as far as the organism involved is concerned; since the elements are undefined, these states do not require definition but merely need labelling. However, we shall speak of elements which are in one state as being "conditioned" to the response, and of elements in the other state as being "non-conditioned."

On a particular trial or occurrence of a response in the learning process, it is conceived that an organism perceives a sub-set of the total stimuli available. It is postulated that the probability of occurrence of the response in a given time interval is equal to the measure of the elements in the sub-set which had been previously conditioned, divided by the measure of the entire sub-set. Speaking roughly, the probability is the ratio of the importance of the conditioned elements perceived to the importance of all the elements perceived. It is further assumed that the sub-set perceived is conditioned to the response if that response is rewarded.

The situation is illustrated in Fig. 1. It would be wrong to suppose that the conditioned and non-conditioned elements are spatially separated in the actual situation as Fig. 1 might suggest; the conditioned elements are spread out smoothly among the non-conditioned ones. In set-theoretic notation, we then have for the probability of occurrence of the response

$$p = \frac{m(X \cap C)}{m(X)}, \qquad (1)$$

where $m(\ )$ denotes the measure of any set or sub-set named between the parentheses, and where $X \cap C$ indicates the intersection of X and C (also called set-product, meet, or overlap of X and C). We then make an assumption of equal proportions in the measures so that

$$p = \frac{m(X \cap C)}{m(X)} = \frac{m(C)}{m(S)}. \qquad (2)$$

Heuristically, this assumption of equal proportions can arise from a fluid model. Suppose that the total situation is represented by a vessel containing an ideal fluid which is a

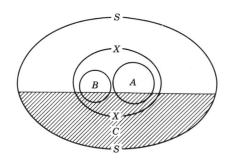

Fig. 1. Set diagram of the single stimulus situation S with the various sub-sets involved in a particular trial. C is the sub-set of elements previously conditioned, X the sub-set of S perceived on the trial. The sub-sets A and B are defined in the text.

mixture of two substances which do not chemically interact but are completely miscible. For discussion let the substances be water and alcohol and assume, contrary to fact, that the volume of the mixture is equal to the sum of the partial volumes. The volume of the water corresponds to the measure of the sub-set of non-conditioned stimuli, $S - C$ (total set minus the conditioned set), and the volume of the alcohol corresponds to the measure of the sub-set C of conditioned stimuli. The sub-set X corresponds to a thimbleful of the mixture and of course if the fluids are well mixed, the volumetric fraction of alcohol in a thimbleful will be much the same as that in the whole vessel. Thus the fraction of measure of conditioned stimuli in X will be equal to the fraction in the whole set S, as expressed by equation (2). Our definition of p is essentially that of Estes (2) except that where he speaks of number of elements, we speak of the measure of the elements.

We next consider another stimulus situation which we denote by a set S'. In general this new set S' will not be disjunct from the set S, i.e., S and S'

will intersect or overlap as shown in Fig. 2. We denote the intersection by

$$I = S \cap S'. \tag{3}$$

We can now define an index of similarity of S' to S by

$$\eta(S' \text{ to } S) = \frac{m(I)}{m(S')}. \tag{4}$$

In words this definition says that the index of similarity of S' to S is the measure of their intersection divided by the measure of the set S'. (Our notation makes clear that we have made a tacit assumption that the measure of an element or set of elements is independent of the set in which it is measured.) Definition (4) also gives the index of similarity of S to S' as

$$\eta(S \text{ to } S') = \frac{m(I)}{m(S)}$$

$$= \frac{m(S')}{m(S)} \eta(S' \text{ to } S). \tag{5}$$

From this last equation it is clear that the similarity of S' to S may not be the same as the similarity of S to S'. In fact, if the measure of the intersection is not zero, the two indices are equal only if the measures of S and S' are equal. It seems regrettable that similarity, by our definition, is non-symmetric. However, we do not care to make the general assumption that (a) the measures of all situations are equal and at the same time make the assumption that (b) measures of an element or set of elements is the same in each situation in which it appears. For then the importance of a set of elements, say a light bulb, would have to be the same in a small situation, say a $2' \times 2' \times 2'$ box, as in a large situation, say a ballroom. Further this pair of assumptions, (a) and (b), leads to conceptual difficulties.

THE GENERALIZATION PROBLEM

We are now in a position to say something about the first experimental problem described in the Introduction. An animal is trained to make a response in one stimulus situation and then his response strength is measured in a similar situation. After the animal has been trained in the first situation whose elements form the set S, a sub-set C of S will have been conditioned to the response as shown in Fig. 2. But part of the sub-set C is also contained in the second situation whose elements form the set S'; we denote this part by $C \cap S'$.

From the discussion preceding equations (1) and (2), we can easily see that the probability of the response occurring in S' is

$$p' = \frac{m(C \cap S')}{m(S')}. \tag{6}$$

We now use the assumption of equal proportions so that

$$\frac{m(C \cap S')}{m(I)} = \frac{m(C \cap I)}{m(I)} = \frac{m(C)}{m(S)}. \tag{7}$$

The first equality in this equation follows from the fact that the only part of C which is in S' is in the inter-

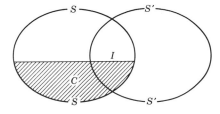

FIG. 2. Diagram of two similar stimulus situations after conditioning in one of them. The situation in which training occurred is denoted by the set S; the sub-set C of S represents the portion of S which was conditioned to the response. The new stimulus situation in which the response strength is to be measured is represented by the set S', and the intersection of S' and S is denoted by I.

section I as shown in Fig. 2. The second equality in equation (7) is an application of our assumption that the measure of C is uniformly distributed over S and so the intersection contains the same fraction of measure of C as does the entire set S.

If now we combine equations (6) and (7), we obtain

$$p' = \frac{m(I)}{m(S')} \cdot \frac{m(C)}{m(S)}. \qquad (8)$$

From equation (4) we note that the first ratio in equation (8) is the index of similarity of S' to S, while from equation (2) we observe that the second ratio in equation (8) is merely the probability p of the response in S. Hence

$$p' = \eta(S' \text{ to } S)p. \qquad (9)$$

Equation (9) now provides us with the necessary operational definition of the index of similarity, $\eta(S' \text{ to } S)$, of the set S' to the set S. The probabilities p and p' of the response in S and S', respectively, can be measured either directly or through measurements of latent time or rate of responding (1). Therefore, with equation (9), we have an operational way of determining the index of similarity.

As a direct consequence of our assumption of equal proportions, we can draw the following general conclusion. *Any change made in a stimulus situation where a response was conditioned will reduce the probability of occurrence of that response, provided the change does not introduce stimuli which had been previously conditioned to that response.* This conclusion follows from equation (9) and the fact that we have defined our similarity index in such a way that it is never greater than unity.

A word needs to be said about the correspondence between our result and the experimental results such as those of Hovland (3). Our model predicts nothing about the relation of the index of similarity defined above to such physical dimensions as light or sound intensity, frequency, etc. In fact, our model suggests that no such general relation is possible, *i.e.*, that any sensible measure of similarity is very much organism determined. Therefore, from the point of view of our model, experiments such as those of Hovland serve only as a clear demonstration that stimulus generalization exists. In addition, of course, such experiments provide empirical relations, characteristic of the organism studied, between the proposed index of similarity and various physical dimensions, but these relations are outside the scope of our model.

We conclude, therefore, that our model up to this point has made no quantitative predictions about the shape of generalization gradients which can be compared with experiment. Nevertheless, the preceding analysis of generalization does provide us with a framework to discuss experiments on stimulus discrimination. In the following sections we shall extend our model so as to permit analysis of such experiments.

THE REINFORCEMENT AND EXTINCTION OPERATORS

In this section we develop some results that will be used later and show that the model of the present paper generates postulates used in our previous paper (1). We shall examine the step-wise change in probability of a response in a single stimulus situation S. We generalize the notions already presented as follows: Previous to a particular trial or occurrence of the response, a sub-set C of S will have been conditioned. On the trial in question a sub-set X of S will be perceived as shown in Fig. 1. According to our previous assumptions, the probability of the response is

$$p = \frac{m(X \cap C)}{m(X)} = \frac{m(C)}{m(S)}. \quad (10)$$

We now assume that a sub-set A of X will be conditioned to the response as a result of the reward given and that the measure of A will depend on the amount of reward, on the strength of motivation, etc. We further assume that another sub-set B of X will become non-conditioned as a result of the work required in making the response. For simplicity we assume that A and B are disjunct. (The error resulting from this last assumption can be shown to be small if the measures of A and B are small compared to that of S.)

We extend our assumption of equal proportions so that we have

$$\frac{m(A \cap C)}{m(A)} = \frac{m(B \cap C)}{m(B)} = \frac{m(C)}{m(S)}. \quad (11)$$

Now at the end of the trial being considered, sub-set A is part of the new conditional sub-set while sub-set B is part of the new non-conditioned sub-set. Thus, the change in the measure of C is

$$\Delta m(C) = [m(A) - m(A \cap C)]$$
$$- m(B \cap C) \quad (12)$$
$$= m(A)(1 - p) - m(B)p.$$

This last form of writing equation (12) results from the equalities given in equations (10) and (11). If we then let

$$a = \frac{m(A)}{m(S)}, \quad b = \frac{m(B)}{m(S)}, \quad (13)$$

and divide equation (12) through by $m(S)$, we have finally for the change in probability:

$$\Delta p = \frac{\Delta m(C)}{m(S)} = a(1 - p) - bp. \quad (14)$$

We thus define a mathematical operator Q which when applied to p gives

a new value of probability Qp effective at the start of the next trial:

$$Qp = p + a(1 - p) - bp. \quad (15)$$

This operator is identical to the general operator postulated in our model for acquisition and extinction in a fixed stimulus situation (1). Hence, the set-theoretic model we have presented generates the basic postulates of our previous model which we applied to other types of learning problems (1). When the operator Q is applied n times to an initial probability p_0, we obtain

$$Q^n p_0 = p_n = p_\infty - (p_\infty - p_0)g^n, \quad (16)$$

where $p_\infty = a/(a+b)$ and $g = 1 - a - b$.

In the next section we shall apply these results to the experiment on stimulus discrimination described in the Introduction.

THE DISCRIMINATION PROBLEM

We are now in a position to treat the second experimental problem described in the Introduction. An animal is presented alternately with two stimulus situations S and S' which are similar, *i.e.*, which have a non-zero

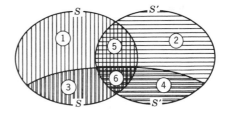

FIG. 3. Set diagram for discrimination training in two similar stimulus situations, S and S'. The various disjunct sub-sets are numbered. Set S includes 1, 3, 5, and 6; S' includes 2, 4, 5, and 6. The intersection I is denoted by 5; T, the complement of I in S, is shown by 1 and 3; T', the complement of I in S', is shown by 2 and 4. C, the conditioned sub-set in S, is represented by 3 and 6, while the conditioned sub-set in S', is represented by 4 and 6. T_c is denoted by 3, T_c' by 4, and I_c by 6.

intersection. The rewards which follow occurrences of the response are different for the two situations, and we are interested in how the response strengths vary with training. At any point in the process, sub-sets of S and S' will be conditioned to the response as shown in Fig. 3. We shall distinguish between that part of S which is also in S' and that part which is not by letting $I = S \cap S'$ and $T = S - (S \cap S') = S - I$. We also distinguish between the part of the conditioned sub-set C of S which is in I and that which is in T, by letting $I_c = C \cap I$ and $T_c = C - (C \cap I) = T \cap C$. The probability of the response in S is

$$p = \frac{m(C)}{m(S)} = \frac{m(T_c) + m(I_c)}{m(S)} . \quad (17)$$

Then we let

$$\alpha = \frac{m(T_c)}{m(T)}, \quad (18) \quad \beta = \frac{m(I_c)}{m(I)}, \quad (19)$$

and, abbreviating $\eta(S \text{ to } S')$ with η, we may write (17) in the form

$$p = \alpha(1 - \eta) + \beta\eta. \quad (20)$$

We write the probability of the response in this form because we shall soon argue that the index η varies during discrimination training. First, however, we shall investigate the variation of α and β with the number of training trials. From the definitions of α and β, equations (18) and (19), we see that these variables are very much like our probability p of equation (17) except that they refer to sub-sets of S rather than to the entire set. By strict analogy with the arguments in the last section, we conclude that

$$\alpha_n = Q^n\alpha_0 = \alpha_\infty - (\alpha_\infty - \alpha_0)g^n, \quad (21)$$

where $\alpha_\infty = a/(a+b)$ and $g = 1 - a - b$. Now, β, the fraction of conditioned stimuli in the intersection I, changes with each presentation of S' as well as

of S. Thus, for each presentation of S, we must operate on β twice, once by our operator Q which describes the effect of the environmental events in S, and once by an analogous operator Q' which describes the effect of the events in S'. Hence, it may be shown that

$$\beta_n = (Q'Q)^n\beta_0 = \beta_\infty - (\beta_\infty - \beta_0)f^n, \quad (22)$$

where

$$\beta_\infty = \frac{a' + a(1 - a' - b')}{\{a' + a(1 - a' - b') + b' + b(1 - a' - b')\}}, \quad (23)$$

and where $f = (1 - a' - b')(1 - a - b)$.

It should be stressed that we are assuming that the response occurs and is rewarded to the same degree on every presentation of S. The same statement, mutatis mutandis, applies to S'. Without this assumption, we are not justified in applying the operators Q and Q' for each presentation. The probability is then the probability that the response will occur in an interval of time, h. The operational measure of this probability is the mean latent time, which according to the response model discussed earlier varies inversely as the probability (1).

We now have cleared the way for discussing the central feature of our model for discrimination problems. We conceive that *the measure of the intersection I of the two sets S and S' decreases as discrimination learning progresses.* This concept seems to make sense intuitively since the measure of any sub-set of stimuli indicates the importance of that sub-set in influencing behavior. If an animal is rewarded for a response in S but not rewarded for it in S', then the stimuli in I are unreliable for deciding whether or not to make the response. And it is just this ambiguity which causes the measure of the intersection to decrease with training. We shall describe this change by introducing a "discrimination operator," denoted by D, which operates on the similarity index η each time the environmental event following the response changes from one type of event to another, e.g., from reward to non-reward. In the present problem, we are considering alternate presentations of S and S' and thus alternate occurrences of the events associated with the operators Q and Q'. So if η_i is the ratio of the measure of I to that of S after the ith presentation of S, the ratio after the $(i + 1)$th presentation is

$$\eta_{i+1} = D\eta_i. \qquad (24)$$

Our next task is to postulate the form of the operator D.

We find that neither experimental data nor our intuition is of much help in guiding our choice of such a postulate. For mathematical simplicity we choose an operator which represents a linear transformation on η. Moreover, we wish to have an operator which always decreases η (or holds it fixed), but which will never lead to negative values of η. Therefore, we postulate that

$$D\eta = k\eta, \qquad (25)$$

where k is a new parameter which is in the range between zero and 1. We then have

$$\eta_n = D^n\eta_0 = k^n\eta_0. \qquad (26)$$

Combining equations (20), (21), (22), and (26), we have

$$p_n = Q^n\alpha_0(1 - D^n\eta_0) + (Q'Q)^n\beta_0 D^n\eta_0$$
$$= [\alpha_\infty - (\alpha_\infty - \alpha_0)g^n](1 - k^n\eta_0)$$
$$+ [\beta_\infty - (\beta_\infty - \beta_0)f^n]k^n\eta_0. \quad (27)$$

This is our final expression for the variation of p_n, the probability of the response in situation S, as a function of the trial number n. This equation is composed of two major terms. The first term corresponds to the relative measures of the stimulus elements of

S which are not in S' (the measure of T_e divided by the measure of S). The second term corresponds to the relative measure of the elements in the intersection of S and S' (the measure of I_e divided by the measure of S).

Because of the symmetry between S and S', we may write for the probability in S':

$$p_n' = [\alpha_\infty' - (\alpha_\infty' - \alpha_0')g'^n](1 - k^n\eta_0')$$
$$+ [\beta_\infty - (\beta_\infty - \beta_0)f^n]k^n\eta_0', \quad (28)$$

where $\alpha_\infty' = a'/(a' + b')$, and $g' = 1 - a' - b'$, and where η_0' is the initial value of

$$\eta' \equiv \eta(S' \text{ to } S)$$
$$= \frac{m(I)}{m(S')} = \frac{m(S)}{m(S')}\eta. \quad (29)$$

We shall now consider some special examples for which certain simplifying assumptions can be made.

(a) *No conditioning before discrimination training.* If no previous conditioning took place in either S or S', it seems reasonable to assume that the "operant" levels of performance in the two situations are the same. Moreover, in view of our assumptions of equal proportions, we may assume that *initially:*

$$\frac{m(C)}{m(S)} = \frac{m(T_e)}{m(T)} = \frac{m(I_e)}{m(I)}$$
$$= \frac{m(T_e')}{m(T')} = \frac{m(C')}{m(S')}. \quad (30)$$

Hence, from equations (17), (18), and (19), we have $p_0 = \alpha_0 = \alpha_0' = \beta_0$. Moreover, inspection of equation (27) shows that, except when $k = 1$, we have $p_\infty = \alpha_\infty$, and in like manner from equation (28) for $k \neq 1$, we have $p_\infty' = \alpha_\infty'$. In Fig. 4 we have plotted equations (27) and (28) with the above assumptions. The values $a = 0.12$, $b = 0.03$, $p_0 = 0.05$, $\eta_0 = \eta_0' = 0.50$, $k = 0.95$ were chosen for these calculations. As can be seen, the proba-

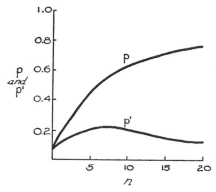

FIG. 4. Curves of probability, p (in S), and p' (in S'), versus trial number, n, for discrimination training without previous conditioning. It was assumed that the response was rewarded in S but not rewarded in S'. Equation (27), equation (28), and the values $p_0 = p_0' = 0.05$, $a = 0.12$, $a' = 0$, $b = b' = 0.03$, $\eta_0 = \eta_0' = 0.50$, and $k = 0.95$ were used.

bility of the response in S is a monotonically increasing, negatively accelerated function of the trial number, while the probability in S' first increases due to generalization, but then decreases to zero as the discrimination

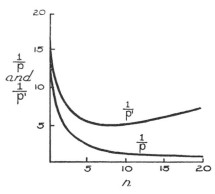

FIG. 5. Reciprocals of probability, p, of the response in S, and p', of the response in S', versus trial number, n, for discrimination training without previous conditioning. In the model described earlier (1), mean latent time is proportional to the reciprocal of probability. The curves were plotted from the values of probability shown in Fig. 4.

is learned. These curves describe the general sort of result obtained by Woodbury for auditory discrimination in dogs (4).

We have argued (1) that the mean latent time varies inversely as the probability. Thus in Fig. 5 we have plotted the reciprocals of p_n and p_n' given in Fig. 4. These curves exhibit the same general property of the experimental curves on running time of rats obtained by Raben (5).

(b) *Complete conditioning in S before discrimination training.* Another spe-

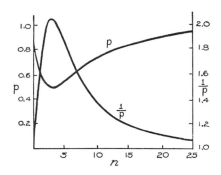

FIG. 6. Curves of probability, p, and its reciprocal versus trial number, n, for the case of complete conditioning in S before the discrimination training. Equation (27) with the values $p_\infty = 1$, $\beta_\infty = 0$, $\eta_0 = 0.80$, $k = 0.90$, and $f = 0.50$ were used.

cial case of interest is that in which the set S is completely conditioned to the response before the discrimination experiment is performed. In this case, $\alpha_0 = \beta_0 = p_0 = p_\infty$. In Fig. 6 we have plotted p_n and $1/p_n$ with these conditions and the values $p_\infty = 1$, $\beta_\infty = 0$, $\eta_0 = 0.80$, $k = 0.90$, and $f = 0.50$. The curve of $1/p$ versus n is similar in shape to the experimental latency curve obtained by Solomon (6) from a jumping experiment with rats.

(c) *Limiting case of S and S' identical.* Another limiting case of the kind of discrimination experiment being considered here obtains when we make the two stimulus situations S and S' identical. The problem degenerates into one type of partial reinforcement where, for example, an animal is rewarded on every second trial in a fixed stimulus situation. The intersection I of S and S' is of course identical to both S and S'. Thus the measure of I must equal the measure of S. From equation (5), we have

$$\eta = \frac{m(I)}{m(S)} = 1, \qquad (31)$$

while according to our postulate about the operator D, equation (26), the similarity index varies from trial to trial:

$$\eta_n = k^n \eta_0. \qquad (32)$$

For S and S' identical, the above two equations are incompatible, unless we take $k = 1$. Thus, we are forced to assume that k depends on how many cues are *available* for discrimination in such a way that $k = 1$ when none are available. Moreover, since I and S are identical, the measure of T, the complement of I in S, must be zero. Since T_e is a sub-set of T, the measure of T_e must also be zero. Therefore, equations (17) and (19) give in place of equation (20)

$$p = \beta\eta. \qquad (33)$$

But we have just argued that for S and S' identical, we have $\eta = 1$. Thus

$$p = \beta. \qquad (34)$$

Equation (22) gives us then

$$p_n = (Q'Q)^n p_0 = p_\infty - (p_\infty - p_0)f^n. \qquad (35)$$

This equation agrees with our previous result on partial reinforcement (1).

(d) *Irregular presentations of S and S'*. In most experiments, S and S' are not presented alternately, but in an irregular sequence so that the animal cannot learn to discriminate on the basis of temporal order. A simple generalization of the above analysis will handle the problem. The usual procedure is to select a block of $(j + j')$ trials during which S is presented j times and S' presented j' times. The actual sequence is determined by drawing "S balls" and "S' balls" at random from an urn containing j "S balls" and j' "S' balls." This sequence is then repeated throughout training. In our model, we can describe the effects on the probability of a known sequence by an appropriate application of our operators Q, Q', and D for presentations of S, presentations of S', and shifts from one to the other, respectively. A less cumbersome method provides a reasonable approximation: for each block of $(j + j')$ trials we describe an effective or expected new value of probability by applying Q to its operand j times, Q' to its operand j' times, and D to the index η a number of times determined by the mean number of shifts from S to S'. For the special case of $j = j'$, the mean number of shifts is j. Since previously, we applied D to η for each *pair* of shifts, we write for the $(i+1)$th block of $(2j)$ trials

$$\overline{p_{i+1}} = Q^j\alpha_i(1 - D^{j/2}\eta_i) + (Q'Q)^i\beta_i D^{j/2}\eta_i. \qquad (36)$$

The rest of the analysis exactly parallels that given above for the case of alternate presentations of S and S'. The results will be identical except for the value of k involved in the operator D.

SUMMARY

A mathematical model for stimulus generalization and discrimination is described in terms of simple set-theoretic concepts. An index of similarity is defined in terms of the model but is related to measurements in generalization experiments. The mathematical operators for acquisition and extinction, discussed in an earlier paper (1), are derived from the set-theoretic model presented here. The model is finally applied to the analysis of experiments on stimulus discrimination.

[MS. received October 13, 1950]

REFERENCES

1. BUSH, R. R., & MOSTELLER, F.   A mathematical model for simple learning. PSYCHOL. REV., 1951, 58, 313–323
2. ESTES, W. K.   Toward a statistical theory of learning. PSYCHOL. REV., 1950, 57, 94–107.
3. HOVLAND, C. I.   The generalization of conditioned responses: I. J. gen. Psychol., 1937, 17, 125–148; The generalization of conditioned responses: II. J. genet. Psychol., 1937, 51, 279–291.
4. WOODBURY, C. B.   The learning of stimulus patterns by dogs. J. comp. Psychol., 1943, 35, 29–40.
5. RABEN, M. W.   The white rat's discrimination of differences in intensity of illumination measured by a running response. J. comp. & physiol. Psychol., 1949, 42, 254–272.
6. SOLOMON, R. L.   Latency of response as a measure of learning in a 'single door' discrimination. Amer. J. Psychol., 1943, 56, 422–432.

Interpretation of Stimulus Generalization

R. C. ATKINSON and W. K. ESTES, *Indiana University*

Our approach to the problem of stimulus generalization is to represent the similarity between two stimuli by the amount of overlap between two sets of elements.[1]   In the simplest experimental paradigm for exhibiting generalization we begin with two stimulus situations, represented by sets S_a and S_b, neither of which has any of its elements conditioned to a reference response A_1. Training is given by reinforcement of A_1 in the presence of S_a only until the probability of A_1 in that situation reaches some value $p_{a1} > 0$. Then test trials are given in the presence of S_b, and if p_{b1} now proves to be greater than zero we say that stimulus generalization has occurred. If the axioms of the component model are satisfied, the value of p_{b1} provides, in fact, a measure of the overlap of S_a and S_b;   for we have,

$$p_{b1} = \frac{N(S_a \cap S_b)p_{a1}}{N(S_b)},$$

where $S_a \cap S_b$ denotes the set of elements common to S_a and S_b, since the numerator of this fraction is simply the number of elements in S_b that are now conditioned to response A_1. More generally, if the proportion of elements of S_b conditioned to A_1 before the experiment were equal to g_{b1}, not necessarily zero, the probability of response A_1 to stimulus S_b after training in S_a would be given by

$$p_{b1} = \frac{N(S_a \cap S_b)p_{a1} + [N(S_b) - N(S_a \cap S_b)]g_{b1}}{N(S_b)},$$

or, with the more compact notation $N_{ab} = N(S_a \cap S_b)$, etc.,

$$p_{b1} = \frac{N_{ab}p_{a1} + (N_b - N_{ab})g_{b1}}{N_b}.$$

This relation can be put in still more convenient form by letting $N_{ab}/N_b = w_{ab}$, namely, $$p_{b1} = w_{ab}p_{a1} + (1 - w_{ab})g_{b1}.$$

This equation may be rearranged to read

$$p_{b1} = w_{ab}(p_{a1} - g_{b1}) + g_{b1},$$

and we see that the difference $(p_{a1} - g_{b1})$ between the posttraining probability of A_1 in S_a and the pretraining probability in S_b can be regarded

---

[1] A model similar in most essentials has been presented in Bush & Mosteller (1951).

This article appeared in *Handbook of mathematical psychology*, Vol. II (pp. 200–206), R. D. Luce, R. R. Bush and E. Galanter, editors. © Copyright 1963 by John Wiley & Sons, Inc.

as the slope parameter of a linear "gradient" of generalization, in which p_{b1} is the dependent variable and the proportion of overlap between S_a and S_b is the independent variable. If we hold g_{b1} constant and let p_{a1} vary as the parameter, we generate a family of generalization gradients which have their greatest disparities at $w_{ab} = 1$ (i.e., when the test stimulus S_b is identical with S_a) and converge as the overlap between S_b and S_a decreases, until the gradients meet at $p_{b1} = g_{b1}$ when $w_{ab} = 0$. Thus the family of gradients shown in Fig. 1 illustrates the picture to be expected if a series of generalization tests is given at each of several different stages of training in S_a, or, alternatively, at several different stages of extinction following training in S_a, as was done, for example, by Guttman and Kalish (1956). The problem of "calibrating" a physical stimulus dimension to obtain a series of values that represent equal differences in the value of w_{ab} has been discussed by Carterette (1961).

The parameter w_{ab} might be regarded as an index of the similarity of S_a to S_b. In general, similarity is not a symmetrical relation, for w_{ab} is not equal to w_{ba} (w_{ab} being given by N_{ab}/N_b and the w_{ba} by N_{ab}/N_a) except in the special case $N_a = N_b$. When $N_a \neq N_b$, generalization from training with the larger set to a test with the smaller set will be greater than general-

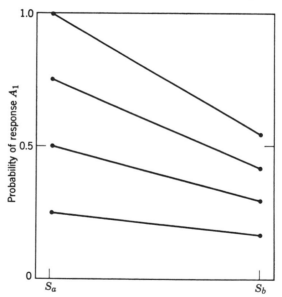

Fig. 1. Generalization from a training stimulus, S_a, to a test stimulus, S_b, at several stages of training. The parameters are $w_{ab} = 0.5$, the proportion of overlap between S_a and S_b, and $g_{b1} = 0.1$, the probability of response A_1 to S_b before training on S_a.

ization from training with the smaller set to a test with the larger set (assuming that the reinforcement given the reference response A_1 in the presence of the training set S_i establishes the same value of p_{i1} in each case before testing in S_j). We shall give no formal assumption relating size of a stimulus set to observable properties; however, it is reasonable to expect that larger sets will be associated with more intense (where the notion of intensity is applicable) or attention-getting stimuli. Thus, if S_a and S_b represent tones a and b of the same frequency but with tone a more intense than b, we should predict greater generalization if we train the reference response to a given level with a and test with b than if we train to the same level with b and test with a.

Although in the psychological literature the notion of stimulus generalization has nearly always been taken to refer to generalization along some physical continuum, such as wavelength of light or intensity of sound, it is worth noting that the set-theoretical model is not restricted to such cases. Predictions of generalization in the case of complex stimuli may be generated by first evaluating the overlap parameter w_{ab} for a given pair of situations a and b from a set of observations obtained with some particular combination of values of p_{a1} and g_{b1} and then computing theoretical values of p_{b1} for new conditions involving different levels of p_{a1} and g_{b1}. The problem of treating a simple "stimulus dimension" is of special interest, however, and we conclude our discussion of generalization by sketching one approach to this problem.[2]

We shall consider the type of stimulus dimension that Stevens (1957) has termed *substitutive* or *metathetic*, that is, one which involves the notion of a simple ordering of stimuli along a dimension without variation in intensity or magnitude. Let us denote by Z a physical dimension of this sort, for example, wavelength of visible light, which we wish to represent by a sequence of stimulus sets. First we shall outline the properties that we wish this representation to have and then spell out the assumptions of the model more rigorously.

It is part of the intuitive basis of a substitutive dimension that one moves from point to point by exchanging some of the elements of one stimulus for new ones belonging to the next. Consequently, we assume that as values of Z change by constant increments each successive stimulus set should be generated by deleting a constant number of elements from the preceding set and adding the same number of new elements to form the

---

[2] We follow, in most respects, the treatment given by W. K. Estes and D. L. LaBerge in unpublished notes prepared for the 1957 SSRC Summer Institute in Social Science for College Teachers of Mathematics. For an approach combining essentially the same set-theoretical model with somewhat different learning assumptions, the reader is referred to Restle (1961).

next set; but, to ensure that the organism's behavior can reflect the ordering of stimuli along the Z-scale without ambiguity, we need also to assume
that once an element is deleted as we go along the Z-scale it must not
reappear in the set corresponding to any higher Z-value. Further, in view
of the abundant empirical evidence that generalization declines in an
orderly fashion as the distance between two stimuli on such a dimension
increases, we must assume that (at least up to the point at which sets
corresponding to larger differences in Z are disjoint) the overlap between
two stimulus sets is directly related to the interval between the corresponding stimuli on the Z-scale. These properties, taken together, enable
us to establish an intuitively reasonable correspondence between characteristics of a sequence of stimulus sets and the empirical notion of
generalization along a dimension.

These ideas are incorporated more formally in the following set of
axioms. The basis for these axioms is a stimulus dimension Z, which may
be either continuous or discontinuous, a collection S_* of stimulus sets,
and a function $x(Z)$ with a finite number of consecutive integers in its
range. The mapping of the set (x) of scaled stimulus values onto the subsets S_i of S_* must satisfy the following axioms:

Generalization Axioms

G1. *For all $i \leqslant j \leqslant k$ in (x), $S_i \cap S_k \subseteq S_j$.*

G2. *For all $i \leqslant j \leqslant k$ in (x), if $S_i \cap S_k \neq \emptyset$, where $\emptyset$ is the null set, then*
$S_j \subseteq (S_i \cup S_k)$.

G3. *For all $h < i, j < k$ in (x), if $i - h = k - j$, then $N_{hi} = N_{jk}$; and*
for all i in (x), $N_{ii} = N$.

The set (x) may simply be a set of Z scale values or it may be a set of
Z-values rescaled by some transformation. The reasons for introducing
(x) are twofold. First, for mathematical simplicity we find it advisable to
restrict ourselves, at least for present purposes, to a finite set of Z-values
and therefore to a finite collection of stimulus sets. Second, there is no
reason to believe that equal distances along physical dimensions will in
general correspond to equal overlaps between stimulus sets. All that is
required, however, to make the theory workable is that for any given
physical dimension, wavelength of light, frequency of a tone, or whatever,
we can find experimentally a transformation x such that equal distances on
the x-scale do correspond to equal overlaps.

Axiom G1 states that if an element belongs to any two sets it also belongs
to all sets that fall between these two sets on the x-scale. Axiom G2 states
that if two sets have any common elements then all of the elements of any
set falling between them belong to one or the other (or both) of the given

sets; this property ensures that the elements drop out of the sets in order as we move along the dimension. Axiom G3 describes the property that distinguishes a simple substitutive dimension from an additive, or intensity (in Stevens' terminology, *prothetic*), dimension. It should be noted that only if the number of values in the range of $x(Z)$ is no greater than $N(S_*)$ $- N + 1$ can Axiom G3 be satisfied. This restriction is necessary in order to obtain a one-to-one mapping of the x-values into the subsets S_i of S_*.

One advantage in having the axioms set forth explicitly is that it then becomes relatively easy to design experiments bearing on various aspects of the model. Thus, to obtain evidence concerning the empirical tenability of Axiom G1, we might choose a response A_1 and a set (x) of stimuli, including a pair i and k such that $\Pr(A_1 \mid i) = \Pr(A_1 \mid k) = 0$, then train subjects with stimulus i only until $\Pr(A_1 \mid i) = 1$, and finally test with stimulus k. If $\Pr(A_1 \mid k)$ is found to be greater than zero, it must be concluded, in terms of the model, that $S_i \cap S_k \neq \emptyset$; that is, the sets corresponding to i and k have some elements in common. Given

$$\Pr(A_1 \mid k) > 0,$$

it must be predicted that for every stimulus j in (x), such that $i < j < k$, $\Pr(A_1 \mid j) \geqslant \Pr(A_1 \mid k)$. Axiom G1 ensures that all of the elements of S_k which are now conditioned to A_1 by virtue of belonging also to S_i must be included in S_j, possibly augmented by other elements of S_i which are not in S_k.

To deal similarly with Axiom G2, we proceed in the same way to locate two members i and k of a set (x) such that $S_i \cap S_k \neq \emptyset$. Then we train subjects on both stimulus i and stimulus k until $\Pr(A_1 \mid i) = \Pr(A_1 \mid k)$ $= 1$, response A_1 being one that before this training had probability of less than unity to all stimuli in (x). Now, by G2, if any stimulus j falls between i and k, the set S_j must be contained entirely in the union $S_i \cup S_k$; consequently, we must predict that we will now find $\Pr(A_1 \mid j) = 1$ for any stimulus j such that $i \leqslant j \leqslant k$.

To evaluate Axiom G3 empirically, we require four stimuli $h < i, j < k$ such that $i - h = k - j$. If the four stimuli are all different, we can simply train subjects on h and test generalization to i, then train subjects to an equal degree on j and test generalization to k. If the amount of generalization, as measured by the probability of the test response, is the same in the two cases, then the axiom is supported. In the special case in which $h = i$ and $j = k$ we would be testing the assertion that the sets associated with different values of x are of equal size. To accomplish this test, we need only take any two neighboring values of x, say i and j, train subjects to some criterion on i and test on j, then reverse the procedure by training (different) subjects to the same criterion on j and testing on i. If the axiom is satisfied, the amount of generalization should be the same in both directions.

Once we have introduced the notion of a dimension, it is natural to inquire whether the parameter that represents the degree of communality between pairs of stimulus sets might not be related in some simple way to a measure of distance along the dimension. With one qualification, which we mention later, the quantity $d_{ij} = 1 - w_{ij}$ could serve as a suitable measure of the distance between stimuli i and j. We can check to see whether the familiar axioms for a metric are satisfied. These axioms are

1. $d_{ij} = 0$ if and only if $i = j$,
2. $d_{ij} \geqslant 0$,
3. $d_{ij} = d_{ji}$,
4. $d_{ij} + d_{jk} \geqslant d_{ik}$,

where it is understood that i, j, and k are any members of the set (x) associated with a given dimension. The first three obviously hold, but the fourth requires a bit of analysis. To carry out a proof, we use the notation N_{ij} for the number of elements common to S_i and S_j, N_{ijk} for the number of elements in both S_i and S_j but not in S_k, and so on. The difference between the two sides of the inequality we wish to establish can be expanded in terms of this notation:

$$d_{ij} + d_{jk} - d_{ik} = \left(1 - \frac{N_{ij}}{N}\right) + \left(1 - \frac{N_{jk}}{N}\right) - \left(1 - \frac{N_{ik}}{N}\right)$$

$$= \frac{1}{N}(N - N_{ij} - N_{jk} + N_{ik})$$

$$= \frac{1}{N}(N_{ijk} + N_{ijk} + N_{ijk} + N_{ijk} - N_{ijk} - N_{ijk} - N_{ijk}$$

$$- N_{ijk} + N_{ijk} + N_{ijk})$$

$$= \frac{1}{N}(N_{ijk} + N_{ijk}).$$

The last expression on the right is nonnegative, which establishes the desired inequality. To find the restrictions under which d is additive, let us assume that stimuli i, j, and k fall in the order $i < j < k$ on the dimension. Then, by Axiom G1, we know that $N_{ijk} = 0$. However it is only in the special cases in which S_i and S_k are either overlapping or adjacent that $N_{ijk} = 0$

and, therefore, that $d_{ij} + d_{jk} = d_{ik}$. It is possible to define an additive distance measure that is not subject to this restriction, but such extensions raise new problems and we are not able to pursue them here.

In concluding this section, we should like to emphasize one difference between the model for generalization sketched here and some of those already familiar in the literature (see, e.g., Spence, 1936; Hull, 1943). We do not postulate a particular form for generalization of response strength or excitatory tendency. Rather, we introduce certain assumptions about the properties of the set of stimuli associated with a sensory dimension; then we take these together with learning assumptions and information about reinforcement schedules as a basis for deriving theoretical gradients of generalization for particular types of experiments. Under the special conditions assumed in the example we have considered, the theory predicts that a family of linear gradients with simple properties will be observed when response probability is plotted as a function of distance from the point of reinforcement. Predictions of this sort may reasonably be tested by means of experiments in which suitable measures are taken to meet the conditions assumed in the derivations (see, e.g., Carterette, 1961); but, to deal with experiments involving different training conditions or response measures other than relative frequencies, further theoretical analysis is called for, and we must be prepared to find substantial differences in the phenotypic properties of generalization gradients derived from the same basic theory for different experimental situations.

References

Bush, R. R., & Mosteller, F. A model for stimulus generalization and discrimination. *Psychol. Rev.*, 1951, **58**, 413–423.

Carterette, Teresa S. An application of stimulus sampling theory to summated generalization. *J. exp. Psychol.*, 1961, **62**, 448–455.

Guttman, N., & Kalish, H. I. Discriminability and stimulus generalization. *J. exp. Psychol.*, 1956, **51**, 79–88.

Hull, C. L. *Principles of behavior: an introduction to behavior theory.* New York: Appleton-Century-Crofts, 1943.

Restle, F. *Psychology of judgment and choice.* New York: Wiley, 1961.

Spence, K. W. The nature of discrimination learning in animals. *Psychol. Rev.*, 1936, **43**, 427–449.

Stevens, S. S. On the psychophysical law. *Psychol. Rev.*, 1957, **64**, 153–181.

An Application of Stimulus Sampling Theory to Summated Generalization[1]

TERESA S. CARTERETTE,[2] *Indiana University*

The general paradigm for experiments demonstrating summated generalization used, for example, by Kalish and Guttman (1957) with pigeons and by Bilodeau, Brown, and Meryman (1956), with human *S*s, is to reinforce a response at two points in a stimulus dimension and, then, to test for generalization along the dimension. The present study represents an attempt to go beyond Bilodeau, Brown, and Meryman by obtaining a more precise determination of the form of the summated gradient for human *S*s and by relating its specific properties to the separation between training stimuli. In addition, the experiment tests a mathematical model for stimulus generalization along a substitutive dimension (Stevens, 1957) derived from the Estes-Burke probabilistic theory of behavior.[3]

Basic to the model is the assumption that, for equal intervals along the dimension, $P(Y) = f(\Delta S)$ is a linear function with negative slope. The dependent variable, $P(Y)$, is the probability of the conditioned response; and (ΔS) is a change along the physical scale of the training stimulus. While Guttman and Kalish's (1956) data for pigeons responding to the wavelength of light generally support the assumption of linearity, human *S*s responding to the position of a light (Brown, Bilodeau, & Baron, 1951) showed such a great drop in response level at the test stimulus immediately adjacent to the training stimulus that clearly most of the gradient was not being adequately sampled. To avoid this high degree of discriminability, the position of the light in the present situation was varied over a continuous field rather than with discrete lamps as in the earlier experiment.

The rationale underlying the simple generalization model and the predictions for summated generalization are elaborated formally in a later section. Briefly, each stimulus in the simple gradient is associated with a set of elements; and some of the elements in each of the sets corresponding to each of the generalized stimuli are assumed to be also present in the set corresponding to the training stimulus. Since the theory relates response probability directly to the proportion of stimulus elements conditioned to a response, the extent to which a test stimulus elicits the reference response reflects the proportion of elements which it shares with the training stimulus. In the summated generalization case where the same response is conditioned to two stimuli in the dimension, response

[1] This paper is based on a PhD dissertation submitted to the Graduate School of Indiana University. The work was executed while the author held a National Institutes of Health Predoctoral Research Fellowship under the sponsorship of W. K. Estes who provided valuable counsel at all stages of the project.

[2] Now at Institute for Psychological Research, Tufts University.

[3] A preliminary presentation of the application of stimulus sampling theory to stimulus generalization phenomena has appeared in mimeographed lectures given by W. K. Estes before the Summer Institute in Social Sciences for College Teachers of Mathematics held at Stanford University in the summer of 1957.

This article appeared in *J. exp. Psychol.*, 1961, **62**, 448–455.

probability should be determined by the proportion of elements which a given test stimulus shares with the two training stimuli.

Application of the assumptions of the set theoretical model (Burke & Estes, 1957) to the simple generalization data obtained in Part I of the experiment provided parameter estimates for the a priori predictions tested in Part II, a summated generalization experiment. Predictions pertained to three aspects of the summated generalization gradients. It was expected that: (a) the height at the two training stimuli would be identical to that obtained in the simple generalization experiment, (b) midway between training stimuli, the height of the gradients would decrease as the separation between training stimuli increased, and (c) the slopes of the outer segments of the summated gradients would be identical for all separation groups.

METHOD

Subjects

The Ss were 240 Indiana University undergraduates. Forty-eight provided the data for the simple generalization gradients; and the remainder provided the summated generalization data.

Apparatus

The apparatus enabled E to present a $2\frac{3}{4}$-in. square of light for 1 sec. at different positions along a horizontal line. The S faced a black panel which supported a 5 in. high by 44 in. wide field of sand blasted plate glass on which the stimulus light appeared. The walls and ceiling of the room were black; and ambient light was provided by a 7.5-w. frosted ceiling bulb situated directly above S.

Design

Simple generalization.—For Group C (Center) the training stimulus was located exactly midway between the left and right limits of the field; and for Group Q (Quarter), it was one-fourth the distance from its left border. The remaining stimuli were to the right of the training stimulus and covered a 3.5-in. range in $\frac{1}{2}$-in. steps.

Summated generalization.—For the Center groups the left-hand training stimulus was at the midway position and for the Quarter groups, at the point one-fourth the distance from the left limit of the stimulus field. The second training stimulus was four $\frac{1}{2}$-in. steps to the right of the first for the T_4 groups; and six and eight steps for the T_6 and T_8 groups, respectively. These separation values were intended to realize two types of situations. In the T_4 groups the stimulus sets associated with the two training stimuli should have a proportion of elements in common. For the T_6 and T_8 groups, these sets should be discrete; but the proportion of elements which the central stimuli share with the training stimuli should differ.

Procedure

Simple generalization.—Each S was tested separately in a 40-min. session with 10 min for dark adaptation and instructions which covered the following points: (a) There would be two types of trials: trials on which E would announce that the stimulus was to appear in the standard position, and test trials on which the unannounced stimulus might be in the standard or in some different position. (b) The stimulus duration would be 1 sec.; and on test trials S must decide whether the light had been in the standard or in some different position. (c) The two keys in front of S were to be used in communicating judgments to E. The training stimulus, presented once at the outset of every block of trials, was followed by 8 test trials in which the standard and seven other stimuli each appeared, these blocks continuing to a total of 180 trials. The order of test stimuli within each block was randomized separately for each S. To indicate the positive response, half the Ss were instructed to use the right-hand key and half, the left key. Approximately 9 sec. elapsed between stimulus presentations.

Summated generalization.—Following dark adaptation and instruction, S was exposed to 210 trials. Instructions were altered as follows: (a) There would be three types of trials: trials on which E would announce the stimulus position as A, trials on which E would announce it as B, and test trials on which the unannounced stimulus might be in A, or in B, or in some different position. (b) On test trials if S believed that the light was in A or B, he was to press the right-hand key; and if he believed that it was in neither position, he was to press the left-hand key. Within each block of 21 trials there were 4 training trials. The two training stimuli each appeared twice, once at the beginning and once midway in the block. The order of test stimuli was randomized with the restriction that each stimulus, including A and B, appear only once in the 17 test trials.

RESULTS

Simple generalization.—Gradients for Groups C and Q were linear over a 2.5-in. range. Comparison of performance for the first 10 blocks of trials with that for the second 10 blocks did not reveal the inhibitory effects observed by Bilodeau, Brown, and Meryman (1956) who found that as test trials progressed, Ss produced fewer responses to generalized stimuli. A straight line fitted to the combined data by the method of least squares had a slope of $-.16$ and its intercept at .82.

Guttman and Kalish (1956) found that gradients for pigeons pecking a key in the presence of different wavelengths of light became flatter as the total number of generalized responses decreased. In the present case three gradients for Ss grouped on the basis of the total number of positive responses did not have different slopes.

Summated generalization.—Figure 1 presents the mean proportion of positive responses at each test position over the 10 blocks of trials. Response level along the center segments decreases as the distance between training stimuli increases. In the T_4 groups these data points are slightly above those at the training stimuli. For the T_6 groups there is virtually no difference between the training stimuli and the intermediate positions; and in the T_8 groups a decline in response level is clear.

In the absence of normal distributions, nonparametric tests were ap-

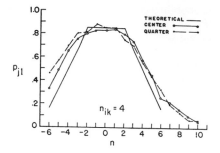
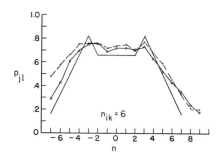
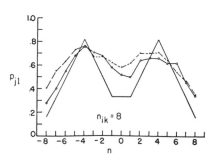

FIG. 1. Theoretical and empirical summated generalization gradients for the T_4, T_6, and T_8 groups. (Zero corresponds to the stimulus exactly midway between training stimuli; and unit changes represent $\frac{1}{2}$-in. steps along the physical scale.)

plied to the data for the entire session. To test the hypothesis that response level at the midway stimulus decreases with increasing separation between training stimuli, each S's mean score at the midway position was subtracted from the mean of his pooled scores at the training stimuli. The Kruskal-Wallis one-way analysis of variance statistic, H, is significant at the .05 level with 2 df for both Group C and Group Q comparisons. The t's comparing the mean proportion of positive responses to the training stimuli with that at the midway stimulus are significant at the .05 level with 62 df for the QT_4 and for the T_8 groups only.

The outer segments of all gradients are linear over four stimulus positions. Two measures were used in comparing the slopes of corresponding outer segments: (a) each S's mean proportion of positive responses over the four outer stimuli adjacent to a given training stimulus, and (b) the difference between each S's pooled mean proportion of positive responses at the first two and second two of these stimuli. The H for Measure 1 on the left side and that for Measure 2 on the right side for Group C gradients are significant at the .05 level with 2 df. Although the corresponding outer segments of the gradients for different separation groups are not far from parallel, the possibility of some significant local deviations cannot be ruled out by the present analysis.

Because Group Q gradients are asymmetrical, an effect probably due to the presence of the left border of the frame near this part of the field, tests for symmetry were restricted to Group C data. The Mann-Whitney U is significant at the .05 level for Measure 2 in Group CT_6. The data for Group CT_8 indicate that departures from symmetry in the Center groups may be due to the use of the center position for one of the training stimuli; but any general statement concerning symmetry irrespective of separation between training stimuli is necessarily tenuous.

Although gradients for the first and second halves of the experimental session show no systematic change in response strength for the Center groups, the response level between training stimuli tends to be lower over the second half of the Quarter groups.

THEORETICAL ANALYSES

Formal Theory

Correspondence between psychological variables and mathematical sets is defined by the application of the Burke-Estes (1957) component model for stimulus variables. A mathematical set, S_i, is associated with each stimulus. Sets S_0, S_1, $\cdots S_k$ denote $k + 1$ distinguishable stimuli; and the overlap between S_i and S_j represents the similarity between stimuli i and j. The number of elements in any set S_i is N; and the number which S_i and S_j have in common is N_{ij}. Behaviors available to S are represented by A_1 and A_2, the mutually exclusive and exhaustive responses formally distinguished in the experiment; and it is assumed that each element in a set is connected to one of these responses so that, given stimulus i, the probability of A_1 is the proportion of elements in i connected to A_1 and sampled by S on that trial.

The relationship between stimulus and response variables, conceptualized in this manner, has been elaborated in theoretical papers by Burke and Estes (Burke & Estes, 1957; Estes & Burke, 1953). The probability of an A_1 when i is presented is expressed by:

$$p_i = \frac{N(C_i)}{N} \qquad [1]$$

where $N(C_i)$ is the number of elements in S_i connected to A_1.

Generalization of response A_1 to stimulus j, given i as the training stimulus, may be expressed as the sum of the proportion of elements common to S_i and S_j which are conditioned to A_1 by virtue of training on i and the proportion of elements in S_j only which are connected to A_1 independently of training on i:

$$p_i = \frac{N_{ij}p_i + (N - N_{ij})\rho_j}{N} \quad [2]$$

where ρ_j, a constant for all j, is the probability of an A_1 given j as the stimulus prior to training on i. Substituting w_{ij} for (N_{ij}/N) and rearranging terms, a more convenient form of Equation 2 is obtained:

$$p_i = w_{ij}(p_i - \rho_j) + \rho_j \quad [3]$$

The range over which generalization will occur is determined by the extent of stimulus overlap between the training stimulus and other stimuli in the series. Given training with reinforcement of response A_1 to stimulus i and nonreinforcement elsewhere along the dimension, or in the case of a voluntary response, following instructions to make response A_1 to stimulus i only, it may be assumed that ρ_j equals zero for $j \neq i$. Equation 3 becomes:

$$p_{(i+n)} = w_{i(i+n)}p_i$$

where n is the number of equal intervals on the physical dimension separating i and j; and it may be restated in the form:

$$p_{(i+n)} = p_i - p_i(1 - w_{i(i+n)})$$
$$= p_i - n(1 - w_{i(i+1)})p_i \quad [4]$$

Equation 4 follows from the fact that stimuli equidistant on the dimension have equal overlaps, so that $w_{i(i+1)} = w_{(i+1)(i+2)} \cdots$ etc. Hence, $n(1 - w_{i(i+1)})$ is the proportion of new elements introduced for a stimulus n steps away from i. If n exceeds $1/(1 - w_{i(i+1)})$, Equation 4 no longer applies.

This equation may be used for predicting generalization along a substitutive dimension. A family of linear gradients may be plotted with p_i as a parameter depending only on learning and n as the independent variable. For experimental convenience it is desirable to determine equal intervals on the physical dimension corresponding to equal decrements in p_i by obtaining a simple generalization gradient empirically. Over the range of physical values for which the gradient fits a straight line, the overlap between i and successive equally separated stimuli may be assumed to decrease by a constant proportion; and the parameters p_i and $w_{i(i+1)}$ may then be estimated from the data and used to test the predictive power of the model in an entirely new situation.

For summated generalization with training on i and k, p_j is the proportion of conditioned elements which j shares with i and k:

$$p_j = \frac{N_{ij}p_i + N_{jk}p_k - N_{ik}p_ip_k}{N}$$
$$= w_{ij}p_i + w_{jk}p_k - w_{ik}p_ip_k$$
$$= p_i[1 - n_{ij}(1 - a)]$$
$$+ p_k[1 - n_{jk}(1 - a)]$$
$$- p_ip_k[1 - n_{ik}(1 - a)] \quad [5]$$

For simplicity in notation $w_{i(i+1)}$ has been replaced with a. The quantity $[1 - n_{ik}(1 - a)]$ is the proportion of overlap between the two training stimuli; n_{ik}, the number of steps between i and k; n_{ij} and n_{jk}, the numbers of steps between a test stimulus j, and i and k, respectively. The third term on the right-hand side corrects for the fact that when training stimuli overlap, the sets associated with stimuli between i and k contain elements common to S_i and S_k which have been included twice in the sum of the first two terms.

Two types of relations are determined by n_{ik}. For n_{ik} between zero and $1/(1 - a)$ the training stimuli overlap; and their intersection must be taken into account. If $n_{ik} \geqslant 1/(1 - a)$, there is no such overlap; and the third term on the right side of Equation 5 is zero. Beyond certain points in the dimension, j will cease to overlap with part of the intersection of i and k, or with either or both training stimuli; and restrictions must be placed on n_{ij} and n_{jk} in both instances. In the present experiment, values of n_{ik} were selected to represent these two types of relations. Given the overlap parameter estimated from the data, training stimuli which are four steps apart, the value of n_{ik} for the T_4 groups, should overlap. Sets associated with stimuli separated by more than four steps should be discrete; and the T_6 and T_8 groups are intended to represent special cases of this type.

Prediction 1.—For all $n_{ik} \leqslant 1/(1-a)$ the sets associated with test stimuli $j = (i+1) \cdots (i+n-1)$, which lie between i and k, are contained in the union of S_i and S_k; and $p_i = p_j = \cdots p_k$. The solid line in the top panel of Fig. 1 presents this type of gradient, the condition expected to obtain for Groups T_4. It should be noted that when $p_i < 1$, the predicted response strength at the training stimuli following summated generalization training is greater when $n_{ik} < 1/(1-a)$ than when $n_{ik} = 1/(1-a)$. Theoretical gradients for Groups T_6 and T_8 are shown in the other two panels of Fig. 1. Since the training stimuli do not overlap, the central test stimuli should contain elements not in i or k; and generalization at this portion should decrease as n_{ik} increases. The flat region should extend over $(n_{ik} + 1)$ points if $n_{ik} < 1/(1-a)$ and over $\left[\dfrac{2}{1-a} - n_{ik} + 1 \right]$ points if $\dfrac{1}{1-a} \leqslant n_{ik} < \dfrac{2}{1-a}$.

Prediction 2.—Corresponding outer segments of the gradients should be linear with identical slopes for all n_{ik}. For $n_{ik} < 1/(1-a)$ and $p_i < 1$, the conditioned overlap between i and k produces a departure from linearity which increases as n_{ik} decreases. Gradients should extend over a range of $\left[n_{ik} - 1 + \dfrac{2}{1-a} \right]$ points.

Adequacy of Predictions for Summated Generalization

The straight line fitted to the simple generalization gradient provided values of p_i and p_j which were substituted in Equation 4 to estimate a. Theoretical and obtained gradients may be compared in Fig. 1.

Prediction 1.—When $n_{ik} = 4$, the discrepancy between theoretical and empirical points along the central segment is in no instance greater than .03. However, the large and consistent disparity between theoretical and obtained values in Groups T_6 and T_8 at these points indicates that predictions from the model are too low when $n_{ik} > 1/(1-a)$.

A salient, and complicating, feature is the downward shift in response strength at the training stimuli. Since, according to the model, response strength at the training stimuli may vary without affecting a, new theoretical gradients might be derived with p_i and p_k estimated from the data for one of the summated generalization groups; but this approach would yield even lower values of p_j than those obtained with $p_i = p_k = .818$.

Statements concerning the symmetry of the center segment and the extent of the plateau must be highly tentative since experimental artifacts discussed in a previous section may have introduced considerable distortion into the gradients. The data do suggest that p_j may be constant over the predicted number of intervals in the central region; but there is no clear indication that the remaining points are symmetrical with those for the outer segments.

Prediction 2.—The outcome of statistical tests comparing the slopes of corresponding outer segments and of tests of symmetry make it impossible to generalize unequivocally concerning the relevance of the results to predictions from the model. On the whole, the data support the assumption that for a substitutive dimension, p_j varies linearly over n. Empirical points over the left outer segments, especially for the Quarter group gradients, generally lie above the predicted values, a disparity which may possibly be due to the conditioning of extraneous cues to the positive response. The ranges over which the empirical gradients extend exceed predictions.

Estimates of a from summated generalization data.—The possibility remains that the stimulus component model may be used to extrapolate across summated generalization situations. An additional estimate of a, obtained by fitting a straight line to the data points for the right hand training stimulus and the six stimuli of the corresponding outer segment of the T_6 groups, yields an overlap parameter equal to .85. In Fig. 2 it can be seen that this estimate results in a better coincidence between theoret-ical and data points, particularly in the case of Groups T_4 and T_8.

Adequacy of the Theory

In general the two main predictions which follow from the model have been supported. First, the decrease in response level as the separation between training stimuli increases is found in all instances. The second prediction, that corresponding outer slopes of the summated gradients should be parallel for all groups, is well substantiated by the data.

Principal discrepancies between theory and data pertain to three aspects: (a) the center dip predicted for the T_6 and T_8 gradients is absent in the T_6 groups and is shallower than expected in the T_8 groups; (b) the range of generalization is greater than predicted; and (c) the left wings of all gradients, especially in the Quarter groups, are consistently too high. Contrary to prediction and perhaps related to (a), the response level for Group QT_4 is significantly higher for the midway stimulus than for tests at the training stimuli. However, it is exactly for the Quarter groups that pronounced asymmetry is present as an experimental artifact. There is the additional possibility that the unequal number of test stimuli on the two outer segments of the T_4 gradients may have interacted with effects of the left border to further increase conditioning to stimuli on the left half of the gradient; consequently, these results remain questionable as legitimate tests of the theory.

If one is mindful of the fact that the parameters used in generating the theoretical curves were estimated from data obtained under different experimental conditions with different Ss, the model appears to possess considerable predictive power. Certainly the extreme elevation of the left segments of the Quarter groups gradients can be corrected by improvements in the apparatus. The shallowness of the central dip and the underestimation of the range of generalization may be due to the omission of factors which should enter

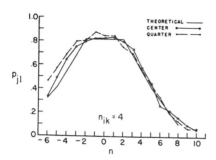

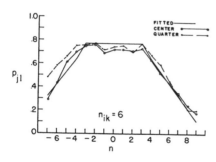

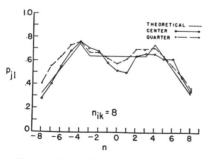

Fig. 2. Theoretical and empirical summated generalization gradients with a estimated from the right hand outer segments of the T_6 groups. (Zero corresponds to the stimulus exactly midway between training stimuli; and unit changes represent $\frac{1}{2}$-in. steps along the physical scale.)

into the application of stimulus sampling theory to generalization phenomena.

The superiority of predictions based on parameters estimated from a portion of the summated generalization data itself, suggests the possibility that much of the discrepancy between theoretical and empirical gradients in the case of a priori predictions may be attributable to sampling variation associated with the use of two different sets of Ss in the two experiments.

SUMMARY

Two experiments were designed to test the predictive power of a mathematical model derived from the Burke-Estes (1957) stimulus sampling theory of behavior. The first, an experiment concerned with simple stimulus generalization, yielded estimates of parameters which were used to generate theoretical curves for the second, concerned with summated stimulus generalization. Procedures in the two experiments were almost identical, except that in the summated generalization experiment the training trials occurred in pairs. On training trials S was shown a square patch of light at one of the two training positions designated for a particular group. On test trials, if S believed the stimulus coincided with either of the training stimuli, he responded "same"; if he believed it differed from both stimuli, he responded "different." Treatments for the six groups differed in two ways: (a) there were three degrees of separation between the two training stimuli and (b) the range of the stimulus field differed across equal separation groups.

A priori predictions pertained to two aspects of the summated generalization gradients. First, it was expected that increasing separation between the training stimuli would lead to progressively lower response levels along intermediate portions of the gradients. Second, it was predicted that corresponding outer segments of the gradients for different separation groups would be parallel.

The two predicted relationships were generally confirmed. Empirical gradients were approximately linear in their outer segments, varying from clear bimodality in the maximum separation groups to curves with virtually horizontal ledges between the training stimuli in the minimum separation groups. Underestimation of the total range of the summated gradients and the shallowness of the curves between training stimuli constituted the systematic departures from exact predictions. However, when the parameters were estimated from the data for one of the summated generalization groups, theoretical and empirical gradients coincided rather well.

REFERENCES

BILODEAU, E. A., BROWN, J. S., & MERYMAN, J. J. The summation of generalized reactive tendencies. *J. exp. Psychol.*, 1956, **51**, 293–298.

BROWN, J. S., BILODEAU, E. A., & BARON, M. R. Bidirectional gradients in the strength of a generalized voluntary response to stimuli on a visual-spatial dimension. *J. exp. Psychol.*, 1951, **41**, 52–61.

BURKE, C. J., & ESTES, W. K. A component model for stimulus variables in discrimination learning. *Psychometrika*, 1957, **22**, 133–145.

ESTES, W. K., & BURKE, C. J. A theory of stimulus variability in learning. *Psychol. Rev.*, 1953, **60**, 276–286.

GUTTMAN, N., & KALISH, H. I. Discriminability and stimulus generalization. *J. exp. Psychol.*, 1956, **51**, 79–88.

KALISH, H. I., & GUTTMAN, N. Stimulus generalization after equal training on two stimuli. *J. exp. Psychol.*, 1957, **53**, 139–144.

STEVENS, S. S. On the psychophysical law. *Psychol. Rev.*, 1957, **64**, 153–181.

(Received August 6, 1960)

A Component Model for Stimulus Variables in Discrimination Learning[*]

C. J. BURKE and W. K. ESTES, *Indiana University*

A general function is derived describing the conditioning of a single stimulus component in a discriminative situation. This function, together with the combinatorial rules of statistical learning theory [5, 12], generates empirically testable formulas for learning of classical two-alternative discriminations, probabilistic discriminations, and discriminations based on the outcomes of preceding trials in partial reinforcement experiments.

From the set-theoretical stimulus model developed by Estes and Burke [5], together with a descriptive theory of reinforcement [4], it is possible to derive a model for certain aspects of discrimination learning. This model is assumed to describe the formation and abolition of conditional relations ("connections") between response classes and the independently variable components or aspects of discriminative stimuli. It does not take account of patterning effects, "observing responses" [13], adaptation of irrelevant cues [11], or many other complications, and thus is not expected to provide a generally adequate account of discrimination learning. The model does, however, describe the data of certain especially simplified experiments [1, 6, 7, 12]; these findings have been taken as evidence for the assumption that it may eventually form a part of a more comprehensive and adequate theory.

Since our primary concern in this paper is with stimulus variables, we shall assume the simplest possible conditions relative to other types of variables. For all functions derived, the reference class of experiments will involve two stimulating situations which are presented in a random order, two alternative response classes with corresponding reinforcing events, and determinate, non-contingent reinforcement.[†]

Definitions and Assumptions

We shall require the following terms:

A_1 and A_2 Mutually exclusive and exhaustive response classes.
E_1 and E_2 Reinforcing events for A_1 and A_2, respectively.

*The researches on which this paper is based were facilitated by a grant from the National Science Foundation.
†By "determinate, non-contingent reinforcement" we mean that exactly one predesignated reinforcing event occurs on each trial and that the probabilities of reinforcing events are not conditional upon the subjects' responses.

This article appeared in *Psychometrika*, 1957, **22**, 133–145.

T_1 and T_2	Types of trials (corresponding to the two stimulating situations which are to be discriminated).
π_{hj} (with $\sum_j \pi_{hj} = 1$)	Probability of E_j on trials of type T_h.
β and $1 - \beta$	Relative frequencies of T_1 and T_2 trials during a learning series.
S_1 and S_2	Sets of stimulus elements available for sampling only on T_1 and only on T_2 trials, respectively.
S_c	Set of stimulus elements available for sampling on all trials (i.e., elements common to the two stimulating situations).
S	Set of all elements associated with either of the two stimulating situations; i.e., $$S = S_1 \cup S_2 \cup S_c,$$ where $\cup$ indicates set-theoretical summation.
N_k	Number of elements in S_k.
θ_{i1} and θ_{i2}	Sampling probability of the ith element of S on trials of type T_1 and T_2, respectively.
$F_{i,n}$	Probability that the ith element of S is "connected to" response A_1 on trial n (i.e., at the beginning of trial n).
F_i	Limiting value of $F_{i,n}$ for large n.
$p_{hj,n}$	Probability of A_j, in the stimulating situation corresponding to T_h, on trial n.
p_n	Probability of a "correct response" on trial n, where a correct response is defined as A_1 on T_1 trials and A_2 on T_2 trials so that

$$(1) \qquad\qquad p_n = \beta p_{11,n} + (1 - \beta) p_{22,n}.$$

Our assumptions about learning are taken directly from previous treatments of learning in elementary, non-discriminative situations [4, 5, 8]. Specifically, we assume:

    a. At any time, each stimulus element in S is "connected to" exactly one of the responses A_1 or A_2.

    b. The $F_{i,n}$ remain fixed in value except when reinforcing events occur.

    c. If E_1 occurs on trial n, then

$$(2) \qquad\qquad F_{i,n} = (1 - \theta_{ih})F_{i,n-1} + \theta_{ih}.$$

    d. If E_2 occurs on trial n, then

$$(3) \qquad\qquad F_{i,n} = (1 - \theta_{ih})F_{i,n-1}.$$

In (2) and (3), $h = 1$ or $h = 2$ according as the trial is of type T_1 or T_2. The $F_{i,n}$ are brought into relation to response probabilities by the assumption that probability of a given response on any trial is equal to the proportion of stimulus elements in the trial sample that are "connected to" the response. Intuitively, a "connection" is obviously intended to represent a learned association, but its formal properties are limited to those expressed above.

Learning Functions for a Single Stimulus Element

General case

    Using the terms and assumptions given above, we can write a general difference equation expressing $F_{i,n}$, the probability that the ith element of S is connected to response A_1 on trial n, as a linear function of the probability on the preceding trial.

$$(4) \quad F_{i,n} = \beta[(1 - \theta_{i1})F_{i,n-1} + \theta_{i1}\pi_{11}] + (1 - \beta)[(1 - \theta_{i2})F_{i,n-1} + \theta_{i2}\pi_{21}]$$
$$= (1 - \beta\theta_{i1} - \theta_{i2} + \beta\theta_{i2})F_{i,n-1} + \beta\theta_{i1}\pi_{11} + (1 - \beta)\theta_{i2}\pi_{21}.$$

If the quantity $F_{i,n-1}$ on the right side of (4) represents a probability associated with a particular subject on trial $n - 1$, then clearly the quantity $F_{i,n}$ on the left represents the expected value on trial n, where the expectation is taken over the possible stimulus sampling outcomes and reinforcing outcomes of trial $n - 1$. If an experiment were repeated many times (or, equivalently if a population of subjects with like parameter values were run simultaneously through an experiment) there would result a distribution of values of $F_{i,n-1}$, and therefore also of $F_{i,n}$. For each value of $F_{i,n-1}$, the conditional mean value of $F_{i,n}$ is given by (4). Therefore the relation between the mean values of $F_{i,n-1}$ and $F_{i,n}$ is also given by (4). We shall now suppose that this averaging has been carried out, and in the remainder of this paper we shall interpret $F_{i,n}$ and $F_{i,n-1}$ in (4) and all following equations as expected values for the population of all repetitions of a given experiment (or, equivalently, for all subjects having a given set of parameter values). With this interpretation, and with the restriction that the parameters θ_{ih} and π_{hj} are constant over trials, (4) can be solved. The resulting expression for $F_{i,n}$, readily verified by induction, is

$$(5) \quad F_{i,n} = F_i - (F_i - F_{i,1})[1 - \beta\theta_{i1} - (1 - \beta)\theta_{i2}]^{n-1},$$

where

$$(6) \quad F_i = \frac{\beta\theta_{i1}\pi_{11} + (1 - \beta)\theta_{i2}\pi_{21}}{\beta\theta_{i1} + (1 - \beta)\theta_{i2}}.$$

The quantity $[1 - \beta\theta_{i1} - (1 - \beta)\theta_{i2}]$ is bounded in the interval 0 to 1, so $F_{i,n}$ describes a negatively accelerated curve with F_i as the asymptote. It will be apparent from inspection of (6) that F_i is also equal to the conditional probability of E_1 on trials when the ith element of S is sampled; i.e.,

$$(7) \quad F_i = \Pr(E_1 \mid X_i = 1),$$

where X_i is a random variable that takes on the values 1 and 0 according as element i is or is not sampled on any trial.

Special cases

Learning functions for simple acquisition, classical discrimination learning, and probabilistic discrimination learning are now obtainable as special cases of (5).

a. A discriminative situation reduces to simple acquisition if only one stimulating situation is ever presented. When we express this restriction by setting $\beta = 1$ and dropping the h subscripts in our general discrimination function, (5) reduces to

$$(8) \qquad F_{i,n} = \pi_1 - (\pi_1 - F_{i,1})(1 - \theta_i)^{n-1}.$$

b. In a classical discrimination problem, the two stimuli to be discriminated (e.g., black card vs. white card, bright light vs. dim light, circle vs. triangle) together with background, or contextual stimulation, are represented by two stimulus sets. On T_1 trials, the set $S_1 \cup S_c$ is available for sampling, and on T_2 trials the set $S_2 \cup S_c$ is available. It will often be assumed that θ values are equal for all elements within each of the three subsets S_1, S_2, and S_c. With this assumption, (5) becomes for S_1:

$$(9) \qquad F_{1,n} = \pi_{11} - (\pi_{11} - F_{1,1})(1 - \beta\theta_1)^{n-1};$$

for S_2:

$$(10) \qquad F_{2,n} = \pi_{21} - (\pi_{21} - F_{2,1})[1 - (1 - \beta)\theta_2]^{n-1};$$

and for S_c:

$$(11) \qquad F_{c,n} = \pi_c - (\pi_c - F_{c,1})(1 - \theta_c)^{n-1},$$

where

$$\pi_c = \beta\pi_{11} + (1 - \beta)\pi_{21}.$$

c. Traditionally, discrimination learning has been regarded as a matter of distinguishing two (or more) stimulating situations which differ with respect to certain component stimuli or stimulus attributes; and discrimination theories have been limited to this paradigm. More generally, however, there is a basis for discrimination learning whenever some of the components or attributes of a situation bear non-random relationships to reinforcing events. If two "situations" to be discriminated include the same stimulus components, and differ only with respect to the sampling probabilities of the components, we shall speak of probabilistic discrimination learning. Just as partial reinforcement represents a natural generalization of simple acquisition and extinction procedures, probabilistic discrimination learning represents a natural generalization of the conventional discrimination paradigm.

In the terms defined above, the condition for probabilistic discrimination learning relative to the two "situations" sampled on trials of types T_1 and T_2 is simply that there be some difference between the distributions of θ_{i1} and θ_{i2}. A simple arrangement which has proved convenient for experimental tests of the theory [cf. 7] is the following. The reinforcement probabilities π_{11} and π_{21} are set equal to unity and zero, respectively; i.e., response A_1 is always reinforced on T_1 trials and A_2 is always reinforced on T_2 trials. The stimulating situation includes N separably manipulable components. On T_1 trials, the sampling probabilities of the components, θ_{i1} for $i = 1, 2, \cdots, N$, are given by the linear function

$$(12) \qquad \theta_{i1} = a_1 + b_1 i;$$

and on T_2 trials the sampling probabilities, θ_{i2} for $i = 1, 2, \cdots, N$, are given by

$$(13) \qquad \theta_{i2} = a_2 + b_2 i.$$

In this case, (5) becomes

$$(14) \qquad F_{i,n} = \frac{\beta(a_1 + b_1 i)}{\bar{a} + \bar{b}i} - \left[\frac{\beta(a_1 + b_1 i)}{\bar{a} + \bar{b}i} - F_{i,1} \right](1 - \bar{a} - \bar{b}i)^{n-1},$$

where

$$\bar{a} = \beta a_1 + (1 - \beta)a_2$$

and

$$\bar{b} = \beta b_1 + (1 - \beta)b_2 .$$

Now if we set $b_1 = -b_2$ and $\beta = 1/2$, values which, in fact, were used in the experimental application referred to above, the asymptotic value of $F_{i,n}$ is a linear function of i:

$$F_i = \frac{1}{\bar{a}}(a_1 + b_1 i).$$

This case is obviously advantageous for statistical tests of the correspondence between predicted and observed values of F_i . A convenient estimator of F_i is the proportion of A_1 responses evoked by the ith stimulus component when presented alone.

Learning Functions in Terms of Response Probability

Given the formulas for $F_{i,n}$, it is a purely mathematical problem to derive expressions for response probability. Two principal cases arise: (a) that in which one wishes to predict response probability in the presence of a specified sample of stimulus elements (as might be the case in an experiment on stimulus compounding or transfer); and (b) that in which one wishes to predict response probability when stimulus elements are being sampled randomly from a specified population (as might be the case in experiments on acquisition and reversal of discriminations). Case (a) is the simpler, since expected response probability will be given directly by the arithmetic mean of the $F_{i,n}$, i.e.,

$$(15) \qquad p_{h1,n} = \frac{1}{K} \sum_i F_{i,n} \, ,$$

where the summation is taken over the K elements in the given sample.

In case (b) we shall follow the procedure used in our earlier treatment of simple learning [5] and replace the arithmetic mean of the $F_{i,n}$ with the weighted mean:

$$(16) \qquad p_{h1,n} = \frac{1}{N_h \bar{\theta}_h} \sum_i \theta_{ih} F_{i,n}$$

(the summation being taken over the set S_h). Equation (16) does not, in general, give the exact value for the mean proportion of A_1-connected elements in trial samples. It does give the exact value when the sample size is fixed, and it approximates the exact value for all cases in which elements are sampled independently and N_h is large. If N_h is very small, (16) may not be a satisfactory estimator, but in this instance direct computation of expected sample proportions will not be difficult.

To illustrate the derivation of learning functions by means of (16), we shall treat a number of special cases which have arisen in experimental applications of the model.

Acquisition with random reinforcement

If an experiment involves but a single stimulating situation, the acquisition function can be obtained by substituting (8) into (16), viz.,

$$(17) \qquad p_{1,n} = \frac{1}{N\bar{\theta}} \sum_i \theta_i [\pi_1 - (\pi_1 - F_{i,1})(1 - \theta_i)^{n-1}]$$

$$= \pi_1 - [\pi_1 - p_{1,1}] \frac{1}{N\bar{\theta}} \sum_i \theta_i (1 - \theta_i)^{n-1}.$$

In the derivation of (17), and in all ensuing derivations, we assume for simplicity that the values of $F_{i,1}$ and θ_i are uncorrelated. The most interesting consequence of (17) is the prediction that asympotically response probability should approach the probability of reinforcement regardless of the distribution of θ_i values. If all of the θ_i are equal, (17) reduces to the function

$$p_{1,n} = \pi_1 - [\pi_1 - p_{1,1}](1 - \theta)^{n-1}$$

used by Estes and Straughan [8], Neimark [10] and others to describe acquisition under non-contingent random reinforcement.

Classical discrimination learning

For discrimination experiments involving two stimulating situations which differ with respect to some of their components, learning functions can be obtained by substituting into (16) from (9) and (11) or from (10) and

(11), the former yielding probability of response A_1 on T_1 trials and the latter probability of A_1 on T_2 trials. Using the notation $\bar{\theta}_{1+c}$ for the mean value of θ over all elements available for sampling on T_1 trials, i.e.,

$$\bar{\theta}_{1+c} = \frac{N_1\theta_1 + N_c\theta_c}{N_1 + N_c} \, ,$$

we obtain for probability of A_1 on T_1 trials

$$p_{11,n} = \frac{1}{N_{1+c}\bar{\theta}_{1+c}} \{N_1\theta_1[\pi_{11} - (\pi_{11} - F_{1,1})(1 - \beta\theta_1)^{n-1}]$$

$$+ N_c\theta_c[\pi_c - (\pi_c - F_{c,1})(1 - \theta_c)^{n-1}]\}.$$

Letting

$$w_1 = \frac{N_1\theta_1}{N_{1+c}\bar{\theta}_{1+c}}$$

and

$$w_c = \frac{N_c\theta_c}{N_{1+c}\bar{\theta}_{1+c}} \, ,$$

this expression simplifies to

(18) $p_{11,n} = w_1\pi_{11} + w_c\pi_c - w_1(\pi_{11} - p_{11,1})(1 - \beta\theta_1)^{n-1}$

$$- w_c(\pi_c - p_{11,1})(1 - \theta_c)^{n-1}.$$

Similarly, for probability of A_1 on T_2 trials, we obtain

(19) $p_{21,n} = w_2\pi_{21} + w_c\pi_c - w_2(\pi_{21} - p_{21,1})[1 - (1 - \beta)\theta_2]^{n-1}$

$$- w_c(\pi_c - p_{21,1})(1 - \theta_c)^{n-1}.$$

The predicted asymptotic accuracy of discrimination is seen to depend both on the amount of overlap between the two stimulating situations and on the values of π_{11} and π_{21}. It has been customary in researches on discrimination learning to give uniform reinforcement in the presence of one situation and uniform nonreinforcement in the presence of the other, i.e., to let $\pi_{11} = 1$ and $\pi_{21} = 0$. This restriction is clearly unessential, however; theoretically, better than chance discrimination will be possible whenever the values of π_{11} and π_{21} differ, provided, of course, that w_c is less than unity. In a recent experiment conducted to test the theory, π_{11} and π_{21} were set equal to unity and 0.5, respectively, and the empirical curves of $p_{11,n}$ and $p_{21,n}$ diverged in accordance with theoretical expectation [6].

Probabilistic discrimination learning

When the "situations" to be discriminated differ only with respect to the sampling probabilities of component stimuli, the discrimination curves for probability of A_1 on T_1 and T_2 trials are given by (16) with $h = 1$ and $h = 2$, respectively:

$$(20) \qquad p_{11,n} = \frac{1}{N\bar{\theta}_1} \sum_i \theta_{i1} F_{i,n}$$

and

$$(21) \qquad p_{21,n} = \frac{1}{N\bar{\theta}_2} \sum_i \theta_{i2} F_{i,n} \, ,$$

$F_{i,n}$ being given by (5) in each case. In general, better than chance discrimination will be theoretically predicted whenever there is any difference in the distribution of θ values on T_1 and T_2 trials. When reinforcement is uniform and the θ_{ih} distributions are linear, as assumed in the derivation of (14), the asymptotic values of $p_{11,n}$ and $p_{21,n}$ are given by

$$(22) \qquad p_{11,\infty} = \frac{1}{N\bar{\theta}_1} \sum_i \frac{\beta(a_1 + b_1 i)^2}{\bar{a} + \bar{b}i}$$

and

$$(23) \qquad p_{21,\infty} = \frac{1}{N\bar{\theta}_2} \sum_i \frac{(1 - \beta)(a_2 + b_2 i)(a_1 + b_1 i)}{\bar{a} + \bar{b}i} \, ,$$

where

$$\bar{\theta}_h = \frac{1}{N} \sum_i (a_h + b_h i).$$

In an experimental test of the theory [7], we have set $b_2 = -b_1$, $a_1 = 0$, and $a_2 = (N + 1)b_1$. With these restrictions,

$$\bar{\theta}_1 = \bar{\theta}_2 = b_1(N + 1)/2$$

and (22) and (23) reduce to

$$(24) \qquad p_{11,\infty} = \frac{2\beta}{N(N + 1)} \sum_i \frac{i^2}{(1 - \beta)(N + 1) + (2\beta - 1)i}$$

and

$$(25) \qquad p_{21,\infty} = \frac{2(1 - \beta)}{N(N + 1)} \sum_i \frac{(N + 1 - i)i}{(1 - \beta)(N + 1) + (2\beta - 1)i} \, ,$$

and we have the curious result that asymptotic response probabilities are independent of b_1, the slope parameter of the θ distributions. For the special case of $\beta = 1/2$, these asymptotic expressions reduce further to

$$(26) \qquad \begin{aligned} p_{11,\infty} &= \frac{2}{N(N + 1)^2} \sum_i i^2 \\ &= \frac{2N + 1}{3(N + 1)} \, , \end{aligned}$$

and

$$p_{21,\infty} = \frac{2}{N(N+1)^2} \sum_i (N+1-i)i$$

$$= \frac{2}{N(N+1)^2} \sum_i [(N+1)i - i^2]$$

(27)

$$= \frac{2}{N(N+1)^2} \left[\frac{N(N+1)^2}{2} - \frac{N(N+1)(2N+1)}{6} \right]$$

$$= 1 - \frac{2N+1}{3(N+1)}.$$

Asymptotic probability of correct responding in this case is seen to vary from 1/2 to 2/3 as N ranges from one to infinity.

One point of interpretation concerning our functions for probabilistic discrimination learning requires especial emphasis. The stimulus sampling probabilities θ_{ih} may be associated either with the hypothetical elements of an experimentally homogeneous stimulating situation or with independently manipulable components of a situation. In the former case, the derived functions should be applicable as they stand. In the latter case, θ_{ih} represents a product of two probabilities, i.e.,

$$\theta_{ih} = \theta'_{ih}\theta.$$

The parameter θ'_{ih} is the (experimenter-determined) sampling probability of the ith stimulus component. The parameter θ is the (subject-determined) probability that any element associated with the ith component will be sampled on trials when the ith component is present. In the experiment cited above [7] the N stimulus components were signal lights with sampling probabilities, θ'_{ih}, prescribed by the experimental design. Since all of the signal lights were similar in physical properties, we assumed that the subsets of stimulus elements associated with the various individual lights all had the same value of θ. When this assumption is satisfied, the asymptotic values of $F_{i,n}$ and $p_{hj,n}$ are independent of θ, and therefore are predictable in advance of an experiment. (6) becomes

$$F_i = \frac{\beta\theta\theta'_{i1}\pi_{11} + (1-\beta)\theta\theta'_{i2}\pi_{21}}{\beta\theta\theta'_{i1} + (1-\beta)\theta\theta'_{i2}}$$

(28)

$$= \frac{\beta\theta'_{i1}\pi_{11} + (1-\beta)\theta'_{i2}\pi_{21}}{\beta\theta'_{i1} + (1-\beta)\theta'_{i2}},$$

and by substitution into (16)

$$p_{h1,\infty} = \frac{1}{N_h \bar{\theta}_h} \sum_i \theta_{ih} F_i$$

(29)
$$= \frac{1}{\sum_i \theta \theta'_{ih}} \sum_i \theta \theta'_{ih} F_i \,,$$

$$= \frac{1}{N_h \bar{\theta}'_h} \sum_i \theta'_{ih} F_i \,,$$

where N_h is the number of stimulus components available for sampling on trials of type T_h , and $\bar{\theta}'_h$ is the mean of their (experimenter-determined) sampling probabilities. The slope parameters of the discrimination learning curves will contain θ as a factor; for example, the exponential term of (5) will become

$$[1 - \beta \theta \theta'_{i1} - (1 - \beta) \theta \theta'_{i2}]^{n-1}.$$

The problem of estimating θ from experimental data in this case will be essentially the same as in the case of simple acquisition functions (cf., e.g., [1, 8]).

Discriminations based on traces of reinforcing stimuli

Numerous experiments concerning learning with partial reinforcement have suggested that when trials are sufficiently massed, the subject forms a discrimination based on the stimulus after-effects of reinforcement and non-reinforcement (see, e.g., [3], pp. 16-18). This type of discrimination learning should be expected to show up especially clearly if experimental arrangements prescribe a non-random relationship between probability of reinforcement on any given trial and the reinforcing outcome of the preceding trial; for an example of such an arrangement, (see [9]). In order to treat trace discrimination in terms of the present model, we shall assume that one set of stimulus elements, S_1 , is available for sampling on trials following reinforcing event E_1 , and a second set, S_2 , is available on trials following occurrences of E_2 . For simplicity we shall limit our derivations to the optimal case in which S_1 and S_2 have no common elements. The parameters π_{11} and π_{21} will now be taken to represent probabilities of E_1 on trials following E_1 and E_2 occurrences, respectively; β will be the average probability of E_1 trials, and must satisfy the relation

$$\beta = \bar{\pi} = \bar{\pi}\pi_{11} + (1 - \bar{\pi})\pi_{21}$$

(30)
$$= \frac{\pi_{21}}{1 - \pi_{11} + \pi_{21}}.$$

Substituting $\bar{\pi}$ for β in (9) and (10), and letting $\theta_1 = \theta_2 = \theta$, we obtain

(31)
$$F_{1,n} = \pi_{11} - (\pi_{11} - F_{1,1})(1 - \theta\bar{\pi})^{n-1}$$

and

(32) $$F_{2,n} = \pi_{21} - (\pi_{21} - F_{2,1})[1 - \theta(1 - \bar{\pi})]^{n-1}.$$

From (31) and (32) we can compute expected probabilities of response A_1 following E_1 and E_2 trials by taking account of the incremental or decremental effect of the reinforcing event:

(33) $$p_{11,n} = (1 - \theta\pi_{11})F_{1,n-1} + \theta\pi_{11}$$

$$= \pi_{11} + \theta\pi_{11}(1 - \pi_{11}) - (\pi_{11} - p_{11,1})(1 - \theta\pi_{11})(1 - \theta\bar{\pi})^{n-2},$$

$$p_{21,n} = (1 - \theta + \theta\pi_{21})F_{2,n-1}$$

(34) $$= \pi_{21} - \theta(1 - \pi_{21})\pi_{21} - (\pi_{21} - p_{21,1})[1 - \theta(1 - \pi_{21})]$$

$$\cdot [1 - \theta(1 - \bar{\pi})]^{n-2},$$

and on the average

$$p_{1,n} = \bar{\pi}p_{11,n} + (1 - \bar{\pi})p_{21,n}$$

(35) $$= \bar{\pi} - \theta(1 - \pi_{11})\pi_{21}\frac{(1 - \pi_{11} - \pi_{21})}{(1 - \pi_{11} + \pi_{21})}$$

$$- \bar{\pi}(\pi_{11} - p_{11,1})(1 - \theta\pi_{11})(1 - \theta\bar{\pi})^{n-2}$$

$$- (1 - \bar{\pi})(\pi_{21} - p_{21,1})[1 - \theta(1 - \pi_{21})][1 - \theta(1 - \bar{\pi})]^{n-2}.$$

The gist of these results is that the probabilities of A_1 on trials following E_1 and E_2 occurrences should tend asymptotically to the conditional probabilities of E_1 and E_2, respectively, plus or minus "correction terms" which are smaller in magnitude than θ; and the average probability of A_1 should tend asymptotically to the average probability of E_1, plus or minus a "correction term" which is smaller in magnitude than θ.

    For purposes of experimental interpretation the functions derived here should be expected to apply when trials are sufficiently massed and the stimuli associated with E_1 and E_2 sufficiently distinct so that the assumption of no overlap between S_1 and S_2 is tenable. As trial spacing is increased, we should expect the communality of S_1 and S_2 to increase until with extreme spacing, they are no longer discriminable. Under the latter condition, the subject is in effect sampling a single stimulus population on all trials, and (33), (34), and (35) reduce to

(36) $$p_{11,n} = \bar{\pi} + \theta(1 - \bar{\pi}) - (\bar{\pi} - p_{11,1})(1 - \theta)^{n-1}$$

(37) $$p_{21,n} = \bar{\pi} - \theta\bar{\pi} - (\bar{\pi} - p_{21,1})(1 - \theta)^{n-1},$$

and

(38) $$p_{1,n} = \bar{\pi} - (\bar{\pi} - p_{1,1})(1 - \theta)^{n-1}.$$

Cases of intermediate spacing should be expected to fall between these two extremes. Explicit expressions for cases involving partial overlap between S_1 and S_2 can be derived by obvious extensions of the methods illustrated here.

The Role of Component Models in Discrimination Theory

How can we characterize the empirical adequacy of the model presented here as a theory of discrimination learning? At a minimum, it provides a quantitative account of data in certain experiments conducted under conditions especially designed to satisfy the simplifying assumptions of the model and predicts some new phenomena, notably those of probabilistic discrimination learning. More generally, the model appears to give a reasonable account of the development of differential S-R correlations under differential reinforcement, of the relation found in some situations between asymptotic accuracy of discriminations and stimulus overlap or "similarity," and of transfer phenomena observed when the components of a discriminative situation are tested in new combinations following the development of discrimination (see, e.g., [7, 12]). The component model does not account for the fact that in some situations subjects, animal or human, are able to achieve essentially perfect discriminations between stimuli which have components or attributes in common.

Formally our stimulus model represents the type of component-sampling model which, with minor variations in detail, underlies numerous contemporary approaches to discrimination theory, e.g., those of Bush and Mosteller [2], Restle [11], and Wyckoff [13] as well as our own. Insofar as stimulus variables are concerned, our model has been elaborated in greater detail than the others, but we have not attempted to handle effects of work or attentional factors. The logical next step in our line of investigation must be to examine possible auxiliary hypotheses, for example those relating to "observing responses" or adaptation of irrelevant cues, in order to determine how the present limited theory may be most effectively extended to cover a broader range of discrimination experiments.

REFERENCES

[1] Burke, C. J., Estes, W. K., and Hellyer, S. Rate of verbal conditioning in relation to stimulus variability. *J. exp. Psychol.*, 1954, **48**, 153-161.
[2] Bush, R. R. and Mosteller, F. A model for stimulus generalization and discrimination. *Psychol. Rev.*, 1951, **58**, 413-423.
[3] Estes, W. K. Learning. In Annual review of psychology, 1956, **7**, 1-38.
[4] Estes, W. K. Theory of learning with constant, variable, or contingent probabilities of reinforcement. *Psychometrika*, 1957, **22**, 113-132.
[5] Estes, W. K. and Burke, C. J. A theory of stimulus variability in learning. *Psychol. Rev.*, 1953, **60**, 276-286.

[6] Estes, W. K. and Burke, C. J. Application of a statistical model to simple discrimination learning in human subjects. *J. exp. Psychol.*, 1955, **50**, 81-88.

[7] Estes, W. K., Burke, C. J., Atkinson, R. C., and Frankmann, J. P. Probabilistic discrimination learning. *J. exp. Psychol.*, 1957, in press.

[8] Estes, W. K. and Straughan, J. H. Analysis of a verbal conditioning situation in terms of statistical learning theory. *J. exp. Psychol.*, 1954, **47**, 225-234.

[9] Hake, H. W. and Hyman, R. Perception of the statistical structure of a random series of binary symbols. *J. exp. Psychol.*, 1953, **45**, 64-74.

[10] Neimark, Edith D. Effects of type of non-reinforcement and number of alternative responses in two verbal conditioning situations. *J. exp. Psychol.*, 1956, **52**, 209-220.

[11] Restle, F. A theory of discrimination learning. *Psychol. Rev.*, 1955, **62**, 11–19.

[12] Schoeffler, M. S. Probability of response to compounds of discriminated stimuli. *J. exp. Psychol.*, 1954, **48**, 323-329.

[13] Wyckoff, L. B., Jr. The role of observing responses in discrimination learning. *Psychol. Rev.*, 1952, **59**, 431-442.

Manuscript received 8/27/56

Probabilistic Discrimination Learning[1]

W. K. Estes, C. J. Burke, R. C. Atkinson,[2] and J. P. Frankmann,
Indiana University

Traditionally, discrimination experiments have been limited to cases in which two situations to be discriminated differ with respect to some or all of their component stimuli or stimulus attributes (henceforth referred to as *cues*). Analyses of discrimination learning in terms of statistical learning theory (1, 4) have led to the study of a more general case which may be termed probabilistic discrimination learning. According to the theory, there is a basis for discrimination learning whenever some of the cues in a situation are differentially correlated with reinforcing events. Classical discrimination learning arises if some of the correlations are unity and others zero; probabilistic discrimination learning arises if the correlations have intermediate values. Otherwise stated, the condition for probabilistic discrimination learning is that differential reinforcement be given relative to two situations which include the same cues and differ only with respect to the sampling probabilities of the cues.

To illustrate these distinctions, consider a standard two-choice discrimination apparatus (e.g., a Grice box or a Lashley stand) with two discriminative cues available, say a light and a tone. To set up a classical discrimination problem, one might present either the light or the tone on each trial and reinforce responses to the left door when the tone is present and responses to the right door when the light is present. To set up a probabilistic discrimination problem, one might assign to the tone and light the probabilities .8 and .4, respectively, of occurring on trials when the left response is reinforced and the probabilities .4 and .8, respectively, of occurring on trials when the right response is reinforced. Now, either the tone or the light or both may occur on any trial, yet there is a basis for better than chance discrimination. According to the theory (1, 4), learning relative to the individual cues should proceed exactly as in simple experiments on acquisition with random reinforcement. Thus the asymptotic probability of a given response to any cue taken alone should approximate the conditional probability of reinforcement in the presence of the cue. Using this principle,

[1] This research was supported in part by a grant to W. K. Estes and C. J. Burke from the National Science Foundation.
[2] Now at U.C.L.A.

This article appeared in *J. exp. Psychol.*, 1957, **54**, 233–239.

together with the compounding laws of the statistical model (**1, 3, 7**), it should be possible in advance of an experiment to predict the asymptotic frequency of correct responding and the asymptotic probability of any given response in the presence of any specified combination of cues. For the illustrative example given above, it would be predicted, employing formulae given in a later section, that asymptotically the relative frequency of correct responses would be .56, the probability of a left response to the tone alone would be .67, the probability of a left response to the tone and light together would be .5, and so on (these computations assume equal frequencies of reinforcement on the left and right).

The experiment to be described was conducted to determine whether a probabilistic discrimination would develop under conditions prescribed by the statistical theory and to test quantitative predictions concerning asymptotic response probabilities. A modified verbal conditioning situation offered several advantages for these purposes. Previous studies (**2, 5, 6**) had established that simple acquisition functions for verbal conditioning are described by the statistical model, and the desired stimulus manipulations could be introduced without changing other aspects of the experimental situation.

METHOD

Apparatus.—The apparatus has been described in detail elsewhere (**5**). The experimental room was dark, except for light coming from the apparatus, and contained four booths and a signal panel. On the panel were mounted 12 12-v., 25-amp. light bulbs, evenly spaced around a circle of 9-in. radius. The booths were placed so that all Ss would have a clear view of the signal panel at a distance of approximately 7 ft. Within each booth was a pair of telegraph keys, each key directly beneath a reinforcing light. The presentations of signal patterns and reinforcing stimuli were controlled by an automatic programming device and the responses of Ss were recorded automatically.

Subjects.—The Ss were 32 non-psychology students obtained from language courses in the Indiana University summer school of 1954 and were paid for their services. They were scheduled in subgroups of four for the experimental sessions.

Design.—For each S, one of the reinforcing lights was designated E_1 and the other E_2, the side of the E_1 light being counterbalanced within each subgroup of four Ss. During discrimination training, either E_1 or E_2 appeared following the signal on each trial; the two types of trials will be designated T_1 and T_2, respectively. On test trials neither of the reinforcing lights appeared.

The stimulating situations obtaining on training trials of types T_1 and T_2 were arranged as follows. First each of the 12 signal lights on the panel was assigned a number between 1 and 12 by a random procedure. Then for T_1 trials the lights in order from 1 to 12 were assigned the probabilities 5/78, 10/78, . . . , 60/78 of being sampled on any one trial; for T_2 trials the lights, in the same order, had sampling probabilities of 60/78, 55/78, . . . , 5/78. In other words, a signal light which had been assigned the ordinal number i appeared on T_1 trials with probability $5i/78$ and on T_2 trials with probability $5(13 - i)/78$, as illustrated in the upper panel of Fig. 1.

During discrimination training, T_1 and T_2 trials occurred in random sequence with the restriction that for one treatment group of 16 Ss the two types occurred equally often within each period and for the other treatment group of 16 Ss the proportions were .25 T_1 to .75 T_2. A new random assignment of numbers to signal lights was made for each subgroup of four Ss in the .5 treatment group and its matched subgroup in the .25 group. The conditional probability of E_1 in the presence of each individual signal light for each group is shown in the lower panel of Fig. 1.

On Days 1 and 2 all groups received 240 training trials. On Day 3 all groups had first a block of 40 additional training trials, bringing the total to 520, then four test blocks of 36 trials each. Each test block included 18 training trials and 18 test trials given in a random order. Each set of 18 test trials included one test on each of the 12 signal lights singly, one test on each of the successive triads (1, 2, 3; 4, 5, 6; 7, 8, 9; 10, 11, 12), and one test each on the mixed triads (1, 3, 11; and 2, 10, 12).

Procedure.—At the first session Ss were seated in the booths and read the instructions

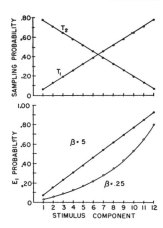

Fig. 1. Upper panel: Sampling probabilities of stimulus components (individual signal lights) on T_1 and T_2 trials (i.e., trials on which reinforcing events E_1 and E_2 occur). Lower panel: Conditional probabilities of E_1 in the presence of individual signal lights for the two treatment groups.

which follow (omitting some repetitive passages):

"I want to see how well you can do in a rather unusual problem situation. At the beginning of each trial some lights will appear on this panel. About a second later, either the left or the right lamp in your compartment will light for a moment. As soon as the signal pattern flashes on the panel, you are to show whether you expect the left or the right lamp in your compartment to light on that trial by pressing the proper key . . . . If you are not sure, guess—your guesses or hunches may turn out to be right, and it is important to have a complete record of your learning.

"Please try not to feel frustrated or irritated if you cannot understand what the experiment is all about. Trying to figure out what the experimenter is up to is not part of your task, and would only tend to spoil your record . . . . The most important thing you can do to ensure the success of the experiment is to indicate as accurately and candidly as possible on each trial which of the compartment lights you expect to appear."

After four practice trials and review of the instructions, the 240 training trials were run off without interruption. Time relations within training trials were approximately: 2-sec. signal duration; 2-sec. delay between signal and rein-

forcement; 1-sec. duration of reinforcing light; 4-sec. intertrial interval.

On Day 2, the instructions were reviewed and 240 additional training trials were given under the same conditions.

On Day 3, the original instructions were reviewed and the following added:

"Up to now, either the left or the right lamp in your compartment has flashed on each trial to show you which key was the correct response to the pattern shown on the panel. During today's session there will be some trials on which neither of the compartment lights will flash. These test trials will be included to see if you can keep up the same level of accuracy when you are not given information as to whether you are right or wrong on every trial. Aside from this one feature, the situation will not be changed in any way, and you are to continue making your best guess on every trial."

Then the 72 test trials and 112 additional training trials were given in the order described above. On test trials the signal duration and intertrial interval were the same as on training trials.

RESULTS AND DISCUSSION

Statistical analyses.—The key-pressing responses corresponding to S's predictions of E_1 and E_2 will be designated as A_1 and A_2, respectively. In analyses of discrimination learning, the dependent variable will be the mean proportion of correct responses per 40-trial block for a given group; a correct response is defined as an A_1 response on a T_1 trial or an A_2 response on a T_2 trial. In analyses of asymptotic probabilities of response to single lights and to compounds, the dependent variable will be the mean proportion of A_1 responses for a given group on all test trials of a given type. Statistical analyses employed F or t tests whenever possible; when variances could not be stabilized by an arcsin transformation of the scores, nonparametric rank tests (8) were used. Statistical significance was defined as the .05 level for a two-tailed t test and the equivalent for other tests.

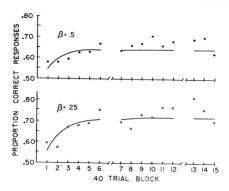

Fig. 2. Theoretical and empirical curves of probabilistic discrimination learning for the two treatment groups. (Note:—the last point on each curve represents only 32 trials.)

Empirical curves of discrimination learning for the two treatment groups are plotted in Fig. 2. Acquisition proceeded at about the same rate in the two groups and was virtually complete by the end of the first period; both curves appear essentially horizontal for the last 400 trials. To estimate the asymptotic probabilities of correct responding, the proportions over the last 40 trials of each period have been averaged. These mean asymptotic proportions are given in Table 1; the group difference is significant by a rank test, and both group means differ significantly from .5 by t tests. Further, both means fall substantially below the values that could be achieved by statistically optimal "strategies."[3]

[3] The optimal strategy would require S to respond to every signal pattern with the response having the higher conditional probability of reinforcement (i.e., the higher probability of being "correct"). The task of calculating exact expected proportions of success for the optimal strategy is beyond our computational resources. However, by analyzing statistically the actual signal-reinforcement sequences which were generated for the present Ss, it is estimated that these maximal proportions are greater than .90 for both of the present groups.

TABLE 1

Asymptotic Proportions of Correct Responses

Group	Observed Proportion	Theoretical Proportion	t
.5	.67	.64	.91
.25	.74	.72	.74

Tests of response probability to single lights yielded the values plotted in Fig. 3; response proportions have been subjected to the arcsin transformation in order to stabilize the variances. It can be seen that for each group, response probability is directly related to and, except at the extreme values, virtually equal to the conditional probability of reinforcement. An analysis of variance on the transformed scores yielded significant F's for differences between Lights and between Groups. (The mean square for Ss-by-Lights interaction was used as the error term in the former case, and the between-Ss mean square in the latter.)

Response proportions obtained on the tests with various triads of lights are summarized in Table 2. The

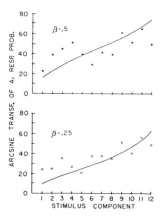

Fig. 3. Predicted and observed probabilities of response to individual signal lights for the two treatment groups.

TABLE 2

PROPORTIONS OF A_1 RESPONSES TO TEST TRIADS

Triads	Proportions				Arcsin Transformations			
	.5 Group		.25 Group		.5 Group		.25 Group	
	Obs.	Th.	Obs.	Th.	Obs.	Th.	Obs.	Th.
1, 2, 3	.22	.15	.03	.06	20	23	4	14
4, 5, 6	.31	.38	.06	.17	29	38	7	24
1, 3, 11	.41	.38	.36	.25	36	38	30	30
7, 8, 9	.59	.62	.42	.35	52	52	38	36
2, 10, 12	.58	.62	.42	.46	51	52	38	43
10, 11, 12	.77	.85	.72	.66	68	67	65	54

triads have been arranged in order of the conditional probabilities of reinforcement, and it can be seen that except for one inversion of an adjacent pair, the observed values fall in the same order for both groups. Group differences are significant, by both t and F tests, for the first two triads, and insignificant for the remainder. Within each group, differences between values for successive triads two or more rows apart are all significant by paired rank tests.

Tests of theoretical predictions.—The theoretical functions required for quantitative predictions of the present data have been derived in detail in another paper (1); here the functions will be simply specialized by inserting the particular parameter values called for by the experimental conditions.

In this study the sampling probability of a stimulus element associated with a signal light of ordinal number i is given by

$$\theta_{ih} = \theta(a_h + b_h i), \qquad (1)$$

where h equals 1 or 2 according to whether the trial in question is of type T_1 or T_2; the parameters a_h and b_h are experimenter-determined, but the value of θ must be estimated from data for a particular S or group of Ss. Inserting the appropriate experimental parameters and averaging, it is found that for both

types of trials

$$\bar{\theta}_h = 5\theta/12.$$

The theoretical probability of A_1 responses on trials of type T_h is given by

$$p_{h1}(n) = \frac{1}{N\bar{\theta}_h} \sum_i \theta_{ih} F_i(n), \qquad (2)$$

where N is the number of cues and $F_i(n)$ is the probability that the ith cue is conditioned to response A_1 after n trials. The latter, in turn, is given by

$$F_i(n) = F_i(\infty) - [F_i(\infty) - F_i(0)] \\ \times (1 - \theta\bar{a} - \theta\bar{b}i)^n. \qquad (3)$$

Under the present experimental conditions, the asymptotic value can be expressed as

$$F_i(\infty) = \frac{\beta i}{(1 - \beta)13 + (2\beta - 1)i} \qquad (4)$$

where β represents the relative frequency of T_1 trials and equals .5 and .25 for our two treatment groups. Also, one has, for the present conditions,

$$\bar{a} = (1 - \beta)5/6$$

and

$$\bar{b} = (2\beta - 1)5/78.$$

Assuming the initial probabilities $F_i(0)$ equal to .5, and estimating θ from obtained total response frequencies as in other studies (2, 5), Equation 2 has been computed for the two treatment groups. The theoretical curves have been plotted together with the empirical values in Fig. 2. The values of θ are .05 and .03 for the $\beta = .5$ and $\beta = .25$ groups, respectively. The fits appear reasonably satisfactory, considering that each curve has only one free parameter and that the theoretical asymptotes, depending solely on experimenter-determined parameters, were predictable in advance of the experiment. Moreover, the estimated values of θ are consistent with the values obtained by similar estimation procedures in studies of simple random reinforcement (**2, 5, 6**) and used to predict the data of a previous discrimination experiment (**4**). Whether the apparently systematic deviations of empirical points from the curves on the first few trial blocks of Day 1 and on the terminal blocks of Days 1 and 2 represent a shortcoming of the theory or merely an effect of the particular stimulus sequences used cannot be decided on the basis of the present data. A numerical comparison of predicted and observed asymptotic values is summarized in Table 1.

Predicted asymptotic probabilities of the A_1 response to single lights are given by Equation 4 and illustrated in the lower panel of Fig. 1; it should be noted that these values are also the conditional probabilities of reinforcing event E_1 in the presence of the single lights. The predicted values are compared with corresponding observed values in Fig. 3, both having been subjected to an arcsin transformation. Throughout the middle range, the correspondence of predicted and observed values seems about as good as could be expected in view of the sizes of our experimental groups. At both extremes the observed points deviate in the direction of .5 from the theoretical curves. It may be noted that this is the pattern of deviation to be expected if there are some background cues in the experimental situation which contribute to response probability on all trials. By appropriate analyses one could estimate the weight associated with the background cues and allow for it in the theoretical functions, thus improving the fits of the curves. However, in this study

the plan was to deal with theoretical curves predicted in advance from the experimental parameters alone.

For the test of response probability to selected triads of lights, the predicted values are obtained by simply averaging the appropriate F_i values. Consider, for example, the triad of Lights 1, 2, 3. Using Equation 4, one obtains 1/13, 2/13, and 3/13 as the three predicted values of $F_i(\infty)$ for the group which had $\beta = .5$. Averaging these, one obtains $2/13 = .15$, which is the first entry in the column of theoretical proportions for the .5 group in Table 2. The theoretical values thus obtained for all triads tested are compared with the corresponding observed values in Table 2, each pair of values being presented on the left side of the table as proportions and on the right side as angles (arcsin transforms). Of the t tests of differences between theoretical and observed transformed values, those for the first two triads in the .25 group were significant; none of the other t's for the .25 group and none of the t's for the .5 group had P values less than .20. On the whole, the accuracy with which observed probabilities of response to compounds are predicted in this study appears comparable to that achieved by Schoeffler (**7**) for similar tests conducted following classical discrimination learning.

SUMMARY

From statistical learning theory it can be predicted that a new experimental phenomenon, "probabilistic discrimination learning," will be observed if two situations to be discriminated include the same cues and differ only with respect to the sampling probabilities of the cues. Just as partial reinforcement represents a natural generalization of simple acquisition and extinction procedures, probabilistic discrimination learning represents a natural generalization of the conventional discrimination paradigm.

For a test experiment, the two "situations" to be discriminated were constructed by assigning two different patterns of sampling probabilities to a set of signal lights, and a key-pressing response was given differential reinforcement relative to these "situations." Two groups of human Ss received 592 training trials, under two different reinforcement schedules, and 72 test trials designed to evaluate asymptotic response probabilities to single cues.

For both groups, curves of correct response proportions approached relatively stable terminal levels intermediate between chance expectations and the maximum values that could be attained by optimal "strategies" under the conditions of the experiment. Rates of probabilistic discrimination learning were very similar to those observed previously for learning under simple partial reinforcement in the same situation. Test trial data confirmed the theoretical prediction that asymptotically the probability of response to any single cue would approach the conditional probability of reinforcement in the presence of the cue.

REFERENCES

1. BURKE, C. J., & ESTES, W. K. A component model for stimulus variables in discrimination learning. *Psychometrika*, 1957, **22**, 133–146.

2. BURKE, C. J., ESTES, W. K., & HELLYER, S. Rate of verbal conditioning in relation to stimulus variability. *J. exp. Psychol.*, 1954, **48**, 153–161.

3. ESTES, W. K., & BURKE, C. J. A theory of stimulus variability in learning. *Psychol. Rev.*, 1953, **60**, 276–286.

4. ESTES, W. K., & BURKE, C. J. Application of a statistical model to simple discrimination learning in human subjects. *J. exp. Psychol.*, 1955, **50**, 81–88.

5. ESTES, W. K., & STRAUGHAN, J. H. Analysis of a verbal conditioning situation in terms of statistical learning theory. *J. exp. Psychol.*, 1954, **47**, 225–234.

6. NEIMARK, E. D. Effects of type of nonreinforcement and number of alternative responses in two verbal conditioning situations. *J. exp. Psychol.*, 1956, **52**, 209–220.

7. SCHOEFFLER, M. S. Probability of response to compounds of discriminated stimuli. *J. exp. Psychol.*, 1954, **48**, 323–329.

8. WILCOXON, F. Individual comparisons by ranking methods. *Biometrics Bull.*, 1945, **1**, 80–82.

(Received August 10, 1956)

The Selection of Strategies in Cue Learning[1]

FRANK RESTLE, *Michigan State University*

In a cue learning problem (discrimination learning, concept formation, and maze learning) the subject chooses one of two or more responses on each trial. The correctness of the response depends on some aspect of the situation at the time of response.

In this paper it is assumed that subjects have difficulty with cue learning problems to the degree that they tend to use strategies (habits, patterns of response) which conflict with the strategy intended by the experimenter. It is often assumed that the subject must also associate correct responses with cues in the situation. However, in most cue learning experiments the subject is instructed or pretrained to make the desired responses before the cue learning process begins. Furthermore, the experimental situation constrains the subject to make exactly one of the available responses per trial. It seems reasonable to assume that cue learning is not so much a matter of the formation as of the selection of responses. The present theoretical discussion begins with a set of strategies and is concerned with the mechanisms by which the subject might select out those strategies intended, and consistently rewarded, by the experimenter.

The term "strategy" is employed in a sense related to the more common terms, "habit" and "hypothesis," to designate a particular pattern of responses to stimuli. Consider, for example, a rat being trained to jump to the larger of two white circles in a Lashley Jumping Stand. Some possible strategies include; jumping to the left side, jumping to the right side, jumping alternately left and right, jumping always to the side last reinforced, jumping to the side which last was punished, jumping in the direction the rat was placed down on the stand, jumping toward the circle with less (or more) acute curvature, jumping toward the side with more white area, jumping toward the side which reflects more total light, and so forth. Each such pattern of behavior, if it occurs in isolation for a sufficiently long sequence of trials, can be identified by the experimenter. It will be seen that there are ordinarily a large number and variety of possible strategies in a cue learning problem, and that a number of strategies may be perfectly confounded. In the example above, jumping to the circle with less acute curvature will always lead to the same result as jumping to the side which reflects more light, since these will both be jumps to the larger circle.

THREE MODELS OF THE SELECTION OF STRATEGIES

The general idea developed here is that the problem gives rise to a set of strategies. The subject uses these various strategies, which at first are selected at random, and attempts to select strategies which will consistently lead to correct responses. For simplicity the discussion is limited to

[1] This research was facilitated by the author's tenure as Faculty Research Fellow of the Social Science Research Council, 1959–61.

This article appeared in *Psychol. Rev.*, 1962, **69**, 329–343.

problems in which there are at least some strategies which are always correct.

Let H be the set of strategies available to the subject at the beginning of the problem. Suppose that some subset C of these strategies are always correct, another subset W are always wrong, and the remainder, I, are sometimes correct and sometimes wrong. For simplicity of presentation, begin with a problem in which the strategies of I are correct and wrong, on successive trials, with independent probabilities all of which are $\frac{1}{2}$, and restrict attention to the two-choice problem.

Presentation of the theory of this conventional discrimination learning problem will begin with a special case in which one strategy is used on each trial. Then an alternative theory will be proposed, in which the subject uses all strategies at once and attempts to narrow down to the correct one. Third, a model will be proposed in which the subject chooses a random sample of all strategies and attempts to narrow down to the correct strategies within his sample. These three models will be shown to be essentially equivalent, in a theorem which may be called the "indifference to sample size" theorem. Following proof of that theorem, some empirical implications of the theory will be derived and compared with relevant data.

One Strategy at a Time

On the first trial of the experiment, the subject selects a certain single strategy from H at random and makes the indicated response. If the response is correct, the same strategy is used on Trial 2. If it is again correct, it is used again on Trial 3, and so forth. If, on any trial, the response is incorrect, the subject returns his strategy to the set H and then chooses a strategy again at random. It is considered possible that the same strategy may be resampled, so that the sampling process is with replacement. Imagine that an error occurs on Trial 2. Then a new strategy is chosen and this strategy is used on Trial 3. If it is correct it is used again on Trial 4. If the response on Trial 3 is wrong, the subject again chooses an hypothesis at random for Trial 4.

Notice that if the subject chooses a correct strategy, he will make no more errors. The correct strategy leads to correct responses, and when the response is correct the subject does not change strategy. Thus, the learning process is terminated by the choice of a correct strategy.

Since sampling is with replacement, the probabilities of choosing a correct, a wrong, or an irrelevant strategy are constant from trial to trial. Let these three probabilities be c, w, and $i = 1 - c - w$.

At the beginning of training the subject chooses a strategy of one of the three types, which have probabilities c, w, and i. After each error he also chooses a strategy, with probabilities c, w, and i. Thus an error is an event which returns the subject to exactly the same condition (in terms of the probabilities of future events) with which he started—it resets the process and makes it begin over. Such an event is called a "recurrent event" (Feller, 1950). Since our experimental interest centers around errors and correct responses, we can limit attention to errors and thus to the theory of recurrent events.

Imagine that at some Trial n the subject makes an error. There is a certain probability f_1 that the next error occurs at Trial $n + 1$, a probability f_2 that the next error occurs at Trial $n + 2$, and in general a probability distribution f_j that the next error after Trial n occurs at Trial $n + j$. In a model of recurrent events like the present one, the distribution f_j is the same for all Trials n on which an error occurs, and is the same as the distribution of probabilities that the first error occurs on Trial 1, 2, etc.

The random process and all of its properties are specified by the distribution f_j. However, the analysis of the process from the distribution f_j will be postponed until two steps have been completed; first, calculation of the distribution f_j for the one-strategy-at-a-time model, and second, the formulation of two other models, very different in assumptions, which also lead to systems of recurrent events with the same distribution. When these steps are completed, the generality of the f distribution will be apparent, and derivations of properties of the process will be justified.

First, f_1 is the probability of an error immediately following another error. The second error can occur because a wrong strategy was chosen (with probability w) or because an irrelevant strategy was chosen and turned out to be wrong (with probability $\frac{1}{2}i$). These are mutually exclusive events and exhaust the possibilities, so that:

$$f_1 = w + \tfrac{1}{2}i.$$

An error occuring on the second trial after the last one, with a correct response intervening, cannot result from the selection of a wrong strategy for the wrong strategy would not lead to an intervening correct response. If the error does occur on the second trial we know that the strategy chosen was not correct. Hence it must be an irrelevant one which led first to a correct and then to a wrong response. In simple discrimination learning, the probability that an irrelevant strategy would lead to a correct and then a wrong response is $\frac{1}{2} \cdot \frac{1}{2} = (\frac{1}{2})^2$. The probability of choosing an irrelevant strategy which gives this sequence, correct-wrong, is therefore:

$$f_2 = i(\tfrac{1}{2})^2$$

By the same reasoning, any value of f_j, $j > 2$, implies that an irrelevant strategy was chosen and then led to $j - 1$ correct responses followed by a wrong response. The probability of a string of exactly $j - 1$ correct responses each with probability $\frac{1}{2}$, followed by an error with probability $\frac{1}{2}$, is $(\frac{1}{2})^j$. Hence, for $j \geq 2$:

$$f_j = i(\tfrac{1}{2})^j$$

Summarizing the results we have the distribution:

$$f_1 = w + \tfrac{1}{2}i$$
$$f_j = i(\tfrac{1}{2})^j$$

for all $j \geq 2$. The distribution f_j is not a proper probability function because it does not sum to unity. Notice that:

$$\sum_{j=1}^{\infty} (f_j) = w + i \sum_{j=1}^{\infty} (\tfrac{1}{2})^j = w + i = 1 - c$$

In Feller's terms this means that errors are *uncertain* recurrent events, for with probability c the subject chooses a correct strategy and never makes another error. Some of the probability of the f distribution is located at the (improper) point ∞, and the proportion so located is c. This merely reflects the fact that learning occurs in the present model and the subject can eliminate errors. The fact that f_j is not a probability function does not place any serious difficulties in the way of analysis.

All Strategies at Once

We now consider a second model of a subject working on the same discrimination learning problem discussed above, with exactly the same set of strategies H divided into correct (C), wrong (W), and irrelevant (I) subsets. Since a strategy corresponds to any specific cue in the situation and these cues are numerous and finely divisible, consider that the set of strategies consists of a fairly sizeable (though finite) number of strategies, each of which is as likely to be used, and has as much influence on behavior, as every other.

In the all-strategies-at-once model we imagine that the subject begins the learning process by considering the entire set H of strategies simultaneously. In informal terms, he then attempts to narrow down to the correct strategy by a process of elimination. However, we suppose that the subject has only a limited memory and cannot remember all of the strategies at once, but only those with which he is presently concerned. The main disability of the subject in this model is that he may accidentally eliminate the correct strategies. When this happens he is unable to remember what they were, for he can remember only the ones he is still using. When the correct strategies have been lost the subject has no recourse but to begin over with the whole set of strategies. This general idea is now stated more precisely.

On the first trial the subject considers all strategies and chooses his response. The correct strategies and some of the irrelevant ones lead toward a correct response, the wrong strategies and the remainder of the irrelevant ones lead to an error. We suppose that the probability of a response is equal to the proportion of the strategies which lead to that response, so that, if we let N_c, N_w, and N_i be the numbers of strategies in sets C, W, and I, and if we let

N_i^- be the number of irrelevant strategies which lead to an error on the next trial, the probability of an error is:

$$f_1 = (N_w + N_i^-)/(N_w + N_c + N_i).$$

When the subject makes this first response we suppose that he eliminates or sets aside all the strategies he does not use. Suppose, for example, that he chooses a correct response. He at the same time eliminates all the wrong strategies and the irrelevant strategies which would have led him to the opposite response. On the next trial he will have only the correct strategies and the surviving irrelevant strategies left.

To complete the discussion and generalize it somewhat we introduce notation for the set of irrelevant strategies which, following any Trial n, first lead to a wrong response on Trial $n + j$. Let $N_{n,j}$ be the number of irrelevant strategies which lead to correct responses on trials $n + 1$, $n + 2$, . . . , $n + j - 1$, and an error on trial $n + j$. Now we can write the probability of an error after an error as:

$$f_1 = (N_w + N_{n,1})/(N_c + N_w + N_i).$$

After one correct response, the only strategies which will lead to an error are those $N_{n,2}$ irrelevent strategies which first lead to an error on the second trial. The total strategies left are N_c correct and $N_i - N_{n,1}$ irrelevant strategies which have not already led toward a wrong response. Thus, the probability of an error following one correct response which follows a given error is:

$$f_2 = (1 - f_1)(N_{n,2}/[N_c + N_i - N_{n,1}])$$
$$= \frac{N_c + N_i - N_{n,1}}{N_c + N_w + N_i} \cdot \frac{N_{n,2}}{N_c + N_i - N_{n,1}}$$

Extension of this line of argument shows that in general:

$$f_j = \frac{N_c + N_i - N_{n,1}}{N_c + N_w + N_i} \cdot \frac{N_c + N_i - N_{n,1} - N_{n,2}}{N_c + N_i - N_{n,1}} \cdots$$

$$\cdot \frac{N_c + N_i - N_{n,1} - \ldots - N_{n,j-2} - N_{n,j-1}}{N_c + N_i - N_{n,1} - \ldots - N_{n,j-3} - N_{n,j-2}} \cdot \frac{N_{n,j}}{N_c + N_i - N_{n,1} - \ldots - N_{n,j-1} - N_{j-1}}$$

In this expression the numerator of each term except the last cancels with the denominator of the following term, so that:

$$f_j = N_{n,j}/(N_c + N_w + N_i)$$

In our ideal experiment, $N_{n,j}$, the number of strategies which first lead to a wrong response on Trial $n + j$ after a given error on Trial n, is independent of n and is given by $N_i(\frac{1}{2})^j$. This statement follows from the idea that irrelevant strategies are correct and wrong with independent probabilities of $\frac{1}{2}$. Actually, $N_i(\frac{1}{2})^j$ is the expected number of irrelevant strategies which first lead to an error on Trial $n + j$, but the derivation to follow does not hinge on the distinction.

If we substitute $N_i(\frac{1}{2})^j$ for $N_{n,j}$ in the expression for f_j and simplify, letting i be the proportion of irrelevant strategies in H, we obtain:

$$f_j = i(\tfrac{1}{2})^j.$$

A similar substitution in the expression for f_1 gives:

$$f_1 = w + \tfrac{1}{2}i.$$

These two results are in agreement with the one-strategy-at-a-time model. We have shown that the one-strategy-at-a-time and the all-strategies-at-once models are both systems in which errors are recurrent events, and we have shown that f_j is the same in both systems. Hence, so far as errors are concerned, the two models are identical.

One remark is in order. In the one-strategy-at-a-time model, the probability of a correct response on any trial is 1, $\frac{1}{2}$, or 0 depending on whether a correct, irrelevant, or wrong strategy is being used. The probability of a correct response in the all-strategies-at-once model can take a variety of values; if there are a great many strategies, the possible values of this probability are numerous and closely packed. The two models are not at all alike in the probabilities involved, and the theorem that they give indistinguishable sequences of errors is by no means obvious on intuitive grounds, even though the proof is easy.

The correspondence of the models extends to the interpretation of the parameters. In the one-strategy-at-a-time model the parameters c, w, and i are the probabilities of selecting a correct, wrong, or irrelevant strategy. In the all-strategies-at-once model the parameters c, w, and i are the proportions of correct, wrong, and irrelevant strategies, where elementary strategies are taken to have equal weight. In terms of experimental realizations of the models, these two sets of parameters are not distinguishable.

It is still possible, of course, to tell which model is more reasonable by any technique which goes beyond the choice data. One might, for example, ask human subjects which strategies they are using, or one might use memory tests to see what parts of the situation have been employed. The equivalence of the models is asserted only for the acquisition of a single problem, and only with respect to the overt choices made: the writer will suggest, in subsequent work, that recognition and transfer tests may permit differential predictions.

A Random Sample of Strategies

The two models discussed above are extremes. One would intuitively imagine that the subject would use, not all strategies and not just one, but some sample of strategies. The third model, called the random-sample-of-strategies model, supposes that on the first trial and after each error the subject draws a random sample of all strategies. So long as he makes no errors the subject discards wrong and irrelevant strategies by the same mechanism as that invoked in the all-strategies-at-once model. If the subject makes an error he takes a new independent sample from H and begins the process over.

The theorem to be proved is, if the sampling process is random in a strict sense to be described below and excludes the possibility that the subject might choose the empty sample, then the random-sample-of-strategies model generates a system of recurrent events which is the same as the other two models given above.

We again consider the set H of strategies, composed of equally potent elementary strategies. Suppose that there are N strategies in H of which N_c are correct, N_w are wrong, and N_i are irrelevant. We shall interpret N_c/N as c, the proportion of correct strategies, N_w/N as w, and N_i/N as i.

In a random sampling model of learning one may assign a fixed probability of being sampled to each element and let the sample size vary randomly, or assign a fixed sample-size, supposing that all such samples are equally probable (Estes, 1959.) To eliminate the possibility of the empty sample it is desirable to deal with a fixed sample size n. The random-sampling specification is that all samples of size n are equally probable.

The total number of samples of size n which can be drawn from a population of N elements is:

$$\binom{N}{n} = \frac{N!}{n!(N-n)!}$$

Similarly, one can draw $\binom{N_c}{n_c}$ samples of n_c correct strategies from the population of N_c strategies. For each of these samples of n_c correct strategies, there are $\binom{N_w}{n_w}$ samples of n_w wrong strategies, so that there are $\binom{N_c}{n_c}\binom{N_w}{n_w}$ ways of drawing n_c correct and n_w wrong strategies. For each of these combinations there are $\binom{N_i}{n_i}$ ways of drawing n_i irrelevant strategies. Hence the total number of ways one could obtain n_c correct, n_w wrong, and n_i irrelevant strategies is:

$$\binom{N_c}{n_c}\binom{N_w}{n_w}\binom{N_i}{n_i}$$

where, of course, it is assumed that $n_c + n_w + n_i = n$. Since every sample of size n is assumed to be as likely as any other, the probability of drawing a sample of exactly n_c correct, n_w wrong, and n_i irrelevant strategies is:

$$P(n_c, n_w, n_i) = \frac{\binom{N_c}{n_c}\binom{N_w}{n_w}\binom{N_i}{n_i}}{\binom{N}{n}}$$

which is the three-category generalization of the hypergeometric distribution (Feller, 1950).

It was asserted, in the statement of the model, that once the subject has chosen a sample his performance follows the rules of the all-strategies-at-once model. Hence, after any error and the choice of a sample with n_c, n_w, and n_i strategies, we can construct the f_j distribution. We may write the f distribution conditional on the constitution of the sample as:

$$f(j \mid \text{sample with } n_c, n_w, n_i \text{ strategies})$$
$$= \begin{vmatrix} (n_w + \tfrac{1}{2}n_i)/n & \text{for } j = 1 \\ (\tfrac{1}{2})^j n_i/n & \text{for } j > 1 \end{vmatrix}$$

directly from our results on the all-strategies-at-once model. To obtain the unconditional f_j we multiply each conditional f by the probability of the sample, and sum. This gives us the expectation of the conditional f. For f_1 we have:

$$f_1 = \mathbf{E}\left[(n_w + \tfrac{1}{2}n_i)/n\right]$$
$$= \mathbf{E}(n_w/n) + \tfrac{1}{2}\mathbf{E}(n_i/n)$$

However, in the hypergeometric distribution the mean proportion of wrong strategies in samples of size n is just the proportion of wrong strategies in the whole population. That is, $\mathbf{E}(n_w/n) = N_w/N = w$. Similar equations hold for irrelevant and correct strategies. Hence:

$$f_1 = w + \tfrac{1}{2}i$$

and, by the same argument:

$$f_j = (\tfrac{1}{2})^j i$$

for j greater than 1. Thus it is shown that the random-sample-of-strategies model with fixed sample size n is a system of recurrent events (this point is obvious and is not proved above) with the same f distribution found in the one-strategy-at-a-time and the all-strategies-at-once models. At this point one can see that the one-strategy-at-a-time model is a special case of the random-sample-of-strategies model with sample size $n = 1$; and similarly, the all-strategies-at-once model is a special case with sample size $n = N$.

One further generalization is possible. Since the final equations of the random-sample-of-strategies model contain no reference to the sample size n, one would get a system of recurrent events with the given f distribution from any mixture of systems which use different sample sizes. One can withdraw the assumption that the sample size is fixed, permitting the possibility that samples are of all different sizes. The only restrictions are that for any n, all samples of size n are equally likely; and there are no empty samples.

The strategy-sampling model differs from Estes' stimulus-sampling model (Estes, 1959) in an important respect. Let the total number of elements (strategies or, in Estes' case, stimulus elements or patterns) be N and the sample size be n. In Estes' formulations, n/N is analogous to the learning rate θ and controls the rate of learning and all the statistical characteristics of the acquisition data. In the present model, learning is independent of the sample size n/N and depends solely on the composition of the basic set H; namely, the proportions of correct, wrong, and irrelevant strategies in H. Thus while the sampling process invoked in this strategy-sampling theory is one of those used by Estes, its place in the theory is entirely different.

In this section it has been shown that three models of the selection of strategies all lead to the same system of recurrent events. Whether or not this is of interest depends largely on whether the resulting description fits the data of cue learning experiments, a question which is considered in the remainder of the paper.

STATISTICAL PROPERTIES OF THE RAW DATA

The discussion above has been restricted to the distribution f_j, the probability that an error follows the last error by exactly j trials. The f distribution can be estimated directly from raw data, but this is neither a conventional nor a very interesting way of describing the data of cue learning. In this section the data generated by this model are analyzed in several of the ways commonly employed by experimenters. Details are given in Restle (1961).

Learning Curve(s)

Consider three versions of the learning curve. One is the succession of correct and wrong responses by an individual subject. A second is the average learning curve of a group of subjects. The third is a corrected or idealized form of the learning curve computed by adjusting a group learning curve (Vincentizing) or by averaging the data of subjects who are selected after the fact for similarity of over-all performance (Spence, 1956).

According to the present theory, the individual data are composed of a sequence of correct and wrong responses in irregular order, followed by an infinite sequence of correct responses. If $w > 0$, there will be somewhat more errors than correct responses on the resolution trials, and there will be a tendency for errors to follow other errors more often than errors follow correct responses. The probability of an error following an error will be $(w + \frac{1}{2}i)/(w + i)$ whereas the probability of an error following a correct response is $\frac{1}{2}$. An individual subject will produce such below-chance behavior for some block of trials and then abruptly, after some error, will either happen on a correct strategy (in the one-strategy-at-a-time model) or will begin a process of elimination which ends up with all correct strategies. This is an extreme form of the "discontinuous" or insightful learning curve. Unfortunately it is difficult to decide whether any individual subject does or does not exhibit this pattern, so data are usually combined.

The group learning curve is merely the average of a set of (theoretically) discontinuous individual curves. If all subjects have the same parameters c, w, and i, they will nevertheless happen to master the problem at different trials, so that the average learning curve is gradual. Its mathematical form is complex but in general appearance, the group learning from this theory resembles the common "growth" curve (Restle, in 1961).

If one selects, from a larger group of subjects, those who make the same number of total errors, or those who reach criterion at the same time, and averages their learning curves; or if one rescales learning trials as by the Vincent-curve method, the resulting curve will usually be **S** shaped. The writer has investigated this question by generating data which arise directly from the assumptions of the present model, by use of tables of random numbers. When, from a large set of such data, one selects a subgroup of "subjects" who all make the same number of errors, or who reach criterion at about the same trial, and average the performance within such a subgroup, the result is an **S** shaped curve. Exact Vincentizing produces a flat (stationary) learning curve before criterion.

The reason for the **S** shaped curves is not difficult to find; the above methods of selecting or rearranging the data tend to put the (theoretically random) times of solution close together. If the times of solution are put exactly together a step-function should result, but if the times of solution are only grouped close to one another, the step is blurred and an S shaped curve results (Spence, 1956).

Summary Statistics of the Data

In the present theory the actual trial on which learning takes place is not in any way fixed, but depends upon the random outcome of the process of selecting strategies. The result is large intrinsic variance in the acquisition phase, which can most conveniently be described in terms of the total errors made by each subject. If each subject is trained until a long sequence of consecutive correct responses has been obtained, one is reasonably sure that the number of errors made approximates the theoretical total errors.

On the first trial or after any error the subject may either make another error, sometime later, or he may make no more errors. The probability that the subject will make at least one more error, the first one in exactly j trials, is f_j. Thus the total probability of at least one more error is:

$$\sum_{j=1}^{\infty} (f_j) = 1 - c$$

With probability c the subject never makes another error at all. From this it is not difficult to show that the probability of exactly k errors is $(1 - c)^k c$. This is the geometric distribution which has mean:

$$\mathbf{E}(k) = (1 - c)/c$$

and variance:

$$\mathrm{Var}(k) = (1 - c)/c^2.$$

The standard deviation of the distribution of error scores should be nearly equal to its mean, according to the theory, and the distribution should show an extreme positive skewness.

Provided that irrelevant strategies are correct just half the time at random, trials-to-criterion behaves very much like total errors.

Methods of Estimating the Parameters w and c

An important step in any mathematical development of a learning theory is the estimation of parameters. Fortunately, in the present model quite simple and efficient estimates are available. A maximum-likelihood estimator of c is given by:

$$\hat{c} = 1/(\bar{T} + 1)$$

where $\bar{T}$ is the mean total error score of a group of subjects. The variance of this estimate, with N subjects in the group, is:

$$\mathrm{Var}(\hat{c}) = c^2(1 - c)/N$$

It is also possible to estimate w by the maximum-likelihood method. As was mentioned earlier, a high frequency of consecutive errors in the presolution phase is an indication of a relatively large proportion of wrong strategies, whereas a chance frequency of consecutive errors is an indication that there are relatively few wrong strategies; provided that the irrelevant strategies are correct and wrong strictly at random. The method is to count "Trial 0," an imaginary trial before training begins, as an error. Then for each subject divide this expanded set of errors into M_0 errors which are followed by correct responses and M_1 errors which are followed by errors. Then computing the means of these statistics one has:

$$\hat{w} = \frac{\bar{M}_1 - \bar{M}_0 + 1}{\bar{M}_0 + \bar{M}_1}$$

as a maximum-likelihood estimator of w (Restle, 1961).

SOME VARIATIONS OF THE BASIC MODEL

The theory stated above is so restrictive in its assumptions that it cannot be applied with success to a great many experimental data. For example, with the theory above, one must expect the standard deviation of error scores to be just slightly less than their mean, and this is not observed with any great regularity. Furthermore, animal subjects often show a strong tendency to remain with one strategy even if it is wrong or irrelevant, for a fairly long string of trials. The model given above says that the subject starts over after each error, and this simply is not a plausible assumption for animal studies.[2]

Perseveration

The model is quite easily generalized to take some account of perseveration of strategies. In place of the assumption that the subject always resamples after an error, one supposes that resampling occurs with some probability r, which may be considered a constant for given experimental conditions and also a constant during the presolution period. The subject chooses some strategy or sample of strategies at Trial 1, whence the probability of making zero errors is c. The probability that any actual error is the last one is only rc, the joint probability that (a) the subject resamples and (b) having resampled, hits on a correct strategy (in the one-strategy-at-a-time model) or goes into a terminal process of narrowing down (in the all-strategies-at-once or the random-sample-of-strategies models.) For this model with perseveration the distribution of total error scores is:

$$P(0) = c$$
$$P(T) = (1 - c)(1 - rc)^{T-1}rc.$$

where $T > 0$. The value of this model in fitting animal data is illustrated by analyzing a set of error scores reported in detail by Harlow, Harlow, Rueping, and Mason (1960), (See Restle, 1960). Harlow's distributions show a relatively high frequency of solutions with zero errors, along with a spread to very large error scores, in original learning by baby monkeys. The result is that the standard deviations of the distributions are somewhat larger than the means. Harlow et al. remarked on the high degree of perseveration shown by some monkeys. Even more striking is Warren's investigation (Warren, 1959b) of the discrimination learning of cats, which show strong perseverative tendencies and which give distributions of error scores with standard deviations much larger than the corresponding means.

It is not at all sure that perseverative effects can be reduced to the single parameter r, and the writer's investigations are entirely insufficient to support the assumption. Within the model there are several symptoms of perseveration; a high frequency of zero error scores relative to the remainder of the distribution, higher standard deviation than mean errors, and consecutive runs of responses which follow a wrong or irrelevant strategy, such as a position habit, object preference, etc. One can imagine that perseverative tendencies would be strong whenever the incentive for learning is not entirely effective, or when the subjects (perhaps from partial reinforcement) have developed an expectation that rewards cannot always be attained. Something of this last effect, in college students, is

---

[2] The writer is indebted to Marvin Levine for pointing out the importance of this factor in animal discrimination learning.

suggested by the results of Morin (1955).

Complexity of Correct Strategies

In the model above it is tacitly assumed that the problem can be solved on the basis of a single correct strategy. This seems a reasonable assumption in the case of simultaneous discrimination. However, when two situations are presented on successive trials it is a question whether complete solution involves learning one strategy (turn right to white and left to black) or two strategies, one for each situation. If two strategies are learned independently and with the same parameters, then the distribution of errors is the distribution of the sum of two random variables (total errors in each situation) each of which has a geometric distribution. This results in a negative binomial distribution (see Restle, 1961) with mean:

$$\mathbf{E}(T) = 2(1 - c)/c$$

and variance:

$$\mathrm{Var}(T) = 2(1 - c)/c^2.$$

These statements follow at once from the fact that the mean of the sum of two independent variables is the sum of the means, and the variance of the sum is the sum of the component variances. With small c the standard deviation will be about $1/\sqrt{2}$ or about 0.7 of the mean.

An interesting fact can be brought forward in favor of this argument, though the writer has not been able to make an exhaustive test. In a case of successive size discrimination by college students (Restle, 1955) the writer found ratios of standard deviation/mean of 1.1 and 0.9 for two problems—both very close to unity, hence in agreement with the orig-

inal model and with the notion that a single strategy is sufficient to solve the problem. In a comparable study using rats in a successive black-white discrimination, Amsel (1952) obtained data on three groups in which the ratio of standard deviation to mean was 0.65, 0.68, and 0.72. The rat results are in excellent agreement with the hypothesis that the rats had to use two separate strategies to solve the problem. One might guess that rats do not integrate the two habits, right turn to white and left turn to black, into a single cognitive structure, whereas humans might make just such an integration. The present analysis may be useful in throwing further light on the nature of successive discriminations for various species of subjects.

ADDITIVITY OF CUES

In several papers regarding another theory the writer has discussed the additivity of cues (Restle, 1955, 1957, 1958, 1959a; see also Bourne & Restle, 1959, and Trabasso, 1960). In simple terms the experiment involves three groups; one learns a problem based on a set A of cues, the second learns a problem based on the set B of cues, and the third learns a problem which can be solved using either A or B cues disjunctively. If the sets A and B are separate then the third set $A \cup B$ should have measure $m(A \cup B) = m(A) + m(B)$, (see Trabasso, 1960). Experimental results have been reconciled with an S-R theory involving adaptation of irrelevant cues (Restle, 1955).

Generally speaking, the calculations from the present model are in good numerical agreement with those from the "adaptation" model. Reanalysis of three of the most satisfactory sets of data used before, and one set not previously used, are reported here. The other data previously discussed are so fragmentary that analysis will hardly be fruitful; and Trabasso (1960) used such difficult problems that many of his subjects failed to learn at all on the more difficult problems, making analysis by the present model unsatisfactory. In general, the estimates reported below are not the maximum-likelihood estimates because the subjects were not run to a strong criterion. However, since learning was nearly complete, the approximate estimates are adequate.

Scharlock (1955; see also Restle, 1957) ran a place-versus-response experiment with rats in which the relative weight of correct place (extramaze) and correct response (intramaze) strategies can be estimated. He also ran one group with both place and response strategies correct, and a group with response strategies correct and no place cues present. In the calculations below it is assumed that the number or wrong strategies of a given type (place or response) equals the number of correct strategies. This is a symmetry assumption which, while not strictly appropriate for Scharlock's experiment, is needed to permit prediction, since separate estimates of wrong strategies cannot be made on the available data.

Rats learned to go to the same place (using extra-maze cues), with response cues irrelevant, making an average of 9.7 errors. Using the estimate $\hat{c} = 1/(1 + \bar{T})$, one estimates that the correct place strategies make up $1/10.7 = .093$ of the total set of strategies. Other rats learned to make a constant response to different places, averaging 6.7 errors. We estimate that correct response strategies constitute $1/7.7 = .130$ of the total set.

The simplest interpretation of the experiment is that when both place and response strategies would work, the proportion of correct strategies would be the sum of the proportions of place and response strategies, since the same total set of strategies is available. One predicts that with place-plus-response learning, $c = .093 + .130 = .223$. We have the formula that the expected errors to solution is $(1 - c)/c$. Hence the expected mean errors is $.777/.223 = 3.4$; the obtained mean was 4.0, which is adequately close. The discrepancy can partly be explained by the fact that the place-learning and response-learning groups were not run to a high criterion and probably would have made more errors if tested longer. The fast-learning place-plus-response group would likely not have made more errors, since their performance was excellent at the end of the training given.

Another group learned a fixed response in the absence of any good place cues. We assume that this group simply had neither correct nor incorrect place strategies. Its predicted proportion of correct strategies is $.130/1 - 2(.093) = .130/.814 = .160$. The expected errors is $.840/.160 = 5.25$; the observed mean was 5.0. Both predictions are close to the obtained results, well within sampling deviations.

Warren (1959a) has reported data on monkeys in an experiment analogous to Scharlock's study of rats. Warren's monkeys had to learn position habits in some problems and object-discriminations in other problems. Warren also used a response-plus-object problem (object discrimination with the objects left in the same place each trial) and a pure response problem (e.g., choose the left one of two indistinguishable objects.) Predictions followed the same formulas as above, and were extremely accurate: the proportions of object and response strategies were estimated from behavior on object (position-varied) and position (object-varied) problems. When these values were added to predict object-plus-position, the prediction was a mean of 0.67 errors, whereas Warren observed 0.63. For pure response learning, the model predicted 3.25 mean errors and the observed value was 3.04. These agreements between theory and data are well within the range of probable sampling error.

Similar results were obtained by analyzing Warren's experiment on the additivity of color, form, and size cues (Warren, 1953). The analysis is substantially the same as that given in a previous paper (Restle, 1958). Learning data are collected on problems involving only color, only form, or only size differences between the objects. These data are used to calculate the proportional weights of the three sources of strategies, and the resulting values are recombined to compute predicted learning rates for problems involving two or more dimensions; for example, discrimination of a red triangle from a green circle involves color plus form cues. In each calculation account is taken of the greater total number of strategies involved in problems with added cues, and it is assumed that whenever a set of correct strategies is introduced by adding cues, an equally large set of wrong strategies also enter the situation.

Calculations on Warren's (1953) data afforded four predictions of total errors to solution. The four predictions were wrong by −17, 0, 5 and 10 percent respectively, and all of the errors can reasonably be attributed to sampling variations.

The hypothesis of additivity of cues has also been applied to human learning (Restle, 1959a) in an experi-ment which required subjects to learn differential verbal responses to con-sonant syllables. The procedure was simple concept formation with indi-vidual letters of the syllables used as cues, and the same sort of additivity of cues as above. The adaptation model gave quite accurate predictions and the present model is, if anything, slightly more accurate; it predicts (given data on the two cues separately) that the added-cue group should make an average of 5.26 errors, whereas the observed mean was 5.25. Consider-ing the variability of the data, the extreme closeness is coincidental.

COMPARISON WITH OTHER THEORIES

The three models of the selection of strategies are conceptually similar to the writer's adaptation theory of dis-crimination learning (Restle, 1955). The "strategies" of the present model resemble the "cues" of the earlier theory. The strategy-selection model has, as a theorem, that the rate of learning depends upon the proportion of correct strategies. A similar idea is expressed in the adaptation model in which it was assumed that the rate of learning (θ) would depend upon the proportion of relevant cues.

Several of the serious faults of the adaptation theory are corrected in the theory of strategy-selection. First, in the adaptation theory the subject was supposed to begin conditioning relevant cues and adapting irrelevant cues, with a rate θ equal to the pro-portion of relevant cues, right from the first trial of training. Of course, at that first trial the subject has no possible way of knowing which cues will turn out to be relevant—it would be possible for the experimenter to change his mind after the first trial is complete. Hence, the adaptation theory could apply only to a prescient subject. The selection-of-strategies theory does not have the subject treat different strategies differently except on the basis of trials already completed, hence avoids the absurdity. Second, the idea that the structure of the problem (proportion of relevant cues or correct strategies) controls the rate of learning was only a simplifying assumption, with no justification, in the adaptation model; but is an inescapable theorem of strategy-selection. Third, the adaptation theory yielded a determinate learning curve in the sense that $p(n)$ was exactly specified for a given θ and $p(1)$. The variance of typical data was in large part left unexplained by the adaptation model and had to be attributed to individual differences, even though it is notoriously difficult to find any strong predictor of such learning. In the strategy-selection model learning itself is a random event and the model generates variability comparable with that obtained in the data.

Despite these important differences, the present theory is close enough to the adaptation theory to make it possible to carry over many of the theoretical insights, though in modified form. The one type of prediction discussed in this paper was additivity of cues, but other ideas such as the proposed basis of learning sets (Restle, 1958) and various quantitative relationships in concept identification (Bourne & Restle, 1959) can be recast in the mold of the selection of strategies. The many similarities and few differences in predictions must be studied in detail and cannot be discussed here, except to mention that most of the results of the Bourne and Restle paper can be reproduced using the strategy-selection model.

In more general terms, it may be remarked that the strategy-selection model is similar to the ideas of Lashley (1928) and Krechevsky (1932) in general intent. In comparison with stimulus-sampling theoreies (Restle, 1959b) the strategy-selection model is like theories of the observing response (Atkinson, 1959a, 1959b; Wyckoff, 1952), except that in the strategy-selection model there is no conditioning, only observing (selecting). The mathematical structure of the model is very close to that of Bower's (1960) one-element association model.

SUMMARY

A stochastic model for the solution of cue learning problems by the selection of strategies was stated and developed. Errors were shown to constitute a system of uncertain recurrent events in Feller's sense. Three models, one-strategy-at-a-time, all-strategies-at-once, and a-random-sample-of-strategies, were formulated and shown to yield the same system of recurrent events, to be identical in terms of data. This is the independence-of-sample-size theorem. The basic distribution of the recurrent-events system was used to generate a description of the data, and also a method for estimating the proportions of correct and wrong strategies in a problem. Variations of the model, which take account of perseveration and complex strategies, were indicated. Experimental evidence, mainly on the additivity of cues, was discussed.

REFERENCES

AMSEL, A. Rate of learning a visual brightness discrimination as a function of discriminanda durations. *J. comp. physiol. Psychol.*, 1952, **45**, 341–346.

ATKINSON, R. C. The observing response in discrimination learning. Technical Report No. 4, 1959, University of California, Los Angeles, Contract Nonr 233(58). (a)

ATKINSON, R. C. A theory of stimulus discrimination learning. *Technical Report No. 1*, 1959, University of California, Los Angeles, Contract Nonr 233(58). (b)

BOURNE, L. E., JR., & RESTLE, F. Mathematical theory of concept identification. *Psychol. Rev.*, 1959, 66, 278–296.

BOWER, G. H. Properties of the one-element model as applied to paired associate learning. *Technical Report No. 31*, 1960, Stanford University, Contract Nonr 225(17).

ESTES, W. K. Component and pattern models with Markovian interpretations. In R. R. Bush & W. K. Estes (Eds.), *Studies in mathematical learning theory*. Stanford: Stanford Univer. Press, 1959.

FELLER, W. *An introduction to probability theory and its applications.* (1st ed.) New York: Wiley, 1950.

HARLOW, H. F., HARLOW, M. K., RUEPING, R. R., & MASON, W. A. Performance of infant Rhesus monkeys on discrimination learning, delayed response, and discrimination learning set. *J. comp. physiol. Psychol.*, 1960, 53, 113–121.

KRECHEVSKY, I. "Hypotheses" in rats. *Psychol. Rev.*, 1932, 39, 516–532.

LASHLEY, K. S. *Brain mechanisms and behavior.* Chicago: Univer. Chicago Press, 1928.

MORIN, R. E. Factors influencing rate and extent of learning in the presence of misinformative feedback. *J. exp. Psychol.*, 1955, 49, 343–351.

RESTLE, F. A theory of discrimination learning. *Psychol. Rev.*, 1955, 62, 11–19.

RESTLE, F. Discrimination of cues in mazes: A resolution of the "place-vs.-response" question. *Psychol. Rev.*, 1957, 64, 217–228.

RESTLE, F. Toward a quantitative description of learning set data. *Psychol. Rev.*, 1958, 65, 77–91.

RESTLE, F. Additivity of cues and transfer in discrimination of consonant clusters. *J. exp. Psychol.*, 1959, 57, 9–14. (a)

RESTLE, F. A survey and classification of learning models. In R. R. Bush & W. K. Estes (Eds.), *Studies in mathematical learning theory*. Stanford: Stanford Univer. Press, 1959. (b)

RESTLE, F. A note on the "hypothesis" theory of discrimination learning. *Psychol. Rep.*, 1960, 7, 194.

RESTLE, F. Statistical methods for a theory of cue learning. *Psychometrika*, 1961, 26, 291–306.

SCHARLOCK, D. P. The role of extramaze cues in place and response learning. *J. exp. Psychol.*, 1955, 50, 249–254.

SPENCE, K. W. *Behavior theory and conditioning.* New Haven: Yale Univer. Press, 1956.

TRABASSO, T. R. Additivity of cues in discrimination learning of letter patterns. *J. exp. Psychol.*, 1960, 60, 83–88.

WARREN, J. M. Additivity of cues in visual pattern discriminations by monkeys. *J. comp. physiol. Psychol.*, 1953, 46, 484–486.

WARREN, J. M. Solution of object and positional discriminations by monkeys. *J. comp. physiol. Psychol.*, 1959, 52, 92–93. (a)

WARREN, J. M. Stimulus perseveration in discrimination learning by cats. *J. comp. physiol. Psychol.*, 1959, 52, 99–101. (b)

WYCKOFF, L. B. The role of observing responses in discrimination learning. Part 1. *Psychol. Rev.*, 1952, 59, 431–442.

(Received November 14, 1960)

Concept Identification

GORDON H. BOWER and THOMAS R. TRABASSO, *Stanford University*

The learning and use of categories (concepts) represents an elementary and general form of cognition by which man adjusts to his environment. As a conceptualizing, classifying animal, man uses language, and the basic units of his language and thoughts are concepts. Although the logical and epistemological study of concepts and their usages is quite advanced, the psychological analysis of conceptual behavior is in a rudimentary stage. Thus a challenging task for present-day experimental psychologists is to construct useful analyses and explanations of how people learn to categorize and classify their social and physical environment.

The development of concepts in young children has been studied by a number of psychologists in attempts to describe the reinforcing environment that influences a child's use of class names such as bird, boy,, and book in appropriate fashion. In schematic outline, at least, we are reasonably certain of the variables that produce and control such learning. At the other extreme, our knowledge is less than adequate in explaining how certain adults develop or form (some would say "create") concepts that are novel and useful representations of nature (e.g., the concept of the gene).

Much is known about how to teach concepts to others. In the past decade, a large number of experimental facts have come to light concerning variables that influence and control the speed with which an adult subject learns a particular concept. It is our contention, however, that with very few exceptions, these facts have been derived from explorations of the process of *concept selection* rather than of *concept formation*. Concept formation refers to the initial development or learning of an equivalence class *de novo*, whereas concept identification refers to the selection of the appropriate classification from among a set of attributes already known by the learner. This distinction

This research was supported by a research grant, M-3849, to the first author from the National Institutes of Mental Health. The same agency provided the second author with a postdoctoral fellowship, MPD-18070.

has been proposed and amplified by Hunt (1962). Most psychologists study how quickly a subject comes to classify his laboratory environment in the same way that the experimenter has chosen to classify it. Thus, the subject is not usually acquiring novel concepts. In most instances, he already has in his repertoire the perceptual discriminations and names of attributes that are relevant to the solution of the problem. His main job is one of selection, through a trial and error process, of the appropriate classifications that the experimenter has decided to reinforce.

This paper presents a theoretical analysis of concept-identification experiments and reports some new experimental results pertinent to the analysis. We deal exclusively with what has been called two-category concept identification, in which the stimulus patterns are constructed from two-valued dimensions or attributes and the subject makes a binary classification of each pattern by using one of two mutually exclusive responses. The logical structure of such problems can best be seen by reference to Table 1, which presents, in a schematic way, the method for construction of the 2^N patterns from N independent binary dimensions. Table 1 illustrates a population of stimuli constructed from three stimulus dimensions. For concreteness, we may suppose that the three stimulus dimensions are the color (red or blue), shape (circle or square), and size (large or small) of geometric patterns. The two values of each dimension are represented by the entries 1 and 0 under each stimulus column.

TABLE 1

SCHEMATIC OUTLINE OF STIMULUS CONSTRUCTION
FOR CONCEPT IDENTIFICATION

D1	D2	D3	Response Assignment
1	1	1	A
1	1	0	A
1	0	1	A
1	0	0	A
0	1	1	B
0	1	0	B
0	0	1	B
0	0	0	B

Each row of Table 1 represents one of the 2^3 possible stimulus patterns that would be presented to a subject learning this concept-identification problem. The responses A and B are assigned according to a systematic rule: if the value of D1 is 1, the answer is A; if the value of D1 is 0, the answer is B. In this example, D1 is called the *relevant* stimulus dimension since the classificatory response is perfectly correlated with D1 values. Dimensions D2 and D3 are independent *irrelevant* dimensions since their values appear equally often as A's and as B's. In an experimental realization of this problem, each pattern is presented, one at a time, and the subject attempts to classify it as an A or B; following his response, the experimenter provides information about the correct classification. The series of 2^N patterns is gone through repeatedly in random order until the subject achieves a criterion of learning, such as 15 consecutive correct responses.

The systematic rule in Table 1 is but one of many rules that could be used for assigning the responses A and B to the eight patterns. A recent monograph by Shepard, Hovland, and Jenkins (1961) has explored six different types of response assignments, which are ordered in their difficulty of being learned. The symmetric assignment in Table 1 was called a "Type I" classification, and it was the easiest for subjects to learn. All of our studies are of Type I concepts; later we shall discuss the other types of response assignments studied by Shepard *et al.* (1961).

In carrying out such experiments, we usually employ stimulus dimensions that are perceived as obvious attributes by nearly all subjects in our population. Thus, the basic perceptual differentiations are assumed to be already part of the subject's repertoire when he enters the experiment. Moreover, the values within a particular dimension are usually clearly discriminable. From the subject's point of view, the presence of a given stimulus dimension depends, in fact, upon there being distinguishable values of it appearing over the series; otherwise, the values of that dimension have no cue properties and in no way will influence the subject's behavior.

A variety of theories has been proposed to explain and account for the major phenomena of two-category concept-identification experiments. These theories may be broadly classified as incremental or all-or-none, according to their expectations regarding the systematic changes that take place in the subject's behavior during the course of the experiment. Theories of the incremental sort are traditional and more plentiful; the all-or-none theories are of more recent vintage. Probably the clearest recent statement of an incremental theory is that provided in an article by Bourne and Restle (1959). They explicitly view concept-identification experiments as simply another class of discrimination studies, and proceed to apply Restle's (1955) theory of discrimination learning to such data. This theory postulates two hypothetical processes: the conditioning of values of the relevant cues to the corresponding correct responses, and the gradual adaptation or elimination of irrelevant cues as determinants of response tendencies. Both processes are conceived to operate trial by trial at a fixed rate, θ. In a two-response problem, the probability that one of the R relevant cues, k, is conditioned to its correct response by trial n will be

$$C(k, n) = 1 - \tfrac{1}{2}(1 - \theta)^{n-1},$$

and the probability that one of the I irrelevant cues is adapted by trial n is

$$A(k, n) = 1 - (1 - \theta)^{n-1}.$$

The probability of a correct response on trial n is given by the average probability that an unadapted cue is conditioned, or

(1)
$$P_n = \sum_k \frac{[1 - A(k, n)]C(k, n)}{\sum\limits_k[1 - A(k, n)]}$$

After substitution and some simplification, Eq. (1) can be reduced to the following final form:

(2)
$$P_n = 1 - \frac{\frac{1}{2}(1 - \theta)^{n-1}}{r + (1 - r)(1 - \theta)^{n-1}},$$

where r is the proportion of relevant cues in the problem. Restle further adds the assumption that $r = \theta$. This assumption leaves only one free parameter and has the theoretical advantage of directly relating the learning rate, θ, to a structural aspect of the stimuli composing the problem. Using this theory, Bourne and Restle (1959) were able to bring a remarkable degree of orderliness into a wide range of data.

The Bourne-Restle model incorporates an incremental theory because it is assumed that each subject changes his response probability in accordance with the values specified by Eq. (2). If θ is sufficiently small, as it usually is, then each individual's response probability will change over a large number of values between the initial value of $\frac{1}{2}$ and the asymptotic value of unity. The sole source of variance for the model is in the customary binomial variance of sampling associated with a given value of P_n.

The alternative theories we shall discuss in this paper have as their basic postulate the notion that the subject's performance changes in discrete, discontinuous steps; moreover, it is assumed that the performance of an individual subject can be characterized by assigning to him one of two possible values of response probability: an initial value, p, usually near the chance level, and a terminal value of unity. The appropriate mathematical model for such theories is a two-state Markov chain. The states refer to the possible values of response probability, p or 1. The subject starts in the initial state, where he has probability p of a correct response; as information accrues to him, some event occurs that changes his probability of a correct response to 1.00. For the moment, we need not specify this theory any further, since it is possible to distinguish it empirically from incremental theories. After we have shown this empirical distinction and have given some evidence pertinent to deciding the issue, we return to filling out the psychological rationale behind the all-or-none models.

The critical distinction between the all-or-none and incremental theories is simply this: according to the all-or-none theory, the performance of an individual subject should show no improvement over trials before he learns; according to an incremental theory, the performance of the individual subject should improve monotonically with practice. The issue may be decided by inspection of those trials before the last error of a given subject. According

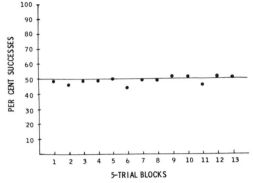

FIG. 1. Stationarity data: percentage of successes prior to the last error plotted in blocks of five trials (Data from Trabasso, 1961).

FIG. 2. Backwards learning curve: percentage of successes plotted over trials before the last error (Data from Trabasso, 1961).

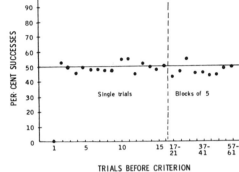

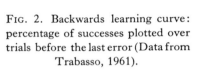

to the all-or-none theory, the probability of a correct response over trials before the last error should remain approximately constant near the chance level; according to the incremental theory, it should increase monotonically. Suppes and Ginsberg (1963) noted this critical distinction between all-or-none and incremental theories, and they inferred from stationary presolution curves that children's learning of certain mathematical concepts could be described by an all-or-none model.

We will present briefly two sets of experimental results on trials prior to the final error; other sets of results showing the same feature will be scattered throughout later parts of the paper. The first set of results is taken from Trabasso's (1961) thesis experiment. Over 200 subjects were trained on a number of two-choice single classification problems. The stimulus materials consisted of flower designs (taken from Hovland, 1953) that varied in a number of attributes, such as the type of flower, its color, number and serration of leaves, etc. These flower designs were to be classified as one of two types. Different subjects had differing combinations of relevant attributes; this affects the learning rate on a problem but is immaterial to deciding whether performance is constant prior to a subject's final error. Hence, we have pooled all subjects for making our analysis. The relevant results are shown in Fig. 1, giving the proportion of correct responses in five-trial blocks; each point plotted involves only those subjects who made their final error on some later block. As subjects make their final error (and learn), they are dropped from consideration; hence the number of subjects involved decreases over successive trials. The number of observations is quite large, averaging around 550 responses per block.

The most striking feature of the successive estimates plotted in Fig. 1 is their constancy over the 65 trials included in the graph. A plot of the backwards learning curve is shown in Fig. 2. This curve contains only subjects who solved the problem (gave 10 consecutive correct responses). The number of observations is quite large (e.g., 213 and 184 on trials 2 and 3, respectively), and again the points are stationary. The probability of a correct response on the two trials preceding the last error is .53 and .50, respectively, neither of which differs from the a priori chance level of .50.

A statistical test for the constancy of the estimates in Fig. 1 has been proposed by Suppes and Ginsberg (1961), and involves calculation of a χ^2 value. For k prelearning trial blocks, the pooled data are arrayed in a $2 \times k$ table (errors and successes by trials). The number of observations in each trial block decreases over blocks. The expected probability of an error is obtained from the ratio of total errors to the total observations in the $2 \times k$ table. The expected frequency for each cell is calculated by multiplying the observations in that trial block by the over-all mean percentage of errors or successes as the case may be. Then the χ^2 value is calculated in the conventional manner from this $2 \times k$ table of observed and expected frequencies. In the present case for Fig. 1, the test yields a χ^2 of 14.41, which, with 12 degrees of freedom, gives a $P > .20$. Thus, there is no evidence for the improvement in performance (before the last error) that is predicted by incremental theories. Instead the picture that emerges is that response probability is constant for a number of trials before the subject learns on a single trial.

One other piece of evidence from Trabasso's data will be mentioned since it is of critical importance to the all-or-none theories. The evidence concerns the independence of successive responses prior to the last error. According to the model sketched above, we expect the sequence of responses the subject generates before he learns to be an independent Bernoulli series with parameter p of a correct response. The independence assumption means that the probability of a correct response on trial $n + 1$ should be the same whether a correct or incorrect classification occurred on trial n. Suppes and Ginsberg (1961) have proposed another χ^2 test for this independence property of the data. One counts the number of times a success or failure is followed on the next trial by a success or failure, summing frequencies over all trials before a subject's last error and summing over all subjects. The 2×2 table for the data represented in Fig. 1 is shown below in Table 2. The conditional probabilities of a success following a success or failure on trial n are about equal;

TABLE 2
TRANSITION FREQUENCIES FOR INDEPENDENCE TEST:
FREQUENCY OF SUCCESS OR FAILURE ON TRIAL $n + 1$ GIVEN A
SUCCESS OR FAILURE ON TRIAL n
(Data from Trabasso, 1961)

		Trial $n + 1$ Success	Trial $n + 1$ Failure	Conditional Probability of Success on $n + 1$
Trial n	Success	1575	1594	.497
	Failure	1614	1697	.487

the χ^2 is .59, which, with one degree of freedom, gives a $P > .30$. This test has considerable power, being based on a total of 6,480 observations. Thus, one cannot reject the assumption that successive responses prior to the last error are statistically independent.

A second illustration of the stationarity predicted by the all-or-none theory is taken from an experiment by Bower (1962b). Twenty-five subjects learned to a criterion of 15 consecutive correct responses the two-choice problem illustrated in Table 3. The stimuli were five-letter consonant clusters. One of two letters appeared in each of the five positions in the left-to-right order. An example is shown in the middle of Table 3. There are 2^5 or 32 different consonant clusters that can be constructed from this array. The solution to the problem depended on the letter in the fourth position: if it was R, the answer was 1; if it was Q, the answer was 2.

The results relevant to the stationarity assumption are given in Fig. 3, which shows the proportion of correct responses in blocks of four trials prior to the last error for any given subject. Figure 3 was constructed in the same manner as was Fig. 1. Again the successive estimates show no trend away from the initial level. The test for stationarity yielded a χ^2 of 11.80 (with 14 df), which gives $P > .50$. Analysis of conditional probabilities, to test the independence assumption, gave results comparable to those reported in

TABLE 3
STIMULUS MATERIALS IN THE BOWER (1962b) STUDY

	Positions 1	2	3	4	5	
Consonant Letter Pairs	$\binom{J}{H}$	$\binom{X}{V}$	$\binom{T}{K}$	$\binom{R}{Q}$	$\binom{L}{Z}$	
Example:	J	V	K	R	Z	
Solution:	—	—	—	R	—	Response 1
	—	—	—	Q	—	Response 2

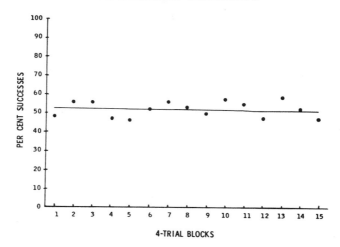

FIG. 3. Stationarity data: percentage of successes prior to the last error plotted in blocks of four trials (Data from Bower, 1962).

Table 2 for the Trabasso data. Again one may conclude that the responses prior to the final error can be represented by a stationary series of independent Bernoulli observations.

1. Psychological interpretations of all-or-none models

We have seen in the preceding section that a subject's performance with respect to the correct classification can be described quantitatively as a two-state process, corresponding to response probabilities of p and 1.00. Accordingly, the psychological interpretations to be considered are restricted principally to those that imply this two-state process at the level of response probabilities.

One theory meeting this requirement has been proposed recently by Restle (1962). He calls it the "strategy-selection" theory. The subject in a concept-identification experiment is viewed as testing out various hypotheses (strategies) about the solution to the problem. Each problem defines for the subject a population of hypotheses. The subject samples one of these hypotheses at random and makes the response dictated by the hypothesis. If his response is correct, he continues to use that hypothesis for the next trial; if his response is incorrect, then he resamples (with replacement) from the pool of hypotheses. The hypotheses are partitioned into a proportion c of correct hypotheses that always lead to a correct response, a proportion w of wrong hypotheses that always lead to an error, and the remaining proportion i of irrelevant hypotheses that lead to correct or incorrect responses randomly with probabilities of one-half. Restle has related the proportion of correct strategies, c, to the proportion of relevant cues and other structural aspects of the stimuli defining the population; these hypotheses will be discussed later.

Restle's theory leads to an all-or-none model at the level of response probabilities. Prior to the trial on which the subject selects a correct hypothesis (by definition, his last error trial), there is no improvement in his average probability of a correct classification. The probability distribution of the total number of errors a subject makes before selecting a correct strategy and reaching criterion is derived easily. The probability that any given error is the last one is c, the likelihood that upon resampling the subject selects a correct hypothesis. The probability that the first hypothesis selected will be correct so that no errors are made is also c. Hence, the probability of exactly k errors is $c(1 - c)^k$, the geometric distribution, with mean $(1 - c)/c$ and variance $(1 - c)/c^2$. An error is an uncertain *recurrent event* in this theory; each error resets the process back to zero, where it starts over again from scratch. This aspect of the theory follows from the assumption that the subject samples hypotheses randomly and with no memory of what previous hypotheses have been tried and rejected (sampling with replacement). If hypotheses were being cast out of the population as they were sampled, tested, and rejected, and if no new hypotheses were added to the initial pool, then the proportion of correct strategies, c, would increase with each error. In this case, the probability of selecting a correct strategy after the nth error would be

$$c_n = \frac{C}{C + W + I - n} \qquad (0 \leq n \leq I + W)$$

$$= \frac{c_0}{1 - n/H},$$

where C, W, and I are the initial number of correct, wrong, and irrelevant strategies, and $C + I + W = H$. The probability that the nth error is the last one increases with n. The probability of exactly k errors is

$$\Pr(T = k) = \frac{c_0}{1 - k/H} \prod_{j=0}^{k-1} \left(1 - \frac{c_0}{1 - j/H}\right).$$

If H is assumed to be large, then sampling with or without replacement makes little material difference in the outcomes expected by the two assumptions. No available data are sufficiently free of sampling error to permit quantitative decisions between the constant-c assumption and the increasing-c assumption with large H. However, some of the results reported later in this paper contradict the notion that c changes appreciably over trials.

The psychological interpretation we propose is but a slight variation on Restle's hypothesis-testing model. We will interpret our results primarily in terms of perceptual acts (attention) and conditioning of cues to which the subject attends. Thus, we will speak of a stimulus-selection process whereby the subject comes to attend principally to the values of the relevant stimulus dimension, and of a conditioning process whereby he learns, in paired-associate fashion, the associations between the various values of the relevant dimension and their assigned responses. In the usual two-choice concept-identification experiment, the latter, paired-associate phase, is apparently very rapid, probably occurring in a single trial. With binary relevant dimensions and a Type I classification, it is really necessary for the subject to form only a single association, between one value and its response, in order to start a criterion run to correct responses. If, say, color (red or blue) is the relevant dimension and the subject learns that red things are A's, by the symmetry of the situation he will respond with B to non-red (blue) things. During the criterion run of correct responses, he can, of course, learn the blue-B association as well. Thus, in applying the theory to two-choice problems, it will be assumed that the stimulus-selection process is being observed throughout, with the necessary paired-associate learning occurring very quickly at the end.

It is clear that the relative difficulty of the stimulus-selection and paired-associate phases can be manipulated experimentally. To lengthen the paired-associate phase, one increases the number of specific values in the relevant dimension, each to be associated with a unique identifying response. Correspondingly, the stimulus-selection phase can be shortened by reducing the number of irrelevant attributes. The limit of this process is a paired-associate task, in which there are no irrelevant cues and the subject's sole task is to form associations between the values of the relevant attribute and the assigned responses. The theory thus identifies an experimental continuum from concept identification to paired-associate learning. A generalization of the model to handle experiments along this continuum is given in Appendix A. No research has yet been done along intermediate points on this experimental continuum.[1] It might be mentioned incidentally that the theoretical unit of analysis changes as one proceeds along this continuum. In paired associates, the unit of analysis is the sequence of responses to the individual stimulus item. In our analysis of concept identification, the unit to which the theory applies is the sequence of responses to the entire series of patterns, without distinguishing whether the pattern on trial n contained the value 1 or 0 of the relevant dimension. From a subject learning a set of 2^N distinct paired-associate items, one obtains 2^N response sequences for analysis; by contrast, for a subject learning a concept-identification problem with 2^N overlapping patterns, one obtains only one sequence for theoretical analysis. This difference in the unit of analysis accounts in large part for the quantitative differences in "total errors," "learning rates," etc., when the same model is applied to the two experiments.

---

[1] Shepard, Hovland, and Jenkins (1961) have suggested another continuum between concept identification and paired-associates which depends upon the assignment of two responses to the 2^N stimulus patterns. The continuum we identify here is one over which the number of irrelevant attributes, number of values of each attribute, and number of responses all vary, but there is a one-to-one assignment of the responses to the values of the relevant attribute. It would be a generalized Type I problem, in the terminology of Shepard et al.

To return to the discussion of two-category problems: We have assumed that we are observing primarily a stimulus-selection process in the subject's behavior. The stimulus selection is conceived to proceed randomly, according to certain structural parameters, until the subject both selects *and* conditions a relevant cue to its appropriate response. Once this joint event occurs, the subject henceforth uses the cue as a basis for responding and the problem is solved. Prior to the occurrence of this critical event, the subject responds systematically to unconditioned relevant cues or to conditioned or unconditioned irrelevant cues, being correct with some chance probability p and in error with probability $q = 1 - p$.

Each stimulus attribute i is represented by a measure or weight w_i. These weights may be interpreted as the attention value of attribute i or as summarizing all factors determining the subject's selection of attribute i as a stimulus to be tested. We will let w_r represent the weight of the relevant attribute and let w_i represent the combined weight of the irrelevant attributes. The relative weight of the relevant attribute defines a structural parameter, r, as

$$(3) \qquad\qquad r = \frac{w_r}{w_r + w_i},$$

which characterizes a particular problem. The parameter r is also the probability that, in a random search of attributes, the subject will focus his attention on the relevant attribute; r also may be described as the probability of sampling the relevant cue in a one-element sample. Given that the subject selects a relevant attribute, there is some probability, θ, that he conditions its value to the reinforced response. Thus, $r \cdot \theta$ is the probability that the critical learning event happens on any particular trial; in an all-or-none theory, $r\theta$ is the probability that on any particular trial the subject leaves the initial state and goes into the terminal state, where he gives errorless performance. In other contexts we would identify $c = r\theta$ with the net "learning rate." We here identify c as the product of two manipulable parameters: r, which reflects aspects of the subject's perceptual processing of the stimulus materials and varies with the weight of the relevant and irrelevant cues, the discriminability of the two values of the relevant dimension, prior instructions, pretraining of the subjects, and so forth; and θ, which is the conditioning parameter governing association learning of values to responses, which will vary with reinforcement variables such as completeness and immediacy of feedback information. Explicit tests of Eq. (3) will be given below, in the section on additivity of cues.

From an abstract point of view, the model we have outlined has the following formal properties: the subject begins in some initial state—call it U for unlearned—where he has probability p of a correct response. On each reinforced trial there is some probability c that he moves into a terminal, absorbing state C (conditioned or correct) where his probability of a correct response is 1.00. Stated in this way, the model is identical to the one Bower

(1961) has used for analysis of elementary forms of paired-associate learning, and its mathematical properties are known in detail.

This model was used to predict details of the data from the 25 subjects in the previously discussed experiment that involved five-letter consonant clusters as stimuli. The estimate of p was the observed proportion of successes prior to the last error, which was .523. The estimate of the learning rate, c, was obtained from the mean errors to criterion. The following rationale for the estimate may help the reader: If the subject has probability c of learning on each trial, then on the average there will be $1/c$ trials before the effective learning event occurs; for each of these $1/c$ prelearning trials, there is a probability $q = 1 - p$ that the subject will make an error; hence, his expected number of errors is q/c. Equating $.477/c$ to the observed mean errors of 12.16, we obtain the estimate $c = .039$. Referring then to the formulas given in Bower's paper (1961), we obtain predictions and compare them with observed values (Table 4).

The predictions fit the detailed data fairly well. It will be noticed that the model predicts and one observes large variance in most statistics. With such variability and with a small sample of 25 subjects, the predictions are as close as can be expected. None of the predictions differ significantly from corresponding observed values by t or F tests of statistical significance. Results of this nature provide encouraging signs for mathematical models of concept identification. In effect, the results establish the depth of analysis and the

TABLE 4

CONSONANT-CLUSTER EXPERIMENT: DETAILED PREDICTIONS

Statistic	Observed	Predicted
Average errors	12.16	12.16
Standard deviation	12.22	12.18
Errors before first success	.92	.89
Standard deviation	.98	1.14
Average trial of last error	25.70	24.50
Standard deviation	28.90	25.00
Probability of an error following an error	.47	.46
Runs of errors	6.44	6.57
Runs of 1 error	3.62	3.57
2 errors	1.32	1.63
3 errors	0.64	0.75
4 errors	0.40	0.35
Alternations of success and failure	12.33	12.41
Error-error pairs		
1 trial apart	5.76	5.45
2 trials apart	5.04	5.22

degree of predictive accuracy that one could routinely expect for further tests of models for concept identification.

2. Additivity of cues

A variety of experiments on concept identification have yielded a body of systematic results relating the speed of learning to the stimulus structure of the problem. The purpose of this section is to show how the theory makes contact with this body of facts.

If the successful solution of a concept problem requires the selection of the relevant cue, the probability of this selection will vary directly with the numbers and weights of the relevant cues and will vary inversely with the numbers and weights of the irrelevant cues. This relation is formalized in the assumption about the net learning rate:

$$(4) \qquad c = \frac{\theta \sum\limits_{i \varepsilon R} w_i}{\sum\limits_{j} w_j},$$

where the sum in the numerator is over the set of R redundant relevant dimensions and the sum in the denominator is over all cues in the stimulus pattern. Equation (4) is adopted directly from Restle's earlier theoretical work (1955, 1957). We shall show how Eq. (4) permits some free predictions in several different "cue-additivity" paradigms, and then we shall test these predictions by some experimental results of Trabasso (1962) and Bourne and Haygood (1959). In all cases, the estimated or predicted c's are related to mean errors by the expression $E(T) = q/c$, where we assume that $q = \frac{1}{2}$ for the two-choice problems.

The first type of additivity experiments we shall consider employ a constant pool of stimulus dimensions 1, 2, 3, $\cdots$, N that are always present for all subjects. In condition 1, subjects learn with cue 1 relevant and the remainder irrelevant; in condition 2, subjects learn with cue 2 relevant; and in condition 3, subjects learn with both cues 1 and 2 redundant and relevant. The theory relates the learning rate in condition 3, call it c_3, to the learning rates, c_1 and c_2, estimated from conditions 1 and 2. The relation is $c_3 = c_1 + c_2$.

PROOF.
$$c_1 = \theta \frac{w_1}{w_1 + w_2 + w_i}, \qquad c_2 = \theta \frac{w_2}{w_1 + w_2 + w_i},$$
$$(5) \qquad c_3 = \frac{(w_1 + w_2)}{\theta w_1 + w_2 + w_i} = c_1 + c_2,$$

where w_i is the combined weights of all other cues in the pool. By elementary algebra the implied relation between average total error scores is

$$(6) \qquad T_3 = \frac{T_1 T_2}{T_1 + T_2}.$$

PROOF.
$$c_1 = \frac{q}{T_1}, \qquad c_2 = \frac{q}{T_2}$$

$$T_3 = \frac{q}{c_3} = \frac{q}{c_1 + c_2} = \frac{q}{q/T_1 + q/T_2} = \frac{T_1 T_2}{T_1 + T_2}.$$

Adequate tests of Eqs. (5) and (6) are not available in the concept-identification literature known to the writers. However, rather than present no results at all, we will illustrate the formula by predicting some results on the discrimination-learning of animals. The material is intended to be purely illustrative and is not advanced to support the idea that rats and humans go about learning discrimination problems in the same way. The original plan for using such data for testing additivity predictions was published in an article by Restle (1957).

The first set of results we shall discuss were reported by Scharlock (1955). He trained rats in a cross-maze having the end of one arm illuminated by a light bulb and the other arm darkened. Three conditions will be considered: "place-learning" rats that were started alternately at the north and south ends of the cross maze and were rewarded for choosing the lighted arm; "response-learning" rats that had alternate starting places and were rewarded for turning right; and "place-plus-response-learning" rats that were always started from the north end of the maze and were rewarded for going to the lighted arm, which always involved a right-turning response. Each condition contained 20 subjects. Average total errors before learning for the three conditions were 9.7 for place learners, 6.7 for response learners, and 4.0 for place-plus-response learners. Substitution of 9.7 and 6.7 for T_1 and T_2 into Eq. (6) leads to the prediction of 3.97 errors for the place-plus-response learners. This prediction is close to the observed value of 4.0 errors. A second example of the prediction of Eq. (6) uses data reported by Warren (1959). Cats were trained on discrimination problems in which position, object, or position-plus-object were relevant cues. Observed mean error was 11.13 on the position problem and 28.63 on the object discrimination. Errors on the problem with both position and objects as relevant cues averaged 8.00, whereas Eq. (6) predicts a value of 8.03.

The second type of cue-additivity experiments we shall consider are those in which the stimulus situation is modified by the addition of new relevant or irrelevant cues. We will consider two experiments of this type. The first, reported by Bourne and Haygood (1959), is based on the assumption that all cues in their experiment had equal weights; the second, reported by Trabasso (1961), uses the theory to estimate the weights of the added cues.

Bourne and Haygood trained groups of 10 subjects in each of 12 different conditions of a two-category concept-identification problem. Geometric forms constituted the stimuli; other cues that could be present were color, size, number, borders, etc. The 12 conditions of the experiment are listed in Table 5, along with the average errors made by the 10 subjects who learned a given problem. The values under columns R and I give the number of relevant and irrelevant attributes for subjects working on a given problem.

Bourne and Haygood interchanged from one subject to the next the particular cues (relevant and irrelevant) associated with a given problem. By this balancing procedure they hoped to average out any unique effects due to the use of particular cues in the various conditions. From the reported mean errors of subjects in a given condition, one cannot estimate the relative weights of the variety of cues involved. In order to generate predictions for these data, we have made the simplifying assumption that all attributes have equal weight. With this assumption, the learning rate for a problem with R relevant and I irrelevant cues is

$$(7) \qquad c = \frac{\theta R}{R + I}.$$

The expression for average total errors is

$$(8) \qquad T = \frac{.5}{c} = \frac{.5}{\theta} \frac{(R + I)}{R} = K \frac{(R + I)}{R}.$$

Using the observed values of T given in Table 5, we obtained a least-squares estimate of $K = 2.24$. Equation (8) was then used to generate the all-or-none predictions listed in Table 5. We have listed also the predictions of these numbers from Restle's incremental theory, which were published in the Bourne-Restle paper (1959). The number of arbitrary parameters estimated for the Bourne-Restle predictions was three; for the all-or-none theory, one

TABLE 5

ADDITIVITY OF CUES PREDICTIONS

(Data from Bourne and Haygood, 1959; incremental prediction from Bourne and Restle, 1959)

			Predicted T	
R	I	T obser.	All-or-none	Incremental
1	1	4.3	4.48	5.5
2	1	3.2	3.37	3.9
3	1	3.1	3.00	3.2
4	1	3.1	2.81	2.8
5	1	2.7	2.69	2.7
6	1	2.1	2.61	2.5
1	3	8.2	8.97	8.2
2	3	6.5	5.61	5.7
3	3	5.7	4.48	4.4
4	3	3.9	3.93	3.8
1	5	13.6	13.47	11.8
2	5	7.4	7.85	7.8

parameter (K) was estimated. The sum of squared deviations, observed minus predicted errors, is 3.51 for the all-or-none model, and is over twice as large (7.93) for the incremental model.

We now use the data from Trabasso's experiment (1961) to illustrate the use of the model to estimate the weights of added cues. The seven experimental conditions of immediate interest are listed in Table 6. Each condition contained 20 subjects. The stimuli were flower designs that varied in a number of attributes such as the angle of the leaves to the stem, the color of the flower, the color of the angle, the type of flower, number and serrations of leaves, etc. All subjects had the same set of irrelevant cues; to this common pool were added the relevant attributes listed in Table 6 for the various experimental conditions. We will not describe the experimental procedure in any more detail here since further details may be obtained by referring to Trabasso's report (1963). In Table 6 we have also listed for each condition the mean errors, T, the number of subjects solving the problem within 65 trials, N_s, the estimate of c based on T and N_s, and, where applicable, the predicted c and T for the additive groups.

Conditions 5 and 7 involve the same type of additivity procedure, and we derive the relation for the general case. Throughout these derivations with the all-or-none model, θ is assumed to equal 1.00; this relieves us of a degree of freedom but does permit predictions to be made. We let w_i represent the combined weight of the common pool of irrelevant cues and let w_a and w_b represent the weights of the added relevant cues. The relations are as follows:

(9a)
$$c_a = \frac{w_a}{w_a + w_i} \qquad \text{with } a \text{ added,}$$

(9b)
$$c_b = \frac{w_b}{w_b + w_i} \qquad \text{with } b \text{ added,}$$

(9c)
$$c_{ab} = \frac{w_a + w_b}{w_a + w_b + w_i} \qquad \text{with } a \text{ and } b \text{ added.}$$

Equations (9a) and (9b) can be solved for w_a and w_b in terms of w_i and the c's. Substitution for these in Eq. (9c) leads to the following relation:

(10)
$$c_{ab} = \frac{c_a + c_b - 2c_a c_b}{1 - c_a c_b}.$$

Equation (10) was used in obtaining predictions for conditions 5 and 7 in Table 6. Inspection shows the predictions to be reasonably close.

The prediction for condition 6 differs slightly because one of the added cues (say, cue b) is irrelevant. For this reason, Eq. (9c) is replaced as follows:

(11a)
$$c_{a/b} = \frac{w_a}{w_a + w_b + w_i}.$$

Substitution for w_a and w_b in terms of Eqs. (9a) and (9b) leads to the result

(11b)
$$c_{a/b} = \frac{c_a(1 - c_b)}{1 - c_a c_b}.$$

Equation (11b) was used to predict c and mean errors for subjects learning under condition 6. The observed c estimate was .029, while the predicted c was .032, not significantly different.

TABLE 6

ADDITIVITY OF CUES PREDICTIONS
(Observed Data from Trabasso, 1961)

Experimental Condition	Obs. $E(T)$	N_s	Est. c	Pred. c	Pred. $E(T)$
1. Angle cue relevant	19.50	14	.0181		
2. Angle, emphasized red	12.45	18	.0363		
3. Flower-color rel.	3.40	19	.1407		
4. Angle-color rel.	4.05	19	.1180		
5. Angle + ang-color rel.	3.45	20	.1450	.145[a]	3.45[a]
6. Angle, with angle-color irrel.	14.65	17	.0292	.032[a]	15.50[a]
7. Angle + flower-color rel.	2.40	20	.2080	.154[b]	3.25[b]

[a] Predicted from groups 2 and 4.
[b] Predicted from groups 1 and 3.

This completes our analysis of the cue-additivity postulate relating learning rate to the relative weight of the relevant cues. The evidence is uniformly supportive to the postulate. The postulate has the additional advantage of permitting one to infer, via estimates of learning rates, something about the attentional or perceptual characteristics of the relevant attributes in the complex stimulus display.

Appendix

The theory proposed for concept identification conceives of two successive processes: a stimulus-selection phase whereby the subject comes to attend principally to the relevant attribute, and a paired-associate phase during which the subject learns associations between the values of the relevant dimension and the classificatory responses. With binary stimulus and response dimensions, the terminal paired-associate phase is brief and the model for stimulus selection gives an adequate description of the data. When the number of stimulus and response values is increased, the terminal paired-associate phase begins to constitute a substantial portion of the later trials. If there are $N > 2$ values of the relevant dimension, each to be assigned one of N classificatory responses, then following the stimulus-selection phase it is likely that the subject will know some of the correct associates but not others. Accordingly, the average probability of a correct response would increase above the initial chance level—that is, with more than binary stimulus and response dimensions, the theory does not predict stationary backward learning curves at the chance level. We have some evidence for this absence of stationarity. For example, in the four-response experiment, the Vincentized quartiles of trials before the last error gave correct response probabilities of .242, .337, .337, and .457 for the first to last quartile. These values gave a borderline $\chi^2 = 8.09$ (df $= 3$, .05 $> P >$ .02).

In this appendix, a general formulation is given that takes into explicit account the terminal paired-associate phase. The model is presented for the general case in which there are N values of the relevant dimension, each occurring with probability $1/N$ in the random series, and in which there are N classificatory responses assigned one-to-one to the N values of the relevant dimension. By specialization of the general model, for $N = 2$ the simple selection model employed throughout the paper is obtained. The response sequences to which the general model applies are the series of correct and incorrect responses, not differentiated according to the stimulus presented.

The general theory essentially attaches the stimulus-selection process onto the front end of the N-element pattern model developed by Estes (1959a). State 0 is defined as the state of the subject during the stimulus-selection phase, before he has selected the relevant attribute for testing. After the subject begins attending to the relevant dimension, there are N equivalence classes of patterns to be conditioned. Each value of the relevant dimension defines, under the subject's encoding operation, a class of equivalent patterns, consisting of N^i members when there are i irrelevant dimensions with N values each. Each equivalence class (or, alternately, each value of the relevant attribute) is identified with a stimulus element. Each element may or may not be connected to its correct response. We identify states j, $1 \leq j \leq N$, of the Markov learning process with the subject's state when he is attending to the relevant attribute and when exactly j of the N values are connected to their correct responses. Let $C_{j,n}$ denote the event of the subject's being in state j at the beginning of trial n. The one-trial, state-to-state transition probabilities, $P(C_{j,n+1} \mid C_{i,n})$, are abbreviated as p_{ij}.

In line with other developments (Bower, 1961), it is assumed that the paired-associate learning between a value and its reinforced response occurs in all-or-none fashion. When the subject is attending to the relevant dimension and an unconditioned value is presented and reinforced, then with probability θ that association is learned. If the N values of the relevant attributes are presented randomly with equal relative frequencies, then the transition probabilities are as follows for $i > 1$:

$$(1a) \qquad p_{ij} = \begin{cases} \left(1 - \dfrac{i}{N}\right)\theta & \text{if } j = i+1, \\[2mm] 1 - \left(1 - \dfrac{i}{N}\right)\theta & \text{if } j = i, \\[2mm] 0 & \text{otherwise}. \end{cases}$$

The factor $1 - i/N$ is the probability that an unconditioned pattern is presented on a trial when i elements are conditioned. Thus $(1 - i/N)\theta$ gives the probability that an unconditioned element is presented and becomes connected; hence, $i + 1$ elements are conditioned after the trial. The transition probability for leaving state 0, where selection of the relevant attribute occurs, is that used in the earlier discussions:

$$(2a) \qquad p_{0i} = \begin{cases} q\varepsilon & \text{for } i = 1, \\ 1 - q\varepsilon & \text{for } i = 0, \\ 0 & \text{otherwise.} \end{cases}$$

In other words, stimulus selection occurs with probability ε when the subject makes a chance error with probability q. Elsewhere we have identified ε as $r\theta$, where r is the probability of selecting the relevant attribute and θ is the probability of conditioning the presented value to the reinforced response.

In the matrix below, the assumptions are illustrated for the case of four relevant values and responses. The subject begins in state 0 and eventually ends in the absorbing state 4.

(3a)

		4	3	2	1	0	P (Correct)
	4	1	0	0	0	0	1
	3	$\dfrac{\theta}{4}$	$1 - \dfrac{\theta}{4}$	0	0	0	1
State on trial n	2	0	$\dfrac{2\theta}{4}$	$1 - \dfrac{2\theta}{4}$	0	0	$\dfrac{3}{4}$
	1	0	0	$\dfrac{3\theta}{4}$	$1 - \dfrac{3\theta}{4}$	0	$\dfrac{2}{4}$
	0	0	0	0	$q\varepsilon$	$1 - q\varepsilon$	$\dfrac{1}{4}$

State on trial $n + 1$

Some axioms relating the state of conditioning to the probability of a correct response are required. If a sampled element is conditioned, then the correct response occurs. However, when the sampled element is not conditioned, then several alternative assumptions can be employed. The appropriate assumption will depend upon procedural and subject variables. The specific assumption tried is that when the subject is confronted with unconditioned patterns, he guesses, using only those responses that he has not yet learned. This assumption seems plausible for intelligent subjects who know that there is a one-to-one correspondence between values of the relevant attribute and the classificatory responses. Thus, when i elements (and responses) are conditioned, the probability of guessing correctly on an unconditioned element will be $1/N - i$. Let $x_n = 0$ be the event of a correct response on trial n; then the response axioms can be stated as follows:

$$(4a) \qquad P(x_n = 0 \mid C_{j,n}) = \begin{cases} 1 & \text{if } j = N, \\ \dfrac{j+1}{N} & \text{if } 0 \leq j \leq N-1. \end{cases}$$

The factor $j + 1/N$ arises directly from our assumption about restricted guessing, viz.,

$$P(x_n = 0 \mid C_{j,n}) = \frac{j}{N} + \left(1 - \frac{j}{N}\right)\frac{1}{N-j} = \frac{j+1}{N}.$$

These response probabilities have been listed opposite the corresponding states of the matrix in Eq. (3a). Response probability reaches unity when state $N - 1$ is entered. For $N = 2$, errors can occur only in state 0, and a stationary backward learning curve is expected. Thus, for $N = 2$ the general model in Eq. (3a) reduces to the one used throughout this paper.

A few results are easily derived for the general Markov chain. Useful results are the distribution of trials and errors in each of the transient error states, 0 to $N - 2$. Define n_i as the number of trials in transient state i. Then the probability distribution of n_i is

$$(5a) \quad P(n_i = k) = \begin{cases} q\varepsilon(1 - q\varepsilon)^{k-1} & \text{for } i = 0, \\ \dfrac{(N-i)\theta}{N}\left[1 - \dfrac{(N-i)\theta}{N}\right]^{k-1} & \text{for } 1 \leq i \leq N-1, \end{cases}$$

having means

$$(6a) \qquad \begin{aligned} E(n_0) &= \frac{1}{q\varepsilon}, \\ E(n_i) &= \frac{N}{(N-i)\theta}. \end{aligned}$$

Define t_i as the number of errors made in transient state i. The distribution of t_0 is $\varepsilon(1 - \varepsilon)^{k-1}$, as was noted before. For $i > 0$, the distribution of t_i is

$$(7a) \qquad P\{t_i = k\} = \begin{cases} a_i b_i & \text{for } k = 0, \\ (1 - a_i b_i)\, b_i(1 - b_i)^{k-1} & \text{for } k \geq 1, \end{cases}$$

where $a_i = 1/N - i$ and $b_i = \theta/[1 - a_i(1 - \theta)]$. The mean value of t_i is

$$(8a) \qquad E(t_i) = \frac{1 - a_i b_i}{b_i} = \frac{1 - 1/N - i}{\theta} \qquad (1 \leq i \leq N-1).$$

Equation (7a) is identical to the distribution of errors per item for the simple one-element model applied to paired-associate data, with $i = 0$ so that guessing is unrestricted (Bower, 1961).

Information about total errors over the entire course of learning may be obtained by summing the t_i over the transient error states. Define total errors, T, as

(9a) $$T = t_0 + t_1 + \cdots + t_{N-2}.$$

The distribution of T will be the convolution of the t_i distributions. The mean and variance of T are the sums of the means and variances of the t_i since the t_i are independent random variables:

$$E(T) = \frac{1}{\varepsilon} + \frac{1}{\theta} \sum_{i=1}^{N-2} \left(1 - \frac{1}{N-i}\right),$$

(10a)

$$\text{var}(T) = \frac{1-\varepsilon}{\varepsilon^2} + \frac{1}{\theta} \sum_{i=1}^{N-2} \left(1 - \frac{1}{N-i}\right) + \frac{(1-2\theta)}{\theta^2} \sum_{i=1}^{N-2} \left(1 - \frac{1}{N-i}\right)^2.$$

The above expressions apply to the case of a one-to-one correspondence of relevant stimulus values and responses. To handle our case with four stimulus values but only two responses, the response rules for unconditioned patterns are modified. In the case of a many-one assignment between relevant values and responses, restricted guessing seems to be an implausible assumption. Rather, it is assumed that to unconditioned patterns, the subject guesses among the r alternatives with equal probabilities. Thus, for $N > r$, the response rule is

$$P(x_n = 0 \mid C_{j,n}) = \frac{j}{N} + \left(1 - \frac{j}{N}\right)\frac{1}{r}.$$

Using these assumptions, the expected total errors for our four-response [from Eqs. (10a)] and two-response subjects will be

$$E(T_2) = \frac{1}{\varepsilon} + \frac{3}{2\theta},$$

(11a)

$$E(T_4) = \frac{1}{\varepsilon} + \frac{7}{6\theta}.$$

The observed average errors for the two groups were $T_2 = 13.36$ and $T_4 = 12.41$. From Eqs. (11a), the difference between the expectations of T_2 and T_4 is

(12a) $$E(T_2) - E(T_4) = \frac{1}{3\theta} \stackrel{\wedge}{=} .95.$$

From this equation, the estimate $\hat{\theta} = .351$ is obtained. If we solve for ε using the observed T_4 and θ estimate, the estimate obtained is $\hat{\varepsilon} = .110$.

There are several points to be noted about these estimates of θ and ε. First, the magnitude of θ is well within the range of θ values we have obtained with short lists of paired-associate items. Second, the ε estimate is just a shade less than $\frac{1}{3}\theta$. Since there were three stimulus dimensions to the problem (color, shape, and angle of line through figure), if one assumes equal weights for all cues, then the proportion of relevant cues is $\frac{1}{3}$. Thus, the hypothesis that $\varepsilon = r\theta$ predicts an ε of .117, compared with the observed estimate of .110. Third, if we use the values $\varepsilon = .110$ and $\theta = .351$, we can predict the standard deviation of total errors using the formula in Eqs. (10a) for the four-response group. The predicted $\sigma(T_4)$ is 8.90 with the observed $\sigma(T_4)$ at 9.74. This prediction is improved over that obtained from the simple one-stage selection model [predicted $\sigma(T_4) = 11.91$]. Fourth, since the initial p-value for the four-response subjects is $\frac{1}{4}$, the average errors before the first success predicted by the general model will be slightly under 3.00 (observed $J_0 = 3.18$). This prediction is improved over that of the simple selection model (predicted $J_0 = 1.79$).

REFERENCES

BINDER, A. M., and FELDMAN, S. E. The effects of experimentally controlled experience upon recognition responses. *Psychol. Monogr.*, 1960, **74**, No. 9 (Whole No. 496).

BLUM, R. A., and BLUM, JOSEPHINE S. Factual issues in the "continuity controversy." *Psychol. Rev.*, 1949, **56**, 33–50.

BOURNE, L. E., Jr. Effects of delay of information feedback and task complexity on the identification of concepts. *J. exp. Psychol.*, 1957, **54**, 201–207.

BOURNE, L. E., Jr., and HAYGOOD, R. C. The role of stimulus redundancy in concept identification. *J. exp. Psychol.*, 1959, **58**, 232–238.

BOURNE, L. E., Jr., and RESTLE, F. Mathematical theory of concept identification. *Psychol. Rev.*, 1959, **66**, 278–296.

BOUSFIELD, W. A., and SEDGEWICK, C. H. W. Analysis of sequences of restricted associative responses. *J. gen. Psychol.*, 1944, **30**, 149–165.

BOWER, G. H. Application of a model to paired-associate learning. *Psychometrika*, 1961, **26**, 255–280.

BOWER, G. H. An association model for response and training variables in paired-associate learning. *Psychol. Rev.*, 1962, **69**, 34–53. (a)

BOWER, G. H. Some experiments related to a learning model. Paper read at Western Psychol. Ass., San Francisco, April, 1962. (b)

BRUNER, J. S., GOODNOW, J. J., and AUSTIN, A. *A study of thinking.* New York: Wiley, 1956.

BUSH, R. R. Sequential properties of linear models. In R. R. Bush and W. K. Estes (Eds.), *Studies in mathematical learning theory.* Stanford, Calif.: Stanford Univer. Press, 1959. Pp. 215–227.

EHRENFREUND, D. An experimental test of the continuity theory of discrimination learning with pattern vision. *J. comp. physiol. Psychol.*, 1948, **41**, 408–422.

ESTES, W. K. Component and pattern models with Markovian interpretations. In R. R. Bush, and W. K. Estes, (Eds.) *Studies in mathematical learning theory.* Stanford, Calif.: Stanford Univer. Press, 1959. Pp. 9–52. (a)

ESTES, W. K. Statistical models for recall and recognition of stimulus patterns by human observers. In Marshall C. Yovits (Ed.), *Self-organising systems: proceedings.* London: Pergamon, 1959. Pp. 51–62. (b)

GARNER, W. R. *Uncertainty and structure as psychological concepts.* New York: Wiley, 1962.

GORMEZANO, I., and GRANT, D. A. Progressive ambiguity in the attainment of concepts on the Wisconsin Card Sorting Test. *J. exp. Psychol.*, 1958, **55**, 621–627.

HOVLAND, C. I. A set of flower designs for experiments in concept formation. *Amer. J. Psychol.*, 1953, **66**, 140–142.

HUGHES, C. L., and NORTH, A. J. Effect of introducing a partial correlation between a critical cue and a previously irrelevant cue. *J. comp. physiol. Psychol.*, 1959, **52**, 126–128.

HUNT, E. B. *Concept learning.* New York: Wiley, 1962.

KENDLER, H. H., and KENDLER, TRACY S. Vertical and horizontal processes in problem solving. *Psychol. Rev.*, 1962, **69**, 1–16.

KRECHEVSKY, I. A study of the continuity of the problem-solving process. *Psychol. Rev.*, 1938, **45**, 107–133.

LAWRENCE, D. H. The nature of a stimulus. In S. Koch (Ed.), *Psychology: a study of a science.* Study II. Vol. 5. *Process Areas.* New York: McGraw-Hill, 1963.

McCULLOCH, T. L., and PRATT, J. G. A study of the pre-solution period in weight discrimination by white rats. *Psychol. Rev.*, 1934, **18**, 271–290.

OSGOOD, C. E. *Method and theory in experimental psychology.* New York: Oxford Univer. Press, 1953.

PETERSON, L. R., and PETERSON, MARGARET J. Short-term retention of individual verbal items. *J. exp. Psychol.*, 1959, **58**, 193–198.

RESTLE, F. A theory of discrimination learning. *Psychol. Rev.*, 1955, **62**, 11–19.

RESTLE, F. Discrimination of cues in mazes: a resolution of the "place-vs-response" question. *Psychol. Rev.*, 1957, **64**, 217–228.

RESTLE, F. Statistical methods for theory of cue learning. *Psychometrika*, 1961, **26**, 291–306.

RESTLE, F. The selection of strategies in cue learning. *Psychol. Rev.*, 1962, **69**, 329–343.

SCHARLOCK, D. P. The role of extramaze cues in place and response learning. *J. exp. Psychol.*, 1955, **50**, 249–254.

SHEPARD, R. N., HOVLAND, C. I., and JENKINS, H. M. Learning and memorization of classifications. *Psychol. Monogr.*, 1961, **75**, No. 13 (Whole No. 517).

SIEGEL, S. *Nonparametric statistics for the behavioral sciences.* New York: McGraw-Hill, 1956.

SPENCE, K. W. Continuous versus noncontinuous interpretations of discrimination learning. *Psychol. Rev.*, 1940, **54**, 223–229.

SUPPES, P., and GINSBERG, ROSE. A fundamental property of all-or-none models; binomial distribution of responses prior to conditioning, with application to concept formation in children. Psychology Series, Technical Report No. 39, Institute for Mathematical Studies in the Social Sciences, Stanford Univer., 1961. (Published in *Psychol. Rev.*, 1963, **70**, 139–161.)

TRABASSO, T. R. The effect of stimulus emphasis on the learning and transfer of concepts. Unpublished doctoral dissertation, Michigan State Univer., 1961.

TRABASSO, T. R. Stimulus emphasis and all-or-none learning in concept identification. *J. exp. Psychol.*, in press.

UNDERWOOD, B. J., and RICHARDSON, J. Some verbal materials for the study of concept formation. *Psychol. Bull.*, 1956, **53**, 84–95.

UNDERWOOD, B. J., and SHULZ, R. W. *Meaningfulness and verbal learning*. Philadelphia: Lippincott, 1960.

WARREN, J. M. Stimulus perseveration in discrimination learning by cats. *J. comp. physiol. Psychol.*, 1959, **52**, 99–101.

WYCKOFF, L. B. The role of observing responses in discrimination learning. Pt. I. *Psychol. Rev.*, 1952, **59**, 431–442.

ZEAMAN, D., HOUSE, B., and FONDA, C. *An attention theory of retardate discrimination learning*. Progress Report No. 3, NIMH USPHS 1961 Res. Grant M-1099, Univer. of Connecticut.

Observable Changes of Hypotheses under Positive Reinforcement

PATRICK SUPPES *and* MADELEINE SCHLAG-REY, *Institute for Mathematical Studies in the Social Sciences, Stanford University*

In mathematical models of concept learning it has consistently been assumed that positive reinforcement cannot lead to a change of the hypothesis determining the overt response. When hypotheses are experimentally identified and recorded along with positive and negative reinforcements of stimulus-response pairs, it can be shown that hypotheses may change after a positive reinforcement. Positive reinforcement has an information content for subjects that has not yet been adequately recognized in concept formation studies.

Various stochastic theories of learning account for the classification or conceptualization of behavior in terms of hypothesis testing. The learning process is described as follows: the subject randomly samples from a population of hypotheses, and when a stimulus is presented he makes the response determined by the hypothesis sampled. In all hypothesis models proposed so far, it has been assumed that the same hypothesis is kept until information is received which infirms it (*1*). As a consequence, the probability is zero that a subject will shift from an incorrect hypothesis to the correct hypothesis on correct trials. The critical assumption of "no-change-if-no-error" has not been checked directly. Indeed, in most of the experiments designed to test these models of learning, it has not been possible to identify the hypotheses used on successive trials. Levine (*2*) attempted such identification by inferring hypotheses from sequences of responses given on blank trials (that is, without outcomes). However, since his procedure did not rule out the possibility that the hypotheses could change in the course of the test responses themselves, identification of the hypotheses could be impaired. This objection may be important, as suggested by the following results.

Three experiments were conducted with three different groups of college students. In experiment I, each subject was given a set of eight white cards; on each card was printed a string of three letters, each letter being either D or K, with all possible combinations represented once in the group of cards. The subject was requested to classify the cards correctly by placing them in two columns, headed by a pink and a blue label, respectively. After the subject had classified the cards once without any clue concerning the "correct" criterion, the experimenter replaced one of the white cards by a colored card, either pink or blue, having exactly the same pattern of letters as that on the white card removed. The subject was instructed to place this card in the group to which it belonged (identified by the color) and, furthermore, to make as many changes in the placement of the other cards, or none, as appeared necessary in order to achieve the correct classification of all cards. When the subject indicated that he was satisfied with his new classification, which might be the same as the previous one, he was given a second colored card. The presentation of each additional colored card started a new trial. The procedure was repeated until all white cards were replaced. As the subject kept all cards before him, the "correct" classification, defining the conceptual problem to be solved, was completely shown after eight trials. In this experiment the problem was the same for all subjects. It is described by the information cards which were given in this fixed order: DKD(blue), KKK(pink), DDD(pink), KDK(blue), DKK(pink), KDD(pink), DDK(blue), KKD(blue).

In experiment II, exactly the same cards and essentially the same procedure were used as in experiment I. But the subjects were given successively six problems to solve, with the same cards, ranging from the simplest (one-dimensional) problem to complex ones (disjunctive three-dimensional). The order of the problems and the sequence of information were constant.

In experiment III, the patterns to be classified included strings of 1, 2, 3, 4, and 5 letters, all 62 possible combinations of D's and K's being represented once. The strings were typed together on single sheets of paper, in fixed order for the individual, and in randomized order for the group of subjects, one sheet being used per trial. The patterns were to be classified by either circling or crossing the strings of letters. After each classification the subject selected one string of letters for which the experimenter indicated the "correct" response (circling or crossing). Each new sheet contained the past as well as the new information given by the experimenter. The single problem, given to all subjects, resembled that of experiment I: circling was the "correct" response requested for all strings of letters ending in DD or KK. Except for the differences in the experimental procedure, the instructions were similar to those given in experiments I and II.

Thus, the three experiments had the following common features: (i) on each trial the subject made a binary classification of the entire set of stimulus patterns (strings of letters); (ii) on each trial the classification of a single stimulus card was reinforced; (iii) the subject had before him a complete record of past information and was prevented from making any classification response inconsistent with this information.

Figure 1A shows, for successive trials of the three experiments, the proportions of subjects who did change their classifications although not forced to do so by the information received—that is, the information card given them agreed with their own classification. The values plotted for experiment II are averages computed over the six problems.

With exception of one peak value (trial 4, experiment I), the proportions of changes on a correct trial fluctuated around 0.20 for experiments I and II, in which the same stimuli and the same procedure were used. The proportions were much higher, ranging between 0.67 and 0.48, in experiment III, which differed from the other two mainly in the complexity of the stimuli and the subject's freedom to select the sequence of information. Inspection of individual data in experiments I and II reveals that changes of hypothesis on a correct trial is not a characteristic either of a few subjects only, or of a particular trial or problem. Actual transitions from specific hypotheses to other hypotheses were analyzed in detail for experiment II. They were quite similar on correct and on incorrect trials. In particular, the proportion of transitions from simple hypotheses to classifications corresponding to no obvious hypotheses remained equally low in both cases. In experiment III the complexity of the task introduced the possibility of clerical errors or inconsistencies that could artificially inflate the proportions of change. But, in fact, changes involving 10 or more individual strings of letters represent more than 90 percent of the changes on correct trials, up to trial 5.

As suggested by the curve obtained for experiment III, the probability of change on a correct trial gradually decreased over trials. If this decline were a simple function of the accrued information or of the shrinkage of the set of hypotheses theoretically available, it should have been more pronounced in experiments I and II which, unlike experiment III, were continued until all information was given. On the contrary, if trials 2 and 3 are compared with trials 6 and 7 the decline, if any, is hardly noticeable in experiments I and II.

There were two peculiarities in trial 4 of experiment I, for which the proportion of changes appeared surprisingly high: it was the first trial on which the preceding information eliminated all simple (one-dimensional) types of classification; it was also the trial on which the proportion of subjects forced by the information to change their classifications was the highest. In fact, the curves of Fig. 1B and Fig. 1A for experiment I suggest that a given piece of information had a particular effect whether it agreed or disagreed with the subject's hypothesis. The peaks and valleys match exactly for the two curves of experiment I.

A tentative interpretation is that, when the set of hypotheses is large (3), the subject "samples" or attends to several hypotheses simultaneously, only one of which will be overt in terms of classification responses. (i) The information received may agree with the overt hypothesis and disagree with

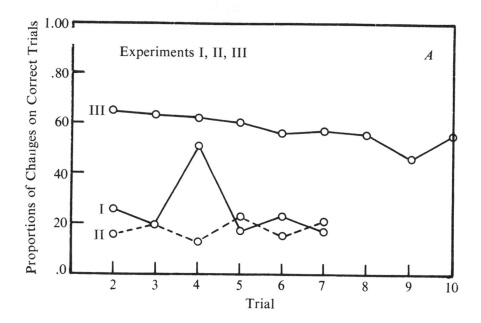

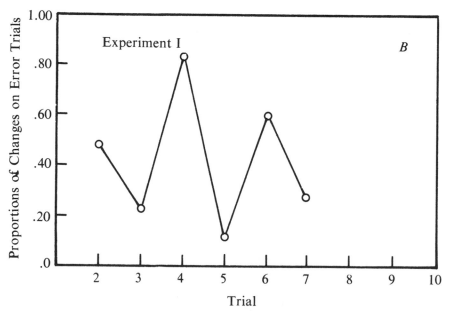

FIG. 1. (A) Plot of proportions of changes of hypotheses on correct trials, for experiments I (157 subjects), II (30 subjects), and III (155 subjects). (B) Plot of proportions of subjects forced to change their hypotheses by the information received, for experiment I.

the covert hypotheses. In this case the subject may be led to alter his subset of hypotheses; this may, in turn, disturb the dominant status of the overt hypothesis. To account for a relation between the probability of change on a correct trial and the overall probability of error on that trial, it must be further assumed that similar subsets of hypotheses were sampled by subjects receiving the same information. This assumption seems supported by the similarity of the transitions between hypotheses, observed on correct and on error trials separately. (ii) If the information received on a given trial agrees with both an overt and a covert hypothesis, it may reinforce either one with a different probability, the reinforcing effect of specific information depending on the hypotheses sampled. This is, indeed, suggested by our data. For example, in experiment I, after the information card DKD was given (4), the conditional probability of a classification based on the middle letter of the pattern was .15, given a previous classification based on the first letter, but it was .00, given a previous classification based on the number of D's (or K's) in the pattern. (iii) It is also conceivable that a subject might sample spontaneously, at any time, or under stimulations other than those planned by the experimenter. A more detailed exploration of these ideas, including a test of Bayesian approaches to information processing, is now being made.

The divergence of our results, for which the assumption "no-change-if-no-error" is clearly wrong, from other studies in which it seems to work, even if not directly checked, may have been enhanced by our procedure of keeping the subject constantly informed of all past reinforcements (5). Our use of a larger universe of hypotheses and a more complex situation yields another source of divergence. At any rate, the present results show that this assumption is unsound for a significant class of concept learning experiments. It would seem that the assumption that the probability of change on a correct trial is zero should be made a special case rather than a postulate in a comprehensive theory of concept learning.

REFERENCES AND NOTES

1. G. H. Bower and T. R. Trabasso, in *Studies in Mathematical Psychology*, R. C. Atkinson, Ed. (Stanford Univ. Press, Stanford, 1964), pp. 32–94; M. Levine, H. Leitenberg, M. Richter, *Psychol. Rev.* **71**, 94 (1964); F. Restle, *ibid.* **69**, 329 (1962); ———, in *Studies in Mathematical Psychology*, R. C. Atkinson, Ed. (Stanford Univ. Press, Stanford, 1964), pp. 116–172.
2. M. Levine, "Hypothesis Behavior by Humans during Discrimination Learning," report presented by the Psychonomic Society Meeting (Oct. 1964).
3. The size of the initial set was $2^8 - 2$ in experiments I and II, and $2^{62} - 2$ in experiment III.
4. Note that this information itself did not infirm any criterion of classification

because the subject could merely reverse his response assignment if necessary.

5. See J. S. Bruner, J. J. Goodnow, G. A. Austin, *A Study of Thinking* (Wiley, New York, 1956), for a discussion of the load put on memory, respectively, by simultaneous scanning and successive scanning of hypotheses.

6. Supported by the Carnegie Corporation of New York and U.S. Office of Education contract OE 3–10–009. These experiments were performed in the Human Communication Laboratory, Department of Psychology, University of California, Los Angeles. We are grateful to Dr. E. C. Carterette for making the facilities of the Laboratory available to us.

February 12, 1965

A Mixed Model

R. C. ATKINSON and W. K. ESTES, *Stanford University*

The pattern model may provide a relatively complete account of discrimination data in situations involving only distinct, readily discriminable patterns of stimulation, as, for example the "paired-comparison" experiment (Atkinson and Estes, 1963. Sec. 2.3) or the verbal discrimination experiment treated by Bower (1962). Also, this model may account for some aspects of the data (e.g., asymptotic performance level, trials to criterion) even in discrimination experiments in which similarity, or communality, among stimuli is a major variable. But, to account for other aspects of the data in cases of the latter type, it is necessary to deal with transfer effects throughout the course of learning. The approach to this problem which we now wish to consider employs no new conceptual apparatus but simply a combination of ideas developed in preceding sections.

In the *mixed model* the conceptualization of the discriminative situation and the learning assumptions is exactly the same as that of the pattern model discussed in Sec. 5.1 of Atkinson and Estes (1963). The only change is in the response rule and that is altered in only one respect. As before, we assume that once a stimulus pattern has become conditioned to a response it will evoke that response on each subsequent occurrence (unless on some later trial the pattern becomes reconditioned to a different response, as, for example, during reversal of a discrimination). The new feature concerns patterns which have not yet become conditioned to any of the response alternatives of the given experimental situation but which have component cues in common with other patterns that have been so conditioned. Our assumption is simply that transfer occurs from a conditioned to an unconditioned pattern in accordance with the assumptions utilized in our earlier treatment of compounding and generalization (specifically, by axiom C2, together with a modified version of C1).*

* Axiom C1. The sample s of stimulation effective on any trial is partitioned into subsets $s_i (i = 1, 2, \ldots, r$, where r is the number of response alternatives), the ith subset containing the elements conditioned to (or "connected to") response A_i.

Axiom C2. The probability of response A_i in the presence of the stimulus sample s is given by

$$\Pr(A_i s) = \frac{N(s_i)}{N(s)}$$

where $N(x)$ denotes the number of elements in the set x.

This article appeared in *Handbook of mathematical psychology*, Vol. II (pp. 243–249), R. D. Luce, R. R. Bush and E. Galanter, editors. © Copyright 1963 by John Wiley & Sons, Inc.

Before the assumptions about transfer can be employed unambiguously in connection with the mixed model, the notion of conditioned status of a component cue needs to be clarified. We shall say that a cue is conditioned to response A_i if it is a component of a stimulus pattern that has become conditioned to response A_i. If a cue belongs to two patterns, one of which is conditioned to response A_i and one to response A_j $(i \neq j)$, then the conditioning status of the cue follows that of the more recently conditioned pattern. If a cue belongs to no conditioned pattern, then it is said to be in the unconditioned, or "guessing," state. Note that a pattern may be unconditioned even though all of its cues are conditioned. Suppose for example, that a pattern consisting of cues x, y, and z in a particular arrangement has never been presented during the first n trials of an experiment but that each of the cues has appeared in other patterns, say wxy and wvz, which have been presented and conditioned. Then all of the cues of pattern xyz would be conditioned, but the pattern would still be in the unconditioned state. Consequently, if wxy had been conditioned to response A_1 and wvz to A_2, the probability of A_1 in the presence of pattern xyz would be $\frac{2}{3}$; but, if response A_1 were effectively reinforced in the presence of xyz, its probability of evocation by that pattern would henceforth be unity.

The only new complication arises if an unconditioned pattern includes cues that are still in the unconditioned state. Several alternative ways of formulating the response rule for this case have some plausibility, and it is by no means sure that any one choice will prove to hold for all types of situations. We shall limit consideration to the formulation suggested by a recent study of discrimination and transfer which has been analyzed in terms of the mixed model (Estes & Hopkins, 1961)

The amended response rule is a direct generalization of Axiom C2 specifically, for a situation involving r response alternatives the following assumptions will apply:

1. If all cues in a pattern are unconditioned, the probability of any response A_i is equal to $1/r$.

2. If a pattern (sample) comprises m cues conditioned to response A_i, m' cues conditioned to other responses, and m'' unconditioned cues, then the probability that A_i will be evoked by this pattern is given by

$$\Pr(A_i) = \frac{m + (m''/r)}{m + m' + m''}.$$

In other words, Axiom C2 holds but with each unconditioned cue contributing "weight" $1/r$ toward the evocation of each of the alternative responses.

To illustrate these assumptions in operation, let us consider a simple classical discrimination experiment involving three cues, a, b, and c, and two responses, A_1 and A_2. We shall assume that the pattern ac is presented on half of the trials, with A_1 reinforced, and bc on the other half of the trials, with A_2 reinforced, the two types of trials occurring in random sequence. We assume further that conditions are such as to ensure the subject's sampling both cues presented on each trial. In a tabulation of the possible conditioning states of each pattern a 1, 2, or 0, respectively, in a state column indicates that the pattern is conditioned to A_1, conditioned to A_2, or unconditioned. For each pair of values under States, the associated A_1-probabilities, computed according to the modified response rule, are given in the corresponding positions under A_1-probability. To reduce algebraic complications, we shall carry out derivations for the special case in which the subject starts the experiment with both patterns unconditioned. Then, under the conditions of reinforcement specified, only

States		A_1-Probability to Each Pattern	
ac	bc	ac	bc
1	2	1	0
1	1	1	1
2	2	0	0
2	1	0	1
0	1	$\frac{3}{4}$	1
0	2	$\frac{1}{4}$	0
1	0	1	$\frac{3}{4}$
2	0	0	$\frac{1}{4}$
0	0	$\frac{1}{2}$	$\frac{1}{2}$

the states represented in the first, seventh, sixth, and ninth rows of the table are available to the subject, and for brevity we number these states 3, 2, 1, and 0, in the order just listed; that is,

State 3 = pattern ac conditioned to A_1, and pattern bc conditioned to A_2.

State 2 = pattern ac conditioned to A_1, and pattern bc unconditioned.

State 1 = pattern ac unconditioned, and pattern bc conditioned to A_2.

State 0 = both patterns ac and bc are unconditioned.

Now, these states can be interpreted as the states of a Markov chain, since the probability of transition from any one of them to any other on a given trial is independent of the preceding history. The matrix of probabilities for one-step transitions among the four states takes the following form:

$$Q = \begin{bmatrix} 1 & 0 & 0 & 0 \\ \dfrac{c}{2} & 1 - \dfrac{c}{2} & 0 & 0 \\ \dfrac{c}{2} & 0 & 1 - \dfrac{c}{2} & 0 \\ 0 & \dfrac{c}{2} & \dfrac{c}{2} & 1 - c \end{bmatrix},$$

where the states are ordered 3, 2, 1, 0 from top to bottom and left to right. Thus State 3 (in which ac is conditioned to A_1 and bc to A_2) is an absorbing state, and the process must terminate in this state, with asymptotic probability of a correct response to each pattern equal to unity. In State 2 pattern ac is conditioned to A_1, but bc is still unconditioned. This state can be reached only from State 0, in which both patterns are unconditioned; the probability of the transition is $\frac{1}{2}$ (the probability that pattern ac will be presented) times c (the probability that the reinforcing event will produce conditioning); thus the entry in the second cell of the bottom row is $c/2$. From State 2 the subject can go only to State 3, and this transition again has probability $c/2$. The other cells are filled in similarly.

Now the probability $u_{i,n}$ of being in state i on trial n can be derived quite easily for each state. The subject is assumed to start the experiment in State 0 and has probability c of leaving this state on each trial; hence

$$u_{0,n} = (1 - c)^{n-1}.$$

For State 1 we can write a recursion,

$$u_{1,n} = \left(1 - \frac{c}{2}\right)^{n-2} \frac{c}{2} + \left(1 - \frac{c}{2}\right)^{n-3}(1 - c)\frac{c}{2} + \ldots + (1 - c)^{n-2}\frac{c}{2},$$

which holds if $n \geqslant 2$. To be in State 1 on trial n the subject must have entered at the end of trial 1, which has probability $c/2$, and then remained for $n - 2$ trials, which has probability $[(1 - (c/2)]^{n-2}$; have entered at the end of trial 2, which has probability $(1 - c)(c/2)$, and then remained for $n - 3$ trials, which has probability $[1 - (c/2)]^{n-3}$; $\ldots$; or have entered at the end of trial $n - 1$, which has probability $(1 - c)^{n-2}(c/2)$. The right-hand side of this recursion can be summed to yield

$$u_{1,n} = \frac{c}{2}(1 - c)^{n-2} \sum_{v=0}^{n-2} \left[\frac{1 - (c/2)}{1 - c}\right]^v$$

$$= (1 - c)^{n-1}\left\{\left[\frac{2 - c}{2(1 - c)}\right]^{n-1} - 1\right\}$$

$$= \left(1 - \frac{c}{2}\right)^{n-1} - (1 - c)^{n-1}.$$

By an identical argument we obtain

$$u_{2,n} = \left(1 - \frac{c}{2}\right)^{n-1} - (1 - c)^{n-1},$$

and then by subtraction

$$u_{3,n} = 1 - u_{2,n} - u_{1,n} - u_{0,n}$$

$$= 1 - 2\left(1 - \frac{c}{2}\right)^{n-1} + (1 - c)^{n-1}.$$

From the tabulation of states and response probabilities we know that the probability of response A_1 to pattern ac is equal to 1, 1, $\frac{1}{4}$, and $\frac{1}{2}$, respectively, when the subject is in State 3, 2, 1, or 0. Consequently the probability of a correct (A_1) response to ac is obtained simply by summing these response probabilities, each weighted by the state probability, namely,

$$\Pr\left(A_{1,n} \mid ac\right) = u_{3,n} + u_{2,n} + \frac{1}{4} u_{1,n} + \frac{1}{2} u_{0,n}$$

$$= 1 - 2\left(1 - \frac{c}{2}\right)^{n-1} + (1 - c)^{n-1} + \left(1 - \frac{c}{2}\right)^{n-1}$$

$$- (1 - c)^{n-1} + \frac{1}{4}\left(1 - \frac{c}{2}\right)^{n-1} - \frac{1}{4}(1 - c)^{n-1}$$

$$+ \frac{1}{2}(1 - c)^{n-1}$$

$$= 1 - \frac{3}{4}\left(1 - \frac{c}{2}\right)^{n-1} + \frac{1}{4}(1 - c)^{n-1}. \tag{1}$$

Equation 1 is written for the probability of an A_1-response to ac on trial n; however, the expression for probability of an A_2-response to bc is identical, and consequently Eq. 1 expresses also the probability p_n of a correct response on any trial, without regard to the stimulus pattern presented. A simple estimator of the conditioning parameter c is now obtainable by summing the error probability over trials. Letting e denote the expected total errors during learning, we have

$$e = \sum_{n=1}^{\infty}(1 - p_n)$$

$$= \frac{3}{4}\sum_{n=1}^{\infty}\left(1 - \frac{c}{2}\right)^{n-1} - \frac{1}{4}\sum_{n=1}^{\infty}(1 - c)^{n-1}$$

$$= \frac{3}{4}\frac{2}{c} - \frac{1}{4}\frac{1}{c}$$

$$= \frac{5}{4c}.$$

An example of the sort of prediction involving a relatively direct assessment of transfer effects is the following. Suppose the first stimulus pattern to appear is ac; the probability of a correct response to it is, by hypothesis, $\frac{1}{2}$, and if there were no transfer between patterns the probability of a correct response to bc when it first appeared on a later trial should be $\frac{1}{2}$ also. Under the assumptions of the mixed model, however, the probability of a correct response to bc, if it first appeared on trial 2, should be

$$\frac{[1 - \frac{1}{2}(1 - c) - c] + \frac{1}{2}}{2} = \frac{1}{2} - \frac{c}{4};$$

if it first appeared on trial 3, it should be

$$\frac{\frac{1}{2}(1 - c)^2 + \frac{1}{2}}{2} = \frac{1}{2} - \frac{c}{2}\left(1 - \frac{c}{2}\right);$$

and so on, tending to $\frac{1}{4}$ after a sufficiently long prior sequence of ac trials.

Simply by inspection of the transition matrix we can develop an interesting prediction concerning behavior during the presolution period of the experiment. By presolution period we mean the sequence of trials before the last error for any given subject. We know that the subject cannot be in State 3 on any trial before the last error. On all trials of the presolution period the probability of a correct response should be equal either to $\frac{1}{2}$ (if no conditioning has occurred) or to $\frac{5}{8}$ (if exactly one of the two stimulus patterns has been conditioned to its correct response). Thus the proportion, which we denote by P_{ps}, of correct responses over the presolution trial sequence should fall in the interval

$$\frac{1}{2} \leqslant P_{ps} \leqslant \frac{5}{8},$$

and, in fact, the same bounds obtain for any subset of trials within the presolution sequence. Clearly, predictions from this model concerning presolution responding differ sharply from those derivable from any model that assumes a continuous increase in probability of correct responding during the presolution period; this model also differs, though not so sharply, from a pure "insight" model that assumes no learning on presolution trials. As far as we know, no data relevant to these differential predictions are available in the literature (though similar predictions have been tested in somewhat different situations: Suppes & Ginsberg, 1963; Theios, 1963). Now that the predictions are in hand, it seems likely that pertinent analyses will be forthcoming.

The development in this section was for the case in which there were only three cues, a, b, and c. For the more general case we could assume that there are N_a cues associated with stimulus a, N_b with stimulus b, and N_c with stimulus c. If we assume, as we have in this section, that experimental conditions are such to ensure the subject's sampling all cues presented on each trial, then Eq. 1 may be rewritten as

$$\Pr(A_{1,n} \mid ac) = 1 - \frac{1}{2}(1 + w_1)\left(1 - \frac{c}{2}\right)^{n-1} + \frac{1}{2}w_1(1 - c)^{n-1}$$

$$\Pr(A_{2,n} \mid bc) = 1 - \frac{1}{2}(1 + w_2)\left(1 - \frac{c}{2}\right)^{n-1} + \frac{1}{2}w_2(1 - c)^{n-1},$$

where

$$w_1 = \frac{N_c}{N_a + N_c} \quad \text{and} \quad w_2 = \frac{N_c}{N_b + N_c}.$$

Further,

$$e = \sum_{n=1}^{\infty}\left\{\frac{1}{2}[1 - \Pr(A_{1,n} \mid ac)] + \frac{1}{2}[1 - \Pr(A_{2,n} \mid bc)]\right\}$$

$$= \frac{1}{c}\left(1 + \frac{1}{2}\bar{w}\right),$$

where $\bar{w} = \frac{1}{2}(w_1 + w_2)$. The parameter $\bar{w}$ is an index of similarity between the stimuli ac and bc; as $\bar{w}$ approaches its maximum value of 1, the number of total errors increases. Further, the proportion of correct responses over the presolution trial sequence should fall in the interval

$$\tfrac{1}{2} \leqslant P_{ps} \leqslant \tfrac{1}{2} + \tfrac{1}{4}(1 - w_1)$$

or in the interval

$$\tfrac{1}{2} \leqslant P_{ps} \leqslant \tfrac{1}{2} + \tfrac{1}{4}(1 - w_2),$$

depending on whether ac or bc is conditioned first.

REFERENCES

Atkinson, R. C. and Estes, W. K. Stimulus sampling theory. In R. D. Luce, R. R. Bush and E. Galanter (Eds.), *Handbook of Mathematical Psychology*. *Vol.* 2. New York: Wiley, 1963. Pp. 121–269.

Bower, G. H. A model for response and training variables in paired-associate learning. *Psychol. Rev.*, 1962, **69**, 34–53.

Estes, W. K. and Hopkins, B. L. Acquisition and transfer in pattern-vs.-component discrimination learning. *J. exp. Psychol.*, 1961, **61**, 322–328.

Suppes, P. and Ginsberg, Rose. A fundamental property of all-or-none models. *Psychol. Rev.*, 1963, **70**, 139–161.

Theios, J. Simple conditioning as two-stage all-or-none learning. *Psychol. Rev.*, 1963, **70**, 403–417.

Acquisition and Transfer in Pattern-Vs.-Component Discrimination Learning

W. K. Estes[1] and B. L. Hopkins, *Indiana University*

Common sense, fortified by a few experimental observations (Hull, 1943; Pavlov, 1927), would lead us to expect that learning to discriminate a stimulus pattern from one or more of its components should proceed in much the same manner as learning to discriminate two entirely dissimilar patterns. The discrimination of *ab* from *a*, say, should be no more difficult than the discrimination of *ab* from *cd*. Contemporary statistical models for discrimination learning, in their simplest form (Burke & Estes, 1957), predict however, that learning should be more difficult in the former instance, and in fact that the limit of accuracy in discriminative performance should be inversely related to the proportion of cues (components) common to the two patterns undergoing discrimination. In the case of *ab* vs. *a*, e.g., the expected asymptotic probability of correct responding would be less than unity (only .625 if the two patterns occurred equally often during the series of differentially reinforced training trials).

We have no doubt that at least for human *S*s, and quite possibly for all animals that demonstrate discrimination learning at all, common sense is right and the model is wrong on this point. Still, an analysis of the problem in terms of the model raises a number of questions to which neither common sense nor the experimental literature provides satisfactory answers. Within

[1] This paper was prepared while the first author held a visiting appointment in the Department of Psychology, Northwestern University, Spring Quarter, 1959.

a pattern-vs.-component discrimination, how will learning proceed on the pattern and the components considered separately? According to some current interpretations the attainment of 100% accuracy on discrimination problems involving overlapping stimuli depends upon the acquisition of an "observing response" (Atkinson, 1958; Wyckoff, 1952) or the equivalent (Restle, 1955); that is, *S* learns to ignore common cues and attend only to those that are unique to one or the other of the discriminative stimuli. In the discrimination of *ab* vs. *a*, *S* learns to respond to the *ab* pattern as a unit, in some sense, but during the course of learning, he should exhibit negative transfer effects from the pattern to the component and vice versa. An alternative view is that the pattern is responded to as a unit from the outset; if so, then an asymptote of 100% accuracy in discrimination between *ab* and *a* can again be predicted, but there should be no negative transfer effects during learning. One purpose of the present study is to obtain quantitative data on learning rates, asymptotes, and transfer effects which may be useful in evaluating these alternative interpretations. A second purpose has to do with some of the specific assumptions of statistical learning theory.

Anticipating that the statistical model developed in relation to simpler learning situations (Burke & Estes, 1957) will prove inadequate, we are interested in seeing whether it can be revised or extended to handle pattern-vs.-component discrimination. The shortcomings of the model may lie either in the assumptions or in the customary interpretations. The principal assumptions are (*a*) that the probability of a given response to any element of a stimulating situation increases by a linear transformation of its

This article appeared in *J. exp. Psychol.*, 1961, **61**, 322–328.

previous value upon each reinforcement, and (b) that probability of a response to a stimulus compound is a weighted average of its probabilities to the constituent elements separately. These assumptions have accumulated considerable empirical support in a variety of contexts (Estes, 1959). Consequently a natural strategy is to see whether a model embodying these assumptions may account for the problem at hand if we reinterpret appropriately the rules of correspondence between terms of the model and terms of the empirical situation.

In particular, it has been the practice in previous applications of the statistical model (e.g., Estes, Burke, Atkinson, & Frankmann, 1957; Schoeffler, 1954) to treat the stimulus elements of the model as the conceptual counterparts of the separably manipulable components of the stimulating situation. In this interpretation, Components a and b in the ab vs. a discrimination would be considered to represent stimulus elements and the response probability to ab would be the average of the probabilities to a and b separately. Possibly these identifications are wrong, and it is not the separate components that act as elements for the learner. What, then, does act as an element? Several possible answers are suggested by considerations arising from contemporary learning theory. In a later section these will be summarized and checked out against our data. In order to be able to differentiate among these possibilities, we have included in our experimental design a number of tests on which components of previously discriminated patterns appear in new combinations. By giving such tests at both intermediate and terminal stages of learning, we may be able to determine precisely what aspects of the stimulating situation, if any, are acting as

TABLE 1

PARADIGM FOR DISCRIMINATION TRAINING

Relative Frequency	Stimulus	Reinforced Response
1/8	a	1
1/8	b	2
1/4	ab	1
1/8	c	1
1/8	d	2
1/4	cd	2

stimulus elements in the sense required by statistical learning theory.

METHOD

Subjects and apparatus.[2]—The Ss were 45 students from undergraduate psychology classes at Indiana University.

Four booths, separated by plywood panels, were located in the experimental room. On a panel at the front of each booth were mounted two 6-v. pilot lights, one above the other and 6 in. apart, and a lever which could be moved up or down from its normal center position.

A black screen was positioned about 8 ft. in front of the booths, well within Ss' lines of vision when they were seated in the booths. A slide projector was used to present stimulus figures on the screen. The durations and intervals between presentations of the stimuli and the pilot lights were controlled by a programer made from a modified Esterline-Angus recorder. Another Esterline-Angus recorder was used to record Ss' lever responses.

The figures shown on the screen were various combinations of four Russian letters, which will henceforth be designated a, b, c, and d, respectively. The letters projected on the screen as figures about $3\frac{1}{2}$ in. high and appeared black against a lighter background.

Experimental design.—Each S was given training concurrently on two pattern-vs.-component discriminations according to the paradigm exhibited in Table 1. The right hand column of the table gives the response reinforced in the presence of each of the stimulus patterns shown in the middle column. By "pattern" is denoted simply the complete stimulus figure shown on a trial, whether it consists of one or more than one

[2] We are indebted to David LaBerge for making the apparatus available to us and to Marcia Johns for the use of the slides.

letter. In the case of the double letters, *ab* and *cd*, the spatial positions of the two constituent letters were the same throughout training. Reinforcement of the upward or downward lever movement consisted in illumination of the upper or lower pilot light, respectively. The two directions of lever movement were assigned randomly to the roles of "Response 1" and "Response 2" in the paradigm. The reason for giving two concurrent problems was to prevent the number of letters per se from being differentially correlated with reinforcement of either response.

Test trials, given midway through training and again at the end, consisted in presentation of 37 different letter combinations. These were: all 12 ordered pairs, 19 triads, and 6 permutations of all four letters. Two random orders of the test patterns were used, one for 24 of the *S*s and the second for the remainder. Since there proved to be no noteworthy differences in results between these subgroups, their data will be pooled.

Procedure.—The *S*s were seated one to a booth, in full sets of four so far as possible, and *E* read the following instructions:

I want to see how well you can do in a rather unusual problem situation. At the beginning of each trial you will see a figure on the screen for about two seconds. About 2 sec. after you see a figure, either the top or the bottom light in your booth will go on. While the figure is being shown on each trial, you are to show whether you expect the top light or the bottom light to come on by pushing the black lever up or down. . . . If you are not sure, guess. Be sure to make your choice while the figure is visible. It is important that you push the lever up or down, never both, on each trial.

During the first few dozen trials, either the upper or the lower light in your booth will flash to show you which way was the correct response to the pattern shown on the screen. Then we will begin having some test trials on which neither of your booth lights will flash. These test trials are included to see if you can keep up the same level of accuracy when you are not being told whether you are right or wrong on every trial. Be sure to continue making your best guess on every trial.

On each training trial, a pattern was projected on the screen for 2 sec.; there was an empty interval of 2 sec.; the pilot light corresponding to the pattern shown was lighted for 2 sec.; then there was another empty interval of 2 sec. before the next pattern was shown. The order of the training patterns was randomized within successive cycles of 8 trials (a single order for all *S*s), each cycle including each single letter once and each of the pairs *ab* and *cd* twice. Test trials were conducted just as the training trials except that the pilot-light interval was omitted. A session began with 8 cycles of training trials, then a block of 37 test trials, 8 more cycles of training trials, and a final block of 37 test trials.

RESULTS AND DISCUSSION

Rate and final level of discrimination learning.—As anticipated, *S*s were approaching 100% accuracy in discriminative performance by the end of the second training series. The proportion of correct responses over the last cycle of eight training trials was .94, and since it was still rising, this proportion would undoubtedly have approximated 1.0 with sufficient additional training. Considering responses to the single letters and the two-letter patterns separately, the proportions correct were .81 and .87, respectively, at the end of the first training series and .92 and .96 at the end of the second. Probably the best single comparison, equating for number of reinforcements and avoiding any complications due to forgetting over the first test series, is that between the proportions of correct responses over the first eight training trials on each stimulus; these values are .68 and .71 for the single and double stimuli, respectively. Thus we find no shadow of evidence that learning was slower on the two-stimulus patterns than on the singles.

Transfer effects during discrimination learning.—If transfer occurs from patterns to components, then we should expect more errors on Components *b* and *c* than on *a* and *d*, since the response correct for *ab* is incorrect for *b* and the response correct for *cd* is incorrect for *c*.

Computation of the mean number of errors per S during learning on each component yields 4.56 and 3.82 for b and c, 2.33 and 2.84 for a and d, respectively. Mean trials to the first correct response on each component in each series exhibit exactly the same pattern. Apparently we may conclude that a response learned to a pattern tends to transfer to constituents of the pattern when they appear alone.

Transfer to new test patterns.—In Table 2 are assembled the two and three-letter patterns tested, the proportion of "correct" responses to each, and the number of observations on which each proportion is based. In the case of Test Patterns ac and bd, the correct responses are of course 1 and 2, respectively. For the patterns of three letters including both a and b, Response 1 is considered correct, and for those including both c and d, Response 2 is considered correct. The patterns of four letters yielded Response 1 proportions ranging from .42 to .49, and since differences among them bear no apparent relation to the ordering of the components, they are not reported individually.

The Training Patterns ab and cd were included in each test series to provide a means of estimating the amount of retention loss during the test series. In both test series these retention tests yielded decrements in correct response proportions from the last training cycle. To quantify the decrement, we may assume that response probability on a test trial is a weighted average of the probability at the end of training and the chance value that would obtain if forgetting were complete. Over the last cycle of the first training series, the proportion correct was .84, and the proportion on the test

TABLE 2

PROPORTIONS OF CORRECT RESPONSES TO
TEST PATTERNS

Pattern	N	First Test P	Second Test P
ab, cd	90	.74	.76
ba, dc	90	.66	.58
ac, bd	90	.72	.79
ca, db	90	.67	.76
abc, cab, bcd, cdb	180	.64	.73
bca, bac, bdc, dcb, dbc	225	.60	.65
abd, dab, acd	135	.38	.39
$bda, bad, adb, dba, dca,$ dac, cad	315	.47	.39

was .74. Letting r be our coefficient of retention, and assuming that test probability would be .5 if forgetting were complete, we can write $.74 = .84r + .5(1-r)$, yielding $r = .7$ for the desired estimate. Similarly, for the second test series, we obtain $r = .6$.

The remaining types of test combinations shown in Table 2 were designed to differentiate between two interpretations which may for brevity be designated the *component hypothesis* and the *pattern hypothesis*, respectively. According to the former, the probability of a response to any given component should tend to approach the marginal relative frequency with which the response is reinforced over all training trials on which the component occurs, whether alone or in combination with others. From Table 1 one can readily calculate that for Response 1 and Components a and b, these relative frequencies are 1.0 and .67, respectively, and similarly for Response 2 in relation to Components d and c, respectively. These are, then, the values which should be averaged in order to predict the asymptotic probabilities of correct responses on test trials. For Test Pattern ba the predicted value is $.5(1.0 + .67) = .83$, for ac (recalling that Response 1 is des-

TABLE 3

THEORETICAL ASYMPTOTIC PROBABILITIES OF
CORRECT RESPONSES TO TEST PATTERNS,
CORRECTED FOR RETENTION LOSS

Pattern	Component Hypothesis	"Molecular" Pattern Hypothesis	"Molar" Pattern Hypothesis
ba	.71	.50	.50
ac	.61	.82	.82
abc	.61	.61	.82
bca	.61	.61	.61
abd	.53	.39	.50
bda	.53	.39	.39

ignated "correct") $.5(1.0+.33)=.67$, for abc $.33(1.0+.67+.33)=.67$, for abd $.33(1.0+.67+0)=.55$, and so on.

According to the pattern hypothesis, the probability of a response to any component or combination of components should tend to approach the relative frequency with which the response is reinforced during training on trials when that component or combination occurs as a pattern. From Table 1 it is apparent that these relative frequencies for Response 1 and Patterns a, b, and ab are 1, 0, and 1, respectively, and it is these values that should be averaged to predict correct response probabilities to test patterns. For Test Pattern ba, the predicted value is .5, for ac 1.0; for abc it is .67 or 1.0 depending on whether a and b separately or ab as a unitary pattern take the role of elements in mediating the transfer, and similarly for abd it is either .33 or .5.

If one of these hypotheses is substantially correct, then the effect of the two training series should be to move the test probabilities progressively away from the original chance level and toward the predicted asymptotic values. It should be noted that in the present experiment the test probabilities cannot be expected to reach the appropriate asymptotic

values, for discrimination training was terminated somewhat short of asymptote and also there was some retention loss over the test series. Having available the results of the retention tests with the training patterns, we can, however, correct the theoretical test probabilities obtained above for retention loss. The "coefficient of retention" r was found to be .7 and .6 for the first and second test series; the mean of these two values has been used in computing the corrected theoretical values shown in Table 3 (corrected value = uncorrected value $\times .65 + .5 \times .35$). For brevity, the first entry under "Pattern" in any row of Table 2 is used to designate the corresponding row of Table 3. Only six rows are needed in Table 3 since all three hypotheses yield the same predictions for the third and fourth rows of Table 2. The labels "molecular" and "molar" in the headings of the last two columns of Table 3 refer to the two forms of the pattern hypothesis; according to the former, a and b (or c and d) separately should behave as elements in mediating transfer to test triads, whereas according to the latter the combination ab (or cd) should behave as an element.

Consideration of the first two rows of Table 3 is sufficient to dispose of the component hypothesis. Comparing these with the corresponding ba and ac rows of Table 2, we see that the test probabilities differ considerably from the predicted values on the first test and move further away on the second test in each instance.

On the other hand, the data for the test pairs appear quite compatible with the pattern hypothesis. In each case the observed proportion moves substantially in the direction of the predicted asymptote between the first and second test and is about as close on the second test as could be expected, considering that the final level of correct responding on the single letters during training was only .92. On test triads of the type *bca* and *bda*, where members of a training pair do not appear in their original arrangement, predictions are again the same for both versions of the pattern hypothesis. For the former, the observed values of .60 and .65 are quite close to the theoretical .61; for the latter, the first test result of .47 is far short but the second test result of .39 agrees with the common prediction.

To differentiate between the "molecular" and "molar" forms of the pattern hypothesis, we must turn to the remaining two test triads. In the case of type *abc*, both observed proportions fall between the two theoretical values, but the change from the first to the second test is distinctly in the direction of the "molar" outcome. In the case of type *abd*, the first test result agrees well with the "molecular" prediction; the change from the first to the second test is in the direction of the "molar" outcome, but the shift is small and does not approach statistical significance ($SE_p = .04$ on each test). Apparently in these ambiguous cases either *a* and *b* separately or the combination *ab* may be responded to as units, but the likelihood of the latter result increases relative to the former as training progresses. The difference in amounts of change between first and second tests for the triads *abc* and *abd* is quite in line with this interpretation. For Ss who had not mastered the discrimination at the time of the first test, and who thus still had chance probabilities of correct response to some or all of the training stimuli, continued learning relative either to the separate compo-

nents or to the two-letter pattern would lead to further increase in the probability of correct response to Test Pattern *abc*. In the case of *abd*, however, learning relative to the separate components would tend to move the test probability downward toward the "molecular" asymptote while learning relative to Pattern *ab* would tend to hold the test probability at .5.

It should be remarked that our data provide no grounds for assuming that the test probabilities specified by the "molar" form of the pattern hypothesis would in all cases be reached with sufficient training. Asymptotic probabilities of response to ambiguous test patterns may well depend on the relative frequencies with which the various subpatterns occur during training.

Theoretical implications.—With respect to the two assumptions of statistical learning theory mentioned earlier, both the "linear operator" representing effects of reinforcement and the "averaging rule" for response to new stimulus compounds receive quantitative confirmation, once it has been determined precisely what aspects of the stimulating situation function as "elements" under the type of experimental arrangement used in this study. These assumptions, appropriately interpreted, apparently account for the discrimination asymptotes, the relative rates of learning on patterns and components, and the probabilities of response to test patterns. One qualification needs emphasis, however.

In previously published applications of the theory to discrimination learning (e.g., Burke & Estes, 1957; Estes et al., 1957), it has been assumed that the probability p_{hi} of response i to stimulus component h changes in accordance with the function

$$p_{hi,n+1} = (1 - \theta)p_{hi,n} + \theta,$$

$(0 < \theta \leq 1)$, upon each occasion when response i is reinforced in the presence of component h, whether h occurs alone or in combination with other components. The transfer effects observed during learning indicate that this assumption may hold during the earlier part of discrimination training even in the pattern-vs.-component situation. But once i has been conditioned to h by virtue of reinforcement on trials involving h alone as the stimulus pattern, the probability of response i to h alone is unaffected by the reinforcement of other responses on later trials when h occurs as a component of a larger pattern.

SUMMARY

Training was given human Ss concurrently on two problems requiring the discrimination of stimulus patterns from subpatterns. Midway through the learning series and again at the end, nonreinforced test trials were given with new compounds of the training stimuli.

During the learning series, the probability of a given response to any stimulus pattern or subpattern was found to approach the relative frequency with which it had been reinforced in the presence of that stimulus alone. Results of the test trials support the assumption that probability of a response to a novel compound is a weighted mean of its probabilities to the constituents. When the test compound is unambiguous, i.e., none of the training patterns appears in it intact, the response probability is simply the arithmetic mean of the component probabilities. When the test compound is ambiguous, i.e., one of the training patterns appears as a component of the test compound, Ss may respond either to the training pattern or to its subpatterns as units, the pattern apparently becoming increasingly dominant over its constituents as training progresses.

REFERENCES

ATKINSON, R. C. A Markov model for discrimination learning. *Psychometrika*, 1958, **23**, 309–22.

BURKE, C. J., & ESTES, W. K. A component model for stimulus variables in discrimination learning. *Psychometrika*, 1957, **22**, 133–45.

ESTES, W. K. The statistical approach to learning theory. In S. Koch (Ed.), *Psychology: A study of a science.* Vol. 2. New York: McGraw-Hill, 1959.

ESTES, W. K., BURKE, C. J., ATKINSON, R. C., & FRANKMANN, J. P. Probabilistic discrimination learning. *J. exp. Psychol.*, 1957, **54**, 233–39.

HULL, C. L. *Principles of behavior.* New York: Appleton-Century-Crofts, 1943.

PAVLOV, I. P. *Conditioned reflexes.* (Trans. by G. V. Anrep) London: Oxford Univer. Press, 1927.

RESTLE, F. A theory of discrimination learning. *Psychol. Rev.*, 1955, 62, 11–19.

SCHOEFFLER, M. S. Probability of response to compounds of discriminated stimuli. *J. exp. Psychol.*, 1954, **48**, 323–29.

WYCKOFF, L. B., JR. The role of observing responses in discrimination learning. *Psychol. Rev.*, 1952, **59**, 431–42.

(Received March 7, 1960)

Transfer Effects in Discrimination Learning[1]

MORTON P. FRIEDMAN and HAROLD GELFAND,[2]
University of California, Los Angeles

Transfer effects which occur during the discrimination of overlapping stimulus compounds were analyzed. The learning materials were paired associates whose stimulus members were simple stimulus compounds. The compounds and responses received a single pairing (reinforcement) and the compounds were presented alone after either 12 or 27 seconds as a test for recall. In different experimental conditions, compounds with common cues were inserted in the training series either before or after reinforcement of the test compound and before recall. Experimental arrangements which might be expected to produce both positive and negative transfer were employed. The principal results were: (1) recall decreased as a function of the interval between reinforcement and test, (2) evidence was found for proactive but not retroactive interference mediated by the common cues, and (3) both proactive and retroactive facilitation mediated by the common cues was obtained. A mixed model arising from stimulus sampling theory was developed for the results. This model, which was in essence an all-or-none retention process coupled with a cue selection process generally did quite well. However, the model failed to provide an adequate description of the obtained proactive interference effects.

This study is concerned with a quantitative analysis of transfer effects which occur during the discrimination of stimulus compounds with common cues. Experimental arrangements which might be expected to produce both positive and negative transfer are considered. For example, in learning a discrimination between the stimulus compounds ab and ac, one would expect negative transfer early in training mediated by the common cue a, but one would also expect that the terminal accuracy of discrimination would reach 100%. Similarly, in a learning task in which the compounds ab and ac were assigned the same response, one would expect positive transfer mediated by the common cue a.

Exactly how to conceptualize common cues in discrimination learning is a problem of some theoretical interest. Within the framework of stimulus sampling theory (for an extensive review see Atkinson and Estes, 1963), two alternative formulations, the

[1] This research was supported in part by a grant from the University Research Committee, University of California, Los Angeles, and in part by the Office of Naval Research (Nonr 233(58)).
[2] Now at the University of Michigan, Ann Arbor.

This article appeared in *J. math. Psychol.*, 1964, **1**, 204–214.

component model (Burke and Estes, 1957) and the pattern model (Estes, 1959), have been suggested to handle discrimination problems with stimulus overlap. The component model correctly predicts the transfer effects which occur early in training, but in the negative transfer example cited above, it predicts less than 100% accuracy of discrimination. On the other hand, the pattern model correctly predicts the asymptotic accuracy of discrimination but fails to predict the transfer effects which occur during training.

Estes and Hopkins (1961), Friedman (1962), and Atkinson and Estes (1963) have suggested some modifications of the pattern model in order to allow a more complete description of simple overlap discrimination problems. The gist of the modified pattern model, termed the "mixed model" is that association or conditioning takes place in terms of patterns, but transfer to new or unconditioned patterns is mediated by responding to component cues.

As an example, consider a discrimination between the compounds *ab* and *ac*. The compounds are presented in random order, response 1 is reinforced in the presence of *ab*, and response 2 is reinforced in the presence of *ac*. According to the mixed model, patterns associated with these compounds will be conditioned separately as units. Once a pattern is conditioned to a response, it will continue to evoke that response on later trials. Thus the stimulus sampling and conditioning assumptions of the mixed model are like those of the simple pattern model. But consider a point in training at which the pattern associated with *ab* is conditioned to response 1, but *ac* is not yet conditioned. Then, according to the mixed model, responding in the presence of *ac* is determined by the conditioning status of the component cues. And, since cue *a* is conditioned to response 1 by virtue of its being a component of the conditioned pattern *ab*, response 1 is likely to occur in the presence of *ac*.

Some of the mixed model's qualitative predictions concerning relative rates of learning and error analyses do quite well, but there are no data detailing the specific trial-by-trial transfer effects which occur during the learning of compounds with common cues. These sorts of data are important for testing both alternative learning assumptions and alternative response rules. The present study was designed to obtain these transfer effects.

METHOD

Subjects. The subjects were 48 students recruited from introductory psychology classes at the University of California, Los Angeles. Participation in experiments was a course requirement.

Procedure. In all experimental conditions, paired associates items were presented together for 3 seconds, which will be denoted the reinforcement, and stimulus members were presented alone for 3 seconds and either 12 or 27 seconds later as a test for recall. Following a procedure used by Peterson, Saltzman, Hillner, and Land (1962), intervals between reinforcement and test on a given item were filled with presentations and tests on other items. The stimulus members of the paired associates were two-element coumpounds. The elements comprising the compounds were common monosyllabic 3-letter English words, and the responses were the digits 1-9. A Hunter Cardmaster was used to present the items, and the inter-item interval was 2 seconds. Subjects were instructed to read the words and numbers aloud when they appeared, and to supply the number when only the words were presented. They were urged to guess, and there were less than 1 % omissions.

Design. A subjects-by-treatments design was employed so that all subjects received all experimental conditions. There were seven experimental conditions in all. The training paradigms for the various conditions are shown in Table 1. The cues comprising the compounds are denoted by letters, and the responses by numbers.

TABLE 1

TRAINING PARADIGMS AND OBTAINED AND PREDICTED PROPORTION OF CORRECT
RECALLS FOR THE SEVEN EXPERIMENTAL CONDITIONS

Experimental condition	Training paradigm			Proportion correct recalls	
	R_1	R_2	T	Obtained	Predicted
Retroaction Control	ab-1	cd-2	ab	0.243	[a]
Proaction Control	cd-2	ab-1	ab	0.375	[a]
2-Reinforcement Control	ab-1	ab-1	ab	0.583	0.559
Retroactive Interference	ab-1	ac-2	ab	0.229	0.215
Intrusion errors				0.263	0.319
Proactive Interference	ac-2	ab-1	ab	0.319	0.363
Intrusion errors				0.167	0.171
Retroactive Facilitation	ab-1	ac-1	ab	0.479	0.467
Proactive Facilitation	ac-1	ab-1	ab	0.461	0.467

[a] These conditions were used to estimate parameters.

All experimental conditions consisted of two reinforced presentation of compounds which are denoted by "R_1" and "R_2" in Table 1, and a single test on one of the compounds, which is denoted by "T." The interval between R_1 and R_2 and R_2 and T was always 12 seconds.

Items in the first condition, Retroaction Control, received one reinforcement and were tested 27 seconds later for recall. Compounds intervening between reinforcement and test had no cues in common with test items. Table 2 contains a sample list of items which gives examples of the various experimental conditions. The Retroaction Control item is the first one on the list. The compound was "eat lie," and the response was "3." Between reinforcement and test there were 5 items or 27 seconds. Thus at number 7 on the list, the compound "eat lie" is presented for recall. The Retroaction Control condition is to be compared with the Retroactive Interference and Retroactive Facilitation conditions. Items in the Retroactive Interference condition also received one reinforced presentation and were tested 27 seconds later for recall, but 12 seconds after the reinforced presentation of the test compound, a compound with a common cue but a different response assignment was inserted in the training series. The Retroactive Interference item on the sample list in Table 2 starts with number 12. The compound "hip rag" is paired with the response "1" and is tested for recall at number 18. But between reinforcement and test, at number 15, the compound "hip ore," paired with a different response "8" but with the common cue "hip," is presented. Items in the Retroactive Facilitation condition were like items in the Retroactive Interference condition except that the inserted compounds were assigned the same response as the test compound.

TABLE 2

SAMPLE LIST OF ITEMS

No.	Condition	Item
1	Retro. Con. (R_1)	eat lie 3
2	Filler	gem dip
3	Retro. Facil. (R_1)	nor top 2
4	Retro. Con. (R_2)	ant saw 6
5	Pro. Inter. (R_1)	pig bet 4
6	Retro. Facil. (R_2)	urn top 2
7	Retro. Con. (T)	eat lie
8	Pro. Inter. (R_2)	sin bet 7
9	Retro. Facil. (T)	nor top
10	2 Rein. Con. (R_1)	but lit 5
11	Pro. Inter. (T)	sin bet
12	Retro. Inter. (R)	hip rag 1
13	2 Rein. Con. (R_2)	but lit 5
14	Pro. Facil. (R_1)	dug his 9
15	Retro. Inter. (R_2)	hip ore 8
16	2 Rein. Con. (T)	but lit
17	Pro. Facil. (R_2)	dug ash 9
18	Retro. Inter. (T)	hip rag
19	Pro. Con. (R_1)	sky rut 3
20	Pro. Facil. (T)	dug ash
21	Filler	pad she 2
22	Pro. Con. (R_2)	yes pry 6
23	Filler	row sap 9
24	Filler	pal mix 1
25	Pro. Con. (T)	yes pry

Items in the Proaction Control condition received one reinforced presentation and were tested 12 seconds later for recall. Items in the Proactive Interference condition were also tested 12 seconds after a reinforced presentation for recall but were preceded by the presentation of a compound with a common cue but with a different response from that assigned to the test compound. Items in the Proactive Facilitation condition were like items in the Proactive Interference condition, except that the response assigned to the inserted compound was the same as the response assigned to the test compound. The Proactive Facilitation item on the sample list is the compound "dug ash" paired with the response "9" at number 17, and tested 12 seconds later at number 20 for recall. Preceding the reinforced presentation at number 14, the compound "dug his," with the common element "dug," is presented paired with the same response.

A 2-Reinforcement Control condition was also run, in which the same compound received two reinforced presentations before test.

Each subject received 6 blocks of trials, and each of the seven experimental conditions was tested once in each block. Within each block, the order of occurrence of the conditions was randomly determined, and the responses were assigned randomly to the experimental conditions. Four experimental conditions contained compounds with common cues. For half of the items from these conditions in each block, the first element was the common cue, and for the other half, the second element was the common cue. This was randomly determined for each block. Dummy or filler items were used to fill out the blocks when necessary.

Two sets of six blocks were constructed, and 24 subjects were run with each set. Four orders of occurrence of the blocks were randomly determined, and 6 subjects were run under each block order in each set.

There was a 1-minute rest interval between blocks 3 and 4 while the cards were changed. The first 3 blocks and the last 3 blocks were run off without separation. The first and fourth blocks were preceded by 5 warm-up items which consisted of 3 reinforced dummy items, and one Proaction Control item. These items were not included in the analysis. Immediately following the warm-up items the experimental blocks began.

RESULTS

For each subject, a total correct score was tabulated for each experimental condition. The results of a subjects X treatments analysis of variance of these scores showed that both the subjects effects ($F = 2.33$, $df = 47,282$) and the treatment effect ($F = 23.34$, $df = 6282$), were significant at the 0.05 level. The Duncan New Multiple Range Test with an 0.05 protection level was used to compare individual treatment means. The statistical comparisons of experimental conditions which follow are based on the results of the Duncan Range Test analysis.

Table 1 shows the proportion of correct recalls for each experimental condition. Each proportion is based on 288 observations. Considering first the control conditions, it can be seen that the 2-Reinforcement Control condition, the third one on the list, produced the highest recall score, 0.583. The proportion of recalls for the Proaction Control condition, in which the interval between the single reinforcement and the test was 12 seconds, was 0.375. This was higher than the obtained score of 0.243 for the Retroaction Control condition, in which the interval between reinforcement and test was 27 seconds. With the Duncan Range test, the obtained differences between the three control conditions were statistically reliable.

It will be recalled that, in the interference conditions, compounds with common cues and different response assignments were inserted in the training series either before (Proactive Interference) or after (Retroactive Interference) reinforcement of the test compound. For the retroactive interference condition, the proportion of correct recalls was 0.229. This is to be compared with the Retroaction Control condition, in which the interval between reinforcement and test was the same, but the items intervening between reinforcement and test had no cues in common with the test compound. The proportion of correct recalls for the control condition was 0.243, which was close to the obtained value of 0.229 for the Retroactive Interference condition; this difference is not statistically reliable. Thus we have no evidence for retroactive interference which can be attributed to the reinforcement of different response in the presence of common cues. However, a different result obtains for the Proactive Interference condition. For the Proaction Control condition, the proportion of correct recalls was 0.375, whereas the corresponding proportion for the Proactive Interference condition was 0.319. This difference is statistically reliable. Thus there appears to be a fair amount of proactive interference due to the reinforcement of common elements in the presence of different responses. An analysis was also made of intrusion errors in the interference conditions; that is, responses occurring on test trials which are appropriate to the inserted compounds. The proportion of intrusion errors for the Retroactive Interference condition was 0.263, which, it might be noted, was higher than the proportion of correct recalls. For the Proactive Interference condition, the proportion of intrusion errors was 0.167.

Remember that the training paradigms for the facilitation conditions were the same as those for the interference conditions except that the compounds with common cues which were inserted in the training series were assigned the same response as the test items. For the Retroactive Facilitation condition, the proportion of correct recalls was 0.479, which is significantly greater than the obtained score of 0.243 for the Retroaction Control condition. The Proactive Facilitation condition alsop reduced significantly better recall than the Proaction Control condition: 0.461 correct recalls as compared with 0.375 for the control condition. The slight difference between the two facilitation conditions was not statistically reliable.

It is possible that the observed facilitation may have been due to a response recency effect; that is, a tendency to repeat responses which had occurred recently in the training series, independently of the compounds with which they were paired. As a rough check on this, a tabulation was made of "psuedo-intrusion" errors for the Retroaction Control condition; that is, responses which were assigned to the compound which occurred 12 seconds before recall of the test item. Assuming that there is no response recency effect, the expected proportion of such error responses is 0.125, which agrees with the obtained proportion of 0.139. It is concluded that the observed facilitation effects in the facilitation conditions can be attributed to the two reinforcements of the response in the presence of the common cues.

As a check for over-all changes in responding during the session, a comparison was made of correct recalls in the first 3 blocks and the last 3 blocks of the experiment. The proportion of correct recalls for all experimental conditions was 0.37 in the first 3 blocks, and 0.38 in the last 3 blocks. A similar analysis of each experimental condition separately also showed little or no changes over the session. This is consonant with the results obtained by Peterson (reviewed in Peterson, 1963), and the experiments of Keppel and Underwood (1962), who showed that proactive inhibition builds up rapidly over the first few presentations and remains fairly constant thereafter.

THEORETICAL ANALYSIS

We will now consider some detailed assumptions concerning the stimulus sampling, associative, and response processes which will allow quantitative predictions of the recall scores for the various experimental conditions.

We assume that there are three sources of stimulation which control behavior on both reinforcement and test trials. First, the cues associated with the compound itself; second, the cues associated with the component stimuli of the compound; and third, background or contextual cues arising from the general experimental situation.

In the case of the associative process, we assume an all-or-none retention model: A pairing of a stimulus compound and response will always result in the formation of an association, but the association may be lost over time in all-or-none manner. The associative process for the compound cues and component cues is assumed to be perfectly correlated. That is, either both the compound cues and the component cues are at full associative strength, or they both are at zero strength. If an association is lost, then the effect of a second reinforcement is the same as the first. If an association is retained over the interval between two reinforcements, then the second reinforcement serves to protect the association and to prevent any future associative loss. We assume that the background cues are randomly associated with the available responses in the situation, and the probability that they are associated with the correct response at any time is $1/N$, where N is the number of response alternatives.

When compounds are presented on a recall test, we assume that responding is determined by a hierarchy of response tendencies. If the association between the reinforced response and the compound cues is retained, then the correct response will always occur; if there is no response associated with the compound cues, then responses associated with the component cues determine the response; and if there are no responses associated with either the compound or component cues, then the background cues determine the response.

From the assumptions above, prediction equations can be derived for the probability of a correct recall for the various experimental conditions. These theoretical

TABLE 3

PREDICTION EQUATIONS FOR PROBABILITIES OF CORRECT RECALL

Retroaction Control	$t + (1 - t) \, 1/N$
Proaction Control	$s + (1 - s) \, 1/N$
2-Reinforcement Control	$s + (1 - s) \, s + (1 - s)^2 \, 1/N$
Retroactive Interference	$t + (1 - s)(1 - t) \, 1/N$
Intrusion errors	$(1 - t) \, s + (1 - s)(1 - t) \, 1/N$
Proactive Interference	$s + (1 - s)(1 - t) \, 1/N$
Intrusion errors	$(1 - s) \, t + (1 - s)(1 - t) \, 1/N$
Retroactive Facilitation	$t + (1 - t) \, s + (1 - t)(1 - s) \, 1/N$
Proactive Facilitation	$s + (1 - s) \, t + (1 - s)(1 - t) \, 1/N$

expressions are given in Table 3. The parameter s is the probability that an association is retained at least 12 seconds, t is the probability that an association is retained at least 27 seconds, and N is the number of response alternatives.

We will illustrate how these equations are derived from our assumptions by going through the derivations for the Proaction Control, Proactive Interference, and Retroactive Facilitation conditions.

It will be recalled that in the Proaction Control condition, a compound received one reinforced presentation and was tested 12 seconds later for recall. According to our assumptions about the associative process, an association between compound cues and the reinforced response is always formed, and with probability s it is retained over the interval between reinforcement and test. If the association is retained, then according to the response assumptions, the correct response is made. If the association is not retained, it was assumed that the response is determined by the component cues. However, for the control items no compounds with common cues were in the training series, and thus the component cues cannot be associated with any response. In this case it was assumed that the response is determined by the background cues. Thus, the probability of a correct recall on a test trial for the Proaction Control condition is the sum of the probability s that an association between compound cues and response is retained, and the probability $(1 - s)(1/N)$ that an association is not retained but the background cues are associated with the correct response.

Consider now the Proactive Interference condition. The paradigm in Table 1 shows that a compound ab is tested for recall 12 seconds after reinforcement. Preceding the reinforcement, the compound ac paired with a different response is presented. A correct recall in the presence of the compound ab can occur in two ways: First, with probability s the compound cues associated with ab elicit the correct response; second with probability $(1 - s)(1 - t)(1/N)$ the compound and component cues elicit no response, but the background cues are associated with the correct response. (The component cues will never elicit a correct response since a different response was reinforced in the presence of the compound ac.)

As a final example of the derivational technique used to obtain the expressions in Table 3 we will consider the Retroactive Facilitation condition. The paradigm for the Retroactive Facilitation condition in Table 1 shows that a compound ab is paired with a response and tested 27 seconds later for recall. Between reinforcement and test, the compound ac with the common cue a and the same response is inserted in the training series. A correct recall could occur in three ways: First, from the assumptions, with probability t, the association between the cues associated with the compound ab and the response will be retained over the interval between reinforcement and test. Second, if the association is lost, then the response is determined by the component cues; and since ac is presented 12 seconds before the test, with probability s the cue a is still associated with the correct response at the time of the recall test. The probability of a correct recall in this case is $(1 - t) s$. Third, a correct recall could result also when the correct response is associated with the background cues, but the responses associated with the compounds ab and ac are not retained; the probability of this event is $(1 - t)(1 - s)(1/N)$.

Estimates of the parameters s and t were obtained from the Proaction and Retroaction Control conditions. Setting the observed proportion of correct recalls in the Proaction Control condition equal to the probability of a correct recall and solving for s yielded an estimate of $s = 0.296$. Similarly, an estimate of $t = 0.148$ was obtained from the Retroaction Control condition. By using these estimates of s and t in the equations of Table 3, predicted probabilities of correct recall were obtained for the other five experimental conditions. These predicted values are shown in Table 1.

An over-all comparison of the observed and predicted results show that the predictions are quite good. An especially striking confirmation of the model is the finding of equal recall in the two facilitation conditions. Except for two predictions, all predicted values are within the standard errors of the obtained proportions. The deviant predictions are, first, for the Proactive Interference condition, where there is associative loss not predicted by the model, and second, for the intrusion errors in the Retroactive Interference condition, which again indicates proactive interference not predicted by the model.

DISCUSSION

In the control conditions recall decreased as a function of the interval between reinforcement and test. This finding is consonant with the results of Peterson *et al.* (1962) and Estes (1961) in similar experimental situations. Because of the observed retention loss, it did not seem reasonable to use an all-or-none association process for this experiment, since the all-or-none association process (Estes, 1959: Bower, 1961) does not allow for associative loss. Estes (1961) has considered a number of modifications of the simple all-or-none process in order to deal with retention loss. In the present paper, we have considered an alternate learning process based on retention. More precisely, an all-or-none retention model was developed.

It is interesting that predictions from the all-or-none retention model are in many cases indistinguishable from the all-or-none association process. For example, if we apply the model to the usual paired-associates experiment involving multiple reinforcements, and assume that the probability of associative loss from reinforcement to reinforcement is constant, we find that the all-or-none retention model described here yields the same predictions in all cases as the all-or-none association model proposed by Bower (1961). According to Bower's model, there is a fixed probability that the correct association is formed on any reinforcement; once the association is formed, the correct response then occurs on all further trials. In the all-or-none retention model proposed here, the correct association is always formed, but there is a fixed probability that it is lost between presentations; but once the association is retained between two reinforcements, then the effect of the second reinforcement is to fix the association. The critical learning events are different for the two models, but it is difficult to distinguish between them since both models predict the same sort of response protocols: a sequence of chance responding which terminates on any trial with a fixed probability followed by a jump to 100% correct responding.

A more general retention process than the simple retention model presented here can easily be formulated. In the simple retention model, if an association survives the interval between two reinforcements, then the second reinforcement always protects the association and prevents further associative loss. In the more general model, it could be assumed that there is a fixed probability that the second reinforcement will protect the association. There would thus be two theoretically distinguishable states of learning. This more general retention model is similar to Atkinson's (1962) strong and weak conditioning theory.

The notion of all-or-none forgetting used in the present model is compatible with recent information-processing theories of human memory. Briefly, these theories assume that items are stored in a finite number of memory cells. A new item placed in a cell may erase the old item in the cell, thus leading to all-or-none forgetting. The response process in these information-processing models consists of scanning the memory cells until the association is found. It is clear that the hierarchy of response tendencies assumed in the present model can be cast in terms of the search notions of the information-processing models.

The interesting finding in the interference and facilitation conditions was the asymmetry of the observed transfer effects. Equal amounts of proactive and retroactive facilitation were obtained. But in the interference conditions, proactive but not retroactive interference mediated by the common cues was observed. The model failed to predict the proactive interference effect. A number of modifications of the model have been considered in order to handle the proactive interference effect, and we will outline two such modifications here.

One possibility is that the proactive interference can be attributed to a true associative decrement. That is, the association between the test compound and response may be interfered with due to the primacy of the compound with common cues which preceded reinforcement of the test compound. Another possibility is that the observed proactive interference is not due to any associative loss, but rather to response competition at recall. That is, we can allow for the possibility that on recall trials, the common cues can evoke both responses with which they were paired. If we assume that a primacy effect is operating, so that the emitted response is the first response reinforced in the presence of the common cues, then the probability of a correct recall in the Proactive Interference condition would be $s(1 - t) + (1 - s)(1 - t) 1/N$. This is the same as the equation for the probability of an intrusion error in the Retroactive Interference condition given in Table 3. Using the estimates of s and t from the control conditions, the predicted probability of a correct recall is 0.319, which is in good agreement with the obtained proportion. Unfortunately, these additional assumptions worsen the prediction for intrusion errors in the Proactive Interference condition. Although the analysis in terms of response competition at recall is suggestive, it is clear that more work is needed on the question of asymmetry of transfer effects. With regard to the theoretical use of primacy, it should be pointed out that Peterson and Peterson (1962) have recently demonstrated the importance of primacy effects in paired-associate learning.

A final comment should be made concerning the generality of the response rule assumed in the model. In the present experiment, subjects never received feedback concerning correctness of responding. However, in situations in which feedback is given, it seems reasonable that the response rule will change as a function of the correctness of responding. Some data on this point is contained in a study of pattern-vs.-component discrimination learning by Friedman (1962), and a theoretical treatment of response rule changes is contained in Atkinson (1960).

REFERENCES

ATKINSON, R. C. A theory of stimulus discrimination learning. In K. J. Arrow, S. Karlin, and P. Suppes (Eds.), *First stanford symposium on mathematical models in the social sciences*. Stanford, Calif.: Stanford Univer. Press, 1960.

ATKINSON, R. C. Choice behavior and monetary payoff: Strong and weak conditioning. In J. Criswell, H. Solomon, and P. Suppes (Eds.), *Mathematical methods in small group processes*. Stanford, Calif.: Stanford Univer. Press, 1962.

ATKINSON, R. C., AND ESTES, W. K. Stimulus sampling theory. In R. Luce, R. Bush, and E. Galanter (Eds.), *Handbook of mathematical psychology*. Vol. 2. New York: Wiley, 1963.

BOWER, G. H. Application of a model to paired-associate learning. *Psychometrika*, 1961, **26**, 255-280.

BURKE, C. K., AND ESTES, W. K. A component model for stimulus variables in discrimination learning. *Psychometrika*, 1957, **22**, 133-145.

ESTES, W. K. Component and pattern models with Markovian interpretations. In R. Bush and W. Estes (Eds.), *Studies in mathematical learning theory*. Stanford, Calif.: Stanford Univer.

ESTES, W. K. New developments in statistical behavior theory: Differential tests of axioms for associative learning. *Psychometrika*, 1961, **26**, 73-84.

Press, 1959.

ESTES, W. K., AND HOPKINS, B. L. Acquisition and transfer in pattern-vs.-component discrimination learning. *J. exp. Psychol.*, 1961, **61**, 322-328.

FRIEDMAN, M. P. Application of statistical learning theory to component-vs.-compound discrimination learning. Unpublished Ph.D. dissertation, Indiana Univer., 1962.

KEPPEL, G., AND UNDERWOOD, B. K. Proactive inhibition in short-term retention of single items. *J. verb. learning verb. Behav.*, 1962, **1**, 153-161.

PETERSON, L. R. Immediate memory: Data and theory. In C. Cofer and B. Musgrave (Eds.), *Verbal behavior and learning*. New York: McGraw-Hill, 1963.

PETERSON, L. R., AND PETERSON, M. J. Minimal paired-associate learning. *J. exp. Psychol.*, 1962, **63**, 521-527.

PETERSON, L. R., SALTZMAN, D., HILLNER, K., AND LAND, V. Recency and frequency in paired-associate learning. *J. exp. Psychol.*, 1962, **63**, 396-403.

RECEIVED: June 26, 1963

CHAPTER V

Multiprocess Models for
Discrimination and Choice

In the preceding chapter we considered two lines of attack upon the problems of generalization and discrimination, both of which were relatively straightforward extensions of models for simple learning. One approach, an extension of the component model, provided a simple description of generalization phenomena but could not predict the occurrence of perfect discrimination between stimuli having elements in common. The second approach, an extension of the pattern model, readily predicts perfect discrimination but cannot describe generalization without an extensive overhaul of the theoretical machinery. A third approach considered was to combine the best features of both simple models into a mixed model which has both component and pattern properties.

In the present chapter we consider modifications of the simple component model, which introduces an auxiliary process operating independently of conditioning and extinction. All variations are alike in that the additional process systematically modifies either the composition of a sample of elements or the relative importance of its components. Chronologically, the first such process to be proposed was one which changed the relative weightings of sampled elements by tuning out, or adapting, the common elements; hence the denotation *adaptative models*. The supplementary process of each of the remaining modifications, on the other hand, serves to focus attention upon the relevant elements rather than to adapt out the irrelevant ones. Although these approaches differ with respect to details of the assumed focusing mechanism (and its mathematical description), they are alike in assuming that the sampling process is an active and selective one rather than a passive registering of elements. For descriptive convenience we shall describe these models under the headings of *observing response* and *scanning models*.

Adaptation models. As was noted earlier, one of the virtues of component models for interpreting generalization and transfer becomes a limitation in applications to discrimination: whenever the stimulus sets associated with discriminative stimuli have elements in common, generalization is proportional to the overlap, even when training has been carried to asymptote. For all experimental tasks traditionally employed to study discrimination it is certainly true that many aspects of the experimental situation remain relatively constant (for example, background cues, the apparatus itself, stimuli associated with the start of a trial, etc.). On the other hand, it is also true that many instances of perfect discrimination have been observed under these conditions. It is, therefore, natural to assume that common elements must come to have a decreasingly important role in determining the occurrence of a response.

Bush and Mosteller (1951) made a frontal assault upon the troublesome common elements through the device of introducing a linear operator which reduced the relative weight of common elements over repeated trials of discrimination training. A subtler version of the same basic approach was proposed by Restle (1955 a,b). Restle defined two categories of elements, relevant and irrelevant (or common) ones; he assumed that relevant cues become conditioned to one of the available response classes whereas irrelevant cues are adapted and lose their capacity to evoke a response. He further introduced the simplifying assumption that the probability of conditioning of a relevant cue is equal to the probability of adaptation of an irrelevant cue. Both probabilities are represented by the quantity θ and $\theta = r/(r + i)$ where r denotes the number of relevant cues and i the number of irrelevant cues. As a result of this assumption, only one additional parameter is introduced.

Although there are no observable psychological processes which may be set in correspondence with the assumed adaptation process, one could live with an arbitrary solution which had compensatory practical advantages. Unfortunately, the mathematical properties of adaptation models turn out to be more complex than those of the patterning and mediational models considered in Chapter IV.

Observing response models. Perhaps the simplest psychological process which can be invoked to account for the decreased importance of common stimulus elements is selective attention to relevant ones. Wyckoff (1952) had proposed a discrimination theory in which selective attention is achieved through the mechanism of an observing response; Atkinson (1958) expressed these assumptions in quantitative form. The major new assumption in Atkinson's observing response model is that at the outset of a trial the subject either makes an observing response O, or he does not, $\bar{O}$. If he makes an O, then the effective stimulus sample on that trial consists solely of the unique elements S_1 or S_2; if he makes $\bar{O}$, then the effective stimulus contains unique elements along with elements common to both stimuli: $S_1 + S_C$ or $S_2 + S_C$. The observing response model has been shown by Atkinson and his associates (Atkinson, 1961; Popper and Atkinson, 1958; Atkinson, Bogartz, and Turner, 1959) to provide more accurate predictions of asymptotic conditional response probabilities, $p(A_1|S_j)$, than a simple component model. However, some other aspects of the data, such as sequential probabilities, are not accurately described by the observing response model.

With the introduction of an observing response, Atkinson has, in effect, treated discrimination as a sequential two-state process comprising the occurrence or nonoccurrence of an observing response followed by a choice response; the outcome of the second stage is dependent upon the outcome of the first. A description of this sort has natural application to a discrimination training procedure, traditionally known as the "successive procedure," in which, on a given trial, only one discriminative stimulus is presented and two or more choices are available, only one of which is associated with reinforcement. An observing response model for a "simultaneous" discrimination procedure has been described by Lovejoy (1965). However, before going on to face the additional complications introduced by the "simultaneous procedure," it is worth considering in more detail some of the applications of models developed in connection with the successive procedure.

Most of the models reviewed previously apply to the successive procedure which is a natural extension of the probability learning task. Although the successive procedure is often used in concept attainment studies, one of the areas of its widest application is in psychophysical judgment tasks. For example, in the determination of thresholds a very common procedure—the method of minimal changes—consists of successive presentations of a stimulus of increasing intensity; on each presentation the subject is to say "yes" (I see or hear it) or "no" (I do not). In a variant of this procedure—the absolute method—stimuli are presented in a random rather than a systematic order, and the subject is to respond "yes" or "no" on each trial. More recently, "forced choice" methods have come to be used; in these, stimulus presentation is broken into a number of successive intervals. A fixed noise level is present throughout all intervals but, in addition, a signal is added to the noise during one of the intervals. The subject's task is to identify the interval during which the signal was presented. All of these psychophysical judgment tasks may naturally be viewed as a sequential two-stage process involving an attentional or perpetual state followed by a choice response. Recently, two-process models have been applied to psychophysical judgment tasks with some success (e.g., Atkinson, 1963; Atkinson, Carterette, and Kinchla, 1962, 1964; Kinchla, 1964). An interesting feature of these studies is the emphasis on relatively neglected independent variables, such as feedback, and the analysis of response sequences.

Scanning processes. For most of the early research on discrimination, a simultaneous procedure was employed based, for the most part, on the then current view that this was the simpler procedure. In the simultaneous procedure all the discriminative stimuli are presented on each trial (with spatial position randomly varied when spatial position is not a relevant cue) and response with respect to one of the discriminative stimuli is associated with reinforcement, whereas response to the other stimuli is not. The T-maze or the Lashley apparatus are common examples of apparatus employing the simultaneous procedure. In such experimental situations, an observing or attentional response may determine which of the discriminative stimuli will be perceived (as contrasted with determining whether cue or cue plus overlap is observed). Following the occurrence of an observing response, the subject may make a choice response or he may make another observing response. In fact, it is possible that many observing responses may be made prior to a choice. Thus the first stage will be expected to vary in duration and composition and an adequate theory should be able to describe both these properties of the data. Within this framework, it is evident that the simultaneous procedure is more complex from the standpoint of developing an adequate discrimination theory.

One of the first detailed analyses of the simultaneous discrimination task is represented by the choice point model proposed by Bower (1959). He assumed that the subject, for example a rat in a T-maze, at the choice point orients either to the right or to the left; in either case, it is exposed to stimulation associated with that arm of the maze. In this example selective attention corresponds to a physical orientation which can be observed directly, and the discriminative stimuli sampled are contingent upon the orienting response which occurs. Having oriented, the rat may run ahead or it may reorient. Bower considers two possible interpretations of the sequence of reorienting; these differ with respect to whether or not the choice point is included as a necessary intervening state between two opposed orientations. Intuitively, it would seem unnecessary to include it and, in this instance, the data are in support of intuition; Bower's second model provides a better description of his data.

Although one of the major aims of discrimination theories has been to relate the development of later choice responses to the contingencies associated with prior choices, it should be evident that the basic approach of

Bower's choice point model has quite a general application to a variety of experimental problems. It may, for example, be extended to any experimental situation in which the individual is confronted with a set of stimuli or objects and is required to choose among them. A model for choice behavior (Estes, 1960; 1961) has been shown to have potential application to such varied experimental problems as preference in paired comparison experiments, choices among bets (Friedman, Padilla, and Gelfand, 1964), and prediction of asymptotes in probability learning with three response alternatives (Cole, 1964). A simple version of a similar model has been considered by Suppes and Atkinson (1960), and a still simpler variant has been applied to problems of visual recognition in tachistoscopic situations (Estes and Taylor, 1964; Estes, 1965; Estes and Taylor, 1966). Another problem for which the choice point model provides a starting point is the prediction of choice time. Two examples of choice time models have been included in this section: Kintsch's (1963) random-walk model, and a somewhat different model of LaBerge (1962) which assumes sequential sampling to the attainment of some critical number of stimulus elements. Still another choice time model, closely related to that of Kintsch, has been proposed by Audley (1960).

A major extension of the scanning, or VTE, model has been noted previously (Chapter III) in relation to multiple choice learning in situations involving variation of both probability and magnitude of reward. In this extension the subject is assumed to scan, not only the stimuli presented on a trial, but also the anticipated consequences of alternative responses (Estes, 1962, 1966).

The developments of this chapter are of special interest with respect to the problem of extrapolating the course of development of stimulus sampling theory into the immediate future. Critics have often taken the view that, although stimulus sampling theory has exhibited power and parsimony in accounting for some simple standard learning experiments, it would undoubtedly proliferate into unmanageable mathematical complexities when extended to handle a wider range of phenomena. That a richer theoretical structure is needed to handle more complex phenomena cannot be gainsaid; yet it is instructive to note that the extensions and elaborations of earlier stimulus sampling models, appearing in the papers of the last two chapters, have followed a relatively simple pattern. Namely, the same elementary processes are found to recur at successively higher levels of analysis. Thus, the simple mechanism of the one-element model applies first at the level of acquisition of stimulus response associations; later the same identical process is found to apply to concept learning involving the selection of hypotheses or strategies. Similarly, the same type of scanning process is found to apply first to relatively simple stimulus elements or components, then to alternative stimulus patterns, and finally to anticipated consequences of alternative courses of action. Although not yet tidily organized and cast in axiomatic form, the body of theory developing within the stimulus sampling approach can thus be seen to be assuming the form, not of a single, highly formalized model, but rather of a hierarchy of models, with the same basic processes of sampling and selection operating at different levels of behavioral organization.

REFERENCES

Atkinson, R. C. A Markov model for discrimination learning. *Psychometrika*, 1958, **23**, 309–322.

Atkinson, R. C. The observing response in discrimination learning. *J. exp. Psychol.*, 1961, **62**, 253–262.

Atkinson, R. C. A variable sensitivity theory of signal detection. *Psychol. Rev.* 1963, **70**, 91–106.

Atkinson, R. C., Bogartz, W. B., and Turner, R. N. Supplementary report: Discrimination learning with probabilistic reinforcement schedules. *J. exp. Psychol.*, 1959, **57**, 349–350.

Atkinson, R. C., Carterette, E. C., and Kinchla, R. A. Sequential phenomena in psychophysical judgments: A theoretical analysis. *IRE Trans. on Information Theory*, 1962, **IT-8**, 155–162.

Atkinson, R. C., Carterette, E. C., and Kinchla, R. A. The effect of information feedback upon psychophysical judgements. *Psychonom. Sci.*, 1964, **1**, 83–84·

Audley, R. J. A stochastic model for individual choice behavior. *Psychol. Rev.*, 1960, **67**, 1–15.

Bower, G. H. Choice-point behavior. In R. R. Bush and W. K. Estes (Eds.), *Studies in mathematical learning theory*. Stanford, Calif.: Stanford Univ. Press, 1959, 109–124.

Bush, R. R. and Mosteller, F. A model for stimulus generalization and discrimination. *Psychol. Rev.*, 1951, **58**, 413–423.

Cole, M. Search behavior: A correction procedure for three-choice probability learning. *J. math. Psychol.*, 1965, **2**, 145–170.

Estes, W. K. A random-walk model for choice behavior. In K. J. Arrow, S. Karlin, and P. Suppes (Eds.), *Mathematical methods in the social sciences*. Stanford, Calif.: Stanford Univ. Press, 1960, 265–276.

Estes, W. K. A descriptive approach to the dynamics of choice behavior. *Behav. Sci.*, 1961, **3**, 177–184.

Estes, W. K. Theoretical treatments of differential reward in multiple-choice learning and two-person interactions. In J. Criswell, H. Solomon, and P. Suppes (Eds.), *Mathematical methods in small group processes*. Stanford, Calif.: Stanford Univ. Press, 1962, 133–149.

Estes, W. K. A technique for assessing variability of perceptual span. *Proc. Nat. Acad. Sci.*, 1965, **54**, 403–407.

Estes, W. K. Transfer of verbal discriminations based on differential reward magnitudes. *J. exp. Psychol.* 1966, **72** (276–283).

Estes, W. K. and Taylor, H. A. A detection method and probabilistic models for assessing information processing from brief visual displays. *Proc. Natl. Acad. Sci.*, 1964, **51**, 446–454.

Estes, W. K. and Taylor H. A. Visual detection in relation to display size and redundancy of critical elements. *Perception and Psychophysics*, 1966, **1**, 9–16.

Friedman, M. P., Padilla, G., and Gelfand, H. The learning of choices between bets. *J. math. Psychol.*, 1964, **1**, 375–385.

Kinchla, R. A. A learning factor in visual discrimination. In R. C. Atkinson (Ed.), *Studies in mathematical psychology*. Stanford, Calif.: Stanford Univ. Press, 1964, 233–249.

Kintsch, W. A response time model for choice behavior. *Psychometrika*, 1963, **28**, 27–32.

Popper, J. and Atkinson, R. C. Discrimination learning in a verbal conditioning situation. *J. exp. Psychol.*, 1958, **56**, 21–26.

Restle, F. A theory of discrimination learning. *Psychol. Rev.*, 1955, **62**, 11–19. (a)

Restle, F. Axioms of a theory of discriminative learning. *Psychometrika*, 1955, **20**, 201–208. (b)

Suppes, P. and Atkinson, R. C. *Markov learning models for multiperson interactions*. Stanford, Calif.: Stanford Univ. Press, 1960, 247–252.

Wyckoff, L. B., Jr. The role of observing responses in discrimination behavior. *Psychol. Rev.*, 1952, **59**, 431–442.

A Theory of Discrimination Learning[1]

FRANK RESTLE,[2] *Stanford University*

This paper presents a theory of two-choice discrimination learning. Though similar in form to earlier theories of simple learning by Estes (**5**) and Bush and Mosteller (**2,3**), this system introduces a powerful new assumption which makes definite quantitative predictions easier to obtain and test. Several such predictions dealing with learning and transfer are derived from the theory and tested against empirical data.

The stimulus situation facing a subject in a trial of discrimination learning is thought of as a set of cues. A subset of these cues may correspond to any thing—concrete or abstract, present, past, or future, of any description—to which the subject can learn to make a differential response. In this definition it does not matter whether the subject actually makes a differential response to the set of cues as long as he has the capacity to learn one. An individual cue is thought of as "indivisible" in the sense that different responses cannot be learned to different parts of it. Informally, the term "cue" will occasionally be used to refer to any set of cues, all of which are manipulated in the same way during a whole experiment.

[1] This paper is adapted from part of a Ph.D. dissertation submitted to Stanford University. The author is especially indebted to Dr. Douglas H. Lawrence and to Dr. Patrick Suppes for encouragement and criticism. Thanks are also due Dr. W. K. Estes who loaned prepublication manuscripts and Dr. R. R. Bush who pointed out some relations between the present theory and the Bush-Mosteller model (**3**).

[2] Now at the Human Resources Research Office, The George Washington University.

This article appeared in *Psychol. Rev.*, 1955, **62**, 11–19.

In problems to be analyzed by this theory, every individual cue is either "relevant" or "irrelevant." A cue is relevant if it can be used by the subject to predict where or how reward is to be obtained. For example, if food is always found behind a black card in a rat experiment, then cues aroused by the black card are relevant. A cue aroused by an object uncorrelated with reward is "irrelevant." For example, if the reward is always behind the black card but the black card is randomly moved from left to right, then "position" cues are irrelevant. These concepts are discussed by Lawrence (**6**).

In experiments to be considered, the subject has just two choice responses. No other activities are considered in testing the theory. Any consistent method of describing these two responses which can be applied throughout a complete experiment is acceptable in using this theory.

THEORY

In solving a two-choice discrimination problem the subject learns to relate his responses correctly to the relevant cues. At the same time his responses become independent of the irrelevant cues. These two aspects of discrimination learning are represented by two hypothesized processes, "conditioning" and "adaptation."

Intuitively, a conditioned cue is one which the subject knows how to use in getting reward. If k is a relevant cue and $c(k,n)$ is the probability that k has been conditioned at the beginning of the nth trial, then

$$c(k,n+1) = c(k,n) + \theta[1 - c(k,n)] \quad [1]$$

is the probability that it will be conditioned by the beginning of the next trial. On each trial of a given problem a constant proportion, θ, of unconditioned relevant cues becomes conditioned.

To the extent that a conditioned cue affects performance, it contributes to a correct response only, whereas an unconditioned relevant cue contributes equally to a correct and to an incorrect response.

Intuitively, an adapted cue is one which the subject does not consider in deciding upon his choice response. If a cue is thought of as a "possible solution" to the problem, an adapted cue is a possible solution which the subject rejects or ignores. If $a(k,n)$ is the probability that irrelevant cue k has been adapted at the beginning of the nth trial, then

$$a(k,n+1)=a(k,n)+\theta[1-a(k,n)] \quad [2]$$

is the probability that it will be adapted by the beginning of the next trial. On each trial of a given problem a constant proportion of unadapted irrelevant cues becomes adapted. An adapted cue is nonfunctional in the sense that it contributes neither to a correct nor to an incorrect response.

It will be noticed that the same constant θ appears in both equations 1 and 2. The *fundamental simplifying assumption* of this theory deals with θ. This assumption is that

$$\theta = \frac{r}{r+i}, \quad [3]$$

where r is the number of relevant cues in the problem and i is the number of irrelevant cues. Thus, θ is the proportion of relevant cues in the problem. This proportion is the same as the fraction of unconditioned cues conditioned on each trial, and the

fraction of unadapted cues adapted on each trial.

The performance function $p(n)$, representing the probability of a correct response on the nth trial, is in accord with the definitions of conditioning and adapting given above. The function is in the form of a ratio, with the total number of unadapted cues in the denominator and the number of conditioned cues plus one-half times the number of other cues in the numerator. Thus conditioned cues contribute their whole effect toward a correct response, adapted cues contribute nothing toward either response, and other cues contribute their effect equally toward correct and incorrect responses. Formally,

$$p(n) = \frac{\overset{r}{\sum} c(k,n)+\tfrac{1}{2}\overset{r}{\sum}[1-c(k,n)]+\tfrac{1}{2}\overset{i}{\sum}[1-a(k,n)]}{r+\overset{i}{\sum}[1-a(k,n)]}. \quad [4]$$

Here $\overset{r}{\sum}$ is the sum taken over the r relevant cues and $\overset{i}{\sum}$ is the sum taken over the i irrelevant cues.

SOME CONSEQUENCES REGARDING SIMPLE LEARNING

If the subject is naive at the beginning of training, so that for any relevant cue k, $c(k,1) = 0$, and for any irrelevant cue k, $a(k,1) = 0$, and if he receives n trials on a given problem, then by mathematical induction it can be shown that if k is relevant,

$$c(k,n + 1) = 1 - (1 - \theta)^n \quad [5]$$

and if k is irrelevant,

$$a(k,n + 1) = 1 - (1 - \theta)^n. \quad [6]$$

Under these circumstances we can substitute equations 5 and 6 into equation 4 and, taking advantage of the simplifying effects of equation 3, we have

$$p(n) = 1 - \tfrac{1}{2} \frac{(1 - \theta)^{n-1}}{\theta + (1 - \theta)^n}. \quad [7]$$

Plotting equation 7 shows that p is an S-shaped function of n with an asymptote (for $\theta > 0$) at 1.00. Also, $p(1) = \tfrac{1}{2}$. Since $p(n)$ is a monotonic increasing function of θ we can estimate θ from observations of performance. If we want to know the theoretical proportion of relevant cues in a problem for a particular subject, we have the subject work on the problem, record his performance curve, and solve equation 7 for θ. This result depends directly upon the simplifying assumption of equation 3.

Since the instability of individual learning curves makes it difficult to fit curves to them, it is fortunate that θ can be determined in a different way. Suppose a subject makes E errors in the course of solving the problem to a very rigorous criterion and it is assumed for practical purposes that he has made all the errors he is going to make. Theoretically, the total number of errors made on a problem can be written

$$E = \sum_{n=1}^{\infty} [1 - p(n)].$$

Under the conditions satisfying equation 7, this can be evaluated approximately by using the continuous time variable t in place of the discrete trial variable n, and integrating. The result of this integration is that

$$E \simeq \tfrac{1}{2} + \tfrac{1}{2} \frac{\log \theta}{(1 - \theta) \log (1 - \theta)}. \quad [8]$$

By equation 8, which relates the total number of errors made on a problem to θ, it is possible to make relatively stable estimates of θ.

AN EMPIRICAL TEST OF THE SIMPLE LEARNING THEORY— COMBINATION OF CUES

Consider three problems, s_1, s_2, and s_3, all of which involve the same irrelevant cues. Two of the problems, s_1 and s_2, have entirely separate and different relevant cues, while in problem s_3 all the relevant cues of s_1 and s_2 are present and relevant. That is, $r_3 = r_1 + r_2$ and $i_1 = i_2 = i_3$. If we know θ_1 and θ_2 we can compute θ_3, since by equation 3

$$\theta_1 = r_1/(r_1 + i)$$
$$\theta_2 = r_2/(r_2 + i)$$
$$\theta_3 = (r_1 + r_2)/(r_1 + r_2 + i).$$

Solving these equations for θ_3 in terms of θ_1 and θ_2 we get

$$\theta_3 = (\theta_1 + \theta_2 - 2\theta_1\theta_2)/(1 - \theta_1\theta_2). \quad [9]$$

This theorem answers the following question: Suppose we know how many errors are made in learning to use differential cue X and how many are used to learn cue Y, then how many errors will be made in learning a problem in which either X or Y can be used (if X and Y are entirely discrete)?

Eninger (4) has run an experiment which tests equation 9. Three groups of white rats were run in a T maze on successive discrimination problems. The first group learned a visual discrimination, *black-white*, the second group learned an auditory discrimination, *tone–no-tone*, and the third group had both cues available and relevant.

Since each group was run to a rigorous criterion, total error scores are used to estimate θ_1 and θ_2 by equation 8.[3] The values estimated are

[3] Total error scores do not appear in Eninger's original publication and are no longer known. However, trials-to-criterion scores were reported. Total error scores were

$\theta_1 = .020$, based on an estimated average of 98.5 errors made on the auditory-cue problem, and $\theta_2 = .029$, based on an estimated average of 64.5 errors on the visual-cue problem. Putting these two values into equation 9 we get

$$\theta_3 = .029 + .020 + 2(.020)(.029)/$$
$$1 - (.020)(.029)$$
$$= .049.$$

This value of θ_3 substituted into equation 8 leads to the expectation of about 33 total errors on the combined cues problem. In fact, an average of 26 errors was made by the four subjects on this problem. The prediction is not very accurate. However, only 14 animals were employed in the entire experiment, in groups of five, five, and four. Individual differences among animals within groups were considerable. If account is taken of sampling variability of the two single-cue groups and of the combined-cue group of subjects, the prediction is not significantly wrong. Further experimentation is needed to determine whether the proposed law is tenable.

It is easily seen that θ_3 will always be larger than θ_1 or θ_2 if all three problems are solved. Learning will always be faster in the combined-cues problem. Eninger (4) in his paper points out that this qualitative statement is a consequence of Spence's theory of discrimination. However, Spence's theory gives no quantitative law.

TRANSFER OF TRAINING

In order to apply this theory to transfer-of-training experiments in which more than one problem is used, certain assumptions are made. It is

estimated from trials-to-criterion scores by using other, comparable data collected by Amsel (1). Dr. Amsel provided detailed results in a personal communication.

assumed that if a cue is conditioned in one problem and appears immediately thereafter as a relevant cue in a new problem, it is still conditioned. Likewise, an adapted cue appearing as an irrelevant cue in a new problem is adapted. However, if a conditioned cue is made irrelevant it is obviously no longer conditioned, since it cannot serve as a predictor of reward. Similarly, it is assumed that if an adapted cue is made relevant in a new problem, it becomes unadapted and available for conditioning.

According to the present definition of conditioning, a conditioned cue contributes to a correct response. Therefore the above assumptions will not hold if the relation between a cue and a reward is reversed in changing the problem. This theory cannot be used to analyze reversal learning, and is applicable only in cases in which relevant cues maintain an unchanging significance.

If two problems are run under the same conditions and in the same apparatus, and differ only in the degree of difference between the discriminanda (as where one problem is a *black-white* and the other a *dark gray-light gray* discrimination), it is assumed that both problems involve the same cues; but the greater the difference to be discriminated, the more cues are relevant and the less are irrelevant.

EMPIRICAL TESTS OF THE TRANSFER-OF-TRAINING THEORY

As Lawrence (7) has pointed out, it seems that a difficult discrimination is more easily established if the subjects are first trained on an easy problem of the same type than if all training is given directly on the difficult discrimination. The experimental evidence on this point raises the question of predicting transfer performance from one problem to another, where the two problems involve the same stimulus dimension but differ in difficulty.

Suppose that problems s_1 and s_2 both require a discrimination along the same stimulus dimension and differ only in that s_2 is more difficult than s_1. Let θ_1 be the proportion of relevant cues in problem s_1 and θ_2 be the proportion of relevant cues in s_2. Suppose that the training schedule involves n trials on problem s_1 followed by j trials on problem s_2. Then the probability of a correct response on trial $n + j$ is

lem without prior experience, their performance on the first problem serves to estimate θ_1, the proportion of relevant cues in the easier pretraining problem. Lawrence replicated the experiment, having two experimental groups, ATG No. 1 and ATG No. 2, each of which transferred abruptly from an easy pretraining problem to the test problem. Group ATG No. 1 had a very easy problem for which we estimate $\theta_1 = .14$. Group ATG No. 2 had a more difficult problem for which $\theta_1' = .07$.

For group ATG No. 1, $\theta_1 = .14$, $\theta_2 = .04$, and $n = 30$ since thirty

$$p(n+j) = \frac{\theta_2 + \frac{1}{2}(1 - \theta_2)^{j-1}[\theta_1 - \theta_2 + (1 - \theta_1)^n(1 - \theta_1 - \theta_2)]}{\theta_2 + (1 - \theta_2)^{j-1}[\theta_1 - \theta_2 + (1 - \theta_1)^{n+1}]}. \quad [10]^4$$

This theorem can be tested against the results of experiments reported by Lawrence (7). He trained white rats in one brightness discrimination and transferred them to a more difficult problem for further training. A control group, which Lawrence called "HDG," learned the hard test problem without work on any other problem. The performance of this control group is used to estimate θ_2, the proportion of relevant cues in the test problem. The value found was .04.[5] Since the experimental subjects first worked on the pretraining prob-

trials of pretraining were given. From this information we can compute $p(n + j)$ for all j, using equation 10. The predicted transfer performance is compared with observed performance in Table 1. For group ATG No. 2, $\theta_1' = .07$, $\theta_2 = .04$, and $n = 50$ since fifty trials of pretraining were given. Here also, $p(n + j)$ can be computed. Prediction is compared with observed performance in Table 1, from which it can be seen that the predictions are

[4] The justification of equation 10 involves no mathematical difficulties. On the first trial of transfer we know the probability that any cue relevant in the second problem is conditioned, since all cues relevant in the second problem were relevant in the first. Similarly, we know the probability that i_1 of the i_2 irrelevant cues are adapted. The other $i_2 - i_1$ cues are unadapted. Equations 1 and 2 can be applied at this point, and all terms divided by $r_1 + i_1 (= r_2 + i_2)$.

[5] These estimates were made by the unsatisfactory method of fitting equation 7 to group average learning curves. Therefore the results regarding Lawrence's experiment are approximate.

TABLE 1

PREDICTION OF EASY-TO-HARD TRANSFER IN RATS*

Trials of Transfer Training	Proportion of Correct Responses			
	Group ATG 1		Group ATG 2	
	Observed	Predicted	Observed	Predicted
1–10	.66	.63	.81	.71
11–20	.70	.68	.83	.77
21–30	.74	.72	.81	.81
31–40	.84	.78		
41–50	.86	.83		

* Data from Lawrence (7).

relatively accurate, though performance is higher than predicted.

Lawrence also considered the possibility that a gradual transition from easy through successively harder problems would result in rapid mastery of the difficult problem. He tested this proposition by giving another group of subjects a series of three pretest problems before the final test problem. The problems in order of ease of learning were, first, the problem learned by ATG No. 1 with $\theta_1 = .14$, an intermediate problem which was not otherwise used, the difficult pretest problem with $\theta_3 = .07$, and finally the test problem with $\theta_4 = .04$.

To estimate θ_2 in Lawrence's experiment where problem s_2 never was used separately in simple learning, we notice the relation of θ to differences between discriminanda in apparent foot-candles for problems s_1, s_3, and s_4 whose θ values are known. We know that if the problems are properly controlled, and the stimulus difference is zero foot-candles, there are no relevant cues and θ is zero. It was found that this assumption, along with available data, made it possible to write a tentative empirical function relating θ to the difference between discriminanda in foot-candles. This equation presumably holds only in the case of Lawrence's apparatus, training procedure, subjects, etc. The equation adopted is

$$\theta = .0988 \log_{10}(.4\,d) \qquad [11]$$

where d is the difference between discriminanda in foot-candles. It is emphasized that this equation has no theoretical significance and is merely expedient. From equation 11 it is possible to determine the θ value of the intermediate pretraining problem by interpolation. Table 2 gives the data and results of this interpolation.

Ten trials were given on each of the first three problems and fifty trials on the final test problem. Using the θ values in Table 2 it is possible to predict the test problem performance of subjects who have gone through gradual transition pretraining.[6] This prediction is compared with observed performance in Table 3. It may be noted that the correspondence between prediction and observation is in this case very close. Again, however, the prediction is consistently a little lower than observed performance.

[6] The general prediction for transfer through a series of problems which get successively more difficult can be derived by following through and repeating the reasoning in footnote 4. Since the resulting equations are extremely large and can be derived rather easily, they are not given here.

TABLE 3
PREDICTION OF TRANSFER PERFORMANCE OF RATS AFTER A SERIES OF PRETRAINING PROBLEMS*

Trials Working on Final Test Problem	Proportion of Correct Responses	
	Observed	Predicted
1–10	.73	.73
11–20	.82	.79
21–30	.87	.84
31–40	.89	.87
41–50	.90	.90

* Data from Lawrence (7).

TABLE 2
THE RELATION OF "DIFFERENCE BETWEEN STIMULI" AND θ VALUE OF PROBLEM*

Difference Between Discriminanda in Apparent Foot-Candles	Corresponding θ Value of Problem
67.7	.14
35.2	.113**
14.0	.07
5.9	.04
0.0	.00†

* Data from Lawrence (7).
** Estimated by interpolation from empirical equation 16.
† Theoretical—see text for explanation.

New Data

The theory has thus far been tested against the behavior of rats. Its generality is now tested with college students in a simple discrimination learning task.

Subjects and procedure. The subjects in this experiment were 23 students in the elementary psychology course at Stanford University. The S was seated at one end of a table and told that his responses could be either "A" or "B". On each trial S saw a single stimulus, which was a black square on a circular white background. The two squares used on alternate trials differed in size. In problem s_1 the squares differed in height by $\frac{1}{4}$ in., in problem s_2 they differed by $\frac{1}{8}$ in. The mean height of each pair of squares was 3 in. The squares were viewed at a distance of about 6 ft.

For half the Ss in each experimental group, the problem was to say "A" to the smaller square and "B" to the larger one. The other Ss had the converse problem. The S was never told that the problem was a size discrimination. Stimuli were alternated randomly. A rest period was called after each ten trials and S was asked what he thought the correct solution to the problem was, and to outline possible solutions which had occurred to him. This method of questioning is a modification of Prentice's method (8).

Twelve Ss were trained first on problem s_1 to a criterion of 15 successive correct responses and then transferred to problem s_2 and run to the same criterion. These Ss made up the "Easy-Hard Transfer Group" called EH. The other 11 Ss were trained first on s_2 and then transferred to s_1. This was the "Hard-Easy Transfer Group" called HE. The two groups were approximately equated for age, sex, and known special visual skills.

Results. Using the pretraining performance of the EH group, the average proportion of relevant cues, θ_1, was estimated at .254 by equation 8. Using the pretraining performance of the HE group, the average proportion of relevant cues in problem s_2 was estimated at $\theta_2 = .138$.

The transfer performance of group EH, which first learned the easy and then the hard problem, is predictable by equation 10. Since these subjects

worked to a high criterion in pretraining, we can assume that $p(n)$ is negligibly different from one at the end of pretraining. Then by equation 7 we see that $(1 - \theta_1)^{n-1}$ is small, and equation 10 simplifies to

$$p(n+j) = \frac{\theta_2 + \frac{1}{2}(1-\theta_2)^{j-1}(\theta_1-\theta_2)}{\theta_2 + (1-\theta_2)^{j-1}(\theta_1-\theta_2)}. \quad [12]$$

This theoretical function of j is compared with observed transfer performance in Table 4. It is seen that the correspondence is quite close with a negligible constant error.

This prediction is based on the formula which also predicted Lawrence's rat data. This confirmation suggests that the law can be applied to human as well as rat performance on this type of task.

Using the line of reasoning which developed equation 10 we can produce an equation to predict transfer performance from hard to easier problems of the same sort. Certain cues are relevant in the easy problem which were irrelevant in the harder one. These cues cannot be identified in the hard problem. For performance to be perfect in the easier problem all relevant cues must be identified. Therefore, when the subject transfers from the hard to the easier

TABLE 4

PREDICTION OF TRANSFER OF TRAINING FROM
EASIER TO HARDER PROBLEM IN
HUMAN SUBJECTS

Trials after Transfer to Second Problem	Proportion of Correct Responses	
	Observed	Predicted
1–5	.817	.821
6–10	.933	.895
11–15	.926	.941
16–20	.933	.966
21–25	.966	.988
26–30	.983	.994
31–35	1.000	1.000

TABLE 5

PREDICTION OF TRANSFER OF TRAINING FROM
HARDER TO EASIER PROBLEM IN
HUMAN SUBJECTS

Trials After Transfer to Second Problem	Proportion of Correct Responses	
	Observed	Predicted
1–4	.932	.883
5–8	.955	.960
9–12	.955	.984
13–16	1.000	.995

problem we should expect some small number of errors to be made. On the assumption that the hard problem was completely learned in pretraining, the formula for transfer performance on the easy problem is

$$p(n+j) = \frac{\theta_2 + (\theta_1 - \theta_2)(1-\theta_1)^{j-1}}{\theta_1} \quad [13]$$

where θ_1 is the proportion of relevant cues in the easy problem and θ_2 is the proportion of relevant cues in the harder problem. The proof of this theorem is similar to that of equation 12 above, and is not given here.

Equation 13 yields the prediction for transfer performance of the *HE* subjects. In Table 5 the prediction is compared with observed transfer performance.

Despite the very small frequencies predicted and observed, the prediction is quite accurate. In all, seven errors were made by eleven subjects, whereas a total of eight were expected. This is an average of .64 errors per subject observed, and .73 predicted.

DISCUSSION

The definition of a "cue" in terms of possible responses is selected because the theoretical results do not depend critically upon the nature of the stimulating agent. While cues are thought of as stimulus elements, these elements need not be of the nature of "points of color" or "elementary tones." If a subject can learn a consistent response to a certain configuration despite changes in its constituents, then the configuration is by definition a cue separate from its constituents. The intention is to accept any cue which can be demonstrated to be a possible basis for a differential response.

The process of conditioning described in this paper is formally similar to the processes of conditioning of Estes (5) and Bush and Mosteller (2,3). In the present theory conditioning takes place at each trial, not only on "reinforced" trials. In earlier theories conditioning is said to occur only on such reinforced trials. In two-choice discrimination the incorrect response has a high initial probability (one-half) because of the nature of the physical situation and the way of recording responses. Therefore, a theory of two-choice learning must account for the consistent weakening of such responses through consistent nonreinforcement.

The notion of adaptation used here is formally analogous to the operation of Bush and Mosteller's Discrimination Operator "*D*" (3). However, whereas Bush and Mosteller's operator is applied only on trials in which the reward condition is reversed for a cue, the present theory indicates that this process takes place each trial. In addition, while the Discrimination Operator and the process of adaptation are both exponential in form, Bush and Mosteller introduce a new exponential constant *k* for this purpose and the present theory uses the conditioning constant θ.

The major point differentiating the present theory from similar earlier theories is the use of the strong simplifying assumption identifying the exponential constant θ with the proportion of relevant cues. This assumption may appear intuitively unlikely, but if it should be shown by further experiment to be tenable, the predictive power of discrimination learning theory is enhanced. There seems to be no reason for abandoning so useful an assumption unless experimental results require it.

Summary

A theory of two-choice discrimination learning has been presented. The theory is formally similar to earlier theories of Estes (5) and Bush and Mosteller (3) but differs somewhat in basic concepts and uses a new simplifying assumption.

From this theory three empirical laws are derived: one dealing with the combination of relevant cues, and two dealing with a special type of transfer of training. These laws permitted quantitative predictions of the behavior of four groups of rats and two groups of human subjects. Five of these six predictions were quite accurate, and the sixth was within the range of reasonable sampling deviation.

REFERENCES

1. Amsel, A. Rate of learning a visual brightness discrimination as a function of discriminanda durations. *J. comp. physiol. Psychol.*, 1952, **45**, 341–346.
2. Bush, R. R., & Mosteller, F. A mathematical model for simple learning. *Psychol. Rev.*, 1951, **58**, 313–323.
3. Bush, R. R., & Mosteller, F. A model for stimulus generalization and discrimination. *Psychol. Rev.*, 1951, **58**, 413–423.
4. Eninger, M. U. Habit summation in a selective learning problem. *J. comp. physiol. Psychol.*, 1952, **45**, 511–516.
5. Estes, W. K. Toward a statistical theory of learning. *Psychol. Rev.*, 1950, **57**, 94–107.
6. Lawrence, D. H. Acquired distinctiveness of cues: II. Selective association in a constant stimulus situation. *J. exp. Psychol.*, 1950, **40**, 175–188.
7. Lawrence, D. H. The transfer of a discrimination along a continuum. *J. comp. physiol. Psychol.*, 1952, **45**, 511–516.
8. Prentice, W. C. H. Continuity in human learning. *J. exp. Psychol.*, 1949, **39**, 187–194.

(Received January 14, 1954)

A Markov Model for Discrimination Learning[*]

RICHARD C. ATKINSON, *University of California, Los Angeles*

A theory for discrimination learning which incorporates the concept of an observing response is presented. The theory is developed in detail for experimental procedures in which two stimuli are employed and two responses are available to the subject. Applications of the model to cases involving probabilistic and nonprobabilistic schedules of reinforcement are considered; some predictions are derived and compared with experimental results.

This paper is a preliminary attempt to develop a quantitativ theory of discrimination learning. For simplicity, the discussion will be limited to two-response problems, but the formulation can be extended readily to certain n-response situations. The model corresponds in some respects to theoretical analysis of discrimination learning presented by Burke and Estes [5] and Bush and Mosteller [6]. In particular, the stimulus conceptualization and response conditioning process are similar to their formulations. The model, however, differs from their work in that an orienting or observing response [16] is postulated. This additional feature leads to predictions which, for some experimental parameter values, are markedly different from those made by either Burke and Estes or Bush and Mosteller, while for other parameter values the predictions are identical. Interrelations among these models will be considered later.

The theory is designed to analyze behavior in an experimental setup where two stimuli, designated T_1 and T_2, are employed and two responses, A_1 and A_2, are available to the subject. Each trial begins with the presentation of either T_1 or T_2; the probability of T_1 is β, and the probability of T_2 is $1 - \beta$. Following T_1, an A_1 response is correct with probability π_1, and an A_2 response is correct with probability $1 - \pi_1$. Following T_2, an A_1 response is correct with probability π_2, and an A_2 response is correct with probability $1 - \pi_2$.

The traditional type of discrimination problem is described when $\pi_1 = 1$ and $\pi_2 = 0$. The subject must learn to respond with A_1 to the presentation of T_1 and respond with A_2 to the presentation of T_2. A form of discrimination learning, involving probabilistic schedules of reinforcement, is specified when π_1, $\pi_2 \neq 0$ or 1. This type of discrimination problem has been only recently investigated [9, 10, 14].

*This research was supported by a grant from the National Science Foundation.

This article appeared in *Psychmetrika*, 1958, **23**, 309–322.

Theoretical Concepts

Stimulus Representation

The stimuli T_1 and T_2 are to be represented conceptually as two sets of stimulus elements, which are designated $\mathfrak{S}_1$ and $\mathfrak{S}_2$, respectively. Further, a set C is designated which represents those stimulus elements common to sets $\mathfrak{S}_1$ and $\mathfrak{S}_2$ ($C = \mathfrak{S}_1 \cap \mathfrak{S}_2$), i.e., those stimulus events common to the presentation of either T_1 or T_2. In regard to the size of the C set, an *index of similarity* between T_1 and T_2 can be defined; the larger the relative size of C with respect to $\mathfrak{S}_1$ and $\mathfrak{S}_2$ the greater the similarity between the stimuli [6].

To simplify subsequent notation let the set S_1 be all stimulus elements in $\mathfrak{S}_1$ but not in C. Similarly, S_2 is the set of all stimulus elements in $\mathfrak{S}_2$ but not in C. Specifically,

$$(1) \qquad S_1 = \mathfrak{S}_1 - C, \qquad S_2 = \mathfrak{S}_2 - C.$$

Let N_1, N_2, and N_c be the number of elements in sets S_1, S_2, and C, respectively. Finally, define

$$(2) \qquad W_1 = \frac{N_1}{N_1 + N_c}, \qquad W_2 = \frac{N_2}{N_2 + N_c}.$$

Orienting Response

It is hypothesized that the organism makes one of two responses at the start of each trial, either an orienting response or a nonorienting response. These responses are designated O and $\bar{O}$, respectively. If O occurs, then the organism is exposed to the unique stimulus elements on that trial. More specifically, the organism will be exposed to only the S_1 stimulus elements if T_1 is presented and to only the S_2 stimulus elements if T_2 is presented. If, on the other hand, $\bar{O}$ occurs, then the organism is exposed to both unique and common stimulus elements on the trial. The organism will be exposed to both S_1 and C stimulus elements if T_1 is presented and to both S_2 and C stimulus elements if T_2 is presented.

It is assumed that the O and $\bar{O}$ responses are elicited by a set $\mathfrak{D}$ of stimuli associated with the beginning of the trial. Thus, the sequence of events on a given trial is as follows.

(i) The onset of the trial is associated with the presentation of a set of stimulus elements $\mathfrak{D}$.

(ii) $\mathfrak{D}$ elicits either an O or $\bar{O}$ response.

(iii) If O occurs, the organism is exposed to the S_1 set on T_1 trials and to the S_2 set on T_2 trials. If $\bar{O}$ occurs, the organism is exposed to S_1 and C on T_1 trials and to S_2 and C on T_2 trials.

Conditioning Relations and Response Probability

On any trial of an experiment, all elements of a given stimulus set are conditioned to one and only one response. The entire $\mathfrak{D}$ set is conditioned to either O or $\bar{O}$. Similarly, the S_i set ($i = 1$ or 2) is conditioned to either A_1 or A_2 and the C set is conditioned to either A_1 or A_2 .

The probability of a response in the presence of particular stimulus elements is defined as the proportion of stimulus elements conditioned to the response [1, 8]. Thus, the probability of O on trial n, $p_n (O)$, is either 1 or 0, depending on whether the $\mathfrak{D}$ set is conditioned to O or $\bar{O}$ at the start of trial n. The probability of A_1 when only S_i ($i = 1$ or 2) is presented (i.e., when an O response has occurred at the start of the trial) is 1 or 0 depending on whether the S_i set is conditioned to A_1 or A_2 . Finally, the probability of A_1 when S_i and C are presented (i.e., when an $\bar{O}$ has occurred at the start of the trial) is, (i) 1 if both the S_i set and the C set are conditioned to A_1 , (ii) W_i if the S_i set is conditioned to A_1 and the C set is conditioned to A_2 , (iii) $1 - W_i$ if the S_i set is conditioned to A_2 and the C set is conditioned to A_1 and, (iv) 0 if both the S_i set and the C set are conditioned to A_2 .

Conditioning Process

A single parameter θ is assumed which governs the conditioning of stimulus sets. On a given trial all elements from $\mathfrak{D}$ and *available* elements from $\mathfrak{S}_i$ will be conditioned with probability θ to an appropriate response, and the conditioned status of all elements will remain unchanged with probability $1 - \theta$. Only those elements in $\mathfrak{S}_1$ and $\mathfrak{S}_2$ which are exposed to the organism on a given trial are available for conditioning. If an O response is made at the start of the trial, then either S_1 or S_2 is available for conditioning on the trial. If an $\bar{O}$ response is made, then either S_1 and C or S_2 and C are available for conditioning. Specifically the following cases encompass all possibilities.

(1) $O \rightarrow T_i \rightarrow A_j \rightarrow$ *correct.* An observing response is made and makes set S_i available. The set S_i elicits A_j , which is designated correct. Given this sequence of events, there is (i) a probability θ that all elements in $\mathfrak{D}$ will be conditioned to O and all elements in S_i will be conditioned to A_j and, (ii) a probability $1 - \theta$ that the conditional status of the element will remain unchanged.

(2) $O \rightarrow T_i \rightarrow A_j \rightarrow$ *not correct.* An observing response is made, and makes set S_i available. The set S_i elicits A_j , which is incorrect. Given this sequence of events there is (i) a probability θ that all elements in $\mathfrak{D}$ will be conditioned to $\bar{O}$ and all elements in S_i will be conditioned to A_j other than the one which occurred on the trial, and (ii) a probability $1 - \theta$ that the conditional status of the elements will remain unchanged.

(3) $\bar{O} \rightarrow T_i \rightarrow A_j \rightarrow$ *correct.* A nonobserving response is made and makes sets S_i and C available; the sets S_i and C elicit A_j , which is correct. Given this sequence of events there is (i) a probability θ that all elements in $\mathfrak{D}$ will be conditioned to $\bar{O}$ response and all elements in both S_i and C will be condi-

tioned to A_j , and (ii) a probability $1 - \theta$ that the conditional status of the elements will remain unchanged.

(4) $\overline{O} \rightarrow T_i \rightarrow A_j \rightarrow$ *not correct*. A nonobserving response is made and makes sets S_i and C available; the sets S_i and C elicit A_j , which is incorrect. Given this sequence there is (i) a probability θ that all elements in $\mathfrak{D}$ will be conditioned to O and all elements in both S_i and C will be conditioned to A_j other than the one which occurred on the trial, and (ii) a probability $1 - \theta$ that the conditional status of the elements will remain unchanged.

The above assumptions for conditioning and response probability are different from those postulated by Estes and Burke in their stimulus sampling model [5, 8]. No attempt will be made to compare the two sets of assumptions, but it should be noted that the ideas fundamental to the model presented in this paper initially were formalized within the framework of the Estes and Burke stimulus sampling theory. Unfortunately, the mathematical analysis resulted in a system of difference equations for which methods of solution are not known. Consequently, certain simplifying assumptions were made which yielded the present model. The difference in complexity between the stimulus sampling formulation and the present analysis is reflected in the state spaces of the respective stochastic processes. For the model presented in this paper the state space includes only six points $\{0, W_1 , W_2 , 1 - W_1 , 1 - W_2 , 1\}$, while the state space for the stimulus sampling model is defined on the closed interval $[0, 1]$.

Mathematical Formulation

Given this conditioning process and the assumption that all stimulus elements in a particular set ($\mathfrak{D}$, S_1 , C, S_2) are conditioned to the same response at the start of the first trial, an organism can be described as being in one of sixteen possible states on any trial. A state will be specified by an ordered four-tuple where:

(i) the first member of the tuple indicates whether all elements in set $\mathfrak{D}$ are conditioned to O or $\overline{O}$;

(ii) the second member indicates whether elements in S_1 are conditioned to A_1 or A_2 ;

(iii) the third member indicates whether elements in C are conditioned to A_1 or A_2 ;

(iv) the fourth member indicates whether elements in S_2 are conditioned to A_1 or A_2 .

As an example, the state $\langle \overline{0}, 1, 1, 2 \rangle$ indicates that the $\mathfrak{D}$ set is conditioned to $\overline{O}$, S_1 is conditioned to A_1 , C is conditioned to A_1 , and S_2 is conditioned to A_2 . If the organism is in this state at the start of trial n, then if T_1 is presented an A_1 will occur, and if T_2 is presented an A_2 will occur with probability W_2 and an A_1 with probability $1-W_2$. The states will be assigned identifying numbers as follows.

1. $\langle 0, 1, 1, 1 \rangle$ 5. $\langle 0, 2, 1, 1 \rangle$ 9. $\langle \bar{0}, 1, 1, 1 \rangle$ 13. $\langle \bar{0}, 2, 1, 1 \rangle$

2. $\langle 0, 1, 1, 2 \rangle$ 6. $\langle 0, 2, 1, 2 \rangle$ 10. $\langle \bar{0}, 1, 1, 2 \rangle$ 14. $\langle \bar{0}, 2, 1, 2 \rangle$

3. $\langle 0, 1, 2, 1 \rangle$ 7. $\langle 0, 2, 2, 1 \rangle$ 11. $\langle \bar{0}, 1, 2, 1 \rangle$ 15. $\langle \bar{0}, 2, 2, 1 \rangle$

4. $\langle 0, 1, 2, 2 \rangle$ 8. $\langle 0, 2, 2, 2 \rangle$ 12. $\langle \bar{0}, 1, 2, 2 \rangle$ 16. $\langle \bar{0}, 2, 2, 2 \rangle$

For these conditioning assumptions and the experimental parameters β, π_1, and π_2 a transition matrix P describing the learning process can be derived and is presented in Table 1. To simplify notation, in writing the P matrix let a $= \theta\beta\pi_1$, b $= \theta\beta(1 - \pi_1)$, c $= \theta(1 - \beta)\pi_2$, and d $= \theta(1 - \beta)(1 - \pi_2)$.

The state at the start of trial n is listed on the row, and the state at the start of trial $n + 1$ is listed on the column. For example, a, the entry in row 15, column 1, is the conditional probability of being in state $\langle 0, 1, 1, 1 \rangle$ at the start of trial $n + 1$ given that the organism was in state $\langle 0, 2, 2, 1 \rangle$ at the start of trial n.

Let $u_i(n)$ be the expected probability of being in state i ($i = 1$ to 16) at the start of trial n, where the first experimental trial is $n = 0$. Define the row matrix

(3) $$ U(n) = [u_1(n), u_2(n), \cdots, u_{16}(n)]. $$

Further, let P represent the one-stage transition matrix of order sixteen presented above, where p_{ij} is the conditional probability of being in state j on trial $n + 1$, given that the system was in state i on trial n. Then the Markov process describing discrimination learning at the start of trial n is

(4) $$ U(n) = U(0)P^n. $$

(For a general consideration of finite Markov processes see [4, 11, or 12]. For applications of Markov processes to learning see [2, 3, 13].)

Experimentally it is impossible to identify individual states of the process on a particular trial. That is, given information about the type of trial and the A_j response which occurred, what state the organism was in at the start of the trial cannot be specified. For example, if T_1 is presented and A_2 occurs, which of the sixteen states the organism was in when the A_2 occurred cannot be established unequivocally. In fact, for this particular combination, any one of the following eight states would have been possible: 1, 2, 3, 4, 9, 10, 11, or 12. Obviously, this confounding is due to the fact that O and $\bar{O}$ responses have been postulated which are not observable.

Since trial descriptions and theoretical states cannot be placed in one-

TABLE 1

The Transition Matrix P

(Zero terms are indicated by blank cells.)

States	1	2	3	4	5	6	7	8	9	10	11	12	13	14	15	16
1	$1-\theta+a+c$															
2		$1-\theta+a+d$														
3			$1-\theta+a+c$													
4				$1-\theta+a+d$												
5					$1-\theta+b+c$				a							
6						$1-\theta+b+d$										
7							$1-\theta+b+c$									
8								$1-\theta+b+d$								
9							b	b	$1-\theta+a+c$							
10	W_2c			$(1-W_2)d$					$(1-W_2)c$	$1-\theta+a$						
11	$(1-W_1)a+(1-W_2)c$			W_2d			W_1b		W_1a+W_2c		$1-\theta$					
12	c	$(1-W_1)a$					$(1-W_1)b$	d	$(1-W_1)a$			$1-\theta+d$				$(1-W_1)b$
13	W_1a						$(1-W_1)b$	W_1b					$1-\theta+c$		W_1b	
14		W_1a			W_2c			$(1-W_1)b+(1-W_2)d$					$(1-W_2)c$	$1-\theta$		W_1b+W_2d
15	a				$(1-W_2)c$			W_2d					W_2c		$1-\theta+b$	$(1-W_2)d$
16	a				c											$1-\theta+b+d$

to-one correspondence, it is necessary (for an experimental evaluation of the theory) to define probabilities of events that are observable. Consequently, the following probabilities are of particular interest: $p_n(A_1 \mid T_1)$, the expected conditional probability on trial n of A_1 given T_1 ; and $p_n(A_1 \mid T_2)$, the expected conditional probability on trial n of A_1 given T_2 . By inspection of the theoretical states it follows that

$$
(5) \quad
\begin{aligned}
p_n(A_1 \mid T_1) = u_1(n) + u_2(n) + u_3(n) + u_4(n) + u_9(n) + u_{10}(n) \\
+ W_1[u_{11}(n) + u_{12}(n)] + (1 - W_1)[u_{13}(n) + u_{14}(n)],
\end{aligned}
$$

and

$$
(6) \quad
\begin{aligned}
p_n(A_1 \mid T_2) = u_1(n) + u_3(n) + u_5(n) + u_7(n) + u_9(n) + u_{13}(n) \\
+ W_2[u_{11}(n) + u_{15}(n)] + (1 - W_2)[u_{10}(n) + u_{14}(n)].
\end{aligned}
$$

Also, for analytical purposes, the probability of an observing response at the start of trial n will be useful.

$$
(7) \quad p_n(O) = u_1(n) + u_2(n) + \cdots + u_8(n).
$$

Analysis of the Model and Some Special Cases

To illustrate certain aspects of the theory, without going into extensive mathematical detail, several special cases will be considered. These cases are of particular interest experimentally. For each case illustrative learning functions will be presented. The computations have been performed with the following restrictions on parameter values: $W_1 = W_2 = W$; the initial probability of O was taken to be zero and the initial probability of A_1 to S_1 , S_2 , or C to be .5. That is, $u_1(0) = u_2(0) = \cdots = u_8(0) = 0$ and $u_9(0) = u_{10}(0) = \cdots = u_{16}(0) = 1/8$.

The computations were performed at the Western Data Processing Center on a 650 IBM computer. The program or punch program deck is available to anyone who is interested in generating theoretical functions for cases or parameter values not presented in this paper. The program is arranged so that the following information must be read into the computer memory: β, π_1 π_2 , θ, W_1 , W_2 , and the vector $U(0)$. The program will compute $U(n)$, $p_n(A_1 \mid T_1)$, $p_n(A_1 \mid T_2)$ and $p_n(O)$ for successive values of n and also asymptotic results for each of these quantities.

However, before examining special cases, a general result can be immediately established; the Cesàro asymptotic probability of any state in the process is independent of the value of θ when $\theta > 0$. This follows from the fact that the main diagonal of the matrix P has terms of the form $(1 - \theta) + \theta X$, while all other nonzero terms are of the form θY. For the case where $\theta = 0$, $u_i(n) = u_i(0)$ for all n.

Traditional Discrimination Learning

The case in which $\pi_1 = 1$, $\pi_2 = 0$, and $\beta \neq 0$ or 1 describes the often investigated situation in which the subject is required to respond with A_1 to the presentation of T_1 and with A_2 to the presentation of T_2. An inspection of the P matrix indicates that, for these particular parameter values, the process eventually will be absorbed in either state $\langle 0, 1, 2, 2 \rangle$ or state $\langle 0, 1, 1, 2 \rangle$ and, therefore, asymptotically

$$p_n(O) \xrightarrow{n} 1$$

$$(8) \qquad p_n(A_1 \mid T_1) \xrightarrow{n} 1$$

$$p_n(A_1 \mid T_2) \xrightarrow{n} 0.$$

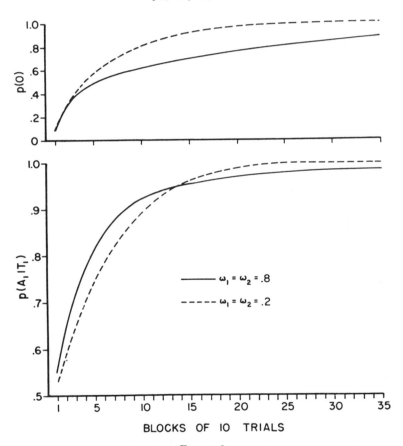

FIGURE 1

Theoretical discrimination learning function for two conditions of stimulus similarity. The case in which $\pi_1 = 1$, $\pi_2 = 0$, and $\beta = 1/2$.

Figure 1 presents several theoretical curves of $p_n(A_1 \mid T_1)$ in blocks of ten trials when $\theta = .05$ and $\beta = .5$. The curves for $p_n(A_1 \mid T_2)$ are not presented, since for $\beta = .5$ and the above initial conditions $p_n(A_1 \mid T_2) = 1 - p_n(A_1 \mid T_1)$. An interesting result is the relation between the functions for different values of W. Taking $W = .8$ as the comparison function, on early trials the $W = .2$ curve is below the comparison curve. However, by approximately trial 130 the $W = .2$ curve crosses the comparison curve and remains above it as they both approach unity. This appears to be a general relationship for a fixed **value** of θ and the above set of initial conditions; given $W^* > W^{**}$ on early trials, the W^* curve for $p_n(A_1 \mid T_1)$ will fall above the W^{**} curve, but at some trial a crossover will occur, and thereafter the W^{**} curve will be above the W^* curve as both approach unity. A proof of this result has not been obtained; however, calculations using many different values of W and θ in no case established a counter example. This is an interesting prediction, and one which should be verifiable. Unfortunately, no evidence has been found in the literature to confirm or negate this result. Research is now under way on this problem and is designed to manipulate W experimentally by varying the apparent similarity between discriminanda.

The Estes and Burke Study

The case in which $\pi_1 = 1.0$, $\pi_2 = .5$, and $\beta = .5$ describes a form of discrimination learning investigated by Estes and Burke [9]. There are several aspects to the study, but for the present analysis only the acquisition process for the constant group will be considered.

Facing the subject is a circular array of 12 lights, and either the onset of the six lights on the left half of the panel or the six on the right half are designated as a T_1 trial and the onset of the other six as a T_2 trial. On each trial the subject makes either an A_1 or A_2 response; this is followed by a signal which informs the subject which response was correct.

In Figure 2 the observed conditional probabilities of $p(A_1 \mid T_1)$ and $p(A_1 \mid T_2)$ in blocks of 20 trials are presented. On the average, for a block of 20 trials there will be 10 T_1 trials and 10 T_2 trials. Consequently, in a block of 20 trials the observed value of $p(A_1 \mid T_1)$ for a given subject is based on approximately 10 observations and $p(A_1 \mid T_2)$ is also based on approximately 10 observations.

Listed on the same graph are some theoretical curves computed for $\theta = .05$ and for $W = .1$, .6, and .9. As can be seen, the $W = .1$ curves provide a fairly close fit to the observed values for $p_n(A_1 \mid T_1)$ and $p_n(A_1 \mid T_2)$. For this value of W the $p_n(A_1 \mid T_1)$ curve approaches an asymptotic level of .907, which closely approximates the observed terminal values. More interesting, however, is the theoretical curve of $p(A_1 \mid T_2)$ for $W = .1$. It starts out at .5, rises to a maximum value at approximately trial 40, and then monotonically decreases to an asymptotic level of .525. This initial

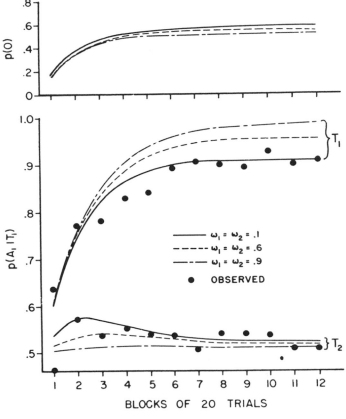

FIGURE 2

Observed values and theoretical functions of discrimination learning for the case in which $\pi_1 = 1$, $\pi_2 = 1/2$, and $\beta = 1/2$. Theoretical results for three conditions of stimulus similarity.

increase and subsequent decrease in the $p(A_1 \mid T_2)$ curve is evident in the Estes and Burke data and is an observation they emphasize in their discussion of the results.

A comparison of the curves in Figure 2 illustrates some general theoretical results for this special case; namely, $p_\infty(A_1 \mid T_1)$ is closer to unity and $p_\infty(A_1 \mid T_2)$ is closer to .5 the greater the value of W. Another prediction of experimental interest is that the smaller the value of W the greater the maximum value of $p_n(A_1 \mid T_2)$, and also the earlier the maximum will be reached. To illustrate, for the above computations, the maximum of $p_n(A_1 \mid T_2)$ for $W = .1$ was .575 and occurred on about trial 40, while the maximum for $W = .9$ was .540 and occurred on about trial 60.

The Popper and Atkinson Study

The final study to be considered used five groups [14]. For all groups $\pi_1 = .85$ and $\beta = .50$. The groups differed with respect to the π_2 parameter which took on the values .85, .70, .50, .30, and .15 for Groups I to V, respectively. In Figure 3 the observed proportions of A_1 responses following both T_1 and T_2 stimuli for the last 120 trials are presented. The experiment was run for a total of 320 trials. An inspection of the response curves by trials indicated that a stable level of responding had been reached during the last 120 trials. Consequently, the proportions presented in Figure 3 can be used as estimates of $p_\infty(A_1 \mid T_1)$ and $p_\infty(A_1 \mid T_2)$.

In fitting this data, the observed asymptotic value of $p_\infty(A_1 \mid T_1)$ for Group IV was used to evaluate W. The resulting estimate was $W = .1$. Using this value, predictions were then generated of $p_\infty(A_1 \mid T_1)$ for the other four groups and of $p_\infty(A_1 \mid T_2)$ for all five groups.

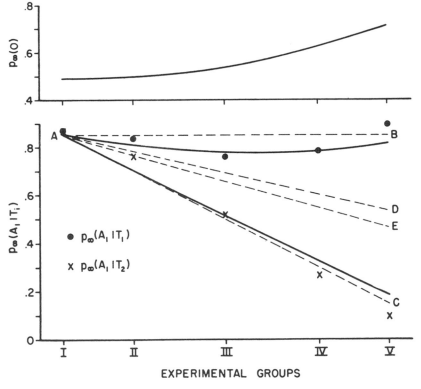

FIGURE 3

Predicted and observed asymptotic values for discrimination problems involving five probabilistic schedules of reinforcement.

The predicted values are given in Figure 3. No attempt will be made to present a detailed analysis of the data except to note that the general trends are approximated by the model. In particular, the model predicts a convex relation between $p_\infty(A_1 \mid T_1)$ and the value of π_2 which is reflected in the data. That is, for a fixed value of π_1, $p_\infty(A_1 \mid T_1)$ first decreases and then increases as π_2 goes from .85 to .15. On the other hand, the theoretical values of $p_\infty(A_1 \mid T_2)$ for $W = .1$ are close to the π_2 value for all groups.

Discussion

No rigorous attempt has been made to test the model for the special cases considered. Nevertheless, qualitatively it appears that the theory accounts for some aspects of traditional types of discrimination learning and can be extended without modification to discrimination problems involving probabilistic reinforcement schedules.

Several studies currently in progress are designed specifically to test various features of the theory. The variables analyzed encompass a broad range of reinforcement schedules and include procedures designed to manipulate the index of similarity between stimuli. It is hoped that these investigations will provide a quantitative evaluation of the present theory and will lead to a more satisfactory formalization of discrimination learning.

For readers familiar with the theoretical work of Burke and Estes [5] and Bush and Mosteller [6] for discrimination learning, it may be helpful to examine some relations between their models and the one presented in this paper. Of particular interest are the asymptotic predictions generated by each model.

In the Bush and Mosteller model,

$$p_n(A_1 \mid T_1) \xrightarrow{n} \pi_1 ,$$

(9)

$$p_n(A_1 \mid T_2) \xrightarrow{n} \pi_2 ,$$

independent of the value of β.

For Burke and Estes

$$p_n(A_1 \mid T_1) \xrightarrow{n} \pi_1 W_1 + (1 - W_1)\pi_c ,$$

(10)

$$p_n(A_1 \mid T_2) \xrightarrow{n} \pi_2 W_2 + (1 - W_2)\pi_c ,$$

where $\pi_c = \beta\pi_1 + (1 - \beta)\pi_2$.

For the model presented in this paper, predicted asymptotes always lie between the predictions of Bush-Mosteller and Burke-Estes. That is, $p_\infty(A_1 \mid T_1)$ is bounded between π_1 and $\pi_1 W_1 + (1 - W_1)\pi_c$, while $p_\infty(A_1 \mid T_2)$ is bounded between π_2 and $\pi_2 W_2 + (1 - W_2)\pi_c$.

These relationships are illustrated in Figure 3. Equation (9) predicts that $p_\infty(A_1 \mid T_1)$ will fall on the straight line AB and $p_\infty(A_1 \mid T_2)$ will fall on the straight line AC. In contrast, (10) predicts for $W_1 = W_2 = .1$ that

$p_\infty(A_1 \mid T_1)$ will fall on the straight line AD, while $p_\infty(A_1 \mid T_2)$ will fall on the straight line AE. As indicated earlier, for the present model the predicted value of $p_\infty(A_1 \mid T_1)$ falls on the convex function bounded between the straight lines AB and AD, while $p_\infty(A_1 \mid T_2)$ falls on the function bounded between lines AC and AE. Actually to compute predictions for the Burke-Estes model, one would estimate W from the data of one group, using an estimation procedure appropriate to their model, and then predict the results of the other groups, as was done for the model presented in this paper. The results undoubtedly would be different from those indicated by lines AD and AE in Figure 3, but would fall on straight lines with origins at A.

In conclusion, it appears that this model generates some interesting predictions regarding both reinforcement schedules and similarity between discriminanda. Objections might be raised concerning the particular assumptions that were selected, but in the final analysis their evaluation will be determined in the laboratory. Nevertheless, several aspects of the theory leave the author uneasy; one feature is particularly disturbing and deserves comment. Reference is made to the assumption in which a single conditioning parameter θ is postulated. In essence, this assumption requires that the acquisition of O or $\bar{O}$ will progress at the same rate as the acquisition of A_1 or A_2. Intuitively this seems an improbable state of affairs which may be approximated only for restricted experimental procedures. If this is the case, a change in the theory will be required such that two conditioning parameters are postulated, one governing the acquisition of O or $\bar{O}$ and the other A_1 or A_2. This modification will still allow formalization of the model as a sixteen-state Markov process. However, the P matrix would have many more nonzero entries, and the theory would no longer yield asymptotic response probabilities which are independent of the conditioning parameters. These complications are not unmanageable, and if the modification proves necessary, theoretical predictions still can be generated easily.

REFERENCES

[1] Atkinson, R. C. A stochastic model for rote serial learning. *Psychometrika*, 1957, **22**, 87–96.

[2] Atkinson, R. C. and Suppes, P. An analysis of a two-person game situation in terms of statistical learning theory. *J. exp. Psychol.*, 1958, **55**, 369–378.

[3] Atkinson, R. C. and Suppes, P. An analysis of non-zero sum games in terms of a Markov model for learning. Tech. Rep. No. 9, Contract NR 171-034, Appl. Math. and Statist. Lab., Stanford Univ., 1957.

[4] Bartlett, M. S. *An introduction to stochastic processes.* Cambridge: Cambridge Univ. Press, 1955.

[5] Burke, C. J. and Estes, W. K. A component model for stimulus variables in discrimination learning. *Psychometrika*, 1957, **22**, 133–145.

[6] Bush, R. R. and Mosteller, F. A model for stimulus generalization and discrimination. *Psychol. Rev.*, 1951, **58**, 413–423.

[7] Bush, R. R. and Mosteller, F. *Stochastic models for learning.* New York: Wiley, 1955.

[8] Estes, W. K. and Burke, C. J. A theory of stimulus variability in learning. *Psychol. Rev.*, 1953, **60**, 276–286.

[9] Estes, W. K. and Burke, C. J. Application of a statistical model to simple discrimination learning in human subjects. *J. exp. Psychol.*, 1955, **50**, 81–88.

[10] Estes, W. K., Burke, C. J., Atkinson, R. C., and Frankmann, J. P. Probabilistic discrimination learning. *J. exp. Psychol.*, 1957, **54**, 233–239.

[11] Feller, W. *An introduction to probability and its applications.* New York: Wiley, 1950.

[12] Fréchet, M. *Recherches théoriques modernes sur le calcul des probabilités*, Vol. 2. Paris: Gauthier-Villars, 1938.

[13] Kemeny, J. G. and Snell, J. L. Markov processes in learning theory. *Psychometrika*, 1957, **22**, 221–230.

[14] Popper, J. and Atkinson, R. C. Discrimination learning in a verbal conditioning situation. *J. exp. Psychol.*, 1958, **56**, 21–25.

[15] Restle, F. A theory of selective learning with probable reinforcements *Psychol. Rev.*, 1957, **64**, 182–191.

[16] Wyckoff, L. B., Jr. The role of observing responses in discrimination behavior. *Psychol. Rev.*, 1952, **59**, 437-442.

Manuscript received 1/10/58
Revised manuscript received 5/30/58

The Observing Response in Discrimination Learning[1]

RICHARD C. ATKINSON, *Stanford University*

Recently, the importance of an orienting or observing response has been emphasized in the formulation of a general theory of discrimination behavior (Atkinson, 1958, 1960; Burke & Estes, 1957; Restle, 1959; Wyckoff, 1952). Unfortunately, for many experimental problems it is not clear how such a theory should be formalized. In particular, there are not enough experimental data available to permit a detailed specification of the postulates relating observing responses and such variables as stimulus dimensions, reinforcement schedules, and stimulus schedules. The purpose of this study is to gain information about this class of relations by modifying the typical discrimination task so that observing responses can be categorized and directly measured.

The experimental situation is considered as a sequence of discrete trials. Each trial is described in terms of the following classifications:

T_1, T_2: *Trial type.* Each trial is either a T_1 or a T_2. Trial type is selected by E and determines in part the stimulus event occurring on that trial.

O_1, O_2: *Observing responses.* At the start of each trial, S makes either an O_1 or O_2. The particular observing response made determines in part the stimulus event for that trial.

s_1, s_c, s_2: *Stimulus events.* Following the observing response, one and only one of these stimulus events (discriminative cues) occurs. On a T_1 trial, s_1 or s_c can occur; on a T_2 trial, s_2 or s_c can occur.

A_1, A_2: *Discrimination responses.* On each trial S makes either an A_1 or A_2 response to the presentation of the stimulus event.

E_1, E_2: *Reinforcing events.* The trial is terminated with the occurrence of one of these events. An E_1 indicates that A_1 was the correct response for that trial and E_2 indicates that A_2 was correct.

The sequence of events on a trial is as follows: (a) ready signal occurs and S makes either an O_1 or O_2; (b) following the observing response s_1, s_2, or s_c is presented; (c) to the onset of s_i, S makes either A_1 or A_2; (d) the trial is terminated with reinforcing event E_1 or E_2.

The trial type and reinforcing event are determined by E. The probability of an E_1 event on a T_1 trial is denoted by π_1, and the probability of an E_1 event on a T_2 trial is denoted by π_2. Consequently, the probability of an E_2 is $1 - \pi_1$ on a T_1 trial and $1 - \pi_2$ on a T_2 trial. The two types of trials are equiprobable in the present experiment.

The particular s_i event that is presented on any trial depends on the trial type and the observing response. If an O_1 is made, then (a) with probability α the s_1 event occurs on a T_1 trial and the s_2 event occurs on a T_2 trial, and (b) with probability $1 - \alpha$ the s_c event occurs, regardless of the trial type. If an O_2 is made, then (a) with probability α the s_c event occurs, regardless of the trial type, and (b) with probability $1 - \alpha$ the s_1 event occurs on a T_1 trial and the s_2 event occurs on a T_2 trial.

To clarify the experimental procedure, consider a case where $\alpha = 1$, $\pi_1 = 1$, and $\pi_2 = 0$. If S is to be correct on every trial, he must make an A_1 on a T_1 trial and an A_2 on a T_2 trial. However, S can gain information about the trial type only by making the appropriate observing response. That is, O_1 must be made in order to identify the trial type; the occurrence of O_2 always leads to the presentation of s_c. Hence, for perfect responding in this case, S must make the O_1 response with probability 1 and then make A_1 to s_1 or A_2 to s_2.

[1] This research was supported by the Office of Naval Research under Contract Nonr 233(58).

This article appeared in *J. exp. Psychol.*, 1961, **62**, 253–262.

The aim of this study is to investigate the effect of various event schedules on observing behavior. In particular, we are interested in the values of π_1, π_2, and α as determiners of the probability of an O_1 response.

THEORY

The analysis of the data will be organized within the framework of a Markov chain model which is closely related to stimulus sampling theory as first formulated by Estes (1950) and Estes and Burke (1953). The mathematical techniques for the model considered in this paper have been presented in detail elsewhere (Atkinson, 1960; Suppes & Atkinson, 1960) and the reader is referred there for a rigorous development.

The basic assumption for observing responses is that if $O_i(i = 1, 2)$ occurs and leads to the selection of a stimulus which in turn elicits a correct discrimination response, then S will tend to repeat that observing response on the next trial. However, if O_i occurs and leads to the selection of a stimulus which elicits an incorrect discrimination response, then S will tend not to repeat that observing response on the next trial. Conceptually, this assumption is similar to that proposed by Wyckoff (1952) and Atkinson (1958).

It is next assumed that S can be described by an ordered four-tuple at the start of trial n where (a) the first member is 1 or 2 and indicates whether O_1 or O_2 will be made on trial n, (b) the second member is 1 or 2 and indicates whether s_1 is conditioned to A_1 or to A_2 (i.e., whether A_1 or A_2 will occur if s_1 is presented), (c) the third member is 1 or 2 and indicates whether s_c is conditioned to A_1 or to A_2, and (d) the fourth member is 1 or 2 and indicates whether s_2 is conditioned to A_1 or to A_2.

These four-tuples will be referred to as subject states and assigned identifying numbers as follows:

1. (1111)	5. (1211)	9. (2111)	13. (2211)
2. (1112)	6. (1212)	10. (2112)	14. (2212)
3. (1121)	7. (1221)	11. (2121)	15. (2221)
4. (1122)	8. (1222)	12. (2122)	16. (2222)

From trial to trial S may change states depending on the sequence of responses and reinforcements. The possible changes are specified by the following axioms:

Axiom 1: With probability θ' the $s_k(k = 1, 2, c)$ stimulus presented on trial n will become conditioned to the reinforced response; if it is already conditioned to that response it remains so. (For example, if s_k is presented and followed by E_j then with probability θ' it will become conditioned to A_j.)

Axiom 2: If $O_i(i = 1, 2)$ is made on trial n and followed by an s_k which elicits a correct discrimination response, then S will repeat the same observing response on the next trial. However, if O_i is made and followed by an incorrect discrimination response, then with probability θ'' S will make the other observing response on the next trial.

From these assumptions and the event schedules employed in this experiment, it can be shown that the sequence of random variables which take the subject states as values is an irreducible, aperiodic Markov chain. This means among other things that a transition matrix $[p_{ij}]$ may be derived from these assumptions where p_{ij} is the conditional probability of being in state j on trial $n + 1$ given state i on trial n. The learning process is completely characterized by these transition probabilities and the initial probability distribution on states.

To clarify the application of the axioms we derive one element of $[p_{ij}]$. Assume S is in State 1211 at the start of Trial n and $T_1 \cdot E_1$ is selected by E with probability $\frac{1}{2}\pi_1$. Then an O_1 occurs with probability 1 and an s_1 is presented with probability α; to the presentation of s_1 an A_2 is made. The S's discrimination response was incorrect and therefore with probability θ'' the observing response changes from O_1 to O_2. Also, with independent probability θ' the conditioning of s_1 changes from A_2 to A_1. Multiplication of the conditional probabilities yields the probability of going from State 1211 to State 2111; i.e., $p_{5,9} = \frac{1}{2}\pi_1\alpha\theta'\theta''$.

In this paper, we shall be primarily interested in the asymptotic behavior of

S. Consequently, $p_{ij}{}^{(n)}$ is defined as the probability of being in state j on trial $n+1$, given that on Trial 1 S was in State i. Then the following limit exists and is independent of i,

$$u_j = \lim_{n \to \infty} p_{ij}{}^{(n)}.$$

The quantity u_j can be interpreted as the asymptotic probability of being in state j no matter what the initial distribution. Experimentally, we will be interested in evaluating the following theoretical predictions:

$$P_\infty(O_1) = u_1 + u_2 + u_3 + u_4 \\ + u_5 + u_6 + u_7 + u_8 \quad [1]$$

$$P_\infty(A_1 \mid T_1) = u_1 + u_2 + u_9 + u_{10} \\ + \alpha[u_3 + u_4 + u_{13} + u_{14}] \\ + (1-\alpha)[u_5 + u_6 + u_{11} + u_{12}] \quad [2]$$

$$P_\infty(A_1 \mid T_2) = u_1 + u_5 + u_9 + u_{13} \\ + \alpha[u_3 + u_7 + u_{10} + u_{14}] \\ + (1-\alpha)[u_2 + u_6 + u_{11} + u_{15}] \quad [3]$$

$$P_\infty(O_1 \cap A_1) = u_1 + \alpha u_3 + (1-\alpha)u_6 \\ + (\alpha/2)[u_4 + u_7] \\ + (1-\alpha/2)[u_2 + u_5] \quad [4]$$

$$P_\infty(O_2 \cap A_1) = u_9 + \alpha u_{14} + (1-\alpha)u_{11} \\ + [(1-\alpha)/2][u_{12} + u_{15}] \\ + [1 - (1-\alpha)/2][u_{10} + u_{13}] \quad [5]$$

Equation 1 gives the asymptotic probability of an O_1 response. Equations 2 and 3 present the asymptotic probability of an A_1 response on T_1 and T_2 trials, respectively. Finally, Equations 4 and 5 present the asymptotic probability of the joint occurrence of each observing response with an A_1 response.

METHOD

Experimental parameter values.—Six groups of Ss were tested. For all groups $\pi_1 = .9$. The groups differed with respect to the experimental parameters π_2 and α; three values of π_2 (.9, .5, and .1) and two values of α (1.00 and .75) were used. Specifically, $\pi_2 = .90$, $\alpha = 1.0$ (Group I); $\pi_2 = .50$, $\alpha = 1.0$ (Group II); $\pi_2 = .10$, $\alpha = 1.0$ (Group III); $\pi_2 = .90$, $\alpha = .75$ (Group IV); $\pi_2 = .50$, $\alpha = .75$ (Group V); and $\pi_2 = .10$, $\alpha = .75$ (Group VI). These particular values of π were

selected because they had been used in a similar discrimination experiment where the observing response was not available (Atkinson, Bogartz, & Turner, 1959).

Subjects.—The Ss were 240 undergraduates obtained from introductory courses in psychology. They were randomly assigned to groups with the restriction of 40 Ss in each group.

Apparatus.—The Ss were run in subgroups of two with each S seated in a private booth. The apparatus, viewed from within S's booth, consisted of a shelf at table level which was 30 in. wide and 13 in. deep. A panel 30 in. wide and 30 in. high was mounted vertically on the edge of the shelf farthest from S. Four red panel lights (the s_i stimuli) were in a column and centered on the vertical panel; the bottom light was 20 in. from the base of the panel; the others were spaced above each other at $1\frac{1}{4}$-in. intervals. Two silent operating keys (the A_1 and A_2 responses) were each mounted $1\frac{1}{2}$ in. in from the edge of the shelf facing S; these keys were 14 in. apart and centered on the column of red lights. On the shelf, 1 in. behind each of these keys, was a white panel light (E_1 and E_2 events). Two additional silent operating keys (the O_1 and O_2 responses) were each mounted 6 in. in from the rear edge of the shelf; these keys were 2 in. apart and also centered on the red lights. A green light (the signal) was centered 3 in. behind the observing response keys on the shelf. The presentation and duration of the lights were automatically controlled.

Procedure.—Within each of the six experimental groups, four subgroups of 10 Ss were formed by counterbalancing right and left positions of the observing response and the discrimination response keys. For each S one of the four red lights was randomly designated s_1, another s_c, and another s_2; the fourth light was not used.

The Ss were read the following instructions:

The present study is designed to determine how well you can do on a very difficult pattern recognition problem. We run subjects in pairs to save time, but you are both working on completely different problems. The experiment for each of you consists of a series of trials. The green light on your panel will go on to indicate the start of each trial. Some time later, one or the other of the two lower white lights will go on. Your job is to predict on each trial which one of the two white lights will go on and to indicate your prediction by pressing one of the two lower keys.

However, before you make your prediction you will receive additional information. That is, as soon as the green light goes on, press one or the other of the two upper keys—which key you press is up to you. Shortly thereafter, one of the four red lights will go on. The particular red light which goes on depends in part on the key you press. Further, the red light which goes on will help you in making your prediction as to which white light goes on. After you have seen one of the red lights go on, you will then predict which white light will go on by pressing the proper key. That is, if you expect the left white light to go on, press the left lower key, and if you expect the right white light to go on, press the right lower key. If the light above the key you pressed goes on, your prediction was correct, but if the light above the key opposite from the one you pressed goes on, you were incorrect and should have pressed the other key. Thus, for a single trial, the sequence of events is as follows: (1) the green light goes on to signal the start of the trial, (2) you press one of the

two upper keys, (3) one of the red lights will go on, (4) you press one of the two lower keys, (5) if the white light goes on above the key you pressed, your prediction was correct; if the light above the key opposite from the one you pressed goes on, you were incorrect and should have pressed the other key.

Questions were answered by paraphrasing the appropriate part of the instructions. Following the instructions, 200 trials were run in continuous sequence. This sequence was followed by a 5-min. rest period; during this period no questions referring to the experiment were answered by E, and Ss were not allowed to discuss the experiment. Following the rest, 200 additional trials were run. For each S, random sequences of s_i and E_i events were generated in accordance with assigned values of π_1, π_2, α, and the observed O_i responses.

On all trials, the signal light was lighted for 2 sec. The appropriate s_i stimulus light immediately followed the cessation of the signal light and remained on for 3 sec. After

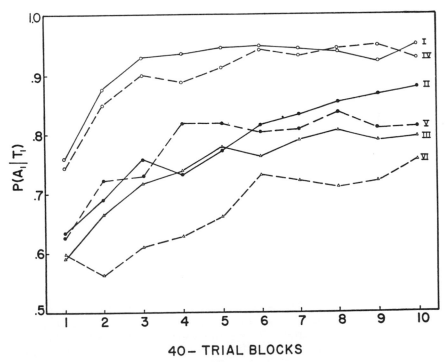

FIG. 1.   The average proportion of A_1 responses on T_1-type trials in successive blocks of 40 trials.

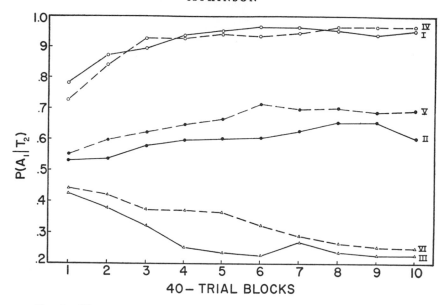

FIG. 2. The average proportion of A_1 responses on T_2-type trials in successive blocks of 40 trials.

the offset of the s_i light, one of the reinforcing lights went on for 2 sec. The time between the offset of the reinforcing light and the onset of the signal light for the next trial was 3 sec.

RESULTS AND DISCUSSION

Mean learning curves and asymptotic results.—Figure 1 presents the average proportion of A_1 responses on T_1-type trials in successive blocks of 40 trials. For each S the proportion of A_1's on T_1 trials was tabulated for a 40-trial block, and these quantities were then averaged over Ss. Similarly, Fig. 2 presents the average proportion of A_1's on T_2-type trials in successive blocks of 40 trials. Finally, Fig. 3 presents the average proportion of O_1 responses. In all three figures the curves appear to be reasonably stable over the last half of the experiment. Consequently,

the proportions computed over the final block of 160 trials were used as estimates of asymptotic performance.

Table 1 presents the observed mean proportions over the last 160-trial block and the related SDs. The observed values of $P_\infty(A_1 | T_i)$ were computed as indicated in the description of Fig. 1 and 2. The observed values of $P_\infty(O_i \cap A_1)$ were computed by obtaining, for individual Ss, the proportion of trials on which both the A_1 response and the O_i response occurred and then averaging over Ss.

The values predicted by the model are also presented in Table 1 for the case where $\theta' = \theta'' = \theta$. Expressions for the u_k's were derived by standard methods (Feller, 1957), and then combined by Equations 1–5 to predict the response probabilities. The computations were performed at the Western Data Processing Center on

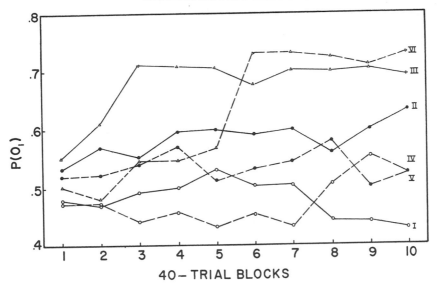

FIG. 3. The average proportion of O_1 responses in successive blocks of 40 trials.

TABLE 1

PREDICTED AND OBSERVED RESPONSE PROBABILITIES OVER THE LAST BLOCK
OF 160 TRIALS

	Group I			Group II			Group III		
	Pred.	Obs.	SD	Pred.	Obs.	SD	Pred.	Obs.	SD
$P_\infty(A_1\|T_1)$	.90	.94	.014	.81	.85	.164	.79	.79	.158
$P_\infty(A_1\|T_2)$	.90	.94	.014	.59	.61	.134	.21	.23	.182
$P_\infty(O_1)$	.50	.45	.279	.55	.59	.279	.73	.70	.285
$P_\infty(O_1\cap A_1)$	.45	.43	.266	.39	.42	.226	.37	.36	.164
$P_\infty(O_2\cap A_1)$	.45	.47	.293	.31	.31	.232	.13	.16	.161

	Group IV			Group V			Group VI		
	Pred.	Obs.	SD	Pred.	Obs.	SD	Pred.	Obs.	SD
$P_\infty(A_1\|T_1)$	.90	.93	.063	.80	.82	.114	.73	.73	.138
$P_\infty(A_1\|T_2)$	.90	.95	.014	.60	.68	.114	.27	.25	.138
$P_\infty(O_1)$	.49	.50	.257	.52	.53	.305	.63	.72	.263
$P_\infty(O_1\cap A_1)$	.44	.47	.241	.35	.38	.219	.32	.36	.138
$P_\infty(O_2\cap A_1)$	.46	.47	.247	.34	.36	.272	.19	.13	.168

an IBM 709 computer.[2] By presenting a single value for each theoretical

[2] The program or punch program deck is
available to anyone interested in generating
theoretical results for parameter values not
considered in this paper.

quantity in Table 1 we imply that
these predicted proportions are independent of θ. Actually this is not
always the case. However for the
event schedules employed in this
experiment the dependency of the

theoretical proportions on θ is negligible. For θ ranging over the interval .00001 to 1.0 the values of the predicted proportions are affected in only the third or fourth decimal place; it is for this reason that we present theoretical values to only two decimal places.[3]

In view of these comments it should be clear that the predictions in Table 1 are based solely on the experimentally assigned values of π_1, π_2, and α. Thus, they are entirely a priori and do not make use of any parameters evaluated from the data. Consequently, differences between Ss, which can be represented by inter-S variability in θ, do not substantially affect these asymptotic predictions. Of course, this implies that the observed proportions for individual Ss and also proportions averaged over Ss should both approach these predicted values with increasing sample size.

An inspection of Table 1 indicates good agreement between observed and predicted quantities. The observed value of $P_\infty(A_1 | T_1)$ decreases from Groups I to III and also from Groups IV to VI as predicted by the model. Similarly the observed values of $P_\infty(A_1 | T_2)$ decrease from I to III and from IV to VI as expected. Column comparisons are also in the appropriate order, that is, on this measure Group I is less than IV, II is less than V, and III is less than VI. Thus, as we increase the frequency of reinforcing the A_2 response on T_2 trials, we not only observe an increment in $P_\infty(A_2 | T_2)$ but also a decrement in $P_\infty(A_1 | T_1)$.

For $P_\infty(O_1)$, an increase occurs from Groups I to III and from Groups IV to VI in accordance with theoretical results. That is, the propor-

[3] Essentially the same statement holds for $\theta' \neq \theta''$. However, in some cases the dependency is slightly larger.

TABLE 2

ANALYSIS OF VARIANCE OF THE NUMBER OF O_1 RESPONSES IN THE LAST BLOCK OF 160 TRIALS

Source	df	MS	F
π (values of π_2)	2	27,533.2	13.8*
α values	1	113.4	0.1
O (O_1 left or right)	1	22,253.0	11.1*
A (A_1 left or right)	1	44.2	0.0
Interactions (11)	18		—[a]
Within	216	2,000.7	

[a] None significant at .05 level.
* $P < .001$.

tion of O_1 responses increases as a function of the difference between π_1 and π_2; of course, this result would be expected in view of the fact that differential reinforcement for the observing responses depends on the difference between the reinforcement schedules on T_1 and T_2 trials. However, column comparisons on the $P_\infty(O_1)$ measure for I–IV and III–VI are in the reverse order; the difference on the $P_\infty(O_1)$ measure is particularly large for Group VI. This difference between data and theory for Group VI is also reflected in $P_\infty(O_2 \cap A_1)$; in fact, the discrepancies of these two quantities from predicted values are greater than any of the others in Table 1.

An analysis of variance on the number of O_1 responses in the last block of 160 trials is presented in Table 2. The effects of the O_1 and A_1 placements on S's panel (i.e., right or left) are included in the analysis. The effect of the π-variable is highly significant as would be expected. However, the α-variable is not significant. This finding might have been anticipated since the theoretical prediction for the over-all effect of α is small for the parameter values used in this study. The most unexpected result of the analysis is with regard to the observing response variable; the placement of the O_1 key turns out to be highly significant while the placement of the A_1 key has no effect. Over all groups and Ss for the last 160 trials, the right hand observing response key was chosen on 55% of the trials while the right hand A_j key was selected on 50% of the trials. This right position preference on the observing response keys is particularly surprising in view of the fact that no similar preference exists for the A_j key. Several variables may account for this finding; for example, the observing response keys are in juxtaposition while the A_j keys are well separated; also, the observing response keys are further from S than the A_j keys.

In order to evaluate statistically the adequacy of the present model we have run a test suggested by Pillai and Ramachandran (1954) on the $P_\infty(O_1)$ measure. The test involves taking the largest absolute difference between an observed mean value and the predicted value in a collection of samples (in this case six). This difference is then divided by an over-all estimate of the standard error of the mean, that is, it is assumed that the observations are randomly selected from populations with homogeneous variance. As noted above, the largest discrepancy on the $P_\infty(O_1)$ measure occurs for Group VI. The predicted number of O_1s in the last block of 160 trials was 100.8 and the observed mean value was 115.7. The within-cells term in Table 2 was used to estimate the standard error of the mean, and in terms of Cochran's test there was no reason to reject the assumption of homogeneous variance. The obtained value of the Pillai-Ramachandran statistic was 2.1 and was not significant at the .05 level. Consequently, in terms of this particular statistical criterion there is no evidence to suggest that we reject the present model.

As noted earlier, not only group means but also the responses of individual Ss should approach the theoretical values

presented in Table 1. A check on the correspondence between individual asymptotic behavior and predicted values is equivalent to evaluating the agreement between observed SDs presented in Table 1 and asymptotic variability predicted by the model. Unfortunately direct computation of the theoretical SD is extremely cumbrous, and we have not obtained an analytical result. However, research reported by Suppes and Atkinson (1960) dealing with a similar model found that observed SDs were substantially larger than predicted values. Considering the rather large SDs reported here, their finding may be applicable to this set of data.

Transition characteristics.—A basic assumption in the model requires that if S is correct on trial n (i.e., A_1-E_1 or A_2-E_2 occurs) then on trial $n + 1$ he will repeat the observing response made on trial n. However, if S is incorrect (i.e., A_1-E_2 or A_2-E_1 occurs) then with probability θ'' he will shift observing responses from trial n to $n + 1$. This is a strong assumption and yields a highly deterministic set of predictions; for example, repetition of an observing response with probability 1 if S is correct on the preceding trial. On the other hand, a weaker form of the assumption which requires only a greater probability of observing response alternation following trials on which incorrect as compared to correct discrimination responses occur seems to be a reasonable conjecture for this type of problem. To test this class of assumptions we have computed the proportions of observing response alternations conditionalized on correct and incorrect discrimination responses over the last 160 trials. Let $N_n(s|c)$ denote the number of Ss who were correct on trial $n - 1$ and shifted observing responses from trial $n - 1$ to n; also, let $N_n(c)$ be the number of Ss who were correct on trial n. Similarly, define $N_n(s|\bar{c})$ and $N_n(\bar{c})$ in terms of incorrect responses. Further, define

$$N(s|c) = \sum_{n=241}^{400} N_n(s|c)$$

and

$$N(c) = \sum_{n=240}^{399} N_n(c)$$

and define $N(s|\bar{c})$ and $N(\bar{c})$ similarly. Then estimates of the conditional probabilities of shifting observing responses following correct or incorrect discrimination responses are, respectively,

$$\hat{P}(s|c) = \frac{N(s|c)}{N(c)},$$

$$\hat{P}(s|\bar{c}) = \frac{N(s|\bar{c})}{N(\bar{c})}$$

Table 3 presents the observed data for each of the groups. No statistical test is needed to see that these observed transition probabilities differ significantly from theoretical values. It suffices to note that theoretically $\hat{P}(s|c)$ should be identically zero for all groups whereas the observed values of this quantity differ markedly from zero. Without regard to the specific assumption considered in this paper, the question can be raised as to whether or not shifting of an observing response is more likely following incorrect or correct trials, that is whether $\hat{P}(s|\bar{c})$ is greater than $\hat{P}(s|c)$. A formal test of this hypothesis is a complex matter and we do not attempt it here. However note that for five of the six groups $\hat{P}(s|\bar{c})$ is greater than $\hat{P}(s|c)$. Further, the difference between these quantities increases as π_2 decreases; that is, the difference increases from Groups I to III and from Groups IV to VI.

TABLE 3

TRANSITION FREQUENCIES AND ESTIMATED PROPORTIONS OVER THE LAST BLOCK OF 160 TRIALS

	Groups					
	I	II	III	IV	V	VI
$N(s\|c)$	1610	880	933	1617	883	735
$N(c)$	5388	4080	4664	5463	4032	4350
$N(s\|\bar{c})$	275	520	446	266	517	524
$N(\bar{c})$	973	2280	1696	897	2328	2010
$\hat{P}(s\|c)$	.299	.216	.200	.296	.219	.169
$\hat{P}(s\|\bar{c})$	.283	.228	.263	.297	.222	.261

In conclusion, the rather striking correspondence between theoretical and observed values in Table 1 lends considerable support to the main features of the model. For the type of discrimination problem considered in this paper, it seems clear that asymptotic behavior can be predicted with accuracy in terms of the particular relations we have postulated among reinforcement schedules, observing responses, and discrimination responses. However, the sequential data reported in Table 3 indicate that some of the detailed features of the stimulus sampling process assumed in the model are certainly incorrect; this finding is not too surprising in view of related research on similar Markov chain models. Fortunately, within the framework of stimulus sampling theory, one can restate our axioms in only slightly modified form and thereby avoid the completely deterministic predictions made by the present model for sequential data. The disadvantage of such a reformulation is that the mathematical complexity of the model is greatly increased. The reader interested in details of such modifications is referred to Suppes and Atkinson (1960).

SUMMARY

An analysis of observing responses in discrimination learning was made. The typical discrimination task was modified so that two mutually exclusive and exhaustive observing responses could be identified and directly recorded. The experimental situation involved a series of 400 trials, each trial belonging to one of two types (T_1 or T_2). The sequence of events on a trial was as follows: (a) ready signal to which S made an observing response; (b) the presentation of one of three stimuli; (c) occurrence of one of two discrimination responses to the stimulus presentation; (d) termination of the trial with the reinforcement of a discrimination response. The particular stimulus presented on a trial depended on the observing response and the trial type. Following one of the observing responses, different stimuli were presented on T_1 and T_2 trials so that it was possible for S to identify the trial type; following the other observing response, the same stimulus was presented on both types of trials and hence S could not identify the trial type.

Six groups of college students were tested. The major independent variable specified different pairs of reinforcement schedules for the two trial types. The results indicated a highly predictable relation between the selection of observing responses and reinforcement schedules. In general, the greater the difference between the reinforcement schedules on T_1 and T_2 trials, the greater the preference for one observing response over the other. The analysis of the data was in terms of a Markov chain model which is closely related to stimulus sampling theory. There was excellent agreement between theoretical and observed values on asymptotic measures of observing and discrimination responses. Hqw- ever, an analysis of the sequential data indicated certain difficulties with the model.

REFERENCES

ATKINSON, R. C. A Markov model for discrimination learning. *Psychometrika,* 1958, **23**, 309–322.

ATKINSON, R. C. A theory of stimulus discrimination learning. In K. J. Arrow, S. Karlin, & P. Suppes (Eds.), *First Stanford symposium on mathematical methods in the social sciences.* Stanford: Stanford Univer. Press, 1960. Ch. 15.

ATKINSON, R. C., BOGARTZ, W. H., & TURNER, R. N. Supplementary Report: Discrimination learning with probabilistic reinforcement schedules. *J. exp. Psychol.,* 1959, **57**, 349–350.

BURKE, C. J., & ESTES, W. K. A component model for stimulus variables in discrimination learning. *Psychometrika,* 1957, **22**, 133–145.

ESTES, W. K. Toward a statistical theory of learning. *Psychol. Rev.,* 1950, **57**, 94–107.

ESTES, W. K., & BURKE, C. J. A theory of stimulus variability in learning. *Psychol. Rev.,* 1953, **60**, 276–286.

FELLER, W. *An introduction to probability theory and its applications.* (2nd ed.) New York: Wiley, 1957.

PILLAI, K. C. S., & RAMACHANDRAN, K. V. On the distribution of the ratio of the ith observation in an ordered sample from a normal population to an independent estimate of the standard deviation. *Ann. math. Statist.,* 1954, **25**, 565–572.

RESTLE, F. A survey and classification of learning models. In R. R. Bush & W. K. Estes (Eds.), *Studies in mathematical learning theory.* Stanford: Stanford Univer. Press, 1959. Ch. 20.

SUPPES, P., & ATKINSON, R. C. *Markov learning models for multiperson interactions.* Stanford: Stanford Univer. Press, 1960.

WYCKOFF, L. B., JR. The role of observing responses in discrimination behavior. *Psychol. Rev.,* 1952, **59**, 431–442.

(Received July 6, 1960)

Discrimination Learning in a Verbal Conditioning Situation[1]

JULIET POPPER, *Stanford University*, and RICHARD C. ATKINSON, *University of California, Los Angeles*

This study deals with an analysis of discrimination learning in a modified verbal conditioning situation (**1, 7**). Two stimuli, designated T_1 and T_2, are employed, and two responses, A_1 and A_2, are available to S. Each trial begins with the presentation of either T_1 or T_2. The probability of a T_1 trial is β and the probability of a T_2 trial is $1 - \beta$. Following the T_1 stimulus, an A_1 response is correct with probability π_1, and an A_2 response is correct with probability $1 - \pi_1$. Following the T_2 stimulus, an A_1 response is correct with probability π_2, and an A_2 response is correct with probability $1 - \pi_2$. The S is instructed to maximize the number of trials on which his response is correct.

Recently Burke and Estes have presented a component model for stimulus variables in discrimination learning (**2**). The theory is a direct extension of their original acquisition model (**4**). The only modification involves the definition of a set of stimulus elements to correspond to each of the stimulus situations to be discriminated (**5, 6**). Their theory is quantitative in a precise sense in that prior to experimentation exact predictions of behavior may be made for a wide range of parameter values.

[1] This research was conducted at the Applied Mathematics and Statistics Laboratory, Stanford University, and was jointly supported by the Behavioral Sciences Division of the Ford Foundation and by the Group Psychology Branch of the Office of Naval Research. The authors are indebted to P. Suppes for several stimulating discussions of the ideas on which this experiment is based.

One of the Burke and Estes discrimination problems deals with probabilistic reinforcement schedules which are contingent on the stimuli to be discriminated. The aim of the present study is to evaluate experimentally the adequacy of some of their predictions. In particular, we will be concerned with how adequately the theory accounts for asymptotic response behavior over a wide range of parameter values of π_2 given a fixed value of π_1.

The principal assumption in the Burke and Estes theory is that the stimuli T_1 and T_2 can be conceptually represented as two sets of stimulus elements which are designated S_1 and S_2, respectively. On T_1 trials S's response is determined by a sample of stimulus elements from S_1; on T_2 trials, by a sample of stimulus elements from S_2. In addition, a set S_c is designated which represents those stimulus elements common to both sets S_1 and S_2 ($S_c = S_1 \cap S_2$), i.e., stimulus events common to the presentation of either T_1 or T_2. One can think of the expected size of the sample from the S_c set as providing an *index of similarity* between T_1 and T_2. The larger the relative size of this sample with respect to the expected size of the samples from S_1 and S_2 the greater the similarity between the stimuli (**3**).

Given the above stimulus representation and rules for conditioning (**2, 4**) one can derive an expression for the probability of an A_1 or A_2 response on Trial n. For our purposes we will be concerned with the long-

This article appeared in *J. exp. Psychol.*, 1958, **56**, 21–26.

run probability of response behavior and, consequently, will present only asymptotic predictions; namely,

$$p_\infty(A_1|T_1) = \pi_1(1-\omega_1) + \pi_c\omega_1 \quad [1]$$

$$p_\infty(A_1|T_2) = \pi_2(1-\omega_2) + \pi_c\omega_2, \quad [2]$$

where $p_\infty(A_1|T_i)$ is the expected conditional asymptotic probability of an A_1 response given a T_i ($i = 1$ or 2) type trial, and $\pi_c = \beta\pi_1 + (1-\beta)\pi_2$.[2]

The quantity ω_i is a theoretical parameter and essentially represents a ratio of the number of elements in S_c to the number of elements in S_i.[3] Consequently $0 \leq \omega_i \leq 1$ and is independent of experimental parameters π_1, π_2, and β. In our situation T_1 and T_2 are symmetric, and it is natural to assume $\omega_1 = \omega_2 = \omega$. The closer ω is to unity, the greater the similarity between T_1 and T_2; the closer ω is to zero, the greater the dissimilarity between T_1 and T_2.

Method

Subjects.—The Ss were 205 undergraduates obtained from introductory courses in psychology. They were run in 20 subgroups, with from 8 to 14 Ss per subgroup.

Procedure.—Each S received a sheet of paper on which numbers from 1 to 320 were printed. Following each number were the letters A and B. The Ss were also provided with two blank sheets of heavy white paper. The instructions began as follows:

"I want to see how well you can do in a rather unusual problem situation. At the beginning of each trial, I will announce the number of the trial, and then I will say one of these two nonsense words: MEF or ZIL. About

[2] These results, in slightly modified form, are presented in Equations 18 and 19 of the Burke-Estes article. In deriving these equations, Burke and Estes denote by S_i the set of stimuli sampled *only* on trials of type T_i. Our use of S_i therefore corresponds to their use of $S_i \cup S_c$.

[3] To be exact, $\omega_i = \dfrac{N_c\theta_c}{N_c\theta_c + N_i\theta_i}$ for $i = 1$ or 2. N_c, N_1, and N_2 are the number of stimulus elements in the sets S_c, $(S_1 - S_c)$, and $(S_2 - S_c)$, respectively. θ_c, θ_1, and θ_2 are the sampling constants associated with these sets.

4 sec. later I will say either A or B. Immediately after I have said ZIL or MEF on each trial, you are to guess whether I will say A or B on that trial by circling either A or B in the appropriate place on your answer sheet. If you expect an A, circle A; if you expect a B, circle B. Guess on every trial even if you are very unsure—your guesses or hunches may turn out to be right, and it is important to have a complete record of your learning. Try to improve as you go along and make as many correct choices as possible.

"I want you to make each choice without seeing any of your previous choices. Therefore, please take the small strip of heavy white paper and slide it down the answer sheet, covering each choice as soon as you have made it. When you have completed a column, use the big piece of paper to cover that whole column, and again use the small strip to slide down the next column." The remainder of the instructions involved repetition of the main points.

The E stood at the back of the room where it was possible to watch Ss to be sure they were following instructions. The number of each trial was announced; 1 sec. later E said either MEF or ZIL, 4 sec. after that either A or B, and 2 sec. later the number of the next trial was announced.

After Trial 4 E interrupted the sequence to ask whether Ss had any questions. Questions were answered by rephrasing appropriate parts of the instructions. The remaining 316 trials were run without interruption. The complete procedure took 45–50 min. for each subgroup.

MEF and ZIL were selected from the list of nonsense syllables with zero association value given by Glaze (8). They met the criteria of being clearly distinguishable, having an unambiguous correct pronunciation, and sounding unlike either A or B.

Design.—There were five experimental conditions. For all experimental groups π_1 was .85 and β was .50. The groups differed with respect to the π_2 parameter; the values of π_2 were .85 (Group I), .70 (Group II), .50 (Group III), .30 (Group IV), and .15 (Group V). Within each of the five experimental groups there were four subgroups distinguished as follows: 1. $T_1 = MEF(T_2 = ZIL)$ and $A_1 = A(A_2 = B)$; 2. $T_1 = ZIL$ and $A_1 = A$; 3. $T_1 = MEF$ and $A_1 = B$; 4. $T_1 = ZIL$ and $A_1 = B$.

For each of the 20 subgroups a different random sequence of events was generated in accordance with the assigned values of π_1 and π_2, with the following restrictions imposed on the randomization: (a) each successive block of 40 trials included 20 T_1 trials and 20 T_2 trials; (b) of the 20 T_1 trials in a 40-trial block, an A_1 response was correct on exactly $\pi_1 \cdot (20)$ of the trials and an A_2 was correct on the remaining $(1 - \pi_1) \cdot (20)$ trials, and (c) of the 20 T_2 trials in a 40-trial block, an A_1 response was correct on exactly $\pi_2 \cdot (20)$ of the trials and an A_2 was correct on $(1 - \pi_2) \cdot (20)$ trials.

Groups I, II, IV, and V consisted of 40 Ss each; there were 45 Ss in Group III.

RESULTS AND DISCUSSION

Figure 1 presents the mean group response behavior over all trials of the experiment. In this figure the proportion of A_1 responses given a T_1 trial and the proportion of A_1 responses given a T_2 trial are plotted in successive blocks of 40 trials. In each block of 40 trials there are 20 T_1's and 20 T_2's; therefore the proportion computed for an individual S is based on 20 observations.

An inspection of this figure indicates that response curves are fairly stable

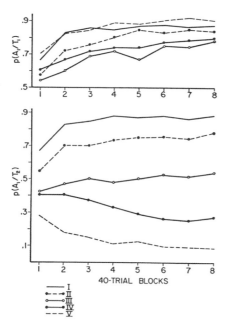

TABLE 1

OBSERVED VALUES OF $p_\infty(A_1|T_1)$ AND $p_\infty(A_1|T_2)$ COMPUTED OVER LAST 120 TRIALS[a]

Group	$p_\infty(A_1|T_1)$		$p_\infty(A_1|T_2)$	
	Mean	SD	Mean	SD
I	.871	.098	.870	.092
II	.838	.099	.766	.105
III	.757	.119	.515	.157
IV	.785	.139	.262	.172
V	.910	.085	.088	.087

[a] Each entry based on 60 observations per S.

over the last 120 trials, and it appears reasonable to assume that a constant level of responding has been reached. Consequently, proportions computed over the last 120 trials were used as estimates of $p_\infty(A_1|T_1)$ and $p_\infty(A_1|T_2)$.

A simple analysis of variance for each experimental group tested for differences between the four subgroups with respect to the total number of A_1 responses in the last 120 trials. None of the five analyses was significant at the .05 level, and for subsequent analyses the subgroup distinctions within an experimental group were not considered.

Table 1 presents the observed means and SDs of proportions for the last 120 trials. Entries for Groups I, II, IV, and V are based on $N = 40$; entries for Group III are based on $N = 45$.

Figure 2 presents a schematic representation of the theoretical predictions as well as the observed asymptotic values given in Table 1. By substituting appropriate parameter values in Equations 1 and 2 the following results are established: (a) If $\omega = 0$, then (for the group designation on the abscissa) $p_\infty(A_1|T_1)$ falls on the straight line ab and $p_\infty(A_1|T_2)$ falls on the straight line ad. (b) If $\omega = 1$, then both $p_\infty(A_1|T_1)$ and $p_\infty(A_1|T_2)$ fall on the straight line ac. (c) If $0 < \omega < 1$, then (i)

FIG. 1. The observed mean values of $p(A_1|T_1)$ and $p(A_1|T_2)$ in successive blocks of 40 trials for Groups I–V. Each point is based on 20 observations per S.

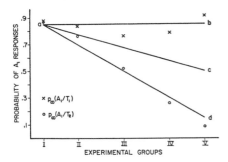

FIG. 2. A schematic representation of theoretical and observed asymptotic predictions.

$p_\infty(A_1|T_1)$ falls on a straight line with origin at point a and bounded between lines ab and ac and (ii) $p_\infty(A_1|T_2)$ falls on a straight line with origin at point a and bounded between lines ac and ad. Further, the amount of displacement of $p_\infty(A_1|T_1)$ from the line ab is the same as the displacement of $p_\infty(A_1|T_2)$ from the line ad and is a function of the value of ω.

Inspection of Fig. 2 suggests certain analyses of the data. In particular, the expected values of $p_\infty(A_1|T_1)$ for the various groups should lie on or between the lines ab and ac. However, the observed values for both Groups I and V are above the ab line. To establish whether these observed points are significantly above the maximum value of .85, t tests were run employing the observed SDs of the mean as the error term. The obtained values of t were 1.36 and 4.46 ($P < .01$, 39 df) for Groups I and V, respectively. Thus, for Group V the observed value of $p_\infty(A_1|T_1)$ was significantly greater than the maximum value predicted by the theory.

Similarly the expected values of $p_\infty(A_1|T_2)$ for the various groups should lie on or between the lines ac and ad. Yet for Group I the observed value is above .85 and for Groups IV and V the observed values are below .30 and .15, respectively. To establish whether the observed results were significantly different from these values, t tests were

again run. The obtained values of t were 1.37, 1.40, and 4.58 ($P < .01$, 39 df) for Groups I, IV, and V, respectively. Thus, for Group V the observed value of $p_\infty(A_1|T_1)$ is significantly smaller than the minimum value predicted by the theory.

A more stringent requirement of the theory is that (a) the expected values of $p_\infty(A_1|T_1)$ fall on a straight line bounded between the lines ab and ac and (b) the expected values of $p_\infty(A_1|T_2)$ fall on a straight line bounded between the lines ac and ad. Inspection of Fig. 2 clearly indicates, at least for $p_\infty(A_1|T_1)$, that this is not the case. The observed values of $p_\infty(A_1|T_1)$ decrease from Groups I to III but, instead of continuing in this trend, show a marked increase for Groups IV and V. Thus we find a convex rather than a linear relationship between $p_\infty(A_1|T_1)$ and the groups when ordered from I to V.

An experiment employing a procedure similar to the one used in this study was reported by Estes and Burke (5). They had two experimental conditions, in both of which $\pi_1 = 1.00$ and $\pi_2 = .50$. The results qualitatively resemble the present observations for Groups II and III in that their observed values of $p_\infty(A_1|T_1)$ are below π_1 and their observed values of $p_\infty(A_1|T_2)$ are slightly above π_2.

In conclusion, the results of the present study indicate substantial disagreement between theoretical predictions and observed values. If one were dealing only with the data of Groups I–III or with the Estes-Burke data (5), a fairly strong case could be made for the model. However, the results on Groups IV and V leave little doubt that the formalization is not adequate in its present form to account for this type of discrimination situation.

In support of the theory, it might be argued from inspection of Fig. 1 that the curves of $p(A_1|T_1)$ for Groups III and IV are still rising, and that the asymptotic values of $p(A_1|T_1)$ and $p(A_1|T_2)$ are in reality π_1 and π_2, respectively, for all groups. As noted above, the theory would predict these asymptotic values when $\omega = 0$. However, if $\omega = 0$, it necessarily follows from the theoretical formulation that the curves of $p(A_1|T_1)$ for all five groups should be identical over trials, approaching π_1 at the same rate. An inspection of the upper panel of Fig. 1 clearly indicates that this is not the case.

If, in fact, $p(A_1|T_1)$ and $p(A_1|T_2)$ are asymptotically equal to π_1 and π_2, respectively, but are approaching the asymptotes at differential rates depending on both π_1 and π_2, one might conjecture that stimuli common to T_1 and T_2 trials (S_c) are initially influencing behavior but are becoming adapted over trials, i.e., losing their influence on response probability (9). The rate of adaptation could be assumed to be a function of the π values. This theoretical approach appears to be worth investigating.

It should be noted that, in one sense, this type of study cannot be viewed as a satisfactory test of the theory. It may be that the relationship of asymptotic response behavior to π_1 and π_2 obtained in the present experiment is an artifact of the massed trial procedure employed. In the derivation of Equations 1 and 2 it was assumed by Burke and Estes that either S_1 or S_2 was sampled *independently* on each trial. If, however, the trials occur in close temporal succession, then the stimulus complex affecting S on any trial may include traces of the stimulation associated with the responses and reinforcing events of one or more preceding trials. Therefore, a more acceptable test of the theory, in the form presented by Burke and Estes, would require a situation where experimental techniques are employed to reduce the carry-over of trace stimulation from one trial to the next (10).

SUMMARY

The study deals with an analysis of discrimination learning. Two stimuli designated T_1 and T_2 are employed and two responses A_1 and A_2 are available. Each trial begins with the presentation of either T_1 or T_2, the probability of T_1 and of T_2 each being $\frac{1}{2}$. Following T_1, an A_1 response is correct with probability π_1 and an A_2 response is correct with probability $1 - \pi_1$. Following T_2, an A_1 response is correct with probability π_2 and an A_2 response with probability $1 - \pi_2$. The S is instructed to maximize the number of trials on which his response is correct.

Five groups were run. For all groups $\pi_1 = .85$. The groups differed with respect to the π_2 parameter which assumed the values .85, .70, .50, .30, and .15. Analysis of the data was in terms of a theoretical model for discrimination learning proposed by Burke and Estes (2). Discrepancies between predicted and observed outcomes were examined. However, it was pointed out that the massed trial procedure employed in the study did not provide an optimal test of the theory.

REFERENCES

1. ATKINSON, R. C. An analysis of the effect of nonreinforced trials in terms of statistical learning theory. *J. exp. Psychol.*, 1956, **52**, 28–32.
2. BURKE, C. J., & ESTES, W. K. A component model for stimulus variables in discrimination learning. *Psychometrika*, 1957, **22**, 133–145.
3. BUSH, R. R., & MOSTELLER, F. A model for stimulus generalization and discrimination. *Psychol. Rev.*, 1951, **58**, 413–423.
4. ESTES, W. K., & BURKE, C. J. A theory of stimulus variability in learning. *Psychol. Rev.*, 1953, **60**, 276–286.
5. ESTES, W. K., & BURKE, C. J. Application of a statistical model to simple discrimination learning in human subjects. *J. exp. Psychol.*, 1955, **50**, 81–88.
6. ESTES, W. K., BURKE, C. J., ATKINSON, R. C., & FRANKMANN, J. P. Probabilistic discrimination learning. *J. exp. Psychol.*, 1957, **54**, 233–239.
7. ESTES, W. K., & STRAUGHAN, J. H. Analysis of a verbal conditioning situation in terms of statistical learning theory. *J. exp. Psychol.*, 1954, **47**, 225–234.
8. GLAZE, J. A. The association value of nonsense syllables. *J. genet. Psychol.*, 1928, **35**, 255–267.
9. RESTLE, F. Theory of selective learning with probable reinforcements. *Psychol. Rev.*, 1957, **64**, 182–191.
10. STRAUGHAN, J. H. An application of statistical learning theory to an escape learning situation using human subjects. *J. exp. Psychol.*, 1956, **52**, 1–8.

(Received August 12, 1957)

Supplementary Report: Discrimination Learning with Probabilistic Reinforcement Schedules[1]

R. C. ATKINSON, W. H. BOGARTZ, and R. N. TURNER,

University of California, Los Angeles

This study deals with discrimination learning in a verbal conditioning situation and is an extension of research reported by Popper and Atkinson (1958). The study differs from theirs in that a new set of parameter values and a more rigorously controlled experimental procedure were employed. Two stimuli, T_1 and T_2, were used and two responses, A_1 and A_2, were available to S. Each trial began by the presentation, with equal probability, of either T_1 or T_2. On a T_1 trial, A_1 was correct with the probability π_1 and A_2 was correct with probability $1 - \pi_1$. For a T_2 trial, π_2 was identically defined.

Method.—Five groups were used. For all groups $\pi_1 = .9$. The groups differed with respect to the π_2 parameter which assumed the values of .9 (G-I), .7 (G-II), .5 (G-III), .3 (G-IV) and .1 (G-V). The Ss were given 400 trials. However, on the first 40 trials all groups were given $\pi_1 = \pi_2 = .5$. The Ss were 180 undergraduates, 36 per group. The experimental design was identical to that of Popper and Atkinson (1958) except that Ss were run in subgroups of three, each S placed in a private booth after instructions. The apparatus, viewed from within S's booth, consisted of two keys attached to the base of a panel, upon the panel were mounted four small lights. Two lights were in a column centered above the keys and served as the T_1 and T_2 stimuli. Each of the two remaining lights (the reinforcing signals) was mounted directly above one of the keys. On all trials the signal light (T_1 or T_2) was lighted for 1.5 sec.; the signal light went off simultaneously with the onset of a reinforcing light. The reinforcing light remained on for 1.8 sec., and was followed by an intertrial interval of 4 sec. Trials were run without interruption and S made his response while the signal light was on. Instructions were similar to those presented in Atkinson and Suppes (1958) except that they were modified to describe the T_1 and T_2 stimuli as in Popper and Atkinson (1958).

Results.—Figure 1 presents mean response curves over all trials of the experiment. In this figure the proportion of A_1's made on T_1 trials, $p(A_1|T_1)$, and the proportion of A_1's made on T_2 trials, $p(A_1|T_2)$, are plotted in successive 40-trial blocks. The corresponding π values are indicated on the far right. The asymptotic and pre-asymptotic characteristics of these curves are identical to those found by Popper and Atkinson (1958). One aspect of these results to be emphasized is the relation between the observed $p_\infty(A_1|T_1)$ and π_2. A convex function was found by Popper and Atkinson when π_2 varied from .85 to .15 (for a fixed $\pi_1 = .85$) and the same relation holds for this study. Specifically, if the proportions computed over the last 120 trials are used as estimates of $p_\infty(A_1|T_1)$, the obtained values are .930, .867, .808, .856, and .895 for Groups I to V, respectively. The convexity was found significant by evaluation of the quadratic component of the treatment sum of squares, $F = 18.2$.

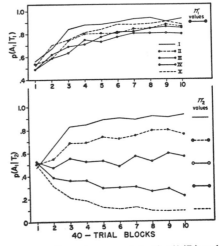

FIG. 1. Observed mean values of $p(A_1|T_1)$ and $p(A_1|T_2)$ in successive blocks of 40 trials. Each point is based on approximately 20 observations per S.

[1] This research was supported in part by a grant to the senior author from the National Science Foundation.

This article appeared in *J. exp. Psychol.*, 1959, **57**, 349–350.

The significance of these findings with regard to stochastic theories of discrimination learning is discussed by Atkinson (1958). In particular, the demonstrated convex relation between π_2 and $p_\infty(A_1|T_1)$ suggests that the Burke and Estes (1957) component model for discrimination learning is not applicable in this type of situation.

(Received August 22, 1958)

REFERENCES

ATKINSON, R. C. A Markov model for discrimination learning. *Psychometrika*, 1958, **23**, 309–322.

ATKINSON, R. C., & SUPPES, P. An analysis of a two-person game situation in terms of statistical learning theory. *J. exp. Psychol.*, 1958, **55**, 369–378.

BURKE, C. J., & ESTES, W. K. A component model for stimulus variables in discrimination learning. *Psychometrika*, 1957, **22**, 133–145.

POPPER, J., & ATKINSON, R. C. Discrimination learning in a verbal conditioning situation. *J. exp. Psychol.*, 1958, **56**, 21–25.

Sequential Phenomena in Psychophysical Judgments: A Theoretical Analysis

R. C. ATKINSON, *Stanford University*, E. C. CARTERETTE, *University of California, Los Angeles, and* R. A. KINCHLA, *Ames Research Center*

This paper deals with an analysis of psychophysical detection experiments designed to assess the limit of a human observer's level of sensitivity. A mathematical theory of the detection process is introduced that, in contrast to previous theories, provides an analysis of the sequential effects observed in psychophysical data. Two variations of the detection task are considered: information feedback and no-information feedback. In the feedback situation the subject is given information concerning the correctness of his responses, whereas in the no-feedback situation he is not. Data from a visual detection experiment with no-information feedback, and from an auditory detection experiment with information feedback are analyzed in terms of the theory. Finally, some general results are derived concerning the relationship between performance in the feedback situation and the no-feedback situation.

INTRODUCTION

This paper presents an analysis of the process by which a human observer detects the occurrence of very weak signals. The theoretical formulation that we offer should apply to signals received via any sensory mode, but our discussion will be restricted to visual and auditory stimuli. Furthermore, the analysis is behavioral rather than physiological since it deals with the subjects' overt responses rather than with biochemical or neurophysiological activity.

A methodology for assessing the limits of a subject's sensitivity to external stimuli based on phenomenal reports was developed quite early (Fechner, 1860) and has remained relatively unchanged since that time. Most simply, these methods offered a means for determining the probability of a "detection" for various signal intensities. Early investigators often interpreted the subject's phenomenal report quite directly; i.e., a reported detection implied that the signal was above the subject's limit of sensitivity and a report of no detection implied that it was below this limit. The limit, or threshold as it has often been called, was viewed as varying randomly in time about a fixed mean value. Therefore, the threshold was defined statistically as that signal intensity reported by the subject on half

This article appeared in *IRE Trans. on information Theory*, 1962, **IT-8**, 155–162.

of the occasions on which it was presented. More recently, alternative interpretations of the subject's performance have been proposed (e.g., see Blackwell[1] and Swets, Tanner, and Birdsall[2]). These proposals all view the subject as utilizing more than the immediate sensory information to determine his response on each trial. However, these newer approaches are still traditional in at least one major respect: they represent the detection process as fixed over long series of trials. This static conception of psychophysical phenomena is surprising in view of the sequential effects that are apparent in the trial-to-trial data. Investigators as far back as Fechner[3] have noted that the subject's response tendency on one trial is markedly influenced by the stimuli and responses that occur on preceding trials. Most investigators either have ignored these sequential effects or treated them as experimental artifacts, to be minimized by randomization, counterbalancing, trial spacing, or by use of trained subjects. In this paper sequential effects will be considered as an important aspect of the subject's performance; furthermore it is our contention that consideration of these effects provides a valuable insight into the character of the detection process. Specifically, we deal with an analysis of sequential statistics in two types of detection situations; one situation involves information feedback on each trial, the other does not.

The type of psychological situation that we analyze is a two-response, forced-choice detection task. On each trial two temporal, or spatial, intervals are defined and the subject is instructed to report which of these two intervals contained a signal. It is a forced-choice task in that on each trial the subject must identify one of the two intervals as containing a signal even if he is uncertain as to what occurred. The following notation will be used to identify each trial:

$T_{i,n}$ = the presentation of a signal in interval i on trial $n(i = 1, 2)$; or the presentation of a signal in neither interval ($i = 0$).

$A_{j,n}$ = the subject's selection of interval j ($j = 1, 2$) as the interval containing the signal on trial n.

$E_{k,n}$ = the occurrence of an information event at the end of trial n which informs the subject that the signal has occurred in interval k ($k = 1, 2$); or no information at the conclusion of trial $n(k = 0)$.

Using this notation, each trial may be described by an ordered triple (T_i, A_j, E_k).

As indicated above, the two variations of the detection task that we analyze in this paper are information feedback and no-information feedback. The *information* condition requires that the experimenter present

E_1 on a T_1 trial and E_2 on a T_2 trial; the *no-information* case requires that E_0 occurs on all trials. In addition to these two cases one can also study the effects of presenting incorrect information on some trials. Carterette and Wyman[4] have investigated the influence of misinformation, and the theory we present here is applicable to their experiment. However, to simplify our discussion we shall not examine the misinformation condition.

When no information is given to the subject it seems natural on occasion to introduce a "blank" trial and note its effect on choice behavior. Hence for the no-information condition we permit T_0 trials. However, the introduction of T_0 trials in the information condition raises problems regarding the type of feedback that should be given on these trials; to avoid these special issues we restrict our analysis of the information case to situations involving only T_1 and T_2 trials. Thus for the no-information case the experimenter has the option of presenting $T_1 - E_0$, $T_2 - E_0$, or $T_0 - E_0$ on each trial. For the information case he may present either $T_1 - E_1$ or $T_2 - E_2$. In this paper we consider only simple probabilistic schedules for presenting events. For the information case we denote the probability of the two events as follows:

$$\gamma = \Pr(T_1 \& E_1)$$
$$1 - \gamma = \Pr(T_2 \& E_2) .$$

For the no-information case:

$$\pi_1 = \Pr(T_1 \& E_0)$$
$$\pi_2 = \Pr(T_2 \& E_0)$$
$$\pi_0 = \Pr(T_0 \& E_0) ,$$

where $\pi_1 + \pi_2 + \pi_0 = 1$.

THEORY

Before we turn to a discussion of the theory on which our analysis is based, a few general remarks will be useful. All psychological theories of signal detection incorporate two distinct processes: an activation process and a decision process. The activation process specifies the relation between external stimulus events and hypothesized sensory states of the subject. The decision process specifies the relation between the sensory states and the observable response of the subject. For example, the model proposed by Blackwell[1] may be interpreted in terms of these two processes. Two sensory states, "true detection" and "no detection," are defined and the activation process is characterized by specifying the probability that one of these two sensory states occurs for a given signal intensity. The decision process is characterized by specifying the probability of the subject's response for each of these two sensory states. In Blackwell's model the subject always makes the correct response given a "true detection," but guesses one response or the other with some fixed probability when the "no detection" state occurs. Other models of the detection process (e.g., Swets, Tanner, and Birdsall[2]) have more complicated views of the activation and decision processes. However, all of these models are similar in one respect: the character of the activation and decision processes is viewed as fixed over long series of trials. It is this common feature that was referred to earlier as a static view of the detection process. The general theory used in our analysis was developed by Atkinson[5,6] and considers both the activation and decision processes as varying from trial to trial. However, a satisfactory treatment of the problems that we consider in this paper can be obtained by using a special case of the general theory; for this case only the decision process is viewed as dynamic.

The theoretical representation that will be used here is a generalization of stimulus sampling concepts as originally formulated by Estes[7]; a comprehensive survey of stimulus sampling theory may be found in Atkinson and Estes.[8] For purposes of this paper the stimulus situation will be represented in terms of two sensory patterns, s_1 and s_2, and a set S of stimulus patterns associated with background stimulation. These patterns are theoretical constructs to which we assign certain properties. Although it is sometimes convenient and suggestive to speak in such terms, one should not assume that these patterns are to be identified with any simple neurophysiological unit such as a receptor cell. At the present stage of theory construction, we mean to assume only that certain properties of the set-theoretical model represent certain properties of the process of stimulation. If these assumptions prove to be adequately substantiated when the model is tested against a wide range of behavioral data, then it will be in order to look for neurophysiological variables that might underlie the correspondence.

On every trial a single pattern is activated from the background set S, and simultaneously one of the sensory patterns may or may not be activated. If the s_1 sensory pattern is activated A_1 occurs; if s_2 is activated A_2 occurs. If neither sensory pattern is activated the subject makes the response to which the background pattern is conditioned. Conditioning of patterns in S may change from trial to trial via a simple learning process. It is the manner in which this conditioning process is conceptualized that distinguishes the information situation from the no-information situation. In the feedback situation the information event itself controls the conditioning process; without feedback the conditioning process is controlled by the sensory pattern activated on each trial. This distinction will become clear after consideration of the axioms. The axioms will be formulated verbally; it is not difficult to state them in mathematically exact form, but for present purposes this is not necessary. The axioms fall into three groups: the first group defines the activation process, the second group defines the decision process, and the third group defines the manner in which the conditioning of background elements occurs. Two sets of conditioning axioms will be stated: one set is applicable to the information case, and the other to the no-information case.

Activation Axioms
A1. If $T_i(i = 1, 2)$ occurs, then sensory pattern s_i will be activated with probability h (with probability $1 - h$ neither s_1 nor s_2 will be activated).

A2. If T_0 occurs, then neither s_1 nor s_2 will be activated.

A3. Exactly one pattern is activated from set S on every trial. Given the set S of N patterns, the probability of activating a particular pattern is $1/N$.

Response Axioms
R1. If sensory pattern s_i is activated, then the A_i response will occur.

R2. If neither sensory pattern is activated, then the response to which the pattern activated from set S is conditioned will occur.

Conditioning Axioms: No Information Feedback
C1. On every trial each pattern in S is conditioned to either A_1 or A_2.

C2. If $s_i(i = 1, 2)$ is activated on trial n, then with probability c' the pattern activated from S on the trial becomes conditioned to A_i at the end of trial n.

C3. If neither s_1 nor s_2 are activated on trial n, then with probability c the pattern activated from S on the trial becomes conditioned with equal likelihood to either A_1 or A_2 at the end of trial n.

Conditioning Axioms: Information Feedback
C1. On every trial each pattern in S is conditioned to either A_1 or A_2.

C2. The pattern activated from S on each trial becomes conditioned with probability θ to the A_i response if E_i occurs on that trial; if it is already conditioned to that response, it remains so.

Thus the information case differs from the no-information case in that in the former the feedback, $E_{i,n}$, is the reinforcing event on trial n, whereas in the no-feedback case the patterns activated on trial n determine the conditioning process.

The symbol p_n will be used to denote the proportion of elements in set S conditioned to A_1 at the start of trial n. The expression for p_n will differ for the information and the no-information conditions. However, once the expression for p_n has been derived (for either the information or no-information case) the equations for the probability of response A_i given event T_i on trial n may be written immediately. These expressions are obtained by the application of axioms R1 and R2 and are as follows:

$$\Pr(A_{1,n}|T_{1,n}) = h + (1 - h)p_n, \tag{1a}$$

$$\Pr(A_{2,n}|T_{2,n}) = h + (1 - h)(1 - p_n), \tag{1b}$$

$$\Pr(A_{1,n}|T_{0,n}) = p_n. \tag{1c}$$

It will be recalled that our discussion is restricted to cases where T_0 trials only occur when there is no information feedback; consequently Eq. (1c) will only be applicable to the no-feedback case.

APPLICATION TO NO-FEEDBACK DATA

In this section we shall evaluate data from a detection study by Kinchla[9] in which no-information feedback was given to the subject. A two-response, forced-choice, *visual* detection task was used and each subject was run for a series of over 800 trials; we shall only consider data from the last 400 trials. Two areas were outlined on a uniformly illuminated milk glass screen and the beginning of each trial was indicated by an auditory signal. During the auditory signal one of three possible events occurred: a fixed increment in radiant intensity occurred on one of the two areas of the visual display, or no change occurred in either area. A trial will be termed a T_1 or T_2 trial depending upon which of the two signal areas had an increment in illumination; trials on which no change occurred will be termed T_0 trials. As indicated earlier, the probability of a T_i trial will be denoted π_i. Subjects were instructed that a change would occur in one of the two areas on each trial. Following the auditory signal the subject was required to make either an A_1 or A_2 response (press one of two keys) to indicate which area he felt had changed in brightness. No information was given him about the correctness of his response.

We shall begin our analysis of this study by considering the expression for p_n. This expression may be derived from the model by applying the conditioning axioms for the no-feedback case. Since detailed derivations of the relevant expressions for this case are available elsewhere (Atkinson[5]) these derivations will not be repeated here. However, the techniques used in the derivations are analogous to those used in the information case which is discussed later in this paper. A direct application of the conditioning axioms and subsequent simplification yields the following expression for p_n:

$$p_n = p_\infty - (p_\infty - p_1)\left[1 - \frac{1}{N}(a + b)\right]^{n-1},\qquad(2)$$

where

$$a = \pi_1 hc' + (1 - h)\frac{c}{2} + \pi_0 h \frac{c}{2},$$

$$b = \pi_2 hc' + (1 + h)\frac{c}{2} + \pi_0 h \frac{c}{2},$$

and

$$p_\infty = \frac{\pi_1 h\psi + \frac{1}{2}(1 - h) + \pi_0 h \frac{1}{2}}{(1 - \pi_0)(1 - h + h\psi) + \pi_0},\qquad(3)$$

where $\psi = c'/c$. It is interesting to note that the asymptotic expression, p_∞, does not depend on the absolute values of c' and c but on their ratio, ψ. Throughout the remainder of this paper we shall only present mathematical results for the limiting case in which $n \to \infty$. The reason is that all the data we consider in this paper was obtained after the subject had already been run for a large number of trials. Hence, the data can best be interpreted in terms of the asymptotic form of the theory.

Using Eq. (3) we shall now consider one aspect of the data from Kinchla's study. Two groups of 24 subjects were run: Group I employed a presentation schedule where $\pi_1 = \pi_2 = .4$, and $\pi_0 = .2$; for Group II, $\pi_1 = .2$, $\pi_2 = .6$, and $\pi_0 = .2$. The average proportion of A_i responses made on T_i trials over the last 400 trials was computed for each group of subjects; the values are given in Table 1. The corresponding asymptotic proportions are specified in terms of Eqs. 1 and 3, and are simply:

$$\lim_{n\to\infty} \Pr(A_{1,n}|T_{1,n}) = h + (1 - h)p_\infty \qquad(4a)$$

$$\lim_{n\to\infty} \Pr(A_{2,n}|T_{2,n}) = h + (1 - h)(1 - p_\infty) \qquad(4b)$$

$$\lim_{n\to\infty} \Pr(A_{1,n}|T_{0,n}) = p_\infty . \qquad(4c)$$

Consideration of Eq. (3) reveals that $p_\infty = \frac{1}{2}$ if $\pi_1 = \pi_2$; thus, $p_\infty = \frac{1}{2}$ for Group I. By setting the observed asymptotic value for $\Pr(A_1|T_1)$ in Group I (i.e., .645) equal to $h + (1 - h)\frac{1}{2}$ an estimate of $h = .289$ was obtained. Since there was no relevant systematic difference in the two groups' experimental situation this estimate of h is appropriate for both groups. An estimate of ψ was obtained by setting the observed value of $Pr(A_1|T_0)$ in Group II equal to Eq. (3) with $h = .289$, $\pi_1 = \pi_0 = .2$ and $\pi_2 = .6$; this method yielded an estimate of $\psi = 2.8$. Using these estimates of h and ψ, Eqs. (3) and (4) generate the asymptotic predictions given in the top panel of Table 1. It is apparent that the model provides a reasonably close fit to this aspect of the data.

In contrast to a static theory of a signal detection the present theory provides a much deeper analysis of the experiment than indicated by the predictions summarized in the top panel of Table 1; the dynamic character of our model allows an analysis of sequential effects as well as average performance. In the model these sequential effects are produced by the trial-to-trial fluctuations that occur in the conditioning of patterns in set S.

The notation $Pr(A_i|T_jA_kT_m)$ will be used to represent the asymptotic probability of an A_i response on a T_j trial when the previous trial had been a T_m trial on which an A_k response was made. Equations (5a) through (5f) are expressions for these quantities derived from the axioms of the model. Since the derivations are quite lengthy they will not be given here; the reader interested in the mathematical techniques involved should consult Atkinson and Estes.[8]

$$Pr(A_1|T_1A_1T_1) = \frac{[h + (1 - h)\delta]p_\infty + (1 - p_\infty)h\xi'}{NX} + \frac{(N - 1)X}{N}, \quad (5a)$$

$$Pr(A_1|T_1A_2T_1) = \frac{(1 - h)\delta'(1 - p_\infty)}{N(1 - X)} + \frac{(N - 1)X}{N}, \quad (5b)$$

$$Pr(A_1|T_1A_2T_2) = \frac{h\xi p_\infty + [h^2 + (1 - h)\delta'](1 - p_\infty)}{NY} + \frac{(N - 1)X}{N}, \quad (5c)$$

$$Pr(A_1|T_1A_1T_2) = \frac{(1 - h)\delta p_\infty}{N(1 - Y)} + \frac{(N - 1)X}{N}, \quad (5d)$$

$$Pr(A_1|T_1A_1T_0) = \frac{\delta}{N} + \frac{(N - 1)X}{N}, \quad (5e)$$

$$Pr(A_1|T_1A_2T_0) = \frac{\delta'}{N} + \frac{(N - 1)X}{N}, \quad (5f)$$

where $\xi = c'h + (1 - c')$, $\xi' = c' + (1 - c')h$, $\delta = (c/2)h + (1 - c/2)$, $\delta' = c/2 + (1 - c/2)h$, $X = h + (1 - h)p_\infty$, and $Y = h + (1 - h)(1 - p_\infty)$. Comparable sets of equations can be written for $Pr(A_2|T_2A_kT_m)$ and $Pr(A_1|T_0A_kT_m)$ and are of the same general form as those in Eq. (5).

Two points of interest regarding these expressions should be noted. First, the average response probabilities defined in Eq. (4) depend only on h and ψ, whereas the quantities in Eq. (5) are functions of all four parameters N, c, c', and h. Second, independently of the parameter values certain relations among the sequential probabilities can be specified; e.g., $\Pr(A_1|T_1A_1T_0) \geq \Pr(A_1|T_1A_2T_0)$ for any stimulus schedule and any set of parameter values. To see this, simply subtract Eq. (5f) from Eq. (5e) and note that $\delta \geq \delta'$.

In Table 1 the observed values for $\Pr(A_i|T_jA_kT_m)$ are presented; these are

TABLE 1. Predicted and observed response probabilities in the visual experiment.

	Group I		Group II	
	Observed	Predicted	Observed	Predicted
$\Pr(A_1|T_1)$	.645	.645	.558	.565
$\Pr(A_2|T_2)$	.643	.645	.730	.724
$\Pr(A_1|T_0)$	.494	.500	.388	.388
$\Pr(A_2|T_2A_1T_1)$	.57	.58	.59	.64
$\Pr(A_2|T_2A_2T_1)$	.65	.69	.70	.76
$\Pr(A_2|T_2A_2T_2)$	.71	.71	.79	.77
$\Pr(A_2|T_2A_1T_2)$	.61	.59	.69	.66
$\Pr(A_2|T_2A_1T_0)$	.54	.59	.68	.66
$\Pr(A_2|T_2A_2T_0)$	.66	.70	.71	.76
$\Pr(A_1|T_1A_1T_1)$	.73	.71	.70	.65
$\Pr(A_1|T_1A_2T_1)$	.62	.59	.59	.52
$\Pr(A_1|T_1A_2T_2)$	.53	.58	.53	.51
$\Pr(A_1|T_1A_1T_2)$	.66	.70	.64	.64
$\Pr(A_1|T_1A_1T_0)$	.72	.70	.61	.63
$\Pr(A_1|T_1A_2T_0)$	.61	.59	.48	.52
$\Pr(A_2|T_0A_1T_1)$	.38	.40	.47	.49
$\Pr(A_2|T_0A_2T_1)$	.56	.58	.59	.66
$\Pr(A_2|T_0A_2T_2)$	.64	.60	.67	.68
$\Pr(A_2|T_0A_1T_2)$	.47	.42	.51	.51
$\Pr(A_2|T_0A_1T_0)$	.47	.42	.50	.51
$\Pr(A_2|T_0A_2T_0)$	.60	.58	.65	.66

based on the same data as the observed values of $\Pr(A_i|T_j)$ presented in Table 1. In order to generate theoretical predictions for the observed sequential entries in Table 1, values of N, c, c', and h are needed. Since estimates of h and $\psi = c'/c$ already have been made for this set of data, it was only necessary to estimate N and either c or c'. The predicted values in Table 1 are based on a least squares estimate of N and c'; i.e., N and c' were chosen so as to minimize the sum of the squared deviations between the 36 observed values in Table 2 and the corresponding theoretical values. The values of the four parameters that were used to generate the predictions are as follows: $N = 4.23$, $c' = 1.00$, $c = .357$, and $h = .289$. Since only four of the 36 possible degrees of freedom represented in Table 1 have been utilized in estimating parameters, the close fit provided by the model lends considerable support to the conception of the detection process made explicit in the axioms.

APPLICATION TO FEEDBACK DATA

To indicate the nature of the predictions for an information feedback problem we shall examine some data from two subjects run in a two-response, forced-choice *auditory* detection task. Two temporal intervals were defined on each trial by a pair of lights. A band-limited Gaussian noise (the masking stimulus) was present continuously throughout the experimental situation and on every trial one of the two intervals contained a fixed intensity, 1000 cps tone. The subject pulled one of two levers to indicate which of the two intervals he believed contained the signal. Each trial ended with the location of the signal being indicated to the subject by another set of lights. The experimental procedure is described in detail in Atkinson and Carterette[10]; that paper deals with an analysis of forced-choice and yes-no data from six subjects, each run for 350 trials per day for 30 days. The preliminary data we present here is not to be regarded as a test of the theory, but only a means of illustrating some of the predictions. A trial will be denoted T_1 or T_2 depending upon whether the first or second interval contained the 1000 cps signal, and a correct response on a T_i trial ($i = 1, 2$) will be termed an A_i response. Thus each T_i trial concludes with an E_i event which indicates to the subject that an A_i response was the correct response on that trial. The probability of a T_1 or T_2 (γ and $1 - \gamma$, respectively) was set at $\frac{1}{2}$ for the data that will be considered.

The first step in our analysis of the information feedback case will be to derive an expression for p_n. To do this we first note that (whatever the value of p_n) the value of p_{n+1} will be either p_n, $p_n + 1/N$, or $p_n - 1/N$; the reason for this is that (by axiom A3) if a change in the conditioning of the background pattern occurs it will only involve *one* of the N patterns. Thus p_{n+1} may be written as an average of these three possible values, with each value weighted by its probability of occurrence. The probability of occurrence of each of these values may be determined directly from the axioms. For example, the probability that $p_{n+1} = p_n + 1/N$ is simply the probability that T_1 occurred on trial $n(\gamma)$, times the probability that the background pattern sampled on that trial is conditioned to an A_2 response, $(1 - p_n)$, times the probability that conditioning is effective on that trial (θ); i.e., $\Pr(p_{n+1} = p_n + 1/N) = \gamma(1 - p_n)\theta$. In a similar fashion $\Pr(p_{n+1} = p_n - 1/N)$ may be shown to equal $(1 - \gamma)p_n\theta$. Finally, since p_{n+1} must be one of three values, $\Pr(p_{n+1} = p_n) = 1 - \gamma(1 - p_n)\theta - (1 - \gamma)p_n\theta$. Thus the following recursive expression for p_{n+1} may be written:

$$p_{n+1} = \gamma(1 - p_n)\theta \left(p_n + \frac{1}{N}\right) + (1 - \gamma)p_n\theta \left(p_n - \frac{1}{N}\right)$$
$$+ [1 - \gamma(1 - p_n)\theta - (1 - \gamma)p_n\theta]p_n . \quad (6)$$

This recursion can be solved by standard methods (see Atkinson and Estes[8]) to yield the explicit formula

$$p_n = p_\infty - (p_\infty - p_1)\left(1 - \frac{\theta}{N}\right)^{n-1}, \quad (7a)$$

where

$$p_\infty = \gamma . \quad (7b)$$

Table 2 presents the observed values for $\Pr(A_1|T_1)$ and $\Pr(A_2|T_2)$. Since $\gamma = \frac{1}{2}$ we have immediately [via Eq. (7)] that $p_\infty = \frac{1}{2}$. Knowing p_∞ and the observed value of $\Pr(A_1|T_1) = .73$ we may use Eq. (4a) to obtain an estimate of $h = .46$. Using this estimate of h the model predicts that $\Pr(A_1|T_2) = .27$ which is quite close to the observed value of .28.

TABLE 2. Predicted and observed response probabilities
in the auditory experiment.

	Observed	Predicted
$\Pr(A_1|T_1)$	.73	.73
$\Pr(A_1|T_2)$	.28	.27
$\Pr(A_1|T_1A_1T_1)$	.80	.78
$\Pr(A_1|T_1A_2T_1)$	.76	.75
$\Pr(A_1|T_1A_1T_2)$	.73	.71
$\Pr(A_1|T_1A_2T_2)$	.67	.68
$\Pr(A_1|T_2A_1T_1)$	.30	.32
$\Pr(A_1|T_2A_2T_1)$	.32	.29
$\Pr(A_1|T_2A_1T_2)$	.26	.25
$\Pr(A_1|T_2A_2T_2)$	.22	.22

Expressions for the sequential probabilities, $\Pr(A_i|T_jA_kT_m)$, may be derived for the feedback case just as they were for the no-feedback case. Once again, since the derivations are rather lengthy, only the expressions themselves will be presented here.

$$\Pr(A_1|T_1A_1T_1) = \frac{p_\infty + (1 - p_\infty)h\{\theta + (1 - \theta)h\}}{NX} + \frac{(N - 1)X}{N}, \quad (8a)$$

$$\Pr(A_1|T_1A_2T_1) = \frac{(1 - p_\infty)(1 - h)\{\theta + (1 - \theta)h\}}{N(1 - X)} + \frac{(N - 1)X}{N}, \quad (8b)$$

$$\Pr(A_1|T_1A_1T_2) = \frac{p_\infty(1 - h)\{1 - \theta + \theta h\}}{N(1 - Y)} + \frac{(N - 1)X}{N}, \quad (8c)$$

$$\Pr(A_1|T_1A_2T_2) = \frac{p_\infty h\{1 - \theta + \theta h\}}{NY} + \frac{(N - 1)X}{N}, \quad (8d)$$

where, as in Eq. (5), $X = h + (1 - h)p_\infty$ and $Y = h + (1 - h)(1 - p_\infty)$. Comparable equations can be written for $\Pr(A_1|T_2A_iT_j)$.

To generate theoretical predictions for $\Pr(A_1|T_iA_jT_k)$ estimates of θ and N are needed, in addition to our estimate of h. Once again, we obtain our estimate of N and θ by a least squares method; i.e., values of N and θ were selected that minimized the sum of the squared deviations between the observed values for $\Pr(A_1|T_iA_jT_k)$ in Table 2 and the corresponding predictions generated by Eq. (8). The values of the three parameters that were used to generate the predictions for Table 2 are $h = .46$, $\theta = .62$, and $N = 3.83$. Since only three of the possible eight degrees of freedom represented in Table 2 have been utilized the fit is reasonably good.

COMPARISON OF THE INFORMATION AND NO-INFORMATION CASES

So far we have examined the types of analyses that are possible in both a feedback situation and a no-feedback situation. We now turn to a comparison of these two situations in terms of our model. Experimentally an obvious way to explore the differences between these two situations would be to conduct a study in which the same subjects were run on two *identical* forced-choice detection tasks that differed only with respect to the presence or absence of information feedback. Either the visual or the auditory detection task discussed previously would be appropriate for such a study. To simplify the comparison we shall permit only T_1 or T_2 type trials to occur in both the information and no-information conditions and will use the notation γ and $1 - \gamma$ to denote the probabilities of a T_1 and T_2 event, respectively. Thus when interpreting the equations for the no-information case we need to set $\pi_1 = \gamma$, $\pi_2 = 1 - \gamma$, and $\pi_0 = 0$.

In our hypothetical study, the same subject would be used in both feedback conditions, and also the same physical signal parameters would be used throughout the experiment. Hence, it would be reasonable to assume that h and N are the same under both the information and no-information conditions. Given this assumption we note, by comparing Eqs. (3) and (7), that

$$p_n{}^I \geq p_n{}^{\bar{I}} \quad \text{for } \gamma > \frac{1}{2},$$

$$p_n{}^I = p_n{}^{\bar{I}} \quad \text{for } \gamma = \frac{1}{2},$$

where I and $\bar{I}$ refer to the information and no-information situations, respectively. Thus using Eq. (1) (which is applicable to both situations) we have for $\gamma \geq \frac{1}{2}$,

$$\begin{aligned} \Pr^I(A_{1,n}|T_{1,n}) &\geq \Pr^{\bar{I}}(A_{1,n}|T_{1,n}), \\ \Pr^I(A_{2,n}|T_{2,n}) &\leq \Pr^{\bar{I}}(A_{2,n}|T_{2,n}). \end{aligned} \tag{10}$$

The equality holds only when $\gamma = \frac{1}{2}$ or when $\psi \to \infty$. With these results in mind consider the overall probability of a correct response on trial n; namely

$$\Pr(C_n) = \gamma \Pr(A_{1,n}|T_{1,n}) + (1 - \gamma)\Pr(A_{2,n}|T_{2,n}).$$

In view of the inequalities in Eq. (10) we immediately have

$$\Pr^I(C_n) \geq \Pr^{\bar{I}}(C_n), \tag{11}$$

where, again, equality holds when $\gamma = \frac{1}{2}$ or when $\psi \to \infty$. Thus, in terms of overall performance, the theory predicts that the subjects will tend to be correct more often in an information feedback situation than in a no-information feedback situation.

A comparison of sequential statistics in the information and no-information cases is more tedious and for purposes of this paper we examine only one prediction; namely

$$\Delta = \Pr(A_1|T_1A_1T_1) - \Pr(A_1|T_1A_2T_2).$$

This equation specifies the largest possible difference between first-order sequential predictions, and it is interesting to examine the effect of the information variable on the value of Δ. To further simplify our analysis we shall let $\gamma = \frac{1}{2}$ and therefore $p_\infty = \frac{1}{2}$ for both the information and no-information cases.

Using Eqs. (8a) and (8d), we may derive an expression for Δ in the information case given that $p_\infty = \gamma = \frac{1}{2}$; namely

$$\Delta(I) = \frac{(1 - h)(1 - h + 2h\theta)}{N(1 + h)}. \tag{12}$$

Similarly, using Eqs. (5a) and (5c) (with $\pi_1 = \gamma$, $\pi_2 = 1 - \gamma$, and $\pi_0 = 0$) we may derive the following expression for Δ in the no-information case given, again, that $p_\infty = \gamma = \frac{1}{2}$:

$$\Delta(\bar{I}) = \frac{(1 - h)(1 - h + c + 2c'h)}{N(1 + h)}. \tag{13}$$

Comparing Eqs. (12) and (13) makes it apparent that the maximum possible difference between first-order sequential predictions may be greater or less in the information case, as compared with the no-information case, depending on the values of θ, c', and h. Namely

$$\Delta(I) > \Delta(\bar{I}), \quad \text{if } \theta > c' + c/2h$$
$$\Delta(I) < \Delta(\bar{I}), \quad \text{if } \theta < c' + c/2h.$$

Thus, at least for this particular comparison, no parameter-free conclusions can be drawn about the overall sequential effects in the information and no-information situations.

It is clear that more comparisons can be made between the feedback and no-feedback situation. However, for our present purposes the results already developed are sufficient to indicate the types of analyses that are possible in terms of the theory presented in this paper.

REFERENCES

1. Blackwell, H. R. "Psychophysical thresholds: Experimental studies of methods of measurement." *Bull. Eng. Res. Inst.*, No. 36, Univ. of Michigan, 1953.
2. Swets, J. A., Tanner, W. P., and Birdsall, T. G. "Decision processes in perception." *Psychol. Rev.*, 1961, **68**, 301–340.
3. Fechner, G. T. *Elemente der psychophysik*. Breitkopf and Hartel, Leipzig, 1860.
4. Carterette, E. C. and Wyman, M. J. "Applications of a Markov learning model to a simple detection situation involving social pressure." In J. Criswell, H. Solomon, and P. Suppes (Eds.), *Mathematical Methods in Small Group Processes*. Stanford Univ. Press, Stanford, California, 1962.
5. Atkinson, R. C. "Mathematical models in research on perception and learning." In M. Marx (Ed.), *Psychological Theory* (2nd Edition). Macmillan Co., New York, 1962.
6. Atkinson, R. C. "A variable sensitivity theory of signal detection." Technical Report No. 47, Psychology Series, Institute for Mathematical Studies in the Social Sciences, Stanford University, 1962.
7. Estes, W. K. "Toward a statistical theory of learning." *Psychol. Rev.*, 1950, **57**, 94–107.
8. Atkinson, R. C. and Estes, W. K. "Stimulus sampling theory." In R. R.

Bush, E. Galanter, and R. D. Luce (Eds.), *Handbook of mathematical psychology*. New York: Wiley, 1962, in press.

9. Kinchla, R. A. "Learned factors in visual discrimination." Unpublished doctor's dissertation, University of California, Los Angeles, 1962.

10. Atkinson, R. C. and Carterette, E. C. "Signal detection as a function of the stimulus presentation schedule: a comparison of forced-choice and yes-no procedures" (in preparation).

A Detection Method and Probabilistic Models for Assessing Information Processing from Brief Visual Displays*

W. K. ESTES and H. A. TAYLOR, *Stanford University*

Read before the Academy, April 29, 1964

The situation investigated in this study is one in which an individual is presented with a visual display containing a number of discrete parts, henceforth referred to as elements, and shortly thereafter is tested for his ability to report what he has seen. An example from outside the laboratory would be a person trying to report the numbers seen during a glimpse of the license plate of a passing auto. One of the best established facts in experimental psychology is the existence of a definite upper limit, termed the span of apprehension, on the number of elements that can be perceived under such conditions. Our first concern in this investigation will be to seek ways of improving existing methods of measuring the apprehension span. The second objective will be to formulate a model of the perceptual process that may provide insight into the reasons why the span of apprehension is so severely limited and at the same time account for the function relating measured span to number of elements in the display.

In ordinary everyday life situations, an individual presented with a visual display

* The research reported in this paper was supported, in part, by a grant from the National Science Foundation and, in part, by contract Nonr 225(73) between the Office of Naval Research and Stanford University. Reproduction in whole or in part is permitted for any purpose of the United States Government.

This article appeared in *Proc. Nat. Acad. Sci.*, 1964, **51**, 446–454.

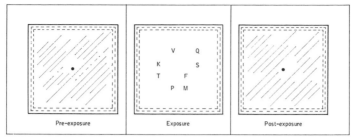

Fig. 1.—Appearance of display panel before, during, and after an exposure of a sample of randomly selected consonants.

moves his eyes about from point to point, thus gaining repeated and partially redundant samplings of the material presented. To attempt to deal immediately with a process of this complexity seems hopeless, and consequently it has been standard procedure in experimental psychology to simplify the situation considerably for purposes of preliminary analysis. To this end, material is presented in a tachistoscope which permits precise control of the time of exposure. By making the exposure time sufficiently short, usually less than 100 msec, it is possible to ensure that the subject will be unable to move his eyes from one fixation point to another and obtain more than one sampling of the material during a single exposure. In the classical experiment on apprehension span, a sample of material is shown for a short interval of time and then the subject is asked to report as much as possible of what he has seen.

A modification of the classical tachistoscopic apparatus[1] used in the present studies is illustrated in Figure 1. The subject is confronted with a panel surrounded by a dark hood (not shown in the figure). At the center of the panel is a window made of half-silvered glass. Behind the window, indicated by the dotted lines in the figure, is a cold cathode fluorescent tube. Rise and decay times for light intensity output are illustrated in Figure 2.

At the beginning of the trial the light behind the window is off so that the window appears to the subject as a mirror. Because of the tilt of the window and the presence of a black screen mounted obliquely below and in front of the window, the window appears dark to the subject but with a small white spot in the center on which he is instructed to fixate just before the beginning of each trial. At the onset of the trial the light behind the window goes on for a designated interval, 50 msec in the present experiments, and the material behind the window becomes visible. In this example, the material is a random sample of consonants filling a randomly selected set of positions from a 16-cell matrix. As soon as the light goes off, the subject again sees only the dark field with the fixation point in the center as indicated in the right-hand panel of the figure.

In order to ensure that our apparatus and procedures were comparable to those used in previous work, we began our present studies by running a few subjects under the classical procedure for determining apprehension spans by verbal report. The displays were linear arrays of randomly selected consonants, and the subject's task on each trial was simply to report as many as possible of the consonants he had seen. Results obtained for these subjects are shown in Figure 3 in the form of

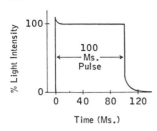

FIG. 2.—Light intensity output during a 100-msec exposure interval.

curves representing numbers of elements correctly reported from displays of various sizes. For displays of five or more elements, each point in the figure represents an average for 40 determinations. For displays of three and four elements, testing was discontinued after fewer determinations if performance was errorless on at least 12 successive trials. It may be noted that the forms of these functions and their limits are very similar from subject to subject. This uniformity is quite usual in this field of investigation. To emphasize it further, we might mention that when we average the mean terminal levels of the functions for these four subjects, the value obtained (4.4 elements) agrees well with that of approximately 4.3 reported by Sperling[2] for a study done several years ago in a laboratory at Harvard with generally similar apparatus. The fact that very similar values are obtained for the report span under a considerable range of experimental conditions and materials suggests that the quantitative properties of these functions, and in particular the upper limits on the amount of material that can be reported, may represent psychological or physiological parameters of some generality.

Despite the orderliness and reliability of these data on report span, they fall short of our purposes in one important respect, namely, that we cannot be confident that we are obtaining estimates of the total amount of information that the subject obtains from the display, or in other terms, the maximum number of elements perceived at the time of exposure. The difficulty is that, in situations of this sort, forgetting occurs very rapidly following the initial exposure. All of us are familar with this fragility of memory for brief displays from many experiences in such situations as that of trying to remember a 10-digit telephone number long enough to get from the telephone book to the phone. Thus, if an individual can correctly report about four or five consonants from a display containing eight or ten, we have good reason to think that he may have perceived more than he could report; but the amount of retention loss during the few seconds needed to give the report is unknown. Further, the very act of giving a report may interfere with retention in ways that are not yet fully understood. Consequently, in order better to assess the number of elements an individual can effectively sample in a display, we seek a method that is free of these perturbations. It appears that we may have developed such a technique in the detection method now to be described.

Following are some sample displays illustrating the schema for a series of trials in an experiment with the detection method.

F-Cards				C-Cards			
F	X	Q	R	C	X	Q	R
X	F	Q	R	X	C	Q	R
X	Q	F	R	X	Q	C	R
X	Q	R	F	X	Q	R	C

For a given series of trials there are exactly two critical elements, both known to the observer before the beginning of the series; in the example, the critical elements are

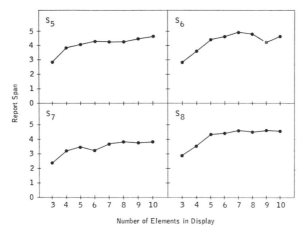

FIG. 3.—Data for individual subjects run with the classical procedure of verbal report and an exposure interval of 50 msec.

C and F. These critical elements represent signals, and the rest of the randomly drawn consonants represent noise, in the terminology of the classical experiments on signal detection. Each display contains exactly one of the critical elements, and the subject's task is to report which of the two critical elements is present in the display. The displays are made up in pairs, the two members of a pair differing only in which of the two critical elements is present in a given position. Since the positions of the critical elements vary randomly from one display to the next, in order to achieve perfect performance with displays of a given length, it is necessary for the subject to sample and process information from all of the elements in the display even though his report, given immediately at offset of the display, is merely an indication of which of the two critical elements is present.

With this technique the problems of retention loss are minimized, since it is not necessary for the subject to give an extended verbal report or, as in other techniques,[2] to be given a test of recall at some arbitrary time following offset of the display. Since each display contains exactly one of the two critical elements, it is possible for an observer to obtain many successes by guessing, even when he has not perceived the critical element in the display. Our answer to this problem is statistical, that is, giving each subject a large number of trials with sets of displays of different lengths and correcting the raw scores for the expected rate of success by guessing.

A sample of data obtained with the detection method is compared with data from the report method in Figure 4. The lower curve represents the mean for the four subjects whose individual data were previously exhibited for the report procedure. The same four subjects were run under the detection technique, with similar arrays of randomly drawn consonants as the displays, and mean scores in terms of estimated number of elements perceived after correction for guessing are shown as the upper curve.

From the raw scores obtained under the two procedures, the estimates shown in Figure 4 were computed in the following way. Each series run with the detec-

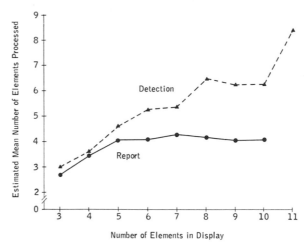

F<small>IG</small>. 4.—Estimates of mean number of elements perceived from displays of various sizes under detection and report procedures.

tion procedure had two critical elements represented equally often. Suppose that, from a display of D elements, the subject effectively processes, or perceives, P elements. If the critical element is included in the subset perceived, an event which has probability P/D, then it is correctly detected. If not, the subject still has probability $1/2$ of giving a correct report by chance (a report was required on all trials). The expected values for proportions of right and wrong reports, $P(R)$ and $P(W)$, respectively, are given by $P(R) = P/D + \left(1 - \dfrac{P}{D}\right)\dfrac{1}{2}$ and $P(W) = \left(1 - \dfrac{P}{D}\right)\dfrac{1}{2}$. Thus, $P(R) - P(W) = P/D$, and our estimate of the number of elements perceived is simply

$$\hat{P} = D[P(R) - P(W)] = R - W,$$

where R and W denote mean numbers of observed right and wrong responses, respectively. This result is well known and the $R - W$ correction has long been a standard procedure for comparable situations.[3] But in the case of the report procedure, there is the complication that the subject's tendency to guess, and therefore the total number of elements per report, may fluctuate from trial to trial even if the number displayed and the number perceived are constant. Denoting by E the number of consonants emitted by the subject on a trial (that is, the total number included in his report), the probability of getting k correct by chance is

$$p_k = \frac{\dbinom{D - P}{k}\dbinom{20 - D}{E - P - k}}{\dbinom{20 - P}{E - P}},$$

given that the display of D elements has been randomly selected from the total set of 20 consonants and that P of those are actually perceived. For any fixed value of E, we have for the expected number of elements correctly reported

$$R = P + \sum_{k=0}^{E-P} k p_k = P + \frac{(E - P)(D - P)}{20 - P}.$$

Solving for P and simplifying, we obtain for the desired estimate,

$$\hat{P} = \frac{20R - DE}{20 - D - E + R}.$$

If the number of elements emitted per report varies over trials with a given display size, then, since the expression for R is linear in E, the mean value of E may be used in the estimation equation for $\hat{P}$.

As anticipated, the estimates of number of elements sampled (Fig. 4) are substantially higher by the detection technique than by the report method and, in particular, there is no suggestion that the detection function is approaching a limit over the range of displays studied.

Now with a better method of measurement at hand, we turn to the problem of formulating a model to represent the perceptual process involved in the assimilation of information from brief displays. An obvious first candidate for evaluation is the fixed-sample-size model that has had much application in statistical learning theory.[4] As applied to the present situation, this model assumes that there is a fixed limit on the number of elements that can be simultaneously processed by the observer from a brief display, this limit being a function of the duration, but independent of the size of the display. When the display contains more than the limiting number, the assumption is that a random sample of this size is drawn from the display presented. In the detection experiment, if the random sample so drawn includes the critical element, a correct detection will result; if the sample does not include the critical element, the subject can achieve success only by random guessing.

Although appealing in its simplicity, this model is clearly inadequate to handle data from the detection experiment. Predicted curves of number of elements effectively sampled versus size of the display would simply comprise two linear segments. For display sizes below the critical sample size, the number of elements processed would be equal to the number in the display and above the critical value the function would be horizontal. Such a function cannot be made to give a reasonable account of the data shown in Figure 4.

Aside from the fact that the fixed-sample-size model is inadequate to handle the present data, its basic conception is unappealing in view of what we know of the eye and the nervous system. When a display contains a relatively large number of elements, there is no reason to think that the stimulation from only four or five of these is registered in the nervous system. Stimulation from a much larger number can certainly activate receptors in the retina and be transmitted to the central nervous system more or less simultaneously. The idea we now propose to account for the small number of elements effectively perceived is that the elements registered in the receptor apparatus must be scanned one at a time by a central mechanism and that the number scanned is limited by the decay of the stimulus traces activated by a brief display.   These notions lead to the *serial processing model* characterized by the following assumptions.

(1)   When a display containing D elements is exposed for a short interval, a sample of d elements is registered in the receptor apparatus.   For the conditions of the present experiments, we assume $d > D$, so d does not appear as a parameter of the model as developed here.

(2)   Following the exposure, the traces of the display in the nervous system fade exponentially.   We assume that there is a fixed parameter s such that during each successive short interval Δt following the display, there is probability s that the traces of the display will have passed below the threshold level at which they can influence behavior.

(3)   During and following the display, until the stimulus traces pass below threshold, the sampled ("registered") elements are scanned one at a time.   As each element is scanned, it is classified either as signal or as noise; and if the former, it leads to a report as to the critical element detected.

(4)   If the stimulus traces fade below threshold before the critical element is scanned, the subject gives a report at random.

From these assumptions, we can readily derive expressions for the probability of scanning any number k of elements from a display,

$$p_k = \begin{cases} s(1 - s)^{k-1} & \text{if } k < D \\ (1 - s)^{D-1} & \text{if } k = D, \end{cases}$$

for the mean number scanned per display,

$$E(k) = \sum_{k=1}^{D} kp_k = \frac{1}{s}[1 - (1 - s)^{D-1}(1 + sD - s)] + D(1 - s)^{D-1}$$

$$= \frac{1}{s}[1 - (1 - s)^{D}],$$

and for the mean proportion of correct detections per display,

$$P(R) = \frac{1}{2} + \frac{1}{2D}E(k) = \frac{1}{2}\left\{1 + \frac{1}{sD}[1 - (1 - s)^{D}]\right\}.$$

These functions appear plausible in form so we return to the data as shown earlier for several subjects run under the detection procedure, with the result shown in Figure 5.   For each subject the theoretical curve from the serial processing model provides a reasonably adequate graduation of the observed values.   Estimates of the decay parameter, s, were .04 for subject number 5, and .08 for subjects 6, 7, and 8.

Using data for individual subjects, the variability is somewhat large to provide a really adequate test of the quantitative adequacy of the model.   Consequently, we have followed up the earlier experiment with one run on a larger scale in which 20 subjects were tested with a series of matrix displays under the detection procedure. Data from this experiment (procedures and results of which will be reported in more detail elsewhere) are summarized in Table 1 in the form of proportions of correct detections for matrix displays of 8, 12, and 16 elements.   Even the fixed-sample-size model, for which theoretical values are shown in the second row, does not do

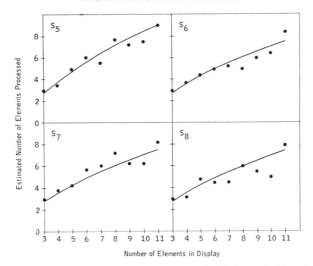

FIG. 5.—Detection data for individual subjects compared with theoretical functions (smooth curves) for the serial processing model.

too badly. However, the deviation for the 8-element displays, although not large by usual standards, is significant. The theoretical values for the serial processing model, shown in the bottom row, appear quite satisfactory.

TABLE 1

PROPORTIONS OF DETECTIONS FROM MATRIX DISPLAYS

	Number of Elements		
	8	12	16
Obs.	.78	.72	.67
FSSM	.82	.71	.66
SPM	.78	.71	.67

It appears that we may have made some progress toward our original objectives. Firstly, the detection method seems to be as free of perturbations due to forgetting as we can well hope to accomplish by any purely psychological technique in this area. Secondly, so far as the data go, the very simple probabilistic theory that we have termed the serial processing model has proved quite satisfactory. Further, the ideas embodied in this model offer some promise of accounting for several well-known but little understood phenomena. One of these is the virtual invariance of observed report span over a wide range of exposure times; another is the curious susceptibility of report span to disruption by events occurring immediately *following* the stimulus exposure.[2] The model now requires more rigorous testing by experiments in which various physical parameters of the experimental situation are systematically varied. A program directed to this end is currently in progress.

[1] The apparatus, including both the exposure unit and the wave generator used to control exposure times, was built by Iconix, Inc., Menlo Park, California. We are indebted to Dr. Nicholas Pappas for determination of the light intensity function.

[2] Sperling, G., "The information available in brief visual presentations," *Psychological Monographs*, **74,** whole no. 498 (1960), pp. 1–29.

[3] Hilgard, E. R., in *Handbook of Experimental Psychology*, ed. S. S. Stevens (New York: John Wiley and Sons, 1951), p. 556.

[4] Estes, W. K., *Psychol. Rev.*, **57,** 94–107 (1950).

Choice-Point Behavior

Gordon H. Bower, *Stanford University*

This paper presents a detailed analysis of the behavior of a subject at a choice point having several discriminative stimuli to which he may respond selectively. It has frequently been observed that a subject in such a situation spends some time sampling, or orienting to, the different stimuli before making his choice response. For example, in a black-white discrimination, a rat often looks back and forth repeatedly between the black stimulus and the white stimulus, as if to "make up his mind," before he approaches one stimulus or the other. Historically, psychologists have referred to orientation back and forth between discriminative stimuli as "vicarious trial and error" or VTE behavior.

It seems likely that our understanding of choice behavior and the variables affecting it will be enhanced by a detailed analysis of the component behaviors which constitute a choice response. Empirically, it seems that choice behavior in the situation described above may be analyzed into two component behaviors: orientation to the separate discriminative stimuli, and approach to these stimuli following orientation. Choices may be regarded as the outcome of the interaction of these underlying component responses. The models of this paper represent ways by which the approach and orientation tendencies to the several discriminative stimuli might combine to determine choices. In addition, the models provide a complete account of the sequences of orienting responses the subjects perform before approaching one stimulus or the other.

The models may be applied to those choice situations in which it is possible to identify orienting responses which serve separately to expose the subject to either of two discriminative stimuli. One simple example is a single-unit T maze with one black and one white arm. On every trial of the experiment, the black and white stimuli are separated spatially and the subject cannot orient to both simultaneously. To give concreteness to the assumptions of the model, the following discussion is referred to the single-unit T maze.

General Assumptions

The stimuli at the choice point of a T maze will be classified as follows: (1) the stimuli the subject samples when he is oriented straight ahead, which

Reprinted from *Studies in mathematical learning theory* (pp. 109–124), Robert R. Bush and William K. Estes, editors, with the permission of the publishers, Stanford University Press. © Copyright 1959 by the Board of Trustees of the Leland Stanford Junior University.

we will denote by the set S_0; and (2) the stimuli, S_1 and S_2, available for sampling on the right or left side of the choice point when the subject orients in that direction. For example, in a black-white discrimination, S_1 may denote the stimuli of the black alley and S_2 the stimuli of the white alley. If the positions of the black-white cues are randomly interchanged over trials, then S_1 appears equally often on the left and right sides of the T maze.

The responses elicited by these stimuli will be described as follows: (1) S_0 elicits orienting responses to the left or right with respect to the subject's body position; (2) when the subject is oriented to S_1 he either approaches S_1 or reorients; when the subject is oriented to S_2 he either approaches S_2 or reorients.

From the sequences of orienting responses that occur on individual trials of an experiment, it is possible to estimate the probabilities of these responses in the presence of the appropriate stimuli. We let F_0 denote the probability that the subject orients to the right after he is oriented to S_0 and $1 - F_0$ the probability that S_0 elicits an orientation to the left. By F_1 we shall denote the probability of an approach response when the subject is oriented to S_1. Similarly, by F_2 we shall denote the probability of an approach response when the subject is oriented to S_2. For convenience, we shall refer to F_0, F_1, and F_2 as the *basic* probabilities.

Over training trials within an experiment, the basic probabilities will undergo changes due to learning. These trial-to-trial changes are not of major interest in the first section of this paper. Instead, the major interest is in testing the implications of the model for orienting behavior on a single experimental trial, given the values of F_0, F_1, and F_2.

The Markovian Assumptions

The assumptions about the choice-point stimuli and the responses elicited by these stimuli permit a Markovian representation of choice-point behavior. The states of the Markov process represent the significant positions of orientation the subject may take at the choice point. We let states 0, 1, and 2 represent the subject's orientation to S_0, S_1, and S_2, respectively. States 3 and 4 will represent the subject's final approach to S_1 or S_2, respectively. States 3 and 4 are " absorbing " states in the sense that choice-point behavior is terminated on a particular experimental trial when the subject approaches S_1 or S_2.

The word " transition " will be used to denote the movement of the subject from one state to another. An experimental trial starts with the subject in state 0 and ends when he enters state 3 or state 4. Between these events, the subject will perform some ordered sequence of orientations and reorientations, corresponding to transitions between states.

The basic probabilities represent transition probabilities among the several states of the system. Thus F_0 is the probability of a transition from state 0 to state 1 if S_1 is on the right side of the maze on that trial, or from state 0 to state 2 if S_2 is on the right on that trial; F_1 is the probability of a transition from state 1 to state 3; and F_2 is the probability of a transition from state 2 to state 4.

In representing choice-point behavior as a Markov process, two assumptions are made: (1) the transition behavior is only one-step dependent—that is, the probability of a transition from state i to state j is independent of the path by which the system entered state i; and (2) the transition probabilities F_0, F_1, and F_2 remain constant for the duration of a single experimental trial.

With these assumptions, we will now consider one particular Markov representation of choice-point behavior. A few implications of this representation will be compared with some experimental results.

Model A

In this model central importance is assigned to state 0. It is assumed that if the subject is oriented to S_1 or S_2 and then turns away from this stimulus, he returns to state 0 (orients to S_0), and S_0 elicits a second orientation to the left or right. A diagram of this process is shown in Fig. 1 for a trial on which S_1 and S_2 are on the right and left side of the maze, respectively.

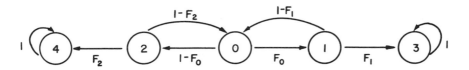

FIGURE 1. The Markovian representation of model A.

Pointed arrows represent the possible one-step transitions. The probabilities of the transitions are indicated beside the arrowed lines. This diagram is equivalent to a 5×5 matrix of transition probabilities. States 3 and 4 are absorbing states; the probability is 1 that the subject remains in these states once he enters them on any trial. The definition of a trial in a T maze ensures that the subject starts every trial at state 0.

Every experimental trial is eventually terminated when the subject approaches S_1 or S_2. To derive the probability that the subject approaches S_1 (is absorbed at state 3), we note that from state 0 to state 3 there is a direct path through state 1. The probability that the subject follows this path is F_0F_1. However, the subject may perform "loops" of orienting responses of the form 0, 1, 0, or 0, 2, 0 before he takes the final path 0, 1, 3. The probability of a 0, 1, 0 loop is $F_0(1 - F_1)$, and the probability of a 0, 2, 0 loop is $(1 - F_0)(1 - F_2)$. The subject may perform an indefinite number of these loops before he takes the final path 0, 1, 3. Therefore, the probability of absorption at state 3 may be written as the infinite sum

$$(1) \qquad \text{Pr}(3) = F_0F_1 \sum_{i=0}^{\infty} [F_0(1 - F_1) + (1 - F_0)(1 - F_2)]^i = \frac{F_0F_1}{F_0F_1 + (1 - F_0)F_2} .$$

This last expression gives the probability that a subject starting in state 0 is eventually absorbed at state 3 (approaches S_1). The probability that the subject approaches S_2 is $\Pr(4) = 1 - \Pr(3)$.

Equation 1 does not constitute a test of the model if estimates of the basic probabilities are first obtained from the data. All the information in the data relevant to $\Pr(3)$ is exhausted in obtaining the estimates of the basic probabilities.

To show this from probability considerations alone, let A and $\overline{A}$ denote the events of orienting to the right or left, respectively. Events B and C will denote approach to right or left, respectively. Without recourse to the model, we may write the analytic expression for the proportion of approaches to the right as

$$(2) \qquad \Pr(3) = \frac{p(A)p(B \mid A)}{p(A)p(B \mid A) + p(\overline{A})p(C \mid \overline{A})}.$$

In the model, the estimates of the basic probabilities are

$$(3) \qquad F_0 \triangleq p(A), \qquad F_1 \triangleq p(B \mid A), \qquad F_2 \triangleq p(C \mid \overline{A}).$$

When these estimates are substituted into Equation 1, Equation 2 follows identically; therefore, all information relevant to $\Pr(3)$ has been used in obtaining the estimates of F_0, F_1, and F_2.

This result cautions us to check every statistic derived from the model to determine whether all information relevant to the statistic has been exhausted by the estimates of F_0, F_1, and F_2. If these estimates do not exhaust all information relevant to the statistic, then the statistic may be considered as a prediction to use in testing the model.

The model may be tested by some of its predictions about the sequences of orienting responses. On any given trial, a subject will perform some particular sequence of orienting responses. A sample protocol of a subject's behavior might be "0, 1, 0, 1, 0, 2, 4." One way to study these sequences is to count the number of times certain patterns of transitions occur. For example, the pattern 0, 1, 0 occurs twice in the protocol above. If the model is correct, it should predict the distribution of the number of occurrences of any pattern of transitions.

As one example, consider the "loop" patterns 0, 1, 0 and 0, 2, 0. Let L, for loops, be a random variable denoting the number of loops that occur on a given trial for one subject. The variable L may have any of the values 0, 1, 2, $\cdots$ of the nonnegative integers. The problem is to derive from the model the distribution of L, i.e., the probability that L takes on some arbitrary value k.

The first few terms of this distribution may be written down by inspection of Fig. 1. The probability that $L = 0$ is given by the probability that the subject is absorbed at 3 or 4 in two steps, which is $F_0 F_1 + (1 - F_0) F_2$. The probability that $L = 1$ is given by the probability that the subject performs exactly one loop and then is absorbed in two steps. The probability of one loop or the other is $F_0(1 - F_1) + (1 - F_0)(1 - F_2)$, and the probability of absorption in two steps following this loop is $F_0F_1 + (1 - F_0)F_2$. The probability that L is exactly 1 is given by the product of these two probabilities. After writing a few more terms for $L = 2$, $L = 3$, $\cdots$, it becomes apparent that the series follows the geometric law given by

$$(4) \qquad \Pr(L = k) = [F_0F_1 + (1 - F_0)F_2][F_0(1 - F_1) + (1 - F_0)(1 - F_2)]^k .$$

Equation 4 gives the probability distribution of the number of loops before absorption occurs. If we set $J = F_0F_1 + (1 - F_0)F_2$, we may write Equation 4 more simply as

$$(5) \qquad \Pr(L = k) = J(1 - J)^k .$$

Equation 5 gives $\Pr(L = k)$ as an exponentially decreasing function of k and is the well-known geometric distribution. In testing the model the empirical distribution of L will be compared with the distribution predicted by the model.

As a second property of orientation sequences, suppose we count the total number of transitions in both directions between states 1 and 2. Let V denote the number of transitions between states 1 and 2. The derivation of the distribution of V will not be presented, since it is rather long. The result which will be used in testing the model is the average, or expected, value of V. The expected value of V derived from the model is given by

$$(6) \qquad E(V) = \frac{F_0(1 - F_0)[(1 - F_1) + (1 - F_2)]}{F_0F_1 + (1 - F_0)F_2} .$$

This expression provides a second prediction from the model to compare with experimental results.

Some Experimental Results

In testing some hypotheses concerning free versus forced choice trials, Milton A. Trapold and the writer recorded the VTE behavior of rats in a place + response learning situation. The experiment employed fifteen pairs of hungry rats run in an all-white T maze with five Noyes food pellets (about .25 gm.) on the right side and one pellet of food on the left side. Prior to the T-maze training, each subject was placed several times in both goalboxes and allowed to eat one pellet of food. Goalbox training was continued until each subject ate promptly upon being placed in either goalbox. Then four spaced trials a day were given for eleven days, after which all subjects were regularly choosing the five-pellet side of the maze.

Each pair of animals consisted of an experimental subject and his " yoked " control mate. On trials 1, 2, and 4 of each training day, the experimental subject of the pair was given free choices (noncorrection) while his control mate was forced to the same side the experimental subject chose on those trials. Forcing was accomplished by lowering a guillotine door at the choice point, blocking one of the maze arms. On the third trial of the day, the control subject was given a free choice and his experimental mate was forced to the side the control subject chose. This procedure ensured that following every trial the experimental subject and his yoked control mate were matched on the sequence of left and right turns and reinforcing events.

A mirror placed three feet above the choice point permitted observation of choice-point behavior. On each free-choice trial, the choice-point behavior of each rat was recorded in terms of his sequence of orienting responses. A typical protocol might read "0, 2, 0, 1, 3," describing a subject that entered the choice point, looked to the left, to the center, and to the right, and then approached the right arm of the maze. The orienting responses were discrete and clearly observable. The two experimenters agreed perfectly in recording the sequences of orienting responses.

The forced-choice versus free-choice comparison will not concern us here. Briefly, it was found that (1) forced trials definitely had a learning effect which appeared in measures of the basic probabilities, and (2) in comparison with a free trial, a forced trial in this situation had a slightly smaller effect on these measures than did an equivalent free trial

The data of primary interest here are the sequences of orienting responses. After estimates of F_0, F_1, and F_2 are obtained, the predictions of the model about these orientation sequences will be tested.

TABLE 1

Observed Values of F_0, F_1, and F_2 (Experimental Group Only)
Blocks of Three Free Trials

Trial Block	F_0	F_1	F_2
1	.50	.55	.37
2	.55	.71	.35
3	.59	.78	.32
4	.69	.93	.26
5	.78	.93	.23
6	.90	.98	.20
7	.90	.98	.20
8	1.00	1.00	—*
9	.98	1.00	0
10	.92	.98	0
11	.98	1.00	0

* No subject looked left during this block of trials. Consequently, F_2 could not be estimated.

In Table 1 the estimated values of F_0, F_1, and F_2 for the experimental group (fifteen subjects) are given in blocks of three free trials. These estimates are easily obtained from the data. For example, F_1 for the nth block of trials is obtained by dividing the number of right turns that occurred during that trial block by the total number of times the subjects looked to the right during that trial block. The estimate of F_0 is given by the proportion of times the subjects looked to the right after they had been oriented straight ahead. By substituting the values of F_0, F_1, and F_2 on the

nth trial block into Equation 1, the probability of a right turn for that trial block is obtained.

In Table 1 both F_0 and F_1 appear to have asymptotes of unity, while F_2 has an asymptote of zero. The corresponding functions for the control group (not shown) have the same asymptotes and approximately the same shapes. The last four values for F_2 are based on small numbers of observations because the subjects made fewer and fewer orientations to the small-reward side.

As the first test of the model, we consider the distribution of L, the number of loops of the form 0, 1, 0 or 0, 2, 0. The model implies that L should have the geometric distribution given by Equation 5, i.e.,

$$\Pr(L = k) = J(1 - J)^k .$$

The results of the experiment show that the daily distributions of L do have a geometric form. The sequence of daily geometric distributions tends to a point distribution with all density at $L = 0$ (corresponding to F_0 and F_1 both reaching asymptotes of unity in Equation 4).

There is one marked deviation from the predicted form of the distribution of L. The distribution on day 1 of the experiment departs significantly from the geometric form for both groups ($P < .01$, Kolmogorov-Smirnov one-sample test). On day 1, the relative frequency of $L = 1$ was larger than the relative frequency of $L = 0$, although all other values were of the expected order of magnitude. This result suggests that the model may be wrong in its description of behavior during the initial trials of the experiment.

If day 1 is excluded and the observations of L are pooled over days 2 through 7 to obtain a large sample, the geometric form of the distribution is clear. In Table 2, the empirical and predicted distributions are shown for the experimental and control groups, respectively. The constant J was estimated by the first point on the empirical distribution (setting $k = 0$ in Equation 5), and the remaining values of the theoretical distribution were calculated from Equation 5 with this estimate substituted for J. In both cases, the geometric distribution fits the data very well.

TABLE 2

Distribution of L

L	Experimental Group		Control Group	
	Observed	Predicted	Observed	Predicted
0	.710	.710	.733	.733
1	.226	.206	.200	.196
2	.041	.060	.059	.052
3	.015	.017	.008	.014
4	.011	.005	0	.004
5	0	.001	0	.001

Further information on the goodness-of-fit may be obtained by comparing the first few moments of the observed and predicted distributions. In Table 3 the first three raw moments are given for the experimental and control groups, respectively. Over all, the predicted values are quite close to the observed values.

TABLE 3

Moments of L Distributions

Moment	Experimental Group		Control Group	
	Observed	Predicted	Observed	Predicted
First (Mean)	.40	.41	.34	.34
Second	.70	.75	.51	.59
Third	1.65	1.30	.89	.98

Note.—The mth raw moment is given by $\sum_{k=0}^{\infty} k^m \Pr(L=k)$.

A second test of the model is the prediction of the average number of transitions between states 1 and 2. Predictions of $E(V)$ over trials were obtained by substituting the successive values of F_0, F_1, and F_2 from Table 1 into Equation 6. In Table 4 the obtained and predicted values of $E(V)$ are compared over trials.

TABLE 4

Trial Changes in Observed and Predicted Values of $E(V)$ by Blocks of Three Free Trials (Experimental Group Only)

Trial Block	$E(V)$	
	Observed	Predicted
1	1.13	.59
2	.76	.42
3	.62	.37
4	.38	.24
5	.24	.19
6	.09	.08
7	.11	.08
8	0	0
9	.02	.02
10	.11	.08
11	.02	.02

It is clear from Table 4 that the predictions are considerably below the observed values of $E(V)$. The predictions for the first four blocks of trials are roughly half as large as the observed values.

The source of this discrepancy is clear. If the subjects were oriented to S_1 and turned away, then they were very likely to orient to S_2 rather than to look back to S_1 again. This observation is supported by further analysis of the data. The orientation sequences of the first four blocks of trials were analyzed for repetition patterns (1, 0, 1 or 2, 0, 2) and alternation patterns (1, 0, 2 or 2, 0, 1). The frequencies of the alternation patterns for the four blocks of trials were 51, 34, 28, and 17, respectively, while the corresponding frequencies of the repetition patterns were 2, 3, 3, and 0. The subjects clearly show a higher degree of alternation of orientations to S_1 and S_2 than is predicted by the model. This indicates that transitions from state 0 do not conform to the path-independence condition. The next orientation of the subject from state 0 depends markedly on whether he was oriented to the left or right before coming back to the center (state 0).

In the next section, we shall consider a revised Markovian representation which does not encounter the "alternation" difficulty of model A. In model B the states 0, 1, and 2 are redefined in such a way that state 0 plays a minor role in the model. State 0 is redefined to be the position of the subject before he makes his first orientation to S_1 or S_2 on a given trial. State 1 is redefined so that head movements from right to center are ignored. The subject is said to leave state 1 only when he approaches state 3 or reorients completely to the other side (state 2). State 2 is defined in a similar manner.

One example of the sequences to be analyzed by model B is 0, 1, 2, 1, 2, 4. Such sequences may be obtained from the earlier protocols by deleting all 0's beyond the first and collapsing all runs of 1's or 2's separated only by zeros. Thus, the earlier protocol 0, 1, 0, 1, 0, 2, 4 will be rewritten as 0, 1, 2, 4. This revised sequence is then ready for analysis by model B.

Model B

The Markovian representation of model B is diagramed in Fig. 2. The new assumption of this model is that the subject orients back and forth between S_1 and S_2 and uses S_0 only to determine the starting point of the cycles of reorientation.

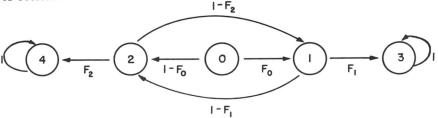

FIGURE 2. The Markovian representation of model B.

The estimates of F_0, F_1, and F_2 for model B differ slightly from the estimates in model A: F_0 is estimated by the proportion of times that subjects orient to the right upon first reaching the choice point; F_1 and F_2 are estimated by the proportion of approach responses per orientation in the S_1 or S_2 direction, respectively.

Four results will be derived from the model: (1) the unconditional probability, $\Pr(3)$, that the subject is absorbed at 3; (2) the conditional probabilities, $\Pr(3|1)$ and $\Pr(3|2)$, that subjects are eventually absorbed at 3 given that their first orientation is to the right or left, respectively; (3) the probability distribution of V, the number of transitions between states 1 and 2; and (4) the average value of V, $E(V)$. The results for $\Pr(3)$ and $E(V)$ cannot be used to test the model since the estimates of F_0, F_1, and F_2 in model B exhaust all information relevant to both statistics. They are derived here for use in a later section of the paper. The model will be tested by its predictions about $\Pr(3|1)$, $\Pr(3|2)$, and the distribution of V.

Consider first the conditional probability that the subject is eventually absorbed in State 3 given that he orients first to the right (to S_1, with the arrangement in Fig. 2). From state 1 the subject is absorbed at 3 in the next step with the probability F_1. However, the subject may make an indefinite number of loops of the form 1, 2, 1 before he finally takes the step from state 1 to state 3. The probability of exactly j loops of the form 1, 2, 1 starting from state 1 is $F_1[(1 - F_1)(1 - F_2)]^j$. From these considerations, we may write $\Pr(3|1)$ as the infinite sum

$$(7) \qquad \Pr(3|1) = F_1 \sum_{j=0}^{\infty} [(1 - F_1)(1 - F_2)]^j = \frac{F_1}{F_1 + F_2 - F_1 F_2}.$$

Equation 7 gives an expression for the probability of eventual absorption at 3, conditional on the subject's looking toward S_1 first upon reaching the choice point.

If the subject starts the trial by orienting to S_2, then with probability $1 - F_2$ a transition to state 1 occurs. Once the subject enters state 1, the probability of eventual absorption at 3 is given by Equation 7. Hence, we may write

$$(8) \qquad \Pr(3|2) = (1 - F_2)\Pr(3|1) = \frac{(1 - F_2)F_1}{F_1 + F_2 - F_1 F_2}.$$

Using Equations 7 and 8 we may write the unconditional probability of absorption at state 3 as

$$(9) \qquad \Pr(3) = F_0 \Pr(3|1) + (1 - F_0)\Pr(3|2)$$
$$= \frac{F_1[F_0 + (1 - F_0)(1 - F_2)]}{F_1 + F_2 - F_1 F_2}.$$

The model may be tested by Equations 7 and 8. To estimate $\Pr(3|1)$ on each trial block, we select all subjects that looked to the right first upon entering the choice point and calculate the proportion of these subjects that were eventually absorbed at 3. A similar estimate of $\Pr(3|2)$ is readily obtained from the data. The observed and predicted values of $\Pr(3|1)$ and $\Pr(3|2)$ are compared in Table 5. The standard deviations of the observed estimates are included to facilitate comparison. In every case, the predicted value is reasonably close to the observed value.

Next, we consider the distribution of V, the number of transitions between states 1 and 2 before absorption occurs. The expression for the probability

TABLE 5

Observed and Predicted Values of Pr (3/2) and Pr (3/1)
(Experimental Group Only)

Trial Block	Pr (3/2)			Pr (3/1)		
	Observed	Predicted	S.D.	Observed	Predicted	S.D.
1	.52	.47	.10	.70	.76	.10
2	.64	.57	.10	.80	.89	.09
3	.59	.62	.10	.96	.93	.04
4	.81	.72	.10	.97	.99	.03
5	.80	.74	.13	1.00	1.00	0
6	.80	.80	.18	1.00	1.00	0
7	.75	.80	.22	1.00	1.00	0
8	1.00	1.00	0	1.00	1.00	0
9	1.00	1.00	0	1.00	1.00	0
10	1.00	1.00	0	1.00	1.00	0
11	1.00	1.00	0	1.00	1.00	0

that V has some value k will depend on whether k is an even or odd integer. The subject can make k transitions from 1 to 2 in either direction by circling the "loop" 1, 2, 1 or 2, 1, 2 on $k/2$ occasions. The probability of one of these loops is $(1 - F_1)(1 - F_2)$. The probability of $k/2$ loops is this factor raised to the power $k/2$. If k is even, the loops begin and end in state 1 with probability F_0F_1, and begin and end in state 2 with probability $(1 - F_0)F_2$. When k is odd, the subject is absorbed on the side opposite his initial orientation after making $(k - 1)/2$ loops. From these considerations we may write the distribution of V as

$$(10) \quad \Pr(V = k) = \begin{cases} [F_0F_1 + (1 - F_0)F_2][(1 - F_1)(1 - F_2)]^{k/2} & \text{if } k \text{ is even} \\ [F_0(1 - F_1)F_2 + (1 - F_0)(1 - F_2)F_1][(1 - F_1)(1 - F_2)]^{(k-1)/2} & \\ & \text{if } k \text{ is odd.} \end{cases}$$

The predicted distribution of V was compared with the obtained daily distributions of V. With the exception of day 1, the daily distributions conformed closely to the predicted form, tending over training to a point distribution with all density at $V = 0$. On day 1, the obtained and predicted distributions differed significantly ($P < .01$, Kolmogorov-Smirnov one-sample

TABLE 6

Observed and Predicted Values of V from Model B
(Experimental Group Only)

V	Observed	Predicted
0	.715	.726
1	.225	.211
2	.041	.046
3	.015	.013
4	.004	.003
5	0	.001

test). The relative frequencies of $V = 0$ and $V = 1$ on day 1 were in the reverse order from their predicted magnitudes.

By excluding day 1 and pooling observations on V over days 2 through 7, the distribution in Table 6 is obtained. The predicted distribution is given for comparison. The values of F_0, F_1, and F_2 were estimated from the pooled data.

The final result to be derived in this section is the average value of V. This may be calculated from the distribution of V given in Equation 10. After simplification, the result of this calculation is

$$(11) \qquad E(V) = \frac{[(1 - F_2)(2 - F_1)] - F_0(F_1 - F_2)}{F_1 + F_2 - F_1 F_2} .$$

This result will be used in the next section to describe the trial-to-trial changes in $E(V)$ implied by certain conditioning assumptions.

To summarize the results of testing model B, it was found that it correctly predicts the distribution of V and the trial-to-trial changes in $\Pr(3|1)$ and $\Pr(3|2)$. The outstanding discrepancy is the difference between the predicted and obtained distributions of V on day 1. Whether this is a sampling error or whether it is the general rule that the model is wrong for the very early trials (e.g., because of failure to take into account visual "exploration" habits) can only be discovered through further experimentation.

Learning Assumptions

In the preceding sections, we have tested some implications of the models for performance at a choice point, using estimates of the basic probabilities obtained from the choice data. In this section, we propose some conditioning assumptions to describe the trial-to-trial changes in the basic probabilities as a function of reinforcement experience.

It should be emphasized that the performance models of the earlier sections and the conditioning assumptions of this section are independent. The following learning assumptions are derived from statistical learning theory [2]. Presumably, at this point the Hullian theorist would prefer to derive the basic probabilities from corresponding reaction potentials which change in a computable manner with reinforcement. Regardless of the rule used in deriving the changes in the basic probabilities during learning, the performance models are available for general use in testing any conditioning assumptions.

In the following, S_0, S_1, and S_2 are identified with sets of stimulus events, or elements, which may be effective when the subject orients to S_0, S_1, and S_2, respectively. We let θ_0 represent the sampling probability of S_0 elements given an orientation to S_0; and we let θ represent the sampling probabilities of S_1 and S_2 elements given an orientation to S_1 or S_2, respectively. By F_0 we denote the proportion of F_0 elements conditioned to orienting right, by F_1 the proportion of S_1 elements conditioned to the approach response, and by $1 - F_1$ the proportion of S_1 elements conditioned to the response of reorienting (to S_2 in model B). A similar interpretation is provided for F_2.

With this as background, the conditioning assumptions may be stated. Consider first the conditioning of S_0 elements to the response of orienting right. If, on trial n, the subject is reinforced for going to the right (which he does just after orienting in that direction), or is nonreinforced for going to the left, then $F_{0,n}$ increases according to

$$(12) \qquad F_{0,n+1} = (1 - \theta_0)F_{0,n} + \theta_0 .$$

If, on trial n, the subject is reinforced for going to the left, or is non-reinforced for going to the right, then $F_{0,n}$ decreases according to

$$(13) \qquad F_{0,n+1} = (1 - \theta_0)F_{0,n} .$$

To illustrate these conditioning assumptions, consider an experiment in which the subject is forced to the right and left sides of the T maze on random proportions ϕ and $1 - \phi$ of the trials, respectively. Further, let a_1 and a_2 be the probabilities that reinforcement follows a forced choice to the right or left side, respectively. Under these conditions, $\phi a_1 + (1 - \phi)(1 - a_2)$ is the probability of applying the operator specified by Equation 12, and $\phi(1 - a_1) + (1 - \phi)a_2$ is the probability of applying the operator specified by Equation 13. The average value of F_0 on trial $n + 1$ may be written as the average of Equations 12 and 13:

$$(14) \qquad F_{0,n+1} = (1 - \theta_0)F_{0,n} + \theta_0[\phi a_1 + (1 - \phi)(1 - a_2)] .$$

The solution to this difference equation is given by

$$(15) \qquad F_{0,n} = F_{0,\infty} - (F_{0,\infty} - F_{0,1})(1 - \theta_0)^{n-1} ,$$

where $F_{0,\infty} = \phi a_1 + (1 - \phi)(1 - a_2)$, and $F_{0,1}$ is the subject's initial probability of orienting to the right in the presence of S_0 stimuli.

The conditioning assumptions for F_1 and F_2 are similar to those for F_0. If reinforcement occurs following an approach to S_i $(i = 1, 2)$, then F_i increases according to

$$(16) \qquad F_{i,n+1} = (1 - \theta)F_{i,n} + \theta .$$

If nonreinforcement occurs following an approach to S_i, then F_i decreases according to

$$(17) \qquad F_{i,n+1} = (1 - \theta)F_{i,n} .$$

Finally, if the subject does not approach S_i on trial n, then F_i remains un-changed. That is, we apply the identity operator if the subject has no ex-perience of reinforcement or nonreinforcement at S_i on trial n. For example, if a forced trial to S_1 occurs on trial n, the value of F_2 is not affected by this event (i.e., $F_{2,n+1} = F_{2,n}$).

To illustrate these assumptions, consider again the forcing situation de-scribed above. Suppose that S_1 (black alley) is always on the right and S_2 (white alley) on the left. This arrangement will be called " place + response " contingencies. The parameter ϕ is the probability that the subject is forced to S_1, and a_1 is the probability of a reinforcement on a forced trial to S_1. The probability of applying to $F_{1,n}$ the operator in Equation 16 is ϕa_1, and the probability of applying the operator in Equation 17 is $\phi(1 - a_1)$. The probability that $F_{1,n}$ remains unchanged is $1 - \phi$ since this is the probability of a forced trial to S_2. From these considerations we may write the average F_1 on trial $n + 1$ as

$$(18) \qquad F_{1,n+1} = (1 - \phi\theta)F_{1,n} + \phi\theta a_1 .$$

By similar reasoning, the average value of $F_{2,n+1}$ is found to be

$$(19) \qquad F_{2,n+1} = [1 - (1 - \phi)\theta]F_{2,n} + \theta(1 - \phi)a_2 .$$

Equations 18 and 19 are difference equations which have the solutions

$$(20) \qquad F_{1,n} = a_1 - (a_1 - F_{1,1})(1 - \phi\theta)^{n-1} ,$$

$$(21) \qquad F_{2,n} = a_2 - (a_2 - F_{2,1})[1 - (1 - \phi)\theta]^{n-1} .$$

Equations 20 and 21 show that the asymptotes of F_1 and F_2 are a_1 and a_2, the probabilities of reinforcement for approach to S_1 and S_2, respectively. The rate of convergence to these asymptotes is $\phi\theta$ for F_1 and $(1 - \phi)\theta$ for F_2.

The expressions derived above for the changes in the basic probabilities in the forced-trial situation may be checked by free-choice test trials. From the results of a free-choice test trial, each of the basic probabilities may be estimated directly and compared with the predicted changes specified by Equations 15, 20, and 21.

The basic probabilities may also be substituted into Equations 9 and 11 of model B to predict the trial-to-trial changes in $\Pr(3)$ and $E(V)$. For example, suppose in the forcing situation described that $a_1 = a_2 = 1$ and $\phi = 2/3$. Equations 20 and 21 imply that F_1 and F_2 approach asymptotes of unity, and Equation 15 implies that F_0 approaches an asymptote of ϕ. By substitution in Equation 9, these values imply that $\Pr(3)$ approaches an asymptote of ϕ. If the initial conditions are $F_{0,1} = .50$ and $F_{1,1} = F_{2,1}$, we may derive the result that $\Pr(3)$ starts at .50, rises with training to a maximum above $2/3$, and then falls to an asymptote of $2/3$.

By substituting the expressions for $F_{0,n}$, $F_{1,n}$, and $F_{2,n}$ into Equation 11, one can derive the prediction that, if $a_1 = a_2 = 1$, then $E(V)$ is a decreasing function of training trials and has an asymptote of zero. It is easy to see the basis for the latter result. Since F_1 and F_2 approach 1, in the limit the subject is absorbed following his first orientation of each trial; hence, $E(V) = 0$.

In the design above, the black alley (S_1) is always on the right and the white alley (S_2) on the left; however, one may randomly interchange the black and white alleys in their left-right positions from trial to trial. In this case, the experimenter may correlate any of several cues with the side on which forced trials and reinforcements are given. In the one case, which we shall call "place" contingencies, the experimenter ignores the left-right dimension and defines ϕ, a_1, and a_2 relative to the black-white dimension. Then ϕ is the probability that the subject is forced to S_1, and a_1 is the probability of reinforcement when the subject is forced to S_1. A second case, called "response" contingencies, arises when the experimenter ignores the black-white dimension and defines ϕ, a_1, and a_2 relative to the right-left positional dimension. In this case, ϕ is the probability of forcing the subject to the right, and a_1 is the probability of reinforcement on a forced trial to the right.

The model may be applied to situations involving "place" and "response" contingencies. One must recall that F_0 is defined as the probability of orienting to whatever stimuli are on the right side of the maze. Thus, the probability of an orientation to S_1 is F_0 if S_1 is on the right, but it is $1 - F_0$ if S_1 is on the left. The Markov expressions (e.g., Equations 9 and 11) in the first section were derived for trials with S_1 on the right. For trials with S_1 on the left, the expressions are correct if F_0 and $1 - F_0$ are interchanged wherever they appear in the equations.

To illustrate briefly the way the model handles "place" contingencies, we consider the case in which the subject is forced to S_1 with probability ϕ, and S_1 is on the left side with probability .50. Here a_1 and a_2 are the probabilities of reinforcement when the subject is forced to S_1 and S_2, respectively. The conditioning rules imply that in such circumstances the asymptote of F_0 will be .50, while the asymptotes of F_1 and F_2 are a_1 and a_2, respectively. If $a_1 = a_2 = 1$ and the initial conditions are as before, Equation 9 implies that the probability of approach to S_1 starts at .50, deviates to a maximum with training, then returns to an asymptote of .50. Note that this asymptotic result differs from the analogous result with the place + response contingencies described above. The difference is due to the different asymptotes of F_0 under the two sets of contingencies. The asymptote is $\phi = 2/3$ in the case of place + response learning, and it is .50 in the present case of place contingencies.

As an additional illustration of the conditioning assumptions, we may consider "response" contingencies such that ϕ is the probability of a forced trial to the right, and .50 is the probability that S_1 is on the right on any given trial of the experiment. Here we identify a_1 and a_2 as the probabilities of reinforcement when the subject is forced to the right and left, respectively. Under these conditions, the asymptotes implied by the conditioning assumptions are

(22) $$F_{0,\infty} = \phi a_1 + (1 - \phi)(1 - a_2) ,$$

(23) $$F_{1,\infty} = F_{2,\infty} = \phi a_1 + (1 - \phi)a_2 .$$

If $a_1 = a_2 = 1$ and we use the same initial conditions as before, then the probability of a right turn starts at .50 and deviates gradually to a limiting value of ϕ, the asymptote of F_0. In this case, the choice probability does not temporarily "overshoot" the eventual asymptote as it did in the two preceding cases.

A novel prediction can be made for the "response" contingencies when $a_1 = 1$ and $a_2 = 0$. That is, the subject is always reinforced when forced to the right side of the maze, but is never reinforced when forced to the left. With $a_1 = 1$ and $a_2 = 0$, Equations 22 and 23 imply that F_0 approaches an asymptote of unity, while F_1 and F_2 approach asymptotes of ϕ. When these values are substituted into Equation 9, the predicted asymptotic probability of a right turn is

$$(24) \qquad \Pr(\text{Right}) = \frac{1}{2 - \phi}.$$

By substituting these same values into Equation 11, we see that the average value of V should decrease to an asymptote given by

$$(25) \qquad E(V) = \frac{1 - \phi}{\phi}.$$

These two predictions seem counter to common-sense expectations. Intuitively, we might expect the subject to learn to ignore the black-white cues [3] and learn simply to "turn right." If they should be verified, these predictions would provide convincing evidence for the conditioning assumptions.

A note is appropriate here to explain the requirement of a forcing procedure for the previous experimental designs. A forcing precedure allows us to specify the probabilities with which certain events (e.g., an approach to left which is nonreinforced) occur on any given trial. Using these probabilities, we can derive mean curves for $F_{0,n}$, $F_{1,n}$, and $F_{2,n}$. By contrast, a free-choice procedure implies that the sequences of events the subjects experience will depend on the choices they make. Because these choices cannot be specified in advance, the probabilities of certain events are unknown before the experiment is performed. In such a case, closed expressions for the mean values of the basic probabilities cannot be derived from the conditioning assumptions; however, they may be computed by Monte Carlo techniques [1]. In principle, then, the model may also be applied to experimental situations involving only free-choice trials.

The foregoing discussion has illustrated some implications of the conditioning assumptions. In principle, the assumptions are relevant to a large body of learning problems. In every case, the predictions of the trial-to-trial changes in choice probability depend jointly on the conditioning assumptions and the Markovian representation. Fortunately, these two classes of assumptions can be tested independently by a single set of experimental results if the experimenter records the sequence of orienting responses exhibited by the subject at the choice point. Thus the model may encourage experimenters to look more closely at these underlying components of choice behavior. It may be at this level of analysis that we will discover sufficient lawfulness to reward our investigations of choice behavior.

REFERENCES

1. Bush, R. R., and Mosteller, F. *Stochastic models for learning*. New York: Wiley, 1955.
2. Estes, W. K., and Burke, C. J. A theory of stimulus variability in learning. *Psychol. Rev.*, 1953, **60**, 276-86.
3. Restle, F. Discrimination of cues in mazes: a resolution of the "place-vs-response" question. *Psychol. Rev.*, 1957, **64**, 217-28.

A Random-Walk Model for Choice Behavior

WILLIAM K. ESTES, *Indiana University*

A common focus of interest for the three groups participating in this conference—economists, mathematicians, and psychologists—lies in the area of preferential choice behavior. Much economic theory rests on an assumption that an individual makes choices among commodities or other entities in such a way as to maximize the value or utility, for him, of the outcomes. Although the generality of this assumption has occasionally been questioned (apparently only by the ever-skeptical psychologists), the combined weight of tradition and intuitive appeal makes its position impregnable.

Problems of mathematical interest have arisen as it has gradually become clear that principles having to do with the maximizing of utility can be effectively applied only to the extent that utility can be measured; for to say that a scale of utility exists for an individual is to say that his choice behavior satisfies the axioms of a particular type of mathematical system. For the experimental psychologist, a maximizing tendency, even if decisively shown to exist, would serve not as an explanatory principle but as a problem itself calling for explanation. Living organisms do not in fact carry utility scales in their heads; how then do they manage, on occasion, to behave as though they did? A psychological explanation of this phenomenon would consist in showing that it can be derived from more elementary assumptions about the behavior of the individual in the choice situation, optimally from assumptions that can claim some independent empirical support.

In this paper we shall consider a mathematical model whose properties are intended to represent in considerable detail the chain of behavioral events that eventuates in an overt manifestation of preference among a set of alternatives. This model represents an extension of earlier ones that have grown out of the assumptions of statistical learning theory. Provision is made for selective sampling ("perceiving") of choice-point cues and for the vacil-

This paper was prepared while the writer held a visiting appointment as Research Associate in the Institute for Mathematical Studies in the Social Sciences, Applied Mathematics and Statistics Laboratories, Stanford University. The work was supported by the Group Psychology Branch of the Office of Naval Research under Contract NR-171–034 with Stanford University.

latory behavior ("vicarious trial-and-error") characteristically observed during the pre-decision period of each trial in a choice experiment. In special cases this model reduces to one recently published by Bower [1] and to the linear or stimulus-sampling models of learning theory [3].

We shall consider two illustrative applications of the model. The first will be to a two-choice learning experiment in which amount of reward is contingent upon the individual's response; it will provide ready comparisons with the more familiar linear model. The second application will concern preferential situations of the kind that have traditionally served as bases for psychological scales of utility; it will enable us to bring out some relationships between this model and one recently published by Luce [6]. Finally, we shall consider the question whether the choice probabilities generated by this model satisfy the constraints summarized by Marschak [7] that justify the assumption of a utility scale.

1. Analysis and Conceptualization of the Choice Situation

The essential ingredients of a choice situation are the organism that is to do the choosing, a set of stimuli (these we shall frequently refer to as "objects," although in experiments with human choosers they may be symbols), and a criterion for the initiation and termination of a trial. By "trial" we denote the temporal unit of primary importance. A trial begins with a signal, which might be the release of a rat into the choice area of a maze or the presentation of a set of stimulus objects to a human subject; continues with a sequence of responses, each of which produces the stimulus for the next; and terminates with the choice of one of the objects. For example, a trial might run as follows:

1. A set of N stimulus objects, S_i $(i = 1, 2, \cdots, N)$, is presented and the subject orients toward ("notices," "looks at") S_3;
2. Subject starts toward S_3;
3. Subject moves further in the direction of S_3;
4. Subject chooses S_3 and terminates the trial.

Or, for a second example,

1. The same set is presented and subject orients toward S_1;
2. Subject reorients toward S_4;
3. Subject starts toward S_4;
4. Subject moves further in direction of S_4;
5. Subject withdraws from path leading to S_4 and reorients toward S_2;
6. Subject chooses S_2 and terminates the trial.

For illustrative purposes, it is convenient to visualize the situation in terms of a rat in a T-maze. Then S_1 and S_2 would be the two goal boxes, and movements toward or away from S_i would be interpreted literally as steps along the pathway leading from the choice point to S_i. This is the context in which Bower conducted his investigation of Markov models for the two-choice situation [1]. More generally, however, the approach movements might be components in the sequence of actions leading to purchase of a commodity or the like (looking in the Yellow Pages, going to the appropriate store to view a sample, asking a salesman the price, etc.); and in the case of human subjects they may be largely verbal and not readily accessible to direct observation by the experimenter. For simplicity, we shall limit consideration here to cases in which the set of alternatives remains fixed throughout a trial and the number of consecutive approach responses required to effectuate a choice (starting from the last return to the choice point) is some finite integer m, the same for all the alternatives S_i.

In the Markovian representation of the choice situation, the state of the system at any step within a trial (each of the numbered statements in the examples above corresponds to a step) will be defined in terms of the response made by the subject. Thus the possible states are:

O_i $(i = 1, 2, \cdots, N)$: Subject at choice point oriented toward S_i;

$A_{i,j}$ $(i = 1, 2, \cdots, N; j = 1, \cdots, m - 1)$: jth consecutive approach response toward S_i;

$A_{i,m}$ $(i = 1, 2, \cdots, N)$: Choice of S_i.

In the special case of $m = 1$, the second subscript will be dropped. From the definition of a trial it follows immediately that $A_{i,m}$ are absorbing states and all other states are transient.

2. Assumptions

1. There exists a set of probabilities o_i $(i = 1, 2, \cdots, N)$ with $\sum_i o_i = 1$, interpreted as the initial probabilities of orientation toward the stimulus objects S_i.

2. There exists a set of probabilities p_i $(i = 1, 2, \cdots, N)$, with $0 < \sum_i p_i \leq N$, which are constant over a trial.

3. If the subject is in either state O_i or state $A_{i,j}$ $(j < m)$, i.e., if the immediately preceding response was either an orientation toward S_i or a movement toward S_i that did not constitute a final choice, then the probability of an approach response toward S_i equals p_i; otherwise this probability equals zero.

4. If the subject is in either state O_i or state $A_{i,j}$ $(j < m)$, then with probability $1 - p_i$ the subject withdraws from S_i and orients toward one of the other stimulus objects S_j $(i \neq j)$, each of these reorientations having probability $1/(N - 1)$.

It should be noted that Assumption 4 as stated here is intended to apply only when the stimulus objects S_i are all distinct and fully discriminable by the subject. In a later section we shall introduce a modification of this assumption for application to the case of duplicate alternatives.

5. If the subject is in state $A_{i,m-1}$, or when $m = 1$ in state O_i, and the next response is an approach toward S_i, the trial terminates and S_i is said to have been chosen.

3. Theorems on Absorption Probabilities

Although choice times can be dealt with in the model in terms of the

ESTES

$$\begin{array}{c|ccccccccc}
 & A_{1,m} & A_{1,m-1} & \cdots & A_{1,1} & O_1 & O_2 & A_{2,1} & \cdots & A_{2,m-1} & A_{2,m} \\
\hline
A_{1,m} & 1 & 0 & \cdots & 0 & 0 & 0 & 0 & \cdots & 0 & 0 \\
A_{1,m-1} & p_1 & 0 & \cdots & 0 & 0 & 1-p_1 & 0 & \cdots & 0 & 0 \\
\vdots & \vdots & \vdots & & & \vdots & \vdots & \vdots & & & \vdots \\
A_{1,1} & 0 & & & 0 & 0 & 1-p_1 & 0 & & & 0 \\
O_1 & 0 & & & p_1 & 0 & 1-p_1 & 0 & & & 0 \\
O_2 & 0 & & & 0 & 1-p_2 & 0 & p_2 & & & 0 \\
A_{2,1} & 0 & & & 0 & 1-p_2 & 0 & 0 & & & 0 \\
\vdots & \vdots & \vdots & & & \vdots & \vdots & \vdots & & & \vdots \\
A_{2,m-1} & 0 & 0 & \cdots & 0 & 1-p_2 & 0 & 0 & \cdots & 0 & p_2 \\
A_{2,m} & 0 & 0 & \cdots & 0 & 0 & 0 & 0 & \cdots & 0 & 1 \\
\end{array}$$

Matrix 1

$$\begin{array}{c|cccc}
 & A_1 & O_1 & O_2 & A_2 \\
\hline
A_1 & 1 & 0 & 0 & 0 \\
O_1 & p_1^m & 0 & 1-p_1^m & 0 \\
O_2 & 0 & 1-p_2^m & 0 & p_2^m \\
A_2 & 0 & 0 & 0 & 0 \\
\end{array}$$

Matrix 2

number of steps to absorption, we shall limit consideration in this report to results concerning choice frequencies. Consequently, the theorems of principal interest are those having to do with probabilities of absorption at the various alternatives. For convenience in exposition, we shall first derive expressions for these probabilities in two important special cases and then indicate the form of the general solution.

First we consider the case of two alternatives with m unrestricted. The matrix of one-step transition probabilities among the states takes the form of Matrix 1, where the ordering of states is as indicated at the top and left. Since the only states with non-zero probabilities at the first step of a trial are O_1 and O_2, we can replace Matrix 1 for our present purposes by the simpler Matrix 2, which obviously yields the same absorption probabilities as the original from initial states O_1 and O_2. Solving for the limit matrix of this auxiliary process in the usual way (see, e.g., [5, chap. 15]), we find it to be

$$\frac{1}{p_1^m + p_2^m - p_1^m p_2^m}\begin{bmatrix} p_1^m + p_2^m - p_1^m p_2^m & 0 & 0 & 0 \\ p_1^m & 0 & 0 & p_2^m(1-p_1^m) \\ p_1^m(1-p_2^m) & 0 & 0 & p_2^m \\ 0 & 0 & 0 & p_1^m + p_2^m - p_1^m p_2^m \end{bmatrix}.$$

Letting $o = o_1 = 1 - o_2$ for the initial orientation probability, we then have for the probability that the first alternative, S_1, will be chosen:

(1)
$$P(1 \mid 1, 2) = \frac{p_1^m[o + (1 - o)(1 - p_2^m)]}{p_1^m + p_2^m - p_1^m p_2^m} .$$

In the case of N alternatives with $m = 1$, the form of the transition matrix again follows in an obvious way from our definitions and assumptions. It is illustrated for $N = 3$ in Matrix 3.

$$
\begin{array}{c|cccccc}
 & A_1 & A_2 & A_3 & O_1 & O_2 & O_3 \\
\hline
A_1 & 1 & 0 & 0 & 0 & 0 & 0 \\
A_2 & 0 & 1 & 0 & 0 & 0 & 0 \\
A_3 & 0 & 0 & 1 & 0 & 0 & 0 \\
O_1 & p_1 & 0 & 0 & 0 & \dfrac{1 - p_1}{2} & \dfrac{1 - p_1}{2} \\
O_2 & 0 & p_2 & 0 & \dfrac{1 - p_2}{2} & 0 & \dfrac{1 - p_2}{2} \\
O_3 & 0 & 0 & p_3 & \dfrac{1 - p_3}{2} & \dfrac{1 - p_3}{2} & 0 \\
\end{array}
$$

Matrix 3

If we impose the restriction of equal initial orientation probabilities for all alternatives, i.e., $o_1 = o_2 = \cdots = o_N = 1/N$ (this restriction is appropriate for all the applications we shall consider for $N > 2$), then it can be shown that the probability of choosing alternative S_i from the set of N is given by

(2)
$$P(i \mid 1, 2, \cdots, N) = \frac{p_i \displaystyle\prod_{j \neq i} \left(1 - \frac{p_j}{N}\right)}{\displaystyle\sum_{k=1}^{N} p_k \prod_{j \neq k} \left(1 - \frac{p_j}{N}\right)} .$$

The proof of this theorem is somewhat involved, so we defer it, together with the statement of the corresponding theorem for m unrestricted, to an appendix.

4. Application to Two-Choice Learning with Differential Amounts of Reward

The reference experiment here can be taken as the running of a rat in a T-maze for a series of free-choice trials under a non-correction procedure. Two different amounts of reward, e.g., different quantities of food or foods of different palatability, are used throughout the series, one always being present in the left goal box and the other always in the right; these will be designated S_1 and S_2.

Now, within any trial, the approach probabilities p_1 and p_2 and the orienting probability $o_1 = 1 - o_2 = o$ are assumed constant in the present model. From one trial to the next, however, the values of these probabilities should be expected to change. If S_1 and S_2, including in each the path leading to it from the choice point, are entirely distinct (i.e., in terms of stimulus-sampling theory, the two sets of stimulus elements are disjoint), then p_i

should change only on trials when S_i is chosen. We shall assume that on these trials the value of p_i changes in accordance with the linear difference equation that has been used previously [3] in interpreting effects of amount of reward within statistical learning theory, viz.,

$$p_{i,n+1} = (1 - \theta)p_{i,n} + \theta c_i ,$$

where θ is a "learning rate" parameter which is the same for all alternatives and falls in the half-open interval $0 < \theta \leq 1$. The "reward coefficient" c_i associated with S_i is assumed to vary with the amount of reward and falls in the closed interval $0 \leq c_i \leq 1$.

The orientation probability o would be expected to change on all trials, increasing if S_1 is chosen and decreasing if S_2 is chosen. The expected change in o, again assuming a linear transformation, is then given by

$$o_{n+1} = (1 - \theta)o_n + \theta P_n(1) ,$$

where $P_n(1)$ is the probability that S_1 is chosen on trial n.

For our present purposes, it will suffice to consider the asymptotic behavior of this system as n, the number of learning trials, becomes large. If both c_1 and c_2 fall between 0 and 1, then the system has no absorbing states, and clearly $P_n(1)$ must remain bounded away from 0 and 1. In this case, both choices continue to occur with non-zero probabilities as n becomes large, and obviously p_i tends to the limit $p_i = c_i$. Also, it is apparent that o_n asymptotically approaches the limit $P(1)$ of $P_n(1)$. Making the appropriate substitutions in equation (1) for the case $m = 1$, we obtain

$$(3) \qquad P(1) = \frac{c_1(1 - c_2)}{c_1 + c_2 - 2c_1c_2} .$$

Note that this expression is independent of the learning rate parameter, and in fact depends only on the "reward coefficients" c_1 and c_2. Although derived under the restriction $0 < c_i < 1$ for $i = 1, 2$, equation (3) clearly yields the correct asymptote if one of the c_i equals unity or if one of the c_i equals zero. For the case $c_1 = c_2 = 0$ the first trial would never terminate, and for $c_1 = c_2 = 1$, the asymptote depends on the initial conditions.

It is of interest to compare asymptotic results for this model with those for the corresponding case of the familiar "linear model." In the latter there is a single dependent variable, the probability p_n that the first alternative is chosen on trial n (the probability that the second alternative is chosen being $1 - p_n$), and this probability is assumed to change in accordance with $p_{n+1} = (1 - \theta)p_n + \theta c_1$ if S_1 is chosen and $p_{n+1} = (1 - \theta)p_n + \theta(1 - c_2)$ if S_2 is chosen. This process has the asymptote

$$p_\infty = \frac{1 - c_2}{2 - c_1 - c_2}$$

(see [2], [4]).

Asymptotic probabilities of choosing the first alternative are compared for the two models in the following table:

c_1	c_2	Random-Walk Model	Linear Model
1	< 1	1	1
> 0	0	1	$\dfrac{1}{2 - c_1}$
$\dfrac{2}{3}$	$\dfrac{1}{3}$	$\dfrac{8}{10}$	$\dfrac{2}{3}$
$\dfrac{3}{4}$	$\dfrac{1}{4}$	$\dfrac{9}{10}$	$\dfrac{3}{4}$

The sharpest difference between the two models appears in the second line of the table. If the second reward coefficient is zero while the first is positive, the random-walk model predicts an asymptote of unity for the first choice regardless of the particular value of c_1, but the linear model predicts an intermediate asymptote depending on c_1. Doubtless most people will intuitively find the first prediction the more congenial. Experimental evidence relevant to this point is so scanty, however, that at the moment one cannot be sure which prediction is more nearly correct.

As one can see in the last two lines of the table, the random-walk model tends to "amplify" differences between c_1 and c_2: that is, for any given difference between c_1 and c_2, the difference in choice probabilities for S_1 and S_2 is generally greater (and never smaller) in the random-walk model than in the corresponding linear model. The only important effect of permitting m to be greater than 1 in equation (1) is that this "amplifying" effect increases with increasing m.

5. Application to the Prediction of Paired Comparisons

The case of the model to be applied is that of N distinct alternatives with the initial orientation probabilities all equal to $1/N$, a tolerable assumption in the usual experimental procedure with randomized presentations. For simplicity of notation we set $m = 1$, but this restriction is of no empirical import; all the results to be discussed in this section and the next hold for any fixed m. The reference experiment is the usual paired-comparison study in which members of a set $[S]$ of N stimulus objects are presented to the subject a pair at a time. Our objective is to use the information gained from observing the results obtained with some pairs in order to make *a priori* predictions about preferences in new pairs.

The theoretical bases for these predictions are the absorption probabilities given by equation (2). These expressions cannot be used directly to generate the desired predictions, for the paired-comparison experiment yields only $N - 1$ independent observation equations from which to estimate the N parameters p_i $(i = 1, 2, \cdots, N)$. We can, however, estimate the ratios of certain simple functions of the p_i. These functions are the quantities $p_i/(1 - \frac{1}{2}p_i)$, and their usefulness arises from the fact that the ratio of the choice probabilities for any two alternatives takes on the very simple form

$$\frac{P(i\mid i, j)}{P(j\mid i, j)} = \frac{p_i(1 - \frac{1}{2}p_j)}{p_j(1 - \frac{1}{2}p_i)} = w_{ij},$$

as may readily be verified by substituting into the left-hand member from equation (2).

Now for any three alternatives, S_i, S_j, and S_k, the following *product rule* obtains:

$$(4) \qquad\qquad w_{ij}w_{jk} = w_{ik},$$

for

$$\frac{p_i(1 - \frac{1}{2}p_j)}{p_j(1 - \frac{1}{2}p_i)} \cdot \frac{p_j(1 - \frac{1}{2}p_k)}{p_k(1 - \frac{1}{2}p_j)} = \frac{p_i}{p_k} \cdot \frac{(1 - \frac{1}{2}p_k)}{(1 - \frac{1}{2}p_i)}.$$

Thus, if $P(i\mid i, j)$ and $P(j\mid j, k)$ have been evaluated empirically for a given subject or group of subjects, then $P(i\mid i, k)$ can be predicted.

For an illustrative application of the product rule, let us consider some data reported by P. T. Young from a study of food palatabilities with rats [8]. The three substances tested were sugar (S), wheat (W), and casein (C), and the first two determinations showed a 55% preference for S over W and a 70% preference for W over C. Thus we have $w_{SW} = .55/.45$ and $w_{WC} = .70/.30$. The product rule yields

$$\frac{.55}{.45} \cdot \frac{.70}{.30} = 2.85 = \frac{.74}{.26}$$

for the predicted value of w_{SC}, which compares favorably with the observed value of .738/.262.

In order to try the product rule on data from human subjects, we may use some results of an unpublished study conducted by the writer. A group of approximately 120 college students was given a mock consumer-preference survey. The students were asked to choose among three color combinations for automobiles: red-white (R), blue-gray (B), and yellow-black (Y). In this case the first two determinations yielded a 71% preference for R over B and a 73% preference for B over Y. Applying the product rule, we obtain

$$\frac{.71}{.29} \cdot \frac{.73}{.27} = 6.62 = \frac{.87}{.13}$$

for the predicted value of w_{RY}, which may be compared with the observed value of .89/.11.

We can readily satisfy ourselves that the present model satisfies the binary constraints that Marschak shows to be conditions for the existence of a utility scale (i.e., a "random utility indicator"; see [7]). As an example, consider Marschak's quadruple condition: for any four objects S_x, S_y, S_z, and S_t,

$$P(x\mid x, y) \geq P(z\mid z, t) \quad \text{if and only if} \quad P(x\mid x, z) \geq P(y\mid y, t).$$

To show that this condition is satisfied, we note that the first inequality holds if and only if $w_{xy} \geq w_{zt}$. Multiplying both sides of this last inequality by w_{yz}, we obtain $w_{xy}w_{yz} \geq w_{yz}w_{zt}$; and applying the product rule, we have $w_{xz} \geq w_{yt}$, which in turn holds if and only if $P(x \mid x, z) \geq P(y \mid y, t)$. Q.E.D.

The reader may have noted that the product rule in this model is identical in form to a theorem arising in Luce's model for choice behavior [6]. It is pertinent to ask whether the present model also yields anything similar to the *constant ratio rule*, which can be regarded as one version of Luce's fundamental choice axiom. The ratio has to do with the probabilities of first choices from subsets of any arbitrary size M taken from $[S]$. For brevity, let s_M represent a subset of M objects from $[S]$, and consider the ratio

$$\frac{P(i \mid s_M)}{P(j \mid s_M)} = \frac{p_i\left(1 - \dfrac{p_j}{M}\right)}{p_j\left(1 - \dfrac{p_i}{M}\right)},$$

which is formed from the probabilities of choosing stimulus objects S_i and S_j from any subset of M objects that includes them both. In Luce's model, this ratio is independent of the number of alternatives, beyond S_i and S_j themselves, added to s_M. In the present model, the ratio depends on M, becoming constant only in the limit as $M \to \infty$. Constancy of the ratio is not essential for predictive purposes, however. Once empirical estimates have been obtained for any $N - 1$ ratios involving independent paired comparisons and any one ratio for a subset with $M > 2$, the p_i can all be evaluated; then predictions can be made for choices from any subsets of any size that can be drawn from the full set of N alternatives. Predictions of this sort will be illustrated in the next section.

6. Application to a Preferential Choice Experiment with Duplicate Alternatives

In the discussion of Marschak's paper in this symposium, Debreu posed the following problem. Suppose that I am asked to choose one of three records; the first is a suite by Debussy (D), the second and third are recordings of the same Beethoven symphony by two different conductors (B_1 and B_2). Assuming that my pairwise preferences are 3/5 for D over either B_1 or B_2 and 1/2 for B_1 over B_2, what will be my probability of choosing D if offered all three alternatives simultaneously? A straightforward application of Luce's choice axiom (the constant ratio rule referred to above) yields 3/7 as the predicted probability; however, Debreu argued on intuitive grounds that 3/5 would more likely be the correct outcome. It may be instructive to analyze this problem within the framework of the present model.

The character of our predictions will turn on the question of whether or not the alternatives are all distinct. If the chooser is able to discriminate between the two Beethoven recordings so that B_1 and B_2 may be considered distinct, then we need only apply equation (2). If, however, B_1 and B_2 are indistinguishable to the chooser, then the transition matrix takes the slightly modified form of Matrix 4, where A_1, A_2, and A_3 designate choices of

	A_1	A_2	A_3	O_1	O_2	O_3
A_1	1	0	0	0	0	0
A_2	0	1	0	0	0	0
A_3	0	0	1	0	0	0
O_1	p_1	0	0	0	$\dfrac{1-p_1}{2}$	$\dfrac{1-p_1}{2}$
O_2	0	p_2	0	$1-p_2$	0	0
O_3	0	0	p_3	$1-p_3$	0	0

Matrix 4

D, B_1, and B_2, respectively. The only change from our previous assumptions is that in this case when the chooser has just oriented toward one of the duplicate alternatives and failed to choose it, his next orientation is always toward the unique alternative. Psychologists will recognize that this modified assumption embodies the notion of an alternation tendency which has become familiar in other experimental contexts under such labels as "stimulus satiation."

The limit matrix is readily found by standard methods for the general case of N alternatives, $N-1$ of which are duplicates. If the initial orientation probabilities all equal $1/N$, the probability that the unique alternative is chosen takes the very simple form

$$(5) \qquad P(u) = \frac{p_u\left(1 - \dfrac{N-1}{N}\right)p_d}{p_u + p_a - p_u p_a} \, ,$$

where the subscripts u and d refer to the unique and duplicate alternatives, respectively. The most notable difference between equations (2) and (5) is that in the latter case, as the number of alternatives is increased, the choice probability approaches a limit which is in general non-zero:

$$\lim_{N \to \infty} P(u) = \frac{p_u(1 - p_a)}{p_u + p_a - p_u p_a} \, .$$

Thus the probability of selection of the unique alternative cannot be swamped (driven to zero) by the addition of a large number of duplicate alternatives. When the number of duplicates is large, it becomes almost certain that one of them will be observed first, but then there is probability $(1 - p_a)p_u$ that the unique alternative will be chosen before any of the duplicates is considered again.

To apply the results of our analysis to Debreu's problem, we consider both possibilities: that B_1 and B_2 are distinct and that they are indistinguishable. Also, we consider two hypothetical choosers: one, who might be a music lover, has relatively high p_i values, and the other has relatively low p_i values. Both sets of p_i values satisfy the hypothesized choice probabilities for binary comparisons. Entering them into equations (2) and (5), we obtain the following probabilities for the choice of alternative D from the set of three.

Alternatives	$p_1 = .80$ $p_2 = p_3 = .62$	$p_1 = .20$ $p_2 = p_3 = .14$
Disjoint	.42	.42
Duplicate	.51	.58

The predicted values for the case of disjoint alternatives are close to the value of .43 which arises from application of Luce's axiom (as is always the case unless some of the p_i are near unity and others near zero). If the chooser is assumed to be unable to distinguish between B_1 and B_2, and is not a music lover, then the outcome conjectured by Debreu on intuitive grounds is very close to that predicted by the present model.

APPENDIX

We wish to prove that equation (2) gives the probability that S_i is chosen if the subject is presented with N distinct alternatives and the initial orientation probabilities are all equal to $1/N$. Since the order of the alternatives is arbitrary, we shall let $i = 1$ and denote by P the probability that alternative 1 is chosen. Also, we denote by t_i' $(i = 1, 2, \cdots, N)$ the probabilities of absorption at A_1 starting from A_i $(i = 1, 2, \cdots, N)$, and by t_i $(i = 1, 2, \cdots, N)$ the probabilities of absorption at A_1 starting from O_i $(i = 1, 2, \cdots, N)$. Obviously $t_1' = 1$, and $t_i' = 0$ for $i \neq 1$. For the t_i we can write

$$t_1 = p_1 + \frac{(1 - p_1)}{N - 1} (t_2 + t_3 + \cdots + t_N)$$

$$t_2 = \frac{(1 - p_2)}{N - 1} (t_1 + t_3 + \cdots + t_N)$$

$$\vdots$$

$$t_N = \frac{(1 - p_N)}{N - 1} (t_1 + t_2 + \cdots + t_{N-1}) ;$$

and these relations can be put in the simpler forms

$$t_1 = p_1 + \frac{(1 - p_1)}{N - 1} (NP - t_1)$$

$$t_2 = \frac{(1 - p_2)}{N - 1} (NP - t_2)$$

$$\vdots$$

$$t_N = \frac{(1 - p_N)}{N - 1} (NP - t_N) ,$$

since under our hypothesis concerning the initial orientation probabilities,

(6) $$P = \frac{1}{N} \sum_i t_i .$$

Substituting into equation (6) in terms of the N relations obtained above, we have

$$P = \frac{1}{N} \sum_i t_i = \frac{1}{N}\left[\frac{(N-1)p_1}{N-p_2} + NP\left(\frac{1-p_1}{N-p_1} + \cdots + \frac{1-p_N}{N-p_N}\right)\right],$$

and, solving for P,

$$P = \frac{(N-1)p_1}{N(N-p_1)\left(1 - \dfrac{1-p_1}{N-p_1} - \cdots - \dfrac{1-p_N}{N-p_N}\right)}$$

$$= \frac{(N-1)p_1(N-p_2)(N-p_3)\cdots(N-p_N)}{N\left[\prod\limits_{i=1}^{N}(N-p_i) - (1-p_1)\prod\limits_{i\neq i}(N-p_i) - \cdots - (1-p_N)\prod\limits_{i\neq N}(N-p_i)\right]}.$$

Now, by straightforward algebra, one can show that

$$\frac{N}{N-1}\left[\prod_i(N-p_i) - \sum_i(1-p_i)\prod_{j\neq i}(N-p_j)\right] = \sum_i p_i\prod_{j\neq i}(N-p_j).$$

Substituting the right-hand expression for the left-hand one in the denominator of the preceding equation yields

$$P = \frac{p_1\prod\limits_{i\neq 1}(N-p_i)}{\sum\limits_i p_i\prod\limits_{j\neq i}(N-p_j)} = \frac{p_i\prod\limits_{i\neq 1}\left(1-\dfrac{p_i}{N}\right)}{\sum\limits_i p_i\prod\limits_{j\neq i}\left(1-\dfrac{p_j}{N}\right)}. \qquad \text{Q.E.D.}$$

Equation (2) was derived for the special case of $m = 1$, where m, it will be recalled, is the number of consecutive steps along the path from the choice point to S_i required for absorption at S_i. By virtue of the same considerations leading to equations (1) and (2), we obtain the following probability of choosing S_1 when there are N distinct alternatives with initial orientation probabilities all equal to $1/N$ but with m arbitrary:

(7)
$$P = \frac{p_1^m\prod\limits_{i\neq 1}\left(1-\dfrac{p_i^m}{N}\right)}{\sum\limits_i p_i^m\prod\limits_{j\neq i}\left(1-\dfrac{p_j^m}{N}\right)}.$$

REFERENCES

1. Bower, G. H. "Choice-Point Behavior," chap. 6 in R. R. Bush and W. K. Estes, eds., *Studies in Mathematical Learning Theory*, Stanford, Calif.: Stanford University Press, 1959.
2. Bush, R. R., and F. Mosteller. *Stochastic Models for Learning*, New York: John Wiley and Sons, 1955.
3. Estes, W. K. "The Statistical Approach to Learning Theory," in S. Koch, ed., *Psychology: A Study of a Science*, II, 380–491, New York: McGraw-Hill, 1959.
4. Estes, W. K., and P. Suppes. "Foundations of Linear Models," chap. 8 in *Studies in Mathematical Learning Theory* (see [1]).
5. Feller, W. *Probability Theory and Some of Its Applications*, New York: John Wiley and Sons, 1950.
6. Luce, R. D. *Individual Choice Behavior*, New York: John Wiley and Sons, 1959.

7. MARSCHAK, J. "Binary-Choice Constraints and Random Utility Indicators" in K. J. Arrow, S. Karlin and P. Suppes, eds., *Mathematical Methods in the Social Sciences, 1959*, Stanford, Calif.: Stanford University Press, 1960.

8. YOUNG, P. T. "Studies of Food Preference, Appetite and Dietary Habit. VII. Palatability in Relation to Learning and Performance," *Journal of Comparative and Physiological Psychology*, **40** (1947), 37–72.

A Response Time Model for Choice Behavior

WALTER KINTSCH,* *University of Missouri*

A subject in a two-choice situation characteristically makes several observing responses before performing the final choice. This behavior can be described by means of a random walk model. The present paper explores some possibilities as to how this model can be extended to include choice time. The assumption is made that the duration of each step in the random walk is a random variable which is exponentially distributed. With this assumption, one can predict the probability distributions of the choice times as well as the moments of these distributions.

Random walk models of choice behavior assume (i) that in a two-choice situation the subject orients himself before making a response and (ii) that the subject's transition from a neutral state to various orienting responses and finally to the overt choice can be described by stable transition probabilities. In these models it is assumed that each step in the random walk process requires a fixed amount of choice time and that this time constant h is equal for all steps [1, 2, 4]. Thus, choice times would be given by h times the number of steps in the random walk. In this case the distribution of choice times is completely determined by the distribution of the number of steps to absorption in the random walk. In the choice model which will be considered below, this distribution will be geometric (eq. 3). The consequent prediction, however, that all choice time distributions must be J-shaped is clearly too restrictive.

The assumption that each step in the random walk has a constant duration must therefore be changed. An obvious alternative assumption is that the duration of each step is a random variable which is exponentially distributed. A strong rationale can be presented for the use of the exponential distribution, and it has been applied successfully in a variety of related situations [cf. 6]. The choice time model proposed here consists essentially in the assumption that a choice can be viewed as a sequence of steps, the orienting responses of the basic random walk model, and that each step is distributed in time according to the exponential distribution. If time is regarded as discrete, the geometric distribution assumes the role of the exponential distribution. It will be advantageous to develop the present

*The author gratefully acknowledges his debt to W. K. Estes and C. J. Burke. This study was initiated while the author held a USPHS postdoctoral fellowship at Indiana University.

This article appeared in *Psychometrika*, 1963, **28**, 27–32.

model first for the discrete case and then for the continuous case; the latter is easier to work with in applications.

Let Q be a transition matrix defining a random walk from a starting state through a sequence of orienting states to one of two absorbing states A or B. Choice A or B occurs whenever the process arrives at A or B, respectively. Let N be the number of steps to absorption in this process. N will be a random variable with $P(N = n) = g(n)$. Let the time required to complete the ith step in this random walk process be a discrete random variable with $P(X_i = x) = f_i(x)$. Furthermore, assume that the distributions of all steps are identical, thus replacing $f_i(x)$ by $f(x)$, and that the time required to complete the ith step is independent of the time required to complete the jth step for all i, j. Mathematically the problem is then to determine the distribution of the sum of N mutually independent random variables X_i ($i = 1, 2, \cdots, N$) with the common distribution $f(x)$, where N is a random variable independent of the X_i with distribution $g(n)$.

For reasons mentioned above, the geometric distribution will be chosen as the distribution of the X_i, i.e.,

$$(1) \qquad P(k \, \triangle t) = p^{k-1}(1 - p),$$

where $P(k \, \triangle t)$ is the probability of a response time of duration $k \, \triangle t$. The expression for $g(n)$ will of course depend upon the characteristics of the random walk model being considered. First a special case will be discussed briefly.

Let the transition matrix Q be such that on each trial the subject starts in the starting state S and moves to either one of two "orienting states" $o_1 A$ or $o_1 B$. This first step determines whether response A or B will be made. After the first step the subject moves on with probability 1 through the remaining orienting states until the process is terminated with the absorption in either A or B, i.e., when one of the overt end responses is performed. The interesting property of this random walk is that the number of steps to absorption is a constant, namely n. In this case the probability distribution of the total response times is given by the distribution of the sums $S_n = X_1 + X_2 + \cdots + X_n$ of n independent random variables, each having an exponential density function. Bush and Mosteller [3] have shown that the distribution of response times will be given by the gamma distribution with parameters n and λ. They have successfully used the gamma distribution to describe running times in the straight runway. As a choice time model, the gamma distribution will be much less useful because of the paucity of the underlying choice model. The latter model assumes that the choice between A and B is determined on the very first step. The remaining $n - 1$ steps add nothing of significance to the choice process and are there merely to fill up time. (Note that this remark does not apply to sequential tasks, such as running to a goal in a straight alley.) A model such as this does not provide for the vacillatory behavior preceding the choice and will therefore be unsatisfactory.

A more realistic choice time model can be obtained by considering the random walk model proposed by Estes [4] and Bower [2]. This model purports to describe the actual sequence of steps involved in a choice and has been successful in accounting for choice behavior. In its simplest version choice behavior is described by the random walk process given by the transition matrix

$$
(2) \qquad Q = \begin{array}{c} \\ S \\ oA \\ oB \\ A \\ B \end{array}
\begin{array}{ccccc}
S & oA & oB & A & B \\
\left[\begin{array}{ccccc}
0 & 1-a & a & 0 & 0 \\
0 & 0 & 1-b & b & 0 \\
0 & 1-c & 0 & 0 & c \\
0 & 0 & 0 & 1 & 0 \\
0 & 0 & 0 & 0 & 1
\end{array}\right].
\end{array}
$$

On each trial the subject begins in the starting state S, goes to one or the other orienting state, and from there he either goes on to make the recorded response or shifts to the other orienting state. As far as a model for response times is concerned, the relevant feature is the distribution of the number of steps to absorption. Now the number of steps is no longer a constant but a random variable. For the case $b = c$ in (2) its distribution is given by

$$
(3) \qquad g(n) = P(N = n) = 0 \qquad \text{for } n < 2,
$$
$$
= (1 - b)^{n-2}b \qquad \text{for } n \geq 2.
$$

The generating function of $g(n)$ will be

$$
(4) \qquad b(s) = \sum_{n=0}^{\infty} P(N = n)s^n = \frac{bs^2}{1 - (1 - b)s}.
$$

The problem is then to determine the distribution of sums $S_n = X_1 + X_2 + \cdots + X_n$, where the number n of terms has probability distribution (3) and generating function (4), and each X_i is independently distributed according to (1), i.e., $P(X = x) = p^x(1 - p)$, which has generating function

$$
(5) \qquad f(s) = \frac{1 - p}{1 - ps}.
$$

A theorem given by Feller ([5], pp. 268–269) states that the required distribution will have the generating function

$$
(6) \qquad h(s) = b(f(s)) = \frac{b(1 - p)^2}{p^2s^2 + \{p^2(b - 1) - p(b + 1)\}s + b + p - bp}.
$$

In order to obtain the complete probability distribution of the response times from the generating function, $h(s)$ will be rearranged by the method of partial fractions ([5], pp. 257–258):

$$(7) \qquad h(s) = \frac{b(1-p)}{(1-b)} \left[\frac{1}{\dfrac{b-p-bp}{p} - s} - \frac{1}{\dfrac{1}{p} - s} \right].$$

Equation (7) can be expanded; $h(k)$, the probability of obtaining a response time of duration $k \, \Delta t$, will be given by the coefficients of s^t and is seen to be

$$(8) \qquad h(k) = \frac{b(1-p)}{(1-b)} \, p^k \left[\left(\frac{1}{1 - (1-b)(1-p)} \right)^{k+1} - 1 \right].$$

The mean and variance of this distribution are given by

$$E(k) = \frac{(1+b)p}{b(1-p)},$$

$$\mathrm{Var}\,(k) = E(k) + (E(k))^2 - \frac{2p^2}{b(1-p)^2} \, .$$

It will usually be practical to treat time as a continuous variable instead of breaking it down into intervals of duration Δt, as is required for (8). It will be necessary to perform the limiting operation upon the moment generating function of (8) instead of directly upon (8), following a similar problem described by McGill [6]. The required moment generating function will be

$$(9) \qquad m_k(\theta) = \sum_{k=0}^{\infty} e^{\theta k} p(k)$$

$$= \frac{b(1-p)}{(1-b)} \left[\frac{1}{1 - (1-b)(1-p)} \right]$$

$$\cdot \left[\frac{1}{1 - e^{\theta}p\{1 - (1-b)(1-p)\}^{-1}} \right] - \frac{b(1-p)}{(1-b)(1-pe^{\theta})} \, ,$$

by choosing θ such that $e^{\theta}p < 1$. Changing now to a new variable $t = k\Delta t$ and going to the limit $\Delta t \to 0$ such that $(p/\Delta t) \to \lambda$, we have

$$(10) \qquad m_t(\theta) = \frac{1}{(1-b)} \left[\frac{b\lambda}{(b\lambda - \theta)} \right] - \frac{b}{(1-b)} \left[\frac{\lambda}{(\lambda - \theta)} \right],$$

after disregarding terms involving Δt^2.

The probability distribution corresponding to (10) will be given by

$$(11) \qquad h(t) = \frac{1}{1-b} \, b\lambda e^{-b\lambda t} - \frac{b}{1-b} \, \lambda e^{-\lambda t}.$$

To prove this assertion, find the moment generating function of (11)

$$m_t(\theta) = \int_0^\infty e^{\theta t} h(t) \, dt = \frac{b\lambda}{(1 - b)(b\lambda - \theta)} - \frac{b\lambda}{(1 - b)(\lambda - \theta)},$$

which equals (10), as required.

Thus the probability of obtaining a choice time smaller than or equal to t will be

(12)
$$H(t) = \int_0^t \left(\frac{1}{1 - b} b\lambda e^{-b\lambda t} - \frac{b}{1 - b} \lambda e^{-\lambda t} \right) dt$$

$$= 1 - \frac{e^{-b\lambda t} - be^{-\lambda t}}{1 - b}.$$

The mean and variance of this distribution are given by

$$E(t) = \frac{1 + b}{b\lambda},$$

$$\text{Var }(t) = \frac{1 + b^2}{b^2 \lambda^2}.$$

The shape of the probability distribution given by (12) is, in general, not unlike the gamma distribution, but its variance will usually be larger. The parameters b and λ may be estimated from mean and variance. It should be noted however, that this model interrelates choice times with other aspects of the choice process. For instance, if it were possible in an experimental situation to record vicarious trial and error behavior by the subject, as has been done by Bower [2], b could be estimated from the VTE data. The model is thus quite strict. If it should prove inadequate in application, several changes are possible. For instance, the restriction placed upon the transition matrix (2) that $b = c$ could be lifted. This has not been done here because the resulting expressions are long and cumbersome.

Equation (12) gives the distribution of all response times, irrespective of which choice has occurred. The distribution of choice times given that choice A has been made can also be derived with the methods used to obtain (12). The mean and variance of the conditional distribution are

$$E(t \mid A) = \left\{ \frac{2 - 2b - b^2}{b(2 - b)} - \frac{1 - a}{1 - ab} \right\} \frac{1}{\lambda},$$

$$\text{Var }(t \mid A) = \frac{8 - 12b + 6b^2 - 2ab^3}{(1 - ab)b^2(1 - b)^2 \lambda^2} + \frac{2}{\lambda} E(t \mid A) - E^2(t \mid A).$$

Since the probability of an A response is given by $P(A) = (1 - ab)/(2 - b)$, the mean latency of the A responses is inversely related to the probability of an A response. The model predicts therefore that the more likely alternative will be responded to faster than the nonpreferred alternative. The choice times of the A and B responses will be equal whenever $a = (1 - a)$

and therefore $P(A) = P(B)$, for b fixed. The relationship between $E(t \mid A)$ and $P(A)$ is not linear, but the predicted deviation from linearity is quite small. The change in $E(t \mid A)$ brought about by variations of the a parameter is always less than or equal to $1/\lambda$. $E(t \mid A)$ is much more sensitive to the b parameter which determines the number of orienting responses that will be made.

REFERENCES

[1] Audley, R. J. A stochastic model for individual choice behavior. *Psychol. Rev.*, 1960, **67**, 1–15.

[2] Bower, G. H. Choice-point behavior. In R. R. Bush and W. K. Estes (Eds.), *Studies in mathematical learning theory*. Stanford, Calif.: Stanford Univ. Press, 1959. Pp. 109–124.

[3] Bush, R. R. and Mosteller, F. *Stochastic models for learning*. New York: Wiley, 1956.

[4] Estes, W. K. A random walk model for choice behavior. In K. J. Arrow, S. Karlin, and P. Suppes (Eds.), *Mathematical methods in the social sciences*. Stanford, Calif.: Stanford Univ. Press, 1959. Pp. 53–64.

[5] Feller, W. *An introduction to probability theory and its applications*. New York: Wiley, 1957.

[6] McGill, W. J. Stochastic latency mechanisms. In R. R. Bush, E. Galanter, and R. D. Luce (Eds.), *Handbook of mathematical psychology*. New York: Wiley, 1963 (in press).

Manuscript received 6/6/62

Revised manuscript received 9/11/62

A Recruitment Theory of Simple Behavior[*]

DAVID LABERGE, *University of Minnesota*

A statistical theory of choice is developed using a sequential sampling assumption. Response latency distributions for certain simple reaction-time situations are derived and tested. Both response probability and response latency measures are developed for a two-alternative judgment situation and the relationship between the two measures explored. The sampling parameter is proposed as a means of representing incentive conditions in choice situations and ROC curves are obtained by appropriate manipulations of this parameter. A solution to the overlap problem in simple discrimination-learning situations is also derived.

The distinctive features of the present theory arise from considerations of the sequence of stimulus events perceived by the organism when it is confronted with a choice. The theoretical framework representing the accumulation of stimulus events of the input process yields its predictions most directly in terms of temporal aspects of responding, while derivations of frequency aspects of responding follow secondarily. It is hoped that this approach may provide a somewhat richer base for describing behavior than has been the case when theories are formulated mainly to describe behavior in terms of relative frequencies of responses.

In its present form, the theory is intended to apply to simplified situations in which the subject responds in a prompt manner, without encountering delays produced by orienting responses, hesitation responses, and the like. If initial tests of the theory prove favorable, then we may consider extensions which seem necessary to account for more complicated situations, such as those involving a series of preparatory responses prior to the occurrence of the choice response.

In the present exposition of the theory, we will be concerned chiefly with stable behavior situations, such as are typically attained after a series of learning trials has brought responding to asymptote. Although we may point out particular implications for learning theory in the ensuing discussions, a comprehensive development of theoretical consequences for the learning process will be postponed at this time.

The plan of the paper is to begin with a general description of the basic

[*]This research was supported in part by a grant from the National Science Foundation. The writer has benefited from discussions with his students, James R. Erickson, James G. Greeno, Duane R. Martin, Kirk H. Smith, and Charles F. Stroebel. For generous suggestions with regard to certain mathematical matters, the writer is indebted to Professors Ingram Olkin, Stephen Orey, and Milton Sobel of the Statistics Department at the University of Minnesota.

This article appeared in *Psychometrika*, 1962, **27**, 375–396.

assumptions of the theory. Following this, the theory will be applied first to simple reaction-time experiments, and then to a particular class of choice situations. We will derive predictions for several important relationships in each of these situations and test some of these predictions against empirical findings.

Definitions and Assumptions

This theory is intended initially to apply to simple judgment situations in which the subject is presented with a single stimulus and is required to make a judgment by responding with one of a set of response alternatives. A typical example of this situation is a simple two-choice intensity discrimination where the subject judges the intensity of a light by pressing one button to indicate the higher intensity, and a second button to indicate the lower intensity. Applications of the theory to the other large category of choice situations, the preference experiment, will not be considered at this time. Preference experiments, which involve a choice among several stimuli presented on a given trial, typically induce the subject to make more than one response per trial. That is, he usually performs several orienting, or VTE, responses toward the various stimuli before he makes a terminal choice response. In this paper we will be interested in the detailed analysis of the characteristics of a single response, and therefore it would seem appropriate to postpone the more complex analysis of the sequence of responses of the preference situation.

In this presentation a trial will involve the following events. Initiating the trial will be a stimulus, followed by one of a set of response alternatives. Following the response, there will occur typically one of a set of outcomes, such as the flashing of a red light over one of the response keys to indicate a correct response. These three events of a trial will be designated in the traditional manner [10] as follows.

S_i ith stimulus alternative.

A_j jth response alternative.

E_k kth outcome alternative.

Stimulus assumptions

The stimulus on a given trial is broadly conceived as the total of all input components to the organism's decision process. We represent these input stimuli in the theory by a finite set of elements. This set is partitioned typically into subsets of elements as follows.

C_j The subset of elements connected to the jth response $(j = 1, 2, \cdots)$.

C_0 The subset of neutral elements which are connected to none of the response alternatives.

The neutral elements are of two types. The first type may be connected to one of the A_i response alternatives through conditioning, though momentarily they may be connected either to an unmeasured response, such as scratching, orienting, etc., or to no response at all. The second type of neutral element is assumed to be incapable of being connected to an A_i response through conditioning. These latter elements may perhaps be best interpreted at this time as noise components of the stimulus input.

The number of elements in each subset C_i of the stimulus will be designated as c_i. The total number of elements in the stimulus population is a parameter, and, along with the c_i, may be quite small without producing mathematical inconveniences.

Response assumptions

We assume that behavior output will be measured in terms of several well-known response classes [10], such as pressing a button or speaking a word. We shall assume that the response classes are mutually exclusive and exhaustive, such that one member of the set always occurs before a trial is terminated. If neutral elements of the first type evoke a response other than the member of the set of measured response alternatives, then the trial simply continues until one of the A_i responses occurs.

Outcome assumptions

The stimulating event following the response, typically labeled reinforcement, will not be analyzed here in terms of its effects on learning. Rather we will be concerned mainly with the rate of reinforcement under which behavior is stabilized. In general, the present theory applies both to probabilistic reinforcement situations, where the reinforcing event E_k is imperfectly correlated with a given stimulus S_i, and to situations where the correlation between E_k and S_i is either unity or zero. Present applications, however, will be confined largely to the latter, non-probabilistic reinforcement case.

Recruitment assumption

The core assumption of the theory is that a succession of stimulus events is necessary to evoke a response. Extending the sequential sampling principle proposed previously [19], we assume that the organism randomly samples elements one by one, in any order, with replacement, until he recruits r_i elements of type C_i. When he has sampled the r_ith element of type C_i, he emits the corresponding response A_i. Other elements may intervene among the sampled series of C_i elements, but the sampling ends when the r_ith element is recruited. For the choice situation, we allow for the general case that the r_i are not equal for the A_i response alternatives.

Before we proceed to the quantitative derivations of the theory for specific behavioral situations, let us consider some of the possible psychological interpretations of the four basic parameters to be used in the behavioral equations.

Proportion of C_i elements in S_i—p_{ii}

The relative proportion of the subset of elements in a stimulus population S_i connected to a particular response A_j corresponds roughly to the strength of that response in the presence of that stimulus. For a reaction-time situation, for example, we would assume that practice trials and increases in the intensity of the stimulus would raise the proportion of conditioned elements in the stimulus. With a consequent greater chance of sampling conditioned cues, the recruitment process should manifest the higher response strength by producing the response with a shorter latency. We would expect this conclusion to hold for choice situations as well, when latency measures are used to assess response strength. However, in choice situations we also have available, as a measure, the relative frequency of a response. This measure would more appropriately be related to the proportion of A_j elements relative to all the other conditioned elements, instead of being related in an absolute sense to the whole population of cues in the stimulus, which includes the neutral cues.

Recruitment factor—r_i

The number of C_i elements needed to evoke response A_j is assumed to be constant in a well-controlled situation where behavior is asymptotic, although it will turn out that small fluctuations in r_i will not appreciably affect quantitative predictions. One effect on the value of r_i is expected to be produced by motivational factors, such as would be established through instructions or through different values of reinforcements. A subject who is instructed to be "sure" before he responds with A_j should increase his value of r_i over that value which obtains under more normal instructions. With a larger value of r_i, the cautious subject should take a longer time to observe before responding. On the other hand, a reduction in the cost of an error should produce a smaller value of r_i, with the result that the less cautious subject uses a shorter observing time before responding. Using information-theory terminology, we could say that the cautious observer requires more redundancy in his stimulus sample before he will respond.

Sampling time—λ

The variable part of the latency of a response is produced by the sampling of the series of elements from the stimulus set. We assume that the sampling of each element requires a certain amount of time. In general an element of type C_i has associated with it the sampling time λ_i. At the present stage of theorizing, it would appear that λ_i should be constant over a wide variety of experimental situations. For purposes of simplicity in our initial analyses, we shall assume that the λ_j are equal for all j.

Time constant—t_0

The constant part of the latency of a response is customarily associated with the minimal time between stimulus onset and response evocation. But for purposes of fitting theoretical equations to data, one may also subsume under t_0 the constant time factors of the mechanical presentation and recording systems. These apparatus factors, however, are expected to be small relative to the minimal time factor ascribed to the organism's judgment processes.

Simple Reaction Time

Few situations in psychology offer the high degree of control obtained in reaction-time experiments, and consequently few situations can yield data of a comparable degree of orderliness. It would seem quite appropriate, then, to select a reaction-time experiment as the initial testing grounds for the quantitative predictions derived from a theory of this sort.

Quantitative expressions

The evocation of the response A involves the sampling of r conditioned elements plus w neutral elements in any order such that the response occurs when the rth conditioned element is sampled. If m elements must be drawn to obtain the rth conditioned element, then the latency is given as

$$(1) \qquad L(A) = \lambda m + t_0 \, .$$

Since m is a stochastic variable, we turn our attention to the computing of the probability of drawing $m = r + w$ elements to obtain the rth conditioned element. If we let p_1 be the proportion of conditioned elements in the stimulus, and p_0 be the proportion of neutral elements in the stimulus, then the probability of making $r + w$ draws resulting in a response is

$$(2) \qquad P(r + w) = \frac{(r + w - 1)!}{(r - 1)! \, w!} \, p_1^r p_0^w \, .$$

Equation (2) is the negative binomial function, which may also be regarded as the convolution of a series of geometric distributions [12], each having an r equal to 1 and a variable w [19].

In appearance the negative binomial distribution resembles the typical reaction-time distribution [29] with its characteristically positive skewness. Even relatively sharply peaked distributions may be derived if p_1 is large and r is small. When comparing theoretical with empirical distributions of latencies, however, it is more convenient mathematically to express (2) in cumulative form

$$(3) \qquad P(r + w \leq m') = \sum_{w=0}^{m'-r} \frac{(r + w - 1)!}{(r - 1)!\, w!} \, p_1^r p_0^w \,.$$

The mathematical advantage of this step accrues from the fact that a finite sum of the negative binomial is equal to the incomplete beta ratio, that is,

$$(4) \qquad \sum_{w=0}^{m'-r} \frac{(r + w - 1)!}{(r - 1)!\, w!} \, p_1^r p_0^w = I_{p_1}(r, m' - r + 1).$$

Proof of (4) can be obtained through a differentiation method, following a suggestion given by Feller [12]. Values of this function have been tabled extensively by Pearson [24] for integral values of r up to 50, with p_1 values ranging over the entire range in steps of .01. Further information about the beta ratio can be obtained from Burington and May [3], from advanced calculus texts, and from articles by McCarthy [21] and Olkin and Sobel [23].

Reinforcement variables

Let us consider the effect on the reaction-time distribution of varying motivational conditions, while holding constant the other factors associated with the main parameters of the theory, namely p_1, λ, and t_0. This procedure reduces the degrees of freedom available for fitting theoretical curves to the data, and thus produces a more challenging test of the theory.

The relevant data were obtained by Johanson [18], who trained two subjects to respond to auditory stimuli under three instruction conditions. The first condition was a "normal" reaction-time instruction. Under a second condition, termed an "incentive" situation, subjects were informed of their previous response time just before the signal of the next trial. For the third condition, the subjects were "punished" by receiving a shock to the fingers of the responding hand when their reaction time was too slow. Johanson combined the data of the two subjects since their latencies were very similar, and the cumulative latency distributions of their data are plotted along with theoretical curves in Fig. 1. The three curves have been fit simultaneously to the data of the three conditions by varying all four parameters, with the restriction that p_1, λ, and t_0 be constant over the three motivational conditions. In order to allow for the possibility that p_1 and λ might be the more appropriate parameters representing motivational effects, we also attempted to fit the three curves by varying p_1 and λ simultaneously, while holding r and t_0 constant. The resulting fits were inferior to that shown in Fig. 1, especially at the lower tails of the distributions. Thus it seems unlikely that the different reinforcement conditions of Johanson's study changed the latency distribution by effecting a change in p_1 or λ either separately or

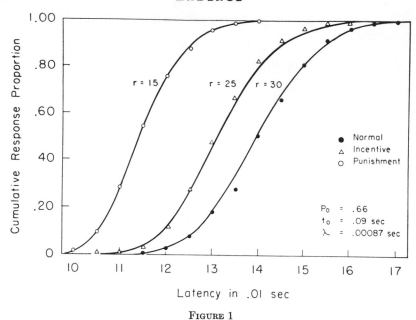

FIGURE 1

Theoretical and empirical (Johanson, 1922) cumulative reaction-time distributions for three motivational conditions

simultaneously. Further, an inspection of the data of Fig. 1 reveals that the distributions do not differ by a simple translation along the time axis, corresponding to a change in t_0. For these data, then, it appears that the parameter r is the critical factor which changes with the motivational variable.

Intensity variable

It is assumed that an increase in intensity of a stimulus corresponds to the addition of more conditionable elements to the stimulus set, thus effectively reducing the proportion of neutral or noise elements. The theoretical cumulative reaction-time distributions for an individual subject assume the form illustrated in Fig. 2. The parameter is the proportion of noise elements p_0. Fig. 2 indicates that variation in intensity yields predictions of changes both in slope and apparent intercept of the curves. Theories which predict simple gamma distributions for reaction time yield families of curves of varying slope such that the lower tails of these curves converge together near zero. Individual cumulative distributions from reaction-time studies involving varying intensities of the stimulus have been reported by McGill, and a typical example [22] is shown in Fig. 3. For these curves the manner of convergence as well as slope variation appear to favor the present beta-function theory. However, more thorough comparisons between theory and

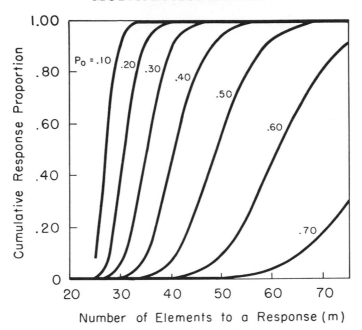

FIGURE 2

Theoretical cumulative reaction-time distributions for several intensities of the stimulus
with $r = 25$

data must wait for the appropriate scaling assumptions which relate p_1
to physical intensity.

Far more common in the literature are curves relating *mean* latency
to intensity. The mean latency is easily obtained from (2), and is

$$(5) \qquad \bar{L}(A) = \lambda E(r + w) + t_0 = \lambda(r/p_1) + t_0 \ .$$

Although this reciprocal relationship between the latency measure and the
intensity variable is in qualitative agreement with the existing relevant
data [29], the more interesting quantitative comparisons between such data
and the present theory again depend upon the sorts of additional assumptions
which might be proposed concerning the relationship between the physical
intensity variable and the psychological variable p_1 . However, a statement
of such a set of scaling assumptions is beyond the scope of the present paper.

A variable closely related to the intensity variable in its effect upon
latency is the number of dimensions in the stimulus. Adding a tone to the
flash of a light would be represented in the theory by adding more conditionable elements. As before, the effect on a response would be that of decreasing
its latency. How successfully one could precisely interchange intensity

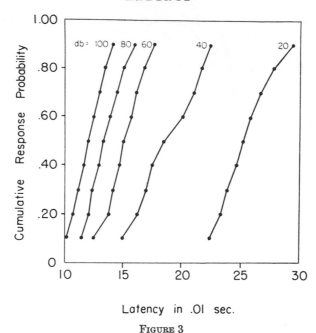

Latency in .01 sec.

FIGURE 3

Empirical cumulative reaction-time distributions for several auditory intensities (Data from a typical subject)

increments with increases in the number of relevant dimensions is an intriguing problem for future research.

Duration variable

One way to decrease response latency in reaction-time experiments is to allow the response to terminate the stimulus. A study by Gregg and Brogden [14] indicated that response termination of the stimulus affects latency through a limitation of the duration of the stimulus. From the point of view of the present theory, this conclusion seems at first bizarre since the continued presence of the stimulus elements following the response should hardly affect the preceding recruitment process which led to the response. On the other hand, we note that the presence of the stimulus after the response is made creates a learning situation in which non-responding is associated with the stimulus. Following this line of reasoning, we would expect stimuli of longer durations to have more of the conditionable elements connected to non-responding with the result that p_1 should be decreased and response time consequently increased.

One way to test this particular hypothesis would be to present different durations of the stimulus in a random order so that the proportion of conditioned elements would stabilize at some constant average level on each trial. We should then expect response latencies to be independent of the particular durations of the individual stimuli. This procedure was carried out by Chernikoff and Brogden [6], and their results showed no differences in latency due to duration of the stimulus, which is in agreement with the present analysis.

Choice Behavior

We turn now to the experimental arrangement in which two responses are available to the subject on a trial. The quantitative relationships to be described in the remaining sections of this paper can be generalized to the n-response alternative case.

When two different stimuli are paired with two responses in a one-to-one relation, we have a situation traditionally labeled the disjunctive reaction [7]. Let us consider the case of two stimuli ordered along a single dimension, represented by the diagram in Fig. 4. In this particular case, the sets representing the two stimuli are of equal size, such as might be realized for metathetic or qualitative dimensions, e.g., dimensions of visual wave length and spacial position of a light. However, for prothetic or intensity dimensions, e.g., loudness or brightness, the set sizes would presumably differ, with the more intense stimulus having the larger size. Referring now to Fig. 4, we note that a given stimulus may be partitioned into two subsets: the subset of elements unique to that stimulus, and the subset of elements held in common with the other stimulus. Ignoring neutral elements for the moment, the unique subset of S_1 contains only C_1 elements, since this subset is present only on trials where response A_1 is reinforced. The common subset, which is present on both S_1 and S_2 trials, contains both C_1 and C_2 elements, presumably in the same proportion that S_1 and S_2 are presented in the training series.

We define η_{ij} [4] as a measure of the similarity between the two stimuli, such that

$$(6) \qquad \eta_{ij} = \frac{N(S_i \cap S_j)}{N(S_i)} ,$$

where $N(S_i)$ is the number of elements in the stimulus set S_i, and $N(S_i \cap S_j)$ is the number of elements in the overlap between S_i and S_j. In general, $\eta_{ij} = \eta_{ji}$ only if $N(S_i) = N(S_j)$.

When the subject is presented with S_1 on a given trial, he has available C_1, C_2, C_0 elements for sampling. Since he must make one of the two responses to terminate the trial, we must consider two recruitment factors, r_1 and r_2. We assume that the subject samples elements one by one until he reaches either the r_1th element of type C_1 or the r_2th element of the type C_2 and emits the corresponding response.

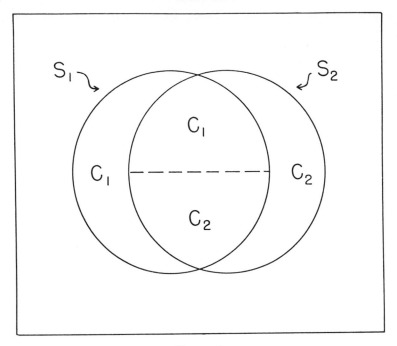

FIGURE 4

Representation of two neighboring stimuli S_1 and S_2 of a metathetic stimulus dimension showing the common and unique sets of stimulus elements

Quantitative expression for response probability

We shall consider the occurrence of an A_1 response, which requires the drawing of r_1 elements of type C_1 , $x < r_2$ elements of type C_2 , and w elements of type C_0 such that

$$(7) \qquad m = r_1 + x + w.$$

For a given m draws, the number of C_1 elements is fixed at r_1 , but the remaining C_2 and C_0 elements may be drawn in varying amounts so long as they sum to $m - r_1$, and so long as the number of C_2 elements is less than r_2 . The probability of response A_1 in m draws is therefore

$$(8) \quad P(A_1 \quad \text{and} \quad m \quad \text{draws}) = \sum_{x=0}^{r_2-1} \frac{(m-1)!}{(r_1-1)!\, x!\, (m-r_1-x)!}\, p_1^{r_1} p_2^{x} p_0^{m-r_1-x}.$$

But response A_1 may occur with varying values of m, so we must sum (8) over all permissible m in order to express the probability of A_1 :

$$(9) \qquad P(A_1) = \sum_{m=r_1}^{\infty} \sum_{x=0}^{r_2-1} \frac{(m-1)!}{(r_1-1)!\, x!\, (m-r_1-x)!}\, p_1^{r_1} p_2^{x} p_0^{m-r_1-x}.$$

Since $w = m - r_1 - x$, we may express (9) also in terms of the component elements as follows:

(10) $$P(A_1) = \sum_{w=0}^{\infty} \sum_{x=0}^{r_2-1} \frac{(r_1 + x + w - 1)!}{(r_1 - 1)!\, x!\, w!}\, p_1^{r_1} p_2^{x} p_0^{w} .$$

This expression may be interpreted as first holding w constant and summing over x, and then summing over all w.

Exchanging the orders of summation of (10) and multiplying by

$$(r_1 + x - 1)!/(r_1 + x - 1)!$$

we obtain

(11) $$P(A_1) = \sum_{x=0}^{r_2-1} \frac{(r_1 + x - 1)!}{(r_1 - 1)!\, x!}\, p_1^{r_1} p_2^{x} \sum_{w=0}^{\infty} \frac{(w + r_1 + x - 1)!}{(r_1 + x - 1)!\, w!}\, p_0^{w} .$$

The second summation term is in the form of an infinite binomial sum and equals ([12], p. 49, 156)

$$(1 - p_0)^{-(r_1+x)} .$$

Since

$$1 - p_0 = p_1 + p_2 ,$$

(11) reduces to

(12) $$P(A_1) = \sum_{x=0}^{r_2-1} \frac{(r_1 + x - 1)!}{(r_1 - 1)!\, x!} \left(\frac{p_1}{p_1 + p_2}\right)^{r_1} \left(\frac{p_2}{p_1 + p_2}\right)^{x} ,$$

which has the same form as (4). Therefore, for the two-choice situation, we have the extremely tidy result that

(13) $$P(A_1) = I_{p_1/(p_1+p_2)}(r_1 , r_2).$$

We observe that $P(A_1)$ depends on the ratio of p_1 to the proportion of conditioned elements and is therefore independent of the proportion of neutral elements, paralleling a similar finding in an earlier theory [19] where $r_i = 1$.

The relation between A_1 probability and the conditioned elements ratio is very easily obtained from the beta-ratio tables [24] and is plotted in Fig. 5 for various values of r_1 , where $r_1 = r_2$. The diagonal line at $r_1 = 1$ represents the matching of A_1 probability with the ratio of conditioned elements. This matching assumption has strongly prevailed among statistical theories ever since Estes' first paper [8]. The most noticeable effect upon $P(A_1)$ due to increasing r_1 is that $P(A_1)$ approaches unity progressively faster as the conditioned element ratio approaches unity. The same general feature holds true as these quantities approach zero. In other words, large values of r_i have the power of overriding the error or confusion produced when c_1 and

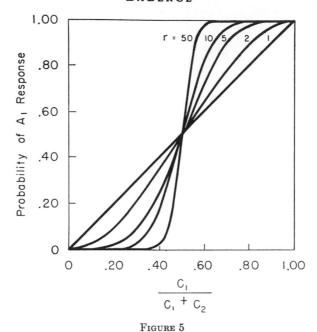

FIGURE 5

Response probability as a function of the conditioned elements ratio with the recruitment
factor as the parameter

c_2 have similar values, by picking out the larger of these and producing the
associated response at a probability approaching unity.

One very interesting consequence of the present probability assumption
is that the overlap between two stimuli (cf., Fig. 4) may be considerable,
such that the conditioned element ratio for each stimulus is well below
unity, and yet the organism can exhibit virtually perfect discrimination
behavior when his r is sufficiently large. For example, in a two-dimensional
discrimination problem where one dimension is relevant and the other
irrelevant [e.g., 13, 16, 17], the present theory allows the organism to show
perfect performance while simultaneously sampling the irrelevant cue dimension to a significant degree. This particular problem of discrimination
behavior has concerned the writer [20] for some years because it seemed
that there should be some way to account for perfect discrimination performance in the presence of common cues without postulating a special
process to eliminate them [cf., 4, 25]. So it was particularly gratifying to
see a simple solution to the overlap problem arise so naturally from the theory.

Returning to the Fig. 5, let us consider what would happen to the curves
if r_2 were greater than r_1. One might produce this condition experimentally
by placing on response A_2 a higher cost for being an error. Raising the re-

cruitment quota for A_2 has the effect of raising the A_1 probability, for a given ratio of conditioned elements. Hence, the curves of Fig. 5 should be translated roughly upward, while maintaining one end of each curve at (0, 0) and the other end at the point (1, 1).

Quantitative expression for response latency

As was the case for reaction-time situations, the response time in a choice situation is represented by the drawing of m elements plus a time constant t_0. We assume that it takes λ_i seconds to draw an element, so that the general expression for response latency is

$$(14) \qquad L(A_1) = \lambda_1 r_1 + \lambda_2 x_2 + \lambda_0 w + t_0 .$$

For simplicity, we assume equal λ_i, so that $L(A_1) \Rightarrow \lambda m + t_0$, where $m = r_1 + x_2 + w$. Since t_0 and λ are assumed to be constant for the sorts of situations to be considered here, we again turn our attention to the variable part of the latency expression—the m draws. We seek, therefore, the conditional probability of m draws given response A_1 :

$$(15) \qquad P(m \text{ draws given } A_1) = \frac{P(m \text{ draws and } A_1)}{P(A_1)}.$$

Since we already have in convenient form the denominator of (15), we will be concerned with the numerator term which is expressed in (8). After removing terms from the summation of (8) and multiplying through by $(m - r_1)!/(m - r_1)!$, we obtain

$P(m \text{ draws and } A_1)$

$$= \frac{(m-1)!}{(r_1-1)!\,(m-r_1)!}\, p_1^{r_1} \sum_{x=0}^{r_2-1} \frac{(m-r_1)!}{x!\,(m-r_1-x)!}\, p_2^x p_0^{m-r_1-x}.$$

Multiplying by $(1 - p_1)^{m-r_2}/(1 - p_1)^{m-r_1}$ yields

$$(16) \qquad P(m \text{ draws and } A_1)$$

$$= \binom{m-1}{r_1-1} p_1^{r_1}(1-p_1)^{m-r_1} \sum_{x=0}^{r_2-1} \binom{m-r_1}{x}\left(\frac{p_2}{1-p_1}\right)^x \left(\frac{p_0}{1-p_1}\right)^{m-r_1-x}.$$

The first part of this expression may be considered as r_1/m times a binomial function; the second part is a finite binomial sum, which is equal to the incomplete beta ratio ([12], p. 163; [3], p. 74), namely

$$I_{p_0/(1-p_1)}(m - r_1 - r_2 + 1, r_2).$$

Therefore, combining expressions into the form of (15), we have

$$(17) \qquad P(m \text{ draws given } A_1)$$

$$= \frac{r_1}{m}\binom{m}{r_1} p_1^{r_1}(1-p_1)^{m-r_1} \frac{I_{p_0/(1-p_1)}(m - r_1 - r_2 + 1, r_2)}{I_{p_1/(p_1+p_2)}(r_1, r_2)}.$$

Formidable as it seems, this expression yields its values very readily with the use of binomial tables [e.g., 15] and the beta-ratio tables [24].

In order to inspect the relationship between latency and the ratio of conditioned elements, we first compute the mean number of draws to a response by going back to (8) and computing the expected value. Dividing the result by $P(A_1)$ in the manner shown in (15) we have

$$(18) \qquad E(m \quad \text{given} \quad A_1) = \frac{r_1}{p_1} \frac{I_{p_1/(p_1+p_2)}(r_1 + 1, r_2)}{I_{p_1/(p_1+p_2)}(r_1, r_2)}.$$

The presence of p_1 in the first term of this expression indicates that response latency is dependent upon the proportion of neutral elements in the stimulus, since p_1 is not divided by the quantity $p_1 + p_2$. However, in order to compare the effect of the conditioned element ratio upon latency we hold p_0 constant and plot in Fig. 6 a family of mean latency curves with r_1 as a

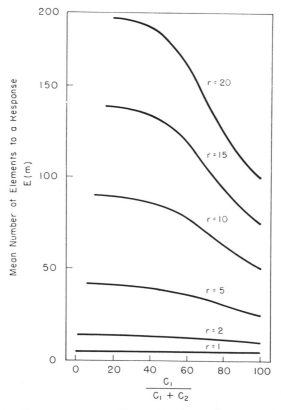

FIGURE 6

Theoretical latency component $E(m)$ as a function of conditioned elements ratio for $p_0 = .80$ with the recruitment factor as the parameter

parameter. Actually these curves represent the mean number of elements sampled before the response is emitted, so if we wish to compare response-time values with data, we must multiply m by λ and add t_0. However, this linear transformation does not alter the essential form of the curves shown in Fig. 6.

Comparing Fig. 6 with Fig. 5, we note that, in general, response latency is more sensitive to the higher values of the conditioned elements ratio, while response probability is more sensitive to the middle range of these values. Moreover, as r increases, both latency and probability curves steepen somewhat in these respective areas, producing a narrowing of their range of sensitivity to the conditioned elements ratio.

Probability–latency relationship

With the quantitative expressions for response probability and latency at hand, we can plot the theoretical relationship between response probability and mean latency using (13) and (18) and varying the ratio of conditioned elements over its entire range. Illustrated in Fig. 7 is a family of probability-latency curves for a constant p_0 and for various values of r_1, where $r_1 = r_2$. We note that the most apparent change in predicted latency occurs as response probability approaches unity. The slight upward swing of latency as probability approaches zero will be very difficult to test since a large number of observations is needed to obtain stable probability estimates at these low probability points.

Reinforcement variables

Following the approach used in our analysis of reaction-time experiments, we expect the main effects of reinforcement value on choice behavior to be represented in the theory by changes in the r factor associated with each response. Let us consider two neighboring stimuli on a single dimension as illustrated in Fig. 4. Suppose that the two responses are reinforced according to the following payoff matrix.

$$\begin{array}{c|cc} & S_1 & S_2 \\ \hline A_1 & +1 & -a \\ A_2 & -b & +1 \end{array}$$

If we present a series of trials at increasing values of a while b is held constant, we should produce an increased caution with respect to making response A_1. That is, the subject will tend to make A_1 only after he has had sufficient information to assure a correct response and thereby avoid the penalty associated with a. Then, when we hold a constant and increase b, we should produce a parallel effect on response A_2. One could say that as a and b change values the subject shifts his criterion of judgment. A convenient

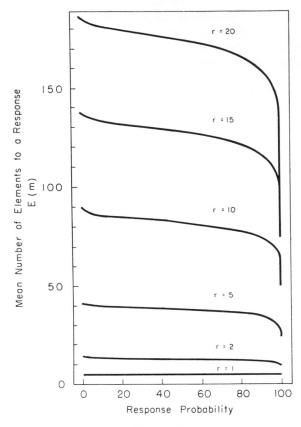

FIGURE 7

Theoretical relationship between the response latency component $E(m)$ and response probability for $p_0 = .80$ with the recruitment factor as the parameter

way of plotting the behavior of the observer in this situation has been given by Tanner and Swets [27] and labeled the "receiver-operating-characteristic."

Following their procedure, we compute the probability of an A_1 response given each stimulus and let the pairs of r values vary in accordance with changes in a and b. In this way we obtain one of the curves illustrated in Fig. 8. The particular curve we obtain depends upon the percent of overlap between the stimuli sets (cf. Fig. 4) which we have labeled η_{12}. This parameter corresponds to d' in signal detection theory [26].

The family of curves illustrated in Fig. 8 is based on the assumption that the set sizes of S_1 and S_2 are equal, as would be expected of two neighboring stimuli along a metathetic stimulus dimension. However, we would expect some change in the shape of the curves of Fig. 8 for prothetic dimensions

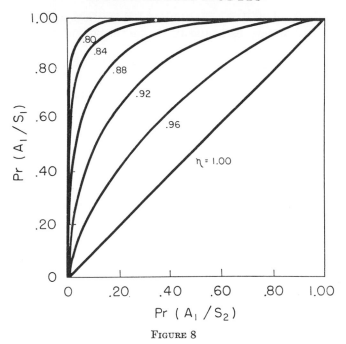

FIGURE 8

Theoretical receiver-operating-characteristic curves with the amount of overlap between
S_1 and S_2 as the parameter

where the stimulus of greater intensity is assumed to have a larger set size. For detection experiments carried out at minimal intensities, we expect S_1 to contain more elements than S_2, the latter containing noise alone in a typical experiment of this sort. For detectable neighboring stimuli well along the prothetic dimension, we similarly expect that the stimulus of greater intensity will have the larger set size. For both prothetic cases, $\eta_{21} > \eta_{12}$, and, therefore, the curves of Fig. 8 would become asymmetric around the positive diagonal, having steeper slopes to the left and shallower slopes to the right of the diagonal. Swets, Tanner, and Birdsall [26] apparently obtained the same sort of effect by assuming different variances for the Gaussian density functions which they employed to represent neural activity level. The reader is referred to their article for encouraging data relevant to the predicted receiver-operating-characteristics for prothetic dimensions. However, it should be noted here that there is apparently little hope of differentiating between theories which predict ROC curves of this general shape on the basis of goodness-of-fit results since data on an individual observer is quite variable [26, 27].

For the present we have not attempted to link r_1 and r_2 with specific payoff patterns in a definitive manner. This is a problem of utility theory and requires a good deal of empirical and theoretical groundwork before it can be inserted in the present theory. So, for the present, we must estimate the r_i from the data.

While discussing reinforcement and its assumed effect upon r, we may point out another implication for learning experiments. On the average, an increase in the value of r_1 , such as produced by an increase in the cost of an A_1 error, will require more elements to be sampled before a response is evoked. If the sample were conditioned at the end of the trial in the manner assumed by traditional statistical learning theory [11], it would be predicted that the higher cost leads to an increased learning rate.

Discussion

The preceding presentation represents an attempt to relate within one theoretical framework several significant stimulus and response variables in choice situations. The qualitative and quantitative evidence which was offered constitutes only a partial test of the theory and further testing must be carried out to ascertain any limits of its application. Since this is a theory of individual behavior, the critical quantitative tests almost surely must come from data analyzed from single subjects. Group curves too often conceal or distort important characteristics of individual data. Critical quantitative tests must also take into account the particular experimental condition stipulated by the recruitment assumption in its present form: namely, that the observer respond promptly to the stimulus input in a trial without permitting intervening hesitation or "checking" operations. For it is conceivable that a very cautious observer may make several provisional covert decisions before he makes an overt choice. Although the perception process for each of these covert decisions may be a single recruitment process, the theoretical structure for handling a sequence of these recruitment chains has not yet been completed.

Turning to the recruitment assumption, it is possible for us to interpret this process at the response side of the organism, although with somewhat less adequacy as compared to the stimulus side. One could conceive that each element produces an implicit response and that a number of these occur before the overt response alternative appears. This conception is not far from those proposed earlier by LaBerge [19] and by Audley [1]. Others such as Bush and Mosteller [5], Bower [2], and Estes [9] have gone a step further on the response side to propose a series of *overt* responses preceding the final measured response, such as characterizes the chain of behavior of a rat in a runway or at a choice point in a T-maze. If one were to draw comparisons instead in terms of the formal aspects of the sequential process, one would probably group Audley, Bower, and Estes together since their theories require that a critical number of responses of the same kind occur consecutively in order to produce the final response. Whereas, one would perhaps group the Bush and Mosteller formulation with the present theory since the critical number of events can occur in any order to produce the final response. The earlier neutral elements model [19] serves as a special case in all of these classes of theories since it requires only one critical event to produce the final response.

In our description of the recruitment process in the first part of this essay, we indicated that the sampling of elements begins with the onset of the signal. That is, we pictured the organism as starting his response process from a relatively "clean slate" at the beginning of a trial. Without serious quantitative modifications of the theory, it is possible to describe cases where the recruitment process begins before the signal appears. For example, a speed-oriented subject in a reaction-time situation may conceivably start his sampling before the signal onset, resulting in an effectively higher r value than when sampling is assumed to start with the signal. Occasionally this preliminary sampling should produce the r critical elements before the signal begins with the result that the subject makes an anticipatory response, a phenomenon well-known by investigators in this area. In the same way certain response biases in the general choice situation may be tantamount to the subject's getting a head start on the recruitment process before the signal is presented. Even the initial presentation of a set of response alternatives to the subject before the first stimulus is given may well start some sort of recruitment toward all the alternatives of this particular set. Whether or not this line of conjecture will open up profitable approaches to the problem of "set" or "attention" remains to be seen.

The recruitment of elements before the stimulus onset is quite possibly related to sequential characteristics of responding when controls are not introduced to eliminate these sequential effects. Although sequential phenomena have been found in the typical psychophysical experiment [e.g., 28], they seem to have their greatest weight in the Humphreys' situation. Subjects who base a given response to some degree on preceding responses and trial outcomes usually have sampled these cues before the signal onset of the trial on which they respond. The composition of the set of cues based on sequential events is unfortunately as variable as the chain of responses and outcomes which precede a given trial in the guessing experiment. Therefore, the set of elements associated with the same physical signal on each trial has a variable and usually unknown amount of each type of conditioned element. Not knowing p_1 and p_2 on a given trial makes the job of predicting response probability and latency a very difficult task indeed. Hence, for our initial derivations and tests of the theory we are trying to limit ourselves to situations where sequential effects on stimulus input are minimized. In this way we hope to gain some assurance that the subject samples only the elements of the trial signal whose cue composition is more directly controlled by the experimenter.

REFERENCES

[1] Audley, R. J. A stochastic model for individual choice behavior. *Psychol. Rev.*, 1960, **67**, 1–15.

[2] Bower, G. H. Choice-point behavior. In R. R. Bush and W. K. Estes (Eds.), *Studies in mathematical learning theory*. Stanford: Stanford Univ. Press, 1959, Ch. 6.

[3] Burington, R. S. and May, D. C. *Handbook of probability and statistics with tables*. Sandusky, Ohio: Handbook Publishers, 1953.

[4] Bush, R. R. and Mosteller, F. A model for stimulus generalization and discrimination. *Psychol. Rev.*, 1951, **58**, 413–423.

[5] Bush, R. R. and Mosteller, F. *Stochastic models for learning*. New York: Wiley, 1955.

[6] Chernikoff, R. and Brogden, W. J. The effect of response termination of the stimulus upon reaction time. *J. comp. physiol. Psychol.*, 1949, **42**, 357–364.

[7] Donders, F. C. Die schnelligkeit psychischer processe. *Arch. anat. Phys.*, 1868, 657–681.

[8] Estes, W. K. Toward a statistical theory of learning. *Psychol. Rev.*, 1950, **57**, 94–107.

[9] Estes, W. K. A random-walk model for choice behavior. In K. J. Arrow, S. Karlin, and P. Suppes (Eds.), *Mathematical methods in the social sciences*. Stanford: Stanford Univ. Press, 1959.

[10] Estes, W. K. The statistical approach to learning theory. In S. Koch (Ed.), *Psychology: a study of a science*. Vol. 2. New York: McGraw-Hill, 1959, Pp. 380–491.

[11] Estes, W. K. and Burke, C. J. A theory of stimulus variability in learning. *Psychol. Rev.*, 1953, **60**, 276–286.

[12] Feller, W. *An introduction to probability theory and its applications* (2nd ed.). New York: Wiley, 1957.

[13] Goodwin, W. R. and Lawrence, D. H. The functional independence of two discrimination habits associated with a constant stimulus situation. *J. comp. physiol. Psychol.*, 1955, **48**, 437–443.

[14] Gregg, L. W. and Brogden, W. J. The relation between duration and reaction time difference to fixed duration and response terminated stimuli. *J. comp. physiol. Psychol.*, 1950, **43**, 329–337.

[15] Hald, A. *Statistical tables and formulas*. New York: Wiley, 1952.

[16] Hughes, C. L. and North, A. J. Effect of introducing a partial correlation between a critical cue and a previously irrelevant cue. *J. comp. physiol. Psychol.*, 1959, **52**, 126–128.

[17] Jeeves, M. A. and North, A. J. Irrelevant or partially correlated stimuli in discrimination learning. *J. exp. Psychol.*, 1956, **52**, 90–94.

[18] Johanson, A. M. The influence of incentive and punishment upon reaction time. *Arch. Psychol.*, 1922, **54**.

[19] LaBerge, D. A model with neutral elements. In R. R. Bush and W. K. Estes (Eds.), *Studies in mathematical learning theory*. Stanford: Stanford Univ. Press, 1959, Ch. 2.

[20] LaBerge, D. and Smith, A. Selective sampling in discrimination learning. *J. exp. Psychol.*, 1957, **54**, 423–430.

[21] McCarthy, P. I. Approximate solutions for means and variances in a certain class of box problems. *Ann. math. Statist.*, 1947, **18**, 349–383.

[22] McGill, W. Stochastic latency mechanisms. In R. R. Bush, R. D. Luce, and E. Galanter (Eds.), *Handbook of mathematical psychology*. Vol. 1. New York: Wiley, in press.

[23] Olkin, I. and Sobel, M. Integral expressions for certain sums of multinomial and negative multinomial probabilities. Tech. Report No. 1, Department of Statistics, Univ. of Minnesota.

[24] Pearson, K. *Tables of the incomplete beta-function*. London: Cambridge Univ. Press, 1932.

[25] Restle, F. A theory of discrimination learning. *Psychol. Rev.*, 1955, **62**, 11–19.

[26] Swets, J. A., Tanner, W. P., Jr., and Birdsall, T. G. Decision processes in perception. *Psychol. Rev.*, 1961. **68**, 301–340.

[27] Tanner, W. P., Jr. and Swets, J. A. A decision-making theory of visual detection. *Psychol. Rev.*, 1954, **61**, 401–409.

[28] Verplanck, W. S., Collier, G. H., and Cotton, J. W. Non-independence of successive responses in measurements of visual threshold. *J. exp. Psychol.*, 1952, **44**, 273–282.

[29] Woodworth, R. S. and Schlosberg, H. *Experimental psychology* (Rev.). New York: Holt, 1956.

Manuscript received 4/15/62
Revised manuscript received 6/18/62